ANNUAL REVIEW
OF PHYSIOLOGY

VOLUME 63, 2001

JOSEPH F. HOFFMAN, *Editor*
Yale University School of Medicine

PAUL De WEER, *Associate Editor*
University of Pennsylvania School of Medicine

www.AnnualReviews.org   science@AnnualReviews.org   650-493-4400

ANNUAL REVIEWS
4139 El Camino Way • P.O. BOX 10139 • Palo Alto, California 94303-0139

ANNUAL REVIEWS
Palo Alto, California, USA

International Standard Serial Number: 0066-4278
International Standard Book Number: 0-8243-0363-6
Library of Congress Catalog Card Number: 39-15404

TYPESET BY TECHBOOKS, FAIRFAX, VA
PRINTED AND BOUND IN THE UNITED STATES OF AMERICA

PREFACE

Readers of the *Annual Review of Physiology* should be apprised that our board of editors is always concerned about the extent of our coverage and responsibilities concerning our field. We are aware of the changing character of different areas, not just the novel advances and new accomplishments, but also the development and application of new approaches leading to better understanding of cellular and systemic processes. We attempt to bridge the reductionist insights into molecular mechanisms with their integrated counterparts in the whole organisms. Taken together, we hope that the subjects reviewed in each edition reflect these various aspects, recognizing that the themes covered in each section change yearly. We continue to encourage our readers to send comments and suggestions concerning topics and/or blind spots in our coverage. We can be reached at our web site, www.Annual Reviews.org.

This year's volume contains, in addition to the articles in the various sections, our prefatory chapter written by Alexander Leaf and two special topics. The purpose of including special topics is to bring to the attention of our readership developments in related fields that lie outside our normal coverage. The first special topic, edited by Amita Sehgal, concerns an in-depth survey of circadian rhythms with special emphasis on molecular aspects. The second topic, written by Robert Shulman and Douglas Rothman, considers new aspects of intermediary metabolism, with implications for systems physiology, and utilizes concepts derived from metabolic control analysis.

Joseph F. Hoffman
Editor

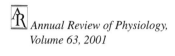*Annual Review of Physiology,*
Volume 63, 2001

CONTENTS

OTHER REVIEWS OF INTEREST TO PHYSIOLOGISTS

From the *Annual Review of Biochemistry*, Volume 69 (2000):

Two-Component Signal Transduction, Ann M Stock, Victoria L Robinson, and Paul N Goudreau

Apoptosis Signaling, Andreas Strasser, Liam O'Connor, and Vishva M Dixit

Protein Tyrosine Kinase Structure and Function, Stevan R Hubbard and Jeffrey H Till

Platelet-Activating Factor and Related Lipid Mediators, Stephen M Prescott, Guy A Zimmerman, Diana M Stafforini, and Thomas M McIntyre

Mediator of Transcriptional Regulation, Lawrence C Myers and Roger D Kornberg

GTPase-Activating Proteins for Heterotrimeric G Proteins: Regulators of G Protein Signaling (RGS) and RGS-Like Proteins, Elliott M Ross and Thomas M Wilkie

Swinging Arms and Swinging Domains in Multifunctional Enzymes: Catalytic Machines for Multistep Reactions, Richard N Perham

From the *Annual Review of Cell and Developmental Biology*, Volume 16 (2000):

Molecular Regulation of Adipogenesis, Evan D Rosen and Bruce Spiegelman

Epithelial M Cells: Differentiation and Function, Jean-Pierre Kraehenbuhl and Marian R Neutra

The Role of Orphan Nuclear Receptors in the Regulation of Cholesterol Homeostasis, Joyce J Repa and David J Mangelsdorf

Structure and Regulation of Voltage-Gated Ca^{2+} Channels, William Catterall

Secretory Protein Trafficking and Organelle Dynamics in Living Cells, Jennifer Lippincott-Schwartz, Theresa Roberts, and Koret Hirschberg

From the *Annual Review of Medicine*, Volume 52 (2001):

Molecular Genetics and Pathogenesis of Autosomal Dominated Polycystic Kidney Disease, MA Arnaout

Novel Platelet Inhibitors, Joel S Bennett

Effects of Neuropeptides and Leptin on Nutrient Partitioning: Dysregulation in Obesity, Bernard Jeanrenaud and Françoise Rohner-Jeanrenaud

From the *Annual Review of Neuroscience*, Volume 24 (2001)

Localization and Globalization in Conscious Vision, S Zeki

Protein Synthesis at Synaptic Sites on Dendrites, Steward Schuman and E Schuman

Neuropeptides and the Integration of Motor Responses to Dehydration, AG Watts

The Vanilloid Receptor: A Molecular Gateway to the Pain Pathway, M Caterina and D Julius

Viktor Hamburger and Rita Levi-Montalcini: The Path to the Discovery of Nerve Growth Factor, WM Cowan

From the *Annual Review of Nutrition*, Volume 20 (2000):

The Behavioral Determinants of Exercise: Implications for Physical Activity Interventions, Nancy E Sherwood and Robert W Jeffrey

Leptin—Much More than a Satiety Signal, Ruth BS Harris

Regulation of Metabolism and Body Fat Mass by Leptin, Clifton A Baile, Mary Anne Della-Fera, and Roy J Martin

Iron Transport, Marianne Wessling-Resnick

Intestinal Transport During Fasting and Malnutrition, Ronaldo P Ferraris and Hannah V Carey

Cellular Copper Transport and Metabolism, Edward D Harris

The Extracellular Ca^{2+}-Sensing Receptor (CAR): Central Mediator of Systemic Calcium Homeostasis, Edward M Brown

The Health Benefits of Wine, J Bruce German and Rosemary L Walzem

Iron Regulatory Proteins and the Molecular Control of Mammalian Iron Metabolism, Richard S Eisenstein

From the *Annual Review of Pharmacology and Toxicology*, Volume 41 (2001):

Genetic Variations and Polymorphisms of G Protein–Coupled Receptors: Functional and Therapeutic Implications, Brinda K Rana, Testuo Shiina, and Paul A Insel

Lysophospholipid Receptors, Nobuyuki Fukushima, Isao Ishii, James JA Contos, Joshua A Weiner, and Jerold M Chun

Molecular Approach to Adenosine Receptors: Receptor-Mediated Mechanisms of Tissue Protection, Joel Linden

Compartmentation of G Protein–Coupled Signaling Pathways in Cardiac Myocytes, Susan F Steinberg and Laurence L Brunton

Physiological Functions of Cyclic ADP-Ribose and NAADP as Calcium Messengers, Hon Cheung Lee

ANNUAL REVIEWS is a nonprofit scientific publisher established to promote the advancement of the sciences. Beginning in 1932 with the *Annual Review of Biochemistry*, the Company has pursued as its principal function the publication of high-quality, reasonably priced *Annual Review* volumes. The volumes are organized by Editors and Editorial Committees who invite qualified authors to contribute critical articles reviewing significant developments within each major discipline. The Editor-in-Chief invites those interested in serving as future Editorial Committee members to communicate directly with him. Annual Reviews is administered by a Board of Directors, whose members serve without compensation.

Alexander Leaf

Annu. Rev. Physiol. 2001. 63:1–14

MEDICINE OR PHYSIOLOGY: My Personal Mix

Alexander Leaf, M.D.

*Departments of Medicine, Massachusetts General Hospital and Harvard Medical School,
Boston, Massachusetts 02129; e-mail: aleaf@partners.org*

Key Words   autobiography, polyunsaturated fatty acids, cell volume regulation,
sodium transport, preventive medicine

INTRODUCTION

As a physician and a clinician, I feel especially honored to be invited to prepare
this prefatory chapter but more than a little intimidated in accepting to do so. In
fact, when first invited by the Editor to do this, I looked up the prefatory chapters
for the past decade. I responded that my small incursions into physiology did not
qualify me to join the ranks of the eminent physiologists who have graced these
Annual Reviews with their comments in the past. So why am I now interrupting that
distinguished succession? Later in a moment of moderate euphoria, engendered
by having just been awarded two separate National Institutes of Health grants, I
have forsaken my better judgement and succumbed to temptation.

Early Life and Education

I was born in 1920 in Yokohama, Japan. My parents had escaped from Russia
via the Trans Siberian railway one year before the Bolshevik revolution, just as
von Hindenburg was beginning his rout of the Czarist's troops, which had been
advancing into Prussia on the German eastern front. We left Japan for the United
States, when I was two-years old, and settled in Seattle. I had an idyllic boyhood
there fully enjoying my playmates; the woods and lake near our house; the mild
but wet winters; swimming and sailing on Lake Washington and Puget Sound;
Mount Rainer, spectacular across the lake; and all the beauties then of the Pacific
Northwest. School was boring with its repetitiveness so I enjoyed the sociability
that it afforded but did poorly scholastically. In high school things changed. There
were several interesting courses. Especially the chemistry and physics courses
were excellent and superbly taught. Unfortunately, the mathematics classes to
which I was assigned were poorly taught so I learned little of that; my other major
deficiency was in reading, which was very slow. Later, I took a speed reading course
at Harvard. I succeeded in doubling my reading speed and exactly halved my
comprehension. I was only little more successful with math. When I was inducted

into the Army Medical Corps, I took a text of integral and differential calculus with me and waded through that in boot camp, during a steaming summer in San Antonio. But both the slow reading and the inability to formulate or summarize concepts in mathematical expression have remained real professional handicaps.

Attending the University of Washington was also enjoyable. I decided to major in chemistry and found the instruction to be stimulating and my classmates good but competitive company. I lived at home. I had been awarded a partial scholarship to Harvard, but my father thought I should remain at home. It was still the Depression years, and the $30 quarterly tuition at the University of Washington did help. My older brother, one year my senior but two years ahead of me scholastically, was soon to go East to pursue his doctoral studies in chemistry.

During my final two years in high school and increasingly during the university time, my father unobtrusively became a pivotal figure in my education. He proved a gold mine of erudition, and I consulted him on many topics. He counseled my brother and me to take as many science courses at school as we could, saying that learning science required demonstrations and laboratory exercises, which were only readily available in schools, whereas cultural subjects we could learn on our own to the extent that we were so motivated. Our home was filled with classical culture from the music and literature, which both my parents loved and encouraged us to hear and read, to lengthy discussions on politics, society, science, religion, philosophy, and literature, at home and with classmates. Both my parents were raised in strict, orthodox Jewish families, and they resolved that their children would not receive any religious indoctrination but be free to make their own choices. My own agnosticism has been strongly bolstered by Karl Popper's analysis of the distinction that science seeks to increase our understanding of our physical and biologic world through careful observation and experimentation, which test negatable hypotheses, whereas the beliefs of religion are not testable but must be accepted on faith.

This lack of a religious identity set me aside from most of my classmates and friends, but even more so did my family's attitude toward how our free time should be spent. With summer school vacations, all of my friends, encouraged by their parents, rushed to get jobs and make money. My father, on the contrary, advised that this was my age of rapid learning and encouraged me to read, take up hobbies, enjoy the outdoors, and practice my flute playing, which with the compositions of Bach, has provided me much pleasure but little expertise. Later, he said, my time would be occupied with supporting a family and there would be little time for scholarship. My father was a dentist, and we were a middle-class family. His own formal education had been very limited in Czarist Russia but that had not diminished his personal, informal scholarly interests.

The summer of my final year in high school I did follow the custom of my neighborhood peers and got a job, working on the construction of the Grand Coulee Dam as a common laborer. My assignment was to brush and sweep clean the tops of the 100-foot square concrete blocks, preparing the surface for the next layer of concrete to be poured. I worked the graveyard shift, from midnight to

8:00 A.M. It seemed grueling, back-breaking work, but it had one salutatory effect; it got me through medical school. I figured there had to be some easier way to make a living!

During my attendance at the university, war clouds were gathering ominously over Europe, creating uncertainty and unrest on our campuses. I made a hasty decision at the beginning of my third year to change my study major from chemistry to premed, feeling that whatever the future might bring, as a physician I would always be helping people. More recent observations and experiences have given me pause to revise that comfortable assumption regarding the role of my profession in society. The courses I had taken during my first two years fulfilled most of the academic requirements of my new major, so I needed to take only a few additional biology classes. This I did by adding them hastily to my chemistry classes, but the class in structural biology, which required dissection of brine-pickled cat cadavers during a warm Seattle summer in the small, unventilated Anatomy Shed almost dissuaded me from pursuing a career in medicine. I even squeezed in my first taste of research during my last two summers in an elective offering in chemical oceanography at the University of Washington's Marine Biology Laboratories in Friday Harbor on San Juan Island in in the Straits of Juan de Fucca. My problem was most mundane–to measure gravimetrically the calcium concentration in sea water sampled from varying depths at specific sites as a means of determining the currents in the Pacific by application of the Bjerknes atmospheric equations—but the setting of the Laboratories was unbelievably beautiful.

By halfway through the third academic year, it seemed likely that I would complete my required courses of study, so I started writing applications for acceptance to medical schools. The University of Washington allowed me to finish my studies in three years, and with satisfactory completion of the first year of medical school, I would be awarded a University of Washington baccalaureate degree in science. It was still possible to enter medical schools with only three years of college and with my high scholastic record, I felt the probability of acceptance was fairly likely. But there was no medical school in Washington in those days so I applied to many schools in the East. There followed a period of increasing anxiety as one after the other of the prestigious schools to which I had applied returned rejection notices to me. This was further heightened when family friends and even my revered atomic energy physics professor advised that it was unlikely that medical schools would accept a Jewish applicant. At last I received an acceptance notice from the University of Michigan and could start to make plans for new experiences in Ann Arbor, where I matriculated in the Fall of 1940.

Medical School

Medical School turned out to be a surprising experience. My previous classmates in chemistry were to be future scientists and engineers, and all seemed motivated to learn as much science as possible. My medical school classmates were a very heterogeneous group. They came from a variety of educational backgrounds, many from families with fathers or uncles who were physicians and who found themselves in medical school through no voluntary choice of their own—they had simply grown up with that natural expectation. Others were there seeking the social status that medicine would provide them. This was not to say there was not a very high degree of competitiveness among a substantial number of classmates, but the motivation for this seemed more the desire to be successful than an intense interest in acquiring knowledge. Our faculty fostered this competitive spirit with frequent quizzes and examinations, the grades of which were publicly posted and listed after our names.

The quality of medical instruction in the basic medical sciences was very spotty. There were many different classes, all required. Some for me were simply terrible (bacteriology, biochemistry) in which masochistic instructors killed potentially exciting fields of inquiry, Others were intolerable (anatomy, morbid pathology) because of the pointless memorization and regurgitation of Latin names and because of the 'know-it-all' professors who lectured to us and again required exact repetition of their dogmas on long examinations. For me, only the pharmacology and physiology courses were exciting owing to the creative laboratory experiences each provided. In the labs we performed classic experiments in groups of two to four and were required to submit in writing our interpretation of our findings. This led to extensive thinking about biologic functions and much library study followed by enlightened, challenging discussions with interested lab instructors. I was thrilled by this stimulating dimension to medical education, so different from the many passive experiences I had.

Not long after I arrived in Ann Arbor the medical school dormitory where I stayed was taken over by the Army Medical Corps and all residents who were physically fit were required to volunteer into the Army Specialized Training Program (ASTP), Navy equivalent, or face immediate military draft. Our curriculum was accelerated by eliminating summer vacations and other holidays. Military discipline did not mix well with medical education, nor did the reveille and squad assembly at 6:00 A.M. and lights out at 10:00 P.M. or the tyrannical diminutive sergeant from Brooklyn with his "Heh, youse guys!" But we were fortunate indeed to be allowed to finish our medical education—the military needed doctors.

The clinical training of the last two years was a big change from the basic science classes. Although there were interminable lectures, covering the major and minor specialties of medicine, the clinical bed-side instruction with diagnostic problems was a new and stimulating experience. Seeking to understand the pathophysiology of the patients' illnesses was an extension of the earlier experience with the physiology labs. We had some excellent teachers of whom Jerome Conn in Endocrinology and Carl Moyer in General Surgery were the most stimulating because of their pursuit of the pathophysiology. But none so influenced my career as did Prof. LH Newburgh, one of the few outstanding physicians at the University of Michigan then. Dr. Newburgh had a son who began medical school with me. David had perhaps the most brilliant mind that I have encountered. I was drawn to him and, as we shared similar interests, we soon became friends. His father erroneously assumed that any friend of David's must also be brilliant, and I was promptly adopted into the Newburgh family. Dr. Newburgh was noted for his interests in endocrinology, especially of diabetes, and his meticulous determinations of energy metabolism in humans, and most recently in body fluids and renal physiology. As a freshman it was thrilling to ride out on my bicycle on weekends and assist the Professor with his gardening while he talked about his research and current medical events. Before the end of that first year my career in medicine was firmly set by the tacit assumption of Dr. Newburgh that there could be no better life for a thinking individual than a specialty in Internal Medicine in an academic career.

In my final year in medical school, like all my classmates, I applied for clinical residency training to fulfill legal requirements to practice. With a high scholastic standing and being the president of my graduating class, I applied to most of the top academic programs. But Dr. Newburgh said I must complete my training at the Massachusetts General Hospital (MGH). It took only a phone call to Dr. James Howard Means, Chief of Medicine at that venerable institution, friend and former classmate of Dr. Newburgh at Harvard, and I was among the class of ten neophyte interns who started intensive clinical training on the medical wards of MGH in January, 1944. With the country at war, all internships (first year residency) were limited to 9 months, following which one third continued for a second 9 months of training, and the others went to serve in the military. The same formula was followed at the end of the second nine months because the military needed some better-trained physicians to staff their referral hospitals. At the end of the first 9 months I was not invited to stay for further training at MGH, but was invited to do so at the Mayo Clinic, where I found the clinical experience to be superb. I had written carefully in the notebook I always carried, all the reading pertaining to the many interesting patients I had seen and cared for at MGH, but had no free time to look up their illnesses. Doing the initial clinical work-up of the patients, with excellent staff supervision during the Clinic's day time hours, left me free to spend my evenings in the library pursuing the many exciting research papers, trying to find answers to my questions. I was one of the fortunate residents who received the full 27-month postgraduate training before starting military service. I had requested overseas duty but was assigned to Beaumont General Hospital in El Paso, Texas for my Army medical service. We saw many interesting medical problems there, but I was ready when Dr. Newburgh secured my early release from the Army to return to my alma mater to assist him with his research program.

Postdoctorate Training

As a consultant for the military Dr. Newburgh had spent most of the war years working for the National Research Council on problems relating to survival in hot climates—clothing, body fluid, and salt requirements. When I arrived, Dr. Newburgh took me to his laboratory room in the sub-basement of University Hospital and said, "This is your laboratory. I will help you in any way I can, but don't ask me what you should be doing. If I knew the answer to that, I would be doing it myself." The next two stimulating years were the beginning of my research into problems of water and electrolyte metabolism. With Dr. Newburgh's retirement impending he advised that I should return to MGH to continue pursuit of an academic career in an environment that fostered research. Again his telephone call to Prof. Means and a providential Rockefeller Fellowship secured that desirable possibility.

I arrived again in Boston, this time with a wonderful wife, two daughters, and a stipend of $300 a month. Without a job assignment from Dr. Means, I spent my first year as a Fellow with the distinguished clinical investigator and endocrinologist, Dr. Fuller Albright, whose writings and lectures had been an inspiration to me. At the end of that very rich learning, but unproductive research experience, I learned from Dr. Means that when he had invited me back to MGH he expected me to set up my own laboratory in his Department of Medicine and to create an independent unit for renal, electrolyte, and water metabolism, thus providing research, clinical, and consulting services, then a new idea for hospitals or medical schools. He had saved a small room in the old Domestic Building for me, one floor above the reach of the elevator, into which, with my rats, I moved with alacrity and gratitude.

Body Fluids, Electrolytes, and Kidneys

That commenced my studies on how sustained hyponatrium and hypoosmolality of extracellular fluids, seen commonly, might occur. The elegant research of Verney (1) at that time on the function of the neurohypophyseal-renal axis clearly showed that a surfeit of water resulted in excretion of large volumes of dilute urine. Conversely, a water deficit resulted in excretion of small volumes of concentrated urine. This feed-back system preserved a normal serum sodium concentration, but it failed to explain the possibility of persistent hyponatremia seen clinically. It was first necessary to demonstrate that some other solute was not accumulating in the extracellular fluids to replace the reduced serum sodium and chloride osmoles. This we did by measuring the colligative properties of the serum water and demonstrating that the freezing point was reduced proportional to the reduction in serum $[Na^+]$ (2). There was at that time an assumption by some influential clinicians that water infused into the extracellular fluid remained exclusively in that compartment, which was disproved by demonstrating in dogs that the volume of distribution of an intravenous water load just equaled that of a tracer amount of deuterium dioxide (3). This compared the net movement of water across cell membranes with the transfer of tracer water by diffusion. Also, it was proposed by some physiologists and pathologists that the osmolality of intracellular fluids was higher than that of extracellular fluids and that this imbalance was maintained by cellular water pumps extruding water from cells to prevent their osmotic swelling. This view could be shown to be incorrect by demonstrating that the mechanism of fluid exchange of tissues, when metabolism was inhibited, resulted from a primary movement of extracellular sodium and chloride into cells (necessarily in excess of potassium lost from the cells) with secondary transfers of water (4). This was followed with a direct demonstration (by a novel method of measuring the melting point of tissues) that extra- and intracellular fluids were indeed isotonic (5). But by the 1950s it was established that water and most of the solutes of the extracellular fluids passively entered cells. This raised the interesting question of how cells could avoid swelling and lysing owing to the fact that they must enclose osmotically active, mainly electrically negatively charged, essential macromolecules, surrounded by an extracellular, interstitial fluid, deficient in comparable concentrations of macromolecules. There seemed only two possible means to avoid this fatal outcome: to surround each cell by a membrane able to resist the considerable osmotic swelling pressures, or to maintain some solute in an obligatory extracellular position to counteract osmotically this swelling pressure. The studies of E Newton Harvey (6) on leukocytes had shown very low surface tensions of cell membranes, insufficient to withstand swelling pressure. But isotopic tracer studies by then showed that the ions of the extracellular fluid entered cells passively. This led us to the hypothesis that sodium ions provided this needed osmotic balance by making the cells effectively impermeable to Na^+ because the Na^+ that entered the cells was promptly extruded by the presence of specific sodium pumps in the plasma membranes. This created a double Donnan equilibrium with the extracellular $[Na^+]$ just balancing the negative intracellular macromolecules and stabilizing the cell volume (7, 8). This choice in allowing for the flexiblity in cells also underlies the mobility of animals. Plants by making the other choice, i.e. surrounding each cell with a strong cellulose sheath, were fated for a sessile existence. Later the ion gradients generated across cell membranes by the extrusion of Na^+ ions could be adapted in specialized systems to create a nervous system, trigger muscle contraction, and provide the free energy required to transport many essential hydrophilic ions and molecules into cells.

This need to protect cells from osmotic lysis indicates that the beginning of life on our planet may have required more than the fortunate combination of elements to produce the building blocks for DNA, RNA, and proteins. The macromolecules formed, it seemed, would be rapidly dispersed in a dilute ocean unless, almost simultaneously, a suitable membrane enclosed the macromolecules to sustain their essential juxtaposition.

Parallel clinical studies allowed us to test some of our new findings in humans. Thus we were able to demonstrate the pathophysiology of the syndrome of inappropriate secretion of antidiuretic hormone by examining the effects on normal subjects of administration of a long-acting vasopressin while varying the daily oral water intake (9). A clinical publication attempted to delineate the various physiologic and clinical states associated with reduced or increased serum sodium concentrations (10).

Copenhagen and Oxford

While enjoying a busy existence, with clinical practice and consulting, research, and teaching activities filling my hours, I came across a publication of a lecture by

HH Ussing on the transport of sodium and water across the frog skin. Although the words he used were mostly familiar, I was dismayed to realize I had no comprehension of his elegant experiments. This was a sobering discovery for one purporting to be an expert on functions of the kidney, when water and sodium transport were the major functions of that organ. This led me to request of my chairman, Prof. Walter Bauer, then Chief of Medicine, a leave of one year in order to spend six months in the laboratory of Hans Ussing and another with Hans Krebs, who then was studying the metabolic requirements for accumulation of K^+ in the retina. But after Bauer consulted with Fritz Lipmann, I was informed that although Lipmann thought it was a good idea, I should forget about the biophysics, as that would lead nowhere, and he had arranged that I spend two years learning biochemistry with Krebs.

In the fall of 1953 I made my first voyage across the Atlantic to Europe. I had learned that Krebs had just been appointed Professor of Biochemistry at Oxford and was moving from Sheffield to Oxford. I had written to Krebs thanking him for granting me the opportunity to join his MRC Unit in Oxford, but that while he was moving, I would be with Ussing in Copenhagen. When he was settled in his new department, he should let me know and I would come promptly to Oxford. That provided four wonderful months in delightful Denmark, the most intensive and profitable learning experience I have had, which allowed me not only to repeat Ussing's classic experiments but also to become familiar with the techniques he had developed. With Ussing's advice and two balanced calomel half cells, I found that the large bilobed transparent urinary bladder of *Bufo marinus*, which fills the abdomen of a hydrated toad, had a spontaneous transmembrane electrical potential of some 100 mV. When I measured the short-circuit current of the bladder in an Ussing chamber and the bi-directional flux of sodium across the bladder wall, as in the Ussing & Zerhan experiment (11), the net excess of Na^+ moved from mucosa to serosa of the bladder just equaled the short-circuit current. This gave me an excellent model for in vitro studies of solute and water transport across a thin, histologically simple epithelium, which mimicked important transport activities in the anatomically complex mammalian kidney and which responded to the same hormones, vasopressin, aldosterone, and others.

The remaining two years in Oxford were delightful, enjoying its rich architectural, artistic, scholarly culture, and rustic surroundings with my family, and trying to learn biochemistry while continuing with my interests in solute and solvent transport processes across cell membranes, which were not unusual interests in this MRC unit. Krebs had received a citation from the Queen shortly before my arrival for his work with Robert E Davies indicating water gradients across cell membranes. By six weeks of my arrival I had completed my experiments on the mechanism of fluid exchange of tissues in vitro and was writing up my results, thinking this was going to be easy. One year later when I was still rewriting this study to obtain Krebs' approval to publish it, I had developed some doubts about how easy scientific life in Oxford was going to be. After responding to all of Krebs' criticisms, he agreed to have my manuscript judged by Kenneth Burton and

Sandy Ogston, two members of his MRC Unit for whose knowledge of quantitative biology he had great respect. With their concurrence my manuscript was published. Although Krebs was focusing his thoughts on intermediary metabolism, I found him a remarkable individual. He made a habit to visit briefly with each of the several research units in his department to keep updated on their progress. Characteristically, he would unexpectedly walk in to the room alone, ask some general questions regarding my work, and then start backing toward the door. I had to make my responses terse and to the point to describe my findings before he reached the door and departed. My subtle attempts to get between him and the exit to prolong the discussions never succeeded. Days later he would appear in my lab with some visiting dignitary, usually an American, introduce the visitor and to my amazement proceed to succinctly describe exactly what my projects were and what I was finding.

My wife, Barbara, and I enjoyed our time in Oxford greatly and returned for a year sabbatical seventeen years later, again with Krebs. He was then retired but Paul Beeson, Chairman of the Department of Medicine, provided Krebs with space in the Radcliffe Infirmary for his MRC Unit. Again we had a wonderful year, punctuated by some exotic and fascinating travels to Hunza, the Russian Caucacuses, and Vilcabamba, Equador for the National Geographic magazine to visit places where people were alleged to live exceptionally long lives, remaining vigorous and healthy. I found each remote site to be fascinating, with seemingly many robust elderly, living a very simple agrarian existence, with lifelong physical labor, an essentially vegetarian diet, and social support, but with grossly exaggerated ages. The latter fact I only suspected at the time and had confirmed later. Today, I still am occasionally introduced as a gerontologist. I still love to travel to exotic places and learn how people have adapted to life with cultures very different from ours, but I don't write about my travels anymore.

Academic Administration

Between these visits to Oxford I had gradually been promoted through the academic ranks to find myself at the start of 1966 occupying the office of the Physician-in Chief of the Medical Services of MGH and Chairman of Harvard's Department of Medicine there. This was a new experience, not really in my plans. Under the wise guidance of my predecessors, the Hospital and the Medical Services had earned a reputation as an outstanding clinical, research, and teaching institution. It was now my responsibility to maintain and build on that reputation. Such a reputation keeps the department stimulating. It is this that affords us the privilege of attracting many of the best students to our Medical School and the best medical students to our post-doctoral clinical and research positions. There have been five Nobel Laureates who graduated from our medical clinical training program during my time here—and very many more who have distinguished themselves as leading figures in both clinical and basic departments of medical schools and government throughout the world. It has been reassuring to me that our very demanding residency program has not stifled their curiosity. I knew that attention to the large geographic full-time staff of some 550 MDs and PhDs—then, I believe Harvard's largest single department—would cut deeply into my research interests, and it was a struggle to keep alive even a glowing ember of that exciting aspect of medicine. But I had the firm belief that the best physicians were those who understood the pathophysiology of their patients' illnesses, so my teaching and rounds were directed by that belief. I also believed that our universities had two central functions: to pass to new generations the knowledge generated by their predecessors and uniquely to perform research to expand that knowledge base. My attitude toward promotions was based on this belief.

Despite the challenges and many satisfactions, I grew increasingly dissatisfied with what was happening on my Medical Service. Our beds were filling up with patients who had suffered their second or third heart attacks, with inoperable cancers, chronic alcoholism, or dementia. But I had seen in my travels that coronary heart disease was practically nonexistent then among perhaps three quarters of the world's population, cancer incidences varied greatly, as did alcoholism. These conditions must be preventable. Yet we physicians waited in our offices until patients came to us with their diseases well advanced. There was very little we could do to cure them of these chronic ailments. Increasingly we responded with ingenious and very expensive technology that mostly provided palliative relief, at best. It seemed to me that these efforts should at least be combined with very active programs in preventive medicine. After 15 years, I resigned from my position as Chief of Medicine. Shortly thereafter I was asked to organize and chair a new Department of Preventive Medicine at Harvard Medical School, which I did and served in that role for another ten years until my mandatory university retirement at age 70. Serving the latter role I became interested in nutrition, especially in fatty acids to promote better health. With new-found freedom from administration, teaching, and practice, I returned to the laboratory to pursue my research interests, now focused on preventive cardiology.

Retirement

By 1990 there were already suggestions that the highly polyunsaturated n-3[1] fatty acids of fish oil might have protective effects against the development of coronary heart disease, and research was increasing on possible antiatherosclerotic effects of fish and fish oil. Meanwhile, two Australian investigators reported that in feeding experiments in rats, fish oil fatty acids virtually prevented ischemia-induced fatal ventricular arrhythmias (12, 13). Perhaps because of the novelty and unusual

---

[1]The n-3 indicates that for this class of polyunsaturated fatty acids one counts back three carbon atoms from the methyl end of the fatty acid to reach the first C=C double bond. The other class of polyunsaturated fatty acids (PUFA) is the n-6 class. Popularly these two classes are also called omega-3 and omega-6. The simple convention is that C20:5n-3 is shorthand for a fatty acid with a chain length of 20 carbons. The:5 indicates 5 C=C double bonds, n-3 is the location of the first C=C bond.

nature of their results, they received very little attention for their remarkable findings. It seemed to me that their carefully conducted and reported experiments deserved at least an effort at confirmation. To do this I turned to George E Billman PhD, Professor of Physiology at Ohio State University School of Medicine at Columbus, as he had a highly reliable dog model of sudden cardiac death. In his prepared, exercising, unanesthetized dogs, the infusion of an emulsion of fish oil free fatty acids, or the fatty acids carried on serum albumin, just prior to inducing ischemia essentially completely prevented the fatal arrhythmias. In the control experiments in the same dog, both before and after the experiment with the fish oil infusion, the animals developed fatal arrhythmias within two minutes of the ischemic insult from which they were defibrillated (14, 15). Subsequently, we found that the three major dietary n-3 fatty acids: pure α-linolenic acid, (C18:3n-3, LNA), eicosapentaenoic acid (C20:5n-3, EPA), and docosahexaenoic acid (C22:6n-3, DHA) were potent antiarrhythmic agents (16). Having confirmed the earlier findings, albeit by a parenteral route of administration, we sought to learn the mechanism of this antiarrhythmic effect of the specific fatty acids containing a free carboxyl group at one end of a long acyl chain with two or more C=C double bonds. As our model for study we used neonatal rat heart cells and adult rat cardiomyocytes. The former were cultured on a microscope cover slip to which they adhered and began beating spontaneously, rhythmically and synchronously. We could both observe the effects of various agents on their beating rate and examine the effects of arrhythmogenic toxins on their function.

We found that the free polyunsaturated fatty acids, if added to the superfusate at low micromolar concentrations, with or without albumin, would prevent the subsequent induction of arrhythmias induced by a large number of cardiotoxins. If the arrhythmias were already induced, then addition of the free n-3 fatty acids to the superfusate would terminate the arrhythmias within a few minutes in the continued presence of the cardiotoxins. Then to our surprise, addition of delipidated bovine serum albumin to the superfusate, which (because of its three high-affinity binding sites extracts the free fatty acids from the cardiomyocytes) resulted in resumption of the arrhythmias (17). This taught us that the free fatty acids need only partition into the lipophilic environment of the phospholipid cell membranes in order to exert their antiarrhythmic action. We would not have been able to extract the fatty acid from the cardiomyocytes if these acids had formed a covalent bond with any constituent in the membrane. In addition, the fatty acids were no longer antiarrhythmic once incorporated into membrane phospholipids (18). Proceeding then to electrophysiologic studies, we found that the fatty acids quickly affected every contractile cell in the myocardium, stabilizing it electrically (19, 20). This effect in turn was found to be due to a modulating action of the free fatty acids on the voltage-dependent Na^+ and the L-type Ca^{2+} currents (21, 22). These findings in rat cardiomyocytes have been confirmed in human cardiac sodium channels with both the α and β subunits, transiently expressed in HEK293t cells (23, 24). The effect of the fatty acids on both the Na^+ and Ca^{2+} channels is to shift the steady-state inactivation potential to more hyperpolarized values, and this effect is highly voltage dependent.

With acute myocardial infarctions, it has been known that in the border zone between ischemic and normally perfused tissue there are partially depolarized myocytes that are potential mischief-makers. With their more positive resting potentials closer to the gating potential for voltage-dependent influx of Na^+, which initiates action potentials, any further small depolarizing stimulus may set off action potentials. If such action potentials occur at a vulnerable moment in the cardiac electrical cycle, an arrhythmia may be started. The fish oil fatty acids shift the steady-state inactivation potential to more negative values required to return the heart cell's Na^+ channels to a closed resting, but activatable state. This requires a much more negative resting state potential than is physiologically attainable and, therefore, the partially depolarized myocytes are quickly eliminated from causing arrhythmias. Also partially depolarized cardiac myocytes can quickly slip into an inactivated state without inducing an action potential. The normally perfused cells, however, having normal resting membrane potentials are largely unaffected functionally by the presence of the fatty acids and continue to contract normally.

The inhibitory effects on the L-type calcium channels, we think, are also very important, because it is well known that excessive cytosolic calcium fluctuations can induce delayed after potentials that again can trigger fatal arrhythmias. By reducing the influx of Ca^{2+} via the L-type calcium channel, reduced release of Ca^{2+} from the sarcoplasmic reticulum stores via the ryanodine receptors occurs, and cytosolic calcium fluctuations are reduced (20, 22). The effects on the sodium and calcium channels, which occur at submicromolar concentrations of the free n-3 polyunsaturated fatty acids, we now think are the major factors in the prevention of fatal ventricular rhythms. But the effects of the fatty acids on ion currents of atrial myocytes have been found to be similar to the effects on ventricular cells, so we suspect supraventricular arrhythmias may likewise be affected by these polyunsaturated fatty acids.

Once we had found an effect of the n-3 fatty acids on an excitable tissue, the heart, we suspected that these fatty acids would affect all excitable tissues because all use essentially the same electrical communicating system—and they do. In the brain we found that they have similar effects on the Na^+ and Ca^{2+} currents of hippocampal neurons (25). One functional consequence of this indicates the same fatty acids are anticonvulsants, as judged in the rat cortical stimulation model of seizure activity (26).

It is apparent that a basic control of cardiac and neural function by common dietary fatty acids exists that has been largely overlooked. The n-3 PUFA have been part of the human diet for some 2–4 million years during which time our genes were being adapted to our diet as hunter-gatherers (27), and they are safe (i.e. nontoxic). With approximately 300,000 sudden cardiac deaths annually, largely owing to ventricular fibrillation, in the United States alone and millions more worldwide, there may be a potential large public health benefit from the practical application of this recent understanding. We are currently in the process of conducting a clinical trial to find if what we have learned in the laboratory will protect patients at high risk from fatal ventricular arrhythmias. Also there are beginning to be reports that the *n*-3 PUFAs are producing beneficial effects in the treatment of depression, bipolar, and other behavioral diseases. The knowledge that these fatty acids have direct physical effects on the fundamental property of the nervous system, namely its electrical activity, should encourage further exploration of potential beneficial effects on brain activities, both normal and pathological. It seems likely that we are just scratching the surface of the potential health effects of these interesting dietary polyunsaturated fatty acids.

I recount these recent experiences, to indicate that the excitement and fun of science and discovery needn't be just the prerogative of the young, as commonly believed. I remember at an early stage of my academic career, my father's concern in stating, "Well, now you have a wife and daughter, how will you support them as a researcher?" "Dad," I replied, "You forget that I am a physician and can always practice Medicine, if an academic career becomes unfeasible." Where upon he stated, "I don't think so. You have already been bitten." The very distinguished respiratory and renal physiologist, Robert F Pitts, whom I greatly admired, once admonished me publicly, saying that I should be in a physiology department, not a department of medicine. I felt quite flattered at such a scolding from him. The fact is I never felt constrained by the medical environment in which I have been fortunate to work, and the problems encountered at the bedside can be a lively stimulus to the fun of seeking answers.

Visit the Annual Reviews home page at www.AnnualReviews.org

LITERATURE CITED

1. Verney EB. 1946. The absorption and excretion of water: the antidiuretic hormone. *Lancet* 2:739–44, 781–93

2. Leaf A, Mamby AR. 1952. An antidiuretic mechanism not regulated by extracellular tonicity. *J. Clin. Invest.* 31:60–71

3. Leaf A, Chatillon JY, Wrong O, Tuttle EP Jr. 1954. The mechanism of the osmotic adjustment of the body cells as determined by the volume of distribution of a large water load. *J. Clin. Invest.* 33:1261–68

4. Leaf A. 1956. On the mechanism of fluid exchange of tissue in vitro. *Biochem. J.* 62:241–48

5. Maffly RH, Leaf A. 1959. The potential of water in mammalian tissues. *J. Gen. Physiol.* 42:1257–75

6. Harvey EN. 1954. Tension at the cell surface. *Protoplasmatologia* 2:E5

7. Leaf A. 1957. On the regulation of intra-cellular fluid volume. Lucknow, India Commemorative Volume. *Scientific Souvenir*, pp. 78–84. Lucknow, India: Indian Council Med. Res.

8. Leaf A. 1959. Maintenance of concentration gradients and regulation of cell volume. *Ann. NY Acad. Sci.* 72:396–404

9. Leaf A, Bartter FC, Santos RF, Wrong O. 1953. Evidence in man that urinary electrolyte loss induced by pitressin is a function of water retention. *J. Clin. Invest.* 33:1261–68

10. Leaf A. 1962. The clinical and physiologic significance of the serum sodium concentration. *N. Engl. J. Med.* 267:24–30, 77–83

11. Ussing HH, Zerhan K. 1951. Active transport as the source of current in the short-circuited isolated frog skin. *Acta Physiol. Scand.* 23:110–27

12. McLennan PL, Abeywardena MY, Charnock JS. 1988. Dietary fish oil prevents ventricular fibrillation following coronary artery occlusion and reperfusion. *Am. Heart J.* 16:709–17

13. McLennan PL. 1993. Relative effects of dietary saturated, monounsaturated, and polyunsaturated fatty acids on cardiac arrhythmias in rats. *Am. J. Clin. Nutr.* 57:207–12

14. Billman GE, Hallaq H, Leaf A. 1994. Prevention of ischemia: induced fatal ventricular arrhythmias by ω3 fatty acids. *Proc. Natl. Acad. Sci. USA* 91:4427–30

15. Billman GE, Kang JX, Leaf A. 1997. Prevention of ischemia-induced cardiac sudden death by n-3 polyunsaturated fatty acids. *Lipids* 32:1161–68

16. Billman GE, Kang JX, Leaf A. 1999. Prevention of ischemia-induced cardiac sudden death by pure n-3 polyunsaturated fatty acids. *Circulation* 99:2452–57

17. Kang JX, Leaf A. 1994. Effects of long-chain polyunsaturated fatty acids on the contraction of neonatal rat cardiac myocytes. *Proc. Natl. Acad. Sci. USA* 91:9886–90

18. Weylandt KH, Kang JX, Leaf A. 1996. Polyunsaturated fatty acids exert antiarrhythmic actions as free fatty acids rather than in phospholipids. *Lipids* 31:977–82

19. Kang JX, Xiao YF, Leaf A. 1995. Free long-chain polyunsaturated fatty acids reduce membrane electrical excitability in neonatal rat cardiac myocytes. *Proc. Natl. Acad. Sci. USA* 92:3997–4001

20. Kang JX, Leaf A. 1996. Prevention and termination of arrhythmias induced by lysophosphatidyl choline and acylcarnitine in neonatal rat cardiac myocytes by free omega-3 polyunsaturated fatty acids. *Eur. J. Pharmacol.* 297:97–106

21. Xiao Y-F, Kang JX, Morgan JP, Leaf A. 1995. Blocking effects of polyunsaturated fatty acids on Na^+ channels of neonatal rat ventricular myocytes. *Proc. Natl. Acad. Sci. USA* 92:11000–4

22. Xiao Y-F, Gomez AM, Morgan JP, Lederer WJ, Leaf A. Suppression of voltage-gated L-type Ca^{2+} currents by polyunsaturated fatty acids in adult and neonatal rat cardiac myocytes. *Proc. Natl. Acad. Sci. USA* 94:4182–87

23. Xiao Y-F, Wright SN, Wang GK, Morgan JP, Leaf A. 1998. N-3 fatty acids suppress voltage-gated Na^+ currents in HEK293t cells transfected with the α-subunit of the human cardiac Na^+ channel. *Proc. Natl. Acad. Sci. USA* 95:2680–85

24. Xiao Y-F, Wright SN, Wang GK, Morgan JP, Leaf A. 2000. Coexpression with the β1-subunit modifies the kinetics and fatty acid block of the voltage-gated human cardiac Na^+ channel α-subunit. *Am. J. Physiol. Heart Circ. Physiol.* 279:H35–H46

25. Vreugdenhil M, Breuhl C, Voskuyl RA, Kang JX, Leaf A, Wadman WJ. 1996. Polyunsaturated fatty acids, modulate sodium and calcium currents in CA1 neurons. *Proc. Natl. Acad. Sci. USA* 93:12559–63

26. Voskuyl RA, Vreugdenhil M, Kang JX, Leaf A. 1998. Anticonvulsant effects of polyunsaturated fatty acids in rats, using the cortical stimulation model. *Eur. J. Pharmacol.* 31:145–52

27. Leaf A, Weber PC. 1987. A new era for science in nutrition. *Am. J. Clin. Nutr.* 45:1048–53

Annu. Rev. Physiol. 2001. 63:15–48

^{13}C NMR OF INTERMEDIARY METABOLISM: Implications for Systemic Physiology

Robert G Shulman* and Douglas L Rothman

*Yale University School of Medicine, Departments of *Molecular Biophysics and Biochemistry and Diagnostic Radiology, 333 Cedar Street, New Haven, Connecticut 06510; e-mail: robert.shulman@yale.edu*

Key Words   metabolism, NMR, muscle, brain, systemic physiology

■ **Abstract**   The study of intermediary metabolism in biomolecules has been given new directions by recent experiments in human muscle and brain by ^{13}C NMR. Labeled substrates, generally glucose, have enabled the fluxes to be determined in vivo, whereas the naturally abundant ^{13}C has enabled concentrations to be measured. In muscle the glycogen synthesis pathway has been measured and the flux control determined by metabolic control analysis of data, which shows that this pathway is mainly responsible for insulin-stimulated glucose disposal and that a deficiency in the glucose transporter in the pathway is responsible for hyperglycemia in non-insulin-dependent diabetics. From a physiological point of view the most surprising result was that the heavily regulated allosteric enzyme, glycogen synthase, does not control flux but is needed to maintain homeostasis during flux changes. This novel role for a phosphorylated allosteric enzyme is proposed to be a general phenomenon in metabolic and signaling pathways, which physiologically link different cellular activities.

In human and rat brains ^{13}C NMR measurements of the flow of labeled glucose into glutamate and glutamine simultaneously determine the rate of glucose oxidation and glutamate neurotransmitter cycling and reveal a 1:1 stoichiometry between the two fluxes. Implications for the interpretation of functional imaging studies and for psychology are discussed.

These results demonstrate how intermediary metabolism serves to connect biochemistry with systemic physiology when measured and analyzed by in vivo NMR methods.

INTRODUCTION AND OBJECTIVES

In the past decade progress in molecular biology and neuroscience has led to a new appreciation of the complexity of the living state. Even for the most basic biological processes, such as the breakdown of glucose for fuel, the products of well over 1000 genes are involved. Recent rapid advances have unveiled great banks of nature's secrets, but as our knowledge has grown, the complexities of the

0066-4278/01/0315-0015$14.00

living state have not been simplified. Molecular genetics and structural biology have identified nucleic acids and proteins involved in an ever-increasing network of biochemical activities, and details of molecular properties are so plentiful they can only be handled by computers. The complicated wall charts of intermediary metabolism whose intricacies could dazzle earlier visitors now seem to be quaint relics of a far simpler time. Biochemistry has provided chemical and physical explanations of many properties, e.g. molecules, structures, genes, and signaling pathways. These explanations derive from reductionist approaches in which more biological and complex entities are broken down into components that can be explained in terms of physics and chemistry.

The analysis of a complex phenomenon in terms of its components, which furthering our understanding of the original complexity, is the methodology responsible for most scientific advances since Descartes' time. The difficulty in applying this model to the study of life is in turning the reductionist understanding back upon the more complex. The power of modern molecular biology and biochemical methods has led to increasing detail at the component level while often neglecting the upward explanatory pathway. For the contemporary biochemist the integrative approach is further hindered by the parallel increase in our understanding of the more complex aspects of the life sciences. The more organismic biological phenomena, such as disease, behavior, evolution, and mind, have also become more complicated, and by their importance, more needful of explanation. As a consequence, modern biochemistry more than ever before sits at the juncture of these two universes—the more complex organismic properties and the equally complex but ever more detailed physical understanding at a molecular level.

To understand the biological functions of genes and proteins and to base future understanding of a complex organism upon molecular findings it is necessary to develop methods that study the living state. Although many directions are promising, we have chosen to explore the much-neglected field of intermediary metabolism, which functions at a level one step up from biochemical molecules. It is here that molecules, produced by the genes and with properties describable by physics and chemistry, coordinate to serve physiological and organismic needs. In this step physiological and cellular activities, based upon molecules, respond to both external conditions and the intrinsic needs of a cell to grow and multiply. Intermediary metabolism and its relation to systemic physiology had been overshadowed by the recent vigorous studies in molecular and structural biology. Although its location on the epistemological ladder between molecular biochemistry and systemic physiology has made it too important to be overlooked, its broad connective nature, spanning so much research, has made it very difficult to study. We propose that this disjuncture can be partially healed with the new physical methods for studying metabolism now available. Furthermore, we propose that metabolism provides one approach to bridging our understanding of complex phenomena at the physiological and behavioral levels with an understanding of molecular mechanisms of gene expression and protein function.

Since 1981 our laboratory has been addressing this challenge of studying bio-chemistry in the living state by developing ^{13}C nuclear magnetic resonance (NMR) spectroscopy for measuring concentrations of metabolites and the rates through metabolic pathways in the human body. In vivo NMR spectroscopy is similar to the better-known magnetic resonance imaging (MRI) in that it measures the signal emitted by nuclei within the human body when placed in a powerful mag-netic field. However, it adds a new dimension to MRI by tracking the resolved NMR signals from different chemicals in the body, a method well developed in organic chemistry. As a result, in vivo NMR can measure the concentrations and synthesis rates of individual biological molecules such as glycogen and neu-rotransmitters within precisely defined areas of specific organs such as brain, liver, and muscle. Thus it has the unique capability of revealing how critical metabolic pathways actually work in healthy individuals and how they are altered in disease.

The use of ^{13}C NMR to track metabolic pathways was pioneered in the 1970s, when metabolic substrates such as glucose were tagged with an NMR-visible stable isotope, ^{13}C. In vivo NMR measurements then followed the metabolism of the labeled glucose through the appearance of the ^{13}C isotope in other com-pounds (1). Rates of these metabolic pathways were determined by measuring the label appearance as a function of time. Initial studies were performed with microorganisms and perfused organs (2). These experiments were extended to intact animal models in 1981 (3) and to human subjects when the Yale School of Medicine established a Magnetic Resonance Center in 1985 that was equipped with superconducting magnets capable of following in vivo NMR spectroscopy in humans (4). Since that time, in vivo ^{13}C NMR has been applied to study a variety of metabolic pathways and systems in animals and humans in our laboratory and several other laboratories world-wide (5–7).

In this review we focus on studies performed primarily at Yale in two areas, the regulation of muscle glycogen metabolism in health and diabetes and the relation-ship between glutamate neurotransmission and metabolism. These studies have probed cellular metabolism in the living human and have provided new understand-ings of the couplings between metabolism and function. In addition, the studies of diabetes have delineated the molecular basis of altered metabolism and physiol-ogy in a human disease. Non-invasive NMR studies of metabolism have provided molecular information bridging the coupled, interactive chemical processes of cell and organ in humans.

Metabolism Occupies a Central Position in Life, Linking Genes and Proteins to Higher-Level Biological Functions

A metabolic pathway is a series of chemical reactions that the cell uses to break down simple molecules such as glucose for fuel, or alternatively to synthesize more complex biomolecules such as hormones and neurotransmitters. These chemical reactions are performed by enzymes produced by the expression of genes. The ability of the body to perform the integrated physiological processes needed for survival, such as providing the energy needed to sustain brain function, depends upon the coordination of metabolic pathways in billions of cells throughout the body. As shown in Figure 1, metabolic pathways occupy a central position in the

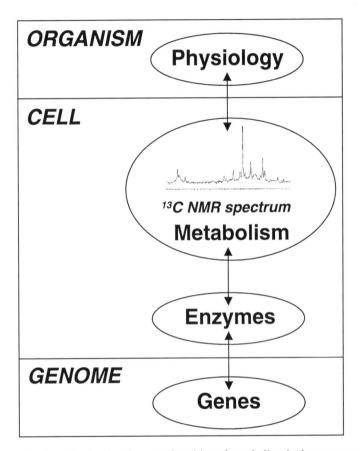

Figure 1   A schematic showing the central position of metabolism in the spectrum of biological organization. Metabolic pathways consist of a chain of chemical reactions catalyzed by enzymes. The cell controls the rate of these pathways through genetic expression and the action of signaling pathways. By modifying enzymes through gene expression and/or signaling pathways, the rate of metabolic pathways can be changed to meet the needs of the organism. Sensing pathways are also metabolic pathways: They detect the presence of specialized biomolecules such as hormones and neurotransmitters used for cell-to-cell communication. At the level of the organism the coordinated response of metabolic pathways is critical for maintaining higher-level function such as systemic physiology, organ function, and behavior. The demands on metabolism are constantly changing in the face of environmental challenges.

levels of biological complexity, extending from gene expression at the level of the individual cell to physiology, organ function, and behavior at the level of the organism.

The research strategy we advocate is to work from metabolism in a step-by-step manner, both upward in complexity to understand how metabolism supports higher-level functions and downward toward understanding the roles of specific genes and proteins in controlling metabolism. There are several advantages of this approach over altering a gene (either directly as in transgenics or indirectly through the study of inherited mutations) and observing the change in complex phenotypes. Most importantly, methods have been developed for determining the quantitative effects of enzyme kinetics on metabolism and of changes in metabolism on systemic physiology. Prominent among the methods is metabolic control analysis (MCA), which evaluates experimental data quantitatively and can guide the design of experiments (8). A key insight of MCA is that the degree of control an enzyme exerts on a metabolic pathway is not constant but, rather, depends upon the environment of the cell, the expression of other enzymes in the pathway, and the activity of other metabolic pathways in the cell. Therefore, it is critical to study metabolism in vivo in order to understand the function of specific enzymes and their regulation through gene expression and cellular signaling. A further implication of MCA is that given the inability to determine from in vitro studies of an isolated enzyme the control of even a single metabolic pathway, it seems unlikely that the functions of proteins may be ascertained through correlation of gene alterations with complex phenotypical traits. Only a more systemic approach can ultimately provide a satisfactory account of protein function in vivo.

STUDIES OF MUSCLE GLYCOGEN METABOLISM

The first example comes from our studies of insulin regulation of the muscle glycogen synthesis pathway. A failure of this regulation leads to non-insulin-dependent diabetes mellitus (NIDDM), which affects ~15% of the population over the age of 65 in the United States. The disease is known to have a strong genetic component because there is ~90% concordance in identical twins. In addition to the genetic contribution, patients respond to environmental factors of exercise and diet (9). In a healthy person, after a meal containing glucose, the pancreas releases insulin that activates glucose metabolism in muscle and liver. In diabetes the ability to maintain the balance between glucose absorption, metabolism, and insulin secretion is lost, which results in chronically elevated blood glucose and subsequent cellular damage.

Prior to the in vivo NMR studies it was widely believed that the molecular defect responsible for NIDDM was in the enzyme glycogen synthase. Glycogen is the major storage compound for glucose in the body. Most glycogen is present in muscle and liver. In both organs glycogen synthesis is stimulated by insulin and high glucose levels. The enzymes responsible for glycogen synthesis and degradation, glycogen synthase (GSase)[1] and phosphorylase (GPase), have been the canonical textbook examples of flux regulation by enzyme phosphorylation (10). When the body needs to eliminate excess systemic glucose, such as after a high-carbohydrate meal, the hormone insulin is released from the pancreas. Insulin binds cellular receptors, which leads to a cascade of signaling events. In the final event, phosphoprotein phosphatase cleaves phosphorylated serines from GSase, which activates it. The key role ascribed to glycogen synthase was based on the belief that phosphorylated enzymes in a metabolic pathway control the rate. (The direct effect of insulin upon GSase phosphorylation was consistent with this view but, as it turns out, was not causative.) An examination of Figure 2, which is a schematic of the pathway of muscle glycogen synthesis (10), shows that the in vivo situation is considerably more complex. Three enzymes in the pathway between plasma glucose and muscle glycogen are regulated by insulin: glucose transporters, hexokinase, and glycogen synthase. Furthermore, these early studies showed that the activities of these enzymes in vivo or in cell cultures correlated with the rate of insulin-stimulated glycogen synthesis.

In addition to uncertainties at the molecular level about the control exerted by glycogen synthase on glycogen synthesis, there were also uncertainties at the level of whole-body physiology about the relative importance of the muscle and liver glycogen synthesis pathways. Studies measuring arteriovenous differences had been interpreted to support muscle as the primary storage point for plasma glucose. However, this interpretation was weakened by the difficulty of making accurate arteriovenous difference measurements of liver glucose uptake in humans and by the inaccuracy of biopsy measurements of muscle glycogen.

The limitations of previous methods were overcome by the development of ^{13}C NMR observations of glycogen. Glycogen, with molecular weight of several million Daltons, would, if it were a rigid molecule, not be visible by high-resolution

---

[1]Abbreviations used throughout the text: ε_s^i in MCA, on the elasticity of enzyme i with respect to metabolite S; ΔN, the incremental activity of a neuronal process; ΔS, the incremental generalized functional imaging signal; C_i^j, flux control coefficient by the ith enzyme; CBF, cerebral blood flow; $CMR_{Glc(ox)}$, cerebral metabolic rate of glucose oxidation; CMR_{glc}, cerebral metabolic rate of glucose (total); $CMRO_2$, cerebral metabolic rate of oxygen; E_i, concentration of ith supply; E_{demand}, group demand enzyme; E_{supply}, group supply enzyme; fMRI, functional magnetic resonance imaging; G6P, glucose-6- phosphate; GABA, gamma-amino-butyric-acid; GPase, glycogen phosphorylase; GSase, glycogen synthase; GT, muscle glucose transporter (Glut 4); Hk, hexokinase; J, flux through pathway; M, mental processes; MCA, metabolic control analysis; NIDDM, non-insulin dependent diabetes mellitus; NMR, nuclear magnetic resonance; NP, rate of neurophysiological energy processes; PET, positron emission tomography; PFK, phosphofructokinase; S, generalized functional imaging signal; V_{cycle}, flux of glutamate+GABA neurotransmitter cycling; V_{TCA}, tricarboxy acid cycle flux.

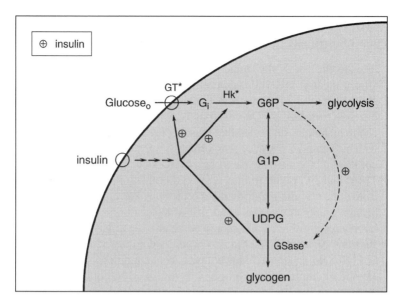

Figure 2   A schematic of a muscle cell showing the metabolic pathway of glycogen synthesis from blood glucose. Glucose is taken up from the blood through the muscle glucose transporter. Once in the muscle cell it is converted by hexokinase to G6P. G6P is then converted to glycogen in a series of enzyme-catalyzed reactions, the final step being performed by glycogen synthase. These three enzymes are activated by insulin, which activates molecular signaling pathways. These signaling pathways adjust the rate of glycogen synthesis in order to meet the needs of the organism for maintaining a stable blood glucose level. In a series of studies using in vivo ¹³C and ³¹P NMR, it was shown that (a) the rate of muscle glycogen synthesis is primarily controlled by the muscle glucose transporter enzyme, (b) a defect in the activation of this enzyme by cellular signaling is responsible for the impairment in this pathway in NIDDM, and (c) this defect is present prior to the development of diabetes and may be a primary cause of the disease.

NMR because its resonance lines would be broadened beyond detectability. However, preliminary observations of a ¹³C resonance assigned to glycogen in perfused livers (5, 11) led us in 1980 to examine this resonance closely and to determine its visibility in vivo (12). A series of experiments, at first in solutions in vitro, then in vivo in the animal muscle, and finally in the human muscle, showed by comparison with standard solutions that the ¹³C glycogen NMR were ~100% visible (13, 14). This meant that they could be used to determine glycogen concentrations in vivo in both liver and muscle, in humans as well as in animal models. The intensity of the 1.1% natural abundance ¹³C peak enabled the muscle glycogen concentration to be determined more accurately than by the existing biopsy method (14). Furthermore, by enriching the ¹³C concentration, starting with an enriched substrate such as 1-¹³C glucose, the sensitivity and therefore the accuracy could be increased by more than a factor of ten.

^{13}C NMR Studies of the Role of Insulin-Stimulated Muscle Glycogen Synthesis in Maintaining Glucose Homeostasis

Prior to the ^{13}C NMR studies it was well known that the elevation of glucose after a meal in NIDDM was primarily due to metabolic pathways in the muscle and/or liver not properly responding to the hormone insulin. Arteriovenous difference studies by DeFronzo and co-workers in conjunction with a glucose clamp technique suggested that muscle played the dominant role (15). However, which metabolic pathway was primarily responsible for insulin resistance was not known, nor were the identities of the key control enzymes in these pathways. The initial ^{13}C NMR studies showed that insulin-stimulated glycogen synthesis in muscle was the major metabolic pathway for disposing of excess glucose in healthy adults after a meal and that a defect in muscle glycogen synthesis was largely responsible for the decreased insulin sensitivity in NIDDM (16). In these studies, ^{13}C-labeled glucose and insulin were infused into both healthy subjects and NIDDM patients to simulate post-meal conditions. Using ^{13}C NMR the flow of glucose into muscle glycogen was measured by following the increase in the intensity of the ^{13}C NMR glycogen signal. A time course of ^{13}C NMR spectra from the muscle glycogen of a healthy subject is shown in Figure 3; Figure 4 compares the time course of muscle glycogen synthesis in the two groups. The twofold slower muscle glycogen synthesis rate in the NIDDM patients was found to quantitatively account for their lower insulin-stimulated glucose uptake, thus establishing muscle glycogen synthesis as the major pathway of insulin resistance in NIDDM.

Muscle therefore was shown to have the major role in insulin-stimulated glucose storage while a meal is being absorbed; however, between meals the level of glucose in the blood is maintained by release of glucose from the liver. Glucose is produced by the liver either by de novo synthesis via gluconeogenesis or by breakdown of stored glycogen (glycogenolysis). By using ^{13}C NMR to measure concentrations of liver glycogen during a fast and measuring the total rates of hepatic glucose output by conventional radiolabels, the separate gluconeogenic and glycogenolytic rates were determined in human livers (17). Gluconeogenesis accounted for 64% of glucose production during the first 22 h of fast in normal subjects, substantially more than had previously been estimated by other methods. Rates of gluconeogenesis in patients with NIDDM accounted for nearly all of the elevated rate of fasting liver glucose production (18).

The initial ^{13}C NMR studies were designed to mimic the blood glucose and insulin profile after a high-carbohydrate meal. The ability to measure both muscle and liver glycogen synthesis by ^{13}C NMR has also allowed the roles of muscle and liver glycogen synthesis in the maintenance of plasma glucose homeostasis to be determined under normal feeding conditions (19). Under these conditions muscle glycogen synthesis remains dominant, but the contributions of liver are larger than under sustained conditions of hyperglycemic hyperinsulinemia.

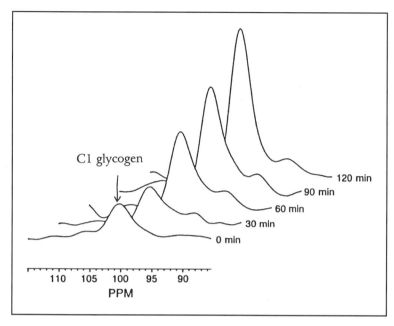

Figure 3   The time course of ^{13}C NMR spectra of muscle glycogen obtained from a healthy subject during an infusion of insulin and ^{13}C-labeled glucose. In the NMR spectrum, signal amplitude is plotted versus time. The resonance frequency of the ^{13}C isotope in the glycogen molecule was resolved from background signals of ^{13}C-labeled glucose and other biological metabolites in the muscle (16).

Determination Using ^{13}C and ^{31}P NMR of the Reduced Activity Enzyme Steps in the Muscle Glycogen Synthesis Pathway in NIDDM

Because of their previously suspected roles in diabetes, the enzymes in the muscle glycogen synthesis pathway had been among the most intensively studied. However, despite decades of studies of the isolated enzymes, control of the rate was not understood. Although GSase was most often described as the key altered step in diabetes, several other enzymes had been proposed for this role, including the glucose transporter and hexokinase (Figure 2). The rates of these enzymes are insulin stimulated and have been reported to correlate with the rate of insulin-stimulated glycogen synthesis in healthy subjects and patients with diabetes.

We distinguished the control exerted in healthy subjects and in subjects with NIDDM by simultaneously measuring in vivo the rate of muscle glycogen synthesis with ^{13}C NMR and the concentration of glucose-6-phosphate (G6P) with ^{31}P NMR (20) at different levels of blood glucose. An increase in blood glucose (at constant insulin) showed a greater increase of G6P in the control subjects than in the diabetic

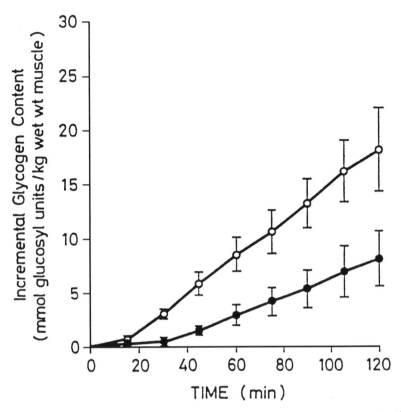

Figure 4 The time courses of muscle glycogen concentration calculated from the ^{13}C NMR spectra during an insulin and glucose infusion for NIDDM subjects and healthy controls. The diabetics (closed symbols) synthesize glycogen more slowly than control subjects (open symbols). Quantitative features of this study showed that insulin-stimulated muscle glycogen synthesis is the major metabolic pathway of glucose disposal in both groups and that impairments in this pathway are responsible for the chronic hyperglycemia in NIDDM subjects.

patients. This showed that changes in the glucose transporter/hexokinase (GT/Hk) steps, not changes in GSase, were responsible for the decreased rate of glycogenesis in NIDDM patients relative to controls. However, control by GT/Hk in the patients with NIDDM could have arisen from a reduction in the rate of those early steps to the point where GT/Hk had taken over control of flux from GSase, still possibly the controlling step in healthy subjects. Subsequent experiments set up in accordance with MCA (as discussed in the next section) showed that GT/Hk was the flux-controlling step in healthy subjects as well as in patients with NIDDM.

In order to distinguish whether a reduction in the glucose transporter or hex-okinase activity is responsible for the reduced rate of insulin-stimulated glycogen synthesis in NIDDM, ^{13}C NMR experiments were done to measure the intracellular free glucose concentration (21). Previous studies using NMR and biopsy methods had demonstrated that intracellular glucose in the muscle was low, but there was ambiguity owing to the contribution of glucose in the extracellular space (22). Labeled mannitol, which is not taken up by the muscle cell, was used as a marker to allow the signal from 1-^{13}C glucose in the blood and extracellular space to be distinguished from the glucose within the muscle. The results demonstrated that intracellular glucose was <200 μM, which would lead to a negligible back flux through the glucose transporter. Therefore, it was concluded that the reduction in glucose transporter activity is responsible for the decreased rate of insulin-stimulated glycogen synthesis in patients with NIDDM.

Impaired Insulin-Dependent Muscle Glycogen Synthesis is a Primary Defect in NIDDM and May Be Corrected by Exercise

Although the activity of the muscle glucose transporter is impaired in diabetes, the question remained as to whether this was the primary defect in NIDDM or was secondary to the loss of glucose homeostasis early in the disease. Young, healthy, normal-weight offspring of NIDDM parents with normal blood glucose levels were studied. Based on previous longitudinal studies of children of parents with NIDDM it was known that these subjects had a high risk of developing the disease (23). In the ^{13}C NMR studies a defect in the muscle glucose transporter and an associated reduction in glycogen synthesis similar to that in the NIDDM subjects were found, suggesting that impaired glucose transporter activity was a primary defect in the pathogenesis of NIDDM (24).

Physical activity has been known for several decades to improve insulin sensitivity. After glycogen-depleting exercise, ^{13}C NMR glycogen concentrations were measured during recovery in control subjects. In a refinement of earlier biopsy studies (25), the recovery was sharply divided into an initial insulin-insensitive period of 1–2 h, followed for many hours by an insulin-sensitive time (26). Similarly, measurements of muscle glycogen repletion after intense depleting exercise in insulin-resistant offspring of NIDDM parents showed (*a*) normal rates of muscle glycogen synthesis during the early insulin-independent phase of recovery from exercise and (*b*) severely diminished rates of muscle glycogen synthesis during the subsequent insulin-dependent period (2–5 h). These experiments provide evidence that exercise and insulin stimulate muscle glycogen synthesis in humans by different mechanisms, in accord with the well-known additive effect of these stimuli on glycogen synthesis.

More recently, in a similar group of young, healthy, insulin-resistant offspring of NIDDM parents, it was found that after six weeks of aerobic training G6P levels and rates of muscle glycogen synthesis normalized during a hyperglycemic clamp, thus demonstrating that this abnormality can be reversed with exercise training (27). The reversal of the defect through regular exercise in these subjects underlines the complex interactions between the environment (lifestyle) and genetics in the development of the disease.

Metabolic Control Analysis of the Rate-Controlling Steps for Muscle Glycogen Synthesis

The main control step (glucose transport) in patients with NIDDM was determined by a comparison of flux and the concentration of G6P in these subjects versus healthy subjects. However, that comparison, which explains the lowered flux in NIDDM subjects, does not necessarily identify the control points in healthy subjects. The glucose transporter activity may be so reduced in patients with NIDDM that it dominates flux control even though it does not exert the majority of flux control in healthy subjects. To pursue this question, experiments were done in healthy subjects to evaluate the flux control coefficients as defined by MCA (8). MCA is a well-developed theory that defines the control of flux in a pathway in terms of the concentrations and kinetic properties of constitutive enzymes and shows how it can be determined by achievable experimental protocols (8, 28). As shown by MCA, the control exerted by an enzyme on a biochemical pathway depends on the relative activities of all the enzymes in the pathway. MCA provides a theoretical basis for analyzing the control of metabolism and has proven to be extremely well suited for interpreting in vivo NMR measurements. MCA, in conjunction with in vivo NMR measurements, offers the opportunity to utilize existing information about biomolecules in furthering our understanding of more complex physiological functions.

A basic concept in MCA is the flux control coefficient (C_i^J), which is defined as

$$C_i^J = \frac{\partial J/J}{\partial E_i/E_i}, \qquad\qquad 1.$$

where C_i^J is the fractional change in the pathway flux, J, achieved by a fractional change in E_i, the concentration of the ith enzyme. If C_i^J approaches unity for a particular enzyme, then this enzyme satisfies the old concept of a rate-limiting step. Generally, however, the control is distributed among several sites. Furthermore because

$$\sum C_i^J = 1 \qquad\qquad 2.$$

for a linear pathway, values of C_i^J for all enzymes depend upon the state of the system. For example, decreasing a particular value of E_i can increase the flux control coefficient of that step, and necessarily, because of the summation rule, it will decrease the coefficients elsewhere in the pathway. In the extreme case of $E_i \sim 0$ all the flux control is localized at that step. The flux control coefficient is a property of the in vivo system and as such can be measured by in vivo NMR, which can follow the flux of a label such as ^{13}C through the pathway. Contributions of individual enzymes to the pathway's kinetics can be evaluated through another parameter, elasticity, ε, defined by MCA. Elasticity measures the sensitivity of the individual enzyme's velocity V_i to changes in any metabolite S. This parameter is determined by the individual enzyme's kinetic properties, measured in vitro under in vivo conditions. The definition of elasticity is

$$\varepsilon_S^i = \frac{\partial V_i/V_i}{\partial S/S.}$$ 3.

Although ε_S^i tends to be most significant for substrates, products, and allosteric effectors of the particular enzyme i, it might be non-vanishing for any enzyme and any metabolite.

Kacser & Burns (28) derived the connectivity theorem, which quantitatively relates elasticities measured in vitro to flux control coefficients in vivo by the relation

$$\sum_{i=1}^{\eta} C_i^J \varepsilon_S^i = 0,$$ 4.

where the summation is over all enzymes in the pathway. This states that for the particular metabolite S, the product of its elasticity with respect to enzyme i times the flux control coefficient of that enzyme C_i^J, when summed over all the enzymes in the pathway, is zero. Although this relationship can be evaluated for a multi-enzyme pathway (because the number of equations increases linearly within the number of intermediates S), it becomes quite workable experimentally for the particularly simple case of two enzymes in a pathway, sharing one metabolite S. In this case

$$\xrightarrow{E_{Supply}} S \xrightarrow{E_{demand}},$$ 5.

and the summation theorem states that

$$C_{Supply}^J + C_{demand}^J = 1.$$ 6.

The connectivity theorem for this two-enzyme system gives

$$C_{Supply}^J \varepsilon_S^{Supply} + C_{demand}^J \varepsilon_S^{demand} = 0.$$ 7.

By measuring the elasticities in vitro under in vivo conditions, these two equations determine the two flux control coefficients. The most useful results have been obtained for a two-enzyme model. A popular, user-friendly reduction of a complex pathway into a two-enzyme system can be achieved by a "top-down" analysis (29). This provides criteria for dividing a multi-step pathway into two lumped enzyme steps, one before and one after a particular metabolite, of the sort shown in Equation 5. The flux control coefficients and other parameters of MCA are experimentally determined for the lumped enzymes, E_{supply} and E_{demand}. To obtain more detailed information, each of the lumped enzymes can be broken down into the individual steps as required.

Muscle glycogen flux has been measured by in vivo NMR and evaluated with sufficient data to use a top-down MCA format, thus illustrating the valuable symbiosis achieved by this combined approach. Top-down analysis of the glycogenic pathway centers on G6P as the bridging metabolite (see Figure 2). In the downstream demand portion, two rapid enzymes from G6P lead to GSase so that the response of GSase to G6P determines the elasticity of this group enzyme to G6P. The elasticity of the GT/Hk supply-side enzymes and of the GSase demand-side enzymes to G6P were measured. The flux through the pathway was varied by changing the level of plasma glucose at a constant insulin level (30). Previous studies, measuring the activity of glycogen synthase from biopsy samples, had shown that the plasma glucose level under these conditions does not affect the activity of the enzyme. Using biopsy values, the connectivity theorem (Equation 4) indicated that $C^J_{supply} \gg C^J_{demand}$. A similar conclusion was reached from the proportional increase in glycogen synthase flux with plasma glucose levels. Therefore, in the healthy, young subjects the majority of flux control was vested in the supply enzymes, consisting of glucose transporter and hexokinase, similar to the patients with NIDDM. As mentioned above, subsequent in vivo ^{13}C NMR experiments measured the intramuscular concentration of glucose. Because it was extremely low ($<$ 0.2 mM), the majority of flux control was assigned to the glucose transporter step.

The kinetics of the isolated GSase enzyme are consistent with an allosteric enzyme (31; D Chan, DL Rothman & RG Shulman, unpublished results). The specific experimental results showing the lack of flux control by GSase are in agreement with the general results of MCA, in which a polymeric enzyme subject to allosteric regulation is an unlikely candidate for a large flux control coefficient. This is directly shown by Equation 4, where the large elasticity of allosteric enzymes necessarily assigns them a small flux control coefficient. This point is made very generally in a recent clear text on MCA (8), where detailed results are presented from other biological and theoretical systems confirming this MCA prediction.

To illustrate the wide applicability of this finding we note that phosphofructokinase (PFK) is another example of an allosteric enzyme that had been incorrectly assigned as flux controlling. PFK is usually identified as the rate-controlling step of glycolysis based on its catalyzing an irreversible reaction and its high sensitivity to allosteric effectors. This assertion was tested in a beautiful experiment on yeast by Davies & Brindle, in which the genetic expression was increased, resulting in a fivefold increase in PFK concentration (32). However, the glycolytic flux increased by less than 10%, as expected from the low flux control coefficient. In PFK, as well as in GSase, the commonly accepted textbook (10) explanation of flux control being exercised by a phosphorylated, allosteric enzyme is incorrect.

The Role of Glycogen Synthase in Maintaining Metabolic Homeostasis

An implication of the low flux control coefficient of GSase is that changing the activity of GSase will have a negligible effect upon the glycogenetic rate. The lack of a major role for GSase in flux control is surprising in light of its complex regulation by signaling pathways (33). Studies of the control of GSase by phosphorylation continue to find new controlling elements; for example, a recent textbook lists as controlling factors three second messengers, three hormones, seven kinases, and two phosphatases plus several phosphatase inhibitors and other enzymes (35). There are also several allosteric inhibitors and activators, yet despite these well-established controls of GSase activity, our results show that this enzyme does not control the rate of glycogen synthesis.

What then is the function of these elaborate controls of GSase? A potential explanation of a functional role of GSase comes from theoretical studies of Kascer & Acarenza (36). They showed that in a branched metabolic pathway, in which intermediates of one pathway are the starting substrates of others, a critical criterion for system-wide metabolic regulation is that the activity of enzymes proximal and distal to the shared intermediates should be regulated in synchrony. In this way flux changes do not require changes in concentrations of intermediates. This constancy provides homeostasis. Homeostasis is a well-recognized physiological criterion. Our use of homeostasis refers to the maintenance of constant concentrations of metabolites in a pathway during changes in flux. In this way homeostasis serves the physiological function of allowing specific local pathways to change flux without requiring flux changes elsewhere. In the glycogen synthesis pathway both intracellular glucose and G6P are key branch points for metabolic pathways, including the sorbitol reductase pathway, the glucosamine synthesis pathway, the pentose shunt, and glycolysis. UDP glucose and F6P, both derived from G6P, serve several other pathways. The analogy between the theoretical shared pathway of Kascer & Acarenza (36) and the glycogen synthesis pathway is shown in Figure 5.

The role of the regulation of GSase activity by phosphorylation was tested theoretically by calculating the concentration of G6P as a function of insulin-stimulated glycogen synthesis flux for a constant level of GSase activity (37). Figure 6 compares the results of this calculation with the experimental results of Rossetti & Giaccari (38). Their measurements of glycogen synthesis rates at different insulin concentrations in rat muscle showed a near constancy of G6P levels during rate changes of an order of magnitude. In contrast, large increases in G6P would be required to increase the rate of GSase by allosteric activation to match the increased flux if the enzyme activity had not been increased by cellular signaling and phosphorylation.

The Role of Insulin Regulation of the Kinetic Properties of Glucose Transport and GSase in Serving the Physiological Needs of the Body While Maintaining Cellular Homeostasis

In their classic studies of isolated muscle GSase, Roach & Larner (39) proposed that the regulation of GSase by phosphorylation serves the higher-level physiological functions of the organism, whereas the allosteric sensitivity to G6P and

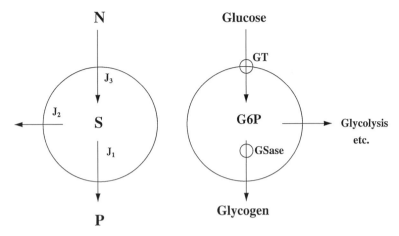

Figure 5   Model of coordinated control proposed by Kascer & Acarenza to accommodate changes in flux from N to the product (P) while maintaining the concentration of the shared intermediate (S) constant. In this way the branching flux J_2 will be independent of J_3. The analogy with the glycogenic pathway is shown where the shared intermediate is G6P.

other effectors reflects local control. "The activity of glycogen synthase results from the integration of two types of regulatory signals: hormonal control via phosphorylation-dephosphorylation, and local cellular control via the concentrations of small molecule modifiers of the enzyme." MCA of the in vivo NMR results extends Roach & Larner's proposal by identifying another function for phosphorylation-dephosphorylation, cellular homeostasis, and by quantitatively defining the roles of glucose transport and GSase in controlling the flux. In this updated view, when the pancreas releases insulin in response to glucose entering the blood from the intestinal tract, a balanced increase in the activity of the glucose transporters and GSase occurs; the activity of glucose transport determines the flux, and the parallel increase in the activity of GSase prevents significant changes in G6P concentration. Under normal conditions this response is sufficient to prevent plasma glucose concentration from substantially rising after a meal. In extreme cases in which the rate of glucose entry from the gastrointestinal tract exceeds the ability of the muscle glycogen synthesis pathway to remove glucose, plasma glucose concentrations will rise. The elevated glucose increases the rate of glucose transport into muscle by mass action due to the high K_m of the transporter. The transported glucose is converted to G6P, which increases slightly and further activates GSase by allosteric mechanisms, thereby limiting the increase in G6P concentrations.

General Implications for Biochemistry

The maintenance of metabolic homeostasis by regulation of GSase activity represents a previously unexplored role for enzyme phosphorylation, with far-reaching

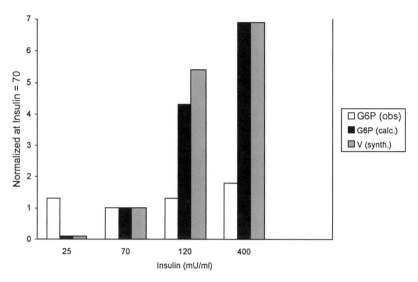

Figure 6   Results replotted from Rossetti & Giaccari (38) of rate of glycogen synthesis (V) in rat muscle versus G6P at different plasma insulin concentrations. The observed values of G6P and V were set to unity at the basal insulin concentration of 70. The concentrations of G6P change very little over the wide range of insulin, changing significantly only at supraphysiological plasma insulin levels despite a large increase in flux. The values of G6P calculated on the assumption of constant GSase activity change significantly over this range as they are linear with flux. The increased activity with insulin levels eliminates the need for a large linear increase in G6P with flux.

implications for cellular control of metabolism. The constancy of pathway intermediates during extreme changes in flux is a widely established but little appreciated result. In muscle (40), heart (41), and brain (42), concentrations of intermediates in the glycolytic and mitochondrial oxidation pathways have been shown to remain constant to within experimental accuracies during several-fold flux changes. Several allosteric enzymes in these pathways are regulated by phosphorylation, and we suggest they play a role in maintaining cellular homeostasis. In Kacser & Acarenza's original formulation and in subsequent reports the "multisite modulation" of activities of the enzyme groups proximal and distal to a branch point was proposed to arise from coupled gene expression (43). There is considerable evidence for this kind of response, but such inducible effects take many minutes to develop in humans, whereas the homeostasis in the face of the flux increases mentioned above responds to changes in much less than a minute. Fell & Thomas (43) have proposed that such rapid multi-site modulation by phosphorylation of allosteric enzymes could possibly serve such a purpose and experimental support has recently been proposed (37; J Chase, DL Rothman & RG Shulman, unpublished observation). The specific case of GSase supports this proposal, while more complete experimental and theoretical studies are evaluating it quantitatively.

The relevance of the use of kinase and phosphatase activity for maintaining metabolic homeostasis may extend beyond metabolic pathways, particularly in light of the extensive families of kinases involved in complex organismic functions (35). The cell division cycle, gene expression signaling pathways, oncogenes, and tumor suppression have all been followed by the expression of kinases and phosphatases (10, 35). Without considerations of homeostasis, all targets of kinases have been implicitly assumed to control the rate of a reaction, either the flux through a metabolic pathway or the rate of gene expression. Based on MCA and the findings of GSase, alternate roles of kinases in maintaining cellular homeostasis in other pathways must be considered. Changes in specific kinase activity, such as by gene expression, can be presumed to be responding to changes in pathway activity, but they cannot, without additional evidence, be assumed to be controlling these pathways.

TURNOVER

One advantage of ^{13}C NMR studies is that they can follow fluxes of labeled precursors. In the absence of labeled substrates, the low 1.1% naturally abundant ^{13}C NMR signal can be used to measure concentrations, while labeled enriched precursors such as 1-^{13}C glucose enable fluxes to be measured even when concentrations are in steady state. This kind of turnover measurement has been very valuable in measuring kinetics during steady-state concentrations, particularly in vivo, where steady-state concentrations are the rule.

In one series of experiments, based on earlier rat liver studies (44), 1-^{13}C glucose was infused to measure rates of glycogenesis and glycogenolysis simultaneously in the human liver. At constant total liver glycogen concentrations, the initial rate of label incorporation determined the rate of glycogenesis, which necessarily equaled the glycogenolytic rate. This experiment showed high rates of both processes; in other words, there was rapid turnover of the liver glycogen pool at constant steady-state concentrations (45). The hepatic function served by this futile cycle has not been identified; however, constant turnover, so readily monitored by ^{13}C NMR, has been subsequently found in exercising muscle, where it has provided insights into a novel role for glycogen (46).

^{13}C NMR STUDIES OF THE ROLE OF METABOLISM IN GLUTAMATE NEUROTRANSMISSION

In the modern view, the function of the brain is to process information. This merger of information theory and neurobiology is the basis of cognitive neuroscience. The transfer of information between neurons occurs at the synapses, which are the junctions connecting neurons. Most such information is carried across synapses by small molecules acting as neurotransmitters. Neurotransmitters are studied from many directions. New species are continually discovered, identified, and localized, while their receptors and regulation of their release are investigated by genetic and chemical methods. Our approach considers neurotransmitters a class of metabolites whose concentrations, reaction pathways, and fluxes can be studied in vivo as one particularly important aspect of intermediary metabolism. Their biochemical pathways serve the brain's primary function of transmitting information across synapses. Because rates of release and recognition of neurotransmitters regulate brain activity, such activity should be related to brain energy consumption. Our studies have focused on just these points: how neurotransmitter fluxes support the transmission of information and how this process depends upon brain energy consumption. Dozens of neurotransmitters have been identified and characterized, and properties of several, e.g. dopamine, serotonin, acetylcholine, and norepinephrine, have been studied intensively for decades. Two neurotransmitters, glutamate and gamma-amino-butyric-acid (GABA), stand out because of their high concentrations (in the millimolar range). Furthermore, in the mammalian cortex, more than 90% of the neurons serve these two neurotransmitters. Glutamate is excitatory, serving to activate neurons, whereas GABA inhibits neuronal activity.

The high concentrations of glutamate and GABA have enabled us to observe their high-resolution NMR signals in vivo. The first observations by ^{13}C NMR of cerebral glutamate were made using indirect detection at the MR Center at Yale in 1983 (47, 48). Glucose is normally the nearly exclusive cerebral carbon source, so that enriched 1-^{13}C glucose was particularly useful in following pathways and quantitating fluxes. These NMR label experiments followed the flow of ^{13}C label into pools of metabolites. Advanced NMR techniques and equipment improvements now enable in vivo measures of fluxes in several cubic centimeters of human brain by ^{1}H-^{13}C NMR, in which the carbon isotope is measured indirectly through scalar coupling to bound proton nuclei (49, 50). This flux measurement provides valuable quantitation of metabolic rates in vivo, not obtainable by any other methods.

The best established ^{13}C NMR measurement in the brain is the flow from 1-^{13}C glucose to 4-^{13}C glutamate, which was used to determine the flux through the tricarboxylic acid cycle (V_{TCA}) (51).[2] The cerebral metabolic rate of oxygen consumption (CMRO$_2$) can be calculated from V_{TCA} because TCA activity is directly coupled to oxidation (10). Values of CMRO$_2$ determined by this method in experiments on rats and humans agreed very well with literature values, thus confirming this in vivo method of measuring oxygen consumption and therefore energy consumption (52).

After technical improvements to NMR were made, it became possible to measure in the human brain the label flow into glutamine from glutamate (53).

---

[2]Although glutamate is not a TCA$_{cycle}$ intermediate, it has been shown to be in fast exchange with α-ketoglutarate, which is in the cycle. Because exchange between these two pools is rapid in brains compared with the TCA$_{cycle}$ flux, the turnover of large glutamate pools determines V_{TCA} (51).

Glutamine, although not a neurotransmitter, had been proposed to be an intermediate in the glutamate neurotransmitter cycle (Figure 7, see color insert). The ability to follow in time, in vivo, the label flow into glutamate and subsequently into glutamine by ^{13}C NMR opened this neurotransmitter cycling to quantitation. The cycle was originally proposed by Berl et al (54) and van den Berg & Garfinkel (55) from ^{14}C and ^{15}N studies of extracts and slices of rat brains. Additional support was provided by enzyme localization studies in neurons and astrocytes (56). However, the importance of this pathway in vivo had not been accepted because of conflicting evidence from studies of brain slices and other in vitro preparations. As shown in Figure 7, glutamate stored in vesicles in the pre-synaptic neuron is released into the synaptic cleft in response to neuronal depolarization. Once released it diffuses across the gap until it is recognized by a glutamate receptor on the post-synaptic surface, which triggers the subsequent post-synaptic potential changes. The majority of released glutamate is not transported by the pre-synaptic terminal, but diffuses to the membranes of the surrounding astrocyte into which it is cotransported down the Na^+ gradient (57). The astrocytic enzyme glutamine synthetase then converts glutamate to glutamine, thus consuming one ATP and one NH_3. Glutamine is transported across the astrocytic membrane, through the intracellular space, and into the neuron, where the enzyme glutaminase reconverts it to glutamate. The glutamate is repackaged into vesicles where it is ready to restart the cycle.

The exciting results of these first experiments were that the flux from glutamate to glutamine was far from negligible but, in fact, on a mole per mole basis, was comparable to the rate of glucose oxidation, thus indicating that the glutamate/glutamine cycle is a major metabolic pathway in the brain. Subsequent studies showed that the rate of neuronal glucose oxidation increases in a close to 1:1 stoichiometry with the rate of the glutamate/glutamine cycle. This finding indicates that brain energy metabolism is coupled directly to glutamate neurotransmission and therefore to brain function. These studies are described below and interpreted in terms of a novel metabolic model that we, in collaboration with Magistretti and co-workers, propose to explain the molecular mechanism of this coupling (58). In addition we present some of the implications of quantitating glutamate neurotransmitter flux for the interpretation of higher-level brain function based on functional imaging studies.

^{13}C NMR STUDIES OF THE RELATIONSHIP BETWEEN THE GLUTAMATE/GLUTAMINE CYCLE AND NEURONAL ENERGY CONSUMPTION

Soon after the first promising experiments on human subjects, a comprehensive study of these rates in the rat brain tested these results in the more easily manipulated animal model (59–61). After several years of rat experiments we and other laboratories turned back to additional human experiments (62, 63). As data accumulated it became clear that the cycling model is equally valid in rat and human

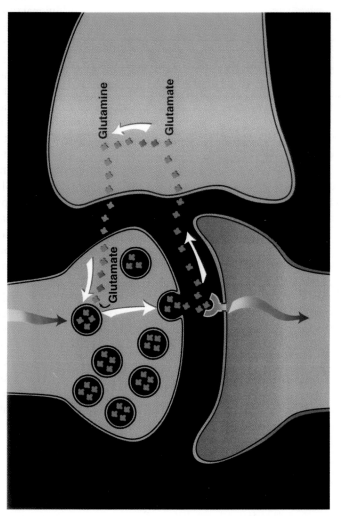

Figure 7 Proposed pathway of glutamate/glutamine neurotransmitter cycling between neurons and glia, whose flux has been quantitated recently by ^{13}C MRS experiments. Action potentials reaching the presynaptic neuron cause release of vesicular glutamate into the synaptic cleft, where it is recognized by glutamate receptors post-synaptically and is cleared by Na^+ - coupled transport into glia. There it is converted enzymatically to glutamine, which passively diffuses back to the neuron and, after reconversion to glutamate, is repackaged into vesicles. The rate of the glutamate-to-glutamine step in this cycle (V_{cycle}), has been derived from recent ^{13}C experiments. (Adapted from Reference 78.)

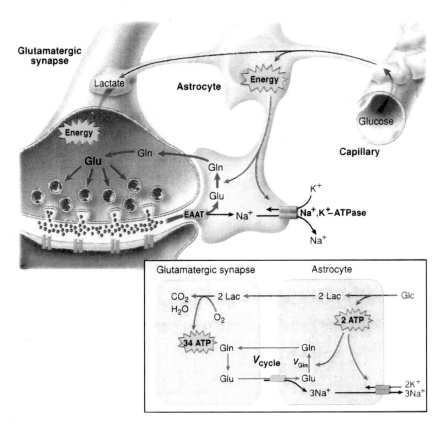

Figure 9 A molecular model of the coupling between the glutamate/glutamine cycle and glucose metabolism. The model was developed in collaboration with the laboratory of P Magistretti. *Upper panel*: The mechanisms by which synaptic activity is coupled to glucose usage. *Lower panel*: Stoichiometry of glutamate-mediated synaptic transmission and glucose usage. V_{cycle} rate of TCA cycle; V_{gln} rate of neurotransmitter cycle. (Adapted from Reference 64.)

brains and that the relative rates of cycling and glucose oxidation are similar in both species (61). These relative rates of oxidation and cycling were studied over a wide range of brain activities in the rat, taking the animals from deep pentobarbital anesthesia, with a flat EEG indicating no neuronal firing, through lighter states of anesthesia, ending with a lightly anesthetized state where neuronal firing had been enhanced by nicotine. Simultaneous measurements of the ^{13}C flow into glutamate and of the subsequent flow into glutamine were converted into V_{TCA} and V_{cycle}, respectively. Cycling flux (V_{cycle}) plotted versus energy consumption $CMR_{glc(ox)}$ in Figure 8 was found to be well fitted with a straight line of

$$CMR_{glc(ox)} = V_{cycle} + 0.10, \qquad \qquad 8.$$

all in units of $\mu M/g \cdot min$. The plot of data is significant in several respects. First, it establishes a quantitative molecular relationship between cortical oxidative energy production and glutamate neurotransmitter flux, the latter measurement explicating the rate of neuronal information transfer. Second, it provides a convenient measurement of this neuronal activity, namely the rate of glucose oxidation. An additional significant finding can be seen at the intercept in Figure 8 where V_{cycle} falls to zero. This corresponds to the state of flat EEG and was brought about by deep pentobarbital anesthesia. At this point the $CMR_{glc(ox)}$ had fallen to 0.1 $\mu M/g \cdot min$. This value of energy consumption in the non-firing brain is $\sim 15\%$ of the value at rest (of 0.8 $\mu M/g \cdot min$). The fact that only $\sim 15\%$ of the basal, resting cerebral cortex energy consumption is needed to support the brain in the absence of electrical activity implies that in the awake, resting, basal state, $\sim 85\%$ of the energy consumption is supporting the neurotransmitter flux. This high level of

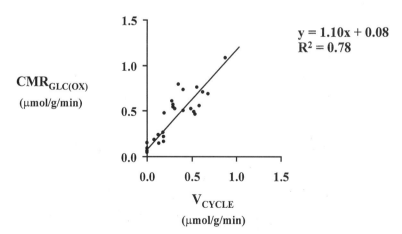

Figure 8 Graph demonstrating the correlation between the rate of oxidative Glc consumption ($CMR_{glc(ox)}$) and the rate of glutamate-neurotransmitter cycling (V_{cycle}). $CMR_{glc(ox)}$ was derived from the measured rate of the TCA cycle (V_{TCA}), and V_{cycle} was determined from the measured rate of Gln synthesis (V_{Gln}) as described in the text.

brain neurotransmitter activity in the absence of specific stimulations is a novel neuroscientific finding from these experiments, which, as discussed below, requires fundamental re-evaluations of modern brain studies of higher-level brain function including functional imaging.

Another unexpected feature of the data plot in Figure 8 is the slope of unity, when V_{cycle} is plotted versus the rate of neuronal glucose oxidation $CMR_{glc(ox)}$. The slope of unity means that for every additional glucose molecule oxidized in a neuron,[3] one glutamate is released as a neurotransmitter, which cycles through glutamine. This stoichiometry allows changes in neurotransmitter flux (which can only be measured directly in this sort of ^{13}C NMR experiment) to be determined from measured changes in oxygen consumption. These results are in accord with a molecular and cellular model (presented below) in which astrocytic uptake of one glutamate requires glycolysis of one glucose, consistent with the NMR observations (58, 60, 63).

The data reported here indicate a 1:1 stoichiometry between incremental cortical neuronal glucose oxidation and neurotransmitter cycling above isoelectric conditions. In addition, the component of glucose oxidation that is independent of synaptic activity is assessed from the value $CMR_{glc(ox)}$ under isoelectric conditions. Previous studies using peripheral neurons have suggested that a substantially smaller fraction of neuronal glucose consumption (5–50% compared with >80% found here) supports functional activity, and the remaining majority of activity had been assumed to subserve so-called housekeeping functions (65, 66). The much higher percentage of energy consumption related to glutamatergic synaptic activity demonstrated here is consistent with the greater degree of synaptic branching found in cortical neurons of the CNS compared with peripheral systems (67). The linear relationship between neuronal glucose oxidation and glutamate-neurotransmitter cycling is in agreement with previous high-resolution 2-deoxyglucose-autoradiographic studies of intact neurons, which demonstrated that, above a baseline metabolic level, synaptic glucose utilization is proportional to stimulation frequency (and by inference neuronal firing and neurotransmitter release) (68, 69). These results indicate that under mild anesthesia, and by extrapolation, in the awake state, ~80% of cortical neuronal energy production is coupled to the metabolic flows from released glutamate and (to a lesser extent GABA) to glutamine.

Given the direct proportionality between neurotransmitter cycling and neuronal glucose oxidation, these results suggest that glutamate-neurotransmitter release is tightly coupled to cortical glucose consumption. The bulk of neuronal glucose oxidation measured by NMR has been shown to account for over 80% of the total

---

[3]The NMR measurement primarily reflects the oxidative requirements of glutamatergic neurons, which based on comparison of NMR measurements with traditional methods account for approximately 80–90% of cortical neuronal glucose oxidation. As described below, the recently developed ability to separately measure GABA will allow the coupling between GABA cycling and glucose oxidation in the GABAergic neuron to be determined.

glucose consumption (52). Based on earlier studies in brain slices, the glutamate-neurotransmitter flux between neurons and astrocytes was thought to be small and, consequently, the energy requirements of this flux were discounted as a factor in the control of cerebral glucose consumption. In contrast to those brain slice studies, our in vivo ^{13}C NMR studies have demonstrated that glutamate-neurotransmitter cycling is energetically very significant. It is important to note that the coupled energy consumption is the total energy for neuronal information-transfer-related processes, including membrane ion pumping, vesicle filling, docking, and release.

Contribution of GABA to Neurotransmitter Cycling

GABA, the major inhibitory transmitter in the brain, is also believed to participate in a neuronal-astrocytic cycle (71). GABA is localized to a subclass of neurons in which it is synthesized from glutamate. The glutamate pool in GABAergic neurons is low in concentration. In the GABA/glutamine cycle the flow is glutamate → GABA → glutamine. In the initial animal studies described above, contributions of the GABA cycle were included in the calculated rate of the glutamate/glutamine cycle. Because of the low glutamate concentration in GABAergic neurons the energy requirements of these cells are not included in the measurement of glucose oxidation from glutamate turnover. More recently new ^{13}C NMR methods have been developed to directly measure GABA/glutamine cycling and the oxidative requirements of GABAergic neurons. These studies of the ^{13}C label flow into GABA have provided a preliminary estimate that this flux is approximately 10% of cortical energy consumption and up to 10% of neurotransmitter cycling (72). This amount of GABA/glutamine cycling would alter the ratio of neuronal glucose oxidation to glutamate/glutamine cycling measured in the animal model by a maximum of 10%.

A Molecular Model of Coupling Between Glucose Consumption and Neuronal Activity and the Control of Functional Glucose Consumption

The ^{13}C NMR data showing a stoichiometry between ΔV_{cycle} and $\Delta_{glc(ox)}$ support a molecular model of coupling in vivo between astrocytic glucose consumption and glutamatergic neuronal activity proposed by Pellerin & Magistretti (73). Based on their findings in cultured astrocytes and other data, Pellerin & Magistretti suggested that the glycolytic glucose consumption in the brain occurs in astrocytes, which subsequently export lactate to neurons as a substrate for oxidative metabolism. Astrocytic uptake of one glutamate molecule with cotransport of two or three sodium ions requires one ATP molecule to restore the transmembrane sodium (and potassium) gradients via the Na^+/K^+-ATPase (Figure 9, see color insert). We have additionally observed that astrocytic conversion of glutamate to Gln (in which form it is returned to the neuron) also requires one ATP per glutamate molecule (60). Therefore, in this extended Magistretti model a total of two ATP molecules will be hydrolyzed within the astrocyte per molecule of glutamate cleared. This energetic cost can be met exactly by the glycolytic production of two ATP molecules per glucose molecule (Figure 9). Therefore, the 1:1 stoichiometry is quantitatively consistent with the extended Magistretti model provided that (within the experimental uncertainties of approximately 15%) all the glucose responsible for incremental activity in vivo is taken up by astrocytes and glycolyzed.

The glycolytic ATP production per glucose molecule is sufficient to support the astrocytic energy-requiring processes that are linked to synaptic glutamate release (glutamate uptake and conversion to Gln). Consequently, the majority of ATP produced from glucose metabolism through lactate/pyruvate oxidation in the TCA cycle is available to support other processes involved in neuronal activities related to information transfer. In vitro and in vivo studies, using high-resolution deoxyglucose autoradiography, have shown that increased glucose uptake in response to functional stimulation is localized primarily in cortical layers rich in dendrites, nerve terminals, and associated glial end processes, but not in layers associated with cell bodies (74). However, although our results indicate that the majority of cortical neuron energy consumption is synaptic, the results have not determined the energetics of specific local processes.

Although the in vivo results demonstrate a clear coupling between the glutamate/glutamine cycle and neuronal glucose oxidation, additional studies can further test the proposed model. At the molecular level, structural studies of the molecular mechanism of coupling between the Na^+/K^+-ATPase and glycolytic enzymes are particularly needed. At the level of metabolic flux determination, it remains to be demonstrated that the oxidized lactate in the neuron is of astrocytic origin. Once these relationships are further established the glutamate/glutamine cycle will be suitable for study by MCA, as was performed for the glycogen synthesis pathway. These studies have the promise of revealing the role of the individual enzymes in the control of glutamate neurotransmission. As described in the next section, the measurement of glutamate neurotransmission through the glutamate/glutamine cycle has significant implications for the interpretation of psychological studies. The study of glutamate metabolism therefore promises to help bridge the kinetics of individual enzymes and enzyme regulatory pathways with higher-level functions such as cognition and behavior.

The Neurophysiological Basis of Functional Imaging Studies

Much of the recent optimism about being able to bridge the brain and the mind derives from positron emission tomography (PET) and functional magnetic resonance imaging (fMRI) (75). These methods are often represented as directly mapping neuronal activity in the functioning human brain. Impressive two- and three-dimensional maps of neuronal activity in the functioning brain have been embraced by scientists and the popular media as providing new insights into the biological basis of how the mind works. In applying modern functional imaging methods to understanding the mind, it is assumed that the imaging signal measures neuronal activity. However, the signal is not a direct measure of neuronal activity. Rather it derives from changes in blood flow, glucose consumption, and glucose oxidation, which are physiological measures of brain energy consumption (76). To interpret these energy signals in terms of neuronal activity one must proceed carefully because the present interpretations of the neuronal basis of the signals are based on assumptions about mental processes (see below). Hence, before functional imaging methods can study "the mental apparatus and its functions," as is generally assumed (77), these assumptions must be examined. A schematic of the various interactions at play in functional imaging experiments is shown in Figure 10. The imaging signal obtained in a functional imaging experiment can be related to specific neuronal processes, as indicated in the lower pathway of Figure 10. To do so, first one must establish the relationship between the intensity of the imaging signal (S) and the rate of neurophysiological energy processes (NP), such as the cerebral metabolic rates of glucose (CMR_{glc}) and of oxygen ($CMRO_2$). The second connection, between the NP and the activity of neuronal processes (N), is provided by the in vivo ^{13}C NMR studies described above (60, 63). It is necessary to understand these relationships before using functional imaging signals to answer questions about the neural basis (i.e. N) of mental processes (M) (78).

Imaging signals obtained in different PET experiments are determined by the regional rate of specific NPs such as CMR_{glc}, $CMRO_2$, and cerebral blood flow (CBF). The fMRI signal is an indirect measure of the difference in changes of $CMRO_2$ and CBF during stimulation. For fMRI, methodological issues remain as to how accurately the imaging signal may be deconvoluted to measure the separate rates of ΔCBF and $\Delta CMRO_2$. These methodological issues are being resolved by ongoing research so that the imaging signals are able, in principle, to provide changes of $\Delta CMRO_2$ or ΔCMR_{glc} and are able to provide, in some PET experiments, measurements of their absolute values (75). Symbolically, the imaging experiments can be interpreted to give a relation between S and the NP parameters.

$$S = NP.$$
9.

In the standard assumptions of neuroscience, mental activity is supported by neuronal activity or

$$N = M,$$
10.

where the equation sign means that the variables are unique functions of each other. In order to relate the imaging signal to mental processes it has been necessary to find a relationship between neuronal activities relevant to mental processes (M), such as spike activity or neurotransmitter flux, and NP. Then a relationship would be made between S and the neuronal activity induced by M. Symbolically the

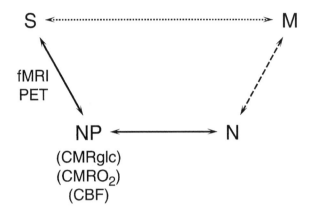

Figure 10   Schematic relations between the signal (S) obtained in functional imaging experiments and mental processes (M). In the usual experimental plan and interpretation, based on psychology, a direct relationship between S and M is assumed, as represented by the upper pathway. The definition of M is based on psychology, whereas the imaging experiment serves to localize and quantitate the signal with the process. The lower pathway, Neuroscience, assumes that M has a molecular and cellular basis, which is broken into three steps leading to S. The signal, S, in fMRI or PET experiments, is primarily a measure of the neurophysiolgical parameters (NP) of cerebral metabolic rate of glucose consumption (CMRglc), cerebral metabolic rate of oxygen consumption ($CMRO_2$), or CBF. PET methods have been developed for measuring each of these separately. fMRI signals respond to differences in the change of CBF and $CMRO_2$, whose quantitative relationships are being investigated. $CMRO_2$ and CMRglc measure cerebral energy consumption, whereas $\Delta CMRO_2$ and $\Delta CMRglc$ measure its increment. The relation between the neurophysiological measure of energy consumption (NP) and neuronal activity (N) has been clarified by the ^{13}C NMR experiments. These recent findings allow measurements of S to be converted into measures of N, which places us squarely facing the unsolved hard problem of neuroscience, i.e. what is the relationship between M and N?

desired relationship may be expressed as

$$S = NP = N = M. \qquad\qquad 11.$$

The ^{13}C NMR results have coupled a specific neuronal activity N (neurotransmitter flux) to the NP parameters of energy consumption and have thereby completed the coupling between S and M in Equation 11. The problem in directly inferring neuronal activity from measurements of neurophysiological energetic processes had been that many brain activities such as protein synthesis and membrane turnover are not directly involved in function but require energy. In previous estimates a majority of the energy was devoted to these non-functional processes. By contrast, the ^{13}C NMR results have shown in the rat that the majority ($\sim$80%) of neuronal energy consumption at rest is linearly coupled to glutamate neurotransmitter cycling (Figure 8). In the human cerebral cortex the ratio of glutamate neurotransmitter cycling to neuronal glucose oxidation is similar (62), suggesting that a similar high level of brain energy metabolism is devoted to functional activity.

For technical reasons, as well as from psychological assumptions, functional imaging experiments are generally set up to measure difference signals, ΔS, observed in the brain image between two behavioral tasks. In the control task, the subject is usually at rest in the absence of the stimulation being evaluated. There is no need for one state to be at rest; the control state merely needs to be missing the stimulation whose effects are being studied. Images collected during rest are subtracted from those collected during a task, and the difference images are evaluated statistically to establish the probability they are not random. Difference images, the usual presentation of results, are plots of regions in which ΔS, the differences between images during the task and at rest, are statistically significant. This presentation does not mean that imaging signals elsewhere are non-existent, but merely that they do not show on the difference image because their magnitudes do not change significantly between task and control. The prevailing interpretation in functional imaging is that ΔS measures the neuronal activity associated with the mental processes involved in the task. In symbols,

$$\Delta S = \Delta N = M. \qquad\qquad 12.$$

It is important to note that Equation 12, differs from Equation 11, which reflects the traditional neuroscientific view of the neuronal support of mental processes. In Equation 12 the mental process M is associated with the difference in neuronal activity, ΔN, as opposed to the total neuronal activity N in the region.

Experimental evidence that the entire neuronal activity of a region is required for mental processing, in support of Equation 12, comes from various rat studies in which sensory stimulations were performed at different degrees of anesthesia reflecting different neuronal activities of glutamate/glutamine cycling (79, 80). Under certain anesthetics, animals respond to sensory stimulations such as forepaw electrical stimulation or vibratory sensory stimulation, and auto-radiographic studies have reported the incremental rate of glucose consumption. If the neuronal activity induced by the stimulus were simply incremental, it should add the same incremental signal ΔS in both the anesthetized and awake states. If, on the other hand, the full neuronal activity were needed to perform the task, then the final state during the task should have the same absolute activity level, regardless of the initial state. In this case the increment during the task would be larger in the more deeply anesthetized state. Animal studies have shown that the latter is actually the case in that ΔS increases with depth of anesthesia, suggesting that the full magnitude of neuronal activity in a region is needed during a mental or sensory process (79). These conclusions are supported by recent experiments in which the same animal was stimulated from two different depths of anesthesia, and ΔS values obtained from both the blood oxygen level–dependent fMRI signals and CBF signals were much larger from the deeper anesthesia (80). In summary, several conclusions from the ^{13}C NMR experiments are relevant for the interpretation of functional imaging experiments.

1. Incremental oxidative glucose consumption is close to a quantitative measure of neurotransmitter activity because glucose oxidation is stoichiometric with glutamate neurotransmitter flux. Hence functional imaging signals, when converted to energy, may be used to measure differences in cortical neurotransmitter flux, which is predominantly glutamate.

2. The rate of the glutamate/glutamine cycle at rest in human cerebral cortex is approximately 70–80% of the rate of glucose oxidation. Hence the resting brain has a high level of functional neuronal activity.

3. Results on the anesthetized animals show that the total regional neuronal functional energy consumption rather than the incremental consumption is required to support function. The traditional functional imaging signal ΔS may localize activity related to a function but it does not measure the total energy (or the total neurotransmitter activity) needed for that function.

Implications of the Glutamate/Glutamine Cycle Flux for Understanding the Mind

The ability to measure regional neurotransmitter activity in the brain has implications for understanding mental activity. Through the use of signal differences many of the results of functional imaging studies are interpreted using modular theories of brain function, in which functionally specialized regions of the brain are selectively activated by external tasks. The finding of a high neurotransmitter activity in the human cerebral cortex at rest is not consistent with modular models that either ignore resting activity or at the least de-emphasize it. However this result can serve a valuable role in the synthesis and testing of new theories of mind. The finding that a high level of neuronal activity is required both at rest and during task performance is supportive of recent experimentally based proposals about the nature of neuronal contributions to brain function. These experiments have led to the hypothesis that there is a need for substantial unfocused neuronal activity at rest for the service of even sensory responses. This hypothesis was suggested by the recent brilliant experiments of Grinvald and colleagues (81). Starting with the recognition that "cortical neurons are spontaneously active in the absence of external input even in primary sensory areas," they studied the correlations between single-unit recordings and real-time optical imaging of the activity (assessed through hemoglobin oxygenation, which is a measure of regional tissue oxygen consumption and blood flow) in large regions of the sensory cortex. They found that large-scale and single-unit activity were highly correlated in both the stimulated and non-stimulated states. They concluded by suggesting that "in the absence of stimulation the cortical network wanders through various states represented by coherent firing of different neuronal assemblies" and that a stimulus pushes the network into a state representing the stimulus.

Analogously the elegant temporal synchronization of neuronal responses upon which Singer's conclusions (82) are based have led to the conclusion that "of the many responses of V1 those that become synchronized best will be particularly effective in influencing neurons in higher areas." This hypothesis, recognizing the large neuronal activity in the absence of stimulation, includes that activity in proposals about brain function. Our results, in agreement with their assumptions, provide measures of the amounts of such unstimulated activity and thereby provide a quantitative basis for analysis.

CONCLUSIONS

Integrating different levels of understanding from the molecular and genetic to the functioning human requires interactions among scientists who specialize in studies at the different levels. This kind of collaboration between disciplines is the usual composition of biomedical research groups. The research described in this article spans 20 years, with over 100 scientists and engineers playing important roles, having backgrounds ranging from molecular biophysics to clinical neurology and medicine. Quantitative measurements of metabolic fluxes by in vivo NMR have provided a certainty from which investigations have proceeded upward in complexity toward integrated physiology and neuroscience, and downward toward the quantitative control effected by enzymes in the pathway. The flow of knowledge between the levels of complexity surrounding metabolic fluxes has resolved methodological controversies between top-down and bottom-up partisans. In our work either approach is used as needed, and the search is for causal mechanisms. Both top-down and bottom-up approaches have their place in biology and mechanistic explanations; the goal to find value from both. This kind of philosophical opportunism is an accurate description of successful biological research, and furthermore there is no reason why it should not be. Our measurements of metabolic fluxes, situated at a slightly higher level of complexity than molecular biochemistry and at a slightly lower level than systemic physiology, contribute to and profit from information available at both levels. Centered around metabolism strengthened by in vivo NMR, our research makes advances in both directions, while retaining the definiteness offered by the NMR results. By taking small steps forward, these explanations of mechanism avoid the oversimplifications created by reductionist top-down or bottom-up paradigms. There is nothing wrong with the idea that genes have some responsibility for disease or that evolution played a role in the nature of the mind, but there is something very wrong with the ideas that either of these theories can jump across layers of complexity and by themselves, neglecting the intermediate complexities, offer causal mechanisms. This kind of reductionist oversimplification is avoided by our methodology. We are not skipping the intermediate levels; instead we are proposing that valid advances can be made by careful quantitative experimentation of intermediary metabolism. In our review we illustrate this methodology by examples. For the moment it suffices to say that intermediary metabolism has given us a platform upon which we stand and hope to exemplify Archimedes' proud claim, "give me a place to stand and I will move the world."

Finally we must face the reductionist hopes of understanding mental functions and ask, to what end should present explorations be directed? To a great extent, the present philosophical position in neuroscience has been sketched in Crick's statement, "our minds—the behavior of our brains—can be explained by the interactions of nerve cells (and other cells) and the molecules associated with them" (83). Molecules and cells are providing structures for explanations of mind. Upon those structures, however, the glutamate neurotransmitter fluxes and their coupled energetics superimpose another level of function, a level in which the dynamics of chemical reactions couple energy to the needs of neuronal signaling. The step beyond structure toward complexity offered by these fluxes has allowed connections to be established between functional imaging, neurochemistry, and neurophysiology. Functional imaging interpreted in terms of neurotransmitter flux can serve as a way station on the explanatory paths connecting mind and brain.

Visit the Annual Reviews home page at www.AnnualReviews.org

LITERATURE CITED

1. Ugurbil K, Brown TR, den Hollander JA, Glynn P, Shulman RG. 1978. High resolution ^{13}C NMR studies of glucose metabolism in *E. coli. Proc. Natl. Acad. Sci. USA* 75:3742–46

2. Cohen SM, Shulman RG, McLaughlin AC. 1979. Effects of ethanol on alanine metabolism in perfused mouse liver studied by ^{13}C NMR. *Proc. Natl. Acad. Sci. USA* 76:4808–12

3. Alger JR, Sillerud LO, Behar KL, Gillies RJ, Shulman RG, et al. 1981. In vivo ^{13}C NMR studies of mammals. *Science* 214:660–62

4. Jue T, Rothman DL, Tavitian BA, Shulman RG. 1989. Natural-abundance ^{13}C NMR study of glycogen repletion in human liver and muscle. *Proc. Natl. Acad. Sci. USA* 86:1439–42

5. Stevens AN, Iles RA, Morris PG, Griffiths JR. 1982. Detection of glycogen in a glycogen storage disease by natural abundance ^{13}C NMR. *FEBS Lett.* 150:489–93

6. Cohen SM. 1983. Applications of NMR to the study of liver physiology and disease. *Hepatology* 738–49

7. London RE. 1988. ^{13}C labeling in studies of metabolic regulation. *Prog. NMR Spectrosc.* 20:337–83

8. Fell D. 1997. In *Understanding the Control of Metabolism*, ed. K Snell, London/ Miami: Portland

9. National Diabetes Data Group 1979. Classification and diagnosis of diabetes mellitus and other categories of glucose intolerance. *Diabetes* 28:1039–57

10. Stryer L. 1988. *Biochemistry.* New York: Freeman

11. Cohen SM. 1983. Simultaneous ^{13}C and ^{31}P NMR studies of perfused rat liver. *J. Biol. Chem.* 258:14294–308

12. Sillerud LO, Shulman RG. 1983. Structure and metabolism of mammalian liver glycogen. *Biochemistry* 22:1087–94

13. Gruetter R, Magnusson I, Rothman DL, Shulman RG, Shulman GI. 1994. In vivo ^{13}C NMR visibility of liver glycogen. *Magn. Reson. Med.* 31:583–88

14. Taylor R, Price TB, Rothman DL, Shulman RG, Shulman GI. 1992. Validation of ^{13}C NMR measurement of human skeletal muscle glycogen by direct biochemical assay of needle biopsy samples. *Magn. Reson. Med.* 27:13–20

15. DeFronzo RA, Jacot E, Jequier E, Maeder E, Wahren J, Felber JP. 1981. The effect of insulin on the disposal of intravenous glucose: results from indirect calorimetry and hepatic and femoral venous catheterization. *Diabetes* 30:1000–7

16. Shulman GI, Rothman DL, Jue T, Stein P, DeFronzo RA, Shulman RG. 1990. Quantitation of muscle glycogen synthesis in normal subjects and subjects with non-insulin dependent diabetes mellitus by ^{13}C nuclear magnetic resonance spectroscopy. *N. Engl. J. Med.* 322:223–28

17. Rothman DL, Magnusson I, Katz LD, Shulman RG, Shulman GI. 1991. Quantitation of hepatic glycogenolysis and gluconeogenesis in fasting humans using ^{13}C NMR. *Science* 254:573–76

18. Magnusson I, Rothman DL, Katz LD, Shulman RG, Shulman GI. 1992. Increased rate of gluconeogenesis in Type II diabetes mellitus: a ^{13}C Nuclear magnetic resonance study. *J. Clin. Invest.* 90:1323–27

19. Taylor R, Magnusson I, Rothman DL, Cline GW, Caumo A, et al. 1996. Direct assessment of liver glycogen storage by ^{13}C nuclear magnetic resonance spectroscopy and regulation of glucose homeostasis after a mixed meal in normal subjects. *J. Clin. Invest.* 97:126–32

20. Rothman DL, Shulman RG, Shulman GI. 1992. ^{31}P NMR measurements of G6P in normal and NIDDM subjects during hyperglycemic-hyperinsulinemia. *J. Clin. Invest.* 89:1069–72

21. Cline GW, Petersen KF, Krssak M, Shen J, Hundal RS, et al. 1999. Impaired glucose transport as a cause of decreased insulin-stimulated muscle glycogen synthesis in type 2 diabetes. *N. Engl. J. Med.* 341:240–46

22. Roussel R, Carlier PG, Robert JJ, Vehlo G, Bloch G. 1998. ^{13}C/^{31}P NMR studies of glucose transport in human skeletal muscle. *Proc. Natl. Acad. Sci. USA* 95:1313–19

23. Eriksson J, Franssila-Kallunki A, Ekstrand A, Saloranta C, Widen E, et al. 1989. Early metabolic defects in persons at increased risk for non-insulin-dependent diabetes mellitus. *N. Engl. J. Med.* 321:337–43

24. Rothman DL, Magnusson I, Cline G, Gerard D, Kahn RC, et al. 1995. Decreased muscle glucose transport/phosphorylation is an early defect in the pathogenesis of non-insulin-dependent diabetes mellitus. *Proc. Natl. Acad. Sci. USA* 92:983–87

25. Maehlum S, Hostmark AT, Hermansen L. 1977. Synthesis of muscle glycogen during recovery after prolonged severe exercise in diabetic and non-diabetic subjects. *Scand. J. Clin. Lab. Invest.* 37:309–16

26. Price TB, Rothman DL, Taylor R, Shulman GI, Avison MJ, et al. 1994. Human muscle glycogen resynthesis after exercise: insulin and concentration dependence. *J. Appl. Physiol.* 76(1):104–11

27. Perseghin G, Price TB, Petersen KF, Roden M, Cline GW, et al. 1996. Increased glucose transport-phosphorylation and muscle glycogen synthesis after exercise training in insulin resistant subjects. *N. Engl. J. Med.* 335:1357–62

28. Kascer H, Burns JA. 1973. The control

of flux. *Symp. Soc. Exp. Biol.* 27:65–104. Reprinted 1995. *Biochem. Soc. Trans.* 23: 341–66

29. Quant PA. 1993. Experimental applications of top-down control analysis to metabolic systems. *Trends Biochem. Sci.* 18:26–36

30. Shulman RG, Bloch G, Rothman DL. 1995. In vivo regulation of muscle glycogen synthase and the control of glycogen synthesis. *Proc. Natl. Acad. Sci. USA* 92:8535–42

31. Roach RJ, Larner J. 1977. Covalent phosphorylation in the regulation of glycogen synthase activity. *Mol. Cell. Biochem.* 15: 179–200

32. Davies SEC, Brindle KM. 1992. Effects of over-expression of PFK on glycolysis in *Saccharomyces cerevisiae*. *Biochemistry* 31:4729–35

33. Hubbard MJ, Cohen P. 1993. On target with a new mechanism for the regulation of protein phosphorylation. *Trends Biochem. Sci.* 18:172–77

34. Deleted in proof

35. Harris RA. 1992. Carbohydrate metabolism II: Special pathways. In *Textbook of Biochemistry: With Clinical Correlations*, ed. TM Devlin, pp. 343–51. New York: Wiley-Liss

36. Kascer H, Acarenza L. 1993. A universal method for achieving increases in metabolite production. *Eur. J. Biochem.* 216:361–67

37. Shulman RG, Rothman DL. 1996. Enzymatic phosphorylation of muscle glycogen synthase: a mechanism for maintenance of metabolic homeostasis. *Proc. Natl. Acad. Sci. USA* 93:7491–95

38. Rossetti L, Giaccari A. 1990. Relative contribution of glycogen synthesis and glycolysis to insulin-mediated glucose update. A dose-response euglycemic clamp study in normal and diabetic rats. *J. Clin. Invest.* 85:1785–92

39. Roach PJ, Larner J. 1977. Covalent phosphorylation in the regulation of glyco-

gen synthase activity. *Mol. Cell. Biochem.* 15:179–200

40. Bucher T, Russman W. 1964. Non-equilibrium in the glycolysis system. *Angew. Chem. Int. Ed.* 3:426–39

41. Kashiwaya Y, Sato K, Tsuchiya N, Thomas S, Fell D, et al. 1994. Control of glucose utilization in working rat heart. *J. Biol. Chem.* 269:25502–14

42. Siesjo BK. 1978. *Brain Energy Metabolism*. New York: Wiley

43. Fell DA, Thomas S. 1995. Physiological control of metabolic flux: the requirement for multisite modulation. *Biochem. J.* 311:35–37

44. David M, Petit WA, Laughlin MR, Shulman RG, King JE, et al. 1990. Simultaneous synthesis and degradation of rat liver glycogen: an in vivo NMR spectroscopic study. *J. Clin. Invest.* 86:612–17

45. Magnusson I, Rothman DL, Jucker B, Shulman RG, Shulman GI. 1994. Liver glycogen turnover in fed and fasted humans. *Am. J. Physiol. Endocrinol. Metab.* 266:E796–E803

46. Price TB, Taylor R, Mason GF, Rothman DL, Shulman GI, Shulman RG. 1994. Turnover of human muscle glycogen during low-intensity exercise. *Med. Sci. Sports Exercise* 26:983–91

47. Behar KL, Petroff OAC, Prichard JW, Alger JR, Shulman RG. 1986. Detection of metabolites in rabbit brain by ^{13}C NMR spectroscopy following administration of [1-^{13}C] glucose. *Magn. Reson. Med.* 3:911–20

48. Rothman DL, Behar KL, Hetherington HP, den Hollander JA, Bendall MR, et al. 1985. [1]H-observe/and ^{13}C-decouple spectroscopic measurements of lactate and glutamate in the rat brain in vivo. *Proc. Natl. Acad. Sci. USA* 82:1633–37

49. Pan JW, Stein D, Mason GF, Rothman DL, Hetherington HP. 2000. Gray and white matter metabolic rate in human brain by spectroscopic imaging. *Magn. Reson. Med.* In press

50. Hyder F, Renken R, Rothman DL. 1999. In vivo carbon detection with proton echo planar spectroscopic imaging (ICED PEPSI): [3,4-^{13}CH$_2$]glutamate/glutamine tomography in rat brain. *Magn. Reson. Med.* 42: 997–1003

51. Fitzpatrick SM, Hetherington HP, Behar KL, Shulman RG. 1990. The flux from glucose to glutamate in the rat brain in vivo as determined by ^{1}H-observed, ^{13}C edited NMR spectroscopy. *J. Cereb. Blood Flow Metab.* 10:170–79

52. Mason GF, Gruetter R, Rothman DL, Behar KL, Shulman RG, Novotny EJ. 1995. Simultaneous determination of rate of TCA cycle, glucose utilization, α-ketoglutarate/glutamate exchange and glutamine synthesis in human brain by NMR. *J. Cereb. Blood Flow Metab.* 15:12–25

53. Gruetter R, Novotny EJ, Boulware S, Mason GF, Rothman DL, et al. 1994. Localized ^{13}C NMR spectroscopy in the human brain of amino acid labeling from [1-^{13}C] glucose. *J. Neurochem.* 63:1377–85

54. Berl S, Takagaki G, Clarke DD, Waelsch H. 1962. Metabolic compartments in vivo: ammonia and glutamic acid metabolism in brain and liver. *J. Biol. Chem.* 237:2562–69

55. van den Berg CJ, Garfinkel D. 1971. A simulation study of brain components. Metabolism of glutamate and related substances in mouse brain. *Biochem. J.* 123:211–18

56. Martinez-Hernandez A, Bell KP, Norenberg MD. 1977. Glutamine synthetase: glial localization in brain. *Science* 195: 1356–58

57. Rothstein JD, Martin L, Levey AI. 1994. Localization of neuronal and glial glutamate transporters. *Neuron* 13:713–25

58. Magistretti PJ, Pellerin L, Rothman DL, Shulman RG. 1999. Perspective: neuroscience "energy on demand." *Science* 283:496–97

59. Sibson NR, Dhankhar A, Mason GF, Behar KL, Rothman DL, et al. 1997. In vivo ^{13}C NMR measurements of cerebral glutamine synthesis as evidence for glutamate-glutamine cycling. *Proc. Natl. Acad. Sci. USA* 94:2699–704

60. Sibson NR, Dhankhar A, Mason GF, Rothman DL, Behar KL, et al. 1998. Stoichiometric coupling of brain glucose metabolism and glutamatergic neuronal activity. *Proc. Natl. Acad. Sci. USA* 95:316–21

61. Shen J, Sibson NR, Cline G, Behar KL, Rothman DL, et al. 1998. ^{15}N NMR spectroscopy studies of ammonia transport and glutamine synthesis in the hyperammonemic rat brain. *Dev. Neurosci.* 20:438–43

62. Shen J, Petersen KF, Behar KL, Brown P, Nixon TW, et al. 1999. Determination of the rate of the glutamate- glutamine cycle in the human brain by in vivo ^{13}C NMR. *Proc. Natl. Acad. Sci. USA* 96:8235–40

63. Gruetter R, Seaquist ER, Kim S, Ugurbil K. 1998. Localized in vivo ^{13}C-NMR of glutamate metabolism in the human brain: initial results at 4 Tesla. *Dev. Neurosci.* 20:380–88

64. Sibson NR, Shen J, Mason GF, Rothman DL, Behar KL, Shulman RG. 1998. Functional energy metabolism: in vivo ^{13}C NMR evidence for coupling of cerebral glucose consumption and glutamatergic neuronal activity. *Dev. Neurosci.* 20:321–30

65. Gjedde A. 1993. The energy cost of neuronal depolarization. In *Functional Organisation of the Human Visual Cortex*, ed. B Gulyas, D Ottoson, PE Roland, pp. 291–306. Oxford, UK: Pergamon

66. Creutzfeldt OD. 1975. Neurophysiological correlates of different functional states of the brain. In *Brain Work. The Coupling of Function, Metabolism and Blood Flow in the Brain*, ed. DH Ingvar, NA Lassen, pp. 21–46. Copenhagen: Munksgaard

67. Shepherd GM. 1994. *The Synaptic Organization of the Brain*. Oxford, UK: Oxford Univ. Press

68. Sokoloff L. 1991. Relationship between functional activity and energy metabolism in the nervous system: Whether, where and why? In *Brain Work and Mental Activity*, ed. NA Lassen, DH Ingvar, ME Raichle, L Friberg, pp. 52–64. Copenhagen: Munksgaard

69. Kadekaro M, Crane AM, Sokoloff L. 1985. Differential effects of electrical stimulation of sciatic nerve on metabolic activity in spinal cord and dorsal root ganglion in the rat. *Proc. Natl. Acad. Sci. USA* 82:6010–13

70. Badar-Goffer RS, Bachelart HS, Morris PG. 1990. Cerebral metabolism of acetate and glucose studied by ^{13}C NMR spectroscopy. *Biochem. J.* 266:133–39

71. Sonnewald U, Westergaard N, Schousboe A, Svendsen JS, Unsgard G, et al. 1993. Direct demonstration by [^{13}C] NMR spectroscopy that glutamine from astrocytes is a precursor for GABA synthesis in neurons. *Neurochem. Int.* 22:19–29

72. Manor D, Rothman DL, Mason GF, Hyder F, Petroff OAC, et al. 1996. The rate of turnover of cortical GABA from [1-^{13}C] glucose is reduced in rats treated with the GABA-transaminase inhibitor vigabatrin (γ-vinyl GABA). *Neurochem. Res.* 12:1031–41

73. Pellerin L, Magistretti PJ. 1994. Glutamate uptake into astrocytes stimulates aerobic glycolysis: a mechanism coupling neuronal activity to glucose utilization. *Proc. Natl. Acad. Sci. USA* 91:10625–29

74. Kennedy C, Des Rosiers MH, Sakurada O. 1976. Metabolic mapping of the primary visual system of the monkey by means of the autoradiographic [^{14}C] deoxyglucose technique. *Proc. Natl. Acad. Sci. USA* 4230–34

75. Raichle ME. 1998. Behind the scenes of functional brain imaging: a historical and physiological perspective. *Proc. Natl. Acad. Sci. USA* 95:765–72

76. Fitzpatrick SM, Rothman DL. 1999. New approaches to functional neuroenergetics. *J. Cogn. Neurosci.* 11:467–71

77. Posner MI, Raichle ME. 1994. *Images of Mind*. New York: Freeman

78. Shulman RG, Rothman DL. 1998. Interpreting functional imaging studies in terms of neurotransmitter cycling. *Proc. Natl. Acad. Sci. USA* 95:11893–98

79. Shulman RG, Rothman DL, Hyder F. 1999. Stimulated changes in localized cerebral energy consumption under anesthesia. *Proc. Natl. Acad. Sci. USA* 96:3245–50

80. Sibson NR, Rothman DL, Behar KL, Wall J, Shulman RG. 1999. *The glycogen shunt and brain energetics*. Presented at ISMRM, 7th. Sci. Meet. Philadelphia, PA. 1, 730

81. Tsodyks M, Kenet T, Grinvald A, Arieli A. 1999. Linking spontaneous activity of single cortical neurons and the underlying functional architecture. *Science* 286:1943–46

82. Singer W. 1994. Putative functions of temporal correlations in neocortical processing. In *Large-Scale Neuronal Theories of the Brain*, ed. C Koch, JL Davis, pp. 201–38. Cambridge, MA: MIT Press

83. Crick FHC. 1994. *The Astonishing Hypothesis: The Scientific Search for the Soul*, p. 7. New York: Scribners

Annu. Rev. Physiol. 2001. 63:49–76

GASTRIN, CCK, SIGNALING, AND CANCER

Enrique Rozengurt and John H Walsh

Department of Medicine, School of Medicine, CURE: Digestive Diseases Research Center and Molecular Biology Institute, University of California, Los Angeles, California 90095; e-mail: erozengurt@mednet.ucla.edu

■ **Abstract** Gastrin, produced by G cells in the gastric antrum, has been identified as the circulating hormone responsible for stimulation of acid secretion from the parietal cell. Gastrin also acts as a potent cell-growth factor that has been implicated in a variety of normal and abnormal biological processes including maintenance of the gastric mucosa, proliferation of enterochromaffin-like cells, and neoplastic transformation. Here, we review the models used to study the effects of gastrin on cell proliferation in vivo and in vitro with respect to mechanisms by which this hormone might influence normal and cancerous cell growth. Specifically, human and animal models of hypergastrinemia and hypogastrinemia have been described in vivo, and several cells that express cholecystokinin $(CCK)_B$/gastrin receptors have been used for analysis of intracellular signaling pathways initiated by biologically active amidated gastrins. The binding of gastrin or CCK to their common cognate receptor triggers the activation of multiple signal transduction pathways that relay the mitogenic signal to the nucleus and promote cell proliferation. A rapid increase in the synthesis of lipid-derived second messengers with subsequent activation of protein phosphorylation cascades, including mitogen-activated protein kinase, is an important early response to these signaling peptides. Gastrin and CCK also induce rapid Rho-dependent actin remodeling and coordinate tyrosine phosphorylation of cellular proteins including the non-receptor tyrosine kinases p125[fak] and Src and the adaptor proteins p130[cas] and paxillin. This article reviews recent advances in defining the role of gastrin and CCK in the control of cell proliferation in normal and cancer cells and in dissecting the signal transduction pathways that mediate the proliferative responses induced by these hormonal GI peptides in a variety of normal and cancer cell model systems.

INTRODUCTION

Multicellular organisms have developed highly efficient mechanisms of cell communication to integrate and coordinate the function and proliferation of individual cell types. Gastrointestinal (GI) peptides, including gastrin and cholecystokinin (CCK), are a structurally diverse group of molecular messengers that function in a rich network of information exchange systems throughout the organism. Gastrin, produced by G cells in the gastric antrum, has been identified as the circulating hormone responsible for stimulation of acid secretion from the parietal cell (1).

0066-4278/01/0315-0049$14.00

49

Gastrin stimulates parietal cell function indirectly by causing the release of histamine from the enterochromaffin-like (ECL) cell, and histamine reaches parietal cell H_2 receptors by paracrine diffusion (for review see 2, 3).

In addition to its role in gastric acid secretion, gastrin also acts as a potent cell-growth factor that has been implicated in a variety of normal and abnormal biological processes including maintenance of the gastric mucosa, proliferation of ECL cells, and neoplastic transformation. CCK, acting through CCK_A receptors, regulates pancreatic secretion and growth, as described by Williams (this volume) (3a). In this review, we focus on the role of these hormonal GI peptides in the control of cell proliferation in normal and cancer cells and on the signal transduction pathways that mediate the proliferative responses induced by gastrin and CCK in a variety of normal and cancer cell model systems.

ASSOCIATIONS BETWEEN GASTRIN AND GASTRIN GENE PRODUCTS WITH HYPERPLASIA AND NEOPLASIA IN VIVO

An association between hypergastrinemia and proliferation of ECL cells, sometimes leading to formation of gastric carcinoid tumors, is now well established in rats (4) and in humans (5, 6). Availability of genetically modified mice has enabled studies of the effects of chronic overproduction or absence of gastrin and its precursors, as well as absence of CCK_B/gastrin receptors (7). These mouse models have produced some unexpected results, including an apparent role for amidated gastrin as an etiologic factor in gastric cancer and of progastrin as a stimulant of colonic proliferation.

Epidemiological evidence has also been obtained that implicates hypergastrinemia as a factor in the development of colorectal cancer (8). Endogenous hypergastrinemia has been associated with rectal cell proliferation defects (9, 10). Colorectal carcinomas have been found to produce progastrin-related peptides and CCK_B/gastrin receptors (11–13).

Therefore, it is appropriate to examine the models used to study the effects of gastrin on cell proliferation in vivo and in vitro with respect to mechanisms by which this hormone might influence normal and cancerous cell growth. Human and animal models of hypergastrinemia and hypogastrinemia have been described in vivo, and several cells that express CCK_B/gastrin receptors are available for detailed analysis of intracellular signaling pathways initiated by biologically active amidated gastrins.

The biosynthesis and processing of gastrin gene products are discussed by Dockray et al (this volume) (13a). It is known that progastrin post-translational processing leads to substantial amounts of C-terminally extended progastrin molecules, including glycine-extended gastrin, in addition to the amidated forms known to be biologically active (14–16). Extended forms have limited biological activity to stimulate gastric acid secretion, although they appear to interact with CCK_B/gastrin receptor to release histamine at about 100-fold lower potency than amidated gastrins (17). However, studies in transgenic mice and in cultured tumors, discussed below, suggest that incompletely processed gastrins may have trophic activity independent of amidated gastrins. Unfortunately, no specific receptor has been characterized and no specific antagonists are available, making the study of potential intracellular signaling pathways difficult.

HUMAN HYPERGASTRINEMIA MODELS: ECL Cell and Parietal Cell Hyperplasia

Gastrinoma

Gastrinoma is the natural model for severe hypergastrinemia produced by gastrin cell neoplasms and produces a disease known as Zollinger-Ellison syndrome. Circulating gastrin concentrations range between 10^{-10} and 10^{-7} M and include a higher proportion of gastrin precursors such as progastrin and glycine-extended gastrin than normal circulating antral and duodenal gastrin (1). These tumors, usually located in the pancreas, duodenum, or adjacent tissues, grow slowly and patients often survive for 10–20 years. Therefore patients with gastrinomas are models for studying the effects of prolonged hypergastrinemia in the presence of normal or increased gastric acid secretion.

Trophic targets of gastrin in the human stomach are parietal cells and ECL cells. Patients who have been cured by successful gastrinoma resection exhibit decreases in basal and stimulated acid secretion from approximately twice normal to normal over a period of several months, implying that parietal cell hyperplasia has been reversed (18). These patients also exhibit ECL cell hyperplasia (19), but they rarely develop ECL carcinoid tumors except in the 20 to 25% who have the inherited multiple endocrine neoplasia type I syndrome in which they also have loss of heterozygosity of the MEN1 gene on chromosome 11q13. The lack of carcinoids in patients with sporadic gastrinoma is compatible with gastrin as a tumor promoter that requires other factors to lead to tumor formation (20).

Chronic Atrophic Gastritis

In chronic atrophic gastritis the acid-secreting gastric mucosa, including parietal cells, is damaged, leading to decreased acid secretion and compensatory hypergastrinemia. Mucosal damage may be caused by either immune mediators (pernicious anemia) or inflammatory mediators (*Helicobacter pylori* infection). ECL cell hyperplasia in these patients is proportional to the degree of hypergastrinemia, and those with the most elevated circulating gastrin often develop carcinoid tumors (21). Thus the combination of mucosal damage and hypergastrinemia is sufficient to lead to ECL cell tumors. The importance of gastrin in formation and growth of these tumors is shown by regression after surgical antrectomy to remove the endogenous source of gastrin (22).

Antisecretory Drug Treatment

Omeprazole and other proton pump inhibitors produce prolonged acid inhibition associated with corresponding moderate hypergastrinemia. ECL cell hyperplasia occurs in less than 10% of patients treated chronically with proton pump inhibitors, and ECL cell tumors have not been described (23). Acid hypersecretion often occurs after these drugs are discontinued and reflects increased parietal cell mass (24). Thus parietal cells may be more responsive to hypergastrinemia than ECL cells in humans with normal gastric mucosa.

RAT HYPERGASTRINEMIA MODELS

Gastrin Infusion

Continuous infusion of gastrin-17 for 28 days to increase gastrin levels by two- to fourfold led to increased oxyntic mucosal mass and increased ECL cell density and activity but had no effects on other parts of the gut (25). Increased ECL cell and stem cell proliferation caused by gastrin infusion were similarly increased during acid inhibition by drugs and were reversed by antrectomy (26).

Chronic Antisecretory Drug Treatment

Lifelong (2 year) administration of omeprazole to rats causes formation of gastric carcinoid tumors preceded by ECL cell hyperplasia that increases progressively during the first 3–5 months of treatment and then becomes micronodular by 1 year (27, 28). Gastrin has been implicated as the etiologic agent for these ECL cell abnormalities because they do not occur after removal of the gastric antrum (28); they also occur in rats in which hypergastrinemia is induced by partial gastric corpectomy (29), and carcinoid tumors also can be induced by chronic administration of H_2 receptor antagonists including ranitidine (30). CCK_B/gastrin (also known as CCK2) receptor antagonists have been found to prevent ECL cell proliferative responses to proton pump inhibitors, as well as to inhibit histamine synthesis and release (31, 32) and to prevent the accompanying increase in parietal cell mass and acid secretory capacity (33).

Gastrin Immunoneutralization

Gastrin-specific monoclonal antibody immunoneutralization in rats, at doses sufficient to prevent acid secretory responses to gastrin and to food, has been used to reveal a role for gastrin in acute gastric proliferative responses to feeding (34) and mucosal hypertrophy in uremic rats (35). Long-term administration of such antibodies has not been used to study ECL and parietal cell proliferative responses to antisecretory agents.

MASTOMYS ECL TUMORS

The African rodent *Mastomys natalensis* is genetically susceptible to spontaneous development of ECL cell gastric carcinoid tumors (36). Its ECL cells also appear to be hypersensitive to endogenous gastrin, and a gastrin antagonist was shown to inhibit growth of transplanted ECL tumors from *Mastomys* (37). However, tumors also can occur in the presence of normal circulating gastrin concentrations, possibly because of spontaneous activation of the CCK_B/gastrin receptor in this species (38).

MOUSE HYPERGASTRINEMIA MODELS

Chronic Antisecretory Drug Treatment

Long-term administration of acid-suppressing agents, including proton pump inhibitors and long-acting histamine H_2 receptor antagonists, to mice produces oxyntic mucosal hypertrophy and hyperplasia, including ECL cell hyperplasia but rarely carcinoid tumors (27, 39). ECL cell carcinoids were reported along with typical changes in foveolar cells similar to those seen in early gastric metaplasia in mice treated with the unsurmountable H_2 antagonist loxtidine (23).

Transgenic Mice Overproducing Amidated Gastrin

Overproduction of amidated gastrin in transgenic mice has led to gastric pathology not predicted from chronic endogenous hypergastrinemic models in rats or mice. There are two reports of overproduction of amidated gastrin by cells other than antral G cells. When the gastrin gene was expressed in fundic epithelial cells, mice developed hyperplasia of mucous cells but not of parietal cells or ECL cells (40). When gastrin was overproduced by pancreatic beta cells, an even more unexpected result was obtained (41). These mice exhibited transient modest parietal cell and ECL cell hyperplasia and acid hypersecretion but later developed gastritis with parietal cell hypoplasia and eventually gastric adenocarcinoma. Concurrent infection with *Helicobacter felis* accelerated the onset of invasive intramucosal carcinoma from 20 to 8 months.

Transgenic Mice Overproducing Gastrin Precursors

Expression of a human progastrin gene in mouse liver resulted in overproduction of gastrin precursors, including glycine-extended gastrin, but not amidated gastrin (42). These mice exhibited no alteration in gastric mucosa but instead had colonic hyperplasia with increased colonic labeling index. Furthermore, expression of a gene that could generate only glycine-extended gastrin but not longer forms led to similar colonic mucosal hyperplasia with expansion of the proliferative zone into the upper portion of the crypts (43). Increased colonic proliferation could also be produced by two-week infusions of glycine-extended gastrin in mice rendered unable to produce endogenous gastrin. Overproduction of progastrin, but not of amidated gastrin, also has been reported to increase aberrant colonic crypt foci in mice treated with the carcinogen azoxymethane (44). Antibodies that neutralize the amidated and glycine-extended forms of gastrin inhibited the growth and metastasis of tumors formed by the colorectal cancer cell line AP5LV in SCID mice (45). Possible proliferative actions of progastrin and glycine-extended gastrin in the human colon have not been studied.

Targeted Disruption of the Progastrin Gene

Mice in which the gastrin gene was disrupted, and therefore had chronic gastrin deficiency, exhibited decreased abundance of gastric parietal and ECL cells but normal proliferative labeling index (46). Colonic labeling index was decreased, but the colon was histologically normal. Functional studies done in other mice subjected to gastrin gene deletion revealed an absence of gastric acid secretion and unresponsiveness to gastrin, histamine, or carbachol (47). These mice had parietal cell and ECL cell hypoplasias that were partially reversed after administration of gastrin for six days, leading to partial restoration of acid secretion. Although gastrin is required for normal proliferation and activity of ECL and parietal cells, gastrin is not necessary for their presence because both cell types are found in gastrin-deficient mice (48).

Targeted Disruption of the CCK$_B$/Gastrin Receptor Gene

Mice genetically lacking the CCK$_B$/gastrin receptor exhibited severe atrophy of the gastric oxyntic mucosa despite marked hypergastrinemia (49, 50). Parietal cell and ECL cell abundance were decreased markedly despite apparently normal numbers of surface mucous cells and mucous neck cells. Because all gastric mucosal cells are derived from the same stem cell, gastrin receptors are likely to be responsible for directing proliferation of already committed parietal cell and ECL cell precursors.

Interactions of Gastrin with Other Growth Factors

Mucosal proliferative effects of gastrin may be produced indirectly through production and release of other growth factors. Infusions of gastrin induce gastric production of two EGF-related growth factors—heparin-binding epidermal growth factor (EGF) and amphiregulin—effects reversed by gastrin receptor antagonist (51). Heparin-binding EGF also is induced in a rat gastric epithelial cell line, RGM1, into which CCK$_B$/gastrin receptors have been transfected (52).

ECL cell tumors in humans have been found in gastrinoma patients with multiple endocrine neoplasia type I but rarely in patients with spontaneous gastrinoma. MEN1 is caused by mutations of a tumor suppressor gene known as menin on chromosome 11q13 (53). The *Reg* gene, originally isolated from regenerating pancreatic islets, is expressed in normal rat ECL cells and is released by gastrin and by stress (54). Mutations of the *RegIα* gene have been identified in human ECL cell carcinoid tumors (55). Increased expression of the apoptosis-suppressing oncoprotein BCL-2 also has been found in ECL carcinoid tumors (56).

GASTRIN AS A GROWTH FACTOR IN CULTURED CELLS

As discussed above, several lines of evidence, using a variety of models of hypogastrinemia and hypergastrinemia, indicate that the CCK_B/gastrin receptor plays an important role in the regulation of gastric cell proliferation (for recent reviews see 7, 48, 57, 58). A number of cellular model systems have been utilized to unravel the signal transduction pathways activated by gastrin and CCK via the CCK_B/gastrin receptor. However, as discussed below, a completely satisfactory cell model system has not been developed.

Gastrin stimulates DNA synthesis in a variety of cell types, including NIH 3T3 (59), Rat-1 (60), and CHO (61, 62) transfected with the human CCK_B/gastrin receptor, and promotes colony formation in semisolid medium of small cell lung cancer (SCLC) cell lines that endogenously express CCK_B/gastrin receptors (63–65). Although the human and rat CCK_B/gastrin receptors are highly homologous (66), agonist stimulation of the rat CCK_B/gastrin receptor expressed in CHO cells has been reported to inhibit cell proliferation, whereas the expression of this receptor in Swiss 3T3 cells mediated induction of DNA synthesis (67).

It should be pointed out that the degree of stimulation of DNA synthesis induced by activation of the CCK_B/gastrin receptor in these model systems has been modest; specifically 1.5-fold in AR4-2J cells (68,69), 1.6-fold in GH3 cells (69), 1.8-fold in CHO cells (70), 3-fold in Rat-1 cells (60), and 4-fold in Swiss 3T3 cells (67). The magnitude of these mitogenic effects contrasts with the stimulation of DNA synthesis elicited by GI peptides and growth factors in other systems [for instance in Swiss 3T3 cells stimulated via endogenously expressed gastrin-releasing peptide receptor (71)]. The small increase in [^{3}H]-thymidine incorporation reported in response to CCK_B/gastrin receptor activation could be from a high level of DNA synthesis in the unstimulated cells (i.e. transformed cells such as AR4-2J, GH3, and CHO do not arrest easily in the G_1 phase of the cell cycle), stimulation of only a small subpopulation of cells by a weak mitogenic signal, or the absence of other growth-promoting factors that are required to cooperate with CCK_B/gastrin receptor in driving a proliferative response.

New model cellular systems are required to elucidate further the mechanisms that mediate the proliferative responses elicited by activation of the CCK_B/gastrin receptor.

SIGNAL TRANSDUCTION PATHWAYS VIA CCK$_B$/GASTRIN RECEPTOR

Gastrointestinal peptides exert their characteristic effects on cellular processes by binding to specific G protein–coupled receptors (GPCRs) on the surface of their target cells (72). These receptors are characterized by an extracellular N-terminal segment, seven transmembrane α-helices, three extracellular loops (exoloops), three cytoplasmic loops (cytoloops), and a C-terminal segment (72). Gastrin, CCK, and CCK-related peptides bind to two receptor subtypes. The CCK$_B$/gastrin receptor binds gastrin and CCK with similar affinity, whereas the CCK$_A$ receptor exhibits a higher affinity for CCK than for gastrin (for review see 73).

The binding of a GPCR agonist to its cognate GPCR triggers the activation of signal transduction pathways that act in a synergistic and combinatorial fashion to relay the mitogenic signal to the nucleus and promote cell proliferation (74–76). In what follows, we review the signal transduction pathways activated by gastrin that lead to cell proliferation.

Phosphatidyl Inositol Turnover, Ca^{2+} Mobilization, and Activation of Protein Kinase C

One of the earliest events to occur after the binding of many GI peptide agonists to their GPCRs is the activation of a pertussis toxin–insensitive G protein of the Gq subfamily, which promotes its dissociation into Gαq and G$\beta\gamma$ subunits and the exchange of GDP bound to the Gαq for GTP. The resulting GTP-Gαq complex, in turn, activates the β isoforms of phospholipase C (PLC), which catalyze the hydrolysis of phosphatidyl inositol 4,5-bisphosphate (PIP$_2$) in the plasma membrane to produce two second messengers: inositol 1,4,5-trisphosphate (IP$_3$) and 1,2,-diacylglycerol (DAG) (77). IP$_3$ binds to its intracellular receptor, a ligand-gated Ca^{2+} channel located in the endoplasmic reticulum, and triggers the release of Ca^{2+} from internal stores (78). In accordance with this signal transduction pathway, gastrin stimulates inositol phosphate production in a variety of cell types (73), and a high-affinity complex between the CCK$_B$/gastrin receptor and Gq has been demonstrated. Conversion of the Asn residue (Asn391) to Ala in the NPXXY motif of the seventh transmembrane domain of the CCK$_B$/gastrin receptor has prevented the activation of PLC. In colonic epithelial cells, however, tyrosine phosphorylation of PLC γ rather than Gq-mediated regulation of PLC β has also been implicated (for review see 58). In addition, novel Ca^{2+}-mobilizing second messengers may also play a role, at least in some cell types (79).

Gastrin stimulates rapid mobilization of Ca^{2+} from intracellular stores followed by a plateau phase in a variety of cell types, including fibroblasts stably transfected with the CCK$_B$/gastrin receptor, e.g. Rat-1 (60), NIH 3T3 (59), CHO (62), and other cell types that express endogenous CCK$_B$/gastrin receptors, including SCLC (63, 64) and colonic epithelial cells (80). In addition to these rapid and transient Ca^{2+} fluxes, gastrin has also been shown to induce long-term Ca^{2+}

oscillations monitored in individual CHO cells transfected with the CCK_B/gastrin receptor (62). These Ca^{2+} oscillations have been linked to cell proliferation because agonist activation of a truncated CCK_B/gastrin receptor mutant lacking the C-terminal 44 amino acids induced early signaling events, including a transient increase in Ca^{2+}, but failed to promote subsequent Ca^{2+} oscillations and DNA synthesis (62). Recently, Ca^{2+} oscillations have been implicated in the regulation of gene expression (81, 82). However, neither the mechanism by which gastrin induces Ca^{2+} oscillations nor the molecular events linking Ca^{2+} oscillations to the progression of the cell cycle are, as yet, understood.

DAG, the other second messenger generated by PLC-mediated hydrolysis of PIP_2, directly activates the classic (α, β, γ) and novel $(\delta, \varepsilon, \eta, \theta)$ isoforms of protein kinase C (PKC) (83). Although some studies using pharmacological inhibitors have implicated PKC in CCK_B/gastrin receptor-mediated signal transduction (68, 84), direct activation of PKC isoforms in response to gastrin has been less frequently measured. The newly identified protein kinase D (PKD), also known as $PKC\mu$, is a serine/threonine protein kinase with distinct structural and enzymological properties (85). PKD is activated by phosphorylation in living cells through a novel Gq-mediated and PKC-dependent signal transduction pathway (86–88). Recent results demonstrate that gastrin induces rapid PKD activation in Rat-1 cells transfected with the human CCK_B/gastrin receptor (89) and thus have identified a novel early event elicited via this receptor.

Gastrin and CCK induce a marked release of arachidonic acid into the extracellular medium (90). As in other cell types, arachidonic acid is likely to be mobilized by the intracellular 85-kDa phospholipase A2 (67, 90), which is regulated by multisite phosphorylation (91) via a pertussis toxin–sensitive pathway (92). Several studies have reported that CCK_B/gastrin receptor activation does not lead to cAMP accumulation (93), except in cells expressing very high levels of this receptor (67).

Stimulation of Mitogen-Activated Protein Kinase

The mitogen-activated protein kinases (MAP kinases), a family of highly conserved serine/threonine kinases, are activated by a range of extracellular signals via protein phosphorylation cascades that relay mitogenic signals to the nucleus, thereby modulating the activity of transcription factors (94). The two best-characterized isoforms, p42[mapk] (ERK-2) and p44[mapk] (ERK-1), are directly activated by phosphorylation on specific tyrosine and threonine residues by the dual-specificity ERK kinase (or MEK). Several pathways leading to MEK activation have been identified. Tyrosine kinase receptors induce p42[mapk] and p44[mapk] activation via the complex between the SH3 domain of the adaptor protein Grb-2 and the guanine nucleotide release factor SOS (son of sevenless), which binds to tyrosine kinase receptors and promotes the accumulation of p21[ras]-GTP. This then recruits p74[raf-1] to the plasma membrane and activates a kinase cascade made up of p74[raf-1], MEK, and p42[mapk]/p44[mapk] (94).

The mechanisms by which mitogenic GPCRs activate p42^{mapk} and p44^{mapk} have been extensively investigated in a variety of cellular model systems but are incompletely understood. These studies led to the identification of Gi- and Gq-dependent pathways and to the recognition of the importance of the cellular context in which the ERK pathway is activated (76, 95).

Gastrin stimulation of ERK activation has been documented in AR4-2J rat pancreatic acinar cells (68, 69, 84, 96), gastric cancer AGS-B cells (97), and gastric ECL cells of *Mastomys natalensis* (98), all of which express endogenous CCK$_B$/gastrin receptors, as well as in Rat-1 (60), CHO (70), and NIH 3T3 cells (59) stably transfected with the CCK$_B$/gastrin receptor. It is generally accepted that gastrin induces ERK activation via pathways insensitive to pertussis toxin (60, 68), which catalyzes the ADP ribosylation and inactivation of the heterotrimeric G proteins of the Gi/Go subfamily.

ERK activation by some GPCRs appears to require receptor endocytosis, linking receptor internalization to receptor signaling (99, 100). However, the role of receptor endocytosis in ERK signaling is the subject of considerable debate (e.g. see 101, 102 for a contrasting view). The relationship, if any, between receptor internalization and ERK signaling has not been investigated with the CCK$_B$/gastrin receptor.

Signal Transduction Pathways Leading to ERK Activation: The Importance of Cell Context

In AR4-2J cells, gastrin-induced stimulation of the ERKs is attenuated by treatments that interfere with either Ca^{2+} mobilization or PKC activation (68, 84). Recent studies with these cells demonstrated that gastrin-induced ERK-mediated phosphorylation and activation of the transcription factors Elk-1 and Sap-1a, which regulate the activity of the serum response element (SRE) located in the c-*fos* promoter, is prevented by pharmacological inhibition of PKC (96), again indicating a critical role of PKCs in this pathway.

The precise mechanism(s) by which the isoforms of the PKC family activate the ERKs remains incompletely understood (103). In some cells, PKC directly phosphorylates and activates p74^{raf-1} (104), whereas in other cells PKC induces the ERK cascade via SOS-Grb2-mediated accumulation of p21^{ras}-GTP (105). In AR4-2J cells, gastrin stimulates rapid tyrosine phosphorylation of Shc, which recruits the SOS-Grb2 complex thereby leading to p21^{ras} activation, thus resembling the pathway utilized by receptor tyrosine kinases (69, 106). However, the tyrosine kinase(s) involved in AR4-2J cells has not been identified.

In epithelial cells a likely chain of events is gastrin-induced (PLC-dependent) PKC activation and Ca^{2+} mobilization, Pyk-2 (proline-rich tyrosine kinase 2)-mediated stimulation of c-Src activation, and MAP kinase activation via tyrosine phosphorylation of adaptor proteins including Shc (107–109). Another potential pathway is the transactivation of the EGF receptor by GPCR agonists, which also leads to p21^{ras}-dependent MAP kinase activation in a variety of cell types (110).

Recently, EGF receptor transactivation was shown to be mediated by the rapid proteolytic formation of EGF-like growth factors (e.g. heparin-binding EGF) at the cell surface (111). Gastrin promotes the synthesis and processing of heparin-binding EGF-like growth factor (HB-EGF) and induces tyrosine phosphorylation of EGF receptor in the rat gastric epithelial cell line RGM1 transfected with the CCK_B/gastrin receptor (52). The localization of HB-EGF to gastric cells, including parietal cells, suggests a physiological role for this mechanism. Future work should define the contribution of these tyrosine kinase pathways to ERK activation induced via the CCK_B/gastrin receptor in AR4-2J cells.

In CHO cells transfected with the CCK_B/gastrin receptor, gastrin induces ERK activation partly via Src and PI3-kinase pathways and partly through PKC (70). In contrast, gastrin-stimulated Raf-1 and ERK activation in Rat-1 fibroblasts stably transfected with the CCK_B/gastrin receptor are independent of PKC (60). These studies reveal that activation of the CCK_B/gastrin receptor stimulates the ERK cascade via separate pathways in different cell types. These pathways are summarized by the scheme shown in Figure 1.

Cell context is likely to reflect the expression and function of specific signal transduction pathways leading to ERK in different cells. For instance, Pyk-2 is expressed in epithelial cells but not in fibroblasts (112), and the EGF receptor transactivation pathway is prominent in Rat-1 cells (113, 114) but is not functional in CHO cells because these cells do not express EGF receptors. Interestingly, parietal cells and ECL cells are known to express CCK_B/gastrin receptors, but gastrin elicits the Ras-ERK pathway and a trophic effect only in ECL cells from *Mastomys natalensis* (98). Furthermore, gastrin does not induce ERK activation in the GH3 pituitary adenoma cell line, which also expresses the CCK_B/gastrin receptor (69). These findings further emphasize the importance of cell context in the regulation of the ERK pathway via the CCK_B/gastrin receptor.

Tyrosine Phosphorylation of Focal Adhesion Kinase, Paxillin, and Crk-Associated Substrate (CAS)

An emerging theme in the elucidation of the signal transduction pathways activated by GPCR agonists is that, in addition to eliciting the synthesis of classic second messengers and the consequent stimulation of multiple serine/threonine protein kinase cascades, these agonists also induce tyrosine phosphorylation of multiple proteins, including focal adhesion kinase (p125[fak]), Pyk-2 (also called cell adhesion kinase β, related adhesion focal tyrosine kinase, or calcium-dependent protein tyrosine kinase), and Src (76).

p125[fak] and Pyk-2 comprise a new family of non-receptor tyrosine kinases. Although p125[fak] is expressed in many cells and tissues, Pyk-2 is found predominantly in neural and epithelial cells. Both proteins are structurally distinct non-receptor protein tyrosine kinases characterized by a centrally located catalytic domain flanked by the N- and C-terminal non-catalytic domains of approximately 400 residues that do not contain Src homology 2 and 3 (SH2 and SH3) domains.

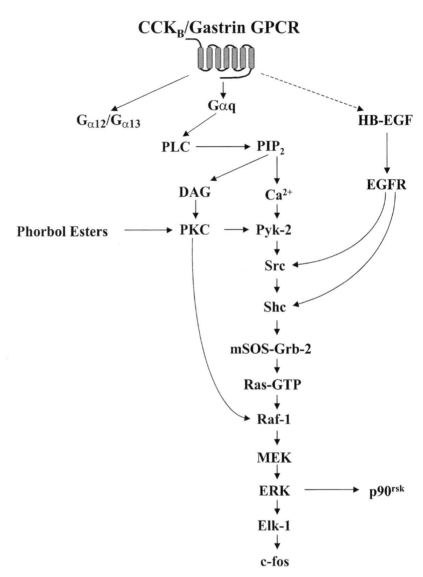

Figure 1   Multiple signal transduction pathways emanate from the CCK_B/gastrin receptor that lead to ERK activation in a variety of cell types. The importance of cellular context for the occurrence of the individual pathways illustrated in this scheme is described in the text. Gastrin and CCK induce many other early events emanating from activation of $G\alpha_{12}/G\alpha_{13}$ (see Figure 2). See text for abbreviations.

The major site of p125^{fak} and Pyk-2 autophosphorylation (i.e. Tyr 397 and 402, respectively) is a high-affinity binding site for the SH2 domain of members of the Src kinase family (reviewed in 115). Complex formation between p125^{fak} and Src results in the tyrosine phosphorylation of p125^{fak} at additional sites that stimulate its activity and provide docking sites for other signaling proteins. The formation of this complex also promotes Src activation. The focal adhesion proteins paxillin (116) and Crk-associated substrate (CAS) (117) are potential downstream targets for p125^{fak} and function as adaptors in signal transduction. The importance of p125^{fak}-mediated signal transduction is underscored by recent experiments showing that this tyrosine kinase is implicated in embryonic development and in the control of cell migration, proliferation, and apoptosis (reviewed in 76).

GPCR agonists have been shown to induce a rapid increase in the tyrosine phosphorylation of p125^{fak}, CAS, and paxillin in many cell types (118). Gastrin has been shown to elicit tyrosine phosphorylation of these focal adhesion proteins in Rat-1 (60) and NIH 3T3 cells (59) transfected with the CCK$_B$/gastrin receptor.

Rho-Dependent Actin Remodeling: Mediation via Gα_{12} and Gα_{13}

In many systems, GPCR-mediated increase in the tyrosine phosphorylation of p125^{fak}, CAS, and paxillin is accompanied by profound alterations in the organization of the actin cytoskeleton and in the assembly of focal adhesions, which, in turn, are mediated by activation of the small G protein Rho. Accordingly, CCK has been shown to induce a striking increase in the formation of actin stress fibers in NIH 3T3 cells transfected with the CCK$_B$/gastrin receptor (119). The formation of stress fibers induced by CCK was prevented by microinjection of Rho GDP dissociation inhibitor or *Clostridium botulinum* ADP-ribosyltransferase C3, treatments that inactivate Rho. These findings imply that Rho activation plays an important role in the actin remodeling induced by CCK$_B$/gastrin receptor activation.

The Ser/Thr protein kinase ROK (Rho kinase) has been identified as a downstream target of Rho-GTP (120–122) that transduces Rho activation into cytoskeletal responses (123), although other targets of Rho also contribute to this process (124). ROK activation leads to a Ca^{2+}-independent increase in the phosphorylation of the light chain of myosin II (MLC) at serine 19 (125), either by phosphorylation and inhibition of the 130-kDa myosin-binding subunit of myosin-associated MLC phosphatase, which dephosphorylates MLC (126, 127), or by direct phosphorylation of MLC (128). In turn, MLC phosphorylation leads to myosin filament formation and stimulates interaction with actin (129). The tension generated by the actin-myosin contractile apparatus has been hypothesized to promote the formation of stress fibers and the clustering of integrins to which they are attached, thus giving rise to focal adhesions (129). The translocation of p125^{fak} into nascent focal adhesions is thought to induce its autophosphorylation, as indicated above (115, 130). The elucidation of the role of ROK in CCK$_B$/gastrin receptor-induced actin remodeling warrants further experimental work.

It is relevant that constitutive active mutants of $G\alpha_{12}$ and $G\alpha_{13}$, which make up the G_{12} subfamily of heterotrimeric G proteins, stimulate Rho-dependent actin stress fiber formation, focal adhesion assembly, and tyrosine phosphorylation of focal adhesion proteins (131–133). The activated forms of $G\alpha_{12}/G\alpha_{13}$ activate Rho exchange factors (e.g. p115RhoGEF) that promote the GTP-bound form of Rho in vivo (134, 135). These findings imply that GPCRs, including the CCK_B/gastrin receptor, couple to Rho via either $G\alpha_{12}$ and/or $G\alpha_{13}$ and thereby lead to tyrosine phosphorylation of p125^{fak}, CAS, and paxillin via stress fiber formation and assembly of focal adhesions. This signal transduction pathway is schematically depicted in Figure 2.

Gastrin Activates Src-Family Tyrosine Kinases

The kinase activity of Src kinase family members (such as Src, Yes, and Fyn) is repressed when a key tyrosine residue in the C-terminal region (corresponding to Tyr-527 of the chicken protein) is phosphorylated by Csk (reviewed in 136). Phosphorylation at Tyr-527 creates a binding site for the Src SH2 domain and allows an intramolecular interaction that locks Src in an inactive conformation. Dephosphorylation of Tyr-527 by a tyrosine phosphatase destabilizes the complex, releases the SH2 domain and thereby activates the kinase activity. An alternative mechanism, involving competition for the SH2 and/or SH3 domains of Src by a high-affinity allosteric ligand, would also lead to enzymatic activation of this kinase (136, 137). In this context, autophosphorylation of p125^{fak} at Tyr-397 creates a putative competitive binding site for the SH2 domain of Src and thus would lead to the formation of a signaling complex in which both p125^{fak} and Src kinases are active (138).

Treatment of CHO cells with gastrin induces a rapid and transient increase in the kinase activity of the Src family of tyrosine kinases and promotes a complex formation between Src and Shc and between Src and IRS1, which leads to the tyrosine phosphorylation of Shc and IRS1 (70). As discussed above, this pathway has been implicated in mediating, at least in part, gastrin-induced ERK and PI3 kinase activation. Gastrin also induces the formation of a Src- p125^{fak} complex that appears to function upstream of PI3 kinase activation (139). PI3 kinase activation has been implicated in the signal transduction pathway that leads to the activation of the p70 ribosomal S6 kinase (p70^{S6K}), a conserved cellular response to many mitogenic stimuli (140), including gastrin (141) and CCK, via the CCK_B/gastrin receptor (142).

The formation of the Src-p125^{fak} complex as well as PI3 kinase activation in response to gastrin is prevented by treatment with cytochalasin D (139), a compound that disrupts actin stress fibers and completely blocks the increase in the tyrosine phosphorylation of p125^{fak} induced by GPCRs (143). Rapid and transient Src activation and cytochalasin D–sensitive complex formation between Src and p125^{fak} have also been shown to be induced by other GPCR agonists (138, 144). These results suggest the existence of two distinct signal transduction pathways that lead to protein tyrosine phosphorylation in GPCR-stimulated cells.

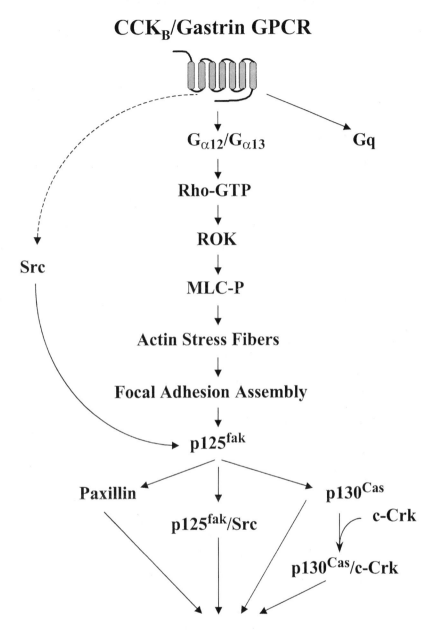

Figure 2 A putative pathway that transduces CCK_B/gastrin receptor signals into tyrosine phosphorylation of focal adhesion proteins via $G\alpha_{12}$/$G\alpha_{13}$. Gastrin and CCK induce many other early events emanating from activation of $G\alpha q$ (see Figure 1). The scheme presented here focuses on the pathway leading to tyrosine phosphorylation of focal adhesion proteins. See text for details and abbreviations. Other abbreviations used: ROK, Rho-associated coiled-coil-forming protein kinase; MLC-(P), phosphorylated form of myosin light chain.

Gastrin also induces Src activation in rat colonic epithelial cells, which leads to tyrosine phosphorylation and activation of PLCγ1 (145). As discussed above, Pyk-2 initiates a distinct pathway leading to Src activation that is downstream of PLC-mediated Ca^{2+} mobilization and PKC activation in certain cell types (108, 146, 147). The delineation of the role of Pyk-2 in CCK_B/gastrin receptor signaling in epithelial and neural cells warrants further experimental work.

Immediate Early Gene Expression

Growth factors induce rapid expression of immediate early genes including c-*myc*, c-*jun*, *jun D*, *jun B*, c-*fos*, *fos B*, *fra-1*, *fra-2*, and *egr1* in multiple cell types. Gastrin and CCK have been shown to induce c-*fos* and c-*jun* in AR4-2J cells (68, 96) and ECL cells (148) and c-*fos* and c-*myc* in NIH 3T3 cells transfected with the CCK_B/gastrin receptor (59). The transcription factors Elk-1 and Sap-1a, which regulate the activity of the serum response element located in the c-*fos* promoter, are known to be activated by multisite phosphorylation catalyzed by the ERKs (149). Gastrin induces ERK-mediated phosphorylation and activation of these transcription factors in AR4-2J cells, an effect prevented by pharmacological inhibition of PKC (96), which indicates an important role of PKCs and ERKs in the transcriptional activation of c-*fos* expression.

The CCK_B/gastrin receptor also couples to members of the G_{12} family, leading to actin remodeling and tyrosine phosphorylation of focal adhesion proteins via Rho. This small G protein interacts with multiple downstream pathways (150), some of which also lead to transcription regulation of the c-*fos* promoter via serum response factor (151) and of the cyclooxygenase-2 promoter (152). Gastrin induction of c-*fos* expression is attenuated by treatment with the C3 exoenzyme of *C. botulinum*, which implicates Rho in the regulation of the expression of this inmediate early gene (96). Gastrin also enhances the translation of ornithine decarboxylase mRNA via a rapamycin-sensitive pathway that involves the phosphorylation of 4E-BP1 (153).

The effect of gastrin and CCK on the activation of the cell cycle machinery, including the accumulation of cyclins, regulation of cyclin-dependent kinases, and the down-regulation of cell cycle inhibitors, remains entirely unexplored.

CCK$_B$/GASTRIN RECEPTOR EXPRESSION IN CANCER

The expression of CCK_B/gastrin receptor in human cancers leads to autocrine/paracrine loops and endocrine stimulation that promote tumor cell proliferation and migration. A well-defined case is small cell lung carcinoma (SCLC), which accounts for 25% of pulmonary cancers and follows a very aggressive clinical course. Tumor growth of SCLC has been proposed to be driven by multiple autocrine/paracrine loops involving neuropeptides that include CCK and gastrin (154). Gastrin, CCK, and unsulfated CCK-8 induce a rapid and transient mobilization of Ca^{2+} from intracellular stores in SCLC cell lines (64). The Ca^{2+}-mobilizing effects of gastrin and CCK-8 are prevented by the specific gastrin/CCKB receptor antagonist L365260 (63). Gastrin stimulates the clonal growth of SCLC cells in semisolid (agarose-containing) medium, increasing both the number and the size of the colonies (63, 155). These findings demonstrate that gastrin can act as a direct growth factor for SCLC cells through gastrin/CCKB receptors and indicates that these peptides can stimulate proliferation of cancer cells outside the GI tract.

Recently Reubi et al examined the expression of CCK_B/gastrin receptors and CCK_A receptors in 406 human tumors of various origins using in vitro receptor autoradiography (156). CCK_B/gastrin receptors were found frequently in medullary thyroid carcinomas (92%), in small cell lung cancers (57%), in astrocytomas (65%), and in stromal ovarian cancers (100%). They were rarely expressed in colorectal cancers, differentiated thyroid cancers, non–small cell lung cancers, meningiomas, neuroblastomas, schwannomas, glioblastomas, lymphomas, renal cell cancers, prostate carcinomas, and the remaining neuroendocrine tumors (i.e. pituitary adenomas, pheochromocytomas, paragangliomas, and parathyroid adenomas). CCK_A receptors were expressed rarely in tumors except in gastroenteropancreatic tumors (38%), meningiomas (30%), and some neuroblastomas (19%). Gastrin mRNA, measured by in situ hybridization, was detected in most CCK_B/gastrin-positive small cell lung cancers, thus supporting the hypothesis of autocrine growth regulation of these tumors. Gastrin and its analogues, which bind preferentially to the CCK_B/gastrin receptor, could provide a new approach for revealing the presence of SCLC using in vivo scintigraphy (157, 158).

The expression and role of CCK_B/gastrin in pancreatic cancer remains controversial. Expression of CCK_B/gastrin receptors has been reported in pancreatic cancer cell lines and pancreatic cancer tissue (159, 160) and autocrine regulation of these tumors via these receptors has been proposed (161). However, functional CCK_B/gastrin receptors were not detected in pancreatic cancer cell lines in another study, and addition of CCK inhibited the growth of these pancreatic cancer cells when they were transfected with the CCK_B/gastrin receptor (162). There is some evidence that CCK_A receptors may be implicated in induction or growth stimulation of pancreatic adenocarcinomas. In humans, CCK_B/gastrin but not CCK_A receptors are found in normal pancreas, but CCK_A receptors were found to be expressed selectively in pancreatic adenocarcinomas (159). An autocrine loop involving the CCK_B/gastrin receptor has also been implicated in the growth of human leukemia cells (163).

CONCLUSIONS AND PERSPECTIVES

Biologically active amidated gastrins act as potent cellular growth factors that are implicated in a variety of normal and abnormal biological processes including maintenance of the gastric mucosa, proliferation of ECL cells, and neoplastic transformation. The expression of CCK_B/gastrin receptor in human cancers has also been documented. Studies in transgenic mice and in cultured tumors also suggest that incompletely processed gastrins may have trophic activity independent of amidated gastrins. An important task for the future will be to identify the specific receptor(s) that mediates the biological responses induced by these gastrins and to develop cell model systems and specific antagonists for studying the intracellular signaling pathways stimulated by these novel receptors.

It will also be important to close the gaps in our understanding of gastrin-mediated signal transduction pathways, define the cross-talks and synergistic interactions between the serine/threonine and tyrosine phosphorylation cascades in the promotion of biological responses, and elucidate the molecular mechanisms by which the early signal transduction pathways induced by gastrin regulate the late molecular events in G_1 and thus the re-initiation of cell proliferation. Indeed, progression from G_1 to the S phase of the cell cycle is regulated by the periodic expression of cyclins D and E and by the elimination of the cyclin-dependent kinase inhibitor $p27^{kip}$, which modulate the activity of the CDKs such as CDK4 and CDK6 (164, 165). The activated CDK complexes are responsible for the hyperphosphorylation of the retinoblastoma (Rb) protein, which antagonizes its cell cycle inhibitory properties and allows passage of the cells through the R point of the cycle in late G_1 (166). Virtually nothing is known about the influence of gastrin and CCK on these fundamental events of the cell cycle. The development of new cellular model systems with a large signal-to-noise ratio in the proliferative response induced by CCK_B/gastrin receptor activation is another important task for the future that will open up an important experimental avenue to accomplish these objectives.

ACKNOWLEDGMENT

This work is supported by National Institutes of Health grants RO1 DK17294 and RO1 DK55003. Dr John H Walsh passed away on June 14, 2000.

Visit the Annual Reviews home page at www.AnnualReviews.org

LITERATURE CITED

1. Walsh JH. 1994. Gastrin. In *Gut Peptides: Biochemistry and Physiology*, ed. JH Walsh, GF Dockray, pp. 75–121. New York: Raven

2. Prinz C, Zanner R, Gerhard M, Mahr S, Neumayer N, et al. 1999. The mechanism of histamine secretion from gastric enterochromaffin-like cells. *Am. J. Physiol. Cell Physiol.* 277:C845–C55

3. Sachs G, Zeng N, Prinz C. 1997. Physiology of isolated gastric endocrine cells. *Annu. Rev. Physiol.* 59:243–56

3a. Williams JA. 2001. Intracellular signaling mechanisms activated by cholecystokinin regulating synthesis and secretion of digestive enzymes in pancreatic acinar cells. *Annu. Rev. Physiol.* 63:In press

4. Carlsson E, Havu N, Mattsson H, Ekman L. 1990. Gastrin and gastric

enterochromaffin-like cell carcinoids in the rat. *Digestion* 47 (Suppl. 1) :17–23; discussion 49–52

5. Rindi G, Azzoni C, La Rosa S, Klersy C, Paolotti D, et al. 1999. ECL cell tumor and poorly differentiated endocrine carcinoma of the stomach: prognostic evaluation by pathological analysis. *Gastroenterology* 116:532–42

6. Solcia E, Rindi G, Paolotti D, La Rosa S, Capella C, Fiocca R. 1999. Clinicopathological profile as a basis for classification of the endocrine tumours of the gastroenteropancreatic tract. *Ann. Oncol.* 10(2): S9–15 (Suppl.)

7. Wang TC, Dockray GJ. 1999. Lessons from genetically engineered animal models. I. Physiological studies with gastrin in transgenic mice. *Am. J. Physiol. Gastrointest. Liver Physiol.* 277:G6–G11

8. Thorburn CM, Friedman GD, Dickinson CJ, Vogelman JH, Orentreich N, Parsonnet J. 1998. Gastrin and colorectal cancer: a prospective study. *Gastroenterology* 115:275–80

9. Renga M, Brandi G, Paganelli GM, Calabrese C, Papa S, et al. 1997. Rectal cell proliferation and colon cancer risk in patients with hypergastrinaemia. *Gut* 41:330–32

10. Sobhani I, Lehy T, Laurent-Puig P, Cadiot G, Ruszniewski P, Mignon M. 1993. Chronic endogenous hypergastrinemia in humans: evidence for a mitogenic effect on the colonic mucosa. *Gastroenterology* 105:22–30

11. Nemeth J, Taylor B, Pauwels S, Varro A, Dockray GJ. 1993. Identification of progastrin derived peptides in colorectal carcinoma extracts. *Gut* 34:90–95

12. McWilliams DF, Watson SA, Crosbee DM, Michaeli D, Seth R. 1998. Coexpression of gastrin and gastrin receptors (CCK-B and delta CCK-B) in gastrointestinal tumour cell lines. *Gut* 42:795–98

13. Baldwin GS, Shulkes A. 1998. Gastrin, gastrin receptors and colorectal carcinoma. *Gut* 42:581–84

13a. Dockray GJ, Varro A, Dimaline R, Wang T. 2001. The gastrins: their production and biological activities. *Annu. Rev. Physiol.* 63:In press

14. Pauwels S, Desmond H, Dimaline R, Dockray GJ. 1986. Identification of progastrin in gastrinomas, antrum, and duodenum by a novel radioimmunoassay. *J. Clin. Invest.* 77:376–81

15. Azuma T, Magami Y, Habu Y, Kawai K, Taggart RT, Walsh JH. 1990. Carboxyl terminal glycine extended progastrin (gastrin-G) in gastric antral mucosa of patients with gastric or duodenal ulcer and in gastrinomas. *J. Gastroenterol. Hepatol.* 5:525–29

16. Huebner VD, Jiang RL, Lee TD, Legesse K, Walsh JH, et al. 1991. Purification and structural characterization of progastrin-derived peptides from a human gastrinoma. *J. Biol. Chem.* 266:12223–27

17. Sandvik AK, Dockray GJ. 1999. Biological activity of carboxy-terminal gastrin analogs. *Eur. J. Pharmacol.* 364:199–203

18. Pisegna JR, Norton JA, Slimak GG, Metz DC, Maton PN, et al. 1992. Effects of curative gastrinoma resection on gastric secretory function and antisecretory drug requirement in the Zollinger-Ellison syndrome. *Gastroenterology* 102:767–78

19. D'Adda T, Corleto V, Pilato FP, Baggi MT, Robutti F, et al. 1990. Quantitative ultrastructure of endocrine cells of oxyntic mucosa in Zollinger-Ellison syndrome. Correspondence with light microscopic findings. *Gastroenterology* 99:17–26

20. Debelenko LV, Emmert-Buck MR, Zhuang Z, Epshteyn E, Moskaluk CA, et al. 1997. The multiple endocrine neoplasia type I gene locus is involved in the pathogenesis of type II gastric carcinoids. *Gastroenterology* 113:773–81

21. Borch K, Renvall H, Liedberg G, Andersen BN. 1986. Relations between circulating gastrin and endocrine cell proliferation in the atrophic gastric fundic mucosa. *Scand. J. Gastroenterol.* 21:357–63

22. Hirschowitz BI, Griffith J, Pellegrin D, Cummings OW. 1992. Rapid regression of enterochromaffinlike cell gastric carcinoids in pernicious anemia after antrectomy. *Gastroenterology* 102:1409–18

23. McCloy RF, Arnold R, Bardhan KD, Cattan D, Klinkenberg-Knol E, et al. 1995. Pathophysiological effects of long-term acid suppression in man. *Dig. Dis. Sci.* 40:96S–120S

24. Gillen D, Wirz AA, Ardill JE, McColl KE. 1999. Rebound hypersecretion after omeprazole and its relation to on-treatment acid suppression and *Helicobacter pylori* status. *Gastroenterology* 116:239–47

25. Ryberg B, Axelson J, Håkanson R, Sundler F, Mattsson H. 1990. Trophic effects of continuous infusion of [Leu15]-gastrin-17 in the rat. *Gastroenterology* 98:33–38

26. Ryberg B, Tielemans Y, Axelson J, Carlsson E, Håkanson R, et al. 1990. Gastrin stimulates the self-replication rate of enterochromaffinlike cells in the rat stomach. Effects of omeprazole, ranitidine, and gastrin-17 in intact and antrectomized rats. *Gastroenterology* 99:935–42

27. Ekman L, Hansson E, Havu N, Carlsson E, Lundberg C. 1985. Toxicological studies on omeprazole. *Scand. J. Gastroenterol. Suppl.* 108:53–69

28. Håkanson R, Tielemans Y, Chen D, Andersson K, Mattsson H, Sundler F. 1993. Time-dependent changes in enterochromaffin-like cell kinetics in stomach of hypergastrinemic rats. *Gastroenterology* 105:15–21

29. Mattsson H, Havu N, Bräutigam J, Carlsson K, Lundell L, Carlsson E. 1991. Partial gastric corpectomy results in hypergastrinemia and development of gastric enterochromaffin-like cell carcinoids in the rat. *Gastroenterology* 100:311–19

30. Havu N, Mattsson H, Ekman L, Carlsson E. 1990. Enterochromaffin-like cell carcinoids in the rat gastric mucosa following long-term administration of ranitidine. *Digestion* 45:189–95

31. Eissele R, Patberg H, Koop H, Krack W, Lorenz W, et al. 1992. Effect of gastrin receptor blockade on endocrine cells in rats during achlorhydria. *Gastroenterology* 103:1596–601

32. Håkanson R, Ding XQ, Norlén P, Lindström E. 1999. CCK2 receptor antagonists: pharmacological tools to study the gastrin-ECL cell-parietal cell axis. *Regul. Pept.* 80:1–12

33. Nishida A, Kobayashi-Uchida A, Akuzawa S, Takinami Y, Shishido T, et al. 1995. Gastrin receptor antagonist YM022 prevents hypersecretion after long-term acid suppression. *Am. J. Physiol. Gastrointest. Liver Physiol.* 269:G699–G705

34. Ohning GV, Wong HC, Lloyd KC, Walsh JH. 1996. Gastrin mediates the gastric mucosal proliferative response to feeding. *Am. J. Physiol. Gastrointest. Liver Physiol.* 271:G470–G76

35. Quintero E, Ohning GV, Del Rivero M, Wong HC, Walsh JH, Guth PH. 1995. Gastrin mediates the increase in gastric cell growth in uremic rats. *Am. J. Physiol. Gastrointest. Liver Physiol.* 268:G586–G91

36. Modlin IM, Tang LH. 1996. The gastric enterochromaffin-like cell: an enigmatic cellular link. *Gastroenterology* 111:783–810

37. Chiba T, Kinoshita Y, Sawada M, Kishi K, Baba A, Hoshino E. 1998. The role of endogenous gastrin in the development of enterochromaffin-like cell carcinoid tumors in *Mastomys natalensis*: a study with the specific gastrin receptor antagonist AG-041R. *Yale J. Biol. Med.* 71:247–55

38. Schaffer K, McBride EW, Beinborn M, Kopin AS. 1998. Interspecies polymorphisms confer constitutive activity to the Mastomys cholecystokinin-B/gastrin receptor. *J. Biol. Chem.* 273:28779–84

39. Betton GR, Dormer CS, Wells T, Pert P, Price CA, Buckley P. 1988. Gastric ECL-cell hyperplasia and carcinoids in rodents following chronic administration of

H2-antagonists SK&F 93479 and oxmetidine and omeprazole. *Toxicol. Pathol.* 16: 288–98

40. Konda Y, Kamimura H, Yokota H, Hayashi N, Sugano K, Takeuchi T. 1999. Gastrin stimulates the growth of gastric pit with less-differentiated features. *Am. J. Physiol. Gastrointest. Liver Physiol.* 277:G773–G84

41. Wang TC, Dangler CA, Chen D, Goldenring JR, Koh T, et al. 2000. Synergistic interaction between hypergastrinemia and Helicobacter infection in a mouse model of gastric cancer. *Gastroenterology* 118: 36–47

42. Wang TC, Koh TJ, Varro A, Cahill RJ, Dangler CA, et al. 1996. Processing and proliferative effects of human progastrin in transgenic mice. *J. Clin. Invest.* 98: 1918–29

43. Koh TJ, Dockray GJ, Varro A, Cahill RJ, Dangler CA, et al. 1999. Overexpression of glycine-extended gastrin in transgenic mice results in increased colonic proliferation. *J. Clin. Invest.* 103:1119–26

44. Singh P, Velasco M, Given R, Wargovich M, Varro A, Wang TC. Mice overexpressing progastrin are predisposed for developing aberrant colonic crypt foci in response to AOM. *Am. J. Physiol. Gastrointest. Liver Physiol.* 278:G390–G99

45. Watson SA, Michaeli D, Morris TM, Clarke P, Varro A, et al. 1999. Antibodies raised by gastrimmune inhibit the spontaneous metastasis of a human colorectal tumour, AP5LV. *Eur. J. Cancer* 35:1286–91

46. Koh TJ, Goldenring JR, Ito S, Mashimo H, Kopin AS, et al. 1997. Gastrin deficiency results in altered gastric differentiation and decreased colonic proliferation in mice. *Gastroenterology* 113:1015–25

47. Friis-Hansen L, Sundler F, Li Y, Gillespie PJ, Saunders TL, et al. 1998. Impaired gastric acid secretion in gastrin-deficient mice. *Am. J. Physiol. Gastrointest. Liver Physiol.* 274:G561–G68

48. Hinkle KL, Samuelson LC. 1999. Lessons from genetically engineered animal models. III. Lessons learned from gastrin gene deletion in mice. *Am. J. Physiol. Gastrointest. Liver Physiol.* 277:G500–G5

49. Nagata A, Ito M, Iwata N, Kuno J, Takano H, et al. 1996. G protein-coupled cholecystokinin-B/gastrin receptors are responsible for physiological cell growth of the stomach mucosa in vivo. *Proc. Natl. Acad. Sci. USA* 93:11825–30

50. Langhans N, Rindi G, Chiu M, Rehfeld JF, Ardman B, et al. 1997. Abnormal gastric histology and decreased acid production in cholecystokinin-B/gastrin receptor-deficient mice. *Gastroenterology* 112: 280–86

51. Tsutsui S, Shinomura Y, Higashiyama S, Higashimoto Y, Miyazaki Y, et al. 1997. Induction of heparin binding epidermal growth factor-like growth factor and amphiregulin mRNAs by gastrin in the rat stomach. *Biochem. Biophys. Res. Commun.* 235:520–23

52. Miyazaki Y, Shinomura Y, Tsutsui S, Zushi S, Higashimoto Y, et al. 1999. Gastrin induces heparin-binding epidermal growth factor-like growth factor in rat gastric epithelial cells transfected with gastrin receptor. *Gastroenterology* 116:78–89

53. Marx SJ, Agarwal SK, Kester MB, Heppner C, Kim YS, et al. 1999. Multiple endocrine neoplasia type 1: clinical and genetic features of the hereditary endocrine neoplasias. *Recent Prog. Horm. Res.* 54:397–438; discussion 438–39

54. Asahara M, Mushiake S, Shimada S, Fukui H, Kinoshita Y, et al. 1996. Reg gene expression is increased in rat gastric enterochromaffin-like cells following water immersion stress. *Gastroenterology* 111:45–55

55. Higham AD, Bishop LA, Dimaline R, Blackmore CG, Dobbins AC, et al. 1999. Mutations of RegI alpha are associated with enterochromaffin-like cell tumor development in patients with hypergastrinemia. *Gastroenterology* 116:1310–18

56. Azzoni C, Doglioni C, Viale G, Delle Fave G, De Boni M, et al. 1996. Involvement of BCL-2 oncoprotein in the development of enterochromaffin-like cell gastric carcinoids. *Am. J. Surg. Path.* 20:433–41

57. Dockray GJ. 1999. Topical review. gastrin and gastric epithelial physiology. *J. Physiol.* 518:315–24

58. Yassin RR. 1999. Signaling pathways mediating gastrin's growth-promoting effects. *Peptides* 20:885–98

59. Taniguchi T, Matsui T, Ito M, Murayama T, Tsukamoto T, et al. 1994. Cholecystokinin-B/gastrin receptor signaling pathway involves tyrosine phosphorylations of p125FAK and p42MAP. *Oncogene* 9:861–67

60. Seufferlein T, Withers DJ, Broad S, Herget T, Walsh JH, Rozengurt E. 1995. The human CCKB/gastrin receptor transfected into rat1 fibroblasts mediates activation of MAP kinase, p74raf-1 kinase, and mitogenesis. *Cell Growth Diff.* 6:383–93

61. Ito M, Matsui T, Taniguchi T, Tsukamoto T, Murayama T, et al. 1993. Functional characterization of a human brain cholecystokinin-B receptor. A trophic effect of cholecystokinin and gastrin. *J. Biol. Chem.* 268:18300–5

62. Akagi K, Nagao T, Urushidani T. 1999. Correlation between Ca(2+) oscillation and cell proliferation via CCK(B)/gastrin receptor. *Biochim. Biophys. Acta* 1452:243–53

63. Sethi T, Rozengurt E. 1992. Gastrin stimulates Ca²⁺ mobilization and clonal growth in small cell lung cancer cells. *Cancer Res.* 52:6031–35

64. Sethi T, Herget T, Wu WSV, Walsh JH, Rozengurt E. 1993. CCKA and CCKB receptors are expressed in small cell lung cancer lines and mediate Ca²⁺ mobilization and clonal growth. *Cancer Res.* 53:5208–13

65. Herget T, Sethi T, Wu WSV, Walsh JH, Rozengurt E. 1994. Cholecystokinin stimulates Ca²⁺ mobilization and clonal growth in small cell lung cancer through CCKA and CCKB/gastrin receptors. *Ann. NY Acad. Sci.* 713:283–97

66. Wank SA, Pisegna JR, de Weerth A. 1994. Cholecystokinin receptor family. Molecular cloning, structure, and functional expression in rat, guinea pig, and human. *Ann. NY Acad. Sci.* 713:49–66

67. Detjen K, Yule D, Tseng MJ, Williams JA, Logsdon CD. 1997. CCK-B receptors produce similar signals but have opposite growth effects in CHO and Swiss 3T3 cells. *Am. J. Physiol. Cell Physiol.* 273:C1449–C57

68. Todisco A, Takeuchi Y, Urumov A, Yamada J, Stepan VM, Yamada T. 1997. Molecular mechanisms for the growth factor action of gastrin. *Am. J. Physiol. Gastrointest. Liver Physiol.* 273:G891–G98

69. Stepan VM, Dickinson CJ, del Valle J, Matsushima M, Todisco A. 1999. Cell type-specific requirement of the MAPK pathway for the growth factor action of gastrin. *Am. J. Physiol. Gastrointest. Liver Physiol.* 276:G1363–G72

70. Daulhac L, Kowalski-Chauvel A, Pradayrol L, Vaysse N, Seva C. 1999. Src-family tyrosine kinases in activation of ERK-1 and p85/p110-phosphatidylinositol 3-kinase by G/CCKB receptors. *J. Biol. Chem.* 274:20657–63

71. Rozengurt E, Sinnett-Smith J. 1983. Bombesin stimulation of DNA synthesis and cell division in cultures of Swiss 3T3 cells. *Proc. Natl. Acad. Sci. USA* 80:2936–40

72. Ji TH, Grossmann M, Ji I. 1998. G protein-coupled receptors. I. Diversity of receptor-ligand interactions. *J. Biol. Chem.* 273:17299–302

73. Wank SA. 1998. G protein-coupled receptors in gastrointestinal physiology. I. CCK receptors: an exemplary family. *Am. J. Physiol. Gastrointest. Liver Physiol.* 274:G607–G13

74. Rozengurt E. 1986. Early signals in the

mitogenic response. *Science* 234:161–66

75. Rozengurt E. 1991. Neuropeptides as cellular growth factors: role of multiple signalling pathways. *Eur. J. Clin. Invest.* 21: 123–34

76. Rozengurt E. 1998. Signal transduction pathways in the mitogenic response to G protein-coupled neuropeptide receptor agonists. *J. Cell. Physiol.* 177:507–17

77. Exton JH. 1996. Regulation of phosphoinositide phospholipases by hormones, neurotransmitters, and other agonists linked to G proteins. *Annu. Rev. Pharmacol. Toxicol.* 36:481–509

78. Mikoshiba K. 1997. The InsP$_3$ receptor and intracellular Ca^{2+} signaling. *Curr. Opin. Neurobiol.* 7:339–45

79. Cancela JM, Churchill GC, Galione A. 1999. Coordination of agonist-induced Ca^{2+}-signalling patterns by NAADP in pancreatic acinar cells. *Nature* 398:74–76

80. Yassin RR, Little KM. 1995. Early signalling mechanism in colonic epithelial cell response to gastrin. *Biochem. J.* 311: 945–50

81. Dolmetsch RE, Xu K, Lewis RS. 1998. Calcium oscillations increase the efficiency and specificity of gene expression. *Nature* 392:933–36

82. Li W, Llopis J, Whitney M, Zlokarnik G, Tsien RY. 1998. Cell-permeant caged InsP$_3$ ester shows that Ca^{2+} spike frequency can optimize gene expression. *Nature* 392: 936–41

83. Nishizuka Y. 1995. Protein kinase C and lipid signaling for sustained cellular responses. *FASEB J.* 9:484–96

84. Daulhac L, Kowalski-Chauvel A, Pradayrol L, Vaysse N, Seva C. 1997. Ca^{2+} and protein kinase C-dependent mechanisms involved in gastrin-induced Shc/Grb2 complex formation and P44-mitogen-activated protein kinase activation. *Biochem. J.* 325: 383–89

85. Valverde AM, Sinnett-Smith J, Van Lint J, Rozengurt E. 1994. Molecular cloning and characterization of protein kinase D: a target for diacylglycerol and phorbol esters with a distinctive catalytic domain. *Proc. Natl. Acad. Sci. USA* 91:8572–76

86. Zugaza JL, Sinnett-Smith J, Van Lint J, Rozengurt E. 1996. Protein kinase D (PKD) activation in intact cells through a protein kinase C-dependent signal transduction pathway. *EMBO J.* 15:6220–30

87. Zugaza JL, Waldron RT, Sinnett-Smith J, Rozengurt E. 1997. Bombesin, vasopressin, endothelin, bradykinin, and platelet-derived growth factor rapidly activate protein kinase D through a protein kinase C-dependent signal transduction pathway. *J. Biol. Chem.* 272:23952–60

88. Yuan JZ, Slice L, Walsh JH, Rozengurt E. 2000. Activation of protein kinase D by signaling through the alpha subunit of the heterotrimeric G protein G(q). *J. Biol. Chem.* 275:2157–64

89. Chiu TT, Duque J, Rozengurt E. 1999. Protein kinase D (PKD) activation is a novel early event in CCKB/gastrin receptor signaling. *Gastroenterology* 116:A597 (Abstr.)

90. Ghrib F, Pyronnet S, Bastié MJ, Fagot-Revurat P, Pradayrol L, Vaysse N. 1998. Arachidonic-acid-selective cytosolic phospholipase A2 is involved in gastrin-induced AR4-2J-cell proliferation. *Int. J. Cancer* 75:239–45

91. Börsch-Haubold AG, Bartoli F, Asselin J, Dudler T, Kramer RM, et al. 1998. Identification of the phosphorylation sites of cytosolic phospholipase A2 in agonist-stimulated human platelets and HeLa cells. *J. Biol. Chem.* 273:4449–58

92. Pommier B, Da Nascimento S, Dumont S, Bellier B, Million E, et al. 1999. The cholecystokinin-B receptor is coupled to two effector pathways through pertussis toxin-sensitive and -insensitive G proteins. *J. Neurochem.* 73:281–88

93. Wu V, Yang M, McRoberts JA, Ren J, Seensalu R, et al. 1997. First intracellular loop of the human cholecystokinin-A receptor is essential for cyclic AMP

signaling in transfected HEK-293 cells. *J. Biol. Chem.* 272:9037–42

94. Widmann C, Gibson S, Jarpe MB, Johnson GL. 1999. Mitogen-activated protein kinase: conservation of a three-kinase module from yeast to human. *Physiol. Rev.* 79:143–80

95. Gutkind JS. 1998. The pathways connecting G protein-coupled receptors to the nucleus through divergent mitogen-activated protein kinase cascades. *J. Biol. Chem.* 273:1839–42

96. Stepan VM, Tatewaki M, Matsushima M, Dickinson CJ, del Valle J, Todisco A. 1999. Gastrin induces c-*fos* gene transcription via multiple signaling pathways. *Am. J. Physiol. Gastrointest. Liver Physiol.* 276:G415–G24

97. Höcker M, Henihan RJ, Rosewicz S, Riecken EO, Zhang Z, et al. 1997. Gastrin and phorbol 12-myristate 13-acetate regulate the human histidine decarboxylase promoter through Raf-dependent activation of extracellular signal-regulated kinase-related signaling pathways in gastric cancer cells. *J. Biol. Chem.* 272: 27015–24

98. Kinoshita Y, Nakata H, Kishi K, Kawanami C, Sawada M, Chiba T. 1998. Comparison of the signal transduction pathways activated by gastrin in enterochromaffin-like and parietal cells. *Gastroenterology* 115:93–100

99. Daaka Y, Luttrell LM, Ahn S, Della Rocca GJ, Ferguson SS, et al. 1998. Essential role for G protein-coupled receptor endocytosis in the activation of mitogen-activated protein kinase. *J. Biol. Chem.* 273:685–88

100. Lefkowitz RJ. 1998. G Protein-coupled receptors. III. New roles for receptor kinases and B-arrestins in receptor signaling and desensitization. *J. Biol. Chem.* 273:18677–80

101. Kranenburg O, Verlaan I, Moolenaar WH. 1999. Dynamin is required for the activation of mitogen-activated protein (MAP) kinase by MAP kinase kinase. *J. Biol. Chem.* 274:35301–4

102. Schramm NL, Limbird LE. 1999. Stimulation of mitogen-activated protein kinase by G protein-coupled alpha(2)-adrenergic receptors does not require agonist-elicited endocytosis. *J. Biol. Chem.* 274: 24935–40

103. Schönwasser DC, Marais RM, Marshall CJ, Parker PJ. 1998. Activation of the mitogen-activated protein kinase/extracellular signal-regulated kinase pathway by conventional, novel, and atypical protein kinase C isotypes. *Mol. Cell. Biol.* 18:790–98

104. Cai H, Smola U, Wixler V, Eisenmann-Tappe I, Diaz-Meco MT, et al. 1997. Role of diacylglycerol-regulated protein kinase C isotypes in growth factor activation of the Raf-1 protein kinase. *Mol. Cell. Biol.* 17:732–41

105. Marais R, Light Y, Mason C, Paterson H, Olson MF, Marshall CJ. 1998. Requirement of Ras-GTP-Raf complexes for activation of Raf-1 by protein kinase C. *Science* 280:109–12

106. Seva C, Kowalski-Chauvel A, Blanchet JS, Vaysse N, Pradayrol L. 1996. Gastrin induces tyrosine phosphorylation of Shc proteins and their association with the Grb2/Sos complex. *FEBS Lett.* 378: 74–78

107. Luttrell LM, Della Rocca GJ, van Biesen T, Luttrell DK, Lefkowitz RJ. 1997. $\beta\gamma$ subunits mediate Src-dependent phosphorylation of the epidermal growth factor receptor. A scaffold for G protein-coupled receptor-mediated Ras activation. *J. Biol. Chem.* 272:4637–44

108. Della Rocca GJ, van Biesen T, Daaka Y, Luttrell DK, Luttrell LM, Lefkowitz RJ. 1997. Ras-dependent mitogen-activated protein kinase activation by G protein-coupled receptors. Convergence of Gi- and Gq-mediated pathways on calcium/calmodulin, Pyk2, and Src kinase. *J. Biol. Chem.* 272:19125–32

109. Wan Kurosaki T, Huang XY. 1996. Tyrosine kinases in activation of the MAP kinase cascade by G-protein-coupled receptors. *Nature* 380:541–44

110. Carpenter G. 1999. Employment of the epidermal growth factor receptor in growth factor-independent signaling pathways. *J. Cell Biol.* 146:697–702

111. Prenzel N, Zwick E, Daub H, Leserer M, Abraham R, et al. 1999. EGF receptor transactivation by G-protein-coupled receptors requires metalloproteinase cleavage of proHB-EGF. *Nature* 402:884–88

112. Li X, Lee JW, Graves LM, Earp HS. 1998. Angiotensin II stimulates ERK via two pathways in epithelial cells: protein kinase C suppresses a G-protein coupled receptor-EGF receptor transactivation pathway. *EMBO J.* 17:2574–83

113. Daub H, Wallasch C, Lankenau A, Herrlich A, Ullrich A. 1997. Signal characteristics of G protein-transactivated EGF receptor. *EMBO J.* 16:7032–44

114. Daub H, Weiss FU, Wallasch C, Ullrich A. 1996. Role of transactivation of the EGF receptor in signalling by G-protein-coupled receptors. *Nature* 379:557–60

115. Hanks SK, Polte TR. 1997. Signaling through focal adhesion kinase. *BioEssays* 19:137–45

116. Brown MC, Perrotta JA, Turner CE. 1996. Identification of LIM3 as the principal determinant of paxillin focal adhesion localization and characterization of a novel motif on paxillin directing vinculin and focal adhesion kinase binding. *J. Cell Biol.* 135:1109–23

117. Sakai R, Iwamatsu A, Hirano N, Ogawa S, Tanaka T, et al. 1994. A novel signaling molecule, p130, forms stable complexes in vivo with v-Crk and v-Src in a tyrosine phosphorylation-dependent manner. *EMBO J.* 13:3748–56

118. Rozengurt E. 1998. Gastrointestinal peptide signaling through tyrosine phosphorylation of focal adhesion proteins. *Am. J. Physiol. Gastrointest. Liver Physiol* 275:G177–G82

119. Taniguchi T, Takaishi K, Murayama T, Ito M, Iwata N, et al. 1996. Cholecystokinin-B/gastrin receptors mediate rapid formation of actin stress fibers. *Oncogene* 12:1357–60

120. Amano M, Mukai H, Ono Y, Chihara K, Matsui T, et al. 1996. Identification of a putative target for Rho as the serine-threonine kinase protein kinase N. *Science* 271:648–50

121. Uehata M, Ishizaki T, Satoh H, Ono T, Kawahara T, et al. 1997. Calcium sensitization of smooth muscle mediated by a Rho-associated protein kinase in hypertension. *Nature* 389:990–94

122. Leung T, Chen XQ, Manser E, Lim L. 1996. The p160 RhoA-binding kinase ROK alpha is a member of a kinase family and is involved in the reorganization of the cytoskeleton. *Mol. Cell. Biol.* 16:5313–27

123. Amano M, Chihara K, Kimura K, Fukata Y, Nakamura N, et al. 1997. Formation of actin stress fibers and focal adhesions enhanced by Rho-kinase. *Science* 275:1308–11

124. Watanabe N, Kato T, Fujita A, Ishizaki T, Narumiya S. 1999. Cooperation between mDia1 and ROCK in Rho-induced actin reorganization. *Nat. Cell Biol.* 1:136–43

125. van Eyk JE, Arrell DK, Foster DB, Strauss JD, Heinonen TY, et al. 1998. Different molecular mechanisms for Rho family GTPase-dependent, Ca^{2+}-independent contraction of smooth muscle. *J. Biol. Chem.* 273:23433–39

126. Kimura K, Ito M, Amano M, Chihara K, Fukata Y, et al. 1996. Regulation of myosin phosphatase by Rho and Rho-associated kinase Rho-kinase. *Science* 273:245–48

127. Essler M, Amano M, Kruse HJ, Kaibuchi K, Weber PC, Aepfelbacher M. 1998.

Thrombin inactivates myosin light chain phosphatase via Rho and its target Rho kinase in human endothelial cells. *J. Biol. Chem.* 273:21867–74

128. Kureishi Y, Kobayashi S, Amano M, Kimura K, Kanaide H, et al. 1997. Rho-associated kinase directly induces smooth muscle contraction through myosin light chain phosphorylation. *J. Biol. Chem.* 272:12257–60

129. Burridge K, Chrzanowska-Wodnicka M. 1996. Focal adhesions, contractility, and signaling. *Annu. Rev. Cell Dev. Biol.* 12:463–518

130. Rozengurt E, Rodriguez-Fernandez JL. 1997. Tyrosine phosphorylation in the action of neuropeptides and growth factors. *Essays Biochem.* 32:73–86

131. Buhl AM, Johnson NL, Dhanasekaran N, Johnson GL. 1995. G alpha 12 and G alpha 13 stimulate Rho-dependent stress fiber formation and focal adhesion assembly. *J. Biol. Chem.* 270:24631–34

132. Gohla A, Harhammer R, Schultz G. 1998. The G-protein G13 but not G12 mediates signaling from lysophosphatidic acid receptor via epidermal growth factor receptor to Rho. *J. Biol. Chem.* 273:4653–59

133. Needham LK, Rozengurt E. 1998. Gα12 and Gα13 stimulate Rho-dependent tyrosine phosphorylation of focal adhesion kinase, paxillin and p130 Crk-associated substrate. *J. Biol. Chem.* 273:14626–32

134. Kozasa T, Jiang X, Hart MJ, Sternweis PM, Singer WD, et al. 1998. p115 RhoGEF, a GTPase activating protein for Gα12 and Gα13. *Science* 280:2109–11

135. Hart MJ, Jiang X, Kozasa T, Roscoe W, Singer WD, et al. 1998. Direct stimulation of the guanine nucleotide exchange activity of p115RhoGEF by Gα13. *Science* 280:2112–14

136. Pawson T. 1995. Protein modules and signalling networks. *Nature* 373:573–80

137. Thomas JW, Ellis B, Boerner RJ, Knight WB, White GC II, Schaller MD. 1998. SH2- and SH3-mediated interactions between focal adhesion kinase and Src. *J. Biol. Chem.* 273:577–83

138. Salazar EP, Rozengurt E. 1999. Bombesin and platelet-derived growth factor induce association of endogenous focal adhesion kinase with Src in intact Swiss 3T3 cells. *J. Biol. Chem.* 274:28371–78

139. Daulhac L, Kowalski-Chauvel A, Pradayrol L, Vaysse N, Seva C. 1999. Gastrin stimulates the formation of a p60Src/p125FAK complex upstream of the phosphatidylinositol 3-kinase signaling pathway. *FEBS Lett* 445:251–55

140. Thomas G, Hall MN. 1997. TOR signalling and control of cell growth. *Curr. Opin. Cell Biol.* 9:782–87

141. Seva C, Kowalski-Chauvel A, Daulhac L, Barthez C, Vaysse N, Pradayrol L. 1997. Wortmannin-sensitive activation of p70S6-kinase and MAP-kinase by the G protein-coupled receptor, G/CCKB. *Biochem. Biophys. Res. Commun.* 238:202–6

142. Desbois C, Le Huerou-Leron I, Dufresne M, Estival A, Clerc P, et al. 1999. The CCKB/gastrin receptor is coupled to the regulation of enzyme secretion, protein synthesis and p70 S6 kinase activity in acinar cells from ElasCCKB transgenic mice. *Eur. J. Biochem.* 266:1003–10

143. Sinnett-Smith J, Zachary I, Valverde AM, Rozengurt E. 1993. Bombesin stimulation of p125 focal adhesion kinase tyrosine phosphorylation. Role of protein kinase C, Ca^{2+} mobilization, and the actin cytoskeleton. *J. Biol. Chem.* 268:14261–68

144. Rodríguez-Fernández JL, Rozengurt E. 1996. Bombesin, bradykinin, vasopressin, and phorbol esters rapidly and transiently activate Src family tyrosine kinases in Swiss 3T3 cells. Dissociation from tyrosine phosphorylation of p125

focal adhesion kinase. *J. Biol. Chem.* 271:27895–901

145. Yassin RR, Abrams JT. 1998. Gastrin induces IP$_3$ formation through phospholipase C gamma 1 and p60c-src kinase. *Peptides* 19:47–55

146. Lev S, Moren H, Martinez R, Canoll P, Peles E, et al. 1995. Protein tyrosine kinase PYK2 involved in Ca(2+)-induced regulation of ion channel and MAP kinase functions. *Nature* 376:737–45

147. Dikic I, Tokiwa G, Lev S, Courtneidge SA, Schlessinger J. 1996. A role for Pyk2 and Src in linking G-protein-coupled receptors with MAP kinase activation. *Nature* 383:547–50

148. Kinoshita Y, Nakata H, Kishi K, Kawanami C, Sawada M, Chiba T. 1998. Comparison of the signal transduction pathways activated by gastrin in enterochromaffin-like and parietal cells. *Gastroenterology* 115:93–100

149. Treisman R. 1996. Regulation of transcription by MAP kinase cascades. *Curr. Opin. Cell Biol.* 8:205–15

150. Mackay DJ, Hall A. 1998. Rho GTPases. *J. Biol. Chem.* 273:20685–88

151. Hill CS, Wynne J, Treisman R. 1995. The Rho family GTPases RhoA, Rac1, and CDC42Hs regulate transcriptional activation by SRF. *Cell* 81:1159–70

152. Slice L, Walsh JH, Rozengurt E. 1999. Gα(13) stimulates Rho-dependent activation of the cyclooxygenase-2 promoter. *J. Biol. Chem.* 274:27562–66

153. Pyronnet S, Gingras AC, Bouisson M, Kowalski-Chauvel A, Seva C, et al. 1998. Gastrin induces phosphorylation of eIF4E binding protein 1 and translation initiation of ornithine decarboxylase mRNA. *Oncogene* 16:2219–27

154. Rozengurt E. 1999. Autocrine loops, signal transduction, and cell cycle abnormalities in the molecular biology of lung cancer. *Curr. Opin. Oncol.* 11:116–22

155. Sethi T, Rozengurt E. 1991. Multiple neuropeptides stimulate clonal growth of small cell lung cancer: effects of bradykinin, vasopressin, cholecystokinin, galanin, and neurotensin. *Cancer Res.* 51:3621–23

156. Reubi JC, Schaer JC, Waser B. 1997. Cholecystokinin (CCK)-A and CCK-B/gastrin receptors in human tumors. *Cancer Res.* 57:1377–86

157. Behr TM, Jenner N, Radetzky S, Béhé M, Gratz S, et al. 1998. Targeting of cholecystokinin-B/gastrin receptors in vivo: preclinical and initial clinical evaluation of the diagnostic and therapeutic potential of radiolabelled gastrin. *Eur. J. Nucl. Med.* 25:424–30

158. Behr TM, Béhé M, Angerstein C, Gratz S, Mach R, et al. 1999. Cholecystokinin-B/gastrin receptor binding peptides: preclinical development and evaluation of their diagnostic and therapeutic potential. *Clin. Cancer Res.* 5:3124s–38s

159. Kaufmann R, Schafberg H, Rudroff C, Henklein P, Nowak G. 1997. Cholecystokinin B-type receptor signaling is involved in human pancreatic cancer cell growth. *Neuropeptides* 31:573–83

160. de Weerth A, von Schrenck T, Löhr M, Mirau S, Greten H, Kalthoff H. 1999. Human pancreatic cancer cell lines express the CCKB receptor. *Hepato-Gastroenterol.* 46:472–78

161. Smith JP, Shih A, Wu Y, McLaughlin PJ, Zagon IS. 1996. Gastrin regulates growth of human pancreatic cancer in a tonic and autocrine fashion. *Am. J. Physiol. Regulatory Integrative Comp. Physiol.* 270:R1078–R84

162. Detjen K, Fenrich MC, Logsdon CD. 1997. Transfected cholecystokinin receptors mediate growth inhibitory effects on human pancreatic cancer cell lines. *Gastroenterology* 112:952–59

163. Iwata N, Murayama T, Matsumori Y,

Ito M, Nagata A, et al. 1996. Autocrine loop through cholecystokinin-B/gastrin receptors involved in growth of human leukemia cells. *Blood* 88:2683–89

164. Bartek J, Bartkova J, Lukas J. 1996. The retinoblastoma protein pathway and the restriction point. *Curr. Opin. Cell Biol.* 8:805–14

165. Sherr CJ, Roberts JM. 1995. Inhibitors of mammalian G1 cyclin-dependent kinases. *Genes Dev.* 9:1149–63

166. Reed SI. 1997. Control of the G1/S transition. *Cancer Surveys* 29:7–23

Annu. Rev. Physiol. 2001. 63:77–97

Intracellular Signaling Mechanisms Activated by Cholecystokinin-Regulating Synthesis and Secretion of Digestive Enzymes in Pancreatic Acinar Cells

John A Williams

Departments of Physiology and Internal Medicine, University of Michigan, Ann Arbor, Michigan, 48109-0622; e-mail: jawillms@umich.edu

Key Words pancreas, secretion, calcium, signal transduction

■ **Abstract** The intracellular signaling mechanisms by which cholecystokinin (CCK) and other secretagogues regulate pancreatic acinar function are more complex than originally realized. CCK couples through heterotrimeric G proteins of the G_q family to lead to an increase in intracellular free Ca^{2+}, which shows spatial and temporal patterns of signaling. The actions of Ca^{2+} are mediated in part by activation of a number of Ca^{2+}-activated protein kinases and the protein phosphatase calcineurin. By the process of exocytosis the intracellular messengers Ca^{2+}, diacylglycerol, and cAMP activate the release of the zymogen granule content in a manner that is poorly understood. This fusion event most likely involves SNARE and Rab proteins present on zymogen granules and cellular membrane domains. More likely related to nonsecretory aspects of cell function, CCK also activates three MAPK cascades leading to activation of ERKs, JNKs, and p38 MAPK. Although the function of these pathways is not well understood, ERKs are probably related to cell growth, and through phosphorylation of hsp27, p38 can affect the actin cytoskeleton. The PI3K (phosphatidylinositol 3-kinase)-mTOR (mammalian target of rapamycin) pathway is important for regulation of acinar cell protein synthesis because it leads to both activation of $p70^{S6K}$ and regulation of the availability of eIF4E in response to CCK. CCK also activates a number of tyrosyl phosphorylation events including that of $p125^{FAK}$ and other proteins associated with focal adhesions.

INTRODUCTION

The primary function of pancreatic acinar cells is to synthesize, package, and secrete a variety of digestive enzymes. In some species acinar cells also secrete a NaCl-rich component of pancreatic juice. Considerable work over the past 25 years

0066-4278/01/0315-0077$14.00

has focused on cellular mechanisms leading to the release by exocytosis of secretory granule contents. Primary attention has been given to signaling mechanisms induced by secretagogues, including the GI hormones cholecystokinin (CCK) and secretin, the neurotransmitters acetylcholine (ACh), vasoactive intestinal polypeptide (VIP), and neuromedin C, the mammalian bombesin equivalent. These secretagogues act through intracellular messengers, particularly Ca^{2+}, diacylglycerol (DAG), and cAMP to induce secretion (1–2). Recently it has become clear that in order to produce an appropriate amount and mixture of digestive enzymes, acinar cells are also regulated by secretagogues with respect to growth, energy production, gene expression, and protein synthesis, in addition to secretion. Moreover, acinar cells are regulated by other external agents that include systemic hormones, growth factors, cytokines, and extracellular matrix components. Some of these affect secretion, but most regulate the other components of cell function. Because many of these non-secretagogue regulators initiate intracellular protein-protein interactions, particularly kinase cascades, and because secretagogues such as CCK also affect these other cell functions, a considerable amount of recent work has addressed these novel signaling mechanisms in acinar cells.

This review focuses on the intracellular mechanisms activated by CCK and cholinergic analogs because these secretagogues either directly or indirectly regulate all of the aforementioned aspects of acinar cell function. I briefly review secretagogue receptors and transmembrane signaling, consider the role of intracellular Ca^{2+} as the primary signaling mechanism controlling secretion, the mechanism of Ca^{2+}-regulated exocytosis, and discuss recent work on novel signaling mechanisms and how they may regulate nonsecretory aspects of acinar cell function (3–5).

MEMBRANE RECEPTORS AND TRANSMEMBRANE SIGNALING

The receptors for pancreatic secretagogues are all G protein–coupled membrane proteins with seven transmembrane domains (6). Two distinct CCK receptors have been molecularly characterized and denoted as A and B or, more recently, as Types 1 and 2. CCKA receptors are specific for CCK, whereas CCKB receptors bind both CCK and gastrin with high affinity (7, 8). Most pancreatic studies have focused on CCKA receptors because they are the predominant form on rodent acinar cells, gall bladder smooth muscle, and vagal afferent nerves; other studies show that CCKB receptors are the primary form in the human pancreas, as well as being present in the brain and stomach. The muscarinic cholinergic receptor present on acinar cells is the M3 isoform. Both CCKA and M3 receptors can assume high- and low-affinity states, and for CCKA receptors in particular, different cellular actions have been assigned to high- or low-affinity receptors (7).

A variety of heterotrimeric G proteins composed of three subunits (α, β, γ) are present in acinar cells, including representatives of all four major families named after the α subunit G_q, G_s, G_i/G_o, and G_{12}. Multiple isoforms of the β and γ subunits are also present. The G proteins responsible for stimulation of secretion have long been assumed to belong to the G_q family (2). All of these heterotrimeric G proteins are primarily localized to the basolateral membrane, but some are also localized intracellularly. G_s is almost certainly responsible for coupling the receptors for secretin, VIP, and in some species CCK to activation of adenylate cyclase, whereas G_i members mediate the action of somatostatin receptors of the SSR2 subtype to inhibit adenylate cyclase and possibly activate tyrosine phosphatase. The physiological regulators of other G_i/G_o members and G_{12} are unknown, but some are likely to be activated by CCK and mediate additional actions of secretagogues.

The major G protein family mediating CCK and M3 receptor action to increase intracellular Ca^{2+} is the G_q family, which includes α_q, α_{11}, and α_{14}, all of which are present in acinar cells (9, 10). In this family, receptor ligand-binding leads to a conformational change such that intracellular portions of the receptor, particularly the third intracellular loop, activate the G protein by facilitating release of GDP and binding of GTP. The α subunit then dissociates and activates a phospholipase C (PLC), which cleaves phosphatidylinositol 4,5-bisphosphate (PIP_2) to form inositol 3,4,5 trisphosphate (IP_3) and DAG. IP_3 binds to an intracellular receptor that functions as a ligand-gated Ca^{2+} channel thereby initiating the release of sequestered Ca^{2+}, and DAG activates protein kinase C (PKC). G_q activation has been followed by measuring PIP_2 hydrolysis, $[Ca^{2+}]_i$ increase, or Ca^{2+}-dependent Cl^- channel activation (10–12). Addition of antibody directed against the carboxyl terminus shared by α_q and α_{11} inhibits G_q protein action in permeabilized, microinjected or patch-clamped cells and in isolated membrane fractions. Although the presence of multiple receptors (CCKA, M3, and bombesin) and multiple G_q family proteins raises the possibility of specific coupling, evidence to date is more in favor of redundancy in that study of pancreas from specific α_q and α_{11} knockout mice did not affect signaling by any of the three receptors (9). Recently RGS proteins (regulators of G protein signaling) have been shown to affect specificity but at the receptor rather than the G protein level (13). RGS1 and RGS4 inhibited carbachol much more than bombesin and CCK, whereas RGS2 inhibited carbachol and CCK equally. G protein $\beta\gamma$ subunits are also known to activate some isoforms of PLCβ, although usually when released from G_i proteins. That this mechanism could apply in acinar cells was demonstrated by Zeng et al (11) who showed that purified $\beta\gamma$ introduced into acinar cells via a patch pipette induced Ca^{2+}-mediated chloride current oscillations and that addition of a $\beta\gamma$ scavenging agent blocked these oscillations as well as those induced by low concentrations of CCK and bombesin. Because infusion or injection of antibody to α_q/α_{11} blocks the oscillatory Ca^{2+} response (9, 10), it seems likely that the $\beta\gamma$ released physiologically is from G_q members and not G_i. Non-secretagogue hormones can modify the expression of G proteins, as is known for insulin in experimental diabetes. Estradiol treatment increased expression of $G_{q/11}$ in ovariectomized rats (14).

Several phosphatidylinositol-specific isoforms of PLC exist. $PLC\beta_1$, $-\beta_3$, $-\gamma_1$, and $-\delta_1$ were identified in rat acinar membranes, but β_2, β_4, and γ_2 were not detected (12). Interestingly, anti-PLC-β1 antibody blocked CCK and bombesin stimulation of PLC activity; anti-PLC-β3 was reported to have a stronger effect on carbachol stimulation. EGF receptor occupancy is known to activate $PLC\gamma$. Activation of PLC by CCK leads to a rapid increase of IP_3, which reaches a peak within several seconds and then declines to a plateau (15). It is this IP_3 that is responsible for the peak and plateau pattern of Ca^{2+} signaling seen with high concentrations of secretagogue. Low concentrations of CCK and carbachol do not induce a measurable IP_3 response, although it is not clear whether this reflects the limits of the assay or an alternate intracellular messenger responsible for Ca^{2+} mobilization (see Cancela 15a). In contrast to IP_3, DAG shows a biphasic time course with an initial peak coinciding with IP_3 and a larger sustained increase that is greater than could be accounted for by PIP_2 hydrolysis. This led to the suggestion that the sustained increase was the result of phosphatidylcholine hydrolysis (15). Alternatively, DAG could result from activation of a phosphatidylcholine-specific phospholipase D by CCK, as reported by Rydzewska et al (16), followed by conversion of phosphatidic acid to DAG. Whether DAG from other sources may act differently in the cell remains to be determined.

INTRACELLULAR CALCIUM SIGNALING

Patterns of Ca^{2+} Signaling

Because of the critical importance of increased Ca^{2+} for stimulating amylase release (see Reference 2) considerable effort has gone into studying the pattern of Ca^{2+} signaling. Most of this work has been performed with Ca^{2+}-sensitive fluorescent dyes, particularly the ratiometric probe fura2. These studies showed that a high concentration of CCK, carbachol, or bombesin induced a rapid increase in $[Ca^{2+}]_i$, which in the presence of extracellular Ca^{2+} declined over 2 to 4 min to a sustained plateau. In the absence of extracellular Ca^{2+} the initial peak was unchanged but declined faster back to baseline or even below. This appeared to indicate that the initial event was a release of Ca^{2+} from intracellular stores followed by both Ca^{2+} extrusion from the cell and Ca^{2+} influx through a store-regulated channel in the membrane. The Ca^{2+} release from stores is primarily mediated by IP_3 because it can be induced by IP_3 microinjection and blocked with intracellular heparin, which acts as an IP_3 receptor antagonist (17, 18). Other studies have confirmed the release of Ca^{2+} from stores using lower affinity Ca^{2+}-sensing dyes such as Mag fura, which enter and report the status of the Ca^{2+} stores in the endoplasmic reticulum (19, 20).

Single-cell Ca^{2+} measurements have shown that low concentrations of CCK, carbachol, and bombesin induce a strikingly different pattern of Ca^{2+} signaling consisting of Ca^{2+} oscillations or spikes that occur at a frequency of 0.5 to 5/min and in some cases are superimposed on a moderate baseline elevation (2, 21).

Since these oscillations can continue for some time in the absence of external Ca^{2+}, they are believed to result from cyclic release of Ca^{2+} from and re-uptake into intracellular stores. The Ca^{2+} oscillations have also been monitored using the Ca^{2+}-dependent Cl^- current as a measure of $[Ca^{2+}]_i$. Oscillations can be induced with IP_3, but oscillating IP_3 levels do not appear necessary because a constant concentration of a non-metabolizable thio-analog can induce Ca^{2+} oscillations (22). Most models that explain the oscillations invoke a mixture of positive and negative feedback by Ca^{2+} on the IP_3 receptor, although other models invoke a separate mediator either to regulate the sensitivity of the IP_3 receptor or to act as an independent Ca^{2+} releaser. Proposed independent releasers include $G\beta\gamma$ (11), arachidonic acid (23), cyclic ADP ribose (24), and NAADP (25). Ca^{2+} oscillations can be dramatically induced by a CCK analog known as JMV-180 or CCK-OPE, which interacts as an agonist only with CCKA receptors in the high-affinity configuration and does not induce a measurable production of IP_3 (26) but whose effect can be blocked with heparin (18).

Evaluation of both Ca^{2+} oscillations and the early time points of stimulation by digital imaging or confocal microscopy, with high-temporal and -spatial resolution, has revealed additional information. First, the primary site of Ca^{2+} release is in the apical pole of the cell in the region filled with zymogen granules (27, 28). Although secretory granules have occasionally been suggested to be a Ca^{2+} source, they do not appear to contain IP_3 receptors (29), which are located predominately in the apical pole and are most concentrated just under the network of sub-apical actin filaments (29, 30). Localized non-propagating Ca^{2+} oscillations have been reported at low concentrations of CCK and are believed to induce amylase release (28, 31). With stronger stimulation an increase in Ca^{2+} appears to propagate toward the base of the cell at a rate of 8–20 μm/s, which is faster for carbachol stimulation and slower for bombesin as compared with CCK (32, 33). This may reflect differences in the activation of protein kinase A (PKA) or PKC, which through phosphorylation of IP_3 receptors regulate the rate of Ca^{2+} release (34). Recent studies using a low-affinity Ca^{2+} dye indicate that agonists could increase Ca^{2+} to more than 10 μM at the apical pole of the cell (35).

In intact acini Ca^{2+} waves appear to spread from cell to cell. Gap junctions remain open during Ca^{2+} wave propagation but close during stimulation by higher secretagogue concentrations under which conditions Ca^{2+} increases simultaneously in all cells (36, 37). Gap junctional blockers affect these Ca^{2+} waves but also have other effects on Ca^{2+} signaling. Microinjection of IP_3 can induce a Ca^{2+} rise in adjacent cells when junctions are open. These studies suggest that the most sensitive cell can drive Ca^{2+} signaling in an acinus accounting for the greater sensitivity of isolated acini compared with isolated acinar cells. Xu et al (38) showed that in the same cell carbachol, CCK, and bombesin initiate a Ca^{2+} increase in separate areas indicative of compartmentalized signaling.

CCK and other secretagogues also increase Ca^{2+} extrusion from the cell, as well as Ca^{2+} influx. Extrusion is believed to be carried out by a Ca^{2+}-ATPase, which was localized to the apical membrane (39), whereas influx is through a channel most likely in the basolateral membrane. Regulation of this channel by nitric oxide, small G proteins, and tyrosine kinases has been proposed (4).

Ca^{2+} Activation of Kinases and Phosphatases

Receptors for Ca^{2+} are generally Ca^{2+}-binding proteins, and the major receptor outside of troponin in striated muscle cells is calmodulin. Calmodulin is a ubiquitous 19,000 kDa protein that binds 4 mol Ca^{2+} per mol protein with an affinity of around 1 μM. Calmodulin is responsible for activating several enzymes in acinar cells including multiple protein kinases, a protein phosphatase, and a cyclic nucleotide phosphodiesterase (2). Other pancreatic calmodulin-binding proteins have been identified by a gel-overlay binding technique.

A number of distinct Ca^{2+}-activated, calmodulin-dependent kinases exist with different substrate specificities. Some such as myosin light chain kinase (MLCK), phosphorylase kinase, and calcium-calmodulin-activated kinase III (Ca^{2+}-CaM KIII) have distinct substrate proteins, and their activation is generally followed in intact cells by analyzing their substrate phosphorylation. MLCK has been purified from acinar cells (40) and is believed to mediate the increased phosphorylation of myosin light chains observed in acini stimulated with CCK (41, 42). A MLCK inhibitor, ML-9, as well as the actin ATPase inhibitor, butanedione monoxime, have been reported to block both reorganization of the actin cytoskeleton and amylase release by rat acini (42), indicating that activation of MLCK may play an important role in digestive enzyme secretion. Ca^{2+}-CaM KIII is known to be relatively specific for its substrate elongation factor 2, a protein involved with the elongation phase of ribosomal translation of mRNA (43). Upon phosphorylation the efficiency of translation is diminished. This may contribute to the effect of high concentrations of CCK to inhibit protein synthesis.

Ca^{2+}-CaM KII can phosphorylate a large number of proteins and is sometimes referred to as a multifunctional protein kinase. It exists in cells as an oligomer with molecular mass of 300–600 kDa and is made up of subunits (α, β, γ, δ) of 50–62 kDa. The pancreas form consists of a 50 kDa subunit (44), but its molecular identity has not been established and it is most likely different from the α form found in brain, which has been studied extensively. All known forms exhibit intramolecular phosphorylation that precedes phosphorylation of exogenous substrate and converts the molecule to a relatively Ca^{2+}-independent form. CCK has been shown to convert Ca-CaM KII to a Ca^{2+}-independent form in pancreatic acini (45). However, the substrate proteins phosphorylated specifically by Ca-CaM KII are still unknown. It is likely that multiple substrates exist because CCK, as well as Ca^{2+} ionophores, increase the phosphorylation of a number of proteins resolved by two-dimensional electrophoresis (2, 46).

The other prominent protein kinase activated in part by Ca^{2+} is PKC, which was originally identified as a Ca^{2+}- and phospholipid-dependent protein kinase activated by DAG. Multiple forms of PKC have subsequently been identified including Ca^{2+}-independent and novel isoforms, but almost all are activated by DAG or pharmacologically by active phorbol ester. Addition of phorbol ester, which both stimulates amylase secretion and leads to the phosphorylation of a number of substrate proteins (46), has been widely used in studies of acinar cell function (see Reference 2 for details). The combination of active phorbol ester and a Ca^{2+} ionophore fully stimulates digestive enzyme secretion in vitro. Several recent studies have focused on identifying the isoforms of PKC present in acini. Western blotting using subtype-specific antibodies showed the presence of PKC-α, -δ, -ε, and -ξ, with only δ and ε isoforms translocating to a membrane fraction in response to CCK (47, 48). Differences were observed for PKC isoform translocation in response to CCK, carbachol, and bombesin. In another study crosslinking the β1 integrin led to membrane association of PKC-α (49). It seems likely that targeting of PKC isoforms within the acinar cell also contributes to their substrate specificity.

CCK is also known to activate the Ca^{2+}-regulated phosphatase, calcineurin, also known as protein phosphatase 2B in acinar cells. CCK or Ca^{2+} ionophore decreased the phosphorylation of multiple proteins on two-dimensional gels (46). Calcineurin can be blocked by the immunosuppressants cyclosporine A (CsA) and FK506 after binding to their intracellular receptors cyclophillin A and FKBP-12, respectively. CsA was shown to block the dephosphorylation of a 24-kDa protein in acinar cells, which was also dephosphorylated following addition of Ca^{2+} and calcineurin to acinar cytosol (50). The 24-kDa protein was then purified, sequenced, cloned, and termed CRHSP-24 (51). It has an apparent M_r of 24,000 kDa (-24) and it is calcium regulated (CR) and heat stable (HS). CRHSP-24 is proline rich and phosphorylated on multiple serine residues. Although the function of CRHSP-24 is not established, activation of calcineurin appears important in acinar cells because CsA may marginally inhibit amylase secretion (50) and strongly block pancreatic growth (52) in response to CCK. Other phosphatases that are not Ca^{2+} regulated also exist in acinar cells and mediate additional CCK-induced dephosphorylation events (2).

Zymogen Granule Exocytosis

The final steps in CCK-stimulated secretion of digestive enzymes involve fusion of the zymogen granule membrane with the apical membrane. This fusion event is believed to share basic mechanisms utilized from yeast to neurons. Models of fusion have been dominated by consideration of two types of proteins, SNARE proteins and small G proteins of the Rab family. In the original SNARE hypothesis (53, 54), transport vesicles in the secretory pathway possess a set of proteins termed v-SNARES that interact with other proteins on the target membrane termed t-SNARES, as well as soluble attachment factors. The terminology derives from the original discovery of the requirement in membrane fusion for a N-ethylmaleimide (NEM)–sensitive factor (NSF) and the subsequent identification of soluble NSF attachment proteins (SNAPs). SNARES were defined as the receptors for SNAPs. Regulated exocytosis in neurons and endocrine and exocrine cells is believed to use a common core machinery (53, 55). Three SNARE proteins, which form a stoi-chiometric complex resistant to low concentrations of SDS, have been identified in brain. These proteins are the vesicle protein VAMP, also called synaptobrevin, and the membrane proteins syntaxin 1 and SNAP-25, the latter being distinct from soluble SNAP proteins and named for its synaptosomal localization and molecular mass. That these proteins are essential to synaptic transmitter release was shown by their being proteolytically cleaved by botulinum and tetanus toxins. These proteins all form coiled coils and their specific pairings, regulated by NSF and SNAPs, are believed to drive fusion. This model has been modified extensively as a result of further studies (56, 57). Multiple forms of most of the SNARE proteins have been identified and their locations appear to be less specific than originally believed. Both VAMPs and syntaxins, for example, exist on synaptic vesicles, and NSF is now believed to separate these molecules, thus priming the SNARES (in an ATP-dependent manner) so they can interact with the appropriate cognate molecules on the target membrane. Other tethering and docking proteins, including Rabs, have also been identified and are involved in regulating the formation of the final SNARE complex and conveying specificity (58). In addition, another protein known as munc18 or nsec-1 is known to be present on the synaptic membrane where it normally binds syntaxin 1, thereby preventing its forming a SNARE complex. Thus exocytosis requires dissociation of munc18, which has been termed a SNARE protector (54). Other forms of munc18 exist in non-neuronal cells.

Abundant evidence exists for the presence of SNARE proteins in the pancreas, although only a modest amount of data confirms a functional role in regulated exocytosis. Ca^{2+}-stimulated acinar secretion is NEM sensitive, although this could affect many proteins. Synaptobrevins or VAMPs, which act as t-SNARES on synaptic vesicles, are known to be present on zymogen granules (59, 60). Both VAMP2 and cellulobrevin, but not VAMP1, are present on zymogen granules (61). Studies with tetanus toxin that completely cleaved VAMP2 in rat acini showed a modest (30%) inhibition of Ca^{2+}-activated amylase secretion (60). Recently the presence of multiple isoforms of the t-SNARE, syntaxin, in acini has been demonstrated with syntaxin 2 present on the apical plasma membrane, syntaxin 4 on the basolateral membrane, and syntaxin 3 on granule membrane (62). Syntaxin 1 has been identified in acinar cells by some but not all investigators, and a specific membrane domain localization has not been identified. In a recent study using a somewhat controversial system combining purified granules and membranes, Edwardson et al (63) reported that botulinum toxin C cleaved syntaxin 2 and 3 but not 4 and blocked granule membrane and granule-granule fusion. They also concluded that synaptobrevin plays a minor role, that syntaxin 2 was the apical membrane t-SNARE, and that the v-SNARE is unknown. The third component of the neuronal SNARE complex, SNAP-25, does not appear to be present in acinar cells. A more widely distributed analog, SNAP-23, is present but has been localized to the basolateral membrane domain where it has been suggested to play a role in basolateral exocytosis that may occur in pancreatitis (64). Munc 18c has also been localized to the basolateral membrane (65). Thus, the basic SNARE complex at the apical membrane of acinar cells has not yet been fully identified. Whether other analogs of the SNARE proteins exist that might localize to the apical membrane remains to be determined. Proteins associated with secretory vesicles in other cells have also been looked for or identified in acinar cells including synaptotagmin (54), syncollin (66), and cysteine string protein (67). The additional importance of cytosolic proteins has been demonstrated by the fact that permeabilizing acini with Staphylococcus α-toxin, which produces small pores and little protein leakage, does not show the rundown of secretion that is seen with streptolysin-O permeabilization, which induces large pores (68). Moreover, cytosol from brain or lacrimal gland restored secretion in streptolysin-O-permeabilized acini. Whether Ca^{2+} in acini directly regulates a SNARE or cytosolic protein or indirectly regulates them through a kinase or phosphatase is not known.

The other major class of proteins regulating vesicular fusion mechanisms are the Rab proteins, which make up the largest family of small G proteins, with 11 identified forms in yeast and over 40 in mammalian cells (69). Different Rabs are present on vesicular elements of secretory and endosomal pathways and are required for vesicular fusion. In intracellular vesicular transport a Rab cycle has been identified whereby the Rab liganded with GDP is inserted into a budding vesicle by Rab GDI. A guanine nucleotide exchange factor (GEF) then releases GDP, which is followed by binding of GTP, after which the vesicle docks to the acceptor compartment and the Rab interacts with an effector protein. Fusion then occurs accompanied by hydrolysis of GTP, and the Rab can be extracted by GDI and re-utilized. The role of GTP hydrolysis in this process is somewhat uncertain because non-hydrolyzable GTPγS inhibits most intracellular vesicular transport but stimulates secretion by mast cells and pancreatic acini. In this model a different Rab protein is involved in each compartment. Exocytosis is believed to involve sec4 in yeast and one of the four isoforms of Rab3 in eukaryotic cells.

In the case of synaptic vesicles, Rab3A and 3C are known to be present on vesicles (54), although their detailed role in exocytosis is unclear. An immunoreactive Rab3 distinct from Rab3A was known to be present in acinar cells and on granules (70, 71). Recent work using PCR amplification and immunocytochemistry with specific antibody has conclusively identified Rab3D as the Rab3 species present on zymogen granules (72, 73), as well as on granules in lacrimal and salivary glands and in chief cells of the stomach. Overexpression of Rab3D in mouse acinar cells via transgenic technology (74) suggests that Rab3D can be rate limiting for the initial phase of amylase secretion induced by CCK in intact cells and Ca^{2+} in permeabilized cells. Furthermore, CCK was shown to alter the rate of GTP binding or turnover to Rab3D. A recent report noted that Rab3D appears to dissociate from zymogen granules as they become coated with actin, and the authors suggest that Rab3D might regulate actin polymerization (75). Further work is needed, however, to establish the regulators and effectors of Rab3D in acinar secretion.

How intracellular messengers (Ca^{2+}, DAG, cAMP) regulate exocytosis in acinar cells is poorly understood. One possibility is that Ca^{2+} binds to and directly regulates a protein on the granule, thereby activating or disinhibiting the SNARE machinery. Another possibility is that a kinase or phosphatase, through reversible phosphorylation, activates the SNARE machinery. In both cases the Rab3D is assumed to be already bound with GTP and ready to play its role. A final possibility is that Ca^{2+}, possibly through a kinase or phosphatase, activates a Rab GEF, thereby increasing the amount of Rab3D-GTP complex, which is then able to activate the SNARE machinery. In some species, such as guinea pig, cAMP can also stimulate considerable enzyme secretion, and in other species cAMP can potentiate the action of Ca^{2+}. Further work in this area is clearly necessary.

NEWER SIGNALING PATHWAYS

Mitogen-Activated Kinase Cascades

Mitogen-activated protein kinases (MAPKs) are serine-threonine-directed kinases originally identified as being activated by mitogens. They are now known to be activated by a variety of stimuli including growth factors, cytokines, neurotransmitters, hormones, extracellular matrix molecules, and cell stress. Known MAPKs are activated by a kinase cascade made up of three protein kinases acting in series (76). Thus, each MAPK is activated by a MAPK kinase (MAPKK), which is in turn activated by a MAPK kinase kinase (MAPKKK). Each MAPK is activated by dual phosphorylation of threonine and tyrosine residues present in a T-X-Y sequence motif and, therefore, all MAPKKs are dual-function kinases. MAPK action is terminated by dephosphorylation, which is carried out in part by a family of dual function phosphatases. At the upstream end of each cascade MAPKKKs receive information from cell surface receptors, usually through a small GTP-binding protein of the Ras superfamily. These family members include Ras, Rho, Rac, and Cdc42, all of which are active when bound with GTP. GEFs catalyze the release of GDP, which leads to GTP binding and the on state. Similarly, GTPase-activating proteins (GAPs) deactivate the small G protein by increasing the rate of hydrolysis of bound GTP.

MAPKs are known to regulate a number of cellular processes including gene transcription, protein translation, metabolism, and the functions of the cytoskeleton. As a result the MAPKs are involved in control of cell growth, differentiation, survival, and apoptosis. These actions are enacted by phosphorylating downstream proteins or by carrying information to the nucleus or cytoskeleton through translocation within the cell. MAPKs phosphorylate and thereby modulate a number of transcription factors. Some of the downstream target proteins, including the small heat shock protein hsp27, regulate the structure and function of the actin cytoskeleton. Currently, there are five independent MAPK cascades, but information on their function in the pancreas and other differentiated cells is limited to the cascades leading to the ERKs, JNKs, and p38 MAPK.

ERK1/2 Cascade Pancreatic secretagogues were first shown to increase the tyrosine phosphorylation and kinase activity of ERK1/2 in isolated rat pancreatic acini and in the in vivo rat pancreas (77, 78). ERKs (extracellular regulated kinase) were originally known as p44 and p42 MAPK based on their apparent molecular mass. These studies showed that CCK, carbachol, bombesin, and active phorbol ester all activate ERK1/2, whereas secretin and VIP do not (77). Maximal activation was seen within 2 to 10 min, with a maximal effect at only modestly supraphysiological concentrations of secretagogues. In several cell types cAMP inhibits activation of ERKs by feedback phosphorylation, but in acini this action was not observed. Subsequently, it was shown that CCK also activates the MAPKKs, MEK1 and 2 (79), and the MAPKKK Raf (80), and increased the binding of GTP to Ras (79), thus demonstrating the existence of the complete kinase cascade in acinar cells. In addition, CCK was shown to activate the downstream kinase MAPKAPK-1, also known as p90^{RSK} (81). Three different forms of Raf—Raf-A, Raf-B, and cRaf-1— were found in acinar cells (80). In the basal state Raf-B had the highest activity, but CCK had a larger stimulatory effect on Raf-A and cRaf-1. All were also activated by EGF and active phorbol ester. Dabrowski et al (80) found, however, that CCK and EGF activate ERK1/2 by different mechanisms. In acinar cells, as in other cells, EGF stimulation led to autophosphorylation of the EGF receptor and tyrosine phosphorylation of the adapter protein Shc, which then bound the adapter protein Grb2 and formed a Shc-Grb2-SOS complex (82) (where SOS is a known Ras GEF). Not surprisingly, EGF increased the fraction of Ras liganded with GTP, which is known to activate Raf. These actions of EGF were unaffected by a PKC inhibitor. By contrast, CCK had no effect on EGF receptor phosphorylation, had a weaker effect on Shc-Grb2-SOS complex formation, and no measurable effect on Ras-GTP. Most importantly, these actions of CCK were blocked by the PKC inhibitor. It was concluded that the major mechanism for CCK activation of ERKs involves PKC-mediated activation of the multiple forms of Raf. Seva et al (83) also showed that PKC and Ca^{2+} are involved with the activation of ERKs by gastrin in pancreas-derived AR42J cells, which are known to possess predominantly CCKB receptors. This group also showed that in AR42J cells, gastrin increased the tyrosine phosphorylation of Shc (84) and that of another docking protein, insulin receptor substrate 1 (IRS-1) (85). IRS-1 has not been identified in normal pancreas but is overexpressed in some forms of pancreatic cancer. Information is lacking on the identity of the tyrosine kinase, which phosphorylates Shc and IRS-1 in response to CCK and gastrin, although it could be a Src family member or Pyk-2. Gastrin is known to increase the growth of AR42J cells, and ERKs seem to be required for this growth based on use of the MEK inhibitor PO98059 (86).

The importance of Ras in CCK action was evaluated by Nicke et al (87) who used in vitro transfection of rat acini by an adenoviral vector to express a dominant-negative N17 Ras. Expression of this dominant-negative Ras did not affect amylase release or Ca^{2+} mobilization and almost totally inhibited ERK activation by EGF, but did not block ERK activation by CCK. It did, however, block activation of JNKs and inhibited DNA synthesis. These results support the different mechanisms of CCK and EGF to activate ERKs and demonstrate that CCK activation of

DNA synthesis requires Ras activation but through a pathway separate from that leading to ERKs.

JNK Cascade   JNKs, named for their activity as Jun kinases, are activated in many cells by proinflammatory cytokines and environmental stress (76). Although they may play a role in mitogenic signaling, their major role is thought to be in regulating apoptosis, although this regulation may be positive or negative depending on the cell type. CCK, carbachol, and bombesin have been shown to activate two isoforms of JNK (p46 and p55), both in isolated acini and in intact rat pancreas, with CCK having the greatest effect (78, 88). VIP had no effect. The activity of JNK in vivo was very low and was increased in isolated acini compared with the activity in in vivo pancreas possibly because of the mechanical stress used to prepare acini. However, both in vitro and in vivo activation of JNKs is slower and requires higher concentrations of agonists as compared with activation of ERKs (78). It is also of interest that increasing intracellular Ca^{2+} and cAMP or addition of active phorbol ester has little effect on JNK activation, thus indicating the existence of different activation mechanisms most likely at the G protein level.

It is well established that high concentrations of CCK but not bombesin can induce pancreatitis in rats and mice (88, 89). Therefore, the increase in JNK activity by high concentrations of CCK may in fact be a stress response (90). This is supported by the fact that JNK activation is one of the earliest events correlating with pancreatitis (89, 91). At present, it is not clear which genes are activated by JNKs and whether this is protective or deleterious. A recent in vivo study of pancreatitis showed that a JNK inhibitor blocked the edema but not other components of pancreatitis (88).

P38 MAPK Cascade   The p38 MAPKs were originally identified in yeast as being activated by hyperosmolarity, but they are known to be activated by both stress and growth stimuli in mammalian cells. The presence of p38 activity in rat pancreatic acini stimulated by CCK was recently demonstrated by Schäfer et al (92). They showed that CCK, carbachol, bombesin, and sorbitol-induced osmotic stress rapidly activate p38 MAPK activity in a dose-dependent manner. Physiological levels of CCK activate p38 in contrast to activation of JNKs. Increased levels of Ca^{2+} and active phorbol ester each had a modest effect but when combined mimicked the action of CCK. VIP had no effect similar to its lack of effect on ERKs and JNKs. p38 MAPK was also activated in the rat pancreas in vivo by a dose of caerulein, which induces maximal secretion via the CCK-A receptor, although maximal p38 activity was seen at a 10-fold higher dose of caerulein (91).

CCK also activated the downstream kinase MAPKAPK-2 and the phosphorylation of its substrate hsp27 (92, 93). The p38 MAPK inhibitor, SB203580 was found to block the phosphorylation of hsp27 in response to CCK and inhibit most of the disaggregation of the actin cytoskeleton induced by CCK (92). That this effect was mediated by hsp27 phosphorylation was confirmed by a study in which hsp27 was overexpressed in CHO cells bearing CCKA receptors and inhibited the effect of CCK to alter the actin cytoskeleton (94). This effect of hsp27 was blocked by mutating the phosphorylatable serine residues to alanine or glycine, as well as by adding SB203580. These studies suggest that p38 MAPK may play a role in acinar cells both in physiological signaling and in stress. Because p38 MAPK is also able to phosphorylate the transcription factor ATF-2 and the translation regulator eIF4E kinase (known as Mnk1), p38 may also play a role in the pancreatic growth response.

PI3K-mTOR Signaling

Another signaling pathway that primarily regulates protein synthesis but is also required for mitogenesis is the PI3K-mTOR-$p70^{S6K}$ pathway. $p70^{S6K}$, one of two S6 kinases, is the one that is physiologically important for phosphorylating the small ribosomal subunit protein S6 and thereby facilitating the synthesis of mRNA with $5'$ polypyrimidine tracts. S6 was the first regulated phosphoprotein identified in acinar cells (2), but only recently has the specific $p70^{S6K}$ enzyme been identified and studied in acini. Bragado et al (95) demonstrated the phosphorylation and activation of $p70^{S6K}$ in rat pancreatic acini by CCK, carbachol, and bombesin, but not by cAMP, phorbol ester, or calcium ionophore. Activation was blocked by rapamycin, which upon binding to its intracellular receptor FKBP-12 inhibits mTOR, and by wortmannin, an inhibitor of PI3K. A similar wortmannin-sensitive inhibition of $p70^{S6K}$ has also been reported in pancreatic AR42J cells where gastrin acts on a CCKB receptor (96). In other cell types this pathway is believed to include Akt, also known as PKB, which is activated by PI3K and acts to phosphorylate mTOR, which can then phosphorylate and activate $p70^{S6K}$. Little is known as to how PI3K is activated by CCK receptors, although an increase in $3'$ phosphoinositide products has been demonstrated in response to CCK (97). This pathway, however, does not appear to be involved in secretion as neither PI3K inhibitors nor rapamycin has significant effects on amylase secretion by acini.

The PI3K-mTOR pathway is now known to play another role in activating protein synthesis in that mTOR phosphorylates the binding protein for eIF4E, the translation initiation factor that binds to the 7 methyl guanosine cap at the $5'$ end of most eukaryotic mRNA molecules (98). This binding protein, known as eIF4E-BP or PHAS-I, was originally identified as a heat- and acid-stable, insulin-regulated phosphoprotein. PHAS-I has multiple phosphorylated sites, and when sufficiently phosphorylated it dissociates from eIF4E, which can then interact with eIF4G (a scaffolding protein) together with eIF4A (a RNA helicase) to form a complex known as eIF4F. CCK stimulation of rat pancreatic acini leads to PHAS-I phosphorylation and the release of eIF4E (99). This also results in formation of an eIF4E-eIF4G complex. These actions are blocked by rapamycin and another PI3K inhibitor, LY294002. Rapamycin, wortmannin, and LY294002 all blocked global protein synthesis in rat acini, reducing basal synthesis and blocking the increase induced by CCK (99). In AR42J cells rapamycin similarly inhibits PHAS-I/eIF4E-BP phosphorylation in response to gastrin and prevents the gastrin-mediated increase in synthesis of ornithine decarboxylase synthesis (100).

Other Signaling Pathways

It is now known that G protein–coupled receptors are able to regulate cellular tyrosine phosphorylation, although the mechanisms of signal transduction are not clear. In rat acini CCK enhanced the tyrosine phosphorylation of multiple proteins, and this effect could be blocked with general tyrosine kinase inhibitors such as genistein (101, 102). Using a nonspecific poly Glu-Tyr substrate, Rivard et al (103) also showed that CCK increased overall tyrosine kinase activity.

The identity of some of these tyrosyl-phosphorylated proteins and the kinases that phosphorylate them is now emerging (5). In addition to the already discussed MAPKs and adaptor proteins (Shc, IRS-1), several tyrosyl-phosphorylated proteins are present as part of the focal adhesion complex. Garcia et al identified p125 focal adhesion kinase (p125^{FAK}) and its substrate paxillin as being phosphorylated in response to CCK (104). Tyrosyl phosphorylation occurred rapidly and at physiological levels of CCK (1–100 pM) but with a maximal effect at nM concentrations. Although active phorbol esters and Ca^{2+} could affect p125^{FAK} phosphorylation, PKC and Ca^{2+} were not required (105). By contrast, an intact cytoskeleton was necessary as shown by the fact that both cytochalasin D and botulinum C3 exotoxin strongly inhibited the action of CCK to increase tyrosyl phosphorylation of p125^{FAK} and paxillin (105). Although there was no effect on amylase release (106), the results suggest a role for Rho, the small G protein that is inactivated by the botulinum toxin in regulating p125^{FAK}. Phosphorylation of p125^{FAK} was also reported to be regulated by bombesin and phorbol ester in AR42J cells (107). Recently, Pyk2, a tyrosine kinase related to p125^{FAK} but known to be Ca^{2+} dependent was shown to be tyrosyl phosphorylated and activated by CCK (108). In acini, Pyk2 activation was mediated synergistically by Ca^{2+} and PKC, with activation also requiring an intact actin cytoskeleton. Following stimulation by CCK, Pyk2 forms a complex with Grb2 and another adapter protein, cCrk, suggesting a potential alternate mechanism for ERK activation. CCK stimulation also increased the tyrosyl phosphorylation of p130^{CAS}, another adapter protein that becomes associated with cCrk (109).

A potential role for the activated p125^{FAK}, Pyk2, and associated proteins is to regulate the actin cytoskeleton and to mediate signaling from the cytoskeleton to the cell interior. High concentrations of CCK have long been known to disrupt the actin cytoskeleton (42, 92), and remodeling of actin may be necessary for normal secretion (110). Recently Leser et al (111) showed that a high concentration of CCK induced redistribution of paxillin with transient localization over the apical and lateral plasma membrane where it colocalized with actin. Subsequently it was redistributed to the basolateral cytosol and degraded. Src activation by p125^{FAK} is another potential signaling pathway in some cells (112). Activation of Src-like kinase activity in rat acini by CCK has also been reported (113). Src or related kinases have also been proposed as mediators of Ca^{2+} influx that occurs following release of intracellular Ca^{2+} (4).

Another signaling pathway recently shown to be activated by CCK involves NF-κB, a transcription factor important in the inflammatory response but with potential other roles. NF-κB in resting cells is sequestered in the cytoplasm through interaction with the inhibitory protein IκB. Cell stimulation by inducers of NF-κB leads to IκB phosphorylation and degradation followed by translocation of NF-κB to the nucleus where it activates target genes. CCK was shown to activate NF-κB through mechanisms involving increased intracellular Ca^{2+} and activation of PKC (114, 115). This activation is part of the events in secretagogue-induced pancreatitis where NF-κB is involved in regulating chemokine gene expression (116). Whether NF-κB activation has a physiological role remains to be determined.

Understanding the mechanisms by which CCK receptors activate the newer signal transduction pathways and their role in acinar cell physiology will be an important area for future investigation. Most of these mechanisms are likely to be involved in coordinating the biosynthetic, growth, and metabolic activities of acinar cells with their secretory function.

Visit the Annual Reviews home page at www.AnnualReviews.org

LITERATURE CITED

1. Johnson LR, ed. 1994. *Physiology of the Gastrointestinal Tract*, Vol. 2. New York: Raven. 3rd. ed. 2202 pp.

1a. Solomon TE. 1994. Control of exocrine pancreatic secretion. See Ref. 1, pp. 1499–529

2. Yule DI, Williams JA. 1994. Stimulus-secretion coupling in the pancreatic acinus. See Ref. 1, pp. 1447–72

3. Scheele GA. 1994. Extracellular and intracellular messengers in diet-induced regulation of pancreatic gene expression. See Ref. 1, pp. 1543–54

4. Williams JA. 1997. Pancreatic acinar cell intracellular signaling mechanisms. *Curr. Opin. Gastroenterol.* 13:369–74

5. Williams JA. 1999. Intracellular regulatory mechanisms in pancreatic acinar cellular function. *Curr. Opin. Gastroenterol.* 15:385–91

6. Logsdon CD. 1994. Molecular structure and function of G-protein-linked receptors. See Ref. 1, pp. 351–80

7. Williams JA, Blevins GT Jr. 1993. Cholecystokinin and regulation of pancreatic acinar cell function. *Physiol. Rev.* 73:701–23

8. Wank SA. 1998. G protein-coupled receptors in gastrointestinal physiology. I. CCK receptors: an exemplary family. *Am. J. Physiol. Gastrointest. Liver Physiol.* 274:G607–G13

9. Xu X, Croy JT, Zeng W, Zhao L, Davignon I, et al. 1998. Promiscuous coupling of receptors to Gq class α subunits and effector proteins in pancreatic and submandibular gland cells. *J. Biol. Chem.* 273:27275–79

10. Yule DI, Baker CW, Williams JA. 1999. Calcium signaling in rat pancreatic acinar cells: a role for Gα_q, Gα_{11}, and Gα_{14}. *Am. J. Physiol. Gastrointest. Liver Physiol.* 276:G271–G79

11. Zeng W, Xu X, Muallem S. 1996. G$\beta\gamma$ transduces [Ca^{2+}]$_i$ oscillations and Gα_q a sustained response during stimulation of pancreatic acinar cells with [Ca^{2+}]$_i$ −mobilizing agonists. *J. Biol. Chem.* 271: 18520–26

12. Piiper A, Stryjek-Kaminska D, Klengen R, Zeuzem S. 1997. CCK, carbachol, and bombesin activate distinct PLC-β isoenzymes via G$_{q/11}$ in rat pancreatic acinar membranes. *Am. J. Physiol. Gastrointest. Liver Physiol.* 272:G135–G40

13. Xu X, Zeng W, Popov S, Berman DM, Davignon I, et al. 1999. RGS proteins determine signaling specificity of

G_q-coupled receptors. *J. Biol. Chem.* 274:3549–56

14. Blevins GT Jr, McCullough SS, Wilbert TN, Isom RM, Chowdhury P, et al. 1998. Estradiol alters cholecystokinin stimulus-response coupling in rat pancreatic acini. *Am. J. Physiol. Gastrointest. Liver Physiol.* 275:G993–G98

15. Matozaki T, Williams JA. 1989. Multiple sources of 1,2-diacylglycerol in isolated rat pancreatic acini stimulated by cholecystokinin. *J. Biol. Chem.* 264:14729–34

15a. Cancela JM. 2001. Specific Ca^{2+} signaling evoked by cholecystokinin and acetylcholine: the roles for NAADP, cADPR, and IP_3. *Annu. Rev. Physiol.* 63:In press

16. Rydzewska G, Rossignol B, Morisset J. 1993. Involvement of phospholipase D in caerulein-induced phosphatidylcholine hydrolysis in rat pancreatic acini. *Am. J. Physiol. Gastrointest. Liver Physiol.* 265:G725–G34

17. Wakui M, Osipchuk YV, Petersen OH. 1990. Receptor-activated cytoplasmic Ca^{2+} spiking mediated by inositol trisphosphate is due to Ca^{2+}-induced Ca^{2+} release. *Cell* 63:1025–32

18. Gaisano HY, Wong D, Sheu L, Foskett JK. 1994. Calcium release by cholecystokinin analogue OPE is IP_3 dependent in single rat pancreatic acinar cells. *Am. J. Physiol. Cell Physiol.* 267:C220–C28

19. Van de Put FHMM, Elliott AC. 1997. The endoplasmic reticulum can act as a functional Ca^{2+} store in all subcellular regions of the pancreatic acinar cell. *J. Biol. Chem.* 272:27764–70

20. Mogami H, Tepikin AV, Petersen OH. 1998. Termination of cytosolic Ca^{2+} signals: Ca^{2+} reeuptake into intracellular stores is regulated by the free Ca^{2+} concentration in the store lumen. *EMBO J.* 17:435–42

21. Thorn P, Lawrie AM, Smith PM, Gallacher DV, Petersen OH. 1993. Ca^{2+} oscillations in pancreatic acinar cells: spatiotemporal relationships and functional implications. *Cell Calcium* 14:746–57

22. Wakui M, Potter BVL, Petersen OH. 1989. Pulsatile intracellular calcium release does not depend on fluctuations in inositol trisphosphate concentration. *Nature* 339:317–20

23. Lankisch TO, Nozu F, Owyang C, Tsunoda Y. 1999. High-affinity cholecystokinin type A receptor/cytosolic phospholipase A2 pathways mediate Ca^{2+} oscillations via a positive feedback regulation by calmodulin kinase in pancreatic acini. *Eur. J. Cell Biol.* 78:632–41

24. Thorn P, Gerasimenko O, Petersen OH. 1994. Cyclic ADP-ribose regulation of ryanodine receptors involved in agonist evoked cytosolic Ca^{2+} oscillation in pancreatic acinar cells. *EMBO J.* 13:2038–43

25. Cancela JM, Churchill GC, Galione A. 1999. Coordination of agonist-induced Ca^{2+} signaling patterns by NAADP in pancreatic acinar cells. *Nature* 398:74–76

26. Matozaki T, Göke B, Tsunoda Y, Rodriguez M, Martinez J, et al. 1990. Two functionally distinct cholecystokinin receptors show different modes of actions of Ca^{2+} mobilization and phospholipid hydrolysis in isolated rat pancreatic acini. *J. Biol. Chem.* 265:6247–54

27. Kasai H, Augustine GJ. 1990. Cytosolic Ca^{2+} gradients triggering unidirectional fluid secretion from exocrine pancreas. *Nature* 348:735–38

28. Thorn P, Lawrie AM, Smith PM, Gallacher DV, Petersen OH. 1993. Local and global cytosolic Ca^{2+} oscillations in exocrine cells evoked by agonists and inositol trisphosphate. *Cell* 74:661–68

29. Yule DI, Ernst SA, Ohnishi H, Wojcikiewicz RJH. 1997. Evidence that zymogen granules are not a physiologically relevant calcium pool. *J. Biol. Chem.* 272:9093–98

30. Lee MG, Xu X, Zeng W, Diaz J, Wojcikiewicz RJH, et al. 1997. Polarized expression of Ca^{2+} channels in pancreatic

and salivary gland cells. *J. Biol. Chem.* 272:15765–70

31. Thorn P, Moreton R, Berridge M. 1996. Multiple, coordinated Ca^{2+}-released events underlie the inositol trisphosphate-induced local Ca^{2+} spikes in mouse pancreatic acinar cells. *EMBO J.* 15:999–1003

32. Kasai H, Li YX, Miyashita Y. 1993. Subcellular distribution of Ca^{2+} release channels underlying Ca^{2+} waves and oscillations in exocrine pancreas. *Cell* 74:669–77

33. Pfeiffer F, Sternfeld L, Schmid A, Schulz I. 1998. Control of Ca^{2+} wave propagation in mouse pancreatic acinar cells. *Am. J. Physiol. Cell Physiol.* 274:C663–C72

34. LeBeau AP, Yule DI, Groblewski GE, Sneyd J. 1999. Agonist-dependent phosphorylation of the inositol 1,4,5-trisphosphate receptor: a possible mechanism for agonist-specific calcium oscillations in pancreatic acinar cells. *J. Gen. Physiol.* 113:851–72

35. Ito K, Miyashita Y, Kasai H. 1997. Micromolar and submicromolar Ca^{2+} spikes regulating distinct cellular functions in pancreatic acinar cells. *EMBO J.* 16:242–51

36. Yule DI, Stuenkel E, Williams JA. 1996. Intercellular calcium waves in rat pancreatic acini: mechanism of transmission. *Am. J. Physiol. Cell Physiol.* 271:C1284–C94

37. Chanson M, Mollard P, Meda P, Suter S, Jongsma HJ. 1999. Modulation of pancreatic acinar cell to cell coupling during ACh-evoked changes in cytosolic Ca^{2+}. *J. Biol. Chem.* 274:282–87

38. Xu X, Zeng W, Diaz J, Muallem S. 1996. Spacial compartmentalization of Ca^{2+} signaling complexes in pancreatic acini. *J. Biol. Chem.* 271:24684–90

39. Belan PV, Gerasimenko OV, Tepikin AV, Petersen OH. 1996. Localization of Ca^{2+} extrusion sites in pancreatic acinar cells. *J. Biol. Chem.* 271:7615–19

40. Bissonnette M, Kuhn D, de Lanerolle P. 1989. Purification and characterization of myosin light-chain kinase from the rat pancreas. *Biochem. J.* 258:739–47

41. Burnham DB, Soling HD, Williams JA. 1988. Evaluation of myosin light chain phosphorylation in isolated pancreatic acini. *Am. J. Physiol. Gastrointest. Liver Physiol.* 254:G130–G34

42. Torgerson RR, McNiven MA. 2000. Agonist-induced changes in cell shape during regulated secretion in rat pancreatic acini. *J. Cell. Physiol.* 182:438–47

43. Nairn AC, Palfrey HC. 1987. Identification of the major M_r 100,000 substrate for calmodulin-dependent protein kinase III in mammalian cells as elongation factor-2. *J. Biol. Chem.* 262:17299–303

44. Cohn JA, Kinder B, Jamieson JD, Delahunt NG, Gorelick FS. 1987. Purification and properties of a multifunctional calcium/calmodulin-dependent protein kinase from rat pancreas. *Biochim. Biophys. Acta* 928:320–31

45. Duan R-D, Guo Y-J, Williams JA. 1994. Conversion to Ca^{2+}-independent form of Ca^{2+}calmodulin protein kinase II in rat pancreatic acini. *Biochem. Biophys. Res. Commun.* 199:368–73

46. Wishart MJ, Groblewski G, Göke Wagner ACC, Williams JA. 1994. Secretagogue regulation of pancreatic acinar cell protein phosphorylation shown by large-scale 2D-PAGE. *Am. J. Physiol. Gastrointest. Liver Physiol.* 267:G676–G86

47. Pollo DA, Baldassare JJ, Honda T, Henderson PA, Talkad VD, et al. 1994. Effects of cholecystokinin (CCK) and other secretagogues on isoforms of protein kinase C (PKC) in pancreatic acini. *Biochim. Biophys. Acta* 1224:127–38

48. Bastani B, Yang L, Baldassare JJ, Pollo DA, Gardner JD. 1995. Cellular distribution of isoforms of protein kinase C (PKC) in pancreatic acini. *Biochim. Biophys. Acta* 1269:307–15

49. Wrenn RW, Herman LE. 1995. Integrin-linked tyrosine phosphorylation increases membrane association of protein kinase Cα in pancreatic acinar cells. *Biochem. Biophys. Res. Commun.* 208:978–84

50. Groblewski GE, Wagner ACC, Williams JA. 1994. Cyclosporin A inhibits Ca^{2+}/calmodulin-dependent protein phosphatase and secretion in pancreatic acinar cells. *J. Biol. Chem.* 269:15111–17

51. Groblewski GE, Yoshida M, Bragado MJ, Ernst SA, Leykam J, et al. 1998. Purification and characterization of a novel physiological substrate for calcineurin in mammalian cells. *J. Biol. Chem.* 273:22738–44

52. Tashiro M, Samuelson LC, Williams JA. 2000. Calcineurin mediates pancreatic growth in protease inhibitor treated mice. *Gastroenterology* 118:A447

53. Rothman JE. 1994. Intracellular membrane fusion. *Adv. Second Messenger Phosphoprotein Res.* 29:81–96

54. Sudhof T. 1995. The synaptic vesicle cycle: a cascade of protein-protein interactions. *Nature* 375:645–63

55. Burgoyne RD, Morgan A. 1998. Analysis of regulated exocytosis in adrenal chromaffin cells: insights into NSF/SNAP/SNARE function. *BioEssays* 20:328–35

56. Hanson PI, Heuser JE, Jahn R. 1997. Neurotransmitter release—four years of SNARE complexes. *Curr. Opin. Neurobiol.* 7:310–15

57. Götte M, Fischer von Mollard G. 1998. A new beat for the SNARE drum. *Trends Cell Biol.* 8:215–18

58. Pfeffer SR. 1999. Transport-vesicle targeting: tethers before SNAREs. *Nat. Cell Biol.* 1:E17–22

59. Braun JEA, Fritz BA, Wong SME, Lowe AW. 1994. Identification of a vesicle associated membrane protein (VAMP)-like membrane protein in zymogen granules of the exocrine pancreas. *J. Biol. Chem.* 269:5328–35

60. Gaisano HY, Sheu L, Foskett JK, Trimble WS. 1994. Tetanus toxin light chain cleaves a vesicle associated membrane protein (VAMP) isoform 2 in rat pancreatic zymogen granules and inhibits enzyme secretion. *J. Biol. Chem.* 269:17062–66

61. Gaisano HY, Sheu L, Grodin G, Ghai M, Bouquillon A, et al. 1996. The vesicle associated membrane protein family of proteins in rat pancreatic and parotid acinar cells. *Gastroenterology* 111:1661–69

62. Gaisano HY, Ghai M, Malkus PN, Sheu L, Bouquillon A. 1996. Distinct cellular locations of the syntaxin family of proteins in rat pancreatic acinar cells. *Mol. Biol. Cell* 7:1019–27

63. Hansen NJ, Antonin W, Edwardson JM. 1999. Identification of SNAREs involved in regulated exocytosis in the pancreatic acinar cell. *J. Biol. Chem.* 274:22871–76

64. Gaisano HY, Sheu L, Wong PPC, Klip A, Trimble WS. 1997. SNAP-23 is located in the basolateral plasma membrane of rat pancreatic acinar cells. *FEBS Lett.* 414:298–302

65. Gaisano HY, Lesser J, Shen L, Tamori Y, Kasuga M, et al. 1999. Minimal PKC activation mediated inhibition of CCK-OPE stimulated enzyme secretion involves munc18c dissociation from the acinar basolateral plasma membrane. *Gastroenterology* 116:A1126 (Abstr.)

66. Edwardson JM, An S, Jahn R. 1997. The secretory granule protein syncollin binds to syntaxin in a Ca^{2+}-sensitive manner. *Cell* 90:325–33

67. Braun JEA, Scheller RH. 1995. Cysteine string protein, a DnaJ family member, is present on diverse secretory vesicles. *Neuropharmacology* 34:1361–69

68. Padfield PJ, Panessar N. 1995. Ca^{2+}-dependent amylase secretion from SLO-permeabilized rat pancreatic acini requires diffusible cytosolic proteins. *Am. J. Physiol. Gastrointest. Liver Physiol.* 269:G647–G52

69. Novick P, Zerial M. 1997. The diversity of Rab proteins in vesicle transport. *Curr. Opin. Cell Biol.* 9:496–504

70. Jena BP, Gumkowski FD, Konieczko E, Fischer von Mollard G, Jahn R, et al. 1994. Redistribution of a Rab3-like GTP-binding protein from secretory granules

to the Golgi complex in pancreatic acinar cells during regulated exocytosis. *J. Cell Biol.* 124:43–53

71. Wagner ACC, Strowski MZ, Williams JA. 1994. Identification of Rab5 but not Rab3A in rat pancreatic zymogen granule membranes. *Biochem. Biophys. Res. Commun.* 200:542–48

72. Ohnishi H, Ernst SA, Wys N, McNiven M, Williams JA. 1996. Rab3D localized to zymogen granules in rat pancreatic acini and other exocrine glands. *Am. J. Physiol. Gastrointest. Liver Physiol.* 271:G531–G38

73. Valentijn JA, Sengupta D, Gumkowski FD, Tang LH, Konieczko EM, et al. 1996. Rab3D localized to secretory granules in rat pancreatic acinar cells. *Eur. J. Cell Biol.* 70:33–41

74. Ohnishi H, Samuelson LC, Yule DI, Ernst SA, Williams JA. 1997. Overexpression of Rab3D enhances regulated amylase secretion from pancreatic acini of transgenic mice. *J. Clin. Invest.* 100:3044–52

75. Valentijn JA, Valentijn K, Pastore LM, Jamieson JD. 2000. Actin coating of secretory granules during regulated exocystosis correlates with the release of rab3D. *Proc. Natl. Acad. Sci. USA* 97:1091–95

76. Widmann C, Gibson S, Jarpe MB, Johnson GL. 1999. Mitogen-activated protein kinase: conservation of a three-kinase module from yeast to human. *Physiol. Rev.* 79:143–80

77. Duan R-D, Williams JA. 1994. Cholecystokinin rapidly activates mitogen-activated protein kinase in rat pancreatic acini. *Am. J. Physiol. Gastrointest. Liver Physiol.* 267:G401–G8

78. Dabrowski A, Grady T, Logsdon CD, Williams JA. 1996. Jun kinases are rapidly activated by cholecystokinin in rat pancreas both in vitro and in vivo. *J. Biol. Chem.* 271:5686–90

79. Duan R-D, Zheng C-F, Guan K-L, Williams JA. 1995. Activation of MAP kinase kinase (MEK) and Ras by cholecystokinin in rat pancreatic acini. *Am.*

J. Physiol. Gastrointest. Liver Physiol. 268:G1060–G65

80. Dabrowski A, Groblewski GE, Schäfer C, Guan K-L, Williams JA. 1997. Cholecystokinin and EGF activate a MAPK cascade by different mechanisms in rat pancreatic acinar cells. *Am. J. Physiol. Gastrointest. Liver Physiol.* 273:G1472–G79

81. Bragado MJ, Dabrowski A, Groblewski GE, Williams JA. 1997. CCK activates p90rsk in rat pancreatic acini through protein kinase C. *Am. J. Physiol. Cell Physiol.* 272:C401–C7

82. Dabrowski A, VanderKuur JA, Carter-Su C, Williams JA. 1996. Cholecystokinin stimulates formation of Shc-Grb2 complex in rat pancreatic acinar cells through a protein kinase C-dependent mechanism. *J. Biol. Chem.* 271:27125–29

83. Seva C, Kowalski-Chauvel A, Blanchet J-S, Vaysse N, Pradayrol L. 1996. Gastrin induces tyrosine phosphorylation of Shc proteins and their association with the Grb2/Sos complex. *FEBS Lett.* 378:74–78

84. Daulhac L, Kowalski-Chauvel A, Pradayrol L, Vaysse N, Seva C. 1997. Ca2+ and protein kinase C-dependent mechanisms involved in gastrin-induced Shc/Grb2 complex formation and P44-mitogen-activated protein kinase activation. *Biochem. J.* 325:383–89

85. Kowalski-Chauvel A, Pradayrol L, Vaysse N, Seva C. 1996. Gastrin stimulates tyrosine phosphorylation of insulin receptor substrate 1 and its association with Grb2 and the phosphatidylinositol 3-kinase. *J. Biol. Chem.* 271:26356–61

86. Todisco A, Takeuchi Y, Urumov A, Yamada J, Vinzenz M, et al. 1997. Molecular mechanisms for the growth factor action of gastrin. *Am. J. Physiol. Gastrointest. Liver Physiol.* 273:G891–G98

87. Nicke B, Tseng M-J, Fenrich M, Logsdon CD. 1999. Adenovirus-mediated gene transfer of RasN17 inhibits specific CCK actions on pancreatic acinar cells. *Am.*

J. Physiol. Gastrointest. Liver Physiol. 276:G499–G506

88. Wagner ACC, Mazzucchielli L, Miller M, Camoratto AM, Göke B. 2000. CEP-1347 inhibits caerulein-induced rat pancreatic JNK activation and ameliorates caerulein pancreatitis. *Am. J. Physiol. Gastrointest. Liver Physiol.* 278:G165–G72

89. Grady T, Dabrowski A, Williams JA, Logsdon CD. 1996. Stress-activated protein kinase activation is the earliest direct correlate to the induction of secretagogue-induced pancreatitis in rats. *Biochem. Biophys. Res. Commun.* 227:1–7

90. Schäfer C, Williams JA. 2000. Stress kinases and heat shock proteins in the pancreas: possible roles in normal function and disease. *J. Gastroenterol.* 35:1–9

91. Wagner ACC, Metzler W, Höfken T, Weber H, Göke B. 1998. P38 map kinase is expressed in the pancreas and is immediately activated following cerulein hyperstimulation. *Digestion* 60:41–47

92. Schäfer C, Ross SE, Bragado MJ, Groblewski GE, Ernst SA, et al. 1998. A role for the p38 mitogen-activated protein kinase/Hsp27 pathway in cholecystokinin-induced changes in the actin cytoskeleton in rat pancreatic acini. *J. Biol. Chem.* 273:224173–80

93. Groblewski GE, Grady T, Mehta N, Lambert H, Logsdon CD, et al. 1997. Cholecystokinin stimulates heat shock protein 27 phosphorylation in rat pancreas both in vivo and in vitro. *Gastroenterology* 112:1354–61

94. Schäfer C, Clapp P, Welsh MJ, Benndorf R, Williams JA. 1999. HSP27 expression regulates CCK-induced changes of the actin cytoskeleton in CHO-CCK-A cells. *Am. J. Physiol. Cell Physiol.* 277:C1032–C43

95. Bragado MJ, Groblewski GE, Williams JA. 1997. P70^{s6k} is activated by CCK in rat pancreatic acini. *Am. J. Physiol. Cell Physiol.* 273:C101–C9

96. Seva C, Kowalski-Chauvel A, Daulhac L, Barthez C, Vaysse N, Pradayrol L. 1997. Wortmannin-sensitive activation of p70S6-kinase and MAP-kinase by the G protein-coupled receptor, G/CCK$_B$. *Biochem. Biophys. Res. Commun.* 238:202–6

97. Rivard N, Rydzewska G, Boucher C, Lods J-S, Calvo E, et al. 1994. Cholecystokinin activation of tyrosine kinases, phosphatidylinositol 3-kinase and phospholipase D: a role in pancreas growth induction? *Endocr. J.* 2:393–401

98. Proud CG, Denton RM. 1997. Molecular mechanisms for the control of translation by insulin. *Biochem. J.* 328:329–41

99. Bragado MJ, Groblewski GE, Williams JA. 1998. Regulation of protein synthesis by cholecystokinin in rat pancreatic acini involves PHAS-1 and the p70 S6 kinase pathway. *Gastroenterology* 115:733–42

100. Pyronnet S, Gingras A-C, Bouisson M, Kowalski-Chauvel A, Seva C. 1998. Gastrin induces phosphorylation of eIF4E binding protein 1 and translation initiation of ornithine decarboxylase mRNA. *Oncogene* 16:2219–27

101. Lutz MP, Sutor SL, Abraham RT, Miller LJ. 1993. A role for cholecystokinin-stimulated protein tyrosine phosphorylation in regulated secretion by the pancreatic acinar cell. *J. Biol. Chem.* 268: 11119–24

102. Duan R-D, Wagner ACC, Yule DI, Williams JA. 1994. Multiple inhibitory effects of genistein on stimulus-secretion coupling in rat pancreatic acini. *Am. J. Physiol. Gastrointest. Liver Physiol.* 266:G303–G10

103. Rivard N, Lebel D, Lainé J, Morisset J. 1994. Regulation of pancreatic tyrosine kinase and phosphatase activities by cholecystokinin and somatostatin. *Am. J. Physiol. Gastrointest. Liver Physiol.* 266:G1130–G38

104. Garcia LJ, Rosado JA, Tsuda T, Jensen RT. 1997. CCK causes rapid tyrosine phosphorylation of p125^{FAX} focal adhesion kinase and paxillin in rat pancreatic

acini. *Biochim. Biophys. Acta* 1358:189–99

105. García LJ, Rosado JA, González A, Jensen RT. 1997. Cholecystokinin-stimulated tyrosine phosphorylation of p125^{FAK} and paxillin is mediated by phospholipase C-dependent and -independent mechanisms and requires the integrity of the actin cytoskeleton and participation of p21^{rho}. *Biochem. J.* 327:461–72

106. Rosado JA, Salida GM, Jensen RT, Garcia LJ. 1998. Are tyrosine phosphorylation of p125^{FAK} and paxillin or the small GTP binding protein, Rho, needed for CCK-stimulated pancreatic amylase secretion? *Biochim. Biophys. Acta* 1404:412–26

107. Feick P, Gilhaus S, Schulz I. 1998. Pervanadate stimulates amylase release and protein tyrosine phosphorylation of paxillin and p125^{FAK} in differentiated AR4-2J pancreatic acinar cells. *J. Biol. Chem.* 273:16366–76

108. Tapai JA, Ferris HA, Jensen RT, García LJ. 1999. Cholecystokinin activated PYK2/CAKβ by a phospholipase C-dependent mechanism and its association with the mitogen-activated protein kinase signaling pathway in pancreatic acinar cells. *J. Biol. Chem.* 275:31261–71

109. Ferris HA, Tapia JA, García LJ, Jensen RT. 1999. CCK$_A$ receptor activation stimulates p130^{Cas} tyrosine phosphorylation translocation, and association with Crk in rat pancreatic acinar cells. *Biochemistry* 38:1497–508

110. Muallem S, Kwaitkowska K, Xu X, Yin HL. 1995. Actin filament dissembly is a sufficient final trigger for exocytosis in nonexcitable cells. *J. Cell Biol.* 128:589–98

111. Leser J, Lührs H, Beil MF, Adler G, Lutz MP. 1999. Cholecystokinin-induced redistribution of paxillin in rat pancreatic acinar cells. *Biochem. Biophys. Res. Commun.* 254:400–5

112. Schaller MD, Hildebrand JD, Parsons JT. 1999. Complex formation with focal adhesion kinase: a mechanism to regulate activity and subcellular localization of Src kinases. *Mol. Biol. Cell* 10:3489–505

113. Tsunoda Y, Yoshida H, Africa L, Steil GJ, Owyang C. 1996. Src kinase pathways in extracellular Ca^{2+}-dependent pancreatic enzyme secretion. *Biochem. Biophys. Res. Commun.* 227:876–84

114. Tando Y, Algul H, Wagner M, Weidenbach H, Adler G, et al. 1999. Caerulein-induced NF-κB/Rel activation requires both Ca^{2+} and protein kinase C as messengers. *Am. J. Physiol. Gastrointest. Liver Physiol.* 277:G678–G86

115. Han B, Logsdon CD. 2000. CCK stimulates mob-1 expression and NF-κB activation via protein kinase C and intracellular Ca^{2+}. *Am. J. Physiol. Cell Physiol.* 278:C344–C51

116. Han B, Logsdon CD. 1999. Cholecystokinin induction of mob-1 chemokine expression in pancreatic acinar cells requires NF-κB activation. *Am. J. Physiol. Cell Physiol.* 277:C74–C84

Annu. Rev. Physiol. 2001. 63:99–117

SPECIFIC Ca^{2+} SIGNALING EVOKED BY CHOLECYSTOKININ AND ACETYLCHOLINE: The Roles of NAADP, cADPR, and IP3

Jose Manuel Cancela

MRC Secretory Control Research Group, The Physiological Laboratory, University of Liverpool, Liverpool L69 3BX, UK; e-mail: j.m.cancela@liverpool.ac.uk

Key Words pancreatic, acinar, mouse, messenger, transduction

■ **Abstract** In order to control cell functions, hormones and neurotransmitters generate an amazing diversity of Ca^{2+} signals such as local and global Ca^{2+} elevations and also Ca^{2+} oscillations. In pancreatic acinar cells, cholecystokinin (CCK) stimulates secretion of digestive enzyme and promotes cell growth, whereas acetylcholine (ACh) essentially triggers enzyme secretion. Pancreatic acinar cells are a classic model for the study of CCK- and ACh-evoked specific Ca^{2+} signals. In addition to inositol 1,4,5 trisphosphate (IP3), recent studies have shown that cyclic ADPribose (cADPr) and nicotinic acid adenine dinucleotide phosphate (NAADP) release Ca^{2+} in pancreatic acinar cells. Moreover, it has also been shown that both ACh and CCK trigger Ca^{2+} spikes by co-activation of IP3 and ryanodine receptors but by different means. ACh uses IP3 and Ca^{2+}, whereas CCK uses cADPr and NAADP. In addition, CCK activates phospholipase A_2 and D. The concept emerging from these studies is that agonist-specific Ca^{2+} signals in a single target cell are generated by combination of different intracellular messengers.

INTRODUCTION

Work on pancreatic acinar cells led to the discovery of the first Ca^{2+}-releasing messenger, inositol 1,4,5 trisphosphate (IP3) (1). In these cells, acetylcholine (ACh) and cholecystokinin (CCK), two important physiological secretagogues, stimulate the production of IP3 by activation of phospholipase C (PLC). In addition to IP3, diacylglycerol (DAG) is produced by the hydrolysis of phosphatidylinositol 4,5 bisphosphate and activates protein kinase C (PKC) (1). This model has become prototypical for hormones and neurotransmitters eliciting calcium release.

With the development of fluorescent Ca^{2+}-sensitive probes and optical techniques cytosolic Ca^{2+} oscillations, agonist-specific Ca^{2+} signals, local Ca^{2+} and global Ca^{2+} elevations, and the role of mitochondria in Ca^{2+} homeostasis (2–8) were discovered. Cells use different elements of Ca^{2+} signaling to respond and adapt specifically to extracellular stimuli. For example, local Ca^{2+} elevations can specifically trigger enzyme secretion, growth cone guidance, or smooth muscle relaxation (4, 9–11), whereas global Ca^{2+} waves control gene expression or smooth muscle contraction (6, 9). In addition, the frequency of Ca^{2+} oscillations has been found to control gene expression (12) and mitochondrial metabolism (5). How cells can generate cytosolic Ca^{2+} elevations with different spatio-temporal patterns is an area of intense research. Recent studies on novel Ca^{2+}-releasing messengers bring fresh information on how cells can generate specific Ca^{2+} signals (13, 14, 19, 20). In pancreatic acinar cells, CCK stimulates secretion of digestive enzymes and also promotes cell growth, whereas ACh mainly stimulates secretion of digestive enzymes. In pancreatic acinar cells, there is a luminal continuity of the endoplasmic reticulum (ER) Ca^{2+} stores from the basolateral to the apical region of the cell (15). However, despite this Ca^{2+} store connectivity, agonist-specific Ca^{2+} signals can be generated. Physiological concentrations of CCK evoke a mixture of local and global Ca^{2+} signals; low physiological concentrations of ACh evoke local Ca^{2+} spikes (Figure 1*a,b*) (4). Recent work on G protein interactions (16); on PLC, phospholipase D (PLD), and phospholipase A_2 (PLA_2) (17); and also on cyclic ADPribose (cADPr) (18, 19) and nicotinic acid adenine dinucleotide phosphate (NAADP) (19, 20) [two recently discovered Ca^{2+}-releasing messengers (21–23)] gives new insight into the basic mechanism underlying the agonist-specific Ca^{2+} signals. The various Ca^{2+} signals could be the consequence of differential distribution of intracellular Ca^{2+}-releasing channels and Ca^{2+} pumps (4, 19, 24, 25) but also of different modulation or activation of the same intracellular receptors and G proteins (14, 16–20).

CCK RECEPTORS

CCK controls gastrointestinal processes such as stimulation of pancreatic digestive enzyme secretion, gallbladder contraction, and the induction of satiety. After food ingestion, small intestine endocrine cells secrete CCK (4, 26–28). CCK is also secreted by neurons from the gastrointestinal tract and from the central nervous system. Therefore, CCK can act both as a hormone and as a neuropeptide to regulate various digestive functions (28).

The CCK receptors belong to the G protein–coupled receptor super family and are of two types: The CCK-A receptor is found in the pancreatic acinar cells, gallbladder, and also in the brain. The CCK-B receptor is found predominantly in the brain but also in pancreatic acinar cells of some species such as guinea pig and dog but not rat or mouse (26, 27, 29). The CCK-A receptor is more sensitive to sulfated CCK than unsulfated CCK and is weakly sensitive to gastrin, whereas CCK-B, also called gastrin receptor, is equally sensitive to CCK and gastrin and does not discriminate between sulfated and unsulfated CCK/gastrin (26, 27, 29). The CCK-B receptor is coupled to IP_3 production, and its physiological role is poorly understood (29).

Mouse pancreatic acinar cells possess only CCK-A receptors. These receptors have a high-affinity binding site and a low-affinity binding site for CCK. The

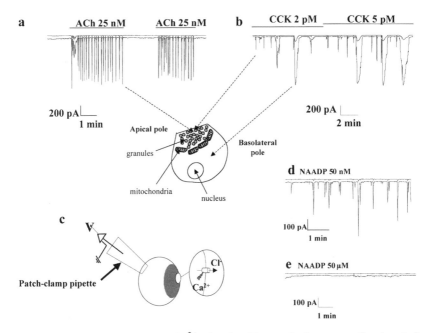

Figure 1 CCK and ACh-evoked Ca^{2+} signals. The patch-clamp recording in whole-cell configuration was used to record the Ca^{2+}-dependent currents (*c*). From a holding potential of -30 mV, steps were made to 0 mV (91, 103). Using our solutions (the extracellular Na$^+$-rich solution contained in mM: 140 NaCl, 4.7 KCl, 1.13 MgCl$_2$, 10 glucose, 1 CaCl$_2$, and 10 HEPES-NaOH, pH 7.2; and the internal solution contained in mM: 140 KCl, 1.13 MgCl$_2$, 0.05 EGTA, 2 ATP, and 10 HEPES-KOH, pH 7.2.), the reversal potential of both the Cl$^-$ and non-selective cation currents were 0 mV. Thus, at -30 mV we obtained both Cl$^-$ and non-selective cation Ca^{2+}-dependent currents that are an index of the cytosolic Ca^{2+} changes (8, 91). Low physiological concentration of ACh (25 nM) evokes short-lasting Ca^{2+} spikes in the apical pole of the cell (*a*). Physiological concentration of CCK evokes a mixture of short-lasting calcium spikes localized in the apical pole and global long-lasting calcium spikes spreading in the basolateral part of the cell (*b*). At 50 nM NAADP evokes short-lasting Ca^{2+} spikes (*d*); at 50 μM NAADP there are no Ca^{2+} spikes (*e*).

physiological relevance of these two binding sites is not fully understood. However, it has been suggested that the high-affinity binding site for CCK stimulates amylase secretion, protein synthesis, and calcium oscillations, whereas the low-affinity binding site mainly inhibits the secretory response and produces a large unique calcium transient (26, 27).

In pancreatic acinar cells, using JMV-180, a CCK analogue, or physiological concentrations of CCK (1–10 pM) (30), stimulation of high-affinity CCK-A receptors leads to the generation of calcium oscillations but does not generate IP$_3$. However, stimulation of the low-affinity binding site generates IP$_3$ (31). The only messenger generated by stimulation of the high-affinity binding site was DAG (27, 31).

Additional signaling pathways, which are not discussed in this review, are activated by CCK, including the mitogen-activated protein kinase (MAPK) cascade, cytosolic tyrosine kinases such as src-family kinases, and PYK2/CAKβ (32–34).

CCK, ACh, AND G PROTEINS

In pancreatic acinar cells, several GTP-binding proteins couple the CCK receptors to enzymes such as phospholipase C, A_2, D, or adenylate cyclase (4, 16, 17, 27, 32, 35). At least 15 different α subunits have been reported in pancreatic acinar cells, including α_i, α_s, and $\alpha_{q/11}$, but also $\beta\gamma$ subunits (16, 36). Interestingly, pancreatic acinar cells express three of the four Gq class subunits, namely, $G_{\alpha q}$, $G_{\alpha 11}$, and $G_{\alpha 14}$, and all interact with every tested Ca^{2+}-releasing agonist such as CCK, ACh, and bombesin (37). Thus far there is no evidence that a G protein can be specifically connected to a plasma membrane receptor (16). Recent studies suggest that regulators of G protein signaling (RGS) are important for the specificity between plasma membrane receptors and G proteins (16, 38). The RGS proteins accelerate the GTP hydrolysis on G_α subunits and therefore reduce G protein activity (16). Thus they can modulate or inhibit Ca^{2+} signals evoked by extracellular agonist. In addition, RGS proteins, which possess a scaffolding property, permit interaction between G proteins and plasma membrane receptors (16). Importantly this scaffolding may give specificity within the signaling receptor–G protein complex (38, 39). In mouse pancreatic acinar cells, RGS4, RGS1, and RGS16 attenuate the muscarinic receptor more potently than CCK, whereas RGS2 is equally potent in attenuating muscarinic and CCK responses (38, 39). The agonist-specific response may rely on specific scaffolding proteins that interact with plasma membrane receptors and G proteins. Interestingly, G proteins coupled to the phospholipase C/enzyme-effector may be differentially regulated by RGS, giving rise to different patterns of production of IP_3 or other second messengers (16).

CCK, ACh, AND CALCIUM OSCILLATIONS

In mouse pancreatic acinar cells, physiological concentrations of the agonists CCK (1–10 pM) and ACh (25 nM) elicit specific Ca^{2+} signals (Figure 1a,b) (4, 14, 19, 40). Despite intensive research, the mechanism underlying such complex Ca^{2+} oscillations remains unclear. It has been shown that heparin, an IP_3 receptor antagonist, blocked the calcium response elicited by ACh, CCK, and the CCK analogue JMV-180 (41, 42). These data suggest that the IP_3 receptors are involved in the secretagogue-evoked calcium spikes, and a two-pool model has been proposed for both ACh and CCK. In this model a steady increase of IP_3 is generated by hormone or neurotransmitter. IP_3 induces a primary calcium release, which then releases more calcium from an IP_3-insensitive pool by a calcium-induced calcium release (CICR) process (4, 41). However, this two-pool model relies on IP_3 generation by CCK and ACh, which is not supported by biochemical data on whole pancreatic acinar cell populations (31). In contrast to ACh, physiological concentrations of CCK do not generate detectable IP$_3$ (31). Taken together, these data led to the search for additional mechanisms responsible for the CCK calcium signal.

To explain the discrepancy between the pharmacological and biochemical data, it has been proposed that the IP$_3$ receptors can be regulated by phosphorylation, and therefore undetectable fluctuations of IP$_3$ levels may well be sufficient to generate a calcium signal (16, 43, 44).

CCK, ACh, AND RYANODINE RECEPTORS

In addition to Ca^{2+} from an IP$_3$-sensitive store, ACh and CCK mobilized Ca^{2+} from a CICR-sensitive pool (17, 19, 41, 45). This store was confirmed to be ryanodine sensitive because both ACh and CCK responses were blocked by ryanodine (19, 45). Cyclic ADPribose (cADPr) is an endogenous regulator of the ryanodine receptor (23, 46, 47). Pancreatic acinar cells were used to determine if cADPr, like IP$_3$, is generally involved in agonist-evoked Ca^{2+} release or linked to a specific agonist (14, 18, 19, 48).

CYCLIC ADPRIBOSE AS AN ENDOGENOUS RYANODINE RECEPTOR STIMULATOR

Lee made the important discovery in 1987 that NAD$^+$, a pyridine-nucleotide, could release calcium from sea urchin microsomes (23). It was shown later that cADPr, a metabolite of NAD$^+$, was the Ca^{2+}-mobilizing messenger (Figure 2a, see color insert) (23). In 1991, Galione et al (46) showed that cADPr releases calcium from a ryanodine-sensitive pool, suggesting that cADPr is an endogenous modulator of the ryanodine receptors. However, ryanodine receptors type II and III are sensitive to cADPr; type I is not (23, 47, 49, 50). These results and others (23) led to the proposal that although the ryanodine receptor is the final effector, cADPr may act through an accessory protein. Consistent with this idea, it has been proposed that in sea urchin eggs, cADPr-mediated calcium release is absolutely dependent on an accessory protein identified as calmodulin (23).

The enzyme responsible for cADPr synthesis is ADPribosyl cyclase (Figure 2), which is widespread in mammalian tissues (13, 23). The enzyme has been located in the plasma membrane, the cytosol, the nucleus, and in mitochondria (13, 23, 51–53). The *Aplysia* cyclase has been purified and cloned and the active site characterized (13, 54). However, how a cell surface receptor stimulates ADPribosyl cyclase is poorly understood. Two other proteins possess ADPribosyl cyclase activity: the leukocyte surface antigen CD38 and BST-1, the latter found in bone marrow stromal cells (23, 55, 56). Surprisingly, both CD38 and BST-1 have the catalytic site facing the extracellular space (23, 55).

Recent work suggests that cell surface receptors control the ADPribosyl cyclase activity and consequently the levels of cADPr (23, 55). In rat pancreatic islets, glucose stimulates insulin secretion by activation of cADPr production (57). In longitudinal intestinal smooth muscle cells, CCK controls the ADPribosyl cyclase activity (58). In addition, ADPribosyl cyclase regulation or cADPr level changes have been reported in other cell systems, such as in PC 12 cells stimulated by nitric oxide (NO) (59), NG 108-15 stimulated by carbachol (60), adrenal chromaffin cells stimulated by ACh (61), and Jurkat T lymphocytes stimulated by anti-CD3 mAb cells (49).

cADPr AND PANCREATIC ACINAR CELLS

Thorn et al (45) showed that cADPr elicits short-lasting Ca^{2+} spikes in pancreatic acinar cells. The cADPr-evoked spikes were blocked by ryanodine (10 μM) and, more surprisingly, by heparin. These results suggest that the calcium spikes elicited by cADPr are primarily the result of activation by ryanodine receptors followed by the recruitment of IP_3 receptors by a CICR process. This important result indicates that activation of the IP_3 receptors may not necessarily need specific IP_3 production—the basal IP_3 level may be high enough to keep the IP_3 receptors just below the threshold for activation. Thus any Ca^{2+} elevation close enough to the IP_3 receptors may activate them.

SPECIFIC ROLE OF cADPr IN CCK SIGNALING

To investigate whether cADPr is involved in agonist-evoked Ca^{2+} spikes, 8-amino-cADPR, a specific cADPr antagonist, was used (18, 62). In pancreatic acinar cells, 8-amino-cADPr specifically blocked cADPr-evoked Ca^{2+} spikes but had little or no effect on IP_3-evoked Ca^{2+} spiking. Indeed, experiments performed with 8-amino-cADPr were very rewarding because the responses to physiological concentrations of CCK (2–5 pM) were blocked (18). Importantly, the ACh response was not blocked by 8-amino-cADPr, although ryanodine blocks the ACh response (19). This important result confirms that cADPr is a relevant and specific calcium-releasing messenger of CCK in pancreatic acinar cells. In contrast, ACh recruits the ryanodine receptors likely by a CICR process, although the participation of an unknown messenger cannot be ruled out (19).

However, a surprising discovery highlighted the complexity and redundancy of calcium signaling. Using a patch-clamp technique in whole-cell configuration, it was observed that intracellular infusion of glucose at a concentration as low as 300 μM inhibited cADPr-evoked Ca^{2+} spikes, whereas IP_3-evoked Ca^{2+} spikes were vigorously potentiated (48). Even more surprising, infusion of glucose, which inhibits the cADPr pathway, had no or little effect on CCK-evoked Ca^{2+} spikes (48). The simplest explanation is that glucose compensated its inhibitory effect on cADPr by stimulating the IP_3 receptors. Perhaps more interestingly, this finding also indicates that glucose and cADPr may share an amplifier role of IP_3 receptor activity.

There is no information available on the resting glucose levels in pancreatic acinar cells. Work on other cell types suggests a resting glucose concentration between 0 and 300 μM. Also, physiological concentrations of CCK of many other hormones and neurotransmitters stimulate glucose uptake (63). Other glycolytic metabolites have recently been reported to modulate Ca^{2+} homeostasis (64). For example, fructose 1,6 bisphosphate potentiates cADPr-evoked Ca^{2+} release and inhibits IP$_3$-evoked Ca^{2+} release (64). The control of Ca^{2+} homeostasis by glycolytic metabolites is an interesting, emerging field.

Finally, the glucose experiment showed that cADPr could be shunted out without altering the CCK response. This surprising result led to investigations of the involvement of additional messengers. One interesting candidate is NAADP because the ADPribosyl cyclase, which forms cADPr, can also form NAADP, a Ca^{2+}-releasing messenger in sea urchin eggs (21–23).

NAADP AS A Ca^{2+}-RELEASING MESSENGER

NAADP, a metabolite of NADP$^+$ synthesized by the ADPribosyl cyclase (Figure 2b), has been shown to release calcium from sea urchin egg microsomes (21, 22). Several important characteristics suggest the existence of a specific NAADP receptor. NAADP releases Ca^{2+} from a thapsigargin-insensitive Ca^{2+} store, which can be physically separated from those mobilized by IP$_3$ and cADPr (22, 23, 65). In addition, ^{32}P-NAADP binding on sea urchin microsomes showed a specific binding site with a K_d of 10 nM, similar to the Ca^{2+}-releasing effective NAADP concentration in sea urchin eggs (13, 65, 66). Another important property of NAADP signaling is the self-desensitization mechanism induced by very low NAADP levels (66, 67). For example, application of subthreshold concentration of NAADP in sea urchin egg microsomes desensitizes the microsomes to further NAADP stimulation, even by supra-maximal concentration. This receptor seems to display a refractory mechanism, suggesting that NAADP acts as a trigger. In support of this view, it was found that the NAADP receptor does not behave as a Ca^{2+}-induced Ca^{2+} release channel (67, 68). In regard to the growing interest in the role of intracellular Ca^{2+} stores in neuronal activity (14, 70), it is also important to point out that L-type Ca^{2+} channel blockers have been reported to inhibit NAADP-evoked Ca^{2+} release in sea urchin eggs (71). However, whether NAADP acts as second messenger or releases calcium in cell systems other than sea urchin cells remained uncertain for a long time.

PHYSIOLOGICAL ROLE FOR NAADP

It was recently reported that NAADP releases Ca^{2+} in mouse pancreatic acinar cells and may transduce the CCK Ca^{2+} response (20). In this study, use of the patch-clamp technique in a whole-cell configuration permitted intracellular infusion of NAADP and recording of the Ca^{2+}-sensitive currents. Surprisingly, the NAADP effect appears to be biphasic; at low concentrations NAADP evokes Ca^{2+} spikes, whereas at high concentrations it does not. NAADP at 50 nM evokes repetitive short-lasting Ca^{2+} spikes mainly localized in the apical part of the cell (Figure 1d) (JM Cancela & A Galione, unpublished observation); however, a more complex mix of short-lasting local Ca^{2+} spikes and global long-lasting Ca^{2+} spikes also occurred (20). When the NAADP concentration was in the micromolar range, no Ca^{2+} release was detected (Figure 1e), suggesting that the NAADP receptors are desensitized. This self-desensitization property of NAADP is specific to NAADP-evoked Ca^{2+} spikes because IP_3 and cADPr-evoked Ca^{2+} spikes were not altered by desensitizing concentrations of NAADP (20).

Pharmacological data on the Ca^{2+} stores recruited by NAADP revealed cooperation between different intracellular receptors. NAADP-evoked Ca^{2+} spikes are inhibited by 8-amino-cADPr and also by heparin, suggesting that the Ca^{2+} released by activation of the NAADP receptors sensitizes the neighboring IP_3 and cADPr receptors to give rise to cytosolic Ca^{2+} spikes. Importantly, NAADP has been proposed to be a second messenger of CCK-mediated Ca^{2+} spikes and therefore physiologically relevant in pancreatic acinar cells. The conclusion is based on the inhibitory effect of desensitizing concentrations of NAADP, which specifically block or partially abolish the response to 2 and 5 pM CCK, whereas the ACh response is not affected (19, 20). Thus, it appears that the responses to physiological concentrations of CCK and NAADP share the same pharmacology because a desensitizing NAADP concentration, 8-amino-cADPr, and heparin inhibit both (Figure 3b).

NAADP, CCK, AND Ca^{2+} OSCILLATION MODELS

A general model for Ca^{2+} spiking in pancreatic acinar cells was recently proposed (19). In this model, Ca^{2+} spikes originate from the concerted activity of IP_3 and ryanodine receptors, irrespective of the agonist triggering them. ACh and

---

Figure 3 (a) General model for agonist-evoked Ca^{2+}-specific signals. ACh and CCK evoke Ca^{2+} spikes by activation of IP_3 and ryanodine receptors, which are the converging element in this model. This element corresponds to an oscillator/amplifier unit. ACh activates these receptors by stimulating IP_3 production, PKC activation, and by CICR (although an unknown messenger that stimulates ryanodine receptors cannot be excluded). In contrast, physiological concentrations of CCK (high-affinity binding site of CCK-A receptor) use NAADP receptors (NAADPR) as a trigger that then recruits IP_3 and ryanodine receptors (IP_3R and RYR, respectively) by CICR and cADPr (14, 19, 20). Stimulation of the high-affinity site by CCK leads to arachidonic acid (AA) production. AA, in turn, modulates the ryanodine receptors (17). Physiological concentrations of CCK likely phosphorylate the IP_3 receptors perhaps via the cAMP/protein kinase A (PKA) pathway (44). NAADP levels in sea urchin eggs can be controlled by cAMP (93). Finally, stimulation of the low-affinity binding site of the CCK-A receptor activates adenylyl cyclase PLC and PLD, which leads to IP_3 generation and greater PKC activation than with ACh (17). Consequently, overstimulation of PKC by CCK slows the speed of Ca^{2+} waves. (b) A summary of the pharmacology of Ca^{2+} spikes evoked by agonists in pancreatic acinar cells. Black circles (●) represent inhibition by various antagonists; open circles (○) represent no effect. Regardless of the agonist trigger, the Ca^{2+} spikes require functional IP_3 and ryanodine receptors.

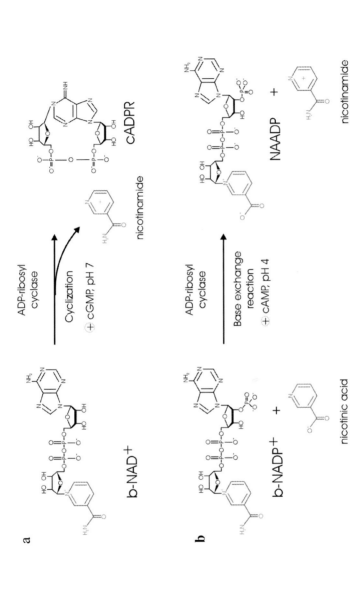

Figure 2 (*a*) The ADPribosyl cyclase forms either cADPr or NAADP depending on the substrates available. In the presence of NAD$^+$, at pH7, the ADPribosyl cyclase forms cADPr by cyclization (23). cGMP is a stimulator of cADPr formation by the ADPribosyl cyclase (93). (*b*) In the presence of NADP$^+$ and nicotinic acid, the ADPribosyl cyclase forms NAADP by base exchange reaction with an optimum pH of 4 (23). The compartment in which this occurs remains to be elucidated. cAMP is a stimulator of NAADP formation by the ADPribosyl cyclase (93).

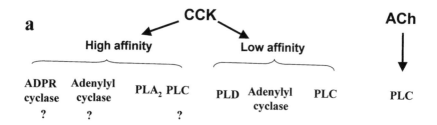

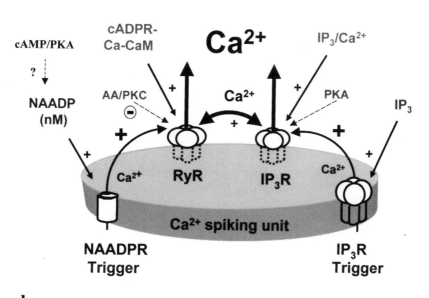

CCK, but also IP$_3$, cADPr, and NAADP, evoke Ca^{2+} spikes by activation of both IP$_3$ and ryanodine receptors, which work as a common oscillator/amplifier unit (Figure 3a) (19).

Specific models of NAADP-evoked Ca^{2+} spikes in pancreatic acinar cells have been proposed (14, 19, 20). These models are based on the pharmacological data available in pancreatic acinar cells (Figure 3b), brain microsomes, and sea urchin eggs (13, 14, 19, 69). An important distinctive property of the NAADP receptor is that it does not behave as a Ca^{2+}-induced Ca^{2+} release channel. In contrast to the IP$_3$ and ryanodine receptors, the NAADP receptor is stimulated by its own ligand. Consequently, a triggering role for Ca^{2+} was suggested (13, 19, 20, 65, 68, 69). In pancreatic acinar cells, this primary release of Ca^{2+} by NAADP would be amplified by IP$_3$ and ryanodine receptors by CICR (20). An important issue is the sequence of events triggered by NAADP. The pharmacological data also indicate that cADPr activates ryanodine receptors and recruits IP$_3$ receptors, probably by a CICR mechanism (14, 19, 45). Finally, IP$_3$ evokes Ca^{2+} spikes by activation of the IP$_3$ receptors without interfering with cADPr or NAADP receptors (14, 18, 20) (Figure 3a,b). This suggests the following sequence: The trigger Ca^{2+} evoked by NAADP is amplified by the cADPr/ryanodine receptor, and the IP$_3$ receptor is the final oscillator (14). Additionally, it has been reported that the Ca^{2+} release in the IP$_3$ receptor is amplified by the ryanodine receptor, although in this case cADPr does not play a role (Figure 3a,b) (18, 19). This model relies on positive and negative Ca^{2+} interactions on the Ca^{2+}-releasing channels (72, 73). However, alternative models, based on different mechanisms, have been proposed (14). The basic mechanism of such models is the oscillations of IP$_3$ levels, which arises from phospholipase C regulation by Ca^{2+} or protein kinase C (2, 5, 74). Considering this type of mechanism, it cannot be excluded that the triggered Ca^{2+} released by NAADP may elicit the production of both cADPr (via activation of a Ca^{2+}-sensitive NO synthase/cGMP/cADPr pathway) (14, 59, 75, 76) and IP$_3$ (14). Similar models apply to the CCK action; however, there is no evidence that physiological CCK levels stimulate cADPr or NAADP formation, and sensitization of those receptors by CCK may also occur. However, it is important to note that an ADPribosyl cyclase activity has been found in pancreatic acinar cells, indicating that the machinery necessary to produce these messengers exists (20).

EVIDENCE FOR INTRACELLULAR RECEPTOR COOPERATIVITY IN INTACT CELLS

Although structural and functional similarities exist between IP$_3$ and ryanodine receptors (1, 77), evidence also exists for separate functional properties (78, 79). Both IP$_3$ and ryanodine receptors are sensitive to Ca^{2+} and therefore can support regenerative Ca^{2+} release. These channels are inhibited by high calcium or Ca^{2+}/calmodulin (79, 80), which make them also suitable for generating Ca^{2+}

oscillations. In addition, the ryanodine receptor possesses a specific and unique property of adaptation (79, 81). Single ryanodine channel recordings showed that Ca^{2+} activates the ryanodine receptor within milliseconds, while the subsequent inactivation occurs over a period of seconds. More interestingly, a second stimulation by Ca^{2+} during the inactivation phase produces an increase in the channel open probability similar to prior stimulation, indicating that the inactivation was only apparent (81). Ryanodine receptors from skeletal muscle and brain cease to adapt when the Ca^{2+} concentration reaches 100 μM, whereas ryanodine receptors from cardiac cells cease to adapt at 1 mM Ca^{2+} (79, 82). The ryanodine receptor property is therefore perfectly adapted to amplify the Ca^{2+} elevation evoked by a primary Ca^{2+}-releasing channel until the Ca^{2+} concentration value for full inactivation is reached. Recent studies on the generation of elementary Ca^{2+} events provide evidence for cooperativity between IP$_3$ and ryanodine receptors (19, 83, 84). Elementary Ca^{2+} signals are highly localized in cells and correspond to small clusters of intracellular Ca^{2+}-releasing channels (85–87). These clusters contain either IP$_3$ or ryanodine receptors, but may also contain both. In particular, it has been shown in portal vein smooth muscle cells that elementary Ca^{2+} signals generated by IP$_3$ are initiated by opening of IP$_3$ receptors, which are then amplified by ryanodine receptors (83). In PC12 cells it has also been proposed that bradykinin-evoked elementary Ca^{2+} signals are triggered by IP$_3$ and amplified by ryanodine receptors (84). In pancreatic acinar cells confocal line scan studies show that the ACh and CCK-evoked elementary Ca^{2+} events are co-localized, suggesting that ryanodine, IP$_3$, and NAADP receptors are present in the same clusters (19).

SPATIAL ORGANIZATION OF THE Ca^{2+} SIGNALS EVOKED BY CCK AND ACH

From recent comparative studies on specific Ca^{2+} signals evoked by ACh or CCK, a new concept has emerged (14, 16, 17, 19, 20, 88). Different extracellular agonists are encoded by several different Ca^{2+}-releasing messengers, which stimulate the same intracellular receptors (Figure 3a).

Ca^{2+} signals evoked by CCK are of a complex nature. CCK elicits a mixture of short-lasting Ca^{2+} spikes localized in the apical pole of the cell and also elicits long-lasting Ca^{2+} spikes, which are global. The relative occurrence of short- and long-lasting Ca^{2+} spikes is dose dependent; higher CCK concentrations will increase the occurrence of long-lasting Ca^{2+} spikes. In contrast, ACh at low concentration mainly evokes repetitive short-lasting spikes in the apical part of the cells. Although it is difficult to explain how such complex patterns are generated, a working model can be produced. It has been reported that the IP$_3$ receptors are mainly localized in the apical pole of the cells (24, 89), although a low density of IP$_3$ receptors in the basolateral part of the cell is likely (90–92). This receptor partition is in agreement with the ability of IP$_3$ to evoke Ca^{2+} spikes in the apical pole of the cell. In contrast, the type II ryanodine receptors have been localized mainly in the basolateral region of the cell (25), whereas a low density of receptors is likely in the apical part (45). Nothing is known about the NAADP receptor distribution in pancreatic acinar cell or in other cell types (13, 14). However, NAADP-evoked Ca^{2+} signals initiated in the apical zone can spread toward the basolateral region of the cell, which indicates that the NAADP receptors are distributed over the whole cell (JM Cancela & A Galione, unpublished observation). Because NAADP is a trigger, the distribution of its receptors is crucial and may explain the CCK ability to produce a global response. In addition to IP_3 receptors, CCK stimulates cADPr and NAADP receptors, and this particular combination of receptors may explain why Ca^{2+} signals evoked by CCK are initiated in the apical region and then spread toward the ryanodine receptor–rich basolateral region of the cell (14, 19). In contrast, ACh stimulates IP_3 and ryanodine receptors but not cADPR or NAADP receptors (19). This may explain why ACh can more consistently evoke local Ca^{2+} spikes in the apical region of the cell and why much higher concentrations of ACh evoke global Ca^{2+} elevations (4, 19, 88).

Additional levels of complexity exist or have been proposed to explain CCK Ca^{2+} signaling. It was recently reported that physiological concentrations of CCK regulate the state of activation-deactivation of the IP_3 receptors by phosphorylation (44). The authors proposed that activation of the cAMP pathway via protein kinase A leads to IP_3 receptor phosphorylation and consequently inactivation (44). This mechanism is attractive considering that NAADP levels in sea urchin eggs can be controlled by cAMP (93). High concentrations of CCK activate adenylyl cyclase, but thus far no evidence indicates that physiological concentrations of CCK can stimulate it (27, 94). In addition, other messenger pathways, such as the PLA_2 and PLD, have been proposed (17, 35, 95). However, in mouse pancreatic acinar cells these pathways do not release Ca^{2+} by themselves but regulate ryanodine receptors or a CICR-channel activity (17). Stimulation of high-affinity CCK receptors by physiological concentrations of CCK leads to arachidonic acid production by activation of phospholipase A_2 (17, 95). It has been proposed that arachidonic acid inhibits CICR and IP_3 receptors and consequently leads to a decrease in the speed of the of Ca^{2+} wave (95, 96). In addition, low-affinity receptors have been found coupled to phospholipase C and phospholipase D, whereas ACh, for example, stimulates only phospholipase C. Consequently the DAG production is greater in CCK-stimulated cells, and therefore protein kinase C is activated to a greater extent. Protein kinase C, in turn, inhibits CICR, leading to a decrease of Ca^{2+} wave speed (17, 95).

ROLE OF MULTIPLE Ca^{2+}-RELEASING MESSENGERS

Many cellular processes are controlled by different Ca^{2+}-signaling elements such as local and global Ca^{2+} signals, distribution of Ca^{2+} stores, capacitative Ca^{2+} entry, and plasma membrane Ca^{2+} channels (4, 7, 70, 92, 97–99). To control so many mechanisms of Ca^{2+} homeostasis, the cells need multiple messengers.

Recent examples found in other cell types also suggest that the complex messenger interaction seen in pancreatic acinar cells may be widespread.

It has been suggested that Ca^{2+}-releasing messengers may have specific tasks but are also integrated in global and physiological responses, such as in *Ascidian* and starfish oocytes, sea urchin eggs, and human T lymphocytes (13, 23, 49, 100, 101). A clear example has been reported in *Ascidian* oocytes where IP$_3$-, cADPr-, and NAADP-evoked Ca^{2+} release have different effects (100). Fertilization of *Ascidian* oocytes triggers a series of local Ca^{2+}-dependent events such as membrane depolarization–activated Ca^{2+} current followed by exocytic membrane insertion in the plasma membrane. Cytoplasmic Ca^{2+} oscillations continue until completion of meiosis (100). Intracellular perfusion of IP$_3$ in unfertilized eggs generates repetitive global Ca^{2+} oscillations but not membrane insertion depolarization–activated Ca^{2+} current. In contrast, cADPr, by elevating Ca^{2+} locally, induces a depolarization-activated Ca^{2+} current followed by membrane insertion. Finally, NAADP evokes only depolarization-activated Ca^{2+} current by local Ca^{2+} elevation (100). The important outcome of this study is that the fertilization of the oocytes requires the coordinated activity of the three different messenger pathways, which mobilize separate Ca^{2+} pools. In addition, cross-talk between IP$_3$ and NAADP receptors has been reported (100). In starfish oocytes, NAADP evokes calcium release in both immature and mature oocytes (101). Interestingly, NAADP-evoked Ca^{2+} release also appears to be dependent on external Ca^{2+} in mature oocytes, indicating that the NAADP-sensitive Ca^{2+} stores are close to the plasma membrane. In immature and mature starfish oocytes, NAADP evokes Ca^{2+} release by activation of NAADP receptors and also by recruiting cADPr and IP$_3$ receptors. These results and the fact that NAADP also triggers the typical cortical reaction usually seen with egg fertilization suggest that NAADP induction of a primary Ca^{2+} release amplified by IP$_3$ and ryanodine receptors represents a sequence of physiological significance during the fertilization process (101). Recent work on T lymphocytes indicates that interaction of NAADP, cADPr, and IP$_3$ pathways occurs during physiological responses (49, 55, 101a). Stimulation of the T-cell receptor/CD3 leads to ADPribosyl cyclase activation followed by sustained Ca^{2+} elevation, T-cell activation, and proliferation. It has been shown that nanomolar concentrations of NAADP elicit Ca^{2+} release in human T lymphocytes, whereas micromolar concentrations of NAADP desensitize the T lymphocytes to NAADP (101a). Most importantly, T lymphocyte activation by stimulation of the T-cell receptor/CD3 is abolished by desensitization of the NAADP receptors. A sequence of events has been proposed whereby a NAADP/Ca^{2+} release system activation is necessary for IP$_3$ and cADPr mediating Ca^{2+} release from internal stores (101a). NAADP pathway activation is also necessary for cADPr mediating the secondary sustained cytosolic Ca^{2+} elevation by activation of the capacitative Ca^{2+}-entry mechanism (49, 55, 101a).

Finally, fertilization of sea urchin eggs triggers global Ca^{2+} waves that can be markedly inhibited when both IP$_3$ and cADPr receptors are blocked (23, 75). There is also evidence that NAADP receptors are involved in the fertilization process (102) and that cooperativity between NAADP and cADPr receptors may exist (13). These results suggest that the global Ca^{2+} waves seen at fertilization require activation of IP_3, cADPr, and NAADP receptors (13).

GENERAL PERSPECTIVES

Important information is still missing for both CCK and NAADP. There is no evidence that a physiological concentration of CCK can stimulate NAADP, cADPr, or even IP_3 production. The NAADP receptor has still to be purified. Accomplishing this is of crucial importance in order to investigate the distribution and the trigger role of this receptor in various tissues. The NAADP field is in its infancy and represents an exciting area of research. In view of the widespread presence of ADPribosyl cyclase and of the coexpression of ryanodine and IP_3 receptors in many cell types, it would appear that cells possess the necessary machinery to generate several Ca^{2+}-releasing messengers.

Finally, work on CCK and ACh suggests that in the same target cell, hormones and neurotransmitters may be linked to a specific combination of messengers and therefore trigger specific Ca^{2+} signals and specific physiological responses.

ACKNOWLEDGMENTS

I am very grateful to Prof. OH Petersen for critical reading of the manuscript. This work was supported by an MRC Programme Grant.

Visit the Annual Reviews home page at www.AnnualReviews.org

LITERATURE CITED

1. Berridge MJ. 1993. Inositol trisphosphate and calcium signalling. *Nature* 361:315–25

2. Tsien RW, Tsien RY. 1990. Calcium channels, stores, and oscillations. *Annu. Rev. Cell Biol.* 6:715–60

3. Cobbold PH, Sanchez-Bueno A, Dixon CJ. 1991. The hepatocyte calcium oscillator. *Cell Calcium* 12:87–95

4. Petersen OH, Petersen CCH, Kasai H. 1994. Calcium and hormone action. *Annu. Rev. Physiol.* 56:297–319

5. Thomas AP, Bird GSJ, Hajnoczky G, Robb-Gaspers LD, Putney JW. 1996. Spatial and temporal aspects of cellular calcium signaling. *FASEB J.* 10:1505–17

6. Berridge MJ, Bootman MD, Lipp P. 1998. Calcium—a life and death signal. *Nature* 395:645–48

7. Meldolesi J, Pozzan T. 1998. The heterogeneity of ER Ca^{2+} stores has a key role in nonmuscle cell signaling and function. *J. Cell Biol.* 142:1395–98

8. Tinel H, Cancela JM, Mogami H, Gerasimenko JV, Gerasimenko OV, et al. 1999. Active mitochondria surrounding the pancreatic acinar granule region prevent spreading of inositol trisphosphate-evoked local cytosolic Ca^{2+} signals. *EMBO J.* 18:4999–5008

9. Jaggar JH, Porter VA, Lederer WJ, Nelson MT. 2000. Calcium sparks in smooth

smuscle. *Am. J. Physiol. Cell Physiol.* 278:C235–C56

10. Petersen OH, Cancela JM. 2000. Nerve guidance: attraction or repulsion by local Ca^{2+} signals. *Curr. Biol.* 10:311–14

11. Zheng JQ. 2000. Turning of nerve growth cones induced by localized increases in intracellular calcium ions. *Nature* 403:89–93

12. Dolmetsch RE, Xu KL, Lewis RS. 1998. Calcium oscillations increase the efficiency and specificity of gene expression. *Nature* 392:933–36

13. Lee HC. 2000. NAADP: an emerging calcium signaling molecule. *J. Membr. Biol.* 173:1–8

14. Petersen OH, Cancela JM. 1999. New Ca^{2+}-releasing messengers: Are they important in the nervous system? *Trends Neurosci.* 22:488–94

15. Mogami H, Nakano K, Tepikin AV, Petersen OH. 1997. Ca^{2+} flow via tunnels in polarized cells: recharging of apical Ca^{2+} stores by focal Ca^{2+} entry through basal membrane patch. *Cell* 88:49–55

16. Muallem S, Wilkie TM. 1999. G protein-dependent Ca^{2+} signaling complexes in polarized cells. *Cell Calcium* 26:173–80

17. Schulz I, Krause E, Gonzalez A, Gobel A, Sternfeld L, Schmid A. 1999. Agonist-stimulated pathways of calcium signaling in pancreatic acinar cells. *Biol. Chem.* 380:903–8

18. Cancela JM, Petersen OH. 1998. The cyclic ADP-ribose antagonist 8-NH$_2$-cADP-ribose blocks cholecystokinin-evoked cytosolic Ca^{2+} spiking in pancreatic acinar cells. *Pflügers Arch.* 435:746–48

19. Cancela JM, Gerasimenko OV, Gerasimenko JV, Tepikin AV, Petersen OH. 2000. Two different but converging messenger pathways to intracellular Ca^{2+} release: the roles of NAADP, cADPR and IP$_3$. *EMBO J.* 19:2549–57

20. Cancela JM, Churchill GC, Galione A. 1999. Coordination of agonist-induced Ca^{2+}-signalling patterns by NAADP in pancreatic acinar cells. *Nature* 398:74–76

21. Chini EN, Beers KW, Dousa TP. 1995. Nicotinate adenine dinucleotide phosphate (NAADP) triggers a specific calcium release system in sea urchin eggs. *J. Biol. Chem.* 270:3216–23

22. Lee HC, Aarhus R. 1995. A derivative of NADP mobilizes calcium stores insensitive to inositol trisphophate and cyclic ADP-ribose. *J. Biol. Chem.* 270:2152–57

23. Lee HC. 1997. Mechanisms of calcium signalling by cyclic ADP-ribose and NAADP. *Physiol. Rev.* 77:1133–64

24. Lee MG, Xu X, Zeng W, Diaz J, Wojcikiewicz JH, et al. 1997. Polarized expression of Ca^{2+} channels in pancreatic and salivary gland cells. *J. Biol. Chem.* 272:15765–70

25. Leite MF, Dranoff JA, Gao L, Nathanson MH. 1999. Expression and subcellular localization of the ryanodine receptor in rat pancreatic acinar cells. *Biochem. J.* 337:305–9

26. Jensen RT. 1994. Receptors on pancreatic acinar cells. See Ref. 26a, pp. 1377–446

26a. Johnson LR, ed. 1994. *Physiology of the Gastrointestinal Tract.* New York: Raven. 3rd ed.

27. Yule DI, Williams JA. 1994. Stimulus-secretion coupling in the pancreatic acinus. See Ref. 26a, pp. 1447–72

28. Liddle RA. Cholecystokinin cells. 1997. *Annu. Rev. Physiol.* 59:221–42

29. Saillan-Barreau C, Clerc P, Adato M, Escrieut C, Vaysse N, et al. 1998. Transgenic CCK-B/gastrin receptor mediates murine exocrine pancreatic secretion. *Gastroenterology* 115:988–96

30. Walsh JH. 1994. Gastrointestinal hormones. See Ref. 26a, pp. 1–128

31. Matozaki T, Goke B, Tsunoda Y, Rodriguez M, Martinez J, Williams JA. 1990. Two functionally distinct cholecystokinin receptors show different modes of action on Ca^{2+} mobilization and phospholipid hydrolysis in isolated rat pancreatic acini. Studies using

a new cholecystokinin analog, JMV-180. *J. Biol. Chem.* 265:6247–54

32. Williams JA. 1999. Intracellular regulatory mechanisms in pancreatic acinar cellular function. *Curr. Opin. Gastroenterol.* 15:385–91

33. Daulhac L, Kowalski-Chauvel A, Pradayrol L, Vaysse N, Seva C. 1999. Src-family tyrosine kinases in activation of ERK-1 and p85/p110-phosphatidylinositol 3-kinase by G/CCK$_B$ receptors. *J. Biol. Chem.* 274:20657–63

34. Tapia JA, Ferris HA, Jensen RT, Garcia L. 1999. Cholecystokinin activates PYK2/CAKβ by a phospholipase C-dependent mechanism and its association with the mitogen-activated protein kinase signaling pathway in pancreatic acinar cells. *J. Biol. Chem.* 274:31261–71

35. Lankisch TO, Nozu F, Owyang C, Tsunoda Y. 1999. High-affinity cholecystokinin type A receptor/cytosolic phospholipase A$_2$ pathways mediate Ca^{2+} oscillations via a positive feedback regulation by calmodulin kinase in pancreatic acini. *Eur. J. Cell Biol.* 78:632–41

36. Schnefel S, Profrock A, Hinsch KD, Schulz I. 1990 Cholecystokinin activates Gi1-, Gi2-, Gi3-, and several Gs-protein in rat pancreatic acinar cells. *Biochem. J.* 269:483–88

37. Xu X, Croy JT, Zeng W, Zhao L, Davignon I, et al. 1998. Promiscuous coupling of receptors to Gq class α subunits and effector proteins in pancreatic and submandibular gland cells. *J. Biol. Chem.* 273:27275–79

38. Xu X, Zeng W, Popov S, Berman DM, Davignon I, et al. 1999. RGS proteins determine signaling specificity of G$_q$-coupled receptors. *J. Biol. Chem.* 274:3549–56

39. Zeng W, Xu X, Popov S, Mukhopadhyay S, Chidiac P, et al. 1998. The N-terminal domain of RGS4 confers receptor-selective inhibition of G-protein signaling. *J. Biol. Chem.* 273:34687–90

40. Petersen CCH, Toescu EC, Petersen OH. 1991. Different patterns of receptor-activated cytoplasmic Ca^{2+} oscillations in single pancreatic acinar cells: dependence on receptor type, agonist concentration and intracellular Ca^{2+} buffering. *EMBO J.* 10:527–33

41. Wakui M, Osipchuk YV, Petersen OH. 1990. Receptor-activated cytoplasmic Ca^{2+} spiking mediated by inositol trisphosphate is due to Ca^{2+}-induced Ca^{2+} release. *Cell* 63:1025–32

42. Thorn P, Petersen OH. 1993. Calcium oscillations in pancreatic acinar cells, evoked by the cholecystokinin analogue JMV-180, depend on functional inositol 1,4,5-trisphosphate receptors. *J. Biol. Chem.* 268:23219–21

43. Xu X, Zeng W, Muallem S. 1996. Regulation of the inositol 1,4,5-trisphosphate-activated Ca^{2+} channel by activation of G-proteins. *J. Biol. Chem.* 271:11737–44

44. LeBeau AP, Yule DI, Groblewski GE, Sneyd J. 1999. Agonist-dependent phosphorylation of the inositol 1,4,5-trisphosphate receptor. *J. Gen. Physiol.* 113:851–71

45. Thorn P, Gerasimenko O, Petersen OH. 1994. Cyclic ADP-ribose regulation of ryanodine receptors involved in agonist evoked cytosolic Ca^{2+} oscillations in pancreatic acinar cells. *EMBO J.* 13:2038–43

46. Galione A, Lee HC, Busa WB. 1991. Ca^{2+}-induced Ca^{2+} release in sea urchin egg homogenates and its modulation by cyclic ADP-ribose. *Science* 253:1143–46

47. Meszaros LG, Bak J, Chu A. 1993. Cyclic ADP-ribose as an endogenous regulator of the non-skeletal type ryanodine receptor Ca^{2+} channel. *Nature* 364:76–79

48. Cancela JM, Mogami H, Tepikin AV, Petersen OH. 1998. Intracellular glucose switches between cyclic ADP-ribose and inositol trisphosphate triggering of cytosolic Ca^{2+} spiking. *Curr. Biol.* 8:865–68

49. Guse AH, da Silva CP, Berg I, Skapenko AL, Weber K, et al. 1999. Regulation of calcium signalling in T lymphocytes by the

second messenger cyclic ADP-ribose. *Nature* 398:70–73

50. Sonnleitner A, Conti A, Bertocchini F, Schindler H, Sorrentino V. 1998. Functional properties of the ryanodine receptor type 3 (RYR3) Ca^{2+} release channel. *EMBO J.* 17:2790–98

51. Ziegler M, Jorcke D, Schweiger M. 1997. Identification of bovine liver mitochondrial NAD+ glycohydrolase as ADP-ribosyl cyclase. *Biochem. J.* 326:401–5

52. Adebanjo OA, Anandatheerthavarada HK, Koval AP, Moonga BS, Biswast G, et al. 1999. A new function for CD38/ADP-ribosyl cyclase in nuclear Ca^{2+} homeostasis. *Nat. Cell Biol.* 1:409–14

53. Liang M, Chini ED, Cheng J, Dousa TP. 1999. Synthesis of NAADP and cADPr in mitochondria. *Arch. Biochem. Biophys.* 15:317–25

54. Munshi C, Thiel DJ, Mathews II, Aarhus R, Walseth TF, Lee HC. 1999. Characterization of the active site of ADP-ribosyl cyclase. *J. Biol. Chem.* 274:30770–77

55. Guse AH. 1999. Cyclic ADP-ribose: a novel Ca^{2+}-mobilising second messenger. *Cell. Signal.* 11:309–16

56. Hirata Y, Kimura N, Sato K, Ohsugi Y, Takasawa S, et al. 1994. ADP ribosyl cyclase activity of a novel bone marrow stromal cell surface molecule, BST-1. *FEBS Lett.* 356:244–48

57. Takasawa S, Nata S, Yonekura H, Okamoto H. 1993. Cyclic ADP-ribose in insulin secretion from pancreatic β cells. *Science* 259:370–73

58. Kuemmerle JF, Makhlouf GM. 1995. Agonist-stimulated cyclic ADP ribose. Endogenous modulator of Ca^{2+}-induced Ca^{2+} release in intestinal longitudinal muscle. *J. Biol. Chem.* 270:25488–94

59. Clementi E, Riccio M, Sciorati C, Nistico G, Meldolesi J. 1996. The type 2 ryanodine receptor of neurosecretory PC 12 cells is activated by cyclic ADP-ribose. *J. Biol. Chem.* 271:17739–45

60. Higashida H, Yokoyama S, Hashii M,

Taketo M, Higashida M, et al. 1997. Muscarinic receptor-mediated dual regulation of ADP-ribosyl cyclase in NG108-15 neuronal cell membranes. *J. Biol. Chem.* 272:31272–77

61. Morita K, Kitayama S, Dohi T. 1997. Stimulation of cyclic ADP-ribose synthesis by acetylcholine and its role in catecholamine release in bovine adrenal chromaffin cells. *J. Biol. Chem.* 272:21002–9

62. Walseth TF, Lee HC. 1993. Synthesis and characterization of antagonists of cyclic ADP-ribose. *Biochim. Biophys. Acta* 1178:235–42

63. Korc M, Wiliams JA, Goldfine ID. 1979. Stimulation of the glucose transport system in isolated mouse pancreatic acini by cholecystokinin and analogues. *J. Biol. Chem.* 254:7624–29

64. Chini EN, Dousa TP. 1999. Differential effect of glycolytic intermediaries upon cyclic ADP-ribose, inositol 1,4,5-trisphosphate-, and nicotinate adenine dinucleotide phosphate-induced Ca^{2+} release systems. *Arch. Biochem. Biophys.* 370:294–99

65. Genazzani AA, Galione A. 1997. A Ca^{2+} release mechanism gated by the novel pyridine nucleotide, NAADP. *Trends Pharmacol. Sci.* 18:108–10

66. Aarhus R, Dickey DM, Graeff RM, Gee KR, Walseth TF, Lee HC. 1996. Activation and inactivation of Ca^{2+} release by NAADP. *J. Biol. Chem.* 271:8513–16

67. Genazzani AA, Empson RM, Galione A. 1996. Unique inactivation properties of NAADP-sensitive Ca^{2+} release. *J. Biol. Chem.* 271:11599–602

68. Chini EN, Dousa TP. 1996. Nicotinate-adenine dinucleotide phosphate-induced Ca^{2+} release does not behave as a Ca^{2+}-induced Ca^{2+} release system. *Biochem. J.* 316:709–11

69. Bak J, White P, Timar G, Missiaen L, Genazzani AA, Galione A. 1999. Nicotinic acid adenine dinucleotide phosphate

triggers Ca^{2+} release from brain microsomes. *Curr. Biol.* 9:751–54

70. Berridge MJ. 1998. Neuronal calcium signaling. *Neuron* 21:13–26

71. Genazzani AA, Mezna M, Dickey DM, Michelangeli F, Walseth TF, Galione A. 1997. Pharmacological properties of the Ca^{2+}-release mechanism sensitive to NAADP in the sea urchin egg. *Br. J. Pharmacol.* 121:1489–95

72. Finch EA, Turner TJ, Goldin SM. 1991. Calcium as a coagonist of inositol 1,4,5-trisphosphate-induced calcium release. *Science* 252:443–46

73. Bezprozvanny I, Watras J, Ehrlich BE. 1991. Bell-shaped calcium-response curves of Ins(1,4,5)P$_3$- and calcium-gated channels from endoplasmic reticulum of cerebellum. *Nature* 351:751–54

74. Hirose K, Kadowaki S, Tanabe M, Takeshima H, Iino M. 1999. Spatiotemporal dynamics of inositol 1,4,5-trisphosphate that underlies complex Ca^{2+} mobilization patterns. *Science* 284:1527–30

75. Galione A. 1994. Cyclic ADP-ribose, the ADP-ribosyl cyclase pathway and calcium signalling. *Mol. Cell. Endocrinol.* 98:125–31

76. Willmott NJ, Sethi J, Walseth TF, Lee HC, White AM, Galione A. 1996. Nitric oxide induced mobilization of intracellular calcium via the cyclic ADP-ribose signalling pathway. *J. Biol. Chem.* 271:3699–705

77. Ehrlich BE, Kaftan E, Bezprozvannaya S, Bezprozvanny I. 1994. The pharmacology of intracellular Ca^{2+} release channels. *Trends Pharmacol. Sci.* 15:145–48

78. Adkins CE, Taylor CW. 1999. Lateral inhibition of inositol 1,4,5-trisphosphate receptors by cytosolic Ca^{2+}. *Curr. Biol.* 9:1115–18

79. Gyorke S. 1999. Ca^{2+} spark termination: inactivation and adaptation may be manifestations of the same mechanism. *J. Gen. Physiol.* 114:163–66

80. Adkins CE, Morris SA, De Smedt H, Sienaert I, Torok K, Taylor CW. 2000. Ca^{2+}-calmodulin inhibits Ca^{2+} release mediated by type-1, -2, and -3 inositol trisphosphate receptors. *Biochem J.* 345:357–63

81. Gyorke S, Fill M. 1994. Ca^{2+}-induced Ca^{2+} release in response to flash photolysis. *Science* 263:987–88

82. Laver DR, Roden LD, Ahern GP, Eager KR, Junankar PR, et al. 1995. Cytoplasmic Ca^{2+} inhibits the ryanodine receptor from cardiac muscle. *J. Membr. Biol.* 147:7–22

83. Boittin FX, Coussin F, Macrez N, Mironneau C, Mironneau J. 1998. Inositol 1,4,5-trisphosphate- and ryanodine-sensitive Ca^{2+} release channel-dependent Ca^{2+} signalling in rat portal vein myocytes. *Cell Calcium* 23:303–11

84. Koizumi S, Bootman MD, Bobanovic LK, Schell MJ, Berridge MJ, Lipp P. 1999. Characteriztion of elementary Ca^{2+} release signals in NGF-differentiated PC12 cells and hippocampal neurons. *Neuron* 22:125–37

85. Parker I, Choi J, Yao Y. 1996. Elementary events of InsP$_3$-induced Ca^{2+} liberation in *Xenopus* oocytes: hot spots, puffs and blips. *Cell Calcium* 20:105–21

86. Berridge MJ. 1997. Elementary and global aspects of calcium signalling. *J. Physiol.* 499:291–306

87. Cannell MB, Soeller C. 1999. Mechanisms underlying calcium sparks in cardiac muscle. *J. Gen. Physiol.* 113:373–76

88. Ito K, Miyashita Y, Kasai H. 1999. Kinetic control of multiple forms of Ca^{2+} spikes by inositol trisphosphate in pancreatic acinar cells. *J. Cell Biol.* 146:405–13

89. Nathanson MH, Fallon MB, Padfield PJ, Maranto AR. 1994. Localization of the type 3 inositol 1,4,5-trisphosphate receptor in the Ca^{2+} wave trigger zone of pancreatic acinar cells. *J. Biol. Chem.* 269:4693–96

90. Kasai H, Li YX, Miyashita Y. 1993. Subcellular distribution of Ca^{2+} release channels underlying Ca^{2+} waves and oscillations in exocrine pancreas. *Cell* 74:669–77

91. Thorn P, Lawrie AM, Smith PM, Gallacher DV, Petersen OH. 1993. Local and

global cytosolic Ca^{2+} oscillations in exocrine cells evoked by agonists and inositol trisphosphate. *Cell* 74:661–68

92. Kasai H, Petersen OH. 1994. Spatial dynamics of second messengers: IP$_3$ and cAMP as long-range and associative messengers. *Trends Neurosci.* 17:95–101

93. Wilson HL, Galione A. 1998. Differential regulation of nicotininc acid-adenine dinucleotide phosphate and cADP-ribose production by cAMP and cGMP. *Biochem J.* 331:837–43

94. Wu V, Yang M, McRoberts JA, Ren J, Seensalu R, et al. 1997. First intracellular loop of the human cholecystokinin-A receptor is essential for cyclic AMP signaling in transfected HEK-293 cells. *J. Biol. Chem.* 272:9037–42

95. Gonzalez A, Schmid A, Sternfeld L, Krause E, Salido GM, Schulz I. 1999. CCK-evoked Ca^{2+} waves in isolated mouse pancreatic acinar cells are modulated by activation of cytosolic phospholipase A$_2$, phospholipase D and protein kinase C. *Biochem. Biophys. Res. Commun.* 261:726–33

96. Maruyama Y. 1993. Control of inositol polyphosphate-mediated calcium mobilization by arachidonic acid in pancreatic acinar cells of rats. *J. Physiol.* 463:729–46

97. Parekh A, Penner R. 1997. Store depletion and calcium influx. *Physiol. Rev.* 77:901–30

98. Putney JW. 1999. "Kissin'cousins": intimate plasma membrane-ER interactions underlie capacitative calcium entry. *Cell* 99:5–8

99. Petersen OH. 1999. Waves of excitement: calcium signals inside cells. *Biologist* 46:227–30

100. Albrieux M, Lee HC, Villaz M. 1998. Calcium signaling by cyclic ADP-ribose, NAADP, and inositol trisphosphate are involved in distinct functions in ascidian oocytes. *J. Biol.Chem.* 273:14566–74

101. Santella L, Kyozuka K, Genazzani AA, De Riso L, Carafoli E. 2000. Nicotinic acid adenine dinucleotide phosphate-induced Ca^{2+} release. *J. Biol. Chem.* 275:8301–6

101a. Berg I, Potter BVL, Mayr GW, Guse AH. 2000. Nicotinic acid adenine dinucleotide phosphate (NAADP$^+$) is an essential regulator of T-lymphocyte Ca^{2+} signaling. *J. Cell Biol.* 150(3):581–88

102. Perez-Tersic CM, Chini EN, Shen SS, Dousa TP, Clapham DE. 1995. Ca^{2+} release triggered by nicotinate adenine dinucleotide phosphate in intact sea urchin eggs. *Biochem. J.* 312:955–59

103. Kidd JF, Thorn P. 2000. Intracellular Ca^{2+} and Cl$^-$ channel activation in secretory cells. *Annu. Rev. Physiol.* 62:493–513

Annu. Rev. Physiol. 2001. 63:119–39

THE GASTRINS: Their Production and Biological Activities

G J Dockray[1], A Varro[1], R Dimaline[1], and T Wang[2]

[1]*Physiological Laboratory, University of Liverpool, Liverpool, L69 3BX, United Kingdom; e-mail: g.j.dockray@liverpool.ac.uk; avarro@liverpool.ac.uk; r.dimaline@liverpool.ac.uk*
[2]*Gastrointestinal Unit, Massachusetts General Hospital, Boston, Massachusetts 02114; e-mail: wang@helix.mgh.harvard.edu*

Key Words   parietal cell, enterochromaffin-like cell, gastric epithelium, gastric acid

■ **Abstract**   Gastric epithelial organization and function are controlled and maintained by a variety of endocrine and paracrine mediators. Peptides encoded by the gastrin gene are an important part of this system because targeted deletion of the gene, or of the gastrin-CCK$_B$ receptor gene, leads to decreased numbers of parietal cells and decreased gastric acid secretion. Recent studies indicate that the gastrin precursor, preprogastrin, gives rise to a variety of products, each with a distinctive spectrum of biological activity. The conversion of progastrin to smaller peptides is regulated by multiple mechanisms including prohormone phosphorylation and secretory vesicle pH. Progastrin itself stimulates colonic epithelial proliferation; biosynthetic intermediates (Gly-gastrins) stimulate colonic epithelial proliferation and gastric epithelial differentiation; and C-terminally amidated gastrins stimulate colonic proliferation, gastric epithelial proliferation and differentiation, and acid secretion. The effects of progastrin-derived peptides on gastric epithelial function are mediated in part by release of paracrine factors that include histamine, epidermal growth factor (EGF)–receptor ligands, and Reg. The importance of the appropriate regulation of this system is shown by the observation that prolonged moderate hypergastrinemia in transgenic mice leads to remodelling of the gastric epithelium, and in the presence of *Helicobacter*, to gastric cancer.

INTRODUCTION

The organization and secretory functions of the gastric epithelium are mediated by endocrine and paracrine factors. The role of the gastric hormone gastrin as an acid secretagogue was first recognized in 1905 (1). Observations in mice in which the gastrin gene has been deleted (Gas-KO) now make it clear that gastrin and related peptides are also important in defining the acid-secreting capacity of the stomach through control of proliferation, differentiation, and maturation of different cell types (2, 3). Two further issues have emerged in recent years that cast new light on the physiology of gastrin. First, it has become clear that peptides derived from the gastrin precursor, preprogastrin, which had previously been considered to be biologically inactive biosynthetic intermediates, now appear to have their own spectrum of activities. In some circumstances, these peptides may even be the main secreted products of gastrin gene expression. Therefore, different patterns of processing of preprogastrin generate multiple active products so that the relevant control mechanisms are of physiological interest. Second, it is now recognized that gastrin stimulates the release of a range of humoral mediators. Histamine is the best studied example, but other examples include ligands of the epidermal growth factor (EGF)-receptor and the pancreatic stone protein, Reg. We review here evidence for the control of gastrin production, the properties of the different products, and the mechanisms by which these peptides influence gastric epithelial organization and function. We focus on recent findings; for reviews of earlier work see (4–6).

THE GASTRIN GENE AND ITS PRODUCTS

The gastrin gene in all mammals consists of three exons and encodes a 101 (human, mouse) or 104 (rat) precursor peptide with an N-terminal signal peptide (5). The signal peptide is removed by cleavage at residues 21 or 25 to generate progastrin. The gastrin (G-) cell of the pyloric antral part of the stomach is the primary site of expression of the gene in adult mammals. However, during development there is expression in pancreatic β-cells and colon, and the gene is also expressed in colorectal tumors and at low levels in pituitary gland and testis (7).

Gastrin Release

Gastrin is secreted in response to stimuli acting at both the luminal and basolateral sides of antral G-cells (5). Gastrin release is suppressed by gastric acid, which probably acts by releasing the paracrine inhibitor somatostatin (5). Gastrin-releasing peptide (GRP), secreted by mucosal nerve fibers, triggers calcium-dependent exocytosis in G-cells through a mechanism that is enhanced by disruption of the cytoskeleton and inhibition of the small GTPase, Rho (8). The well-recognized luminal stimuli are amino acids (particularly aromatic amino acids), dietary amines, and calcium. Human G-cells express receptors detecting extracellular calcium (9). It now seems possible that the same receptor also responds to aromatic amino acids because L-phenylalanine and L-tryptophan have been shown to activate the extracellular Ca^{2+}-sensing receptor in cells stably transfected with this receptor (10). Two different classes of luminal stimuli may therefore converge on a single pathway.

In patients infected with *Helicobacter pylori*, basal plasma gastrin concentrations are elevated approximately twofold, and responses to food or to GRP may be elevated up to sixfold (11); these phenomena have attracted much attention, but the relevant cellular mechanisms are still poorly understood. Studies on human G-cells in culture suggest that *H. pylori* has only a small effect on basal gastrin release, and no effect on release in response to the GRP homologue, bombesin (12). This is compatible with the view that in vivo cytokines, e.g. IL-8 and inflammatory cells, might mediate the effects of *H. pylori* infection on gastrin release (13, 14).

Gene Expression

Long-term increases in gastrin release are supported by increased synthesis. Thus gastrin mRNA abundance is increased by food in the stomach and is inhibited by gastric acid via the paracrine mediator, somatostatin. Reduction of acid secretion, for example by administration of proton pump inhibitors such as omeprazole, increases gastrin release, mRNA abundance, and mRNA translation (15–18). Separate mechanisms appear to control transcription, translation, post-translational processing, and secretion (Figure 1). Thus in omeprazole-treated rats, translation of gastrin mRNA, measured by incorporation of [^{3}H]-tyrosine into progastrin, increased before mRNA abundance indicating differential regulation of gastrin transcription and translation (18). There is also differential control of gastrin gene expression and gastrin secretion in response to humoral factors. Thus human gastrin gene expression is increased by EGF, which is a weak gastrin secretagogue, but is not increased by bombesin, which is a strong secretagogue (19, 20).

Several distinct *cis*-regulatory elements have been identified in the promoter of the human gastrin gene, including a GC-rich element that binds Sp1 and appears to mediate the action of EGF (20). In colorectal carcinoma cells, gastrin gene expression is increased by oncogenic mutations in *Ras*, and there is evidence that this effect is mediated through activation of the Ras-Raf-Mek-MAP kinase cascade (21). This pathway is activated by EGF, and recent studies suggest this leads to Sp1-induced gastrin gene expression (22). The Sp1 element also binds a Kruppel-like

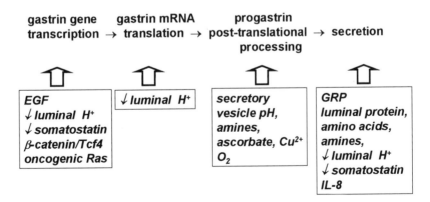

Figure 1 Summary of control mechanisms in gastrin synthesis and secretion. Factors known to regulate gastrin gene transcription, translation, progastrin processing, and gastrin release are shown.

zinc finger protein (ZBP-89), which inhibits the action of EGF (23). Mechanisms involving Sp1 activation are likely to be complex because Sp1 control of a CACC element in the gastrin promoter has also been shown to be inhibited by a novel zinc finger protein, RIN ZF (24). In any case, it is likely that additional mechanisms contribute to gastrin gene expression in colorectal cancer cells, as recent studies suggest the gastrin gene is a down-stream target for the β-catenin/Tcf-4 signaling pathway, which is activated in most colorectal cancers (24a).

Post-Translational Modification

The mechanisms and regulation of progastrin processing are interesting because different progastrin-derived peptides exhibit different biological properties (Figure 2, see color insert). There are three pairs of basic residues in progastrin that are sites for cleavage by prohormone convertases (PC). Progastrin is also modified by sulfation of Tyr residues (Tyr-86), phosphorylation of Ser (Ser-96), and C-terminal amidation (Phe-92) (25–27). Sulfation and phosphorylation occur in a distal compartment of the Golgi complex, and cleavage normally follows rapidly after sequestration of progastrin into secretory vesicles. There is, therefore, limited cleavage of the precursor in cells in which secretory vesicles of the regulated pathway are poorly represented, e.g. colon cancer cell lines (28–30). In these cells, the products mostly pass directly from the *trans*-Golgi network (TGN) to the cell surface via the constitutive pathway of secretion, and the main products are progastrin and Gly-gastrins.

In rat G-cells, cleavage of progastrin at pairs of Arg residues is completed with a $t_{1/2}$ of about 12 min after progastrin leaves the TGN; in human this cleavage occurs more slowly ($t_{1/2}$, 60 min). But in both species the main product is G34-Gly, which is converted via a C-terminal hydroxy-glycine intermediate to G34 (Figure 2). Cleavage of G34-Gly or G34 at Lys-Lys gives rise to G17Gly or G17 (27, 31) and occurs over the following 1 to 2 h. In rat G-cells, amidation occurs up to 90 min after production of Gly-gastrins and thereafter stops (even though substrate in the form of G17-Gly remains), suggesting that optimal conditions for PAM activity are lost. Consequently in rat G-cells, approximately equal amounts of G17-Gly or G17 are generated and secreted, and the evidence suggests G17-Gly is not normally converted to G17. In contrast, in human G-cells there is more complete conversion of Gly-gastrins, and G17 is the predominant product (27, 31). The amidation reaction is mediated by peptidyl α-amidating mono-oxygenase (PAM) in two steps; initially the mono-oxygenase domain of the enzyme yields a C-terminal hydroxyglycine intermediate in a reaction requiring molecular oxygen, copper, and ascorbate. The intermediate is then converted to a C-terminal amide by the lyase domain of the enzyme. Alternative mRNA splicing generates multiple forms of PAM differing in the presence of the lyase domain and *trans*-membrane domains, several of which occur in G-cells (32). The physiological factors that account for the species differences in gastrin amidation are uncertain. These factors are, however, interesting because it has been suggested that species differences in the gastric responses to prolonged hypergastrinemia might be attributed to variation in the relative secretion of amidated gastrin compared with progastrin or Gly-gastrins (33).

Control of Processing

Progastrin cleavage is modified by differential expression of prohormone convertases (PCs), by prior sulfation or phosphorylation, and by modulation of the interior environment of secretory vesicles, e.g. pH (32, 34–36). Rat G-cells contain PC1/3, PC2, the secretory protein 7B2, which is a chaperone for PC2, as well as other members of the PC family (32), and human G-cells have both PC2 and PC1/3 (37). The abundance of PC1/3 and PC2 mRNA in the rat antrum is up-regulated by omeprazole (32). Studies in cell lines indicate that PC2 mediates cleavage of progastrin at each of the three pairs of basic residues (38). A patient lacking PC1 has been found to have normal plasma concentrations of amidated gastrin so that this enzyme is not essential for progastrin cleavage at Arg-94,95; however, there were higher than normal plasma progastrin concentrations in this patient, and these increased progressively after a meal indicating a contribution of PC1 to progastrin cleavage (A Varro, GJ Dockray, RS Jackson & S O'Rahilly, unpublished observations). Following cleavage at pairs of residues there is carboxypeptidase removal of C-terminal basic residues, which liberates the C-terminal Gly-extended gastrins. Mice that lack carboxypeptidase E exhibit increased concentrations of gastrin precursor peptides in the antrum but variable reductions in amidated gastrin; interestingly, they show evidence of impaired local regulation of G-cell function (39–41).

Phosphorylation and Sulfation Modify Cleavage

The proximity of the Ser-96 phosphorylation site to Arg-94,95 and the conservation of this motif in all mammalian gastrin and cholecystokinin precursors suggest that phosphorylation modulates cleavage. Site-directed mutagenesis indicates that loss of Ser-96 or deletion of the kinase recognition site (Glu-98) increases cleavage of progastrin in the endocrine cell line HIT-T15 (34). The relevant kinase is believed to be physiological casein kinase, which is a widely distributed Golgi-resident enzyme that phosphorylates peptides with the general sequence Ser-X-acidic residue. Physiological casein kinase requires millimolar calcium concentrations, and disruption of calcium stores inhibits progastrin phosphorylation, although it is not yet clear whether this provides a physiological route to modulate processing (34).

Sulfation of Tyr residues depends on acidic amino acids on the N-terminal side. Site directed mutagenesis suggests that in the case of progastrin, the consensus sequence for sulfation differs from that commonly found in other proteins. In particular, a basic residue two positions to the N terminus of Tyr-86 has been reported to increase sulfation, suggesting the possibility of a cell-specific tyrosine sulfotransferase activity (36). It seems possible that Tyr-sulfation also modifies subsequent cleavage, although the details are unclear (42).

Secretory Vesicle pH Selectively Modifies Cleavage

The internal pH in neuroendocrine cell secretory vesicles is typically about 5.5 owing to the activity of the $vH^+ATPase$ (43). The proton gradient provides energy for accumulation of biogenic amines via the activity of vesicular monoamine transporters (VMAT) and also provides an internal pH close to the optimum for PC activity. Raising intravesicular pH in rat G-cells inhibited cleavage of Lys-Lys but not Arg-Arg residues in progastrin (35). Similar effects were produced by incubation with biogenic amine precursors, e.g. L-DOPA and 5-HTP, and these were reversed by the VMAT inhibitor reserpine, compatible with the idea that amines raise intravesicular pH, thereby modulating cleavage (35). In HIT-T15 cells transfected with a pH-sensitive form of green fluorescent protein targeted to secretory vesicles as a chimeric protein with preprogastrin, co-expression of VMAT2 was associated with a reserpine-sensitive increase in vesicle pH from approximately 5.5 to 6.4 (44). Interestingly, dietary amines also inhibit progastrin processing, and although some, e.g. tyramine, may be VMAT substrates, they appear to act in this case as weak bases because their effects are not blocked by reserpine (45). It is possible that either loss of protons through VMAT activity or re-protonation of amines in secretory vesicles is responsible for increased vesicle pH. Further work is now needed to determine whether increased vesicular pH influences prohormone maturation by directly reducing PC activity, by inhibiting PC2 maturation, or by dissipating the organization of secretory vesicle cores (35). However, because the metabolic clearance rate of G34 is about 20% that of G17 (46), it is already clear that one consequence of inhibiting G34 cleavage would be higher plasma concentrations of total amidated gastrins.

THE ACTIONS OF AMIDATED GASTRINS

The Effects of Targeted Gene Deletion

Mice in which the genes encoding either gastrin (Gas-KO mice) or the gastrin-CCK_B receptor have been deleted exhibit similar phenotypes (2, 3, 47, 48). In both cases, there are reduced numbers of parietal and enterochromaffin-like (ECL) cells, the mice have elevated gastric pH, and they do not secrete acid in response to gastrin, histamine, or carbachol (3, 47). However, following continuous administration of gastrin for 24 h or longer, acid secretion reappears in Gas-KO mice (3, 49). Together these observations suggest amidated gastrins acting at gastrin-CCK_B receptors regulate the proportions of different cell types in the epithelium and, in the case of parietal cells, their maturation.

Overexpression of Amidated Gastrin

The observations in mice with gene knockouts complement those made in mice that overexpress the gastrin gene. In mice transgenic for a gastrin minigene consisting of 0.4 kb of the insulin promoter upstream of the human gastrin coding sequence (INS-GAS mice), expression of human gastrin is targeted to pancreatic β-cells (50). The pattern of post-translational processing of progastrin in these cells is similar to antral G-cells, i.e. the major secretory products are amidated gastrins. These mice exhibit increased proliferation of the gastric and colonic epithelium. In young animals (up to about 4 months) there are also increased numbers of parietal cells and acid secretion is augmented (33). Interestingly, however, there is then a progressive loss of parietal cells, decreased acid secretion, and the development of foveolar hyperplasia. Similar findings have been reported in a second transgenic model in which the chicken β-actin promoter was linked to a mutant progastrin that possessed a furin-cleavage site in G34 and terminated in Gly (after amidation, the main product is therefore G17). The transgene was shown to be expressed in gastric mucosa, and the mice had approximately six-fold elevated plasma gastrin concentrations (51). At 8 months these mice also exhibited expansion of the mucus neck and surface epithelial cell populations, whereas parietal cell numbers and the length of the glandular region of gastric tubules were depressed. In older hypergastrinemic mice ($\sim$20 months) there was a tendency to develop gastric cancer; this progression was exacerbated in animals infected with *Helicobacter felis*; many of these animals had gastric cancer by 8 months (33). At plasma concentrations above the physiological range, gastrin therefore disrupts the processes controlling the tubular organization of gastric glands, i.e. tubulogenesis, and together with other factors accelerates oncogenic progression.

Receptor-Overexpressing Mice

Human, but not mouse, pancreatic acinar cells express the gastrin-CCK$_B$ receptor. Saillan-Barreau et al (52) used the promoter of the elastase 1 gene to generate a mouse model of human acinar cells by directing expression of the gastrin-CCK$_B$ receptor to these cells. Pancreatic acinar cells in the resulting animals secreted enzymes in response to gastrin. The latter did not increase expression of the genes encoding digestive enzymes, but there was increased mRNA translation owing to activation of p70 S6 kinase (53). When these mice were crossed with INS-GAS mice to produce a strain in which there are locally high gastrin concentrations in the pancreas and local expression of the receptor, the offspring exhibited tubular dysplasia and increased fibrosis in the pancreas (54). Thus in both stomach and pancreas increased stimulation of gastrin-CCK$_B$ receptors disrupts tubulogenesis.

Secretion and Expression of Genes Linked to Secretory Function

The activation of gastrin-CCK$_B$ receptors on ECL cells is associated with stimulation of histamine release, changes in gene expression (particularly of genes involved in histamine synthesis and storage), enzyme activity, and proliferation (Figure 3, see color insert). Recent work using submucosal microdialysis in conscious rats has directly confirmed the view that release of gastrin by food in turn stimulates gastric histamine secretion (55). Gastrin-stimulated exocytosis in isolated ECL cells is dependent on increased intracellular Ca^{2+} mediated both by release from intracellular stores and activation of calcium channels (56–58). The maintenance of histamine secretion as cellular stores diminish requires increased activity of histidine decarboxylase (HDC), which synthesizes histamine from histidine. Both HDC enzyme activity and mRNA abundance in the rat stomach are decreased by fasting and increase rapidly on feeding, which can be attributed to stimulation by gastrin of both transcription and translation (59–61). In addition, recent studies suggest that gastrin increases the stability of HDC by inhibition of proteosome-dependent degradation (60–62). In parallel with changes in HDC activity, there are also feeding-related increases in the abundance of mRNA encoding chromogranin A, which is packaged in secretory vesicles in ECL cells (63), and VMAT2, which sequesters histamine in secretory vesicles (64). The ECL cell response to gastrin therefore includes coordinated regulation of the expression of several genes required for histamine synthesis and storage.

The mechanisms by which gastrin regulates expression of HDC, chromogranin A, and VMAT2 have been studied in human gastric adenocarcinoma (AGS) epithelial cells transfected with the gastrin-CCK_B receptor. Increased human HDC gene transcription in response to gastrin is mediated by an enhancer-like response element, +2 to +24 bases relative to the transcriptional start site, which consists of two overlapping sequences binding distinct nuclear factors (+1 to +19, +11 to +27) (65). Stimulation of HDC transcription by gastrin was shown to be mediated by protein kinase C (PKC), indirect activation of c-*fos* and c-*jun*, and stimulation of MAP kinase (66–68). The latter step depends on activation of Raf, but interestingly activation of Ras, which is frequently upstream of Raf, was not required (68). In the case of chromogranin A transcription, both Sp1 and CREB appear to mediate the effect of gastrin (69). Transcription of VMAT2 is increased in response to raised intracellular calcium (70), but in AGS cells the action of gastrin appears to be mediated by a novel AP-2-like site (F Watson & R Dimaline, unpublished observations).

The importance of histamine in mediating the acute effects of gastrin on acid secretion is widely recognized. Parietal cells do, however, express functional gastrin receptors. Gastrin stimulates calcium oscillations in isolated parietal cells, although this seems to have only a small effect on acid secretion (71). Interpretation of the data is complicated by the fact that gastrin releases transforming growth factor (TGF)α and related peptides from parietal cells (see below). These exert acute, autocrine inhibitory effects, although on prolonged stimulation, for example of isolated canine parietal cells, there may be a small stimulatory effect on aminopyrine uptake, which is used as an index of acid secretion (72). Gastrin also stimulates the p42/44 MAP kinase pathway in canine parietal cells (72) but apparently not in *Mastomys* parietal cells (73). The gastrins are known to regulate the expression of genes encoding proteins essential for parietal cell function (74). Presumably, however, the mechanisms by which gastrin regulates parietal cell maturation in the intact mucosa include both direct effects and indirect actions secondary to release of paracrine mediators (histamine, TGFα, etc) (75, 76).

Proliferation and Differentiation

The gastric hypertrophy produced by prolonged administration of gastrin was described over a generation ago (77). It is now clear that gastrin also stimulates the growth of some tumor cells and that elevated plasma gastrin concentrations are a risk factor for colon and gastric cancer (particularly in the presence of *H. pylori*) (78, 79). However, observations in Gas-KO mice suggest that amidated gastrins might also cause some cells to leave the cell cycle. The rates of gastric proliferation in Gas-KO mice, demonstrated by BrdU labeling, are similar to wild type, but parietal cell numbers are reduced, and the parietal cells present are refractory to secretagogues (2, 3). It seems then that gastrin stimulates parietal cell differentiation, and because these cells are terminally differentiated, gastrin may cause their immediate precursors to leave the cell cycle.

Proliferating cells in gastric glands are located in the isthmus region and give rise to all the cell types of the gastric epithelium. Following administration of a test meal to fasted rats, there is increased BrdU labeling of gastric epithelial cells, which is inhibited by gastrin immuno-neutralization (80). However, while it is clear that gastrin receptors are expressed by parietal and ECL cells, it is not clear that proliferating cells also express the receptor. The proliferative response to gastrin in the stomach may therefore reflect indirect effects mediated by release of other growth factors including TGFα and heparin-binding (HB)-EGF (Figure 4, see color insert). Because proliferation rates are, in any case, similar in Gas-KO and wild-type mice, other growth factors presumably maintain proliferation in the absence of gastrin. Unlike parietal cells, it appears that at least in the rat, ECL cells are capable of proliferation and are stimulated to do so by gastrin. Gastrin increases the numbers of isolated rat ECL cells in culture, suggesting a direct mitogenic effect (81), and stimulates replication of ECL cells in vivo measured by thymidine incorporation (82). Moreover, hypergastrinemia is associated with increased ECL cell numbers in human and rat, and with the occurrence of gastric ECL cell carcinoid tumors (83–85). Gastric ECL cell carcinoid tumors also develop spontaneously in the small sub-Saharan rodent, *Mastomys*. The development of carcinoid tumors in this case is not dependent on gastrin, although hypergastrinemia has a potentiating effect (86). Instead, it seems these tumors arise as a consequence of three species-specific amino acid substitutions in the gastrin-CCK$_B$ receptor that lead to its constitutive activation (87).

Several groups have studied the transduction pathways associated with the proliferative effects of gastrin using the pancreatic AR4-2J cell line. In these cells, gastrin activates protein kinase C, stimulates the MAP kinase pathway, activates RhoA, and induces c-*fos* (88–91). It is thought that the activation of phospholipase C via Gα$_{q/11}$ stimulates PKC and increases intracellular calcium, which leads to Shc phosphorylation, activation of the Shc/Grb2 complex, and then stimulation of the MAP kinase pathway (91, 92). In other cells, however, proliferative responses appear to be mediated by different mechanisms; thus in the pituitary GH3 cell line, gastrin-stimulated proliferation was dependent on increased intracellular calcium but not MAP kinase activation or induction of c-*fos* (90). Increased intracellular calcium stimulated by gastrin was also linked to proliferation in CHO cells, but increased intracellular calcium in response to carbachol did not stimulate proliferation; the different responses in this case were attributed to differential desensitization of muscarinic and gastrin-CCK$_B$ receptors (93). Interestingly, in some cell lines amidated gastrins act at the gastrin-CCK$_B$ receptor to inhibit proliferation, e.g. certain pancreatic cancer cell lines, CHO cells, and AGS-cells transfected with the gastrin-CCK$_B$ receptor (94–96). The relevant transduction mechanisms remain uncertain, and it seems likely that the cellular context determines whether gastrin-CCK$_B$ receptor activation leads to stimulation or inhibition of proliferation.

THE PROPERTIES OF PROGASTRIN AND GLY-GASTRINS

Overexpression of Progastrin and Gly-Gastrins in Vivo

Observations on mice overexpressing either progastrin or Gly-extended gastrins suggest the colon is a target for these peptides. Mice transgenic for 1.3 kb of the human gastrin promoter and the coding sequence of human preprogastrin express the transgene in hepatocytes (H-Gas mice) (50). The liver is unable to process the product and progastrin is constitutively secreted. These mice exhibit high plasma progastrin concentrations (but normal amidated gastrin) and increased proliferation in the colon. In addition, mice transgenic for progastrin terminated at Gly, and driven by the metallothionien promoter constitutively secrete Gly-gastrins and exhibit increased thickness of the colon, and increased BrdU labeling in colon, increased colon goblet cell numbers, and some develop bronchoalveolar tumors in the lung (97). Recent studies have shown that H-Gas mice also exhibit increased aberrant crypt foci in the colon and are predisposed to the development of colon adenomas and carcinomas in response to a carcinogen (azoxymethane), compared with wild-type mice or INS-GAS mice (98, 99). It seems, then, that progastrin and Gly-gastrins are colon growth factors and that progastrin may act as a co-carcinogen, i.e. it does not initiate tumorigenesis but expands the pool of transformed cells.

Cellular Actions of Gly-Gastrins: Proliferation

The affinities of progastrin or Gly-gastrins for the gastrin-CCK$_B$ receptor are approximately three orders of magnitude lower than that of amidated gastrin. However, radio-ligand-binding studies suggest the existence of a receptor for Gly-gastrin with low affinity for amidated gastrin; this receptor is therefore distinct from the gastrin-CCK$_B$ receptor, although its molecular identity remains uncertain (100–104). Different cell lines may express one or both types of receptor. Care is needed in interpreting the data because at least in the case of AGS and LoVo cells it seems possible that different laboratories are using clones that vary in their expression of the putative Gly-gastrin receptor (102, 103, 105; A Varro & GJ Dockray, unpublished observations). It is unclear at present whether there is a distinct progastrin receptor.

The trophic effects of progastrin and Gly-gastrin in vivo are compatible with observations made in cell lines expressing the gastrin gene that are unable to complete the full program of post-translational processing events; thus the main secretory products are progastrin or Gly-gastrin. Singh et al showed that in colon cancer cell lines expressing progastrin, antisense inhibition of gastrin synthesis was associated with reduced proliferation (106). A gastrin antisense mRNA also inhibited proliferation of an immortalized mouse colon cell line (YAMC) producing mainly Gly-gastrin and some progastrin. Proliferation was stimulated by exogenous G17-Gly, but not by amidated gastrin; interestingly, an antibody to Gly-gastrin fully inhibited the effect of exogenous G17-Gly but only partially reversed the effects attributed to endogenous peptides (104). These observations have led to the suggestion that progastrin-derived peptides have an autocrine intracellular mechanism of action (104, 107).

The Gly-gastrins increased [^{3}H]-thymidine incorporation in some colon cancer cell lines (LoVo, HT29) reported to express a Gly-gastrin receptor but not the gastrin-CCK$_B$ receptor (102). Amidated gastrins had no effect in these cells, and the response to Gly-gastrin was apparently not mediated by the MAP kinase pathway, although it was associated with stimulation of Jun-N-terminal kinase (JNK). Other cell lines that express both gastrin-CCK$_B$ receptors and Gly-gastrin receptors, e.g. AR4-2J cells, human embryonic kidney (HEK) cells, and at least one clone of the gastric epithelial cell AGS, respond to stimulation of both receptors by increased proliferation (100, 101, 103). However, separate signaling pathways appear to be involved because Gly-extended gastrin does not increase intracellular calcium; its effects appear to involve stimulation of tyrosine kinases and activation of PI-(3)-kinase and JNK (101, 102, 108).

Actions of Gly-Gastrins: Parietal Cells

The Gly-gastrins do not stimulate acid secretion when infused intravenously in rats, but when co-administered with amidated gastrin, potentiation of the acid-secretory response is reported (109). In isolated canine parietal cells, Gly-gastrin, unlike amidated gastrin, did not increase intracellular Ca^{2+} or stimulate c-*fos* expression; however, it did activate JNK. Gly-gastrin also induced expression of the α-subunit of the proton pump through a mechanism associated with tyrosine-kinase activation and enhanced secretory responses to amidated gastrin after prolonged treatment (110). These results are compatible with a role for Gly-gastrins in the differentiation or maturation of parietal cells. In keeping with this idea, Chen et al (49) found that administration of Gly- and amidated gastrins to Gas-KO mice using osmotic mini-pumps stimulated and maintained acid secretion for up to 14 days; in contrast, amidated gastrin given alone initially stimulated acid secretion, which then declined. Therefore, the Gly-gastrins are not acid secretagogues, but they can act as modulators of parietal cell function by regulating the capacity of the parietal cell to respond to secretagogues.

GASTRIN AND THE ORGANIZATION
OF THE GASTRIC EPITHELIUM

The evidence discussed above makes it clear that gastrin regulates the organization and function of the gastric epithelium. Because the secretion of gastrin is inhibited by gastric acid, treatments that reduce acid secretory responses reflexively increase gastrin release and so may indirectly influence corpus epithelial cells. A well-recognized example is the increase in ECL cell numbers in human and rat owing to increased circulating gastrin after administration of proton pump inhibitors. A number of genetically modified mice have been characterized recently in which there are marked changes in gastric epithelial architecture, e.g. targeted expression of diphtheria toxin to parietal cells (111); constitutive stimulation of the activin II receptor (112); deletion of IQGAP1, a target of the small GTPase Cdc42 (113); deletion of the gene encoding trefoil peptide pS2 (114); TGFα overexpression (115, 116); loss of sodium-proton exchanger type II (117); loss of secretory phospholipase A2 (118); and proton pump mutations that inhibit recycling from the plasma membrane (119). Loss of parietal cells through several different mechanisms is associated with depletion of chief cells and expansion of mucus cell populations. Depressed parietal cell function is expected to stimulate gastrin release, and this response has been sought and verified in some, but not all, animal models. The extent to which hypergastrinemia contributes to the phenotype in many of these models remains unclear, but as noted above, prolonged moderate hypergastrinemia is sufficient to produce long-term loss of parietal cells and foveolar hyperplasia in mice so that gastrin should be considered a candidate contributor to these gastric phenotypes. It is worth noting that changes in mucosal architecture similar to those described above are also associated with *H. felis* infection in mice, and again it seems possible that gastrin plays a part in mediating these changes.

Many actions of gastrin are exerted via release of paracrine or autocrine mediators, including histamine (55, 120) and somatostatin (121), which together determine acute acid-secretory responses to gastrin (for review see 5). In addition, the amidated gastrins increase the expression of several growth factors that are putative mediators of mucosal proliferative responses (Figure 4). These may be relevant both in normal mucosa and in disease, e.g. increased fibroblast growth factor production in gastric carcinoid tumors (83). In rat stomach, gastrin increases the abundance of mRNA encoding TGFα, HB-EGF, and amphiregulin (122). At least in part this may reflect direct stimulation of transcription (123, 124). But in addition, in rat gastric mucus cells transfected with the gastrin receptor, gastrin has been shown to liberate HB-EGF by proteolysis from the cell surface; moreover, neutralization of HB-EGF inhibits proliferative responses to gastrin (124).

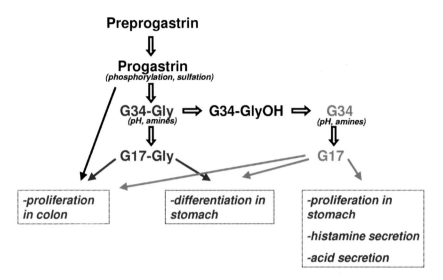

Figure 2 Major pathways of progastrin post-translational processing. The conversion of preprogastrin to progastrin occurs in endoplasmic reticulum; progastrin cleavage occurs in secretory vesicles in G-cells. The major biological activities of progastrin, the C-terminal Gly-extended gastrins (G34-Gly and G17-Gly) and the C-terminal amidated gastrins (G34 and G17) are shown. In rat G-cells, similar proportions of G17-Gly and G17 are generated, but in humans G17 predominates. Factors regulating cleavage are indicated in brackets.

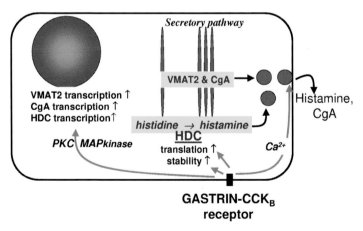

Figure 3 Summary of gastrin-dependent control mechanisms in enterochromaffin-like cells. There is regulation of transcription of histidine decarboxylase (HDC), vesicular monoamine transporter type 2 (VMAT2), and chromogranin A (CgA). Gastrin also stimulates HDC mRNA translation and inhibits HDC degradation. Histamine is generated by HDC and packaged in vesicles by VMAT2; gastrin regulates vesicular exocytosis.

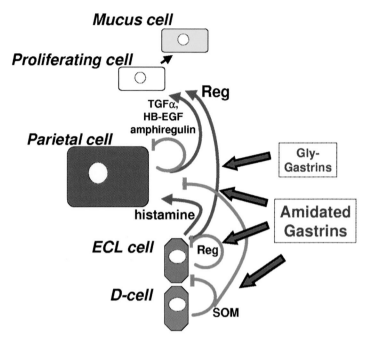

Figure 4 Gastrin-activated paracrine and autocrine regulatory pathways in the gastric mucosa. Stimulatory pathways are shown in blue, and inhibitory mediators in orange. Amidated gastrins act on parietal and ECL cells to release TGFα-related peptides, and Reg, which are autocrine inhibitors, but paracrine stimulants of proliferating cells leading to increased mucus cell numbers. Acute regulation of acid secretion depends on release of the stimulant histamine and inhibitor somatostatin.

In INS-Gas mice, TGF-α and HB-EGF are both increased in stomach (33). The parietal cell is a major source of gastric HB-EGF (125), and because there are similarities in the phenotypes of mice overexpressing TGF-α and gastrin, it has been proposed that gastrin activates a sequence of events that leads to EGF receptor-mediated autocrine inhibition of parietal cell numbers and paracrine stimulation of mucus cell numbers (33). Physiologically, this would provide a mechanism to balance the development of parietal and other cells in the base of the gastric gland with the development of mucus cells in the neck and surface.

Recent work has suggested a further possible mediator of the effects of gastrin on mucosal architecture. Thus gastrin increases the expression in gastric mucosa of Reg (other names include pancreatic stone protein, lithostathine, pancreatic thread protein), a protein originally found in pancreas that is associated with islet regeneration and binding of calcium in pancreatic juice. There is a family of Reg genes that are structurally similar to pancreatitis-associated proteins. In humans, Reg1α is expressed in ECL and chief cells, and in rat Reg is expressed in ECL cells (126, 127). The expression of Reg is strongly stimulated by gastrin both in vivo, and in AR42-J cells (126, 127). Reg is reported to stimulate proliferation of mucus cells in the rat (128). In some ECL cell carcinoid tumors there is a mutation in the codon for the initiator methionine that leads to disruption of the signal sequence and blocks secretion of Reg (127). This has given rise to the suggestion that Reg is a carcinoid tumor suppressor and that it may act physiologically as an autocrine depressant of ECL cell numbers, but a stimulant of mucus cell proliferation (Figure 4). Recently, a putative Reg receptor was cloned from rat pancreatic islets that appears to be homologous to the human EXT-like gene 3 (EXTL3) (129). Members of the EXT family have been implicated as tumor suppressors in multiple exostoses. There is a single putative membrane-spanning domain in EXTL3, which apparently is not conserved in other members of this family; instead the latter are thought to be Golgi resident proteins. Interestingly, Reg stimulation of EXTL3 expressed in RINm5F cells was associated with increased proliferation at low concentrations, but at high concentrations, with apoptosis. In addition, EXTL3 has been implicated as a tumor suppressor in colon cancer cell lines (130). It seems possible, then, that within gastric glands there is a loss of cells where concentrations of Reg are locally high, reflecting, for example, a putative tumor suppressor function around ECL cells, whereas lower Reg concentrations elsewhere in the gastric gland stimulate proliferation.

OVERVIEW

The maintenance of gastric epithelial organization and function depends on regulation of epithelial cell proliferation, migration, differentiation, and secretion. Gastrins acting at gastrin-CCK$_B$ receptors are regulators of these processes. Some of these effects are likely to be mediated directly, but others require the release of autocrine or paracrine mediators. Gastrin controls both acute acid-secretory responses to food and, over longer periods, it determines the capacity to secrete acid by regulating the relative proportions of different gastric epithelial cell types. It is now recognized that there are several active peptides derived from the gastrin gene that do not act at gastrin-CCK$_B$ receptors. These peptides appear to stimulate colonic proliferation, but their significance for physiological control of gastric function remains largely unexplored.

Plasma gastrin is increased in *Helicobacter* infections. Some of the effects of *H. pylori* infection may be due to prolonged hypergastrinemia. In addition, there are synergistic interactions between gastrin and *Helicobacter* infection in determining the progression to gastric neoplasia. It is now timely to examine the relevant cellular mechanisms.

Visit the Annual Reviews home page at www.AnnualReviews.org

LITERATURE CITED

1. Edkins JS. 1905. On the chemical mechanism of gastric secretion. *Proc. R. Soc. London Ser. B* 76:376
2. Koh TJ, Goldenring JR, Ito S, Mashimo H, Kopin AS, et al. 1997. Gastrin deficiency results in altered gastric differentiation and decreased colonic proliferation in mice. *Gastroenterology* 113:1015–25
3. Friis-Hansen L, Sundler F, Li Y, Gillespie PJ, Saunders TL, et al. 1998. Impaired gastric acid secretion in gastrin-deficient mice. *Am. J. Physiol. Gastrointest. Liver Physiol.* 274:G561–G68
4. Sawada M, Dickinson CJ. 1997. The G cell. *Annu. Rev. Physiol* 59:273–98
5. Walsh JH. 1994. Gastrin. In *Gut Peptides: Biochemistry and Physiology*, ed. JH Walsh, GJ Dockray, pp. 75–121. New York: Raven
6. Dockray GJ, Varro A, Dimaline R. 1996. Gastric endocrine cells: gene expression, processing and targeting of active products. *Physiol. Rev.* 76:767–98
7. Wang TC, Dockray GJ. 1999. Lessons from genetically engineered animal models. I. Physiological studies with gastrin in transgenic mice. *Am. J. Physiol. Gastrointest. Liver Physiol.* 277:G6–G11
8. Seensalu R, Avedian D, Barbuti R, Song M, Slice L, Walsh JH. 1997. Bombesin-induced gastrin release from canine G cells is stimulated by Ca^{2+} but not by protein ki-

nase C, and is enhanced by disruption of rho/cytoskeletal pathways. *J. Clin. Invest.* 100:1037–46
9. Ray JM, Squires PE, Curtis SB, Meloche MR, Buchan AM. 1997. Expression of the calcium-sensing receptor on human antral gastrin cells in culture. *J. Clin. Invest.* 99:2328–33
10. Conigrave AD, Quinn SJ, Brown EM. 2000. L-Amino acid sensing by the extracellular Ca^{2+}-sensing receptor. *Proc. Natl. Acad. Sci. USA* 97:4814–19
11. Calam J. 1994. Circulating hormones in peptic ulcer disease. In *Gut Peptides: Biochemistry and Physiolgy*, ed. JH Walsh, GJ Dockray, pp. 655–73. New York: Raven
12. Richter-Dahlfors A, Heczko U, Meloche RM, Finlay BB, Buchan AM. 1998. *Helicobacter pylori*-infected human antral primary cell cultures: effect on gastrin cell function. *Am. J. Physiol. Gastrointest. Liver Physiol.* 275:G393–G401
13. Lehmann FS, Golodner EH, Wang J, Chen MCY, Avedian D, et al. 1996. Mononuclear cells and cytokines stimulate gastrin release from canine antral cells in primary culture. *Am. J. Physiol. Gastrointest. Liver Physiol.* 270:G783–G88
14. Beales I, Blaser MJ, Srinivasan S, Calam J, Perez-Perez GI, et al. 1997. Effect of *Helicobacter pylori* products and recombinant

cytokines on gastrin release from cultured canine G cells. *Gastroenterology* 113:465–71

15. Brand SJ, Stone DL. 1988. Reciprocal regulation of antral gastrin and somatostatin gene expression by omeprazole-induced achlorhydria. *J. Clin. Invest.* 82:1059–66

16. Larsson H, Carlsson E, Mattsson H, Lundell L, Sundler F, et al. 1986. Plasma gastrin and gastric enterochromaffinlike cell activation and proliferation: studies with omeprazole and randitidine in intact and antrectomized rats. *Gastroenterology* 90:391–99

17. Wu SV, Giraud A, Mogard M, Sunii K, Walsh JH. 1990. Effects of inhibition of gastric secretion on antral gastrin and somatostatin gene expression in rats. *Am. J. Physiol. Gastrointest. Liver Physiol.* 258:G788–G93

18. Bate GW, Varro A, Dimaline R, Dockray GJ. 1996. Control of preprogastrin messenger RNA translation by gastric acid in the rat. *Gastroenterology* 111:1224–29

19. Merchant JL, Demediuk B, Brand SJ. 1991. A GC-rich element confers epidermal growth factor responsiveness to transcription from the gastrin promoter. *Mol. Cell Biol.* 11:2686–96

20. Ford MG, Valle JD, Soroka CJ, Merchant JL. 1997. EGF receptor activation stimulates endogenous gastrin gene expression in canine G cells and human gastric cell cultures. *J. Clin. Invest.* 99:2762–71

21. Nakata H, Wang S-L, Chung DC, Westwick JK, Tillotson LG. 1998. Oncogenic ras induces gastrin gene expression in colon cancer. *Gastroenterology* 115:1144–53

22. Merchant JL, Du M, Todisco A. 1999. Sp1 phosphorylation by Erk 2 stimulates DNA binding. *Biochem. Biophys. Res. Commun.* 254:454–61

23. Merchant JL, Iyer GR, Taylor BR, Kitchen JR, Mortensen ER, et al. 1996. ZBP-89, a Kruppel-like zinc finger protein, inhibits epidermal growth factor induction of the gastrin promoter. *Mol. Cell Biol.* 16:6644–53

24. Tillotson LG. 1999. RIN ZF, a novel zinc finger gene, encodes proteins that bind to the CACC element of the gastrin promoter. *J. Biol. Chem.* 274:8123–28

24a. Koh TJ, Bulitta CJ, Fleming JV, Dockray GJ, Varro A, Wang TC. 2000. Gastrin is a target of the beta-catenin/TCF-4 growth-signaling pathway in a model of intestinal polyposis. *J. Clin. Invest.* 106:533–39

25. Brand SJ, Klarlund J, Schwartz TW, Rehfeld JF. 1984. Biosynthesis of tyrosine *O*-sulfated gastrins in rat antral mucosa. *J. Biol. Chem.* 259:13246–52

26. Varro A, Henry J, Vaillant C, Dockray GJ. 1994. Discrimination between temperature- and brefeldin A-sensitive steps in the sulfation, phosphorylation, and cleavage of progastrin and its derivatives. *J. Biol. Chem.* 269:20764–70

27. Varro A, Voronina S, Dockray GJ. 1995. Pathways of processing of the gastrin precursor in rat antral mucosa. *J. Clin. Invest.* 95:1642–49

28. Nemeth J, Taylor B, Pauwels S, Varro A, Dockray GJ. 1993. Identification of progastrin derived peptides in colorectal carcinoma extracts. *Gut* 34:90–95

29. Ciccotosto GD, McLeish A, Hardy KJ, Shulkes A. 1995. Expression, processing, and secretion of gastrin in patients with colorectal carcinoma. *Gastroenterology* 109:1142–53

30. Kochman ML, Delvalle J, Dickinson CJ, Boland CR. 1992. Post-translational processing of gastrin in neoplastic human colonic tissue. *Biochem. Biophys. Res. Comm.* 189:1165–69

31. Varro A, Dockray GJ, Bate GW, Vaillant C, Higham A, et al. 1997. Gastrin biosynthesis in the antrum of patients with pernicious anemia. *Gastroenterology* 112:733–41

32. Macro JA, Bate GW, Varro A, Vaillant C, Seidah NG, et al. 1997. Regulation by

gastric acid of the processing of progastrin-derived peptides in rat antral mucosa. *J. Physiol.* 502:409–19

33. Wang TC, Dangler CA, Chen D, Goldenring JR, Koh TJ, et al. 2000. Synergistic interaction between hypergastrinemia and *Helicobacter* infection in a mouse model of gastric cancer. *Gastroenterology* 118:36–47

34. Bishop L, Dimaline R, Blackmore C, Deavall D, Dockray GJ, Varro A. 1998. Modulation of the cleavage of the gastrin precursor by phosphorylation. *Gastroenterology* 115:1154–62

35. Voronina S, Henry J, Vaillant C, Dockray GJ, Varro A. 1997. Amine precursor uptake and decarboxylation: significance for processing of the rat gastrin precursor. *J. Physiol.* 501:363–74

36. Bundgaard JR, Vuust J, Rehfeld JF. 1997. New consensus features for tyrosine O-sulfation determined by mutational analysis. *J. Biol. Chem.* 272:21700–5

37. Scopsi L, Gullo M, Rilke F, Martin S, Steiner DF. 1995. Proprotein convertases (PC1/PC3 and PC2) in normal and neoplastic human tissues: their use as markers of neuroendocrine differentiation. *J. Clin. Endocrinol. Metab.* 80:294–301

38. Dickinson CJ, Sawada M, Guo YJ, Finniss S, Yamada T. 1995. Specificity of prohormone convertase endoproteolysis of progastrin in AtT-20 cells. *J. Clin. Invest.* 96:1425–31

39. Udupi V, Gomez P, Song L, Varlamov O, Reed JT, et al. 1997. Effect of carboxypeptidase E deficiency on progastrin processing and gastrin messenger ribonucleic acid expression in mice with the fat mutation. *Endocrinology* 138:1959–63

40. Lacourse KA, Friis-Hansen L, Rehfeld JF, Samuelson LC. 1997. Disturbed progastrin processing in carboxypeptidase E-deficient fat mice. *FEBS Lett.* 416:45–50

41. Friis-Hansen L, Rehfeld JF. 2000. Impaired feedback of gastric functions in carboxypeptidase E-deficient mice. *Biochem. Biophys. Res. Commun.* 267:638–42

42. Bundgaard JR, Vuust J, Rehfeld JF. 1995. Tyrosine O-sulfation promotes proteolytic processing of progastrin. *EMBO J.* 14:3073–79

43. Mellman I, Fuchs R, Helenius A. 1986. Acidification of the endocytic and exocytic pathways. *Annu. Rev. Biochem.* 55:663–700

44. Blackmore CG, Bishop LA, Dimaline R, Varro A, Gallacher DV, Dockray GJ. 1999. Vesicular monoamine transporter type-2 modulation of intravesicular pH detected by green fluorescent protein *J. Physiol.* 520:13P–14

45. Hussain I, Bate GW, Henry J, Djali PK, Dimaline R, et al. 1999. Identification of vesicular monoamine transporter type 1 (VMAT1) in G-cells and its role in modulating cleavage of G34. *J. Physiol.* 517:495–505

46. Walsh JH, Isenberg JI, Ansfield J, Maxwell V. 1976. Clearance and acid-stimulating action of human big and little gastrins in duodenal ulcer subjects. *J. Clin. Invest.* 57:1125–31

47. Langhans N, Rindi G, Chiu M, Rehfeld JF, Ardman B, et al. 1997. Abnormal gastric histology and decreased acid production in cholecystokinin-B/gastrin receptor-deficient mice. *Gastroenterology* 112:280–86

48. Nagata A, Ito M, Iwata N, Kuno J, Takano H, et al. 1996. G protein-coupled cholecystokinin-B/gastrin receptors are responsible for physiological cell growth of the stomach mucosa in vivo. *Proc. Natl. Acad. Sci. USA* 93:11825–30

49. Chen D, Wang TC, Dockray GJ, Varro A, Zhao CM, et al. 2000. Glycine-extended gastrin synergizes with gastrin 17 to stimulate acid secretion in gastrin deficient mice. *Gastroenterology* 116:A136 (Abstr.)

50. Wang TC, Koh TJ, Varro A, Cahill RJ, Dangler CA, et al. 1996. Processing and

proliferative effects of human progastrin in transgenic mice. *J. Clin. Invest.* 98:1918–29

51. Konda Y, Kamimura H, Yokota H, Hayashi N, Sugano K, Takeuchi T. 1999. Gastrin stimulates the growth of gastric pit with less-differentiated features. *Am. J. Physiol. Gastrointest. Liver Physiol.* 277:G773–G84

52. Saillan-Barreau C, Clerc P, Adato M, Escrieut C, Vaysse N, et al. 1998. Transgenic CCK-B/gastrin receptor mediates murine exocrine pancreatic secretion. *Gastroenterology* 115:988–96

53. Desbois C, Huerou-Luron IL, Dufresne M, Estival A, Clerc P, et al. 1999. The CCKB/gastrin receptor is coupled to the regulation of enzyme secretion, protein synthesis and p70 S6 kinase activity in acinar cells from ElasCCKB transgenic mice. *Eur. J. Biochem.* 266:1003–10

54. Clerc P, Saillan-Barreau C, Desbois C, Wang TC, Dockray GJ, et al. 1999. Transgenic CCK-B/G receptor alters pancreatic proliferation and differentiation. *Digestion* 60:611

55. Kitano M, Norlen P, Hakanson R. 2000. Gastric submucosal microdialysis: a method to study gas. *Regul. Pept.* 86:113–23

56. Zeng N, Walsh JH, Kang T, Helander KG, Helander HF, Sachs G. 1996. Selective ligand-induced intracellular calcium changes in a population of rat isolated gastric endocrine cells. *Gastroenterology* 110:1835–46

57. Sachs G, Zeng N, Prinz C. 1997. Physiology of isolated gastric endocrine cells. *Annu. Rev. Physiol.* 59:243–56

58. Prinz C, Zanner R, Gerhard M, Mahr S, Neumayer N, et al. 1999. The mechanism of histamine secretion from gastric enterochromaffin-like cells. *Am. J. Physiol. Cell Physiol.* 277:C845–C55

59. Dimaline R, Sandvik AK, Evans D, Forster ER, Dockray GJ. 1993. Food stimulation of histidine decarboxylase messenger RNA abundance in rat gastric fundus. *J. Physiol.* 465:449–58

60. Ohning GV, Song M, Wong HC, Wu SV, Walsh JH. 1998. Immunolocalization of gastrin-dependent histidine decarboxylase activity in rat gastric mucosa during feeding. *Am. J. Physiol. Gastrointest. Liver Physiol.* 275:G660–G67

61. Chen D, Zhao CM, Yamada H, Norlen P, Hakanson R. 1998. Novel aspects of gastrin-induced activation of histidine decarboxylase in rat stomach ECL cells. *Regul. Pept.* 77:169–75

62. Fleming JV, Wang TC. 2000. Amino- and carboxy-terminal PEST domains mediate gastrin stabilization of rat L-histidine decarboxylase isoforms. *Mol. Cell Biol.* 20:4932–47

63. Dimaline R, Evans D, Forster ER, Sandvik AK, Dockray GJ. 1993. Control of gastric corpus chromogranin A messenger RNA abundance in the rat. *Am. J. Physiol. Gastrointest. Liver Physiol.* 264:G583–G88 ·

64. Dimaline R, Struthers J. 1996. Expression and regulation of a vesicular monoamine transporter (VMAT2) in rat stomach: a putative histamine transporter. *J. Physiol.* 490:249–56

65. Raychowdhury R, Zhang Z, Hocker M, Wang TC. 1999. Activation of human histidine decarboxylase gene promoter activity by gastrin is mediated by two distinct nuclear factors. *J. Biol. Chem.* 274:20961–69

66. Zhang Z, Hocker M, Koh TJ, Wang TC. 1996. The human histidine decarboxylase promoter is regulated by gastrin and phorbol 12-myristate 13-acetate through a downstream *cis*-acting element. *J. Biol. Chem.* 271:14188–97

67. Hocker M, Zhang Z, Merchant JL, Wang TC. 1997. Gastrin regulates the human histidine decarboxylase promoter through an AP-1 dependent mechanism. *Am. J. Physiol. Gastrointest. Liver Physiol.* 272:G822–G30

68. Hocker M, Henihan RJ, Rosewicz S, Riecken EO, Zhang Z, et al. 1997.

Gastrin and phorbol 12-myristate 13-acetate regulate the human histidine decarboxylase promoter through Raf-dependent activation of extracellular signal-regulated kinase-related signaling pathways in gastric cancer cells. *J. Biol. Chem.* 272:27015–24

69. Hocker M, Raychowdhury R, Plath T, Wu H, O'Connor DT, et al. 1998. Sp 1 and CREB mediate gastrin-dependent regulation of chromogranin A promoter activity in gastric carcinoma cells. *J. Biol. Chem.* 273:34000–7

70. Watson F, Deavall DG, Macro JA, Kiernan R, Dimaline R. 1999. Transcriptional activation of vesicular monoamine transporter 2 in the pre-B cell line Ea3.123. *Biochem. J.* 337:193–99

71. Urushidani T, Forte JG. 1997. Signal transduction and activation of acid secretion in the parietal cell. *J. Membr. Biol.* 159:99–111

72. Takeuchi Y, Yamada J, Yamada T, Todisco A. 1997. Functional role of extracellular signal-regulated protein kinases in gastric acid secretion. *Am. J. Physiol. Gastrointest. Liver Physiol.* 273:G1263–G72

73. Kinoshita Y, Nakata H, Kishi K, Kawanami C, Sawada M, Chiba T. 1998. Comparison of the signal transduction pathways activated by gastrin in enterochromaffin-like and parietal cells. *Gastroenterology* 115:93–100

74. Campbell VW, Yamada T. 1989. Acid secretagogue-induced stimulation of gastric parietal cell gene expression. *J. Biol. Chem.* 264:11381–86

75. Kaise M, Muraoka A, Yamada J, Yamada T. 1995. Epidermal growth factor induces H^+, K^+-ATPase alpha-subunit gene expression through an element homologous to the $3'$ half-site of the c-fos serum response element. *J. Biol. Chem.* 270:18637–42

76. Tari A, Yamamoto G, Yonei Y, Sumii M, Sumii K, et al. 1994. Effect of histamine on rat gastric H(+)-K(+)-ATPase alpha-subunit expression. *Am. J. Physiol. Gastrointest. Liver Physiol.* 266:G444–G50

77. Johnson LR. 1988. Regulation of gastrointestinal mucosal growth. *Physiol. Rev.* 68:456–502

78. Thorburn CM, Friedman GD, Dickinson CJ, Vogelman JH, Orentreich N, Parsonnet J. 1998. Gastrin and colorectal cancer: a prospective study. *Gastroenterology* 115:275–80

79. Hansen S, Vollset SE, Ardill JES, El-Omar E, Melby K, et al. 1997. Hypergastrinaemia is a strong predicator of distal gastric adenocarcinoma among *Helicobacter pylori* infected persons. *Gastroenterology* 112:A575 (Abstr.)

80. Ohning GV, Wong HC, Lloyd KCK, Walsh JH. 1996. Gastrin mediates the gastric mucosal proliferative response to feeding. *Am. J. Physiol. Gastrointest. Liver Physiol.* 271:G470–76

81. Mahr S, Neumayer N, Kolb HJ, Schepp W, Classen M, Prinz C. 1998. Growth factor effects on apoptosis of rat gastric enterochromaffin-like cells. *Endocrinology* 139:4380–90

82. Ryberg B, Tielemans Y, Axelson J, Carlsson E, Hakanson R, Mattsson H, et al. 1990. Gastrin stimulates the self-replication rate of enterochromaffinlike cells in the rat stomach: effects of omeprazole, ranitidine and gastrin-17 in intact and antrectomized rats. *Gastroenterology* 99:935–42

83. Bordi C, D'Adda T, Azzoni C, Ferraro G. 1998. Pathogenesis of ECL cell tumors in humans. *Yale J. Biol. Med.* 71:273–84

84. Delle FG, Helander H, Holt S, Modlin IM, Powers R, et al. 1994. Acid suppression and gastric mucosal cell biology. *Dig. Dis. Sci.* 39:1843–52

85. Lamberts R, Creutzfeldt W, Struber HG, Brunner G, Solcia E. 1993. Long term omeprazole therapy in peptic ulcer disease: gastrin, endocrine cell growth and gastritis. *Gastroenterology* 104:1356–70

86. Modlin IM, Tang LH. 1996. The gastric

enterochromaffin-like cell: an enigmatic cellular link. *Gastroenterology* 111:783–810

87. Schaffer K, McBride EW, Beinborn M, Kopin AS. 1998. Interspecies polymorphisms confer constitutive activity to the mastomys cholecystokinin-B/gastrin receptor. *J. Biol. Chem.* 273:28779–84

88. Dabrowski A, Detjen KM, Logsdon CD, Williams JA. 1997. Stimulation of both CCK-A and CCK-B receptors activates MAP kinases in AR42J and receptor-transfected CHO cells. *Digestion* 58:361–67

89. Stepan VM, Tatewaki M, Matsushima M, Dickinson CJ, del Valle J, Todisco A. 1999. Gastrin induces c-*fos* gene transcription via multiple signaling pathways. *Am. J. Physiol. Gastrointest. Liver Physiol.* 276:G415–24

90. Stepan VM, Dickinson CJ, del Valle J, Matsushima M, Todisco A. 1999. Cell type-specific requirement of the MAPK pathway for the growth factor action of gastrin. *Am. J. Physiol. Gastrointest. Liver Physiol.* 276:G1363–G72

91. Daulhac L, Kowalski-Chauvel A, Pradayrol L, Vaysse N, Seva C. 1997. Ca2+ and protein kinase C-dependent mechanisms involved in gastrin-induced Shc/Grb2 complex formation and P44-mitogen-activated protein kinase activation. *Biochem. J.* 325:383–89

92. Daulhac L, Kowalski-Chauvel A, Pradayrol L, Vaysse N, Seva C. 1999. Src-family tyrosine kinases in activation of ERK-1 and p85/p110-phosphatidylinositol 3-kinase by G/CCKB receptors. *J. Biol. Chem.* 274:20657–63

93. Akagi K, Nagao T, Urushidani T. 1999. Correlation between Ca(2+) oscillation and cell proliferation via CCK(B)/gastrin receptor. *Biochim. Biophys. Acta* 1452:243–53

94. Detjen K, Yule D, Tseng MJ, Williams JA, Logsdon CD. 1997. CCK-B receptors produce similar signals but have opposite growth effects in CHO and Swiss 3T3 cells. *Am. J. Physiol. Cell Physiol.* 273:C1449–C57

95. Varro A, Wroblewski L, Noble P-J, Bishop L, Ashcroft F, et al. 2000. Gastrin inhibits proliferation and promotes differentiation of AGS cells. *Gut* 46:A56 (Abstr.)

96. Detjen K, Fenrich MC, Logsdon CD. 1997. Transfected cholecystokinin receptors mediate growth inhibitory effects on human pancreatic cancer cell lines. *Gastroenterology* 112:952–59

97. Koh TJ, Dockray GJ, Varro A, Cahill RJ, Dangler CA, et al. 1999. Overexpression of glycine-extended gastrin in transgenic mice results in increased colonic proliferation. *J. Clin. Invest.* 103:1119–26

98. Singh P, Velasco M, Given R, Wargovich M, Varro A, Wang TC. 2000. Mice overexpressing progastrin are predisposed for developing aberrant colonic crypt foci in response to AOM. *Am. J. Physiol. Gastrointest. Liver Physiol.* 278:G390–G99

99. Singh P, Velasco M, Given R, Varro A, Wang TC. 2000. Progastrin expression predisposes mice to development of colon carcinomas and adenomas in response to AOM. *Gastroenterology* 119:162–71

100. Seva C, Dickinson CJ, Yamada T. 1994. Growth-promoting effects of glycine-extended progastrin. *Science* 265:410–12

101. Stepan VM, Krametter DF, Matsushima M, Todisco A, Delvalle J, Dickinson CJ. 1999. Glycine-extended gastrin regulates HEK cell growth. *Am. J. Physiol. Regulatory Integrative Comp. Physiol.* 277:R572–R81

102. Stepan VM, Sawada M, Todisco A, Dickinson CJ. 1999. Glycine-extended gastrin exerts growth-promoting effects on human colon cancer cells. *Mol. Med.* 5:147–59

103. Iwase K, Evers BM, Hellmich MR, Guo Y-S, Higashide S, et al. 1997. Regulation of growth of human gastric cancer by

gastrin and glycine-extended progastrin. *Gastroenterology* 113:782–90

104. Hollande F, Imdahl A, Mantamadiotis T, Ciccotosto GD, Shulkes A, Baldwin GS. 1997. Glycine-extended gastrin acts as an autocrine growth factor in a nontransformed colon cell line. *Gastroenterology* 113:1576–88

105. Artru P, Attoub S, Levasseur S, Lewin MJ, Bado A. 1998. Gastrin-17 and G17-gly induce proliferation of LoVo cells through the CCK B/gastrin receptor. *Gastroenterol. Clin. Biol.* 22:607–12

106. Singh P, Owlia A, Varro A, Dai B, Rajaraman S, Wood T. 1996. Gastrin gene expression is required for the proliferation and tumorigenicity of human colon cancer cells. *Cancer Res.* 56:4111–15

107. Baldwin GS, Shulkes A. 1998. Gastrin, gastrin receptors and colorectal carcinoma. *Gut* 42:581–84

108. Kowalski-Chauvel A, Pradayrol L, Vaysse N, Seva C. 1997. Tyrosine phosphorylation of insulin receptor substrate-1 and activation of the PI-3-kinase pathway by glycine-extended gastrin precursors. *Biochem. Biophys. Res. Commun.* 236:687–92

109. Higashide S, Gomez G, Greeley GH, Townsend CM, Thompson JC. 1996. Glycine-extended gastrin potentiates gastrin-stimulated gastric acid secretion in rats. *Am. J. Physiol. Gastrointest. Liver Physiol.* 270:G220–G24

110. Kaise M, Muraoka A, Seva C, Takeda H, Dickinson CJ, Yamada T. 1995. Glycine-extended progastrin processing intermediates induced H^+, K^+-ATPase α-subunit gene expression through a novel receptor. *J. Biol. Chem.* 270:11155–60

111. Li Q, Karam SM, Gordon JI. 1996. Diphtheria toxin-mediated ablation of parietal cells in the stomach of transgenic mice. *J. Biol. Chem.* 271:3671–76

112. Li Q, Karam SM, Coerver KA, Matzuk MM, Gordon JI. 1998. Stimulation of

activin receptor II signalling pathways inhibits differentiation of multiple gastric epithelial lineages. *Mol. Endocrinol.* 12:181–92

113. Li S, Wang Q, Chakladar A, Bronson RT, Bernards A. 2000. Gastric hyperplasia in mice lacking the putative Cdc42 effector IQGAP1. *Mol. Cell Biol.* 20:697–701

114. Lefebvre O, Chenard MP, Masson R, Linares J, Dierich A, et al. 1996. Gastric mucosa abnormalities and tumorigenesis in mice lacking the pS2 trefoil protein. *Science* 274:259–62

115. Dempsey PJ, Goldenring JR, Soroka CJ, Modlin IM, McClure RW, et al. 1992. Possible role of transforming growth factor α in the pathogenesis of Menetrier's disease: supportive evidence from humans and transgenic mice. *Gastroenterology* 103:1950–63

116. Sharp R, Babyatsky MW, Takagi H, Tagerud S, Wang TC, et al. 1995. Transforming growth factor α disrupts the normal program of cellular differentiation in the gastric mucosa of transgenic mice. *Development* 121:149–61

117. Schultheis PJ, Clarke LL, Meneton P, Harline M, Boivin GP, et al. 1998. Targeted disruption of the murine Na^+/H^+ exchanger isoform 2 gene causes reduced viability of gastric parietal cells and loss of net acid secretion. *J. Clin. Invest.* 101:1243–53

118. Wang TC, Goldenring JR, Dangler C, Ito S, Mueller A, et al. 1998. Mice lacking secretory phospholipase A2 show altered apoptosis and differentiation with *Helicobacter felis* infection. *Gastroenterology* 114:675–89

119. Courtois-Coutry N, Roush D, Rajendran V, McCarthy JB, Geibel J, et al. 1997. A tyrosine-based signal targets H/K-ATPase to a regulated compartment and is required for the cessation of gastric acid secretion. *Cell* 90:501–10

120. Black JW, Shankley NP. 1987. How does

gastrin act to stimulate oxyntic cell secretion? *Trends Physiol. Sci.* 8:486–90

121. Zavros Y, Shulkes A. 1997. Cholecystokinin (CCK) regulates somatostatin secretion through both the CCK-A and CCK-B/gastrin receptors in sheep. *J. Physiol.* 505:811–21

122. Tsutsui S, Shinomura Y, Higashiyama S, Higashimoto Y, Miyazaki Y, et al. 1997. Induction of heparin binding epidermal growth factor-like growth factor and amphiregulin mRNAs by gastrin in the rat stomach. *Biochem. Biophys. Res. Commun.* 235:520–23

123. McLaughlin JT, Koh TJ, Wang TC. 1999. Gastrin activates the human heparin binding-EGF promoter via a PKC/MAP kinsase-dependent pathway in AGS cells. *Gastroenterology* 116:A626 (Abstr.)

124. Miyazaki Y, Shinomura Y, Tsutsui S, Zuchi S, Higashimoto Y, et al. 1999. Gastrin induces heparin-binding epidermal growth factor-like growth factor in rat gastric epithelial cells transfected with gastrin receptor. *Gastroenterology* 116:78–89

125. Murayama Y, Miyagawa J, Higashiyama S, Kondo S, Yabu M, et al. 1995. Localization of heparin-binding epidermal growth factor-like growth factor in human gastric mucosa. *Gastroenterology* 109:1051–59

126. Asahara M, Mushiake S, Shimada S, Fukui H, Kinoshita Y, et al. 1996. Reg gene expression is increased in rat gastric enterochromaffin- like cells following water immersion stress. *Gastroenterology* 111:45–55

127. Higham AD, Bishop LA, Dimaline R, Blackmore CG, Dobbins AC, et al. 1999. Mutations of Reg alpha are associated with enterochromaffin-like cell tumor development in patients with hypergastrinemia. *Gastroenterology* 116:1310–18

128. Fukui H, Kinoshita Y, Maekawa T, Okada A, Waki S, et al. 1998. Regenerating gene protein may mediate gastric mucosal proliferation induced by hypergastrinemia in rats. *Gastroenterology* 115:1483–93

129. Kobayashi S, Akiyama T, Nata K, Abe M, Tajima M, et al. 2000. Identification of a receptor for Reg (regenerating gene) protein, a pancreatic beta-cell regeneration factor. *J. Biol. Chem.* 275:10723–26

130. Arai T, Akiyama Y, Nagasaki H, Murase N, Okabe S, et al. 1999. EXTL3/EXTR1 alterations in colorectal cancer cell lines. *Int. J. Oncol.* 15:915–19

Annu. Rev. Physiol. 2001. 63:141–64

CONTROL OF GROWTH BY THE SOMATROPIC AXIS: Growth Hormone and the Insulin-Like Growth Factors Have Related and Independent Roles[1]

Andrew A. Butler

The Vollum Institute for Advanced Biomedical Research, Oregon Health Sciences University, Portland Oregon 97201-3098; e-mail: butlera@ohsu.edu

Derek Le Roith

Clinical Endocrinology Branch, NIDDK, National Institutes of Health, Bethesda Maryland 20892-1758; e-mail: derek@helix.nih.gov

Key Words conditional knockouts, somatomedin hypothesis, cell proliferation

■ **Abstract** The traditionally accepted theory has been that most of the biological effects of growth hormone (GH) are mediated by circulating (endocrine) insulin-like growth factor-I (IGF-I). This dogma was modified when it was discovered that most tissues express IGF-I that can act via an autocrine/paracrine fashion. In addition, both GH and IGF-I had independent effects on various target tissues. Using tissue-specific gene deletion of IGF-I in the liver, it has been shown that circulating IGF-I is predominantly liver-derived but is not essential for normal postnatal growth. Therefore, it is proposed that non-hepatic tissue-derived IGF-I may be sufficient for growth and development. Thus the original somatomedin hypothesis has undergone further modifications.

INTRODUCTION

The last decades of the 20th century witnessed remarkable developments in our understanding of the basic biology of growth and development. These achievements were made possible by combining traditional cell biology with newly developed molecular tools. Development is a broad term that covers many different processes. At its most basic level, development involves the coordinated regulation of cell proliferation, cell death (apoptosis), cell migration, and differentiation. Growth must also involve the integration of the intrinsic genetic programs

---

[1] The US Government has the right to retain a nonexclusive, royalty-free license in and to any copyright covering this paper.

141

with environmental cues. The specific environmental signals may vary from organism to organism; however, most if not all multicellular complex organisms must coordinate growth with variations in nutrition. This is requisite for the fetus as well as the juvenile because maternal nutrition can also vary considerably. Thus the endocrine and autocrine/paracrine factors that control growth must respond to multiple signals and adapt when environmental conditions are not optimal.

The regulation of growth hormone (GH) secretion and its action at target tissues is believed to be the most fundamental determinant of body size. While other growth factors have been discovered, GH seems to fit the role of the primary growth hormone. GH is regulated by nutrition and by the hormonal and genetic milieu that controls the timing and rate of growth. The most significant effects of GH are postnatal; there are little or no effects of GH on regulation of fetal growth. Many of the effects of GH on growth and metabolism are actually mediated indirectly via control of the synthesis of other growth factors. Of these, the insulin-like growth factors (IGFs) are generally considered to be the most important. The insulin-like growth factor system consists of a diverse family of ligands, receptors, and soluble binding proteins. Although the IGF system was originally characterized as an intermediate of GH action, this system is ubiquitous and is frequently involved in regulation of cellular processes that are completely independent of GH. For example, in distinct contrast to GH, the IGFs are essential for normal fetal development. Thus the IGF and, to a lesser degree, the GH systems are highly decentralized. A far more complicated model involving autocrine/paracrine roles for both GH and the IGF systems has largely replaced old concepts of a simple, top-down system with GH at the apex.

GROWTH HORMONE AND THE GROWTH HORMONE RECEPTOR

Growth Hormone

GH and the GH receptor (GHR) belong to the large family of cytokine peptides and their receptors (1–5). The pattern of GH release from somatotroph cells located in the anterior pituitary gland is at least as important in determining growth rate than in the basal GH levels. In the male rat, GH secretion occurs in discrete pulses with low interpeak levels. In contrast, secretion of GH in the female rat exhibits less pulsatility and relatively high interpeak levels (6–8). A similar sexually dimorphic pattern of GH release also occurs in humans (9). In all species studied, serum IGF-I levels and growth rates correlate with the peak amplitude of GH and not with concentrations between pulses. In addition, intermittent infusion to rodents of GH is a more potent stimulus of growth rate than is continuous infusion (10, 11). Continuous versus intermittent stimulation of the GHR in liver may explain the sex-specific pattern in the expression of liver enzymes such as isoforms of cytochrome P-450 (12, 13). In addition to the pituitary, GH is produced in brain, lymphocytes, placenta, mammary tissue, and pineal gland. These findings suggest that GH has local paracrine/autocrine effects possibly distinct from its classic effects that are mediated by circulating IGF-I. These local paracrine/autocrine effects may result either from local production of IGF-I or from other factors (14).

Two hypothalamic factors, growth hormone-releasing hormone (GHRH) (15, 16) and the inhibitory hormone somatostatin (17), interact to regulate GH secretion from pituitary somatotrophs. In addition to GHRH and somatostatin, other factors that influence GH release include free fatty acids, leptin, and neuropeptide Y (18, 19). These factors appear to coordinate the metabolic status of the organism with GH secretion. The direct action of free fatty acids on the pituitary to inhibit GH release is postulated to complete a feedback loop since GH stimulates lipid mobilization (20, 21). The adipostat hormone leptin stimulates GH secretion in rodents at the level of the hypothalamus by regulating GHRH and somatostatin activity (22–24). The effect of leptin on GH secretion in the rodent may also involve neuropeptide Y because leptin suppresses expression of this peptide. Further, infusion of neuropeptide Y suppresses GH secretion (25, 26). Leptin can attenuate the decline in GH levels during starvation in rodents; however, the human clinical significance of this observation is unclear, as the regulation of GH synthesis and release by nutrition exhibits marked species specificity. Although they display a reduced response to GH-stimulation tests, homozygous leptin-deficient humans have circulating GH levels in the normal range and are normal in height; a similar defect occurs in obese children (27).

Both hypothalamic and peripheral factors appear to be important for controlling GH release and action. Hexarelin, a synthetic hexapeptide, belongs to a family of GH-releasing peptides (e.g. GHRP-1, GHRP-2, GRH-6) (28). A G protein–coupled receptor expressed in the pituitary is activated by the small synthetic growth hormone secretagogue (GHS-R) (18). Cloning of the GHS-R has led to the isolation of the 28 residue peptide Ghrelin from stomach extracts (29). Ghrelin mRNA and immunoreactivity are expressed at high levels in endocrine cells of the stomach and at lower levels in the arcuate nucleus of the hypothalamus. Circulating levels of ghrelin in the plasma are relatively high (around 120 fmol/ml). Somatostatin analogues, such as octreotide and lanreotide, are useful in the treatment of the GH-hypersecretion disorder acromegaly (30). In addition to suppressing GH secretion, octreotide also inhibits the stimulation of longitudinal growth, supresses expression of hepatic IGF-I mRNA, and lowers serum IGF-I levels in GH-deficient rats treated with exogenous GH (31, 32). Indeed, the general antiproliferative activity of somatostatin analogs, which is mediated at least in part through inhibition of the GH/IGF-I system, has led to the investigation of these agents as antineoplastic agents (33). A potential mechanism for the antiproliferative effects of somatostatin in peripheral tissues may be the stimulation of tyrosine phosphatase activity (34, 35).

States such as malnutrition, in which glucocorticoid levels are elevated, are associated with general resistance to the stimulatory effects of GH on growth and on serum IGF-I levels (36). In hypophysectomized rats, dexamethasone treatment inhibits the stimulation by GH of IGF-I mRNA levels in liver and other tissues (37), and that effect is probably mediated by glucocorticoid receptors.

Dexamethasone also inhibits GH-induced expression of IGF-I mRNA in primary cultures of hepatocytes (38) and in cultured chondrocytes (39). Given the inhibitory effect of glucocorticoids on GH action, it was unexpected that the maturation of the somatotropic axis in the fetus requires the surge in glucocorticoids observed in late gestation (40).

Growth Hormone Receptor

GHR, the first member of the Type I cytokine receptor family to be cloned, shares a single transmembrane domain structure with other receptors that include the prolactin receptor, the interleukin receptor, and colony-stimulating factor receptor (3). Post-transcriptional and post-translational mechanisms produce two forms of the GHR that differ in the length of the intracellular domain. In rats and mice, a soluble GH-binding protein (GHBP), composed of the GHR extracellular ligand-binding domain, is produced by alternate splicing of the GHR hmRNA (41). A truncated human GHR mRNA encodes a membrane-bound receptor lacking 98% of its cytoplasmic domain (42). Cells transfected with truncated cDNA produce soluble GHBP more efficiently than cells transfected with full-length GHR cDNAs. Rats and rabbits also express this transcript (42), suggesting that proteolysis of membrane-bound truncated GHR is a common mechanism for producing GHBP. In primates, both mechanisms (i.e. proteolysis and alternate splicing) are utilized (43). The primary function of circulating GHBP is to act as a physiological buffer, stabilizing GH levels by extending its half-life in the circulation (44).

The Physiological Effects of Growth Hormone

GH is an anabolic hormone that induces positive nitrogen balance in intact animals and protein synthesis in muscle (45). At all ages, treatment of humans with human GH increases muscle size in GH-deficient individuals (45). Growth hormone enhances amino acid uptake into skeletal muscle, suggesting that this tissue is a primary target of the physiological effects of GH (45). However, other tissues may be important in the effect of GH on nitrogen balance. Furthermore, the effects of GH on nitrogen balance may or may not be mediated by IGF-I. GH therapy increases whole body protein synthesis (46) and enhances nitrogen retention, concomitant with the increase in lean body mass (47). To determine whether the effects of GH on protein synthesis in muscle require IGF-I, the metabolic effects of GH, IGF-I and insulin were compared by infusing these factors into the forearms of human volunteers in whom systemic amino acid levels were held constant. All three factors enhanced phenylalanine balance. The uptake of phenylalanine was increased by GH and IGF-I, whereas phenylalanine release was inhibited by IGF-I and insulin, but not by GH (48). These studies strongly support the hypothesis that many of the anabolic effects of GH in muscle are dependent on IGF-I. On the other hand, IGF-I may have additional effects, such as inhibiting proteolysis. These and other studies imply that the effects of GH are mediated by local production of IGF-I, which acts in an autocrine/paracrine manner.

The long-term effects of GH include a decrease in deposition of fat and an increase in fat mobilization. Growth hormone exerts lipolytic effects on fat and muscle, and circulating free fatty acids and glycerol levels rise following acute administration of GH. This hormone also reduces fat mass, particularly in individuals who have accumulated excess fat during periods of GH deficiency (49). A similar effect occurs in adults treated with recombinant human GH (50), an effect that appears to be mediated by the inhibition of lipoprotein lipase (51, 52). GH administration also causes mild reductions in LDL cholesterol levels and small elevations in HDL cholesterol (53).

Acute administration in vitro of GH to fat and other tissue explants causes a temporary insulin-like effect on glucose uptake. In contrast, chronic GH treatment causes insulin resistance associated with hyperinsulinemia and a postreceptor defect in insulin signaling (54). The acute insulin-like effects of GH on carbohydrate metabolism are most likely independent of both IGF-I and insulin because these effects also occur in isolated tissue preparations and in cultured cells (55). The precise mechanism(s) by which GH regulates metabolism are not defined, but GH-induced tyrosine phosphorylation of insulin receptor substrate-1 (IRS-1) and/or IRS-2 may be involved (56). Ultimately, prolonged GH stimulation causes hyperglycemia associated with enhanced hepatic gluconeogenesis and glycogenolysis. These effects may be indirect results of GH-induced lipolysis and of elevated plasma free fatty acids that inhibit insulin activity at its target tissues. This type of lipotoxic effect was first noted by Randle and others and is known as the glucose/fatty acid or Randle cycle (57).

Systemic administration of GH stimulates longitudinal bone growth and skeletal muscle growth, whereas IGF-I treatment preferentially increases the size of lymphoid tissues (spleen and thymus) and kidney (58). Growth hormone causes more robust longitudinal bone growth than IGF-I in animals, and the effects of these factors may be additive (59–61); furthermore, administration of recombinant human GH is more potent than that of recombinant IGF-I in humans (62). Systemic GH administration increases circulating levels of IGF-I, IGF-binding protein-3 (IGFBP-3), and the acid labile subunit (ALS). IGF-I administration, on the other hand, transiently increases circulating levels of IGF-I, inhibits GH secretion and may actually decrease levels of IGFBP-3 and ALS, thereby leading to faster clearance of IGF-I from the circulation. Indeed, this finding led to clinical trials using a complex of IGF-I/IGFBP-3 rather than IGF-I alone. Co-administration of IGFBP-3 with IGF-I to hypophysectomized rats markedly reduces the hypoglycemia associated with IGF-I treatment (63); however, the effects of co-administration of IGFBP-3 on the anabolic actions of IGF-I are variable and show no change or an enhanced effect on growth (63).

Growth hormone regulates the synthesis of IGF-I, IGF-binding proteins (IGF-BPs), and ALS. For example, GH treatment in humans increased serum levels of IGF-I, IGFBP-3, and ALS and reduced levels of IGFBP-1 and IGFBP-2. However, only the promoter for the ALS of the large (150 kDa) ternary IGF:IGFBP-3/5:ALS complex has an identifiable GH-responsive element (64). The tissues in which IGF-I expression correlates most closely with GH levels are the liver, white adipose tissue, and skeletal muscle. The majority of circulating IGF-I is derived from liver, which also has the highest level of ALS mRNA. Interestingly, the mRNAs encoding IGF-I, IGFBP-3, and ALS do not co-localized in the same cells in the liver (65). mRNAs encoding IGF-I and ALS are expressed by hepatocytes, whereas IGFBP-3 mRNA is exclusively expressed in endothelial cells of the hepatic sinusoids. Unlike hepatocytes, sinusoidal endothelial cells of the liver do not express detectable levels of GHR mRNA. Thus the regulation of IGFBP-3 synthesis by GH is probably indirect and may be mediated by IGF-I. Conversely, hepatocytes do not express detectable levels of IGF-I receptor mRNA. Therefore, IGF-I does not appear to act on hepatocytes directly. Thus ALS levels may be controlled directly by GH, whereas IGF-I may regulate IGFBP-3.

THE INSULIN-LIKE GROWTH FACTOR SYSTEM

To date, the IGF family includes three known ligands (IGF-I, IGF-2, and insulin), six characterized binding proteins (IGFBP-1 through -6), and cell surface receptors that mediate the actions of the ligands (IGF-I receptor, insulin receptor, and the IGF-II mannose-6-phosphate receptor) (66–68). IGF-I and IGF-2 share ~50% amino acid identity with insulin, the major structural difference being retention of the C chain that is cleaved from pro-insulin (69–71). The cellular responses to both IGF-I and IGF-2 are mediated by the IGF-I receptor. The effects of insulin are mediated by the insulin receptor, and a subset of alternately spliced insulin receptors also stimulate proliferation in response to IGF-2. The IGF-II/mannose-6-phosphate receptor is not believed to have a major role in IGF signal transduction, but is primarily responsible for clearing IGF-2, thereby reducing the extracellular levels of this hormone during fetal development (72).

There is ~60% overall amino acid identity between the IGF-I and insulin receptors (73). Certain regions are highly homologous, particularly the tyrosine kinase domain, which is ~85% homologous in the two receptors. Both receptors contain α and β subunits; the α subunit is localized entirely in the extracellular region, and the β subunit spans the membrane and is primarily intracellular (74). The receptors assemble in an $\alpha_2\beta_2$ configuration, with ligand binding primarily mediated by the α subunits, which form a binding pocket. The intracellular domains of the β subunits contain the tyrosine kinase activity and tyrosine residues that are phosphorylated upon activation of the receptor.

Unlike insulin, IGFs in the circulation are bound by high-affinity binding proteins (IGFBPs) (66). The identification of six IGFBPs indicates that the IGF system is complex. In the circulation, IGFBPs act as carrier proteins that transport the IGFs to the target tissues and prolong IGF half-lives by protecting them from proteolytic degradation. The major circulating form of IGF is a high molecular weight (~150) complex consisting of the IGFs, IGFBP-3, and ALS (75). Mortensen and colleagues showed that administration of recombinant IGFBP-1 leads to increased secretion of insulin in rats, suggesting that circulating IGFs may inhibit insulin release and thereby impart a tonic glycemic effect (76). As mentioned above, glucocorticoids regulate the somatotropic axis at the level of the GHR. Regulation of IGFBP synthesis by glucocorticoids provides an additional level of regulation of the somatotropic axis. For example, the synthesis of IGFBP-1 in liver, which inhibits IGF action in vivo (77), is stimulated by glucocorticoids.

Although IGFBP-3 was the first IGFBP to be identified in the ternary complex, recent data suggest that IGFBP-5 can complex with IGF and ALS (78). The release of IGFs from these large complexes leads to the formation of smaller complexes with other IGFBPs, complexes that are believed to transport the IGFs out of the circulation. In addition to their roles in the circulation, most target tissues also express IGFBPs, which regulate the local action of IGFs (79). More detailed discussion of the physiological function of IGFBPs is beyond the scope of this review (66, 79, 80).

Physiological Effects of Insulin-Like Growth Factors

Mice carrying null mutations in the IGF-I gene are born small and fail to grow postnatally (72, 81, 82). Mice in which the GH and GHR genes are deleted have almost normal birth weights, strongly supporting GH-independent effects of IGF-I on fetal growth. Plasma IGF-I levels in humans usually correlate with body size. For example, constitutional tall children have elevated plasma IGF-I levels (83). Infusions of recombinant IGF-I also enhances body weight and size in a number of models, further supporting a role for IGF-I in growth (84). Previous studies indicated that GH is most effective in promoting bone growth and that IGF-I is more effective in promoting kidney and spleen growth (58). One interpretation of these findings is that IGF-I functions alone in certain tissues and may mediate the effects of GH in other tissues. The role of IGF-I in ovarian follicular development and uterine growth appears to be independent of GH because mice with GHR gene deletions are fertile, whereas mice with IGF-I gene-deletions are infertile (85). Furthermore, humans with Laron dwarfism, GH receptor mutations, and GH resistance are fertile (86). GH also increases the levels of certain IGFBPs. Thus the higher potency of GH, compared with IGF-I, might be due to the fact that GH simultaneously stimulates the synthesis of IGF-I and facilitates IGF-I action via modification of the overall IGFBP profile.

IGF-I and insulin have both shared and unique actions. Administration of IGF-I increases whole body protein metabolism by increasing protein synthesis and inhibiting proteolysis (48, 87). These actions are distinct from the metabolic effects of insulin, which are primarily from inhibition of proteolysis. This evidence strongly suggests that IGF-I functions in muscle via the IGF-I receptor and not via the insulin receptor. However, IGF-I also enhances the uptake of glucose into peripheral tissues, an insulin-like effect (88). The effect on glucose uptake could conceivably be mediated either by IGF-I or by insulin receptors. Hybrid IGF-I/insulin receptors exist, although the function of such hybrid receptors is unclear.

Interestingly, the incidence of hybrid receptors is increased in states of insulin-resistance, and glucose levels may regulate hybrid formation. In patients with poorly controlled type 1 diabetes mellitus, levels of circulating IGF-I are low and those of GH are elevated. Administration of recombinant IGF-I often restores the high levels of GH to normal, thereby leading to improved insulin sensitivity and enhanced glucose uptake in peripheral tissues (90). In patients with type 2 diabetes mellitus, who are usually insulin-resistant, IGF-I therapy leads to some improvement, primarily from enhanced muscle glucose uptake (91–94). Whether this effect is mediated by the IGF-I receptor, the insulin receptor, or the hybrid receptors in muscle is not known (95, 96). Nevertheless, these findings illustrate the distinct physiological effects of GH and IGF-I.

The IGF system is also involved in processes not regulated by GH. For example, the intra-ovarian IGF system is important for normal development of the ovarian follicle by stimulating mitosis and steroidogenesis and by inhibiting apoptosis. The IGF system may also play a role in regulating adrenal steroidogenesis (97). Tumorigenesis is still another example of a GH-independent role of the IGF system. For example, the tumor suppressor p53 inhibits proliferation by stimulating IGFBP-3 synthesis and inhibiting IGF-IR synthesis (98).

Regulation of the Cell Cycle by the IGF-IR

The role of IGF-I as a mitogen was deduced largely from in vitro studies of growth-arrested fibroblast cell lines (99). Peptides such as PDGF, FGF, and EGF were termed competence factors, as they stimulated quiescent cells to enter the G1 phase of the cell cycle. IGF-I spurs progression through G1 to S phase and was designated a G1-progression factor (100). Studies using cells derived from knockout models of the IGF-I and IGF-I receptor suggest that IGF-I is not indispensable for progression through G1. Rubin & Baserga (101) reported that fibroblasts derived from IGF-I receptor null embryos have a fourfold longer duration G2/M phase in the cell cycle than comparable wild-type cells. In this model, G1 is not blocked but is longer in duration. Moreover, in intact IGF-I null mice, progression through G1 and S phases is normal, indicating that IGF-1 has a minor role as a G1 progression factor in vivo (102). On the other hand, IGF-I null cells progress through G2/M slowly, at least in cells from the estradiol-stimulated uterus (102). Thus IGF-I appears to be required for normal progression through the latter phases of the cell cycle. In contrast, IGF-2 shortens the cell cycle time and decreases the G1 checkpoint after DNA damage (103). Further studies are required to resolve the significance of these effects.

THE SOMATOMEDIN HYPOTHESIS

Original Somatomedin Hypothesis

The somatomedin hypothesis originated in efforts to understand how somatic growth is regulated by the pituitary. Experiments, performed almost 50 years ago, utilized an assay that measured the incorporation of $^{35}SO_4$ into chondroitin sulfate from cartilage. Injections in vivo of pituitary extracts and of purified bovine GH restored $^{35}SO_4$ incorporation into cartilage (104, 105). However, when bovine GH was added to cartilage slices in vitro, only a minimal effect was observed, suggesting that an intermediary substance was involved in regulating sulfate incorporation (106). The term somatomedin was later coined to reflect the growth-promoting substance (107). Two decades after somatomedins were postulated to exist, IGF-I (and IGF-II) were characterized. IGF-I is the somatomedin regulated by GH (71, 108). Both IGFs were named insulin-like because of their ability to stimulate glucose uptake into fat cells and muscle. The original somatomedin hypothesis became the widely accepted model of IGF action: namely, the concept that GH stimulates IGF-I synthesis and release from the liver and that IGF-I reaches the main target organs, such as cartilage and bones, via the circulation to act as an endocrine agent (Figure 1, *left panel*). Circulating IGF-I was also assumed to feedback on the somatotropic axis and suppress the release of GH from the pituitary (109).

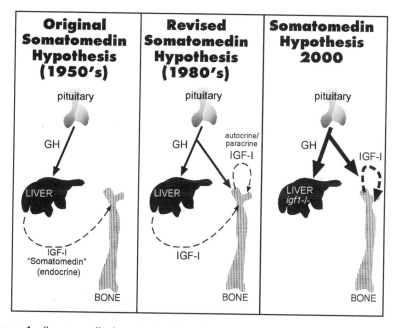

Figure 1 Somatomedin hypothesis. The original hypothesis proposed that the effect of GH on longitudinal body growth was mediated solely by liver-derived IGF-I. The revised hypothesis proposed that extra-hepatic tissues expressed IGF-I as well and are also involved in mediating GH action. The data presented in this review and derived from tissue-specifc gene-deletion experiments suggest that liver-derived IGF-I may not be essential for GH-stimulated postnatal growth and development, at least in the mouse.

The Alternative or Revised Somatomedin Hypothesis

The original somatomedin hypothesis was challenged in 1980 with the discovery that IGF-I and IGF-II are produced in most, if not all, tissues (110–112). Indeed, the IGF-I gene is expressed in many tissues throughout embryonic and postnatal development and during adult life (112, 113). Injection of GH in hypophysectomized rats increases IGF-I mRNA in lung, kidney, heart, skeletal muscle, and white adipose tissue, as well as in liver. Further studies confirmed that IGF-I is produced locally in diverse tissues under the control of GH or other hormones (Figure 1, *middle panel*).

The Dual Effector Theory

Green and co-workers (114) proposed the "dual effector hypothesis," to explain the roles played by GH and IGF-I in growth and differentiation. This theory suggests that GH stimulates the differentiation of adipocytes and that IGF-I stimulates clonal expansion (114). Furthermore, differentiation but not mitosis of 3T3 pre-adipocytes was believed to be dependent on an adipogenic factor in serum. A hormone(s) secreted from the pituitary was considered a possible candidate by Morikawa et al (115) because pituitary extracts and recombinant human GH showed this activity, whereas serum from hypophysectomized rats showed reduced activity (115). Thus in contrast to the original concept of the somatomedin hypothesis that IGF-I mediated all the functions of GH, these authors showed that pre-adipocytes could be induced to differentiate directly into adipocytes by GH (116). Furthermore, because somatomedins could not replace GH in their studies, they suggested that IGF-I induced clonal expansion of these differentiated cells (117). Direct injection of GH into the tibial growth plate of hypophysectomized rats stimulated growth plate expansion and increased longitudinal bone growth, whereas the contralateral tibia was unaffected. Subsequent studies by this and other groups confirmed and expanded these findings (118, 119). By analogy with the adipocyte work of Greene et al (114–117), the Isaakson group extended the dual effector theory to the growth plate, proposing that GH acts directly at the germinal zone of the growth plate to stimulate the differentiation of chondrocytes. Growth hormone also acts to induce local synthesis of IGF-I, which is thought to stimulate the clonal expansion of chondrocytes in an autocrine/paracrine manner, as reviewed elsewhere (120, 121).

Evidence Inconsistent with the Dual Effector Theory: IGF Gene Knockouts

Insulin at high doses and IGF-I at physiological concentrations cause pre-adipocytes to differentiate into mature adipocytes (122, 123), most likely by activating IGF-I receptors. Furthermore, additional findings are not consistent with the dual effector hypothesis. The concept that GH has direct, non-IGF-I dependent effects on growth plate germinal zone was confirmed in studies showing that GH induces proliferation of germinal zone cells in the growth plate (124, 125); IGF-I has a similar effect (125). However, the growth plate germinal zones are expanded in IGF-I null mice (126). Given the absence of IGF-I in these mice, elevated endogenous GH levels probably mediate this effect on the germinal zone.

While the hypothesis that GH has direct, non-IGF-I dependent effects on growth plate germinal cells has been widely confirmed, the findings by Isaksson et al that GH induces IGF-I synthesis in proliferative chondrocytes in vivo has not been confirmed (121). For example, both Shinar et al (127) and Wang et al (128) were unable to detect IGF-I mRNA in growth plate chondrocytes of rats or mice of any age, although both groups found abundant IGF-2 mRNA in proliferative chondrocytes from both species.

Analysis of long bone growth and growth plate characteristics in IGF-I null mice indicates that the number of chondrocytes in the growth plate and their pro-liferation are normal, despite a 35% reduction in the rate of long bone growth (126). However, chondrocytes from IGF-I null mice are smaller than those from wild-type mice throughout the growth plate. The terminal hypertrophic chondro-cytes, the scaffold upon which linear growth occurs, are reduced by 30% in linear dimension. This may account for most of the decreased longitudinal growth in IGF-I null mice. In chondrocytes from IGF-I null mice, the level of the insulin-sensitive glucose transporter (GLUT4) is reduced, glycogen synthase kinase 3b is hypo-phosphorylated, glycogen stores are depleted, and ribosomal RNA levels are reduced (126). These and other data suggest that IGF-I may have anabolic effects on bone. Such actions promote hypertrophy rather than mitogenesis of chondro-cytes as previously thought. In contrast to IGF-I, IGF-2 is normally expressed by proliferating chondrocytes (127, 128), and IGF-2 expression is not impaired by deletion of IGF-I. Taken together, these findings may explain the normal prolifer-ation observed in the igf-1 null growth plate. The source of IGF-I that promotes chondrocyte hypertrophy remains uncertain. IGF-I mRNA is expressed in the murine periosteum and perichondrium (127, 128) and by muscle and fat cells. These tissues may provide sufficient IGF-I to enhance longitudinal bone growth, and circulating IGF-I derived from the liver may also serve this role.

GH is clearly not essential for the differentiation of adipocytes or chondrocytes because these differentiated cells are abundant in GH-deficient and GH receptor-deficient states. Indeed, adiposity is excessive in GH deficiency, and GH treatment reduces the mass of adipose tissue (49). This suggests that the lipolytic effects of GH are more important than effects on differentiation of adipocytes. Moreover, growth plate chondrocytes proliferate normally in the absence of IGF-I. There-fore, IGF-I is apparently not required for their clonal expansion. Thus while GH and IGF-I and possibly IGF-2 have complementary roles in promoting long bone growth (Figure 2), these roles are not the same as proposed in the original dual ef-fector scheme (121). Other examples of divergence from the dual effector scheme include the findings that differentiating myoblasts are unable to proliferate (129) and that IGF-I itself is capable of inducing myoblast differentiation into mature myotubes (130).

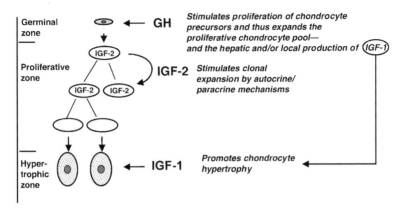

Figure 2   GH and IGF interactions in long bone growth.

NEW APPROACHES: Conditional Knockouts Using the Cre/LoxP System

One problem with gene targeting studies is that disruption of a gene that is critical for normal development may preclude using the resulting animals as appropriate models to study normal function of the gene in the adult. Furthermore, compensatory mechanisms, such as the up-regulation of another gene with a similar function, may obscure the loss of function of the gene of interest. Thus the ability to inactivate genes in a specific tissue in a temporally regulated manner represents a powerful tool for biology. Genes may be excised from the genome utilizing a site-specific recombination technology adapted from bacteriophage. For example, bacteriophage P1 Cre recombinase, a 38-kDa protein, recognizes 34 bp DNA sequences called loxP sites (locus of crossover P1) (131, 132). When the loxP sites are in tandem and flanking an essential exon of the gene of interest, Cre induces an intra-molecular recombination and excision of the intervening DNA, resulting in deletion of the exon (Figure 3). By placing the Cre recombinase under the control of tissue-specific or inducible promoters, the function of a gene in a

---

Figure 3   Cre-loxP system for tissue-specific IGF-I gene deletion. Exon 4 (ex4) in the IGF-I gene is flanked by two tandem repeats of loxP sequences and inserted into the genome using homologous recombination. These mice are bred with transgenic mice that express *cre* in liver only under the influence of the albumin promoter. *Cre* recognizes loxP sequences and causes a recombination event resulting in deletion of exon 4 in the liver. At the bottom are representative examples of Southern blot analyses of liver (Li) and other tissues (H = heart, B = brain, K = kidney, S = spleen, Lu = lung, F = fat) demonstrating that the recombination event occurs only in the liver. The reduction of the 4.9 kb band to 2.8 kb represents recombination.

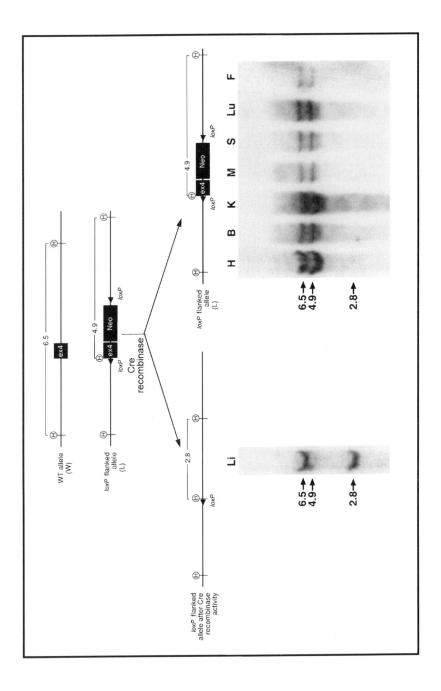

certain tissue(s) can be examined in the absence of potentially critical developmental abnormalities.

Using homologous recombination, we established a mouse line in which two loxP sites in tandem flank the fourth exon of the IGF-I gene (Figure 3). Exon 4 encodes amino acids 26–70 of the IGF-I peptide, including part of the B domain and the entire C, A, and D domains. This region of the peptide is responsible for the binding of IGF-I to its cognate receptor (IGF-I receptor) and has been targeted to create a total IGF-I knockout for developmental studies (72). To create a liver-specific deletion of the IGF-I gene, we generated transgenic mice expressing Cre recombinase exclusively in the liver by expressing Cre under the control of the albumin promoter. The albumin promoter is highly active in the liver and weakly active in certain other tissues. Cross-breeding of the loxP-flanked IGF-I mice and the albumin Cre-expressing mice resulted in deletion of the IGF-I gene in the liver (133). Southern blot analysis revealed that levels of IGF-I in gene-deleted animals were reduced by ∼95% in the liver and unchanged in other tissues. Furthermore, IGF-I mRNA levels in liver, as determined by solution hybridization RNAse protection assays, were <1% of that in wild-type animals.

Circulating IGF-I levels in liver of IGF-I-/- mice were reduced at 6 weeks of age to 25% of those in wild-type animals. This decrease was associated with an approximately fourfold increase in circulating GH levels, presumably caused by the decrease in negative feedback control by circulating IGF-I on GH secretion by the pituitary. Postnatal growth and development was assessed from ages 3 to 6 weeks (Figure 4). Mice were killed at age 6 weeks, and body length (nose to anus) was measured, femoral length was assessed by X-ray, and the weights of individual organs were determined. Except for the spleen, none of these parameters were different in liver-specific IGF-I knockout animals and their wild-type littermates. The spleen was reduced in the knockout animals, perhaps reflecting the chronically reduced levels of circulating IGF-I. Sexual maturation was normal, with respect to fertility, litter size, lactation, and weaning. In brief, gross phenotypic distinctions between the liver-specific IGF-I gene-deleted animals and their wild-type littermates were minimal. In a second model, we produced a liver-specific deletion of the IGF-I gene by using an inducible interferon promoter to drive the expression of Cre (134). Although the expression of Cre is not liver specific, in this model the deletion of the IGF-I gene was largely specific to the liver and spleen. Once again, the circulating levels of IGF-I were reduced by ∼75%; however, post-natal growth and development was normal.

Serum GH levels are increased in the liver of IGF-I-/- mice. Therefore, we considered the possibility that the normal growth and development of these mice was the result of compensation from non-hepatic tissues. Using the solution hybridization/RNAse protection assay, which provides high specificity and sensitivity, IGF-I mRNA levels were measured in various tissues. In all tissues examined, including heart, muscle, fat, spleen, and kidney, IGF-I mRNA levels were not different from wild-type levels. From these results we have concluded that

Growth curve

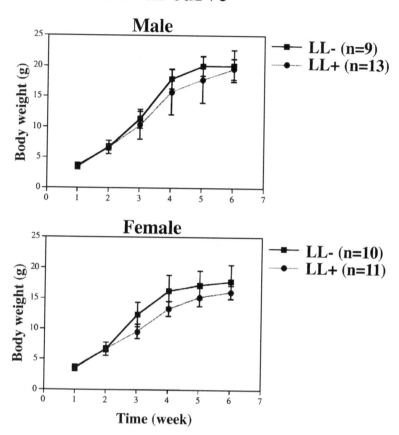

Figure 4 Growth curves. Body weights of male and female mice were measured weekly from postnatal week 1 until week 6. There was no significant difference between liver-specific IGF-I gene-deleted mice (LL+) and littermates (LL−). The + sign represents *cre* positive, i.e. recombination event positive (see Figure 3).

these tissues do not show compensation, although we cannot exclude the possibility that compensation could occur at the level of IGF-I translation or turnover (135).

At this stage it is unclear whether the normal growth and development in these mice is entirely from local production of IGF-I or whether the free circulating IGF-I levels are sufficient to maintain this function. This latter possibility could explain why IGF-I receptor mRNA levels were not different from those in wild-type mice in the peripheral tissues analyzed. Lower circulating IGF-I levels can cause up-regulation of IGF-I receptor gene expression in some models (136, 137).

Alternatively, free IGF-I levels might be normal and sufficient to maintain endocrine IGF-I-induced growth. However, no compensation in IGF-II levels occurs, because neither IGF-II mRNA levels in tissue nor IGF-II protein levels in serum were detectable in the IGF-I gene deleted mice.

CONCLUSIONS

Investigators can now re-evaluate many of the hypotheses that have become dogma over the years (Figure 1, *right panel*). While the role of IGF-I had assumed a central role in the mediation of the biological actions of GH, GH-independent functions clearly exist for for IGF-I, and similarly, some of the actions of GH appear to be IGF-I-independent. Tissue-specific gene deletion has made it possible to investigate these roles in vivo. Many unanswered questions remain: (*a*) What is the role of liver IGF-I? (*b*) What other tissues contribute to circulating IGF-I levels? (*c*) Are the residual IGF-I levels in the circulation of the conditional IGF-I knockout animal adequate for normal growth and development, or are these functions the result of local tissue IGF-I production?

Many of these questions may be investigated using gene deletion studies of the non-hepatic tissues and by crossing these various animal models.

Visit the Annual Reviews home page at www.AnnualReviews.org

LITERATURE CITED

1. Bazan JF. 1989. A novel family of growth factor receptors: a common binding domain in the growth hormone, prolactin, erythropoietin and IL-6 receptors, and the p75 IL-2 receptor beta-chain. *Biochem. Biophys. Res. Commun.* 164:788–95
2. Bazan JF. 1990. Haemopoietic receptors and helical cytokines. *Immunol. Today* 11:350–54
3. Cosman D, Lyman SD, Idzerda RI, Beckmann MP, Park LS, et al. 1990. A new cytokine receptor superfamily. *Trends Biochem. Sci.* 15:265–70
4. Miller WL, Eberhardt NL. 1983. Structure and evolution of the growth hormone gene family. *Endocr. Rev.* 4:97–130
5. Niall HD, Hogan ML, Sauer R, Rosenblum IY, Greenwood FC. 1971. Sequences of pituitary and placental lactogenic and growth hormones: evolution from a primordial peptide by gene reduplication. *Proc. Natl. Acad. Sci. USA* 68:866–70
6. Clark RG, Carlsson LM, Robinson IC. 1987. Growth hormone secretory profiles in conscious female rats. *J. Endocrinol.* 114:399–407
7. Eden S. 1979. Age- and sex-related differences in episodic growth hormone secretion in the rat. *Endocrinology* 105:555–60
8. Saunders A, Terry LC, Audet J, Brazeau P, Martin JB. 1976. Dynamic studies of growth hormone and prolactin secretion in the female rat. *Neuroendocrinology* 21:193–203
9. Pincus SM, Gevers EF, Robinson IC, van den Berg G, Roelfsema F, et al. 1996. Females secrete growth hormone with more process irregularity than males in both humans and rats. *Am. J. Physiol. Endocrinol. Metab.* 270:E107–E15

10. Maiter D, Underwood LE, Maes M, Davenport ML, Ketelslegers JM. 1988. Different effects of intermittent and continuous growth hormone (GH) administration on serum somatomedin-C/insulin-like growth factor I and liver GH receptors in hypophysectomized rats. *Endocrinology* 12:1053–59

11. Isgaard J, Moller C, Isaksson OG, Nilsson A, Mathews LS, Norstedt G. 1988. Regulation of insulin-like growth factor messenger ribonucleic acid in rat growth plate by growth hormone. *Endocrinology* 122:1515–20

12. Davey HW, Park SH, Grattan DR, McLachlan MJ, Waxman DJ. 1999. STAT5b-deficient mice are growth hormone pulse-resistant. Role of STAT5b in sex-specific liver p450 expression. *J. Biol. Chem.* 274:35331–36

13. Park SH, Liu X, Hennighausen L, Davey HW, Waxman DJ. 1999. Distinctive roles of STAT5a and STAT5b in sexual dimorphism of hepatic P450 gene expression. Impact of STAT5a gene disruption. *J. Biol. Chem.* 274:7421–30

14. Waters MJ, Shang CA, Behncken SN, Tam SP, Li H, et al. 1999. Growth hormone as a cytokine. *Clin. Exp. Pharmacol. Physiol.* 26:760–64

15. Spiess J, Rivier J, Vale W. 1983. Characterization of rat hypothalamic growth hormone-releasing factor. *Nature* 303:532–35

16. Ling N, Esch F, Bohlen P, Brazeau P, Wehrenberg WB, Guillemin R. 1984. Isolation, primary structure, and synthesis of human hypothalamic somatocrinin: growth hormone-releasing factor. *Proc. Natl. Acad. Sci. USA* 81:4302–6

17. Brazeau P, Vale W, Burgus R, Ling N, Butcher M, et al. 1973. Hypothalamic polypeptide that inhibits the secretion of immunoreactive pituitary growth hormone. *Science* 179:77–79

18. Howard AD, Feighner SD, Cully DF, Arena JP, Liberator PA, et al. 1996. A receptor in pituitary and hypothalamus that functions in growth hormone release. *Science* 273:974–77

19. Smith RG, Pong SS, Hickey G, Jacks T, Cheng K, et al. 1996. Modulation of pulsatile GH release through a novel receptor in hypothalamus and pituitary gland. *Recent Prog. Horm. Res.* 51:261–85

20. Muggeo M, Tiengo A, Fedele D, Crepaldi G. 1975. The influence of plasma triglycerides on human growth hormone response to arginine and insulin: a study in hyperlipemics and normal subjects. *Horm. Metab. Res.* 7:367–74

21. Imaki T, Shibasaki T, Shizume K, Masuda A, Hotta M, et al. 1985. The effect of free fatty acids on growth hormone (GH)-releasing hormone-mediated GH secretion in man. *J. Clin. Endocrinol. Metab.* 60:290–93

22. Carro E, Senaris R, Considine RV, Casanueva FF, Dieguez C. 1997. Regulation of in vivo growth hormone secretion by leptin. *Endocrinology* 138:2203–6

23. Tannenbaum GS, Gurd W, Lapointe M. 1998. Leptin is a potent stimulator of spontaneous pulsatile growth hormone (GH) secretion and the GH response to GH-releasing hormone. *Endocrinology* 139:3871–75

24. Vuagnat BA, Pierroz DD, Lalaoui M, Englaro P, Pralong FP, et al. 1998. Evidence for a leptin-neuropeptide Y axis for the regulation of growth hormone secretion in the rat. *Neuroendocrinology* 67:291–300

25. Chan YY, Steiner RA, Clifton DK. 1996. Regulation of hypothalamic neuropeptide-Y neurons by growth hormone in the rat. *Endocrinology* 137:1319–25

26. Kamegai J, Minami S, Sugihara H, Hasegawa O, Higuchi H, Wakabayashi I. 1996. Growth hormone receptor gene is expressed in neuropeptide Y neurons in hypothalamic arcuate nucleus of rats. *Endocrinology* 137:2109–12

27. Ozata M, Ozdemir IC, Licinio J. 1999. Human leptin deficiency caused by a

missense mutation: multiple endocrine defects, decreased sympathetic tone, and immune system dysfunction indicate new targets for leptin action, greater central than peripheral resistance to the effects of leptin, and spontaneous correction of leptin-mediated defects. *J. Clin. Endocrinol. Metab.* 84:3686–95. Erratum. 2000. *J. Clin. Endocrinol. Metab.* 85:416

28. Deghenghi R, Cananzi MM, Torsello A, Battisti C, Muller EE, Locatelli V. 1994. GH-releasing activity of Hexarelin, a new growth hormone releasing peptide, in infant and adult rats. *Life Sci.* 54:1321–28. Erratum. 1994. *Life Sci.* 55:1309

29. Kojima M, Hosoda H, Date Y, Nakazato M, Matsuo H, Kangawa K. 1999. Ghrelin is a growth-hormone-releasing acylated peptide from stomach. *Nature* 402:656–60

30. Turner HE, Vadivale A, Keenan J, Wass JA. 1999. A comparison of lanreotide and octreotide LAR for treatment of acromegaly. *Clin. Endocrinol.* 51:275–80

31. Serri O, Brazeau P, Kachra Z, Posner B. 1992. Octreotide inhibits insulin-like growth factor-I hepatic gene expression in the hypophysectomized rat: evidence for a direct and indirect mechanism of action. *Endocrinology* 130:1816–21

32. Ambler GR, Butler AA, Padmanabhan J, Breier BH, Gluckman PD 1996. The effects of octreotide on GH receptor and IGF-I expression in the GH-deficient rat. *J. Endocrinol.* 149:223–31

33. Pollak MN, Schally AV. 1998. Mechanisms of antineoplastic action of somatostatin analogs. *Proc. Soc. Exp. Biol. Med.* 217:143–52

34. Liebow C, Reilly C, Serrano M, Schally AV. 1989. Somatostatin analogues inhibit growth of pancreatic cancer by stimulating tyrosine phosphatase. *Proc. Natl. Acad. Sci. USA* 86:2003–7

35. Srikant CB, Shen SH. 1996. Octapeptide somatostatin analog SMS 201-995 induces translocation of intracellular PTP1C to membranes in MCF-7 human breast adenocarcinoma cells. *Endocrinology* 137:3461–68

36. Thissen JP, Triest S, Underwood LE, Maes M, Ketelslegers JM. 1990. Divergent responses of serum insulin-like growth factor-I and liver growth hormone (GH) receptors to exogenous GH in protein-restricted rats. *Endocrinology* 126:908–13

37. Luo JM, Murphy LJ. 1989. Dexamethasone inhibits growth hormone induction of insulin-like growth factor-I (IGF-I) messenger ribonucleic acid (mRNA) in hypophysectomized rats and reduces IGF-I mRNA abundance in the intact rat. *Endocrinology* 125:165–71

38. Beauloye V, Ketelslegers JM, Moreau B, Thissen JP. 1999. Dexamethasone inhibits both growth hormone (GH)-induction of insulin-like growth factor-I (IGF-I) mRNA and GH receptor (GHR) mRNA levels in rat primary cultured hepatocytes. *Growth Horm. IGF Res.* 9:205–11

39. Jux C, Leiber K, Hugel U, Blum W, Ohlsson C, et al. 1998. Dexamethasone impairs growth hormone (GH)-stimulated growth by suppression of local insulin-like growth factor (IGF)-I production and expression of GH- and IGF-I-receptor in cultured rat chondrocytes. *Endocrinology* 139:3296–305

40. Freemark M. 1999. The fetal adrenal and the maturation of the growth hormone and prolactin axes. *Endocrinology* 140:1963–65

41. Baumann G, Stolar MW, Amburn K, Barsano CP, DeVries BC. 1986. A specific growth hormone-binding protein in human plasma: initial characterization. *J. Clin. Endocrinol. Metab.* 62:134–41

42. Dastot F, Sobrier ML, Duquesnoy P, Duriez B, Goossens M, Amselem S. 1996. Alternatively spliced forms in the cytoplasmic domain of the human growth hormone (GH) receptor regulate its ability to generate a soluble GH-binding protein. *Proc. Natl. Acad. Sci. USA* 93:10723–28

43. Martini JF, Pezet A, Guezennec CY,

Edery M, Postel-Vinay MC, Kelly PA. 1997. Monkey growth hormone (GH) receptor gene expression. Evidence for two mechanisms for the generation of the GH binding protein. *J. Biol. Chem.* 272:18951–58

44. Baumann G, Amburn KD, Buchanan TA. 1987. The effect of circulating growth hormone-binding protein on metabolic clearance, distribution, and degradation of human growth hormone. *J. Clin. Endocrinol. Metab.* 64:657–60

45. Kostyo JL. 1968. Rapid effects of growth hormone on amino acid transport and protein synthesis. *Ann. NY Acad. Sci.* 148:389–407

46. Wolf RF, Heslin MJ, Newman E, Pearlstone DB, Gonenne A, Brennan MF. 1992. Growth hormone and insulin combine to improve whole-body and skeletal muscle protein kinetics. *Surgery* 112:284–91

47. Horber FF, Haymond MW. 1990. Human growth hormone prevents the protein catabolic side effects of prednisone in humans. *J. Clin. Invest.* 86:265–72

48. Fryburg DA. 1994. Insulin-like growth factor I exerts growth hormone- and insulin-like actions on human muscle protein metabolism. *Am. J. Physiol. Endocrinol. Metab.* 267:E331–E36

49. Russell-Jones DL, Weissberger AJ, Bowes SB, Kelly JM, Thomason M, et al. 1993. The effects of growth hormone on protein metabolism in adult growth hormone deficient patients. *Clin. Endocrinol.* 38:427–31

50. Richelsen B, Pedersen SB, Borglum JD, Moller-Pedersen T, Jorgensen J, Jorgensen JO. 1994. Growth hormone treatment of obese women for 5 weeks: effect on body composition and adipose tissue LPL activity. *Am. J. Physiol. Endocrinol. Metab.* 266:E211–E16

51. Ottosson M, Vikman-Adolfsson K, Enerback S, Elander A, Bjorntorp P, Eden S. 1995. Growth hormone inhibits lipoprotein lipase activity in human adipose tissue. *J. Clin. Endocrinol. Metab.* 80:936–41

52. Dietz J, Schwartz J. 1991. Growth hormone alters lipolysis and hormone-sensitive lipase activity in 3T3-F442A adipocytes. *Metabolism* 40:800–6

53. Asayama K, Amemiya S, Kusano S, Kato K. 1984. Growth-hormone-induced changes in postheparin plasma lipoprotein lipase and hepatic triglyceride lipase activities. *Metabolism* 33:29–31

54. Rosenfeld RG, Wilson DM, Dollar LA, Bennett A, Hintz RL. 1982. Both human pituitary growth hormone and recombinant DNA-derived human growth hormone cause insulin resistance at a postreceptor site. *J. Clin. Endocrinol. Metab.* 54:1033–38

55. Goodman HM. 1984. Biological activity of bacterial derived human growth hormone in adipose tissue of hypophysectomized rats. *Endocrinology* 114:131–35

56. Carter-Su C, King AP, Argetsinger LS, Smit LS, Vanderkuur J, Campbell GS. 1996. Signalling pathway of GH. *Endocr. J.* 43:S65–70 (Suppl.)

57. Randle PJ, Garland PB, Hales CN, Newsholme EA. 1963. The glucose-fatty acid cycle: its role in insulin sensitivity and the metabolic disturbances of diabetes mellitus. *Lancet* 1:785–89

58. Guler HP, Zapf J, Scheiwiller E, Froesch ER. 1988. Recombinant human insulin-like growth factor I stimulates growth and has distinct effects on organ size in hypophysectomized rats. *Proc. Natl. Acad. Sci. USA* 85:4889–93

59. Clark R, Carlsson L, Mortensen D, Cronin M. 1994. Additive effects on body growth of insulin-like growth factor-I and growth hormone in hypophysectomized rats. *Endocrinol. Metab.* 1:49–54

60. Clark R, Mortensen D, Carlsson L. 1995. Insulin-like growth factor-I and growth hormone (GH) have distinct and overlapping effects in GH-deficient rats. *Endocrine* 3:297–304

61. Fielder PJ, Mortensen DL, Mallet P, Carlsson B, Baxter RC, Clark RG. 1996.

Differential long-term effects of insulin-like growth factor-I (IGF-I) growth hormone (GH), and IGF-I plus GH on body growth and IGF binding proteins in hypophysectomized rats. *Endocrinology* 137:1913–20

62. LeRoith D, Yanowski J, Kaldjian EP, Jaffe ES, LeRoith T, et al. 1996. The effects of growth hormone and insulin-like growth factor I on the immune system of aged female monkeys. *Endocrinology* 137:1071–79

63. Clark RG, Mortensen D, Reifsnyder D, Mohler M, Etcheverry T, Mukku V. 1993. Recombinant human insulin-like growth factor binding protein-3 (rhIGFBP-3): effects on the glycemic and growth promoting activities of rhIGF-1 in the rat. *Growth Regul.* 3:50–52

64. Boisclair YR, Seto D, Hsieh S, Hurst KR, Ooi GT. 1996. Organization and chromosomal localization of the gene encoding the mouse acid labile subunit of the insulin-like growth factor binding complex. *Proc. Natl. Acad. Sci. USA* 93:10028–33

65. Chin E, Zhou J, Dai J, Baxter RC, Bondy CA. 1994. Cellular localization and regulation of gene expression for components of the insulin-like growth factor ternary binding protein complex. *Endocrinology* 134:2498–504

66. Jones JI, Clemmons DR. 1995. Insulin-like growth factors and their binding proteins: biological actions. *Endocr. Rev.* 16:3–34

67. LeRoith D, Baserga R, Helman L, Roberts CT Jr. 1995. Insulin-like growth factors and cancer. *Ann. Intern. Med.* 122:54–59

68. Nissley P, Lopaczynski W. 1991. Insulin-like growth factor receptors. *Growth Factors* 5:29–43

69. Blundell TL, Bedarkar S, Rinderknecht E, Humbel RE. 1978. Insulin-like growth factor: a model for tertiary structure accounting for immunoreactivity and receptor binding. *Proc. Natl. Acad. Sci. USA* 75:180–84

70. Blundell TL, Bedarkar S, Humbel RE.

1983. Tertiary structures, receptor binding, and antigenicity of insulinlike growth factors. *Fed. Proc.* 42:2592–97

71. Rinderknecht E, Humbel RE. 1978. The amino acid sequence of human insulin-like growth factor I and its structural homology with proinsulin. *J. Biol. Chem.* 253:2769–76

72. Baker J, Liu JP, Robertson EJ, Efstratiadis A. 1993. Role of insulin-like growth factors in embryonic and postnatal growth. *Cell* 75:73–82

73. Ullrich A, Gray A, Tam AW, Yang-Feng T, Tsubokawa M, et al. 1986. Insulin-like growth factor I receptor primary structure: comparison with insulin receptor suggests structural determinants that define functional specificity. *EMBO J.* 5:2503–12

74. Steele-Perkins G, Turner J, Edman JC, Hari J, Pierce SB, et al. 1988. Expression and characterization of a functional human insulin-like growth factor I receptor. *J. Biol. Chem.* 263:11486–92

75. Baxter RC, Martin JL, Beniac VA. 1989. High molecular weight insulin-like growth factor binding protein complex. Purification and properties of the acid-labile subunit from human serum. *J. Biol. Chem.* 264:11843–48

76. Mortensen DL, Won WB, Siu J, Reifsnyder D, Gironella M, et al. 1997. Insulin-like growth factor binding protein-1 induces insulin release in the rat. *Endocrinology* 38:2073–80

77. Van Buul-Offers SC, Van Kleffens M, Koster JG, Lindenbergh-Kortleve DJ, Gresnigt MG, et al. 2000. Human insulin-like growth factor (IGF) binding protein-1 inhibits IGF-I-stimulated body growth but stimulates growth of the kidney in snell dwarf mice. *Endocrinology* 141:1493–99

78. Twigg SM, Kiefer MC, Zapf J, Baxter RC. 2000. A central domain binding site in insulin-like growth factor binding protein-5 for the acid-labile subunit. *Endocrinology* 141:454–57

79. Rechler MM. 1993. Insulin-like growth

factor binding proteins. *Vitam. Horm.* 47:1–114

80. Martin JL, Baxter RC. 1999. IGF binding proteins as modulators of IGF action. In *Contemporary Endocrinology: The IGF System*, ed. RG Rosenfeld, CT Roberts Jr, 17:227–55. Totowa, NJ: Humana

81. Liu JL, Grinberg A, Westphal H, Sauer B, Accili D, et al. 1998. Insulin-like growth factor-I affects perinatal lethality and postnatal development in a gene dosage-dependent manner: manipulation using the Cre/loxP system in transgenic mice. *Mol. Endocrinol.* 12:1452–62

82. Powell-Braxton L, Hollingshead P, Warburton C, Dowd M, Pitts-Meek S, et al. 1993. IGF-I is required for normal embryonic growth in mice. *Genes Dev.* 7:2609–17

83. Gourmelen M, Le Bouc Y, Girard F, Binoux M. 1984. Serum levels of insulin-like growth factor (IGF) and IGF binding protein in constitutionally tall children and adolescents *J. Clin. Endocrinol. Metab.* 59:1197–203

84. Blair HT, McCutcheon SN, Mackenzie DD, Ormsby JE, Siddiqui RA, et al. 1988. Genetic selection for insulin-like growth factor-1 in growing mice is associated with altered growth. *Endocrinology* 123:1690–92

85. Zhou J, Kumar TR, Matzuk MM, Bondy C. 1997. Insulin-like growth factor I regulates gonadotropin responsiveness in the murine ovary. *Mol. Endocrinol.* 11:1924–33

86. Laron Z. 1999. Natural history of the classical form of primary growth hormone (GH) resistance (Laron syndrome). *J. Pediatr. Endocrinol. Metab.* 12(l)1:231–49 (Suppl.)

87. Fryburg DA, Jahn LA, Hill SA, Oliveras DM, Barrett EJ. 1995. Insulin and insulin-like growth factor-I enhance human skeletal muscle protein anabolism during hyperaminoacidemia by different mechanisms. *J. Clin. Invest.* 96:1722–29

88. Jacob R, Barrett E, Plewe G, Fagin KD,

Sherwin RS. 1989. Acute effects of insulin-like growth factor I on glucose and amino acid metabolism in the awake fasted rat. Comparison with insulin. *J. Clin. Invest.* 83:1717–23

89. Bailyes EM, Nave BT, Soos MA, Orr SR, Hayward AC, Siddle K. 1997. Insulin receptor/IGF-I receptor hybrids are widely distributed in mammalian tissues: quantification of individual receptor species by selective immunoprecipitation and immunoblotting. *Biochem. J.* 327:209–15

90. Cheetham TD, Holly JM, Clayton K, Cwyfan-Hughes S, Dunger DB. 1995. The effects of repeated daily recombinant human insulin-like growth factor I administration in adolescents with type 1 diabetes. *Diabetes Med.* 12:885–92

91. Moses AC, Morrow LA, O'Brien M, Moller DE, Flier JS. 1995. Insulin-like growth factor I (rhIGF-I) as a therapeutic agent for hyperinsulinemic insulin-resistant diabetes mellitus. *Diabetes Res. Clin. Pract.* 28:S185–94 (Suppl.)

92. Moses AC, Young SC, Morrow LA, O'Brien M, Clemmons DR. 1996. Recombinant human insulin-like growth factor I increases insulin sensitivity and improves glycemic control in type II diabetes. *Diabetes* 45:91–100

93. Schalch DS, Turman NJ, Marcsisin VS, Heffernan M, Guler HP. 1993. Short-term effects of recombinant human insulin-like growth factor I on metabolic control of patients with type II diabetes mellitus. *J. Clin. Endocrinol. Metab.* 77:1563–68

94. Zenobi PD, Jaeggi-Groisman SE, Riesen WF, Roder ME, Froesch ER. 1992. Insulin-like growth factor-I improves glucose and lipid metabolism in type 2 diabetes mellitus. *J. Clin. Invest.* 90:2234–41

95. Moxham CP, Duronio V, Jacobs S. 1989. Insulin-like growth factor I receptor beta-subunit heterogeneity. Evidence for hybrid tetramers composed of insulin-like growth factor I and insulin receptor heterodimers. *J. Biol. Chem.* 264:13238–44

96. Dozio N, Scavini M, Beretta A, Sartori S, Meschi F, et al. 1995. In vivo metabolic effects of insulin-like growth factor-I not mediated through the insulin receptor. *J. Clin. Endocrinol. Metab.* 80:1325–28

97. l'Allemand D, Penhoat A, Blum W, Saez JM. 1998. Is there a local IGF-system in human adrenocortical cells? *Mol. Cell. Endocrinol.* 140:169–73

98. Neuberg M, Buckbinder L, Seizinger B, Kley N. 1997. The p53/IGF-1 receptor axis in the regulation of programmed cell death. *Endocrine* 7:107–9

99. Pardee AB. 1989. G1 events and regulation of cell proliferation. *Science* 246:603–8

100. Stiles CD, Capone GT, Scher CD, Antoniades HN, Van Wyk JJ, Pledger WJ. 1979. Dual control of cell growth by somatomedins and platelet-derived growth factor. *Proc. Natl. Acad. Sci. USA* 76:1279–83

101. Rubin R, Baserga R. 1995. Insulin-like growth factor-I receptor. Its role in cell proliferation, apoptosis, and tumorigenicity. *Lab. Invest.* 73:311–31

102. Adesanya OO, Zhou J, Samathanam C, Powell-Braxton L, Bondy CA. 1999. Insulin-like growth factor 1 is required for G2 progression in the estradiol-induced mitotic cycle. *Proc. Natl. Acad. Sci. USA* 96:3287–91

103. Zhang L, Kim M, Choi YH, Goemans B, Yeung C, et al. 1999. Diminished G1 checkpoint after gamma-irradiation and altered cell cycle regulation by insulin-like growth factor II overexpression. *J. Biol. Chem.* 274:13118–26

104. Salmon WD, Daughaday WH. 1957. A hormonally controlled serum factor which stimulates sulfate incorporation by cartilage in vitro. *J. Lab. Clin. Med.* 49:825–26

105. Denko CW, Bergenstal DM. 1955. The effect of hypophysectomy and growth hormone on cartilage sulfate metabolism. *Proc. Soc. Exp. Biol. Med.* 84:603–5

106. Daughaday WH, Reeder C. 1966. Synchronous activation of DNA synthesis in hypophysectomized rat cartilage by growth hormone. *J. Lab. Clin. Med.* 68:357–68

107. Daughaday WH, Hall K, Raben MS, Salmon WD Jr, Van der Brande JL, Van Wyk JJ. 1972. Somatomedin: proposed designation for sulphation factor. *Nature* 235:170

108. Klapper DG, Svoboda ME, Van Wyk JJ. 1983. Sequence analysis of somatomedin-C: confirmation of identity with insulin-like growth factor I. *Endocrinology* 112:2215–17

109. Berelowitz M, Szabo M, Frohman LA, Firestone S, Chu L, Hintz RL. 1981. Somatomedin-C mediates growth hormone negative feedback by effects on both the hypothalamus and the pituitary. *Science* 212:1279–81

110. D'Ercole AJ, Applewhite GT, Underwood LE. 1980. Evidence that somatomedin is synthesized by multiple tissues in the fetus. *Dev. Biol.* 75:315–28

111. Kajimoto Y, Rotwein P. 1989. Structure and expression of a chicken insulin-like growth factor I precursor. *Mol. Endocrinol.* 3:1907–13

112. Roberts CT Jr, Lasky SR, Lowe WL Jr, Seaman WT, LeRoith D. 1987. Molecular cloning of rat insulin-like growth factor I complementary deoxyribonucleic acids: differential messenger ribonucleic acid processing and regulation by growth hormone in extrahepatic tissues. *Mol. Endocrinol.* 1:243–48

113. Han VK, Lund PK, Lee DC, D'Ercole AJ. 1988. Expression of somatomedin/insulin-like growth factor messenger ribonucleic acids in the human fetus: identification, characterization, and tissue distribution. *J. Clin. Endocrinol. Metab.* 66:422–29

114. Green H, Morikawa M, Nixon T. 1985. A dual effector theory of growth-hormone action. *Differentiation* 9:195–98

115. Morikawa M, Nixon T, Green H. 1982. Growth hormone and the adipose conversion of 3T3 cells. *Cell* 29:783–89
116. Nixon T, Green H. 1983. Properties of growth hormone receptors in relation to the adipose conversion of 3T3 cells. *J. Cell. Physiol.* 115:291–96
117. Morikawa M, Green H, Lewis UJ. 1984. Activity of human growth hormone and related polypeptides on the adipose conversion of 3T3 cells. *Mol. Cell. Biol.* 4:228–31
118. Russell SM, Spencer EM. 1985. Local injections of human or rat growth hormone or of purified human somatomedin-C stimulate unilateral tibial epiphyseal growth in hypophysectomized rats. *Endocrinology* 116:2563–67
119. Schlechter NL, Russell SM, Spencer EM, Nicoll CS. 1986. Evidence suggesting that the direct growth-promoting effect of growth hormone on cartilage in vivo is mediated by local production of somatomedin. *Proc. Natl. Acad. Sci. USA* 83:7932–34
120. Ohlsson C, Bengtsson BA, Isaksson OG, Andreassen TT, Slootweg MC. 1998. Growth hormone and bone. *Endocr. Rev.* 19:55–79
121. Isaksson OG, Lindahl A, Nilsson A, Isgaard J. 1987. Mechanism of the stimulatory effect of growth hormone on longitudinal bone growth. *Endocr. Rev.* 8:426–38
122. Accili D, Taylor SI. 1991. Targeted inactivation of the insulin receptor gene in mouse 3T3-L1 fibroblasts via homologous recombination. *Proc. Natl. Acad. Sci. USA* 88:4708–12
123. Steinberg MM, Brownstein BL. 1982. A clonal analysis of the differentiation of 3T3-L1 preadipose cells: role of insulin. *J. Cell. Physiol.* 113:359–64
124. Ohlsson C, Nilsson A, Isaksson O, Lindahl A. 1992. Growth hormone induces multiplication of the slowly cycling germinal cells of the rat tibial growth plate. *Proc. Natl. Acad. Sci. USA* 89:9826–30
125. Hunziker EB, Wagner J, Zapf J. 1994. Differential effects of insulin-like growth factor I and growth hormone on developmental stages of rat growth plate chondrocytes in vivo. *J. Clin. Invest.* 93:1078–86
126. Wang J, Zhou J, Bondy CA. 1999. Igf1 promotes longitudinal bone growth by insulin-like actions augmenting chondrocyte hypertrophy. *FASEB J.* 13:1985–90
127. Shinar DM, Endo N, Halperin D, Rodan GA, Weinreb M. 1993. Differential expression of insulin-like growth factor-I (IGF-I) and IGF-II messenger ribonucleic acid in growing rat bone. *Endocrinology* 132:1158–67
128. Wang E, Wang J, Chin E, Zhou J, Bondy CA. 1995. Cellular patterns of insulin-like growth factor system gene expression in murine chondrogenesis and osteogenesis. *Endocrinology* 136:2741–51
129. Nadal-Ginard B. 1978. Commitment, fusion, and biochemical differentiation of a myogenic cell line in the absence of DNA synthesis. *Cell* 15:855–64
130. Florini JR, Ewton DZ, Coolican SA. 1996. Growth hormone and the insulin-like growth factor system in myogenesis. *Endocr. Rev.* 17:481–517
131. Gu H, Marth JD, Orban PC, Mossmann H, Rajewsky K. 1994. Deletion of a DNA polymerase beta gene segment in T cells using cell type-specific gene targeting. *Science* 265:103–6
132. Sauer B. 1993. Manipulation of transgenes by site-specific recombination: use of Cre recombinase. *Methods Enzymol.* 225:890–900
133. Yakar S, Liu JL, Stannard B, Butler A, Accili D, et al. 1999. Normal growth and development in the absence of hepatic insulin-like growth factor I. *Proc. Natl. Acad. Sci. USA* 96:7324–29
134. Sjogren K, Liu JL, Blad K, Skrtic S, Vidal O, et al. 1999. Liver-derived insulin-like growth factor I (IGF-I) is the principal

source of IGF-I in blood but is not required for postnatal body growth in mice. *Proc. Natl. Acad. Sci. USA* 96:7088–92

135. Foyt HL, LeRoith D, Roberts CT Jr. 1991. Differential association of insulin-like growth factor I mRNA variants with polysomes in vivo. *J. Biol. Chem.* 266:7300–5

136. Hernandez-Sanchez C, Werner H, Roberts CT Jr, Woo EJ, Hum DW, et al. 1997. Differential regulation of insulin-like growth factor-I (IGF-I) receptor gene expression by IGF-I and basic fibroblastic growth factor. *J. Biol. Chem.* 272:4663–70

137. Eshet R, Werner H, Klinger B, Silbergeld A, Laron Z, et al. 1993. Up-regulation of insulin-like growth factor-I (IGF-I) receptor gene expression in patients with reduced serum IGF-I levels. *J. Mol. Endocrinol.* 10:115–20

Annu. Rev. Physiol. 2001. 63:165–92

ROLE OF ESTROGEN RECEPTOR BETA IN ESTROGEN ACTION

Katarina Pettersson and Jan-Åke Gustafsson

Department of Medical Nutrition and Department of Biosciences, Karolinska Institute, NOVUM, Huddinge S-141 86, Sweden; e-mail: jan-ake.gustafsson@mednut.ki.se

Key Words SERM, prostate, mammary gland, phytoestrogen

■ **Abstract** There was a time when the classification of sex hormones was simple. Androgens were male and estrogens female. What remains true today is that in young adults androgen levels are higher in males and estrogen levels higher in females. More recently we have learned that estrogens are necessary in males for regulation of male sexual behavior, maintenance of the skeleton and the cardiovascular system, and for normal function of the testis and prostate. The importance of androgen in females was never in doubt, it is after all the precursor of estrogen as the substrate for aromatase, the enzyme that produces estrogen. In addition, the tissue distribution of androgen receptors suggests that androgens themselves are important in the ovary, uterus, breast, and brain.

New information promises to clarify some of the complex issues of the physiological roles of estrogen and the contribution of estrogen to the development of neoplastic diseases in humans. The discovery of the second estrogen receptor, the creation of mutant mice defective in both estrogen receptors and in the aromatase gene, the solution of the structures of the ligand-binding domains of estrogen receptor alpha (ERα) and estrogen receptor beta (ERβ), the finding of novel routes through which estrogen receptors can modulate transcription, and the identification of a man with a bi-allelic disruptive mutation of the ERα gene are but some of the milestones. This review focuses on the mechanistic aspects of signal transduction mediated by ERs and on the physiological consequences of deficiency of estrogen or estrogen receptor in the available mouse models.

MECHANISMS OF ACTION OF ESTROGEN

The existence of a protein responsible for specific binding of 17β estradiol (E2) in the uterus was recognized almost 40 years ago (1). The actual cloning of ERα took place a quarter of a century later (2, 3). During the following decade, this receptor was believed to be the single mediator of the physiological effects of estrogens (reviewed 4). In 1996, however, a novel ER was discovered in the rat prostate (5–7). This receptor was named ERβ to distinguish it from the other receptor, ERα.

0066-4278/01/0315-0165$14.00

Both ERs belong to the nuclear receptor (NR) gene family of transcription factors, which show an evolutionarily and functionally conserved structure (8). The action of NRs involves binding of the liganded receptor to *cis*-regulatory DNA elements in the promoter region of target genes to influence transcription rate through physical interaction with cofactors and the transcription machinery. Phylogenetic analysis and functional characterization of NRs form the basis for classification into subfamilies: The steroid receptor subgroup (Type 1 receptors) consists of the receptors for glucocorticoids, mineralocorticoids, progesterone, androgens, and estrogens (GR, MR, PR, AR, and ER, respectively) (9). These receptors act principally as homodimers and rely on ligand activation for efficient DNA-binding and transcriptional activity.

NRs have an N-terminal domain of variable length termed the A/B domain. This region has the lowest degree of sequence similarity among NR family members, but in any single family there is generally good conservation of sequence homology between species, suggesting that evolutionary changes are subjected to functional constraints. The A/B domain of NRs usually harbors an activation function (AF-1) that contributes to transcriptional activity. Adjacent to the A/B domain is the DNA-binding or C domain, the most highly conserved region of the NR super-family. The DNA-binding function consists of two zinc finger motifs coordinated by eight strictly conserved cysteine residues. The DNA-binding domain (DBD) also contains a dimerization interface that mediates cooperativity in DNA binding.

The DBD is linked to the ligand-binding domain (LBD) by the D domain or hinge region. This region is less well characterized and is poorly conserved between different NRs and is involved in association with the molecular chaperone heat shock protein 90 (hsp90). C terminal to the hinge domain is the ligand binding or E/F domain, which displays a high degree of homology among members of the NR superfamily. This multifunctional region is involved in binding of NR agonists and antagonists, dimerization, cofactor binding, and transactivation and, in members of the steroid receptor subgroup of NRs, is involved in a second hsp90 interaction and nuclear localization. Dimerization is important in NR action and is a characteristic of a majority of NRs. The LBD contains a strong dimerization interface that for many receptors functions in the absence of ligand. The transactivation function (AF-2) located in the LBD is in most cases dependent on binding by an agonist ligand to the receptor for proper function.

DNA BINDING

The DBD is the most conserved region in NRs (reviewed in 10, 11). Nine cysteine residues are invariably conserved. Eight of the residues are coordinated around two Zn^{2+} ions forming two Zn finger motifs that confer specific DNA-binding capacity. Within the Zn fingers, several subdomains mediate distinct functions. The so-called P-box encompasses six amino acids at the C-terminal base of the first Zn finger and includes the third and fourth cysteines (Figure 1).

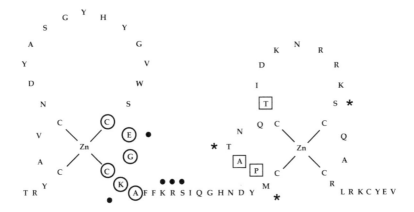

Figure 1 Human ER*α* zinc finger organization. Circled residues signify the P-box. Residues indicated by a dot make direct basepair contacts with the estrogen responsive element (ERE). Amino acids making direct contacts in the dimerization interface are boxed. Asterisks indicate residues making dimerization contacts via ordered water molecules.

The P-box confers DNA-binding specificity on NRs and is therefore critical in recognition of target genes (see Table 1). The ER P-box (CEGCKA) is most similar to the P-boxes of the estrogen receptor-related receptors (ERRs, CEACKA), and similar to the P-boxes of retinoic acid receptor (RAR), retinoid X receptor (RXR), thyroid hormone receptor (TR), vitamin D receptor (VDR), and others (CEGCKG), reflecting the common recognition of the AGGTCA DNA core sequence displayed by these receptors. In contrast, glucocorticoid receptor (GR), mineralocorticoid receptor (MR), progesterone receptor (PR), and androgen receptor (AR) have deviating P-boxes (CGSCKV) and bind to AGAACA core sequences (10, 11).

Although the P-box is not the sole determinant of DNA sequence recognition, the specificity of DNA binding can be altered by changing a few amino acids within the P-box. An ER mutant with three amino acid substitutions in the P-box,

TABLE 1   P-boxes and corresponding DNA recognition sequences of various NRs

P-box	NR	Core sequence
CGSCKV	GR, MR, PR, AR	AGAACA (palindrome)
CEGCKA	ER*α*, ER*β*	AGGTCA (palindrome)
CEACKA	ERR*α*, ERR*β*	AGGTCA (palindrome) TCAAGGTCA
CEGCKG	RAR, RXR, ThR, VDR, PPAR, and others.	AGGTCA (direct repeat)
CESCKG	SF-1, FTZ-F1	TCAAGGTCA

which transform it into a GR-like P-box (from CEGCKA to CGSCKV), binds to a glucocorticoid responsive element (GRE) instead of an estrogen responsive element (ERE) (12).

Hormone response elements are generally composed of two repeats of core sequences arranged as palindromes, direct repeats, or sometimes as inverted repeats, reflecting the fact that dimerization is important in efficient DNA binding by most NRs. The number of nucleotides separating the two repeats influences the efficiency of DNA binding, with differing requirements displayed by different NRs. A dimerization interface referred to as the D-box is present within the DBD at the N-terminal half of the second Zn finger. Dimerization via the DBDs facilitates cooperative DNA binding, and the interactions of the D-boxes further stabilize NR-DNA contact (10, 11). A small subset of NRs interact with DNA as monomers. These receptors recognize and bind to isolated half sites, generally with a requirement for a specific extended 5′ trinucleotide (reviewed in 13). The consensus ERE is composed of two core sequences, organized as palindromes and spaced by three nucleotides.

The three-dimensional structures of ERα DBD bound to an ERE and of GR DBD bound to a GRE have been determined (14–17). ER and GR show both similarities and differences in amino acid residues within their respective DBDs that make direct contact with nucleotides of their cognate DNA response elements, and these findings provide a basis for understanding the selective recognition of response elements by NRs. Cooperative interactions between the two DBDs is facilitated by the spacing between the two core elements, which enhances the exposure of the dimerization interfaces of each subunit to one another. Dimerization of the ERα DBDs enhances binding to imperfect EREs, thus contributing to increase the number of sequences with which ERα can interact (18). The D-boxes differ considerably between NRs, perhaps reflecting the different modes of DNA-binding displayed by various NRs.

COMPARISON OF THE TWO ESTROGEN RECEPTORS

As expected, the DBDs of the two ERs share approximately 97% sequence similarity. In the LBD, the overall amino acid identity is 55%. Regions directly involved in ligand binding and the AF-2 display a higher degree of sequence similarity. ERβ binds E2 with high affinity, and the ERβ-E2 complex activates transcription of an ERE-containing reporter construct (5). ERβ homologs have been cloned from human (19, 20) and mouse (21, 22), and several splicing variants of ERβ have been described (discussed in more detail below; see References 21, 23–27).

Ligand-Binding

ERα and ERβ are similar in those parts of the LBD involved in the actual binding of ligand and have similar binding specificities (29). The major differences in ligand binding between ERα and ERβ lie in the affinities for various compounds

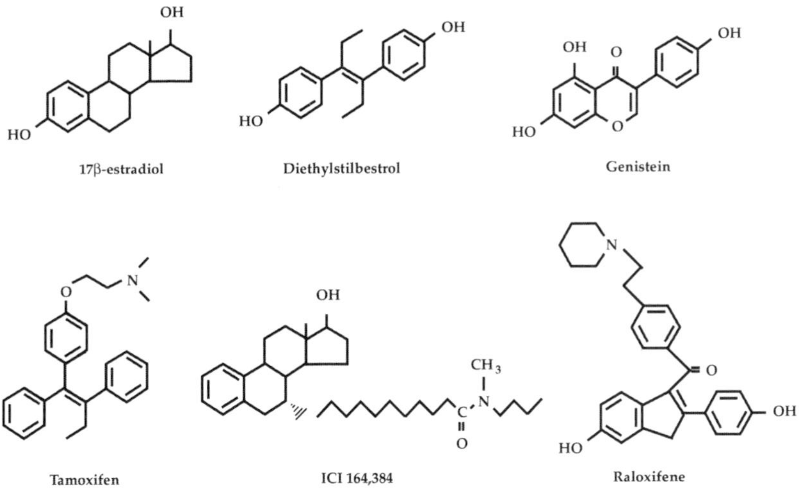

Figure 2   Molecular structures of estrogen receptor agonists and antagonists.

and the transcriptional response a given compound is able to elicit. For instance, tamoxifen is a cell- and tissue-specific mixed agonist-antagonist for ERα but is a pure antagonist on ERβ (30–32). This phenomenon is perhaps not surprising in view of the fact that in ERα it is mediated principally via the N-terminal AF-1, a region where ERα and ERβ differ. Phytoestrogens such as coumestrol and the isoflavonoid genistein have a generally higher affinity (up to ten times higher) for ERβ (33). However, despite their higher affinity, the maximal transcriptional stimulation by phytoestrogens achieved with ERβ is only about half that of ERα (32) (Figure 2).

ER-LBD Structure

Binding of an agonist to an NR induces a conformational change that is associated with the transition to a transcriptionally active complex. Analysis of the crystal structures of several NR LBDs has revealed a conserved architecture composed of 12 helices termed H1–H12 (reviewed in 34).

The crystal structures of ERα LBD bound to the agonists E2 and diethyl-stilbestrol (DES) and to the antagonists raloxifen and 4-OH-tamoxifen have been determined (35–37), and the three-dimensional structure of the ERβ LBD bound to the isoflavonoid genistein and to raloxifene has been described (38). In the ERα LBD bound to E2 or DES, the protein is folded into a three-layered, anti-parallel, α helical sandwich. A central core layer of three helices is packed between two additional layers of helices creating a molecular scaffold with the ligand-binding cavity in one end. In the agonist-binding configuration, H12 is typically positioned across the ligand-binding cavity in a groove created by H3, H5/6, and H11, separating the ligand-binding cavity from the outside. This configuration facilitates contact between ERα and the p160 class of coactivators by exposing the coactivator-binding interface of the receptor to the LXXLL motif(s) of the coactivator (36). The hormone-binding pocket of the ERs is relatively large compared with that of several other NRs for which the crystal structure has been solved (39–41). E2 accordingly does not occupy the entire cavity. The large ligand-binding cavity may explain the unique ability of the ERs to bind to a variety of steroids and other compounds. When DES is bound, the conformation of the ERα LBD is similar to that with E2. However, when the anti-estrogens raloxifene or 4-OH-tamoxifen are bound, H12 is translocated to a position that obscures the coactivator interaction site. This conformation appears to prevent coactivator binding and may be a primary mechanism of ER antagonism (35, 36). The overall three-dimensional structure of ERβ LBD bound to raloxifene is similar to ERα LBD/raloxifene complex (38). When genistein is bound to the ERβ LBD, H12 does not adopt the typical agonist conformation but is positioned in a manner reminiscent of antagonist binding (38). This arrangement of H12 could account for the fact that genistein is a partial agonist (32).

COFACTORS AND OTHER INTERACTING PROTEINS: The Basis for Cofactor Interaction

A number of NR-interacting proteins have been identified. In addition to factors that coactivate transcriptional initiation by NRs, cointegrators and corepressors have been described and are now referred to as cofactors (reviewed in 42, 43). The interaction of cofactors with NRs depends on conserved so-called NR-boxes within the cofactors, composed of the consensus sequence LXXLL (where L is a leucine and X is any other amino acid). One or more of these motifs is present in all NR-interacting cofactors, and mutations in the NR-boxes disrupt NR-cofactor interaction (44).

Coactivators

Several factors increase ER-mediated transcription (reviewed in 42, 43). One group is referred to as the p160 or SRC (steroid receptor coactivator) class of coactivators. For clarity the nomenclature system is that of McKenna et al (43): SRC-1 (human SRC-1 and mouse NCoA-1), SRC-2 (human TIF2, mouse GRIP1/NCoA-2), and SRC-3 (human RAC3/ACTR/AIB1/TRAM-1/SRC-3 and mouse p/CIP). Three LXXLL/NR box motifs are conserved in all members of the SRC family. The NR-boxes form amphipathic α helices with the conserved leucine residues forming a hydrophobic surface on one face of the helix. Interestingly, amino acids flanking the NR-boxes appear to impart receptor-specificity in interaction between SRC-1, SRC-2, and different NRs (45–47). SRC-1 coactivates ligand-dependent transactivation of numerous NRs; ER, PR, GR, ThR, RXR, HNF-4 (hepatocyte nuclear factor), and PPARγ. Interaction between ER and SRC-1 is abolished in the presence of anti-estrogens, possibly because steric interference inhibits coactivator-binding conformation in ERα, as discussed above. Furthermore, SRC-1 mediates functional interactions between AF-1 and AF-2 of ER, PR, and AR via individual domains resulting in AF-1/AF-2 synergy. SRC-3 selectively augments transcriptional activity of ERα over that of ERβ (48). SRC members also interact with p300/CBP (CBP; CREB binding protein) (CREB; cAMP regulatory element binding protein) (49, 50).

Cointegrators

p300/CBP was initially characterized as a coactivator required for CREB-dependent activation of cAMP-regulated promoters (51) and was later found to coactivate multiple factors such as NRs, p53, STATs (signal transducer and activator of transcription), and NF-κB (nuclear factor) (43). p300/CBP acts synergistically with ligand-activated ERα in enhancing in vitro transcription of chromatin templates (52). p300/CBP contains an N-terminal NR-box that is indispensable for NR interaction. In addition, p300/CBP interacts with coactivators of the SRC family via its C-terminal region. The CBP/SRC-1 complex is rather unstable, but a stable ternary complex is formed in the presence of an NR, containing NR, SRC, and CBP (53, 54). p300/CBP interacts weakly with ER or PR but can synergize with SRC-1 in coactivation of these receptors (55).

Corepressors

Several factors repress transcriptional activity of NRs. NCoR (nuclear receptor corepressor) and SMRT (silencing mediator for retinoid and thyroid hormone receptors) have been shown to interact with and repress transcriptional activity of Type II receptors (56, 57). NCoR and SMRT interact with the non-ligand bound receptor, which contributes to obstruction of ligand-independent recruitment of coactivators. Upon ligand binding the corepressor is released and interaction with coactivators can occur (58, 59). Binding conventional corepressors does not appear to be an essential feature of the steroid receptor subgroup of NRs. SMRT corepresses the activity of ER and PR only in the presence of their cognate partial agonists tamoxifen and RU486 (60, 61). One explanation for this may be the constitutive DNA-binding character of Type II receptors. Corepressor binding may represent an important regulatory step preventing ligand-independent transactivation. In the case of the steroid receptors, ligand binding precedes DNA binding, and the requirement of additional regulators such as corepressors may be less of a priority. The ability of corepressors to interact only with antagonist-bound ERα and PR may indicate that steroid receptors contain cryptic corepressor-binding sites that are exposed in the antagonist-binding receptor conformation.

Short heterodimer partner (SHP) is an unusual member of the NR family in that it lacks a conventional DBD (62). SHP interacts with several NRs, including RAR and TR, and inhibits transactivation by these receptors. It displays a ligand-dependent interaction with ERα and ERβ that results in repression of transcriptional activity (63, 64). SHP interacts with ERs via two NR-box-related motifs that may antagonize binding of p160 coactivators to the ERs. SHP also contains an active repressor mechanism (65).

HISTONE ACETYLATION

Chromatin accessibility influences transcription regulation. Acetylation of histone tails disrupts higher-order chromatin structure and is associated with increased transcriptional activity. Histone acetylation may facilitate access of transcription factors to promoter elements (reviewed in 66). p300/CBP possesses histone acetyl-transferase (HAT) activity and is tightly associated with the RNA polymerase II holoenzyme (67, 68). SRC-1 and SRC-3 also have intrinsic HAT activity located in the C termini (49, 69), whereas no HAT activity has been demonstrated for SRC-2. The HAT activity of p300/CBP is very strong compared with that of the SRC factors. P/CAF (p300/CBP associated factor) is a histone acetyl-transferase that associates with p300/CBP, SRC-1, or SRC-3 in concert with RAR, TR, or ER (70). The HAT activity of coactivators and/or their ability to act as bridging factors recruiting other proteins with HAT activity may account for their capacity to enhance transcriptional activity of NRs. Conversely, histone deacetylase complexes specifically interact with DNA-binding repressor proteins such as Mad or the corepressors NCoR and SMRT. The capacity of these factors to repress transcription correlates with their ability to interact with the histone deacetylase complexes (71–73).

CHAPERONE COMPLEXES

In the non-active state, members of the steroid receptor subgroup are found in a heterocomplex consisting of heat shock proteins (hsp), immunophilins, and p23. HsP and immunophilins are conserved and ubiquitously expressed proteins (reviewed in 74, 75). Immunophilins bind immuno-suppressant drugs (such as FK506, cyclosporin A, and rapamycin). Three immunophilins of high molecular weight associate with the steroid receptor chaperone complex through a direct binding to hsp90; FKBP50 (FK binding protein), FKBP52 and Cyp40. p23 forms an ATP-dependent complex with hsp90 and stabilizes the interaction between hsp90 and the different target proteins. The mature steroid receptor chaperone complex consists of an hsp90 dimer, one immunophilin, and a p23 monomer. Hsp70 can be coprecipitated with several steroid receptors; its association with the chaperone complex appears transient, and its role is unclear. In ER an additional region of several basic amino acids in the C-terminal part of the DBD, also recognized as a nuclear localization signal (NLS), is required for stable hsp90 interaction (76, 77). No physical interaction has been detected between hsp90 and the ERα NLS region. Interestingly, the immunophilin FKBP52 contains a negatively charged domain that may bind to the basic NLS in ERα and account for the stabilization of the hsp90 complex (75).

TRANSCRIPTIONAL ACTIVITY: Two Transactivation Functions

Two activation functions, termed AF-1 and AF-2, are present in ERα. The core of AF-2 is located on H12 in the LBD. Ligand-induced conformational changes create the functional AF-2 surface. AF-1 is located in the N-terminal A/B domain and functions autonomously and in the absence of ligands. Different portions of AF-1 in ERα are required for tamoxifen- and estrogen agonism (78, 79). Although AF-1 and AF-2 function autonomously in a cell and promoter context-dependent manner, the intact ER is generally a stronger transactivator than the isolated AF-1 or AF-2 (reviewed in 80). Functional interaction between AF-1 and AF-2 is required for full activity of ERα under conditions where individual action of AF-1 or AF-2 is not supported (81, 82).

Comparison of Transcriptional Activity of ERα and ERβ

With regard to the ability to activate transcription with constructs that contain ERE (5), ERβ is weaker than ERα in most cell systems tested (20, 31, 83–85). ERβ fails to show agonistic response to tamoxifen, which appears to be due to functional differences in the A/B domains in ERα and ERβ (22, 31, 32). When the A/B domain of ERβ was exchanged with that of ERα, the resulting chimeric receptor responded agonistically to tamoxifen in HEC-1 cells (human endometrial cancer). Conversely, tamoxifen acted as a pure antagonist of an ERα chimera containing the A/B domain of ERβ. However, in another cell system (breast cancer cell line MDA-231), which supports the agonistic effect of tamoxifen by wild-type ERα, there was no response with the ERβ chimera, indicating that cellular context is important in determining transcriptional activity of the ERs and that agonistic response to tamoxifen is also influenced by receptor regions other than AF-1 (86). When the isolated AF-1 and AF-2 of ERα and ERβ, respectively, were fused to the DBD of the yeast factor Gal4, ERβ AF-1 was unable to initiate transcription autonomously in co-transfection experiments, in contrast to ERα AF-1. Both full-length ERβ and ERβ AF-2 induced transcription from a TATA-containing promoter less efficiently than full-length ERα or ERα AF-2, whereas each AF-2 was equally potent in transcriptional activity on a heterologous thymidine kinase promoter (87). ERβ, in contrast to ERα, interacts with SRC-1 in the absence of ligand. This interaction results in ligand-independent transcriptional activity (22), is independent of AF-2, and occurs as a consequence of phosphorylation of serine residues in the A/B domain (88). Other laboratories report low or negligible AF-1 activity of ERβ. These apparent conflicts could be due to cell-specific differences in ERβ AF-1 activity.

ERα and ERβ show opposite effects in regulation of AP1 in an AF-1-dependent manner (89). Anti-estrogens induce activity of an AP1 promoter in the presence of ERβ, whereas E2 blocks transcription. In the presence of ERα the pattern is reversed (90). A similar observation of activation of the RARα promoter by E2 has been described (91). Both receptors regulate transcription of the quinone reductase gene in response to anti-estrogens but not E2 (92).

Dimerization

Transcriptional activity of ERs depends on receptor dimerization. Both receptor subtypes dimerize independently of ligand in solution and on DNA in vitro, but whether dimerization is ligand independent in vivo is unclear. Heterodimerization between the glucocorticoid and mineralocorticoid receptors contributes to tissue-specific actions of glucocorticoids (93). ERα and ERβ have almost identical DBDs, and the parts of the LBDs involved in dimerization also share a significant degree of similarity. ERα and ERβ form functional heterodimeric complexes both in vitro and in cells (27, 83, 85, 94). ERα/ERβ heterodimers bind to ERE sequences with a specificity and affinity similar to those of the respective homodimers, and ERα and ERβ are co-expressed in the same cells in mouse mammary gland and in rat cardiac myocytes and fibroblasts, suggesting that heterodimerization probably occurs in vivo (Figure 3) (95–97).

The physiological role of ER heterodimeric complexes remains to be determined. Creation of mutations in the DBD of ERα or ERβ resulted in receptors with altered DNA-binding specificity (from ERE to GRE). Co-transfection experiments, performed with a reporter construct containing a composite response element consisting of one ERE half site and one GRE half site, and the mutated ERα, together with wild-type ERβ or mutated ERβ with wild-type ERα, permitted measurement of transcriptional activity exclusively induced by α/β heterodimers (98). Transcriptional activity of heterodimeric complexes was found to be dependent on a functionally intact AF-2 within both receptor subunits, supporting earlier findings with ERα and ERβ dominant-negative F domain mutants (99). The complex initiated transcription when only one ER subunit was competent to bind ligand, albeit to a lower extent than if both subunits interacted with ligand. In addition, subtype-specific AF-1 functions were retained within the context of the heterodimeric complex (98). Co-expression of ERα with ERβ modulates responses to tamoxifen and low levels of E2 in an ERβ dose-dependent manner, probably owing to formation of heterodimeric complexes (100).

ERβ ISOFORMS

Analysis of ERβ transcripts revealed additional open reading frames upstream of the first reported sequence, with two putative translation start sites. Translation from these upstream ATGs gives rise to proteins containing 548 or 530 amino acids, respectively, in addition to the 485 amino acid ERβ first reported. These open reading frames are present in the human, mouse, and rat ERβ (27, 101).

Another variant, termed ERβ2, contains 54 extra nucleotides within the reading frame, which causes an 18 amino acid insertion in the LBD of ERβ1 (21, 23, 24, 26). ERβ2 shows severely impaired E2-binding ability and consequently initiates

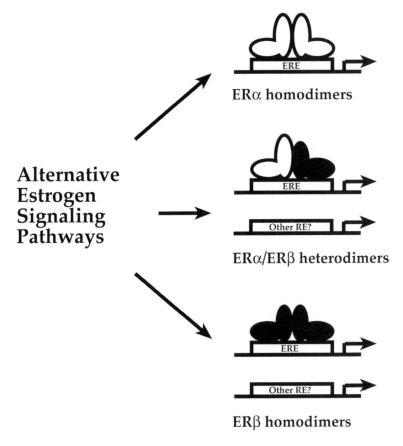

ERα homodimers

ERα/ERβ heterodimers

ERβ homodimers

Figure 3 Putative pathways by ERα/ERβ homo- and heterodimeric complexes.

transcription of reporter constructs poorly in transient transfection experiments. ERβ2 binds to ERE sequences in vitro and can form heterodimeric complexes with both ERβ and ERα. Co-expression in cells of ERβ2 with ERα or ERβ results in loss of transcriptional activity in an ERβ2 dose-dependent fashion, indicating that ERβ2 functions as a dominant-negative partner of both ERα and ERβ1. Another splice variant in human tissue, ERβcx, has an alternative C terminus and is unable to bind either ligand or DNA . It selectively heterodimerizes with ERα and inhibits its transcriptional activity (102). In addition, several other ERβ isoforms have varying C-terminal ends (103).

Phosphorylation and Ligand-Independent Activity

The transition of NRs from silent into transcriptionally active states is more complex than initially proposed. Activation of ER appears to be a multistep process relying on a number of events, including dimerization, the binding of ligand, phosphorylation, interaction with cofactors, and DNA binding. Phosphorylation of ERs occurs as part of both the ligand-induced activity and ligand-independent transcriptional activation (reviewed in 104, 105).

Phosphorylation of the LBD

A conserved tyrosine residue in the LBD in both ER subtypes of all species, located in position 537 in human ER α (Tyr 541 in mouse ERα), appears to be important in the regulation of ERα transcriptional activity. Tyr 537 is phosphorylated by the Src family of tyrosine kinases in the absence of E2 (106). Mutation in human ERα of Tyr 537 to Ser or Ala produces a constitutively active receptor, whereas Lys, Phe, and Glu substitutions retain E2-dependent transcriptional activity (107). Peptide profiles of proteolytic digests of an ERα mutant, in which Tyr 537 has been replaced by Ser, show that this mutant appears to be in a ligand-bound conformation in the absence of E2 (108). Mouse ERα with Tyr 541 replaced by Asp, Glu, or Ala, but not Phe, also displays ligand-independent activity (109). Mouse and human ERα with cognate tyrosine substitutions show E2-independent interaction with SRC-1. SRC-1 furthermore enhances ligand-independent transcriptional activity of these mutant receptors. Interestingly, SRC-1 peptides stabilize the H12 position in the agonist-bound ERα and slow the dissociation rate of the agonist (36, 110). The three-dimensional structure of ERα shows that Tyr 537 is located at the C-terminal end of the loop preceding H12. Interestingly, in the crystal structure of ERα LBD bound to 4-OH-tamoxifen, Tyr 537 contacts residues in H3 and H4, which were not observed in the ERα DES three-dimensional structure. These contacts appear to stabilize the N-terminal turn of H12, albeit not in the agonist position observed in the DES-bound structure (36). Mutation of the corresponding tyrosine to asparagine in ERβ LBD also results in a receptor that is active in the absence of ligand (30).

Because phosphorylation of Tyr 537 in ERα occurs in the absence of E2, without inducing ligand-independent transcriptional activity, the phosphorylation status of Tyr 537 may regulate the ability of ERα to bind E2. Substitutions of this residue with a charged or an alanine residue result in a constitutively active receptor, probably the result of conformational changes within the ERα LBD that mimic ligand activation. This notion is supported by the observation that anti-estrogens inhibit the ligand-independent activity of both ER subtypes with tyrosine to asparagine substitutions, probably through disruption of the agonist-like conformation of these mutant receptors (30).

EGF-Induced Phosphorylation

The fact that growth factors and protein kinase A (PKA) activators induce transcriptional activity of ERα in the absence of E2 challenged the view of ER as a strictly ligand-dependent transcription factor. Peptide growth factors, PKA-activating agents, neurotransmitters, and cyclins can induce or enhance ER-mediated transcriptional activity (reviewed in 104). Phosphorylation appears to be important in ligand-independent activation of ERα in all of these pathways.

The N terminus of ERα contains several conserved serine residues within AF-1 that are targets for phosphorylation. Phosphorylation of Ser 118 of human ERα is induced by EGF and is dependent on the Ras-MAPK (mitogen-activated protein kinase) pathway (111, 112). Phosphorylation of Ser 118 via MAPK occurs in the absence of E2 and results in ligand-independent activity of ERα. E2 also induces phosphorylation of Ser 118, but this appears to be independent of MAPK (113), indicating that alternative signal transduction pathways can act on the same residue, depending on the E2 status of the cell. Serine residues in ERβ are also phosphorylated via the MAPK pathway. Co-expression of a dominant form of H-Ras (an integral factor in MAPK signaling) enhances E2-induced activity of mouse ERβ, indicating that alternative signal transduction pathways can act on the same residue, depending on the E2 status of the cell (22). In addition, phosphorylation of Ser 106 and Ser 124 in ERβ (numbered assuming 548 amino acids in mERβ) by MAPK results in ligand-independent recruitment of SRC-1 and concomitant increase in transcriptional activity (88).

The physiological relevance of EGF-activation of ERα is supported by the observation that EGF imitates the effects of E2 in the murine female reproductive tract and in breast epithelial cells (114, 115). Mice deficient in ERα (ERKO) lack a uterotropic response to EGF, demonstrating the involvement of ERα in mediating EGF action in vivo (116). EGF alone can increase the expression of PR in the mammary gland of sexually mature mice in an ER-dependent manner, mimicking the effects of E2. Inhibition of EGF action in the mammary gland blocks E2-induced expression of PR and development of the terminal end buds (117 and references therein). Another phosphorylation target in the A/B domain of ER is Ser 167, which is phosphorylated by casein kinase II upon binding of E2 in vitro (118). This residue is also phosphorylated by pp90rsk1 (90-kDa ribosomal S6 kinase, a Ser/Thr protein kinase) (119).

cAMP-Dependent Phosphorylation

In addition to ligand-independent activation through phosphorylation of serine residues in the AF-1 of ERα, other compounds induce transcriptional activity in the absence of ligand but in a manner depending on AF-2 rather than AF-1 (120). cAMP activates PKA by inducing the release of the regulatory element from the catalytic subunit. Agents that increase cellular content of cAMP (forskolin, okadaic acid, and cholera toxin) evoke ligand-independent transcriptional activity of ERα and also synergize with E2-mediated activation (121). The partial agonistic response to tamoxifen increases with increased cellular cAMP (122). Activation via cAMP signaling pathways requires ERα AF-2 and appears to be dependent on PKA and thus represents a pathway distinct from activation via peptide growth factors (123). However, no specific phosphorylation targets for PKA have been determined within the AF-2 (124). PKA phosphorylates Ser 236 in the DBD of ERα, which enhances receptor dimerization.

Cyclins

Cyclins and their kinases, cyclin-dependent kinases (cdks) regulate cell cycle progression, and defects in the regulation of cyclins or cdks play an important role in the development and progression of cancer. Interestingly, E2 increases the protein levels of G1 regulatory cyclins A, B1, D1, D3, and E in mammary carcinoma female 7 (MCF7) cells (125). Cyclin D1, in addition, induces transcriptional activity of unliganded ER (126, 127), which is interesting because cyclin D1 is frequently expressed abnormally in breast tumors. Cyclin D1 activation of ERα occurs independently of the cognate cdk and direct phosphorylation of ERα; cyclin D1 acts as a bridging factor between unliganded ERα and SRC-1 (128). E2 also increases cyclin D1 expression in an ER-dependent manner in breast cancer cell lines, which may be of relevance in explaining the mitogenic effects of E2 on breast tumors (129, 130). Ser 104 and Ser 106 in human ERα are phosphorylated by the cyclin A-cdk2 complex, enhancing transcriptional activity of ERα in both the absence and presence of ligand, which may be of consequence for cellular proliferation (131, 132).

THE PHYSIOLOGICAL IMPORTANCE OF ESTROGENS AND THE ROLE OF HERS

In addition to their role in reproduction, estrogens influence a number of systems in females, including the mammary gland, the cardiovascular system, and bone. E2 is synthesized in the granulosa cells of the mature ovary through aromatization of testosterone supplied by the thecal cells. The rate-limiting enzyme in E2 synthesis is aromatase, a member of the P450 family. Synthesis of estrogens also occurs in adipose tissue, skeletal muscle, skin, hair follicles, and bone. As illustrated by the increased risk of fractures in post-menopausal women and the decreased risk with hormone replacement therapy (reviewed 133), estrogens are important for maintenance of female bone mass.

Estrogens also exert a protective effect on the cardiovascular system, possibly accounting for the low incidence of heart disease in women of reproductive age. After menopause the risk of cardiovascular disease increases and at 60 years of age or older the sexes converge in incidence of heart disease. Hormone replacement therapy has a beneficial effect on the cardiovascular system in post-menopausal women (reviewed in 134). In adult men endogenous estrogens are produced by the adrenals, testes, and adipose tissue. The role of estrogen production and ERs in males has historically been unclear, but testicular responses to exogenous estrogens in men includes an increase in Leydig cell number, atrophy of seminiferous tubules, and hyperplasia of the rete testis (reviewed in 135). Steroidogenesis and proper development of Leydig cells are impaired in rats treated with exogenous E2 (reviewed in 136). ERs are present in all fetal reproductive organs in male mice. Furthermore, ERα is present in seminal vesicles, epididymis, and nonhyperplastic prostate in men.

EXPRESSION PATTERN OF ERβ IN THE BODY

ERβ was originally cloned from a rat prostate cDNA library and is expressed in parts of the rat prostate (reviewed in 137). ERβ is also expressed in human prostate (138). In the testis ERβ is present in Sertoli cells at all developmental stages, in fetal Leydig cells, peritubular cells, and gonocytes. In pubertal rats, ERβ is expressed in spermatogonia and pachytene spermatocytes (139). ERβ in the ovaries is mainly found in the granulosa cells of primary, secondary, and mature follicles (5,140–144). The expression of ERβ in rat ovaries fluctuates during the estrus cycle; lowest levels occur in the estrus phase (140). ERα is not detected in granulosa cells but is present in theca cells, interstitial gland cells, and germinal epithelium (142). In the adult rat uterus ERβ is found only in the glandular epithelial cells, whereas ERα is present in both luminal and glandular epithelial cells and in the stroma (140, 142). Both ER subtypes are expressed in rat pituitary (145, 146), and ERβ is present in multiple human tissues (138).

AROMATASE AND ER DEFICIENCY

During the 1990s, two men and five women with mutations in the CYP19 (aromatase) gene were reported to have negligible aromatase activity (reviewed in 147). The men were born with normal genital development and had normal onset of puberty, but linear growth persisted into adulthood. Examination of the skeleton showed unfused epiphyseal plates, delayed bone age, and osteoporosis. The women had ambiguous external genitalia at birth. Internal reproductive organs were normal, but at puberty several effects of the lack of sufficient E2 included failure of breast growth, amenorrhea, enlargement of the clitoris (androgenization), absence of a growth spurt, delayed bone age, and later multicystic ovaries as well as unfused epiphyses. Treatment with estrogens and progesterone resulted in regression of ovarian cysts, restored ovarian function, and normal pubertal development. Levels of testosterone, FSH, and LH in serum were elevated in both sexes, confirming the long-held concept of a role for estrogens in regulation of gonadotropin secretion in both males and females.

The generation of mutant mice lacking functional aromatase (ArKO) has been described by two groups (148, 149). Mice homozygous for the mutation are viable with normal genital development. However, at the time of puberty female mice display atrophic but histologically otherwise normal uteri; complete lack of corpora lutea in the ovaries, which in addition show hypertrophied stroma; and an increased number of granulosa cells and follicles arrested before ovulation.

Mammary glands remain in a prepubertal stage. FSH, LH, and testosterone levels are elevated. Treatment with E2 resulted in normal response of uteri of mutant mice compared with wild-type mice.

Male mutant mice showed an age-related disruption of spermatogenesis with increased germ cell apoptosis, Leydig cell hypertrophy and hyperplasia, and normal numbers of Sertoli cells and germ cells (150). In addition, ArKO male mice showed impaired sexual behavior, with reduced mounting frequency and increased latency between mounts; however, young males were able to sire litters (148, 149). Mice of both sexes showed increased internal fat. The normal fetal development of aromatase-deficient mice and humans is attributed to the transfer of maternal estrogens during pregnancy. The question still remains as to whether estrogen signaling is required for embryonic development (reviewed in 151).

At the time of the creation of ERα KO (ERKO) [ERα (-/-) and ERβ (+/+)] mice, only one ER had been identified, and ERKO mice were thought to be completely devoid of estrogen signaling. Not long afterward a man was identified with a bi-allelic disruptive mutation of the ERα gene. This patient was externally normal with normal genitalia but suffered from osteoporosis and was still growing at the age of 28 because the epiphyseal plates were unfused (152). Both male and female ERKO mice are infertile. Females do not ovulate. The ovaries are hyperemic and lack corpora lutea. LH levels are elevated, and the ovarian phenotype of females can be successfully rescued by prepubertal treatment with a gonadotropin-releasing hormone antagonist (153). The uteri are hypoplastic and have very reduced response to E2 treatment. The mammary glands of ERKO females appear to exhibit normal prepubertal development, but no pubertal growth (154). Ductal growth of the mammary gland during puberty normally occurs in response to ovarian synthesis of E2, and ERα appears to be indispensable in mediating the growth-stimulation.

In ERKO males the testes are normal at birth and develop normally to puberty when they begin to degenerate. By 5 months of age the testes are atrophic. Luminal fluid appears to accumulate in the seminiferous tubules, rete testes, and efferent ductules owing to a lack of reabsorption in the efferent ductules that results in reduced sperm concentrations in the epididymis (155). Sperm from ERKO mice have severely impaired motility and fertilization ability indicating a critical role for ERα in the maturation process of spermatozoa. ERKO mice, in addition, show compromised sexual behavior at several levels. The males appear normal with regard to interest in receptive females and mounting attempts; however, latency between mounts is prolonged, number of intromissions is reduced, and ejaculations do not occur. ERKO males, furthermore, display less offensive aggressive behavior and an increased rate of pup-killing compared with heterozygous or wild-type mice (156). Comparison with ArKO male mice (which are exposed to maternal estrogens during the gestation period) and which show less severe impairment of sexual behavior, indicates that development of appropriate sexual behavior may be dependent on estrogen signaling via ERα during early brain development or, alternatively, that maintenance of sexual behavior in the adult mouse involves other signals than those mediated by ERα. ERKO females show increased aggressive behavior toward other females, reject mating advances by males, and exhibit impaired parental behavior including a higher degree of infanticide (84, 157, 158).

The phenotype of BERKO mice [ERβ (-/-), ERα (+/+)] is different from that of ERKO mice (159). BERKO mice develop normally and are viable. BERKO females have very reduced fertility. When they do have pups, the litter size is no more than three. Poor reproductive capacity in BERKO females is due to defects in both the ovary and the uterus. Unlike ERKO females, where the ovarian defects are the result of pituitary dysfunction, the defects in BERKO females are in the ovary itself. There is a marked paucity of corpora lutea and an increase in the number of follicles with premature atresia. It appears that follicles are actively recruited into the growth pool but they fail to mature. The oocytes are not released and die within the preantral follicles. By 1.5 years of age no follicles are left in the BERKO ovary. Surprisingly, in the heterozygote females, the ovary also ages much more rapidly than in the wild-type littermates, and breeding becomes very inefficient after a few matings. Uterine dysfunction probably contributes to infertility in BERKO mice because in pregnant BERKOs most of the fetuses are resorbed. Because the uterus is traditionally thought of as ERα-regulated tissue, it was most surprising to find defects in BERKO uteri. In both immature and adult BERKO females expression of the proliferation marker, Ki-67, was increased, and the uterus was hyperresponsive to estradiol, as indicated by the over-expression of VEGF and IGF-I (160).

BERKO males appear to be normal, but develop prostatic hyperplasia as young as 3 months of age. This suggests that estrogens may control prostatic growth via ERβ. Double-mutant mice lacking both ERs are viable with normal development (161). Phenotypes appear essentially similar to ERKO mice except for the appearance of structures in the ovary that resemble seminiferous tubules of the testis. These structures have not been fully characterized, but the phenomenon has been described as post-natal sex reversal.

THE MAMMARY GLAND

Until the onset of puberty in humans there is no significant difference in the primitive mammary gland between the sexes. In females, the growth rate of the mammary epithelia accelerates during puberty to eventually fill the mammary fat pad. The functional portion of the human mammary gland is called the terminal ductal lobular unit (TDLU), corresponding to the terminal end buds in mice. After development is completed these structures are the major hormone-sensitive areas of the mammary epithelium in all species (reviewed in 162). Most mammary cancers also originate from these structures because they constitute the major proliferative cell population in the mammary gland. The TDLU responds by DNA synthesis to both estrogen and progesterone during the luteal phase of the human menstrual cycle. This is in contrast to the endometrium, where the bulk of proliferation occurs in response to E2 during the follicular phase, and progesterone secretion during the luteal phase opposes E2-stimulated proliferation (163 and references therein).

During pregnancy the mammary glands of all species form side buds that either branch or form alveoli. This process continues to fill the entire fat pad with alveolar structures. In the post-lactating mammary gland regression takes place with death of most of the functional cells. The early phases of regression are characterized by widespread apoptosis. In post-menopausal women TDLU also regresses. ERβ appears to be ubiquitously expressed during all developmental stages, whereas ERα expression fluctuates, with an increase around puberty, gradual decline during pregnancy, up-regulation during lactation, and a decrease in the post-lactating gland (97).

The role of estrogen receptors in the proliferative response of the breast to estrogen is not understood. In the normal mammary gland, ERα is not expressed in proliferating epithelial cells, which indicates that the growth stimulatory effect of E2 occurs indirectly (97, 164, 165). In contrast, breast cancers that express ERα respond to estrogen by proliferation, and their growth is blocked by the anti-estrogen tamoxifen. It is thought that ER in the stroma mediates growth-stimulatory effects of estrogen by increasing growth factor secretion (163). Growth factors are the mediators of proliferation in the epithelial cells. This still does not explain why ERα-containing epithelial cells do not divide in response to estrogen in normal mammary gland but do so in breast cancer. It appears that ERβ might down-regulate growth factor receptors or some key protein involved in proliferative pathways. The respective roles of the two ERs in estrogen-mediated breast growth remains to be delineated.

ERβ IN BREAST CANCER

ERβ is present in breast cancer (166–176), but it is not clear what this means in development, progression, and treatment of breast cancer. Clearly, in the rodent breast ERβ is the more highly expressed of the two receptors. If this is also true in the human breast, the presence of ERβ in breast cancer would not be surprising. If ERβ plays a role in growth repression, and if repression is mediated through EREs, anti-estrogen therapy would inhibit this growth repression. If, on the other hand, ERβ exerts its growth repressive effects via AP-1 or SP-1 sites, anti-estrogens would limit growth via ERβ. What is needed are more studies with larger numbers of both normal and malignant breast samples. Such studies would permit an evaluation of the ERβ content of the breast as disease progresses and its correlation with responsiveness to anti-estrogen treatment.

SUMMARY AND CONCLUSIONS

The biological effects of estrogens are mediated via two estrogen receptors, ERα and ERβ, which regulate transcription through direct interaction with specific binding sites on DNA (EREs) in promoter regions of target genes. In addition, ERs are transcriptional regulators at AP-1 and SP-1 sites.

Both ERα and ERβ bind specifically to estrogen responsive elements (EREs) and activate ERE-containing promoters in response to 17β-estradiol (E2). ERβ

requires approximately five- to tenfold higher concentrations of E2 than ERα for maximal transcriptional activity to occur, and ERβ is only approximately 30% as efficient as ERα in a variety of reporter systems. The anti-estrogen, tamoxifen, is a mixed agonist/antagonist on ERα but is a pure antagonist on ERβ. ERα and ERβ can form functional DNA-binding heterodimeric complexes both in vitro and in cell systems, and in these complexes ERβ is the dominant partner repressing transcriptional activity at low concentrations of E2 and in the presence of tamoxifen. At AP-1 and SP-1 sites, ERα and ERβ can have opposite actions. This is true in the presence of both agonists and antagonists. These opposing effects of the two estrogen receptors may be very important in helping the understanding of the good and bad effects of estrogens. How, for example, can estrogen be the cause of breast malignancies and yet phytoestrogens perhaps be the factor responsible for the low incidence of the same malignancy in the Asian population? In conclusion, signal transduction by ERs involves multiple pathways, depending on tissue-selective expression of different receptor subtypes, the nature of the DNA target, concentration of agonistic or antagonistic ligand, and formation of heterodimeric complexes.

ACKNOWLEDGMENT

Supported by a grant from the Swedish Cancer Fund.

Visit the Annual Reviews home page at www.AnnualReviews.org

LITERATURE CITED

1. Jensen EV, Jacobson HI. 1962. Basic guides to the mechanism of estrogen action. *Recent Prog. Horm. Res.* 18:387–414
2. Green S, Walter P, Kumar V, Krust A, Bornert JM, et al. 1986. Human oestrogen receptor cDNA: sequence, expression and homology to v-erb-A. *Nature* 320:134–39
3. Greene GL, Gilna P, Waterfield M, Baker A, Hort Y, Shine J. 1986. Sequence and expression of human estrogen receptor complementary DNA, *Science* 231:1150–54
4. Parker MG. 1995. Structure and function of estrogen receptors. *Vitam. Horm.* 51:267–87
5. Kuiper GGJM, Enmark E, Pelto-Huikko M, Nilsson S, Gustafsson J-Å. 1996. Cloning of a novel estrogen receptor expressed in rat prostate and ovary. *Proc. Natl. Acad. Sci. USA* 93:5925–30
6. Enmark E, Gustafsson J-Å. 1999. Oestrogen receptors—an overview. *J Intern. Med.* 246:133–38
7. Muramatsu M, Inoue S. 2000. Estrogen receptors: How do they control reproductive and nonreproductive functions? *Biochem. Biophys. Res. Comm.* 270:1–10
8. Laudet V, Hanni C, Coll J, Catzeflis F, Stehelin D. 1992. Evolution of the nuclear receptor gene superfamily. *EMBO J.* 11:1003–13
9. Beato M, Truss M, Chavez S. 1996. Control of transcription by steroid hormones. *Ann. NY Acad. Sci.* 784:93–123
10. Freedman LP. 1992. Anatomy of the steroid receptor zinc finger region. *Endocr. Rev.* 13:129–45
11. Glass CK. 1994. Differential recognition of target genes by nuclear receptor monomers, dimers, and heterodimers. *Endocr. Rev.* 15:391–407
12. Mader S, Kumar V, de Verneuil H, Chambon P. 1989. Three amino acids of the oestrogen receptor are essential to its ability to distinguish an oestrogen from a

glucocorticoid-responsive element. *Nature* 338:271–74

13. Laudet V, Adelmant G. 1995. Nuclear receptors. Lonesome orphans. *Curr. Biol.* 5:124–27

14. Härd T, Kellenbach E, Boelens R, Maler BA, Dahlman K, et al. 1990. Solution structure of the glucocorticoid receptor DNA-binding domain. *Science* 249:157–60

15. Schwabe JW, Neuhaus D, Rhodes D. 1990. Solution structure of the DNA-binding domain of the oestrogen receptor. *Nature* 348:458–61

16. Luisi BF, Xu WX, Otwinowski Z, Freedman LP, Yamamoto KR, Sigler PB. 1991. Crystallographic analysis of the interaction of the glucocorticoid receptor with DNA. *Nature* 352:497–505

17. Schwabe JW, Chapman L, Finch JT, Rhodes D. 1993. The crystal structure of the estrogen receptor DNA-binding domain bound to DNA:how receptors discriminate between their response elements. *Cell* 75:567–78

18. Kuntz MA, Shapiro DJ. 1997. Dimerizing the estrogen receptor DNA binding domain enhances binding to estrogen response elements. *J Biol. Chem.* 272:27949–56

19. Enmark E, Peltohuikko M, Grandien K, Lagercrantz S, Lagercrantz J, et al. 1997. Human estrogen receptor beta-gene structure, chromosomal localization, and expression pattern. *J. Clin. Endocrinol. Metab.* 82:4258–65

20. Mosselman S, Polman J, Dijkema R. 1996. ERbeta—identification and characterization of a novel human estrogen receptor. *FEBS Lett.* 392:49–53

21. Petersen DN, Tkalcevic GT, Koza-Taylor PH, Turi TG, Brown TA. 1998. Identification of estrogen receptor beta2, a functional variant of estrogen receptor beta expressed in normal rat tissues. *Endocrinology.* 139:1082–92

22. Tremblay GB, Tremblay A, Copeland NG, Gilbert DJ, Jenkins NA, et al. 1997. Cloning, chromosomaal localization, and

functional analysis of the murine estrogen receptorβ. *Mol. Endocrinol.* 11:353–65

23. Chu S, Fuller PJ. 1997. Identification of a splice variant of the rat estrogen receptor beta gene, *Mol. Cell. Endocrinol.* 132:195–99

24. Hanstein B, Liu H, Yancisin MC, Brown M. 1999. Functional analysis of a novel estrogen receptor-beta isoform. *Mol. Endocrinol.* 13:129–37

25. Leygue E, Dotzlaw H, Watson PH, Murphy LC. 1999. Expression of estrogen receptor beta1, beta2, and beta5 messenger RNAs in human breast tissue. *Cancer Res.* 59:1175–79

26. Maruyama K, Endoh H, Sasaki-Iwaoka H, Kanou H, Shimaya E, et al. 1998. A novel isoform of rat estrogen receptor beta with 18 amino acid insertion in the ligand binding domain as a putative dominant negative regular of estrogen action. *Biochem. Biophys. Res. Commun.* 246:142–47

27. Ogawa S, Inoue S, Watanabe T, Hiroi H, Orimo A, et al. 1998. The complete primary structure of human estrogen receptor beta (hER beta) and its heterodimerization with ER alpha in vivo and in vitro. *Biochem. Biophys. Res. Commun.* 243:122–26

28. Deleted in proof

29. Kuiper GGJM, Carlsson B, Grandien K, Enmark E, Häggblad J, et al. 1997. Comparison of the ligand binding specificity and transcript tissue distribution of estrogen receptors alpha and beta. *Endocrinology* 138:863–70

30. Tremblay GB, Tremblay A, Labrie F, Giguere V. 1998. Ligand-independent activation of the estrogen receptors alpha and beta by mutations of a conserved tyrosine can be abolished by antiestrogens. *Cancer Res.* 58:877–81

31. Watanabe T, Inoue S, Ogawa S, Ishii Y, Hiroi H, et al. 1997. Agonistic effect of tamoxifen is dependent on the cell type, ERE-promoter context, and estrogen receptor subtype: Functional difference

between estrogen receptors α and β. *Biochem. Biophys . Res. Comm.* 236:140–45

32. Barkhem T, Carlsson B, Nilsson Y, Enmark E, Gustafsson J-Å, Nilsson S. 1998. Differential response of estrogen receptor alpha and estrogen receptor beta to partial estrogen agonists/antagonists, *Mol. Pharmacol.* 54:105–12

33. Kuiper GG, Lemmen JG, Carlsson B, Corton JC, Safe SH, et al. 1998. Interaction of estrogenic chemicals and phytoestrogens with estrogen receptor beta. *Endocrinology* 139:4252–63

34. Wurtz JM, Bourguet W, Renaud JP, Vivat V, Chambon P, et al. 1996. A canonical structure for the ligand-binding domain of nuclear receptors. *Nat. Struct. Biol.* 3:87–94

35. Brzozowski AM, Pike ACW, Dauter Z, Hubbard RE, Bonn T, et al. 1997. Molecular basis of agonism and antagonism in the estrogen receptor. *Nature* 389:753–58

36. Shiau AK, Barstad D, Loria PM, Cheng L, Kushner PJ, et al. 1998. The structural basis of estrogen receptor/coactivator recognition and the antagonism of this interaction by tamoxifen. *Cell* 95:927–37

37. Tanenbaum DM, Wang Y, Williams SP, Sigler PB. 1998. Crystallographic comparison of the estrogen and progesterone receptor's ligand binding domains. *Proc. Natl. Acad. Sci. USA.* 95:5998–6003

38. Pike ACW, Brzozowski AM, Hubbard RE, Bonn T, Thorsell AG, et al. 1999. Structure of the ligand-binding domain of oestrogen receptor beta in the presence of a partial agonist and a full antagonist. *EMBO J.* 18:4608–18

39. Bourguet W, Ruff M, Chambon P, Gronemeyer H, Moras D. 1995. Crystal structure of the ligand-binding domain of the human nuclear receptor RXR-alpha. *Nature* 375:377–82

40. Renaud JP, Rochel N, Ruff M, Vivat V, Chambon P, et al. 1995. Crystal structure of the RAR-gamma ligand-binding domain bound to all-trans retinoic acid. *Nature* 378:681–89

41. Wagner RL, Apriletti JW, McGrath ME, West BL, Baxter JD, Fletterick RJ. 1995. A structural role for hormone in the thyroid hormone receptor. *Nature* 378:690–97

42. Glass CK, Rosenfeld MG. 2000. The coregulator exchange in transcriptional functions of nuclear receptors. *Genes Dev.* 14:121–41

43. McKenna NJ, Lanz RB, O'Malley BW. 1999. Nuclear receptor coregulators:cellular and molecular biology. *Endocr. Rev.* 20:321–44

44. Henttu PM, Kalkhoven E, Parker MG. 1997. AF-2 activity and recruitment of steroid receptor coactivator 1 to the estrogen receptor depend on a lysine residue conserved in nuclear receptors. *Mol. Cell Biol.* 17:1832–39

45. Darimont BD, Wagner RL, Apriletti JW, Stallcup MR, Kushner PJ, et al. 1998. Structure and specificity of nuclear receptor-coactivator interactions. *Genes Dev.* 12:3343–56

46. Mak HY, Hoare S, Henttu PM, Parker MG. 1999. Molecular determinants of the estrogen receptor-coactivator interface. *Mol. Cell Biol.* 19:3895–903

47. McInerney EM, Rose DW, Flynn SE, Westin S, Mullen TM, et al. 1998. Determinants of coactivator LXXLL motif specificity in nuclear receptor transcriptional activation. *Genes Dev.* 12:3357–68

48. Suen CS, Berrodin TJ, Mastroeni R, Cheskis BJ, Lyttle CR, Frail DE. 1998. A transcriptional coactivator, steroid receptor coactivator-3, selectively augments steroid receptor transcriptional activity. *J. Biol. Chem.* 273:27645–53

49. Spencer TE, Jenster G, Burcin MM, Allis CD, Zhou J, et al. 1997. Steroid receptor coactivator-1 is a histone acetyltransferase. *Nature* 389:194–98

50. Torchia J, Rose DW, Inostroza J, Kamei Y, Westin S, et al. 1997. The transcriptional co-activator p/CIP binds CBP and

mediates nuclear-receptor function. *Nature* 387:677–84

51. Kwok RP, Laurance ME, Lundblad JR, Goldman PS, Shih H, et al. 1996. Control of cAMP-regulated enhancers by the viral transactivator Tax through CREB and the co-activator CBP. *Nature* 380:642–46

52. Kraus WL, Kadonaga JT. 1998. p300 and estrogen receptor cooperatively activate transcription via differential enhancement of initiation and reinitiation. *Genes Dev.* 12:331–42

53. Hanstein B, Eckner R, DiRenzo J, Halachmi S, Liu H, et al. 1996. p300 is a component of an estrogen receptor coactivator complex. *Proc. Natl. Acad. Sci. USA* 93:11540–45

54. Li H, Chen JD. 1998. The receptor-associated coactivator 3 activates transcription through CREB-binding protein recruitment and autoregulation. *J. Biol. Chem.* 273:5948–54

55. Smith CL, Onate SA, Tsai MJ, O'Malley BW. 1996. CREB binding protein acts synergistically with steroid receptor coactivator-1 to enhance steroid receptor-dependent transcription. *Proc. Natl. Acad. Sci. USA* 93:8884–88

56. Chen JD, Evans RM. 1995. A transcriptional co-repressor that interacts with nuclear hormone receptors. *Nature* 377:454–57

57. Horlein AJ, Naar AM, Heinzel T, Torchia J, Gloss B, et al. 1995 Ligand-independent repression by the thyroid hormone receptor mediated by a nuclear receptor co-repressor. *Nature* 377:397–404

58. Nagy L, Kao HY, Love JD, Li C, Banayo E, et al. 1999. Mechanism of corepressor binding and release from nuclear hormone receptors. *Genes Dev.* 13:3209–16

59. Perissi V, Staszewski LM, McInerney EM, Kurokawa R, Krones A, et al. 1999. Molecular determinants of nuclear receptor-corepressor interaction. *Genes Dev.* 13:3198–208

60. Smith CL, Nawaz Z, O'Malley BW. 1997.

Coactivator and corepressor regulation of the agonist/antagonist activity of the mixed antiestrogen, 4-hydroxytamoxifen. *Mol. Endocrinol.* 11:657–66

61. Wagner BL, Norris JD, Knotts TA, Weigel NL, McDonnell DP. 1998. The nuclear corepressors NCoR and SMRT are key regulators of both ligand- and 8-bromo-cyclic AMP-dependent transcriptional activity of the human progesterone receptor. *Mol. Cell. Biol.* 18:1369–78

62. Seol W, Choi HS, Moore DD. 1996. An orphan nuclear hormone receptor that lacks a DNA binding domain and heterodimerizes with other receptors. *Science* 272:1336–39

63. Johansson L, Thomsen JS, Damdimopoulos AE, Spyrou G, Gustafsson J-Å Treuter E. 1999. The orphan nuclear receptor SHP inhibits agonist-dependent transcriptional activity of estrogen receptors ERalpha and ERbeta. *J. Biol. Chem.* 274:345–53

64. Seol W, Hanstein B, Brown M, Moore DD. 1998. Inhibition of estrogen receptor action by the orphan receptor SHP (short heterodimer partner), *Mol. Endocrinol.* 12:1551–57

65. Johansson L, Båvner A, Thomsen JS, Farnegardh M, Gustafsson JÅ, Treuter E. 2000. The orphan nuclear receptor SHP utilizes conserved LXXLL-related motifs for interactions with ligand-activated estrogen receptors. *Mol. Cell. Biol.* 20:1124–33

66. Struhl K. 1998. Histone acetylation and transcriptional regulatory mechanisms. *Genes Dev.* 12:599–606

67. Bannister AJ, Kouzarides T. 1996. The CBP co-activator is a histone acetyltransferase. *Nature* 384:641–43

68. Ogryzko VV, Schiltz RL, Russanova V, Howard BH, Nakatani Y. 1996. The transcriptional coactivators p300 and CBP are histone acetyltransferases. *Cell* 87:953–59

69. Chen H, Lin R, Schiltz R, Chakravarti D, Nash A, et al. 1997. Nuclear receptor coactivator ACTR is a novel histone acetyltransferase and forms a multimeric activation

complex with P/CAF and CBP/p300. *Cell* 90:569–80

70. Korzus E, Torchia J, Rose DW, Xu L, Kurokawa R, et al. 1998. Transcription factor-specific requirements for coactivators and their acetyltransferase functions. *Science* 279:703–7

71. Alland L, Muhle R, Hou H Jr, Potes J, Chin L, Schreiber-Agus N, DePinho RA. 1997. Role for N-CoR and histone deacetylase in Sin3–mediated transcriptional repression. *Nature* 387:49–55

72. Heinzel T, Lavinsky RM, Mullen TM, Soderstrom M, Laherty CD, et al. 1997. A complex containing N-CoR, mSin3 and histone deacetylase mediates transcriptional repression. *Nature* 387:43–48

73. Nagy L, Kao HY, Chakravarti D, Lin RJ, Hassig CA, et al. 1997. Nuclear receptor repression mediated by a complex containing SMRT, mSin3A, and histone deacetylase. *Cell* 89:373–80

74. Csermely P, Schnaider T, Soti C, Prohaszka Z, Nardai G. 1998. The 90-kDa molecular chaperone family:structure, function, and clinical applications. A comprehensive review. *Pharmacol. Ther.* 79:129–68

75. Pratt WB, Toft DO. 1997. Steroid receptor interactions with heat shock protein and immunophilin chaperones. *Endocr. Rev.* 18:306–60

76. Chambraud B, Berry M, Redeuilh G, Chambon P, Baulieu EE. 1990. Several regions of human estrogen receptor are involved in the formation of receptor-heat shock protein 90 complexes. *J. Biol. Chem.* 265:20686–91

77. Picard D, Kumar V, Chambon P, Yamamoto KR. 1990. Signal transduction by steroid hormones:nuclear localization is differentially regulated in estrogen and glucocorticoid receptors. *Cell Regul.* 1:291–99

78. Tzukerman MT, Esty A, Santiso-Mere D, Danielan P, Parker MG, et al. 1994. Human estrogen receptor transactivational capacity is determined by both cellular and promoter context and mediated by two functionally distinct intramolecular regions. *Mol. Endocrinol.* 8:21–30

79. McInerney EM, Katzenellenbogen BS. 1996. Different regions in activation function-1 of the human estrogen receptor required for antiestrogen- and estradiol-dependent transcription activation. *J. Biol. Chem.* 271:24172–78

80. Katzenellenbogen JA, Omalley BW, Katzenellenbogen BS. 1996. Tripartite steroid hormone receptor pharmacology–interaction with multiple effector sites as a basis for the cell- and promoter-specific action of these hormones. *Mol. Endocrinol.* 10:119–31

81. Gandini O, Kohno H, Curtis S, Korach KS. 1997. Two transcription activation functions in the amino terminus of the mouse estrogen receptor that are affected by the carboxy terminus. *Steroids* 62:508–15

82. Kraus WL, McInerney EM, Katzenellenbogen BS. 1995. Ligand-dependent, transcriptionally productive association of the amino- and carboxyl-terminal regions of a steroid hormone nuclear receptor. *Proc. Natl. Acad. Sci. USA* 92:12314–18

83. Cowley SM, Hoare S, Mosselman S, Parker MG. 1997. Estrogen receptors α and β form heterodimers on DNA. *J. Biol. Chem.* 272:19858–62

84. Ogawa S, Eng V, Taylor J, Lubahn DB, Korach KS, Pfaff DW. 998. Roles of estrogen receptor-alpha gene expression in reproduction-related behaviors in female mice. *Endocrinology* 139:5070–81

85. Pettersson K, Grandien K, Kuiper GGJM, Gustafsson J-Å. 1997. Mouse estrogen receptor β forms estrogen response element-binding heterodimers with estrogen receptor α. *Mol. Endocrinol.* 11:1486–96

86. McInerney EM, Tsai MJ, O'Malley BW, Katzenellenbogen BS. 1996. Analysis of estrogen receptor transcriptional enhancement by a nuclear hormone receptor coactivator. *Proc. Natl. Acad. Sci. USA* 93:10069–73

87. Cowley SM, Parker MG. 1999. A comparison of transcriptional activation by ER alpha and ER beta. *J. Steroid Biochem. Mol. Biol.* 69:165–75

88. Tremblay A, Tremblay GB, Labrie F, Giguere V. 1999. Ligand-independent recruitment of SRC-1 to estrogen receptor beta through phosphorylation of activation function AF-1. *Mol. Cell* 3:513–19

89. Webb P, Nguyen P, Valentine C, Lopez GN, Kwok GR, et al. 1999. The estrogen receptor enhances AP-1 activity by two distinct mechanisms with different requirements for receptor transactivation functions. *Mol. Endocrinol.* 13:1672–85

90. Paech K, Webb P, Kuiper GG, Nilsson S, Gustafsson J-Å, et al. TS. 1997. Differential ligand activation of estrogen receptors ERalpha and ERbeta at AP1 sites. *Science* 277:1508–10

91. Zou AK, Marschke B, Arnold KE, Berger EM, Fitzgerald P, et al. 1999. Estrogen receptor beta activates the human retinoic acid receptor alpha-1 promoter in response to tamoxifen and other estrogen receptor antagonists, but not in response to estrogen. *Mol. Endocrinol.* 13:418–30

92. Montano MM, Jaiswal AK, Katzenellenbogen BS. 1998. Transcriptional regulation of the human quinone reductase gene by antiestrogen-liganded estrogen receptor-alpha and estrogen receptor-beta. *J. Biol. Chem.* 273:25443–49

93. Trapp T, Holsboer F. 1996. Heterodimerization between mineralocorticoid and glucocorticoid receptors increases the functional diversity of corticosteroid action. *Trends Pharmacol. Sci.* 17:145–49

94. Pace P, Taylor J, Suntharalingam S, Coombes RC, Ali S. 1997. Human estrogen receptor beta binds DNA in a manner similar to and dimerizes with estrogen receptor alpha. *J. Biol. Chem.* 272:25832–38

95. Grohe C, Kahlert S, Lobbert K, Stimpel M, Karas RH, et al. 1997. Cardiac myocytes and fibroblasts contain functional estrogen receptors. *FEBS Lett.* 416:107–12

96. Grohe C, Kahlert S, Lobbert K, Vetter H. 1998. Expression of oestrogen receptor alpha and beta in rat heart—role of local oestrogen synthesis. *J. Endocrinol.* 156:R1–7

97. Saji S, Jensen EV, Nilsson S, Rylander T, Warner M, Gustafsson J-Å 2000. Estrogen receptors alpha and beta in the rodent mammary gland. *Proc. Natl. Acad. Sci. USA* 97:337–42

98. Tremblay GB, Tremblay A, Labrie F, Giguere V. 1999. Dominant activity of activation function 1 (AF-1) and differential stoichiometric requirements for AF-1 and -2 in the estrogen receptor alpha-beta heterodimeric complex. *Mol. Cell. Biol.* 19:1919–27

99. Ogawa S, Inoue S, Orimo A, Hosoi T, Ouchi Y, Muramatsu M. 1998. Cross-inhibition of both estrogen receptor alpha and beta pathways by each dominant negative mutant. *FEBS Lett.* 423:129–32

100. Hall JM, McDonnell DP. 1999. The estrogen receptor beta-isoform (ERbeta) of the human estrogen receptor modulates ERalpha transcriptional activity and is a key regulator of the cellular response to estrogens and antiestrogens. *Endocrinology* 140:5566–78

101. Bhat RA, Harnish DC, Stevis PE, Lyttle CR, Komm BS. 1998. A novel human estrogen receptor beta: identification and functional analysis of additional N-terminal amino acids. *J. Steroid Biochem. Mol. Biol.* 67:233–40

102. Ogawa S, Inoue S, Watanabe T, Orimo A, Hosoi T, et al. 1998. Molecular cloning and characterization of human estrogen receptor betacx: a potential inhibitor of estrogen action in human. *Nucleic Acids Res.* 26:3505–12

103. Moore JT, McKee DD, Slentz-Kesler K, Moore LB, Jones SA, et al. 1998. Cloning and characterization of human estrogen receptor beta isoforms. *Biochem. Biophys. Res. Commun* 247:75–78

104. Cenni B, Picard D. 1999. Ligand-independent activation of steroid receptors: new roles for old players. *Trends Endocrinol. Metab.* 10:41–46

105. Weigel NL, Zhang Y. 1998. Ligand-independent activation of steroid hormone receptors, *J. Mol. Med.* 76:469–79

106. Arnold SF, Obourn JD, Jaffe H, Notides AC. 1995. Phosphorylation of the human estrogen receptor on tyrosine 537 in vivo and by src family tyrosine kinases in vitro. *Mol. Endocrinol.* 9:24–33

107. Weis KE, Ekena K, Thomas JA, Lazennec G, Katzenellenbogen BS. 1996. Constitutively active human estrogen receptors containing amino acid substitutions for tyrosine 537 in the receptor protein. *Mol. Endocrinol.* 10:1388–98

108. Lazennec G, Ediger TR, Petz LN, Nardulli AM, Katzenellenbogen BS. 1997. Mechanistic aspects of estrogen receptor activation probed with constitutively active estrogen receptors: correlations with DNA and coregulator interactions and receptor conformational changes. *Mol. Endocrinol.* 11:1375–86

109. White R, Sjöberg M, Kalkhoven E, Parker MG. 1997. Ligand-independent activation of the oestrogen receptor by mutation of a conserved tyrosine. *EMBO J.* 16:1427–35

110. Gee AC, Carlson KE, Martini PG, Katzenellenbogen BS, Katzenellenbogen JA. 1999. Coactivator peptides have a differential stabilizing effect on the binding of estrogens and antiestrogens with the estrogen receptor. *Mol. Endocrinol.* 13:1912–23

111. Bunone G, Briand PA, Miksicek RJ, Picard D. 1996. Activation of the unliganded estrogen receptor by EGF involves the MAP kinase pathway and direct phosphorylation. *EMBO J.* 15:2174–83

112. Kato S, Endoh H, Masuhiro Y, Kitamoto T, Uchiyama S, et al. 1995. Activation of the estrogen receptor through phospho-rylation by mitogen-activated protein kinase. *Science* 270:1491–94

113. Joel PB, Traish AM, Lannigan DA. 1998. Estradiol-induced phosphorylation of serine 118 in the estrogen receptor is independent of p42/p44 mitogen-activated protein kinase. *J. Biol. Chem.* 273:13317–23

114. Briand P, Lundholt BK, Skouv J, Lykkesfeldt AE. 1999. Growth response of breast epithelial cells to estrogen is influenced by EGF. *Mol. Cell. Endocrinol.* 153:1–9

115. Ignar-Trowbridge DM, Nelson KG, Bidwell MC, Curtis SW, Washburn TF, et al. 1992. Coupling of dual signaling pathways: Epidermal growth factor action involves the estrogen receptor. *Proc. Natl. Acad. Sci. USA* 89:4658–62

116. Curtis SW, Washburn T, Sewall C, DiAugustine R, Lindzey J, et al. 1996. Physiological coupling of growth factor and steroid receptor signaling pathways: Estrogen receptor knockout mice lack estrogen-like response to epidermal growth factor. *Proc. Natl. Acad. Sci. USA* 93:12626–30

117. Ankrapp DP, Bennett JM, Haslam SZ. 1998. Role of epidermal growth factor in the acquisition of ovarian steroid hormone responsiveness in the normal mouse mammary gland. *J. Cell. Physiol.* 174:251–60

118. Arnold SF, Obourn JD, Jaffe H, Notides AC. 1994. Serine 167 is the major estradiol-induced phosphorylation site on the human estrogen receptor, *Mol. Endocrinol.* 8:1208–14

119. Joel PB, Smith J, Sturgill TW, Fisher TL, Blenis J, Lannigan DA. 1998. pp90rsk1 regulates estrogen receptor-mediated transcription through phosphorylation of Ser-167. *Mol. Cell. Biol.* 18:1978–84

120. Lahooti H, White R, Danielian PS, Parker MG. 1994. Characterization of ligand-dependent phosphorylation of the

estrogen receptor. *Mol. Endocrinol.* 8:182–88

121. Cho H, Katzenellenbogen BS. 1993. Synergistic activation of estrogen receptor-mediated transcription by estradiol and protein kinase activators. *Mol. Endocrinol.* 7:441–52

122. Fujimoto N, Katzenellenbogen BS. 1994. Alteration in the agonist/antagonist balance of antiestrogens by activation of protein kinase A signaling pathways in breast cancer cells: antiestrogen selectivity and promoter dependence. *Mol. Endocrinol.* 8:296–304

123. El-Tanani MK, Green CD. 1997. Two separate mechanisms for ligand-independent activation of the estrogen receptor. *Mol. Endocrinol.* 11:928–37

124. Chen D, Pace PE, Coombes RC, Ali S. 1999. Phosphorylation of human estrogen receptor alpha by protein kinase A regulates dimerization, *Mol. Cell. Biol.* 19:1002–15

125. Prall OWJ, Sarcevic B, Musgrove EA, Watts CKW, Sutherland RL. 1997. Estrogen-induced activation of Cdk4 and Cdk2 during G1-S phase progression is accompanied by increased cyclin D1 expression and decreased cyclin-dependent kinase inhibitor association with cyclin E-Cdk2. *J. Biol. Chem.* 272:10882–94

126. Neuman E, Ladha MH, Lin N, Upton TM, Miller SJ, DiRenzo J, et al. 1997. Cyclin D1 stimulation of estrogen receptor transcriptional activity independent of cdk4. *Mol. Cell. Biol.* 17:5338–47

127. Zwijsen RM, Wientjens E, Klompmaker R, van der Sman J, Bernards R, Michalides RJ. 1997. CDK-independent activation of estrogen receptor by cyclin D1. *Cell* 88:405–15

128. Zwijsen RM, Buckle RS, Hijmans EM, Loomans CJ, Bernards R. 1998. Ligand-independent recruitment of steroid receptor coactivators to estrogen receptor by cyclin D. *Genes Dev.* 12:3488–98

129. Buckley MF, Sweeney KJ, Hamilton JA, Sini RL, Manning DL, et al. 1993. Expression and amplification of cyclin genes in human breast cancer. *Oncogene* 8:2127–33

130. Sabbah M, Courilleau D, Mester J, Redeuilh G. 1999. Estrogen induction of the cyclin D1 promoter: involvement of a cAMP response-like element. *Proc. Natl. Acad. Sci. USA* 96:11217–22

131. Rogatsky I, Trowbridge JM, Garabedian MJ. 1999. Potentiation of human estrogen receptor alpha transcriptional activation through phosphorylation of serines 104 and 106 by the cyclin A-CDK2 complex. *J. Biol. Chem.* 274:22296–302

132. Trowbridge JM, Rogatsky I, Garabedian MJ. 1997. Regulation of estrogen receptor transcriptional enhancement by the cyclin A/Cdk2 complex. *Proc. Natl. Acad. Sci. USA* 94:10132–37

133. Pinkerton JV, Santen R. 1999. Alternatives to the use of estrogen in postmenopausal women. *Endocr. Rev.* 20:308–20

134. Mendelsohn ME, Karas RH. 1999. The protective effects of estrogen on the cardiovascular system. *N. Engl. J. Med.* 340:1801–11

135. Ciocca DR, Roig LM. 1995. Estrogen receptors in human nontarget tissues: biological and clinical implications. *Endocr. Rev.* 16:35–62

136. Abney TO. 1999. The potential roles of estrogens in regulating Leydig cell development and function: a review. *Steroids* 64:610–17

137. Chang WY, Prins GS. 1999. Estrogen receptor-beta: implications for the prostate gland. *Prostate* 40:115–24

138. Taylor AH, Al-Azzawi F. 2000. Immunolocalisation of oestrogen receptor beta in human tissues. *J. Mol. Endocrinol.* 24:145–55

139. Saunders PTK, Maguire SM, Gaughan J, Millar MR. 1997. Expression of oestrogen receptor beta (ER-beta) in multiple rat

tissues visualised by immunohistochemistry. *J. Endocrinol.* 154:R3–16

140. Hiroi H, Inoue S, Watanabe T, Goto W, Orimo A, et al. 1999. Differential immunolocalization of estrogen receptor α and β in rat ovary and uterus. *J. Mol. Endocrinol.* 22:37–44

141. O'Brien ML, Park K, In Y, Park-Sarge O. 1999. Characterization of estrogen receptor β mRNA and protein expression in rat granulosa cells. *Endocrinology* 140:4530–41

142. Sar M, Welsch F. 199. Differential expression of estrogen receptor and estrogen receptor a in the rat ovary. *Endocrinology* 140:963–71

143. Byers M, Kuiper GGJM, Gustafsson J-Å and Park-Sarge OK. 1997. Estrogen receptor-beta mRNA expression in rat ovary–down-regulation by gonadotropins. *Mol. Endocrinol.* 11:172–82

144. Shughrue PJ, Lane MV, Merchenthaler I. 1997. Comparative distribution of estrogen receptor-alpha and -beta mRNA in the rat central nervous system. *J. Comp. Neurol.* 388:507–25

145. Shughrue PJ, Lane MV, Scrimo PJ, Merchenthaler I. 1998. Comparative distribution of estrogen receptor-alpha (ER-alpha) and beta (ER-beta) mRNA in the rat pituitary, gonad, and reproductive tract. *Steroids* 63:498–504

146. Wilson ME, Price RH, Handa RJ. 1998. Estrogen receptor mRNA in the pituitary gland. *Endocrinology* 139:5151–56

147. Faustini-Fustini M, Rochira V, Carani C. 1999. Oestrogen deficiency in men: where are we today? *Euro. J. Endocrinol.* 140:111–29

148. Fisher CR, Graves KH, Parlow AF, Simpson ER. 1998. Characterization of mice deficient in aromatase (ArKO) because of targeted disruption of the cyp19 gene. *Proc. Natl. Acad. Sci. USA* 95:6965–70

149. Honda S, Harada N, Ito S, Tagaki Y, Maeda S. 1998. Disruption of sexual behavior in male aromatase-deficient mice lacking exons 1 and 2 of the cyp19 gene. *Biochem. Biophys. Res. Commun.* 252:445–49

150. Robertson KM, O'Donnell L, Jones ME, Meachem SJ, Boon WC, et al. 1999. Impairment of spermatogenesis in mice lacking a functional aromatase (cyp 19) gene. *Proc. Natl. Acad. Sci. USA* 96:7986–91

151. Couse JF, Korach KS. 1999. Estrogen receptor null mice: what have we learned and where will they lead us? *Endocr. Rev.* 20:358–417

152. Smith EP, Boyd J, Frank GR, Takahashi H, Cohen RM, et al. 1994. Estrogen resistance caused by a mutation in the estrogen-receptor gene in a man. *N. Engl. J. Med.* 331:1056–61

153. Couse JF, Bunch DO, Lindzey J, Schomberg DW, Korach KS. 1999. Prevention of the polycystic ovarian phenotype and characterization of ovulatory capacity in the estrogen receptor-alpha knockout mouse. *Endocrinology* 140:5855–65

154. Bocchinfuso WP, Korach KS. 1997. Mammary gland development and tumorigenesis in estrogen receptor knock out mice. *J. Mammary Gland Biol. Neoplasia* 2:323–34

155. Hess RA, Bunick D, Lee KH, Bahr J, Taylor JA, et al. 1997. A role for oestrogens in the male reproductive system. *Nature* 390:509–12

156. Ogawa S, Lubahn DB, Korach KS, Pfaff DW. 1997. Behavioral effects of estrogen receptor gene disruption in male mice. *Proc. Natl. Acad. Sci. USA* 94:1476–81

157. Ogawa S, Taylor JA, Lubahn DB, Korach KS, Pfaff DW. 1996. Reversal of sex roles in genetic female mice by disruption of estrogen receptor gene. *Neuroendocrinology* 64:467–70

158. Rissman EF, Early AH, Taylor JA, Korach KS, Lubahn DB. 1997. Estrogen receptors are essential for female sexual

receptivity. *Endocrinology* 138:507–10

159. Krege JH, Hodgin JB, Couse JF, Enmark E, Warner M, et al. 1998. Generation and reproductive phenotypes of mice lacking estrogen receptor beta. *Proc. Natl. Acad. Sci. USA* 95:15677–82

160. Weihua Z, Saji S, Makinen S, Cheng G, Jensen EV, et al. 2000. ERβ, a modulator of ERα in the uterus. *Proc. Natl. Acad. Sci. USA* 97:5936–41

161. Couse JF, Hewitt SC, Bunch DO, Sar M, Walker VR, et al. 1999. Postnatal sex reversal of the ovaries in mice lacking estrogen receptors. *Science* 286:2328–31

162. Cardiff RD, Wellings SR. 1999. The comparative pathology of human and mouse mammary glands. *J. Mammary Gland Biol. Neoplasia* 4:105–22

163. Dickson RB, Lippman ME. 1995. Growth factors in breast cancer. *Endocr. Rev.* 16:559–89

164. Zeps N, Bentel JM, Papadimitriou JM, D'Antuono MF, Dawkins HJ. 1998. Estrogen receptor-negative epithelial cells in mouse mammary gland development and growth. *Differentiation* 62:221–26

165. Zeps N, Bentel JM, Papadimitriou JM, Dawkins HJ. 1999. Murine progesterone receptor expression in proliferating mammary epithelial cells during normal pubertal development and adult estrous cycle. Association with ERalpha and ERbeta status. *J. Histochem. Cytochem.* 47:1323–30

166. Dotzlaw H, Leygue E, Watson PH, Murphy LC. 1997. Expression of estrogen receptor-beta in human breast tumors. *J. Clin. Endocrinol. Metab.* 82:2371–74

167. Dotzlaw H, Leygue E, Watson PH, Murphy LC. 1999. Estrogen receptor-beta messenger RNA expression in human breast tumor biopsies: relationship to steroid receptor status and regulation by progestins. *Cancer Res.* 59:529–32

168. Leygue E, Dotzlaw H, Watson PH, Murphy LC. 1998. Altered estrogen receptor alpha and beta messenger RNA expression during human breast tumorigenesis. *Cancer Res.* 58:3197–201

169. Robertson JF. 1996. Oestrogen receptor: a stable phenotype in breast cancer. *Br. J. Cancer* 73:5–12

170. Sasano H, Suzuki T, Matsuzaki Y, Fukaya T, Endoh M, et al. 1999. Messenger ribonucleic acid in situ hybridization analysis of estrogen receptors alpha and beta in human breast carcinoma. *J. Clin. Endocrinol. Metab.* 84:781–85

171. Speirs V, Malone C, Walton DS, Kerin MJ, Atkin SL. 1999. Increased expression of estrogen receptor beta mRNA in tamoxifen-resistant breast cancer patients. *Cancer Res.* 59.:5421–24

172. Speirs V, Parkes AT, Kerin MJ, Walton DS, Carleton PJ, et al. 1999. Coexpression of estrogen receptor alpha and beta: poor prognostic factors in human breast cancer? *Cancer Res.* 59:525–28

173. Vladusic EA, Hornby AE, Guerra-Vladusic FK, Lupu R. 1998. Expression of estrogen receptor beta messenger RNA variant in breast cancer, *Cancer Res.* 58:210–14

174. Vladusic EA, Hornby AE, Guerra-Vladusic FK, Lakins J, Lupu R. 2000. Expression and regulation of estrogen receptor beta in human breast tumors and cell lines. *Oncol. Rep.* 7:157–67

175. Ciocca DR, Fanelli MA. 1997. Estrogen receptors and cell proliferation in breast cancer, *Trends Endocrinol. Metab.* 8:313–21

176. Clarke R, Brünner N. 1996. Acquired estrogen independence and antiestrogen resistance in breast cancer. *Trends Endocrinol. Metab.* 7:291–301

Annu. Rev. Physiol. 2001. 63:193–213

StAR Protein and the Regulation of Steroid Hormone Biosynthesis

Douglas M Stocco

Department of Cell Biology and Biochemistry, Texas Tech University Health Sciences Center, Lubbock, Texas 79430; e-mail: doug.stocco@ttmc.ttuhsc.edu

Key Words   steroidogenic cells, steroid hormones, cholesterol transfer, mitochondria, StAR, START domain

■ **Abstract**   Steroid hormone biosynthesis is acutely regulated by pituitary trophic hormones and other steroidogenic stimuli. This regulation requires the synthesis of a protein whose function is to translocate cholesterol from the outer to the inner mitochondrial membrane in steroidogenic cells, the rate-limiting step in steroid hormone formation. The steroidogenic acute regulatory (StAR) protein is an indispensable component in this process and is the best candidate to fill the role of the putative regulator. StAR is expressed in steroidogenic tissues in response to agents that stimulate steroid production, and mutations in the StAR gene result in the disease congenital lipoid adrenal hyperplasia, in which steroid hormone biosynthesis is severely compromised. The StAR null mouse has a phenotype that is essentially identical to the human disease. The positive and negative expression of StAR is sensitive to agents that increase and inhibit steroid biosynthesis respectively. The mechanism by which StAR mediates cholesterol transfer in the mitochondria has not been fully characterized. However, the tertiary structure of the START domain of a StAR homolog has been solved, and identification of a cholesterol-binding hydrophobic tunnel within this domain raises the possibility that StAR acts as a cholesterol-shuttling protein.

STEROIDOGENESIS

Steroidogenesis is the process in which specialized cells in specific tissues synthesize steroid hormones, an important class of terpene-based, small lipid molecules. Examples of steroid hormones are adrenal glucocorticoids, which regulate carbohydrate metabolism and manage stress, and adrenal mineralocorticoids, which regulate salt balance and maintain blood pressure. Further examples are the ovarian and placental progestogens and estrogens, which regulate reproductive function and secondary sex characteristics in the female, and testicular androgens, which are essential for fertility and secondary sex characteristics in the male. Lastly, a class of steroids referred to as neurosteroids in the brain function to both stimulate and inhibit GABAergic responses (1), modulate the response of Purkinje cells

0066-4278/01/0315-0193$14.00

to excitatory amino acids (2), and control memory (3). Thus the steroid hormones have diverse functions but are synthesized by biosynthetic pathways that are identical in the initial stages (4). In all steroidogenic tissues, regardless of the hormones synthesized, the initial step in steroidogenesis is the conversion of cholesterol to the first steroid, pregnenolone. This conversion occurs via the action of the cytochrome P450 side-chain cleavage enzyme (P450scc), which is present in the inner mitochondrial membrane in all steroidogenic cells (5). Pregnenolone then exits the mitochondria and is converted to progesterone by 3β-hydroxysteroid dehydrogenase (3β-HSD) in the microsomal compartment. In some steroidogenic cells, a mitochondrial form of the 3β-HSD can convert pregnenolone to progesterone prior to its exit from the mitochondria (6, 7). However, in most species and in most steroidogenic tissues, pregnenolone is converted to progesterone in the microsomal compartment and then to a variety of other steroids, the final product resulting from the complement of enzymes in those tissues (8). For example, adrenal glomerulosa cells preferentially synthesize and secrete the mineralcorticoid aldosterone, and adrenal fasciculata cells synthesize and secrete the glucocorticoids cortisol or corticosterone. Likewise, ovarian theca cells synthesize and secrete androgens; ovarian granulosa cells convert androgens to estradiol, ovarian corpora lutea; placental syncytiotrophoblasts synthesize and secrete progesterone; and testicular Leydig cells synthesize and secrete the androgen testosterone. Neurosteroids are synthesized in specialized regions of the brain, with the most prevalent being pregnenolone, progesterone, 5 α-dihydroprogesterone, allopregnanolone and dehydroepiandrosterone (DHEA) (9). The biosynthetic pathways that lead to the steroid hormones described above and the steroidogenic enzymes in these pathways are illustrated in Figure 1 (see color insert). Understanding the enzymes involved in steroidogenesis and, most importantly, their intracellular location, is key to understanding how the synthesis of steroid hormones is regulated.

REGULATION OF STEROIDOGENESIS

The biosynthesis of steroid hormones is regulated mainly by the pituitary trophic hormones such as adrenocorticotropin (ACTH), luteinizing hormone (LH), and follicle stimulating hormone (FSH) but other agents also control steroidogenesis (see below). In all tissues the regulation of steroid production occurs in two phases. The acute phase occurs on the order of minutes and is responsible for the rapid production of steroids in response to immediate need (10). The biosynthesis of glucocorticoids to combat stressful situations and the rapid synthesis of aldosterone to regulate blood pressure quickly are examples of this type of of regulation. More chronic regulation also occurs and encompasses synthesis of the mRNAs and enzymes for steroidogenesis to enhance synthetic capacity in the cells. Chronic regulation of the steroidogenic pathway enzymes has been covered in great detail (4, 11–13) and thus is not further discussed here. This review focuses on the events that result in the rapid biosynthesis of steroid hormones in response to steroidogenic stimuli, i.e. the acute phase. As indicated above the key to understanding the acute regulation of steroidogenesis is knowing where the steroidogenic components are located within the cell and how they are regulated.

Like most biosynthetic pathways, steroidogenesis has a rate-limiting step. For a long time, the rate-limiting step was believed to be the activation of the P450scc enzyme, the enzyme that converts cholesterol to pregnenolone (14, 15). However, it soon became clear that the P450scc enzyme is active even in unstimulated cells (16, 17), and the search for the true rate-limiting step culminated in the finding that the critical step is the delivery of the substrate cholesterol from the outer mitochondrial membrane to the inner mitochondrial membrane where the P450scc enzyme is located (5, 18). This step is rate-limiting because the hydrophobic cholesterol cannot traverse the aqueous intermembrane space of the mitochondria and reach the P450scc enzyme rapidly enough by simple diffusion to support acute synthesis. More detailed descriptions of the observations can be found elsewhere (10, 19–24). Suffice it to say that this important step makes possible the rapid transfer of cholesterol from the outer to the inner mitochondrial membrane in response to steroidogenic signals.

Investigation of the acutely regulated step began in the adrenal gland where adrenocorticotropic hormone (ACTH) controls the biosynthesis of steroids (14). One of the most important observations concerning steroidogenesis was that acute stimulation of steroid production requires the synthesis of new proteins. Early studies by Ferguson (25, 26) demonstrated that the acute stimulation of glucocorticoid synthesis in adrenal glands by ACTH is sensitive to the protein synthesis inhibitor, puromycin. Garren and co-workers confirmed that steroidogenesis in adrenal tissue is dependent on the ACTH-stimulated synthesis of new proteins (27–29). The ACTH controlled step was distal to the hydrolysis of cholesterol esters (the intracellular source for steroidogenic cholesterol), but proximal to its side chain cleavage, i.e. at the delivery of cholesterol to the P450scc enzyme (30). Simpson & Boyd (31) determined that the step sensitive to protein synthesis inhibition is located in the mitochondria; it was subsequently noted that protein synthesis inhibitors have no effect on the activity of the P450scc itself (32). These results indicated that the unknown protein(s) probably function at the level of the delivery of cholesterol to the P450scc enzyme. Studies on the relationship between newly synthesized protein(s) and cholesterol transfer to the P450scc enzyme culminated in the demonstration that inhibition of protein synthesis has no effect on the increased delivery of cholesterol to the outer mitochondrial membrane but does inhibit the transfer of this substrate from the outer to the inner membrane (33, 34). Thus the precise site of the rate-limiting reaction was shown to be the transfer of cholesterol to the P450scc enzyme in the inner mitochondrial membrane.

The effort to identify and characterize this acute regulatory protein(s) continues. Several candidate proteins and the data supporting their roles have been reviewed (10). Evidence for the role of the steroidogenic acute regulatory (StAR) protein is summarized here. It has been approximately 17 years since the StAR phosphoprotein was first described in ACTH-stimulated adrenal cortex and approximately

6 years since it was purified, cloned, sequenced, and expressed. This protein has been the subject of approximately 250 manuscripts, reviews and commentaries, and the preponderance of evidence indicates that it is the putative regulatory protein whose existence was predicted almost four decades ago.

THE STEROIDOGENIC ACUTE REGULATORY PROTEIN

The candidate protein ultimately characterized as StAR was first described by Orme-Johnson and colleagues as an ACTH-induced 30-kDa phosphoprotein in hormone-treated rat and mouse adrenocortical cells and as an LH-induced protein in rat corpus luteum cells and mouse Leydig cells (35–42). This series of studies indicated a close relationship between the appearance of the 30-kDa protein and steroid hormone biosynthesis in these tissues and that their synthesis, as was steroidogenesis, was sensitive to protein synthesis inhibition. Similarly, our laboratory described a family of proteins in hormone-stimulated MA-10 mouse Leydig tumor cells that we now know to be identical to the protein described by Orme-Johnson (43–49). In both laboratories these proteins were shown to be localized to the mitochondria and consisted of several forms of a newly synthesized 30-kDa protein. The 30-kDa mitochondrial proteins are processed from a 37-kDa precursor form whose N terminus contains a mitochondrial-signaling sequence (37, 45). Many subsequent studies have confirmed the tight correlation between the synthesis of steroids and the synthesis of the 30-kDa proteins (35–42, 46–49). However, a direct cause-and-effect relationship between 30-kDa protein expression and steroidogenesis was lacking, and it was necessary to clone the 30-kDa protein to prove unequivocally its function in steroidogenesis. Purification of the protein and cloning and sequencing of the cDNA for the 37-kDa protein precursor were accomplished in 1994 (50). Both the nucleic acid sequence of the cDNA and the amino acid sequence of the 37-kDa protein indicate that it is a novel protein, and transient transfection experiments demonstrated that expression of the cDNA-derived protein in MA-10 mouse Leydig tumor cells increased steroid synthesis in the absence of ACTH. In addition, transient transfection of COS-1 cells with the cDNA for the 37-kDa protein increased the conversion of cholesterol to pregnenolone (10, 51, 52). These results confirm a direct role for the protein in hormone-regulated steroid production.

Following the cloning of the StAR cDNA, collaborative studies with the laboratories of Miller and Strauss demonstrated that mutations in the StAR gene caused the disease congenital lipoid adrenal hyperplasia (lipoid CAH), providing even more compelling evidence for the role of this protein in steroidogenesis (51). Lipoid CAH is a lethal condition characterized by an almost complete inability of the newborn to synthesize steroids, by large adrenals containing high levels of cholesterol and cholesterol esters, and by testicular Leydig cells that contain increased amount of lipid. The accumulation of cholesterol and cholesterol esters and the apparent inability to convert these substrates to pregnenolone led to the belief that lipoid CAH might be the result of mutations in the P450scc gene (53, 54). When this was proved to be incorrect (55), attention shifted to other potential targets and ended when mutations in the StAR cDNAs and genes were found in these patients (51). Mutations in the StAR gene are the only known cause of the disease (22).

In a corroborating study, Caron and co-workers used targeted disruption of the StAR gene to produce StAR knockout mice (56). All StAR (-/-) mice have female external genitalia, fail to grow normally, and die prematurely, presumably as a result of adrenocortical insufficiency. Serum levels of corticosterone and aldosterone are depressed, and levels of ACTH and CRH are elevated, indicating that impairment of adrenal steroid production interferes with feedback regulation of the hypothalamus/pituitary. The adrenal medulla is normal but the fascicular zone of the adrenal cortex is disrupted and contains elevated lipid deposits. Thus the StAR knockout mouse phenotype is similar to that of human lipoid CAH.

LOCALIZATION OF StAR EXPRESSION

Reagents are now available for the further characterization of the tissue distribution of StAR. Methodologies such as Western analysis, Northern analysis, in situ hybridization, immunocytochemistry, RNAse protection assays, and RT PCR all indicate that StAR expression is confined to steroidogenic tissues. StAR is expressed in the adrenal cortex (both glomerulosa and fasciculata-reticularis cells) (57–66), ovarian theca (59, 67–70), granulosa (67, 68, 70–75), and ovarian corpora lutea cells (59, 67, 76–82), fetal mouse giant trophoblast cells (83), fetal and adult testes, ovaries, and adrenals (84), adrenal tumors (57), and testicular Leydig cells (59, 85–91). Interestingly, StAR is also expressed in testicular Sertoli cells (59, 92), which are not generally considered to be steroidogenic. However, Sertoli cells can be induced to express cytochrome P450scc enzyme and synthesize small amounts of pregnenolone, indicating that they have some steroidogenic capacity (93). StAR is also expressed in brain, where its cellular distribution overlaps with that of P450scc and 3β-HSD (94). These findings implicate StAR in the biosynthesis of neurosteroids.

Although StAR appears to be absent in the human placenta (59, 95), it is present in the placenta of the cow (76), the pig (84), and the rodent (83). The absence of StAR in the human placenta implies that this tissue has an alternative mechanism to supply cholesterol to the P450scc enzyme, but to date this mechanism has not been identified (96). In any event, if StAR were required for placental progesterone biosynthesis in the human, the fetuses afflicted with lipoid CAH would not develop to term because the human placenta is the source of progesterone after the first trimester (8). StAR is also present in human kidney tissue, but its role in this tissue remains unknown (59, 95). Perhaps it is involved in some aspect of vitamin D metabolism in the kidney. Also, MLN64, a protein with a high degree of homology to a region in the C terminus of the StAR protein, is expressed in high levels in human breast tumors, and it is possible that this protein may contribute to the high levels of steroidogenesis seen in some such tumors (97).

REGULATION OF StAR EXPRESSION

Positive Regulation of the StAR Gene

The cloning of StAR made it possible to investigate the regulation of its expression by trophic hormones and by other steroidogenic agents. In virtually every system studied, agents that increase steroid biosynthesis also increase the expression of the StAR protein. In addition to the signals generated through membrane receptors, some stimulators may act directly on the *StAR* gene, indicating that its promoter may contain many regulatory elements. Thus steroid production and StAR expression are up-regulated by LH (88, 89, 98, 99), LH + insulin (75), chorionic gonadotropin (CG) (70, 86, 100–103), pregnant mare's serum gonadotropin (PMSG) (100), ACTH (58, 64, 65), FSH (71, 72, 74), angiotensin II (104), corticotropin-releasing hormone (CRH) (105), cAMP analogs (71, 72, 99, 104–106), intracellular cAMP-inducing agents (81), IGF-1 (72, 74, 79, 86), insulin (81), growth hormone (90), growth differentiation factor 9 (107), thyroid hormone (108), estradiol (77), retinoic acid (109), oxysterols (110), calcium ions (7, 61, 103), angiotensin II and potassium ions (104), and aspartate (111). Also, when added in the presence of a low-chloride concentration, a cAMP analog was more effective in stimulating steroid biosynthesis and StAR protein expression in rat Leydig cells, indicating a role for this ion in the control of steroidogenesis (106).

Secretions from medullary chromaffin cells of the bovine adrenal are able to stimulate both steroid biosynthesis and StAR mRNA and protein levels in cultured adrenal cortex cells from the same animal (112), and epinephrine mimics this effect. In addition, activation of the muscarinic receptor in human granulosa cells with carbachol increases progesterone biosynthesis and StAR protein levels (113).

Other studies have demonstrated that intracellular release of arachidonic acid (AA) from phospholipids and other stores in the cell is required in the biosynthesis of steroid hormones (114–116). They indicated that AA acts at the locus following activation of protein kinase A (PKA) but prior to P450scc activity; therefore, we investigated the relationship between AA release, steroid biosynthesis, and StAR expression. Blockage of AA release by inhibiting phospholipase A2 (PLA$_2$) resulted in a dose-dependent inhibition of steroid synthesis and a concomitant decrease in StAR protein (99). The inhibition of StAR protein expression occurred at the level of transcription, and a metabolite in the lipoxygenase pathway of AA metabolism was involved in the regulation of the StAR gene (117). These observations demonstrated that in addition to the role of the cAMP pathway, AA, or more likely one of its lipoxygenase pathway metabolites, is also required for StAR gene expression and ultimately for steroid biosynthesis.

In summary, many steroidogenic stimuli that increase steroid hormone biosynthesis increase StAR protein production.

Negative Regulation of the StAR Gene

Several studies designed to determine the mechanisms responsible for the negative regulation of steroidogenesis found that disruption of StAR expression was the causative factor. Some of the extensive descriptions of compounds and experimental conditions known to inhibit steroidogenesis by this mechanism include diethylumbelliferyl phosphate (118), prostaglandin F2α (78, 82,119–121), endotoxemia as induced by lipopolysaccharide (85), inhibition of transcription by actinomycin D (122), heat shock (123), over-expression of the DAX-1 protein (dosage sensitive sex reversal-adrenal hypoplasia congenita-x-linked) (124, 125), interferon-γ (126), transforming growth factor β1 (63, 127), atrial natriuretic peptide (61), GnRH agonist (128), tumor necrosis factor α (80, 87, 129), ethane dimethane sulfonate (130), inhibitors of phosphoprotein phosphatases PP1 and PP2A (131), induction of sepsis (132), aging (91), disruption of the mitochondrial electrochemical gradient (133), interleukin 1β (134), the herbicide Roundup (135), the pesticide lindane (136), and the pesticide dimethoate (137).

It appears that StAR occupies a sensitive place in both the positive regulation of steroid hormone output and the inhibition of steroid biosynthesis. These observations could take on added significance in view of the possibility that environmental endocrine disruptors that are known to decrease reproductive function in wildlife and humans may have StAR as a primary target (138).

The StAR Promoter

With StAR expression being subject to both positive and negative regulation by many different agents, studies to determine the regulatory elements in the StAR promoter and the manner in which transcription factors interact with these elements were undertaken. Hormone-stimulated steroid production in steroidogenic cells is accompanied by a rapid increase in StAR mRNA levels (50, 139, 140). Because trophic hormone stimulation usually results in a rapid increase in intracellular cAMP levels, the role of cAMP in the regulation of the StAR gene was investigated (52, 74,140–143). The fact that the promoter region of the StAR gene lacks a recognizable cAMP response element (CRE) suggests that the cAMP response element–binding protein (CREB) does not act directly on sequences found in the StAR promoter. However, CREB may act indirectly on the StAR promoter. The cAMP-responsive site is retained within the first 254 nucleotides before the transcription start site (140), and this region has been the focus of studies to identify promoter elements and their cognate-binding proteins that could mediate the cAMP response.

A transcription factor that may be important in the regulation of the StAR gene is steroidogenic factor 1 (SF-1), and SF-1 knockout mice do not express StAR mRNA (140). Several SF-1 consensus-binding sites have been identified in the

StAR promoter, including the five SF-1 sites in the rat (143) and additional sites in human and mouse (140, 142). Two of these sites, located at positions −97 and −42, are highly conserved in several species, whereas the −132 site has been identified only in mouse and rat. Utilizing transient transfection protocols, SF-1 transactivates the StAR promoter in several cell types (140–143). SF-1 may also play some role in the developmental regulation of the StAR gene because StAR mRNA is not detected in the urogenital ridge of the SF-1 knockout mouse (140).

Additional factors are involved in tissue- and time-specific expression of StAR, and the search for additional *trans*-acting factors involved in the regulation of the StAR gene has continued. The CCAAT/enhancer-binding proteins (C/EBPs) are a family of basic region/leucine zipper transcription factors implicated as regulators of differentiation and function of multiple cell types (144). Two members of this family, C/EBPα and C/EBPβ, are expressed in Leydig cells and ovarian granulosa cells (145, 146), and two putative C/EBP binding sites in the StAR promoter have been identified (147–149). Furthermore, the StAR promoter is transactivated by C/EBPβ during transient transfection assays, and SF-1 transactivation of the StAR promoter is dependent on the presence of functional C/EBP-binding sites, suggesting that SF-1 and C/EBPβ form a complex on this promoter (147, 148). The GATA-4 site in the StAR promoter may be partially responsible for the acute activation of the StAR gene in rat granulosa cells (148). The sterol regulatory element-binding protein (SREBP) may also be involved in the regulation of the StAR gene because SREBP-1α can transactivate the StAR promoter (110). No consensus-binding sites for SREBP-1α have yet been found in the StAR promoter, but this may prove to be an example of the convergence of the regulation of cholesterol metabolism and steroidogenesis.

In spite of the findings that several transcription factors are required for transactivation of the StAR gene, mutation of these sites produces similar effects on both basal and stimulated promoter activity. Thus the fold stimulation does not change. These observations indicate that all the elements responsible for the rapid activation of the StAR promoter and hence for the acute expression of StAR are not known.

While the studies outlined above focus on postive regulation, the StAR promoter may also harbor elements involved in repression of transcription. The transcription factor DAX-1 is an unusual member of the nuclear hormone receptor family, with homology to the ligand-binding domain of the nuclear hormone receptors (150). The DNA-binding domain lacks zinc finger motifs and consists of 3.5 repeats of a 65–67 amino acid sequence in its N terminus (150). Over-expression of DAX-1 inhibits the synthesis of steroids in Y-1 mouse adrenal tumor cells by binding to a hairpin structure in the promotor region of the StAR gene (124). The DAX-1 protein contains a powerful transcriptional silencing domain in its C-terminal region (151), and DAX-1 inhibits P450scc and 3β-HSD gene expression as well (125). One possible mechanism for these effects is that DAX-1 can interact directly with SF-1, resulting in an inhibition of SF-1-mediated transactivation (152). Combined, these data implicate DAX-1 as a key factor in the regulation of StAR gene expression.

MECHANISM OF StAR ACTION

Models of StAR Action

How does StAR mediate the transfer of cholesterol from the outer mitochondrial membrane to the inner mitochondrial membrane? We earlier proposed a model in which StAR was synthesized in the cytosol in response to trophic hormone stimulation, and during import into the mitochondrial inner compartment forms contact sites between the inner and outer membranes that serve as a hydrophobic bridge for outer mitochondrial membrane cholesterol to transfer to the inner membrane (10, 45). Evidence that this model was incorrect and would require modification was obtained when it was observed that N-terminal truncations of the StAR protein that removed as many as 62 amino acids and were not imported into the mitochondria had no effect on cholesterol transfer or steroid production when transfected into MA-10 or COS-1 cells (153, 154). Also, bacterially produced StAR protein lacking the first 62 N-terminal amino acids supported full steroidogenesis when added to isolated mitochondria but was not imported into the mitochondrian (155). However, when mitochondria were incubated with StAR protein whose C terminus was truncated by 28 amino acids, the capacity to stimulate production was lost (153, 154). These data all indicate that a region in the C terminus of the StAR protein is instrumental in cholesterol transfer.

The role of the C-terminal region of the StAR protein in cholesterol transfer was confirmed (156) by studies of MLN64, a protein with homology to the C-terminal region of StAR. MLN64 expression in transfected COS-1 cells increases steroid production. Furthermore Ponting & Aravind (157) showed that sequences in the C terminus of StAR are homologous to sequences in several other proteins, including MNL64, which display diverse functions. They named these sequences START domains, for StAR-related lipid tansfer domains. These domains are capable of binding lipids, and StAR may be a lipid-binding carrier protein as is discussed below.

Kallen and colleagues demonstrated that StAR can act as a sterol transfer protein to enhance sterol desorption from one membrane to another (158). They showed that StAR is directed to the mitochondria via its N terminus and, presumably utilizing C-terminal sequences, produces alterations in the outer mitochondrial membrane that result in the transfer of cholesterol from the outer to the inner membrane. This transfer of cholesterol is specific. This hypothesis is pertinent to the situation in steroidogenic mitochondria because the outer mitochondrial membrane is cholesterol rich, whereas the inner membrane is relatively devoid of cholesterol (158, 159).

Although the mechanism of action of the StAR protein is still unknown, it is likely that StAR interacts with proteins, lipids and/or other factors on the outside of the outer mitochondrial membrane to transfer cholesterol. The identification of the mitochondrial factors responsible for the interaction has proven elusive (160). The suggestion that StAR promotes cholesterol transfer by its direct interaction with the outer mitochondrial surface and not through an intermediary came from studies in which the addition of recombinant StAR protein to purified mitochondria caused an increase in pregnenolone production (158). Attempts to identify StAR-interacting proteins using the yeast two-hybrid assay system have failed to identify StAR-binding partners (160). Perhaps, StAR stimulates cholesterol transfer either through a few high-affinity stable interactions with the outer mitochondrial membrane, which are difficult to detect because of their low number, or through transient interactions, that are also difficult to detect (155).

Miller and colleagues also attempted to determine how StAR might promote cholesterol transfer to the inner mitochondrial membrane; they subjected StAR to limited proteolysis at different pH values and found that the molecule behaves differently as the pH decreases (161). Namely, at pH values in the 3.5–4.0 range StAR can form a molten globule structure. They speculated that if the pH microenvironment surrounding the mitochondria is acidic, the StAR molecule may undergo a conformational shift, forming an extended structure and increasing the flexibility of the linker region located between the N terminus and the biologically active C terminus while acting on the outer mitochondrial membrane. They suggested that the transition to a molten globule may lower the energy required to open the StAR structure further, possibly exposing a cholesterol channel or that it may prolong the interval with which StAR can reside on the outer membrane thus allowing increased transfer of cholesterol during this period. This theory is heavily dependent upon the pH of the microenvironment near the mitochondria being much lower than the rest of the cytosol, a condition not yet unequivocally demonstrated.

Structure of the START Domain

While the search for interacting partners for StAR on the outer mitochondrial membrane continues, such partners may not be necessary. Elucidation of the crystal structure of all or part of the StAR protein has proven difficult. First, wild-type StAR protein is easy to express but difficult to purify. However, it is possible to purify large amounts of StAR protein that lacks the N-terminal 62 amino acids. This truncated protein is difficult to crystallize because it is not soluble to the extent required to form crystals. As a result, information on the tertiary structure of StAR was not available until Tsujishita & Hurley (162) crystallized and solved the structure for the START domain of the MNL64 protein. The START domain of MLN64 shows a high degree of homology with StAR-START domain, and StAR-START and MLN64-START bind cholesterol in essentially an identical manner at a ratio of 1:1. The crystal structure of the MLN64-START at 2.2 Å has an $\alpha + \beta$ fold built around a U-shaped incomplete β-barrel. Most importantly, the tertiary structure of MLN64-START has a hydrophobic tunnel that is $26 \times 12 \times 11$ Å in size and is large enough to bind a single molecule of cholesterol. The authors propose that StAR functions in transferring cholesterol to the inner mitochondrial membrane via its ability to bind cholesterol and act as a cholesterol-shuttling protein.

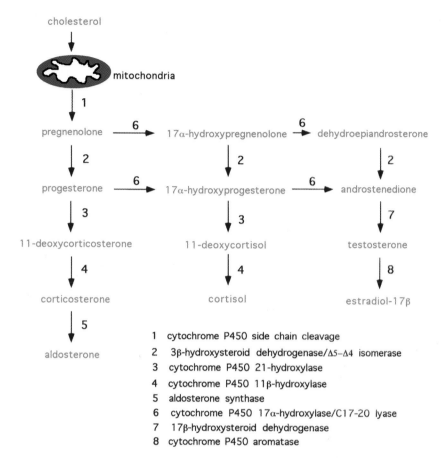

1 cytochrome P450 side chain cleavage
2 3β-hydroxysteroid dehydrogenase/Δ5–Δ4 isomerase
3 cytochrome P450 21-hydroxylase
4 cytochrome P450 11β-hydroxylase
5 aldosterone synthase
6 cytochrome P450 17α-hydroxylase/C17-20 lyase
7 17β-hydroxysteroid dehydrogenase
8 cytochrome P450 aromatase

Figure 1 The biosynthetic pathway of steroid hormones. Shown are the biosynthetic pathways leading from cholesterol to the major steroids produced in the adrenal, ovary, and testis. Conversions of cholesterol to pregnenolone and 11-deoxycortisol to cortisol occurs in the mitochondria; the remaining reactions occur in the microsomal compartment. The enzymes involved in the conversions of steroids are numbered in the reactions and named at the bottom of the figure.

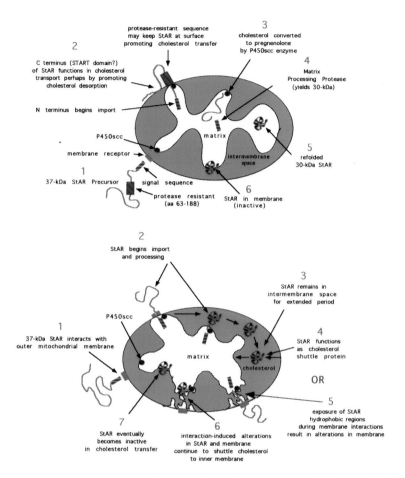

Figure 2 Proposed mechanisms of StAR action. Shown are several of the ways in which StAR has been hypothesized to deliver cholesterol to the inner mitochondrial membrane. The top figure represents earlier models and essentially describes those in which StAR promotes cholesterol transfer through interactions with as yet unknown factors on the outer mitochondrial membrane. These models are highlighted by the proposals that StAR may act as a sterol transfer protein that desorbs outer membrane cholesterol to the inner membrane or as a molten globule that alters membrane structure and allows cholesterol to reach the inner membrane. The bottom figure depicts a more recent model, based on the solving of the tertiary structure of the START domain, hypothesizing that StAR may function by itself as a cholesterol-shuttling protein. This model was proposed as a result of finding that the START domain contains a hydrophobic cholesterol-binding tunnel. Two facets of this model are pertinent: first, that StAR may transfer cholesterol molecules, one at a time, to the inner membrane and second, that hydrophobic regions in the START domain may alter mitochondrial membrane and StAR structure to allow for the passage of cholesterol.

A number of previous observations are not easily reconciled by the proposal that StAR acts as a cholesterol-shuttling protein, moving cholesterol to the inner mitochondrial membrane one molecule at a time. For instance, StAR can be fully active in steroidogenesis without being imported into the mitochondria (153, 154), and the fact that once StAR is imported and processed from the 37-kDa precursor to the 30-kDa mature form it is no longer active in cholesterol transfer is at odds with the concept that StAR acts as a carrier protein on a continuous basis (10, 45). In addition, one must determine the stoichiometry of StAR molecules synthesized and cholesterol molecules transferred to the inner membrane to determine if sufficient cholesterol molecules can be delivered to the P450scc to account for the level of steroids synthesized. Mitochondrial proteins must be in an unfolded state before import and processing can occur and it is not known if any hydrophobic tunnel remains intact and if cholesterol is still bound in the unfolded state. If not, how does the refolding of StAR occur in the intermembrane space so that it can act as a shuttling protein when the refolding factors are thought to reside in the matrix? However, action of StAR by itself in transferring cholesterol to the inner membrane could account for the inability to identify StAR-binding partners on the mitochondrial membrane.

In summary, while many questions remain, solving of the tertiary structure of the part of the StAR molecule that is functional in cholesterol transfer represents a significant step in solving the riddle of its mechanism of action.

ACKNOWLEDGMENTS

The author acknowledges the support of National Institutes of Health grant HD 17481 during the course of these studies. He also thanks Ms Deborah Alberts and Mr Lance Walsh for help in constructing this review.

Visit the Annual Reviews home page at www.AnnualReviews.org

LITERATURE CITED

1. Majewska MD, Harrison NL, Schwartz RD, Barker JL, Paul SM. 1986. Steroid hormone metabolites are barbiturate-like modulators of the GABA receptor. *Science* 232:1004–7
2. Smith SS. 1991. Progesterone administration attenuates excitatory amino acid responses of cerebellar Purkinje cells. *Neuroscience* 42:309–20
3. Flood JF, Morley JE, Roberts E. 1992. Memory-enhancing effects in male mice of pregnenolone and steroids metabolically derived from it. *Proc. Natl. Acad. Sci. USA* 89:1567–71

4. Miller WL. 1988. Molecular biology of steroid hormone synthesis. *Endocr. Rev.* 9:295–318
5. Farkash Y, Timberg R, Orly J. 1986. Preparation of antiserum to rat cytochrome P-450 cholesterol side chain cleavage, and its use for ultrastructural localization of the immunoreactive enzyme by protein A-gold technique. *Endocrinology* 118:1353–65
6. Cherradi N, Defaye G, Chambaz EM. 1994. Characterization of the 3β-hydroxysteroid dehydrogenase activity associated with bovine adrenocortical

mitochondria. *Endocrinology* 134:1358–64

7. Cherradi N, Rossier MF, Vallotton MB, Timberg R, Friedberg I, et al. 1997. Submitochondrial distribution of three key steroidogenic proteins (steroidogenic acute regulatory protein and cytochrome p450scc and 3β-hydroxysteroid dehydrogenase isomerase enzymes) upon stimulation by intracellular calcium in adrenal glomerulosa cells. *J. Biol. Chem.* 272:7899–907

8. Miller WL. 1998. Early steps in androgen biosynthesis: from cholesterol to DHEA. *Clin. Endocrinol. Metab.* 12:67–81

9. Baulieu EE. 1997. Neurosteroids: of the nervous system, by the nervous system, for the nervous system. *Recent Prog. Horm. Res.* 52:1–32

10. Stocco DM, Clark BJ. 1996. Regulation of the acute production of steroids in steroidogenic cells. *Endocr. Rev.* 17:221–44

11. Waterman MR, Simpson ER. 1985. Regulation of the biosynthesis of cytochromes P-450 involved in steroid hormone synthesis. *Mol. Cell. Endocrinol.* 39:81–89

12. Simpson ER, Waterman MR. 1988. Regulation of the synthesis of steroidogenic enzymes in adrenal cortical cells by ACTH. *Annu. Rev. Physiol.* 50:427–40

13. Simpson E, Lauber M, Demeter M, Means G, Mahendroo M, et al. 1992. Regulation of expression of the genes encoding steroidogenic enzymes in the ovary. *J. Steroid Biochem. Mol. Biol.* 41:409–13

14. Stone D, Hechter O. 1954. Studies on ACTH action in perfused bovine adrenals: site of action of ACTH in corticosteroidogenesis. *Arch. Biochem. Biophys.* 51:457–69

15. Karaboyas GC, Koritz SB. 1965. Identity of the site of action of cAMP and ACTH in corticosteroidogenesis in rat adrenal and beef adrenal cortex slices. *Biochemistry* 4:462–68

16. Tuckey RC, Atkinson HC. 1989. Pregnenolone synthesis from cholesterol and hydroxycholesterols by mitochondria from ovaries following the stimulation of immature rats with pregnant mare's serum gonadotropin and human choriogonadotropin. *Eur. J. Biochem.* 186:255–59

17. Tuckey RC. 1992. Cholesterol side-chain cleavage by mitochondria from the human placenta. Studies using hydroxycholesterols as substrates. *J. Steroid Biochem. Mol. Biol.* 42:883–90

18. Black SM, Harikrishna JA, Szklarz GD, Miller WL. 1994. The mitochondrial environment is required for activity of the cholesterol side-chain cleavage enzyme, cytochrome P450scc. *Proc. Natl. Acad. Sci. USA* 91:7247–51

19. Stocco DM. 1997. A StAR search: implications in controlling steroidgenesis. *Biol. Reprod.* 56:328–36

20. Stocco DM. 1999. Steroidogenic acute regulatory protein. *Vitam. Horm.* 55:399–441

21. Miller WL. 1995. Mitochondrial specificity of the early steps in steroidogenesis. *J. Steroid Biochem. Mol. Biol.* 55:607–16

22. Miller WL. 1997. Congenital lipoid adrenal hyperplasia: the human gene knockout for the steroidogenic acute regulatory protein. *J. Mol. Endocrinol.* 19:227–40

23. Miller WL. 1998. Lessons from congenital lipoid adrenal hyperplasia. *Curr. Opin. Endocrinol. Diabetes* 5:155–61

24. Miller WL, Strauss JF, 3rd. 1999. Molecular pathology and mechanism of action of the steroidogenic acute regulatory protein, StAR. *J. Steroid Biochem. Mol. Biol.* 69:131–41

25. Ferguson JJ. 1962. Puromycin and adrenal responsiveness to adrenocorticotropic hormone. *Biochim. Biophys. Acta* 57:616–17

26. Ferguson JJ. 1963. Protein synthesis and adrenocorticotropin responsiveness. *J. Biol. Chem.* 238:2754–59

27. Garren LD, Ney RL, Davis WW. 1965. Studies on the role of protein synthesis in

the regulation of corticosterone production by ACTH in vivo. *Proc. Natl. Acad. Sci. USA* 53:1443–50

28. Garren LD, Davis WW, Crocco RM. 1966. Puromycin analogs: action of adrenocorticotropic hormone and the role of glycogen. *Science* 152:1386–88

29. Garren LD. 1968. The mechanism of action of adrenocorticotropic hormone. *Vitam. Horm.* 26:119–45

30. Davis WW, Garren LD. 1968. On the mechanism of action of adrenocorticotropic hormone. The inhibitory site of cycloheximide in the pathway of steroid biosynthesis. *J. Biol. Chem.* 243:5153–57

31. Simpson ER, Boyd GS. 1966. The cholesterol side-chain cleavage system of the adrenal cortex: a mixed function oxidase. *Biochem. Biophys. Res. Commun.* 24:10–17

32. Arthur JR, Boyd GS. 1976. The effect of inhibitors of protein synthesis on cholesterol side-chain cleavage in the mitochondria of luteinized rat ovaries. *Eur. J. Biochem.* 49:117–27

33. Privalle CT, Crivello JF, Jefcoate CR. 1983. Regulation of intramitochondrial cholesterol transfer to side-chain cleavage cytochrome P-450 in rat adrenal gland. *Proc. Natl. Acad. Sci. USA* 80:702–6

34. Ohno Y, Yanagibashi K, Yonezawa Y, Ishiwatari S, Matsuba M. 1983. A possible role of "steroidogenic factor" in the corticoidogenic response to ACTH; effect of ACTH, cycloheximide and aminoglutethimide on the content of cholesterol in the outer and inner mitochondrial membrane of rat adrenal cortex. *Endocrinol. Jpn.* 30:335–38

35. Krueger RJ, Orme-Johnson NR. 1983. Acute adrenocorticotropic hormone stimulation of adrenal corticosteroidogenesis. *J. Biol. Chem.* 258:10159–67

36. Epstein LF, Orme-Johnson NR. 1991. Acute action of luteinizing hormone on mouse Leydig cells: accumulation of mitochondrial phosphoproteins and stimulation of testosterone synthesis. *Mol. Cell. Endocrinol.* 81:113–26

37. Epstein LF, Orme-Johnson NR. 1991. Regulation of steroid hormone biosynthesis. Identification of precursors of a phosphoprotein targeted to the mitochondrion in stimulated rat adrenal cortex cells. *J. Biol. Chem.* 266:19739–45

38. Pon LA, Orme-Johnson NR. 1988. Acute stimulation of corpus luteum cells by gonadotrophin or adenosine 3′,5′-monophosphate causes accumulation of a phosphoprotein concurrent with acceleration of steroid synthesis. *Endocrinology* 123:1942–48

39. Pon LA, Orme-Johnson NR. 1986. Acute stimulation of steroidogenesis in corpus luteum and adrenal cortex by peptide hormones. Rapid induction of a similar protein in both tissues. *J. Biol. Chem.* 261:6594–99

40. Pon LA, Hartigan JA, Orme-Johnson NR. 1986. Acute ACTH regulation of adrenal corticosteroid biosynthesis. Rapid accumulation of a phosphoprotein. *J. Biol. Chem.* 261:13309–16

41. Pon LA, Epstein LF, Orme-Johnson NR. 1986. Acute cAMP stimulation in Leydig cells: rapid accumulation of a protein similar to that detected in adrenal cortex and corpus luteum. *Endocr. Res.* 12:429–46

42. Alberta JA, Epstein LF, Pon LA, Orme-Johnson NR. 1989. Mitochondrial localization of a phosphoprotein that rapidly accumulates in adrenal cortex cells exposed to adrenocorticotropic hormone or to cAMP. *J. Biol. Chem.* 264:2368–72

43. Stocco DM, Kilgore MW. 1988. Induction of mitochondrial proteins in MA-10 Leydig tumour cells with human choriogonadotropin. *Biochem. J.* 249:95–103

44. Stocco DM, Chaudhary LR. 1990. Evidence for the functional coupling of cyclic AMP in MA-10 mouse Leydig tumour cells. *Cell Signal* 2:161–70

45. Stocco DM, Sodeman TC. 1991. The 30-kDa mitochondrial proteins induced by hormone stimulation in MA-10 mouse

Leydig tumor cells are processed from larger precursors. *J. Biol. Chem.* 266: 19731–38

46. Stocco DM, Chen W. 1991. Presence of identical mitochondrial proteins in unstimulated constitutive steroid-producing R2C rat Leydig tumor and stimulated nonconstitutive steroid-producing MA-10 mouse Leydig tumor cells. *Endocrinology* 128:1918–26

47. Stocco DM. 1992. Further evidence that the mitochondrial proteins induced by hormone stimulation in MA-10 mouse Leydig tumor cells are involved in the acute regulation of steroidogenesis. *J. Steroid Biochem. Mol. Biol.* 43:319–33

48. Stocco DM, Ascoli M. 1993. The use of genetic manipulation of MA-10 Leydig tumor cells to demonstrate the role of mitochondrial proteins in the acute regulation of steroidogenesis. *Endocrinology* 132:959–67

49. Stocco DM, King S, Clark BJ. 1995. Differential effects of dimethylsulfoxide on steroidogenesis in mouse MA-10 and rat R2C Leydig tumor cells. *Endocrinology* 136:2993–99

50. Clark BJ, Wells J, King SR, Stocco DM. 1994. The purification, cloning, and expression of a novel luteinizing hormone-induced mitochondrial protein in MA-10 mouse Leydig tumor cells. Characterization of the steroidogenic acute regulatory protein (StAR). *J. Biol. Chem.* 269:28314–22

51. Lin D, Sugawara T, Strauss JF III, Clark BJ, Stocco DM, et al. 1995. Role of steroidogenic acute regulatory protein in adrenal and gonadal steroidogenesis. *Science* 267:1828–31

52. Sugawara T, Lin D, Holt JA, Martin KO, Javitt NB, et al. 1995. Structure of the human steroidogenic acute regulatory protein (StAR) gene: StAR stimulates mitochondrial cholesterol 27-hydroxylase activity. *Biochemistry* 34:12506–12

53. Shimizu K, Hayano M, Gut M, Dorfman RI. 1961. The transformation of 20α-hydroxycholesterol to isocaproic acid and C21 steroids. *J. Biol. Chem.* 236:695–99

54. Degenhart HJ, Visser HK, Boon H, O'Doherty NJ. 1972. Evidence for deficient 20α-cholesterol-hydroxylase activity in adrenal tissue of a patient with lipoid adrenal hyperplasia. *Acta Endocrinol.* 71:512–18

55. Lin D, Gitelman SE, Saenger P, Miller WL. 1991. Normal genes for the cholesterol side chain cleavage enzyme, P450scc, in congenital lipoid adrenal hyperplasia. *J. Clin. Invest.* 88:1955–62

56. Caron KM, Soo SC, Wetsel WC, Stocco DM, Clark BJ, et al. 1997. Targeted disruption of the mouse gene encoding steroidogenic acute regulatory protein provides insights into congenital lipoid adrenal hyperplasia. *Proc. Natl. Acad. Sci. USA* 94:11540–45

57. Liu J, Heikkila P, Kahri AI, Voutilainen R. 1996. Expression of the steroidogenic acute regulatory protein mRNA in adrenal tumors and cultured adrenal cells. *J. Endocrinol.* 150:43–50

58. Nishikawa T, Sasano H, Omura M, Suematsu S. 1996. Regulation of expression of the steroidogenic acute regulatory (StAR) protein by ACTH in bovine adrenal fasciculata cells. *Biochem. Biophys. Res. Commun.* 223:12–18

59. Pollack SE, Furth EE, Kallen CB, Arakane F, Kiriakidou M, et al. 1997. Localization of the steroidogenic acute regulatory protein in human tissues. *J. Clin. Endocrinol. Metab.* 82:4243–51

60. Peters B, Clausmeyer S, Obermuller N, Woyth A, Kranzlin B, et al. 1998. Specific regulation of StAR expression in the rat adrenal zona glomerulosa. An in situ hybridization study. *J. Histochem. Cytochem.* 46:1215–21

61. Cherradi N, Brandenburger Y, Rossier MF, Vallotton MB, Stocco DM, et al. 1998. Atrial natriuretic peptide inhibits calcium-induced steroidogenic acute regulatory

protein gene transcription in adrenal glomerulosa cells. *Mol. Endocrinol.* 12:962–72

62. Nicol MR, Wang H, Ivell R, Morley SD, Walker SW, et al. 1998. The expression of steroidogenic acute regulatory protein (StAR) in bovine adrenocortical cells. *Endocr. Rev.* 24:565–69

63. Brand C, Cherradi N, Defaye G, Chinn A, Chambaz EM, et al. 1998. Transforming growth factor β1 decreases cholesterol supply to mitochondria via repression of steroidogenic acute regulatory protein expression. *J. Biol. Chem.* 273:6410–16

64. Fleury A, Ducharme L, LeHoux JG. 1998. In vivo effects of adrenocorticotrophin on the expression of the hamster steroidogenic acute regulatory protein. *J. Mol. Endocrinol.* 21:131–39

65. Lehoux JG, Fleury A, Ducharme L. 1998. The acute and chronic effects of adrenocorticotropin on the levels of messenger ribonucleic acid and protein of steroidogenic enzymes in rat adrenal in vivo. *Endocrinology* 139:3913–22

66. Lehoux JG, Hales DB, Fleury A, Briere N, Martel D, et al. 1999. The in vivo effects of adrenocorticotropin and sodium restriction on the formation of the different species of steroidogenic acute regulatory protein in rat adrenal. *Endocrinology* 140:5154–64

67. Kiriakidou M, McAllister JM, Sugawara T, Strauss JF, 3rd. 1996. Expression of steroidogenic acute regulatory protein (StAR) in the human ovary. *J. Clin. Endocrinol. Metab.* 81:4122–28

68. Ronen-Fuhrmann T, Timberg R, King SR, Hales KH, Hales DB, et al. 1998. Spatiotemporal expression patterns of steroidogenic acute regulatory protein (StAR) during follicular development in the rat ovary. *Endocrinology* 139:303–15

69. Bao B, Calder MD, Xie S, Smith MF, Salfen BE, et al. 1998. Expression of steroidogenic acute regulatory protein messenger ribonucleic acid is limited to theca of healthy bovine follicles collected during recruitment, selection, and dominance of follicles of the first follicular wave. *Biol. Reprod.* 59:953–59

70. Kerban A, Boerboom D, Sirois J. 1999. Human chorionic gonadotropin induces an inverse regulation of steroidogenic acute regulatory protein messenger ribonucleic acid in theca interna and granulosa cells of equine preovulatory follicles. *Endocrinology* 140:667–74

71. Pescador N, Houde A, Stocco DM, Murphy BD. 1997. Follicle-stimulating hormone and intracellular second messengers regulate steroidogenic acute regulatory protein messenger ribonucleic acid in luteinized porcine granulosa cells. *Biol. Reprod.* 57:660–68

72. Balasubramanian K, Lavoie HA, Garmey JC, Stocco DM, Veldhuis JD. 1997. Regulation of porcine granulosa cell steroidogenic acute regulatory protein (StAR) by insulin-like growth factor I: synergism with follicle- stimulating hormone or protein kinase A agonist. *Endocrinology* 138:433–39

73. Thompson WE, Powell J, Thomas KH, Whittaker JA. 1999. Immunolocalization and expression of the steroidogenic acute regulatory protein during the transitional stages of rat follicular differentiation. *J. Histochem. Cytochem.* 47:769–76

74. LaVoie HA, Garmey JC, Veldhuis JD. 1999. Mechanisms of insulin-like growth factor I augmentation of follicle-stimulating hormone-induced porcine steroidogenic acute regulatory protein gene promoter activity in granulosa cells. *Endocrinology* 140:146–53

75. Sekar N, Garmey JC, Veldhuis JD. 2000. Mechanisms underlying the steroidogenic synergy of insulin and luteinizing hormone in porcine granulosa cells: joint amplification of pivotal sterol-regulatory genes encoding the low-density lipoprotein (LDL) receptor, steroidogenic acute regulatory (StAR) protein and cytochrome P450

side-chain cleavage (P450scc) enzyme. *Mol. Cell. Endocrinol.* 159:25–35

76. Pescador N, Soumano K, Stocco DM, Price CA, Murphy BD. 1996. Steroidogenic acute regulatory protein in bovine corpora lutea. *Biol. Reprod.* 55:485–91

77. Townson DH, Wang XJ, Keyes PL, Kostyo JL, Stocco DM. 1996. Expression of the steroidogenic acute regulatory protein in the corpus luteum of the rabbit: dependence upon the luteotropic hormone, estradiol-17β. *Biol. Reprod.* 55:868–74

78. Chung PH, Sandhoff TW, McLean MP. 1998. Hormone and prostaglandin F2α regulation of messenger ribonucleic acid encoding steroidogenic acute regulatory protein in human corpora lutea. *Endocrine* 8:153–60

79. Pescador N, Stocco DM, Murphy BD. 1999. Growth factor modulation of steroidogenic acute regulatory protein and luteinization in the pig ovary. *Biol. Reprod.* 60:1453–61

80. Chen YJ, Feng Q, Liu YX. 1999. Expression of the steroidogenic acute regulatory protein and luteinizing hormone receptor and their regulation by tumor necrosis factor alpha in rat corpora lutea. *Biol. Reprod.* 60:419–27

81. Mamluk R, Greber Y, Meidan R. 1999. Hormonal regulation of messenger ribonucleic acid expression for steroidogenic factor-1, steroidogenic acute regulatory protein, and cytochrome P450 side-chain cleavage in bovine luteal cells. *Biol. Reprod.* 60:628–34

82. Juengel JL, Haworth JD, Rollyson MK, Silva PJ, Sawyer HR, et al. 2000. Effect of dose of prostaglandin F2α on steroidogenic components and oligonucleosomes in ovine luteal tissue. *Biol. Reprod.* 62:1047–51

83. Arensburg J, Payne AH, Orly J. 1999. Expression of steroidogenic genes in maternal and extraembryonic cells during early pregnancy in mice. *Endocrinology* 140:5220–32

84. Pilon N, Daneau I, Brisson C, Ethier JF, Lussier JG, et al. 1997. Porcine and bovine steroidogenic acute regulatory protein (StAR) gene expression during gestation. *Endocrinology* 138:1085–91

85. Bosmann HB, Hales KH, Li X, Liu Z, Stocco DM, et al. 1996. Acute in vivo inhibition of testosterone by endotoxin parallels loss of steroidogenic acute regulatory (StAR) protein in Leydig cells. *Endocrinology* 137:4522–25

86. Lin T, Wang D, Hu J, Stocco DM. 1998. Upregulation of human chorionic gonadotrophin-induced steroidogenic acute regulatory protein by insulin-like growth factor-I in rat Leydig cells. *Endocrine* 8:73–78

87. Mauduit C, Gasnier F, Rey C, Chauvin MA, Stocco DM, et al. 1998. Tumor necrosis factor-α inhibits Leydig cell steroidogenesis through a decrease in steroidogenic acute regulatory protein expression. *Endocrinology* 139:2863–68

88. Luo L, Chen H, Stocco DM, Zirkin BR. 1998. Leydig cell protein synthesis and steroidogenesis in response to acute stimulation by luteinizing hormone in rats. *Biol. Reprod.* 59:263–70

89. Lejeune H, Sanchez P, Chuzel F, Langlois D, Saez JM. 1998. Time-course effects of human recombinant luteinizing hormone on porcine Leydig cell specific differentiated functions. *Mol. Cell. Endocrinol.* 144:59–69

90. Kanzaki M, Morris PL. 1999. Growth hormone regulates steroidogenic acute regulatory protein expression and steroidogenesis in Leydig cell progenitors. *Endocrinology* 140:1681–86

91. Leers-Sucheta S, Stocco DM, Azhar S. 1999. Down-regulation of steroidogenic acute regulatory (StAR) protein in rat Leydig cells: implications for regulation of testosterone production during aging. *Mech. Ageing Dev.* 107:197–203

92. Gregory CW, DePhilip RM. 1998. Detection of steroidogenic acute regulatory

protein (StAR) in mitochondria of cultured rat Sertoli cells incubated with follicle-stimulating hormone. *Biol. Reprod.* 58:470–74

93. Ford SL, Reinhart AJ, Lukyanenko Y, Hutson JC, Stocco DM. 1999. Pregnenolone synthesis in immature rat Sertoli cells. *Mol. Cell. Endocrinol.* 157:87–94

94. Furukawa A, Miyatake A, Ohnishi T, Ichikawa Y. 1998. Steroidogenic acute regulatory protein (StAR) transcripts constitutively expressed in the adult rat central nervous system: colocalization of StAR, cytochrome P-450SCC (CYP XIA1), and 3β-hydroxysteroid dehydrogenase in the rat brain. *J. Neurochem.* 71:2231–38

95. Gradi A, Tang-Wai R, McBride HM, Chu LL, Shore GC, et al. 1995. The human steroidogenic acute regulatory (StAR) gene is expressed in the urogenital system and encodes a mitochondrial polypeptide. *Biochim. Biophys. Acta* 1258:228–33

96. Strauss JF, 3rd, Martinez F, Kiriakidou M. 1996. Placental steroid hormone synthesis: unique features and unanswered questions. *Biol. Reprod.* 54:303–11

97. Moog-Lutz C, Tomasetto C, Regnier CH, Wendling C, Lutz Y, et al. 1997. MLN64 exhibits homology with the steroidogenic acute regulatory protein (STAR) and is over-expressed in human breast carcinomas. *Int. J. Cancer* 71:183–91

98. Juengel JL, Larrick TL, Meberg BM, Niswender GD. 1998. Luteal expression of steroidogenic factor-1 mRNA during the estrous cycle and in response to luteotropic and luteolytic stimuli in ewes. *Endocrine* 9:227–32

99. Wang X, Walsh LP, Stocco DM. 1999. The role of arachidonic acid on LH-stimulated steroidogenesis and steroidogenic acute regulatory protein accumulation in MA-10 mouse Leydig tumor cells. *Endocrine* 10:7–12

100. Sandhoff TW, McLean MP. 1996. Hormonal regulation of steroidogenic acute regulatory (StAR) protein messenger ribonucleic acid expression in the rat ovary. *Endocrine* 4:259–67

101. Soumano K, Price CA. 1997. Ovarian follicular steroidogenic acute regulatory protein, low-density lipoprotein receptor, and cytochrome P450 side-chain cleavage messenger ribonucleic acids in cattle undergoing superovulation. *Biol. Reprod.* 56:516–22

102. Duncan WC, Cowen GM, Illingworth PJ. 1999. Steroidogenic enzyme expression in human corpora lutea in the presence and absence of exogenous human chorionic gonadotrophin (HCG). *Mol. Hum. Reprod.* 5:291–98

103. Manna PR, Pakarinen P, El-Hefnawy T, Huhtaniemi IT. 1999. Functional assessment of the calcium messenger system in cultured mouse Leydig tumor cells: regulation of human chorionic gonadotropin-induced expression of the steroidogenic acute regulatory protein. *Endocrinology* 140:1739–51

104. Clark BJ, Pezzi V, Stocco DM, Rainey WE. 1995. The steroidogenic acute regulatory protein is induced by angiotensin II and K$^+$ in H295R adrenocortical cells. *Mol. Cell. Endocrinol.* 115:215–19

105. Huang BM, Stocco DM, Li PH, Yang HY, Wu CM, et al. 1997. Corticotropin-releasing hormone stimulates the expression of the steroidogenic acute regulatory protein in MA-10 mouse cells. *Biol. Reprod.* 57:547–51

106. Ramnath HI, Peterson S, Michael AE, Stocco DM, Cooke BA. 1997. Modulation of steroidogenesis by chloride ions in MA-10 mouse tumor Leydig cells: roles of calcium, protein synthesis, and the steroidogenic acute regulatory protein. *Endocrinology* 138:2308–14

107. Elvin JA, Clark AT, Wang P, Wolfman NM, Matzuk MM. 1999. Paracrine actions of growth differentiation factor-9 in the mammalian ovary. *Mol. Endocrinol.* 13:1035–48

108. Manna PR, Tena-Sempere M, Huhtaniemi IT. 1999. Molecular mechanisms of thyroid hormone-stimulated steroidogenesis in mouse Leydig tumor cells. Involvement of the steroidogenic acute regulatory (StAR) protein. *J. Biol. Chem.* 274:5909–18

109. Lee HK, Yoo MS, Choi HS, Kwon HB, Soh J. 1999. Retinoic acids up-regulate steroidogenic acute regulatory protein gene. *Mol. Cell. Endocrinol.* 148:1–10

110. Christenson LK, McAllister JM, Martin KO, Javitt NB, Osborne TF, et al. 1998. Oxysterol regulation of steroidogenic acute regulatory protein gene expression. Structural specificity and transcriptional and posttranscriptional actions. *J. Biol. Chem.* 273:30729–35

111. Nagata Y, Homma H, Matsumoto M, Imai K. 1999. Stimulation of steroidogenic acute regulatory protein (StAR) gene expression by D-aspartate in rat Leydig cells. *FEBS Lett.* 454:317–20

112. Haidan A, Bornstein SR, Liu Z, Walsh LP, Stocco DM, et al. 2000. Secretory products of chromaffin cells stimulate the expression of the steroidogenic acute regulatory (StAR) protein in adrenocortical cells. *Mol. Cell. Endocrinol..* 165:25–32

113. Fritz S, Grunert RA, Stocco DM, Hales DB, Mayerhofer A. 2000. StAR protein is increased by muscarinic receptor activation in human luteinized granulosa cells. *Mol. Cell. Endocrinol.* In press

114. Wang J, Leung PC. 1989. Arachidonic acid as a stimulatory mediator of luteinizing hormone-releasing hormone action in the rat ovary. *Endocrinology* 124:1973–79

115. Band V, Kharbanda SM, Murugesan K, Farooq A. 1986. Prostacyclin and steroidogenesis in goat ovarian cell types in vitro. *Prostaglandins* 31:509–25

116. Cooke BA, Dirami G, Chaudry L, Choi MS, Abayasekara DR, et al. 1991. Release of arachidonic acid and the effects of corticosteroids on steroidogenesis in rat testis Leydig cells. *J. Steroid Biochem. Mol. Biol.* 40:465–71

117. Wang X, Walsh LP, Reinhart AJ, Stocco DM. 2000. The role of arachidonic acid in steroidogenesis and steroidogenic acute regulatory(StAR) gene and protein expression. *J. Biol. Chem.* 275:20204–9

118. Choi YS, Stocco DM, Freeman DA. 1995. Diethylumbelliferyl phosphate inhibits steroidogenesis by interfering with a long-lived factor acting between protein kinase A activation and induction of the steroidogenic acute regulatory protein (StAR). *Eur. J. Biochem.* 234:680–85

119. Sandhoff TW, McLean MP. 1996. Prostaglandin F2α reduces steroidogenic acute regulatory (StAR) protein messenger ribonucleic acid expression in the rat ovary. *Endocrine* 5:183–190

120. Sandhoff TW, McLean MP. 1999. Repression of the rat steroidogenic acute regulatory (StAR) protein gene by PGF2α is modulated by the negative transcription factor DAX-1. *Endocrine* 10:83–91

121. Fiedler EP, Plouffe L Jr, Hales DB, Hales KH, Khan I. 1999. Prostaglandin F2α induces a rapid decline in progesterone production and steroidogenic acute regulatory protein expression in isolated rat corpus luteum without altering messenger ribonucleic acid expression. *Biol. Reprod.* 61:643–50

122. Clark BJ, Combs R, Hales KH, Hales DB, Stocco DM. 1997. Inhibition of transcription affects synthesis of steroidogenic acute regulatory protein and steroidogenesis in MA-10 mouse Leydig tumor cells. *Endocrinology* 138:4893–901

123. Liu Z, Stocco DM. 1997. Heat shock-induced inhibition of acute steroidogenesis in MA-10 cells is associated with inhibition of the synthesis of the steroidogenic acute regulatory protein. *Endocrinology* 138:2722–28

124. Zazopoulos E, Lalli E, Stocco DM, Sassone-Corsi P. 1997. DNA binding and transcriptional repression by DAX-1

blocks steroidogenesis. *Nature* 390:311–15

125. Lalli E, Melner MH, Stocco DM, Sassone-Corsi P. 1998. DAX-1 blocks steroid production at multiple levels. *Endocrinology* 139:4237–43

126. Lin T, Hu J, Wang D, Stocco DM. 1998. Interferon-γ inhibits the steroidogenic acute regulatory protein messenger ribonucleic acid expression and protein levels in primary cultures of rat Leydig cells. *Endocrinology* 139:2217–22

127. Brand C, Souchelnytskiy S, Chambaz EM, Feige JJ, Bailly S. 1998. Smad3 is involved in the intracellular signaling pathways that mediate the inhibitory effects of transforming growth factor-β on StAR expression. *Biochem. Biophys. Res. Commun.* 253:780–85

128. Sridaran R, Philip GH, Li H, Culty M, Liu Z, et al. 1999. GnRH agonist treatment decreases progesterone synthesis, luteal peripheral benzodiazepine receptor mRNA, ligand binding and steroidogenic acute regulatory protein expression during pregnancy. *J. Mol. Endocrinol.* 22:45–54

129. Budnik LT, Jahner D, Mukhopadhyay AK. 1999. Inhibitory effects of TNFα on mouse tumor Leydig cells: possible role of ceramide in the mechanism of action. *Mol. Cell. Endocrinol.* 150:39–46

130. King SR, Rommerts FF, Ford SL, Hutson JC, Orly J, et al. 1998. Ethane dimethane sulfonate and NNN'N'-tetrakis-(2–pyridylmethyl)ethylenediamine inhibit steroidogenic acute regulatory (StAR) protein expression in MA-10 Leydig cells and rat Sertoli cells. *Endocr. Res.* 24:469–78

131. Jones PM, Sayed SB, Persaud SJ, Burns CJ, Gyles S, et al. 2000. Cyclic AMP-induced expression of steroidogenic acute regulatory protein is dependent upon phosphoprotein phosphatase activities. *J. Mol. Endocrinol.* 24:233–39

132. Sam AD, 2nd, Sharma AC, Lee LY, Hales DB, Law WR, et al. 1999. Sepsis produces depression of testosterone and steroidogenic acute regulatory (StAR) protein. *Shock* 11:298–301

133. King SR, Liu Z, Soh J, Eimerl S, Orly J, et al. 1999. Effects of disruption of the mitochondrial electrochemical gradient on steroidogenesis and the Steroidogenic Acute Regulatory (StAR) protein. *J. Steroid Biochem. Mol. Biol.* 69:143–54

134. Ogilvie KM, Held Hales K, Roberts ME, Hales DB, Rivier C. 1999. The inhibitory effect of intracerebroventricularly injected interleukin 1β on testosterone secretion in the rat: role of steroidogenic acute regulatory protein. *Biol. Reprod.* 60:527–33

135. Walsh LP, McCormick C, Martin C, Stocco DM. 2000. The role of the steroidogenic acute regulatory (StAR) protein in environmental pollutant disrupted steroidogenesis: Roundup inhibits steroidogenesis by disrupting StAR expression. *Environ. Health Persp.* 108:769–76

136. Walsh LP, Stocco DM. 2000. The effects of Lindane on steroidogenesis and steroidogenic acute regulatory protein expression. *Biol. Reprod.* 63:1024–33

137. Walsh LP, Webster DR, Stocco DM. 2000. Dimethoate inhibits steroidogenesis by disrupting transcription of the steroidogenic acute regulatory (StAR) gene. *J. Endocrinol.* In press

138. Walsh LP, Stocco DM. 2000. The role of the steroidogenic acute regulatory (StAR) protein in environmental endocrine disruptor inhibited steroidogenesis. Presented at the *Proc. 52nd Yamada Conf., Molecular Steroidogenesis*, Tokyo, Japan

139. Clark BJ, Stocco DM. 1997. Steroidogenic acute regulatory protein: the StAR still shines brightly. *Mol. Cell. Endocrinol.* 134:1–8

140. Caron KM, Ikeda Y, Soo SC, Stocco DM, Parker KL, et al. 1997. Characterization

of the promoter region of the mouse gene encoding the steroidogenic acute regulatory protein. *Mol. Endocrinol.* 11:138–47

141. Sugawara T, Holt JA, Kiriakidou M, Strauss JF, 3rd. 1996. Steroidogenic factor 1-dependent promoter activity of the human steroidogenic acute regulatory protein (StAR) gene. *Biochemistry* 35:9052–59

142. Sugawara T, Kiriakidou M, McAllister JM, Kallen CB, Strauss JF III. 1997. Multiple steroidogenic factor 1 binding elements in the human steroidogenic acute regulatory protein gene 5'-flanking region are required for maximal promoter activity and cyclic AMP responsiveness. *Biochemistry* 36:7249–55

143. Sandhoff TW, Hales DB, Hales KH, McLean MP. 1998. Transcriptional regulation of the rat steroidogenic acute regulatory protein gene by steroidogenic factor 1. *Endocrinology* 139:4820–31

144. Johnson PF. 1993. Identification of C/EBP basic region residues involved in DNA sequence recognition and half-site spacing preference. *Mol. Cell Biol.* 13:6919–30

145. Nalbant D, Williams SC, Stocco DM, Khan SA. 1998. Luteinizing hormone-dependent gene regulation in Leydig cells may be mediated by CCAAT/enhancer-binding protein-β. *Endocrinology* 139:272–79

146. Sirois J, Richards JS. 1993. Transcriptional regulation of the rat prostaglandin endoperoxide synthase 2 gene in granulosa cells. Evidence for the role of a *cis*-acting C/EBPβ promoter element. *J. Biol. Chem.* 268:21931–38

147. Reinhart AJ, Williams SC Stocco DM. 1999. Interactions between SF-1 and C/EBPβ are required for high level expression from the murine StAR promoter. *Mol. Endocrinol.* 13:729–41

148. Silverman E, Eimerl S, Orly J. 1999. CCAAT enhancer-binding protein β and GATA-4 binding regions within the promoter of the steroidogenic acute regulatory protein (StAR) gene are required for transcription in rat ovarian cells. *J. Biol. Chem.* 274:17987–96

149. Christenson LK, McAllister JM, Martin K, Javitt NB, Osborne TF, et al. 1998. Oxysterol regulation of steroidogenic acute regulatory protein (StAR) gene expression: structural specifictiy, transcriptional and post-transcriptional actions. *J. Biol. Chem.* 273:30729–35

150. Bardoni B, Zanaria E, Guioli S, Floridia G, Worley KC, et al. 1994. A dosage sensitive locus at chromosome Xp21 is involved in male to female sex reversal. *Nat. Genet* 7:497–501

151. Lalli E, Bardoni B, Zazopoulos E, Wurtz JM, Strom TM, et al. 1997. A transcriptional silencing domain in DAX-1 whose mutation causes adrenal hypoplasia congenita. *Mol. Endocrinol.* 11:1950–60

152. Ito M, Yu R, Jameson JL. 1997. DAX-1 inhibits SF-1-mediated transactivation via a carboxy-terminal domain that is deleted in adrenal hypoplasia congenita. *Mol. Cell Biol.* 17:1476–83

153. Arakane F, Sugawara T, Nishino H, Liu Z, Holt JA, et al. 1996. Steroidogenic acute regulatory protein (StAR) retains activity in the absence of its mitochondrial import sequence: implications for the mechanism of StAR action. *Proc. Natl. Acad. Sci. USA* 93:13731–36

154. Wang X, Liu Z, Eimerl S, Timberg R, Weiss AM, et al. 1998. Effect of truncated forms of the steroidogenic acute regulatory protein on intramitochondrial cholesterol transfer. *Endocrinology* 139:3903–12

155. Arakane F, Kallen CB, Watari H, Foster JA, Sepuri NB, et al. 1998. The mechanism of action of steroidogenic acute regulatory protein (StAR). StAR acts on the outside of mitochondria to stimulate steroidogenesis. *J. Biol. Chem.* 273:16339–45

156. Watari H, Arakane F, Moog-Lutz C,

Kallen CB, Tomasetto C, et al. 1997. MLN64 contains a domain with homology to the steroidogenic acute regulatory protein (StAR) that stimulates steroidogenesis. *Proc. Natl. Acad. Sci. USA* 94:8462–67

157. Ponting CP, Aravind L. 1999. START: a lipid-binding domain in StAR, HD-ZIP and signalling proteins. *Trends Biochem. Sci.* 24:130–32

158. Kallen CB, Billheimer JT, Summers SA, Stayrook SE, Lewis M, et al. 1998. Steroidogenic acute regulatory protein (StAR) is a sterol transfer protein. *J. Biol. Chem.* 273:26285–88

159. Martinez F, Strauss JF, 3rd. 1997. Regulation of mitochondrial cholesterol metabolism. In *Subcellular Biochemistry*, ed. R Bittman, 28:205–34. New York: Plenum

160. Kallen CB, Arakane F, Christenson LK, Watari H, Devoto L, et al. 1998. Unveiling the mechanism of action and regulation of the steroidogenic acute regulatory protein. *Mol. Cell. Endocrinol.* 145:39–45

161. Bose HS, Whittal RM, Baldwin MA, Miller WL. 1999. The active form of the steroidogenic acute regulatory protein, StAR, appears to be a molten globule. *Proc. Natl. Acad. Sci. USA* 96:7250–55

162. Tsujishita Y, Hurley JH. 2000. Structure and lipid transport mechanism of a StAR-related protein. *Nat. Struct. Biol.* 7:408–14

Annu. Rev. Physiol. 2001. 63:215–33

THE GUANYLYL CYCLASE FAMILY AT Y2K

BJ Wedel and DL Garbers

Cecil H and Ida Green Center for Reproductive Biology Sciences, Howard Hughes Medical Institute and Department of Pharmacology, University of Texas Southwestern Medical Center, Dallas, Texas 75390; e-mail: dgarbe@mednet.swmed.edu

Key Words cyclic GMP, adenylyl cyclase, natriuretic peptides, heat-stable enterotoxins, hypertension, nitric oxide, olfaction, vision, genetic diseases

■ **Abstract** During the 1980s the purification, cloning, and expression of various forms of guanylyl cyclase (GC) revealed that they served as receptors for extracellular signals. Seven membrane forms, which presumably exist as homodimers, and four subunits of apparent heterodimers (commonly referred to as the soluble forms) are known, but in animals such as nematodes, much larger numbers of GCs are expressed. The number of transmembrane segments (none, one, or multiple) divide the GC family into three groups. Those with no or one transmembrane segment bind nitric oxide/carbon monoxide (NO/CO) or peptides. There are no known ligands for the multiple transmembrane segment class of GCs. Mutational and structural analyses support a model where catalysis requires a shared substrate binding site between the subunits, whether homomeric or heteromeric in nature. Because some cyclases or cyclase ligand genes lack specific GC inhibitors, disruption of either has been used to define the functions of individual cyclases, as well as to define human genetic disease counterparts.

GENERAL OVERVIEW OF THE GUANYLYL CYCLASE FAMILY

Three general topological variants of the enzyme are known and can be defined as containing no, one, or multiple transmembrane segments (Figure 1, see color insert).

No Apparent Transmembrane Segments

Those enzymes that contain no apparent transmembrane segments are generally referred to as the soluble forms of the enzyme, although subunits from some species contain a consensus isoprenylation site at the carboxyl tail, possibly targeting them to the membrane (1, 2). The soluble forms are also thought to function normally as heterodimers (α and β subunit), although exceptions may exist (e.g. *Manduca Sexta*) (2) (see below). Within the carboxyl tail of both subunits is a cyclase homology domain (CHD) similar to those of the other GC isoforms and similar to adenylyl cyclases (AC) (Figure 1). A heme group is bound within the amino terminus of at least one of the members of this group, the so-called α_1/β_1 form, where it binds principally to the β subunit (for review see 3). Both the α_1/β_1 and α_2/β_1 forms of heterodimeric cyclases have been isolated from tissues, and both respond to NO (4, 5). It is assumed, therefore, that the effects of NO that are mediated by cGMP are the result of binding to one or more of the enzymes in this group.

The completion or near-completion of genome projects for various species will define the numbers of GCs and will clarify the generality of the α/β paradigm that has been established in mammals. In *Drosophila*, of the five predicted soluble GC isoforms, four share characteristics of the β subunit, whereas only one α-like subunit exists. This finding suggests that the four β subunits share the single α subunit or that the β-like subunits combine as heterodimers or homodimers to form active enzymes.

Work in the insect *Manduca sexta* may shed light on this quandary. One soluble guanylyl cyclase in this species (MsGC-β_3) is closely related to mammalian soluble β subunits but is catalytically active in the absence of other subunits (2), suggesting the formation of an active β homodimer that contains a conserved putative heme-binding histidine but lacks conserved cysteine residues that when mutated reduce the affinity of the α_1/β_1 heterodimer for heme (6). MsGC-β_3 is not responsive to NO stimulation, even after attempts to reconstitute the enzyme with heme, suggesting a different ligand or mechanism of activation.

There are also soluble GC isoforms in *Caenorhabditis elegans*, where a total of seven are predicted (gcy-31 to −37). They appear more closely related to mammalian β isoforms, and all contain the conserved histidine (β_1H105) (7). The two conserved cysteines (β_1C78 and β_1C214) that reduce the heme content of purified α_1/β_1 heterodimer when mutated to serine are not present in these isoforms (6). That these isoforms may not contain heme is supported by the failure of NO to stimulate cGMP production in homogenates of *C. elegans* (8). Also, no genes with homology to NO synthases are apparent within the *C. elegans* genome. Thus if these enzymes are receptors for NO, the source is likely not in the worm itself. Considering the lack of a α-like subunit, either heterodimeric or homomeric active β/β forms of GC seem likely.

Single Apparent Transmembrane Segments

The membranous forms of the enzyme are separated into two classes, those with a single transmembrane span and those with multiple membrane spans (Figure 1). The single transmembrane span divides the molecule into an extracellular ligand binding domain (ECD) and an intracellular region consisting of a protein kinase-homology domain (KHD), an amphipathic helical or hinge region (H), and a cyclase-homology domain (CHD). The CHD represents the catalytic domain. There are seven isoforms of the single transmembrane class of cyclases in mammals (abbreviated GC-A through GC-G) (for review see 9, 10). GC-A and GC-B are also referred to as NPR-A and NPR-B. Three of these isoforms possess identified ligands and fall into two groups. GC-A and GC-B share identity within the ECD, and both bind natriuretic peptides, whereas GC-C contains an ECD with limited sequence similarity to the above two isoforms and binds heat-stable enterotoxins (STa). Ironically, although the first three isoforms were cloned based on low stringency hybridization or PCR, they are the only three with known ligands.

The natriuretic peptides, atrial natriuretic peptide (ANP), B-type natriuretic peptide (BNP), and C-type natriuretic peptide (CNP), are synthesized as prepro-hormones and share a common 17-amino acid disulfide-linked ring structure. CNP acquired the functional name natriuretic peptide mostly because of its structural similarity to ANP and BNP, but its normal function remains unclear. Although ANP and BNP are present in relatively high levels in the heart and circulate in the bloodstream, CNP is produced in a variety of tissues, including endothelial cells (for review see 11). GC-A is expressed in the kidney, smooth muscle vasculature, adrenal gland, and in many other tissues, whereas GC-B, although found in many tissues, is expressed at particularly high levels in the fibroblast.

GC-C is expressed principally in the intestine but is also found in kidney, testis, liver, and placenta in various animals (12–14). The types of infant or adult (traveler's) diarrhea caused by a heat-stable enterotoxin of *Escherichia coli* (STa) are the result of activation of this receptor. The proposed endogenous ligands for GC-C are guanylin, uroguanylin, and lymphoguanylin (for review see 15, 16). These three peptides are expressed in a variety of tissues and cells (15, 16), and although they activate GC-C and compete with STa in binding assays, it is not known whether they bind exclusively to GC-C (i.e. no cross-linking or similar studies have been performed on intestinal or other cells to determine the number of different proteins to which these peptides bind); GC-C may not be the primary receptor in all tissues. All three peptides also have been suggested to possess natriuretic properties in intact animals and to regulate sodium balance (15, 16).

GC-D through GC-G are expressed in many tissues. GC-D is expressed predominately in olfactory epithelium; GC-E and GC-F are present in photoreceptors and the pineal gland; and GC-G is expressed in lung, intestine, and skeletal muscle (9, 10). The cell types that express GC-G are not known. These enzymes are believed to be orphan receptors because of several features: First, the topology of these proteins is the same as that of the known receptors. Second, a chimera between mammalian GC-B and a *C. elegans* CHD generates a CNP-sensitive GC (17). Third, six cysteine residues within the ECD are highly conserved across the various single transmembrane segment forms of GC (18). These conserved cysteines form disulfide bonds in the ANP clearance receptor (19). These cysteine residues are believed to be conserved because of the necessity of maintaining a general ECD conformation required to bind the various ligands.

GC-D is expressed in a unique subset of olfactory neurons that also contain other unique proteins (20, 21). These neurons project back to a set of glomeruli in the olfactory bulb known as necklace glomeruli that are believed to play a role in pheromone sensing (21). Although considerable work on GC activating proteins

(GCAPs) shows regulation of GC-E and GC-F, possibly through binding to the KHD and CHD, the function of the ECD, if any, remains unknown (22–24).

Preliminary analysis of annotated sequences in the *Drosophila* genome predicts seven single transmembrane forms of GC, corresponding to the number found in mammals, but none closely resemble any of the mammalian forms within the ECD.

There are 27 annotated single transmembrane isoforms of GC (gcy-1 to −27) in *C. elegans*. Several of these isoforms have been shown through expression of promoter:GFP fusions to be located in single discrete sensory neurons; some exhibit left or right sidedness in expression (18).

A GC (gyc-10; *odr-1*) has been identified as defective in worms deficient for chemotaxis to certain odorants (25). The extracellular domain of odr-1 is not required for the chemosensory response because an amino-terminal truncation of *odr-1* restores odorant responsiveness in an *odr-1* mutant strain defective in chemotaxis (25). However, the intracellular region could still form a heterodimeric complex with a full-length receptor to rescue a ligand-dependent event. Thus the intracellular piece may participate in a receptor complex.

Multiple Apparent Transmembrane Segments

The class of guanyl cyclases containing multiple transmembrane segments is not known to serve as receptors for ligands (Figure 1). So far they have been discovered in a restricted number of cells *(Paramecium tetraurelia, Tetrahymena pyriformis, Plasmodium falciparum, Dictyostelium discoideum)* (26–28). Two apparent CHDs, each lying to the carboxyl side of a stretch of 6 transmembrane segments, much the same as in mammalian ACs, are predicted, although the C1 and C2 domains appear reversed. In addition to the 12 transmembrane segments that separate the CHDs, this class of cyclases may contain other segments (26–28). The alveolate GCs possess an additional amino-terminal part with 10 transmembrane spanning segments that show strong similarity to P-type ATPases (Figure 1). However, key amino acids involved in ATPase activity are altered, suggesting a different function for this part of the protein (26). This form of GC is found in protozoa and in the malarial parasite *Plasmodium falciparum*, where it appears to be expressed during the sexual blood stages of the life cycle (28). Another apparent member of this class of GCs originates from the slime mold *Dictyostelium discoideum* (Genbank accession # CAB42641).

IDENTIFICATION OF REGIONS ESSENTIAL FOR CATALYSIS

The X-ray crystal structures of various ACs provide insight into substrate specificity, catalytic mechanisms, and means of regulation by effectors (29, 30). These structures also have allowed modeling of the GC putative catalytic domain (31, 32). Several characteristics of the enzyme have been explained as a result of modeling studies, in particular the minimal requirement of dimer formation for significant rates of catalysis. Co-expression of both subunits of the soluble form of GC is required for detectable activity in mammals (33, 34), as is also the case with the C1 and C2 domains of the ACs (for review see 35, 36). The CHDs are believed to form two pseudosymmetric potential substrate-binding sites at their interface, while aligning head to tail (31, 32, 37). In the case of AC, one of these shared sites binds the substrate ATP, and the other binds the diterpene activator forskolin (30). The molecule that normally binds to the forskolin site has not been identified. The fact that certain residues predicted to make contacts with ATP/GTP are present in C1 or α_1 but not in C2 or β_1, and vice versa (Figure 2, see color insert), provides an explanation for linear Michaelis Menton-type kinetics with both the soluble GCs and ACs (38, 39). In contrast, the membrane forms of GC, which function as homodimers, display positive cooperative kinetics as a function of substrate concentration (38).

Two metal ions are required for catalysis, analogous to DNA polymerases (40). Because both types of enzyme catalyze a nucleophilic attack of the 3' hydroxyl of ribose on the α phosphate of a nucleoside triphosphate, the similar response is not unexpected. Two aspartates are predicted to contact two Mg-ions (Figure 2). Structural studies (41) demonstrate that there is a free metal site in addition to a MeNTP site. Possibly the most unexpected result from the structural modeling was that two amino acids dictate substrate specificity (32, 37, 42). While K938 and D1018 of AC IIC2 appear to form hydrogen bonds with the N-1 and N-6 atoms of the adenine ring of ATP, the corresponding residues E473 and C541 of the β_1 subunit of soluble GC appear to contact the N-2 and O-6 atoms of the guanine ring (Figures 2 and 3, see color insert). These respective amino acid residues are invariant in the ACs or GCs. Mutation of these residues in β_1 to those in IIC2 switches substrate specificity of the soluble GC to that of an AC with retention of NO sensitivity (32). Mutation of an additional amino acid (R592Q) enhances cAMP formation rates. Although this arginine residue probably does not directly interact with GTP, interaction with β_1E473 may stabilize the active site. The same mutations in GC-E have similar effects to those in the soluble form of GC (42).

REGULATORY REGIONS OF MAMMALIAN SINGLE TRANSMEMBRANE FORMS OF GUANYLYL CYCLASE

Kinase Homology Domain (KHD)

Deletion of the KHD causes ligand-independent cyclase activity and may act as a negative regulator of cyclase activity (43). Although the KHD contains many residues conserved in the catalytic domain of protein kinases, catalytic activity has not been detected, except possibly in one case (44). Here, apparent autophosphorylation of GC-E occurred but may have been the result of contamination by another protein kinase. A highly conserved aspartic acid, suggested as the catalytic base in protein kinases, is absent from all GC KHDs (Figure 4, see color insert). Mutation of this residue in protein kinases reduces or destroys enzyme activity, suggesting that GCs are either not protein kinases or not conventional protein kinases (Figure 4). Additionally, a glycine-rich loop conserved in protein kinases is only partially retained in some of the GC isoforms (Figure 4). The glycine-rich loop ($G_1XG_2XXG_3XV$) serves as a nucleotide-positioning loop in protein kinases and interacts with the three phosphate groups of ATP. G_1 and G_2 are the most critical glycine residues in PK-A, and mutation of G_2 results in a 300-fold reduction in the rate of phosphoryl transfer (45). However, the effects on ATP binding have not been reported.

KHDs similar to those of the GCs are also found in another group of enzymes, the JAK kinases (Figure 4). The binding of specific cytokines and their receptors seems to cause activation of JAK kinases by auto- or transphosphorylation (46–48). The four known JAK kinases (JAK1, JAK2, JAK3, and TYK2) consist of seven JAK homology domains (JH1-7) (Figure 4). Two of these domains are similar to protein kinase catalytic domains, but only one (JH1) is known to express protein kinase activity. JH2, in contrast, like the KHD of the GCs, contains modifications within the glycine-rich loop region and an invariant aspartate that is altered in all GCs (Figure 4). The function of the KHD in JAKs and in GCs is potentially similar. Deletion of the KHD in JAKs and GCs results in constitutively active enzymes, suggesting that in both cases the KHD functions as a negative regulator of catalytic activity (49). Another activating point mutation within a JAK-KHD (JAK3: C759R) has been identified in patients with severe combined immunodeficiency (SCID) (50). The mutation results in cytokine-independent, constitutive JAK3 protein tyrosine phosphorylation. The respective cysteine is part of the $CW(X)_6RP$ motif and is conserved in most active protein tyrosine kinases and in all KHDs. A possible explanation for the effect of these mutations is that they inhibit the interaction of the KHD with the protein kinase domain, thereby relieving inhibition. Whether ATP relieves the inhibition in the JAKs, as in the GCs, is unknown.

In screening the database for other proteins with KHDs resembling those of the JAKs or the GCs, a family of proteins in *Arabidopsis thaliana* was found that contains an extracellular domain with leucine-rich repeats, a predicted single transmembrane segment, and an intracellular KHD (Figure 4). Since no other domain is apparent within the intracellular region of these proteins, the function of the KHD in these cases is intriguing. These KHDs may act as docking sites or scaffolds for other proteins in both plants and animals. Alternatively these may actually act as specific protein kinases or possess other enzyme activity.

Protein Phosphorylation

In the sea urchin GCs are phosphorylated in the absence of added ligand. The addition of ligand (egg peptides in this case) causes a rapid dephosphorylation and desensitization of the enzyme (51). GC-A or GC-B can be desensitized by either homologous or heterologous mechanisms, and Potter & Garbers subsequently demonstrated a strong correlation between the phosphorylation state and the sensitivity of GC-A to ANP (52, 53). When membranes from NIH 3T3 cells that stably over-express GC-A were incubated with ATP, AMPPNP, or ATPγS, only ATPγS potentiated ANP-dependent cyclase activity. When the membranes were incubated with ATPγS and then washed, GC-A became sensitive to ANP/AMPPNP stimulation (54). These and other experiments indicate that GC-A can be sensitized and desensitized in a membrane preparation and that such ligand sensitivity is dependent on protein phosphorylation. Potter & Hunter mapped the phosphorylation sites of GC-A and GC-B, and demonstrated that alteration of these amino acids to glutamic acid produced an enzyme that could no longer be desensitized (see Figure 4) (55–57).

Chrisman & Garbers concentrated their efforts on enzyme regulation in the fibroblast, a cell central to wound remodeling (58). Relatively high activities of GC-B in the fibroblast suggest that this cGMP signaling pathway regulates fibroblast functions, and elevations of cGMP induced by CNP blocked activation of the mitogen-activated protein kinase cascade in fibroblasts. Furthermore, PDGF or FGF rapidly (within 5 min) impaired CNP-dependent elevations of cyclic GMP (58). The NO-sensitive guanylyl cyclase, in contrast, was not affected, demonstrating that the growth factors specifically targeted GC-B for inactivation. The effects of the mitogens were explained fully by a direct and stable inactivation of GC-B in membranes. The stable inactivation correlated with the dephosphorylation of GC-B, but a direct cause-effect relationship has not been established.

Associated Proteins

Genetic screens have identified a possible associated protein in the *C. elegans* cGMP signaling pathway, the chaperone HSP90. Mutations in either a putative membrane GC receptor *(daf-11)* or HSP90 *(daf-21)* result in animals defective in response to certain nonvolatile chemicals sensed primarily by ASE neurons (59). The HSP90 mutant can be rescued with a cGMP analogue, suggesting that GC and HSP90 function in a common pathway. HSP90 associates with a variety of proteins, including steroid hormone receptors, protein kinases, and protein phosphatases (60, 61). Although the amino terminus of HSP90 interacts with unfolded proteins in an ATP-sensitive manner, the carboxyl-terminal domain functions as an ATP-independent chaperone. In light of the genetic similarity of GCs and HSP90, the ATP effects on GCs could, in part, be explained by the binding of ATP to HSP90. ATP is necessary for maximal ANP or CNP activation of GC-A or GC-B, and it appears to stabilize GC-C and GC-E (62–64).

The protein phosphatase PP5 interacts with the KHD of GC-A, based on a yeast two-hybrid screen (65). Although the physiological relevance of this interaction remains unclear, PP5 also interacts with HSP90, where the sites of interaction reside around four basic residues within a tratricopeptide repeat domain of PP5 and in acidic residues in the carboxyl-terminal domain of HSP90 (66, 67). Based on analogy with steroid hormone receptors, HSP90/ATP may transform GC-A or GC-B into a ligand-sensitive state. Upon binding of ligand, HSP90 could be released from the protein, thereby leading to PP5 binding which, in turn, could dephosphorylate the receptor switching it to the ligand-insensitive state. Alternatively, the proteins could remain associated throughout the entire process.

FUNCTIONS OF SPECIFIC GUANYLYL CYCLASE RECEPTORS

Given the lack of specific inhibitors of the individual forms of GC, gene disruption has been used to define function. In addition, the over-expression of various gene products provides considerable insight into the physiological roles of the GC pathways (Table 1). Targeted gene disruption in the mouse also creates animal models that can define the basis of specific human genetic diseases and provides a basis for development of therapeutic intervention. The ANP-clearance receptor (ANP-CR) and GC-A, GC-C, and GC-E genes have been disrupted along with a number of putative ligand or ligand-generating genes (summarized in Table 1). We discuss only a few of the gene disruption models in detail.

Elimination of BNP

Disruption of the BNP gene leads to cardiac fibrosis in the absence of hypertension or cardiac hypertrophy (68). This is in sharp contrast to ANP gene disruption (see Table 1). Thus although ANP and BNP appear to signal through the same receptor, the physiological consequences of removal of either peptide is different. Based on this finding, it has been suggested that BNP acts as an antifibrolytic factor within the heart. Fibroblasts contain GC-A and GC-B, as well as soluble forms of GC, but GC-B activity predominates (see below). The antagonism by cGMP of certain growth factor signaling pathways may explain the proliferative response of fibroblasts in the absence of BNP, in this case presumably because of failure to activate fibroblastic GC-A (58). These studies, in conjunction with those on GC-A (see below), point to the importance of local signaling by these peptides, even in the face of substantial concentrations in the circulation.

Elimination of GC-A

Genetic analyses of families with hereditary hypertension have led to the identification of several genetic forms of hypertension (69). Although there are as yet no clear human homologues, the elimination of specific cGMP pathways in the mouse causes hypertension. One such gene disruption model is that of GC-A (58).

At least four prominent manifestations are evident after disruption of the mouse GC-A gene: elevated basal blood pressure, resistance to dietary salt-induced hypertension, cardiac hypertrophy, and cardiac fibrosis (70–72). The salt-resistant hypertension suggests that GC-A is not a critical regulator of the response to

TABLE 1 Mouse models resulting from genetic alteration of cGMP signaling pathways

Gene	Gene disruption	Transgene (overexpression)	Phenotype	References
nNOS (NOS1)	+		Grossly enlarged stomach, hypertrophy of the pyloric sphincter and circular muscle layer, resistance to stroke injury, aggression in males	(95–97)
iNOS (NOS2)	+		Impaired liver regeneration	(98)
eNOS (NOS3)	+		Elevated blood pressure, pulmonary hypertension protection against vascular injury	(97, 99–104)
eNOS (NOS3)		+	Lowered blood pressure, reduced to reactivity NO-mediated vasodilators	(105)
ANP	+		Salt-sensitive hypertension, pulmonary hypertension	(106–110)
ANP		+	Lowered blood pressure	(111–113)
BNP	+		Cardiac fibrosis	(68)
BNP		+	Skeletal overgrowth	(114)
ANP-C receptor	+		Reduced ability to concentrate urine, mild diuresis, lowered blood pressure, skeletal deformations	(115)
GC-A	+		Salt-resistant hypertension, cardiac hypertrophy, cardiac fibrosis	(70–74, 116, 117)
GC-A		+	Hypotension, protection against high dietary salt (dependent on copy number)	(118)
GC-C	+		Resistance to heat-stable enterotoxins	(78, 79)
GC-E	+		Cone-specific dystrophy, paradoxical rod behavior	(84)
cGK I	+		Vascular dysfunction, intestinal dysfunction, erectile dysfunction	(119, 120)
cGK II	+		Intestinal secretory defects, dwarfism	(77)

high- or low-salt diets. Yet, the infusion of an isooncotic solution to null mice to expand vascular volume caused no natriuretic or diuretic response (73). An attractive explanation for this disparity in response to dietary salt compared with intravenous salt would be direct communication between the gastrointestinal tract and the kidney. Indeed, as pointed out elsewhere, guanylin and uroguanylin may regulate the kidney, possibly through GC-C (for review see 15, 16).

In fact, when physiological saline was given by gavage, the kidney response of wild-type and GC-A null mice was equivalent, in apparent support of a direct link between the gastrointestinal tract and the kidney (74). However, the administration of 0.9% saline through an intraperitoneal route also resulted in equal kidney responses in wild-type and GC-A null mice. When 0.9% saline was infused intravenously, wild-type and null mice then showed an equivalent natriuretic and diuretic response. Thus GC-A does not appear essential for regulation of sodium excretion in response to changes in dietary sodium concentration, but likely becomes critical in volume expansions, where the isooncotic pressure remains constant, such as head-out immersion, or during the initial and correctable stages of congestive heart failure (74).

Elimination of GC-C

Heat-stable enterotoxins (STa) from various pathogenic bacteria, including some strains of E. coli, are peptides with two to three intramolecular disulfide bridges (75). The common explanation of their mechanism of action is that the peptides bind to and activate GC-C, thus increasing the levels of intracellular cGMP (76). The resultant activation of a specific membrane-associated form of cGMP-dependent protein kinase type II (cGK II) and phosphorylation of the chloride channel, CFTR thus causes the acute secretory diarrhea. Gene disruptions have fully supported the model in that elimination of GC-C or cGK II blocks STa-induced diarrhea in mice (77–79). The acute secretory diarrhea caused by STa can result in the death of human infants or other young animals. Therefore, one would predict that unless GC-C is critical for survival, selective pressure would have eliminated the receptor during evolution. However, the receptor is highly conserved in mammalian species and is likely expressed in frogs, snakes, and other animals (80, 81). Nevertheless, disruption of the GC-C gene in mice does not cause an apparent phenotype except resistance to STa (78). The apparent paradox is not explained but may be due to the highly controlled environment within animal colonies in comparison with conditions in the wild.

Elimination of GC-E

The two GCs expressed in the retina and the pineal gland possess the key features of the known GC receptors (82). Expression of the cyclases is prominent on the disk membrane, suggesting that the ECD is harbored within an exceptionally small area (83). Nevertheless, the ligands for these putative receptors have not been identified, and therefore they are still considered orphan receptors.

The gene for GC-E was disrupted in mice at exon 5, which encodes the transmembrane region (84). GC-E -/- mice exhibit a severe reduction in cone function within the first post-natal month and a complete loss of cone function after the first two months. Rod function is somewhat impaired in GC-E -/- compared with wild-type mice; however, differences are not statistically significant. GC-E, therefore, may be the major or the only GC in cones, whereas another cyclase, possibly GC-F, may sustain rod function.

The mapping of GC-E and GC-F to mouse and human chromosomes showed that GC-E is located in a region containing three known gene defects, retinitis pigmentosa, Leber's congenital amaurosis (LCA), and a specific cone-rod dystrophy (CRD; CORD6); GC-F maps to the X chromosome where no linkage to a visual disease has yet been reported.

Mutations within the GC-E receptor gene are responsible for certain cases of LCA and CRD (see Table 2). LCA is one of the earliest and most severe forms of inherited retinal dystrophies, characterized by total blindness or greatly impaired vision, normal fundus, and an extinguished electroretinogram at birth (85). The clinical features of CRD are less severe and include diminished visual acuity and loss of color discrimination, followed by progressive peripheral visual field loss. Early loss of cone responses is followed by progressive loss of rod responses. Mutations within RPE65 (retinal pigment epithelium protein involved in metabolism of vitamin A), CRX (photoreceptor transcription factor), and GC-E have been linked to different forms of LCA (85). Several of the mutations in GC-E would yield truncated proteins lacking the catalytic domain (Figure 5, see color insert). The *F565S* mutant is a point mutation within the KHD, a region that appears to bind GCAPs (24, 86). The mutation seems to dramatically decrease basal cGMP production and cause a loss of GCAP1 responsiveness of GC-E (86).

A phenotype similar to LCA causing blindness of chickens at hatch has been linked to mutations in GC-E (87). The retinas appear morphologically normal at hatching but do not respond to light. The photoreceptor cells subsequently degenerate progressively. This disorder results from a 642 bp deletion in a region corresponding to exons 4–7, which is replaced by a reverse 81 bp fragment with homology to exon 9.

The mutations found in CRD patients are localized within the H region of GC-E (see Figure 5), an amphipathic region predicted to form a coiled coil leucine zipper-like structure. Three groups have identified missense mutations *E837D, R838C, R838S,* and *T839M* (88–90). Mutation of *E837D* decreases basal cGMP production and GCAP-1 stimulation, whereas it increases GCAP-2 stimulation (91). Mutation of *R838C* reduces basal activity and GCAP-2 sensitivity, while GCAP-1 sensitivity is increased and shifted to higher Ca^{2+} concentrations (91, 92). Because the *E837D* and *R838C* mutants are catalytically active, it seems unlikely that these mutations block dimerization. A point mutation within GCAP-1 (Y99C) associated with CRD may disrupt one of the calcium binding EF hands and therefore interfere with the calcium feedback mechanism (93). In addition, the Y99C mutant of GCAP-1

TABLE 2   Phenotype and biochemical consequences of mutations within the GC-E receptor gene found in human and chicken

Phenotype	Organism	Mutation in GC-E	Biochemical characterization	References
LCA	Human	■ Exon 2 (227 G to T) *A52S* (polymorphism?) ■ Exon 2 (bp 460 C deleted) premature stop at aa 165 ■ Exon 2 base 693 C deleted; premature stop at aa 215 ■ Exon 8 (bp 1767 T to C) *F565S* (falsely reported as F589S) ■ Exon 13 (bp 2646 C to T) premature stop	*F565S mutant:* F514S in bovine GC-E (corresponds to F565S in human GC-E) ~10-fold reduced cGMP formation, loss of GCAP-1 responsiveness	(86, 121, 122)
rd	Chicken	■ Exon 4-7 642 bp deleted; replaced by 81 bp fragment	cGMP levels in the retina drop to 10–20% of wild type	(87)
CRD	Human	■ Exon 13 (bp 2584 G to C) *E837D* ■ Exon 13 (bp 2585 C to T) *R838C* ■ Exon 13 *R838S* ■ Exon 13 (bp 2589 C to T) *T839M*	*E837D mutant:* No effect on basal activity or GCAP-1 stimulation; Increased GCAP-2 stimulation *R838C mutant:* Reduced basal cGMP levels and reduced Mn/TritonX-100 activity; Altered Ca^{2+} sensitivity of GCAP-1; Diminished response to GCAP-2	(88–92)

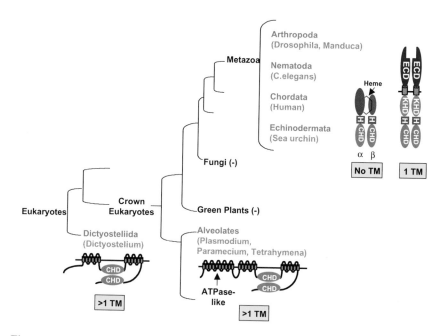

Figure 1 Expression of three general classes of GCs across eukaryotes. The GCs are separated into those containing no, one, or multiple transmembrane segments. Those containing no apparent transmembrane segment are generally referred to as the soluble forms, although β subunits of various species often contain a consensus isoprenylation site.

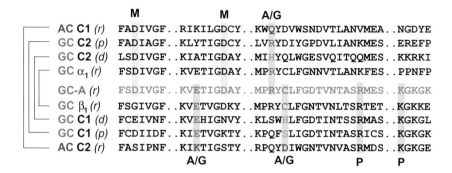

	M	M	A/G		
AC C1 *(r)*	FADIVGF..RIKILGDCY..KWQYDVWSNDVTLANVMEA..NGDYE
GC C2 *(p)*	FADIAGF..KLYTIGDCY..LVRYDIYGPDVLIANKMES..EREFP
GC C2 *(d)*	LSDIVGF..KIATIGDAY..MIHYQLWGESVQITQQMES..KKRKI
GC α₁ *(r)*	FSDIVGF..KVETIGDAY..MPRYCLFGNNVTLANKFES..PPNFP
GC-A *(r)*	FSDIVGF..KVETIGDAY..MPRYCLFGDTVNTASRMES..KGKGK
GC β₁ *(r)*	FSGIVGF..KVETVGDKY..MPRYCLFGNTVNLTSRTET..KGKKE
GC C1 *(d)*	FCEIVNF..KVEHIGNVY..KLSWHLFGDTINTSSRMAS..KGKGL
GC C1 *(p)*	FCDIIDF..KIETVGKTY..KPQFSLIGDTINTASRICS..KGKGK
AC C2 *(r)*	FASIPNF..KIKTIGSTY..RPQYDIWGNTVNVASRMDS..KGKGE
	A/G	A/G	P	P

Figure 2 Identification of the amino acids predicted as critical for substrate binding in ACs (blue) or GCs (red). Segments of the rat *(r)* AC type I C1 and C2 domains, equivalent C1 and C2 domains of *Paramecium (p)* and *Dictyostelium (d)* GCs, α₁ and β₁ subunits of soluble GC and GC-A are shown. Highlighted in blue are the predicted metal-binding sites (M); green, the contact sites to the phosphates (P) of the substrate ATP or GTP; yellow, the residues that are major determinants of substrate specificity (ATP versus GTP; A/G).

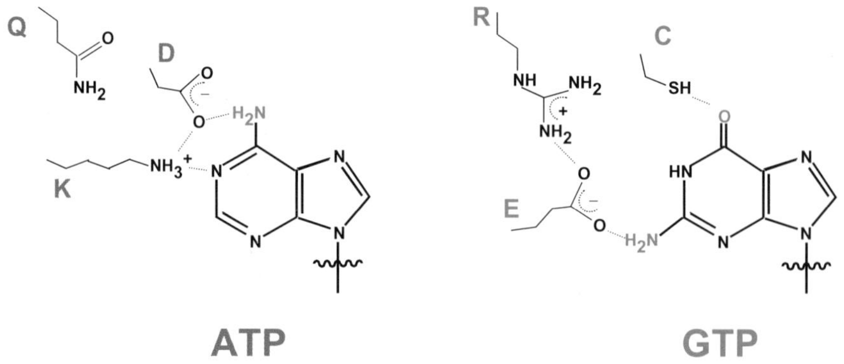

Figure 3 Amino acids predicted to coordinate with the purine base of ATP (blue) or GTP (red). The Q (blue) or R (red) do not appear to coordinate directly with the purine base, but likely stabilize the active site through charge-charge interactions.

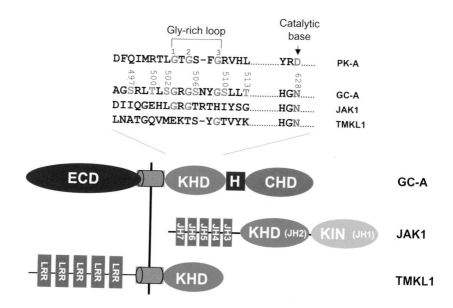

Figure 4 Protein families with KHDs and comparison with known active protein kinases. GC-A, JAK1 and TMKL1 represent families of proteins with KHDs (green). JAK kinases share JAK-homology domains (JH1-JH7), with JH1 corresponding to the active protein kinase domain (KIN) and JH2 to the KHD. Putative plant receptors such as TMKL1 contain an extracellular domain with leucine-rich repeats (LRR) separated from the KHD by a transmembrane segment. The primary sequences of an active kinase (PK-A) and of KHDs are aligned on the top. The glycine-rich loop that is found in protein kinases is only partially retained in the KHDs. The predicted catalytic base (D) of protein kinases is always a different amino acid in the KHDs, most often an N. The sites of phosphorylation of GC-A are shown in blue.

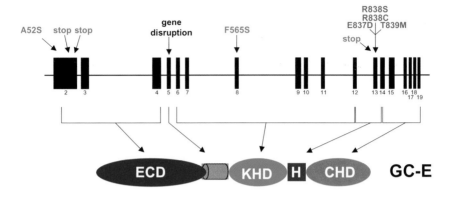

Figure 5 Sites of mutations in GC-E that appear to account for either Leber's congenital amaurosis (LCA; red) or cone rod dystrophy (CRD; blue). The site of disruption of the GC-E receptor gene in mice is exon 5, which encodes the transmembrane segment.

activates GC-E over a broad range of free Ca^{2+} concentrations, probably resulting in the constitutive activation of cGMP synthesis (23, 94).

CONCLUSION

Disruption of the genes for the guanylyl cyclase receptors and their peptide ligands have provided a framework for defining the functions of the signaling pathways in animals, and mouse genetic models are beginning to lead to an identification of the genes responsible for various human genetic diseases. However, the mechanisms of direct regulation of the cyclases and the importance of the guanylyl cyclases in the regulation of other signaling pathways are still poorly understood. Four cyclases found in a variety of animals remain orphan receptors. Therefore, the search for orphan receptor ligands and molecules that directly regulate guanylyl cyclases or that impinge on the regulation of other signaling pathways remain the major focus of this field.

Visit the Annual Reviews home page at www.AnnualReviews.org

LITERATURE CITED

1. Yuen PST, Potter LR, Garbers DL. 1990. A new form of guanylyl cyclase is preferentially expressed in rat kidney. *Biochemistry* 29:10872–78
2. Nighorn A, Byrnes KA, Morton DB. 1999. Identification and characterization of a novel beta subunit of soluble guanylyl cyclase that is active in the absence of a second subunit and is relatively insensitive to nitric oxide. *J. Biol. Chem.* 274:2525–31
3. Koesling D. 1999. Studying the structure and regulation of soluble guanylyl cyclase. *Methods* 19:485–93
4. Gerzer R, Böhme E, Hofmann F Schultz G 1981. Soluble guanylate cyclase purified from bovine lung contains heme and copper. *FEBS Lett.* 132:2:71–74
5. Russwurm M, Behrends S, Harteneck C, Koesling D. 1998. Functional properties of a naturally occurring isoform of soluble guanylyl cyclase. *Biochem. J.* 335 (Pt 1):125–30
6. Friebe A, Wedel B, Harteneck C, Foerster J, Schultz G, Koesling D. 1997. Functions

of conserved cysteines of soluble guanylyl cyclase. *Biochemistry* 36:1194–98
7. Wedel B, Humbert P, Harteneck C, Foerster J, Malkewitz J, et al. 1994. Mutation of His-105 in the beta 1 subunit yields a nitric oxide-insensitive form of soluble guanylyl cyclase. *Proc. Natl. Acad. Sci. USA* 91:2592–96
8. Morton DB, Hudson ML, Waters E, O'Shea M. 1999. Soluble guanylyl cyclases in *Caenorhabditis elegans*: NO is not the answer. *Curr. Biol.* 9:R546–47
9. Wedel BJ, Garbers DL. 1997. New insights on the functions of the guanylyl cyclase receptors. *FEBS Lett.* 410:29–33
10. Wedel BJ, Garbers DL. 1998. Guanylyl cyclases: approaching year thirty. *Trends Endocrinol. Metab.* 9:213–19
11. Nakao K, Itoh H, Saito Y, Mukoyama M, Ogawa Y. 1996. The natriuretic peptide family. *Curr. Opin. Nephrol. Hypertens.* 5:4–11
12. Laney DWJ, Mann EA, Dellon SC, Perkins DR, Giannella RA, Cohen MB. 1992.

Novel sites for expression of an *Escherichia coli* heat-stable enterotoxin receptor in the developing rat. *Am. J. Physiol. Gastrointest. Liver Physiol.* 263:G816–G21

13. Vaandrager AB Schulz S, DeJonge HR, Garbers DL. 1993. Guanylyl cyclase-C is an N-linked glycoprotein receptor that accounts for multiple heat-stable enterotoxin binding proteins in the intestine. *J. Biol. Chem.* 268:2174–79

14. London RM, Eber SL, Visweswariah SS, Krause WJ, Forte LR. 1999. Structure and activity of OK-GC: a kidney receptor guanylate cyclase activated by guanylin peptides. *Am. J. Physiol. Renal Physiol.* 276:F882–F91

15. Forte LR. 1999. Guanylin regulatory peptides: structures, biological activities mediated by cyclic GMP and pathobiology. *Regul. Pept.* 81:25–39

16. Forte LR, London RM, Freeman RH, Krause WJ. 2000. Guanylin peptides: renal actions mediated by cyclic GMP. *Am. J. Physiol. Renal Physiol.* 278:F180–F91

17. Baude EJ, Arora VK, Yu S, Garbers DL, Wedel BJ. 1997. The cloning of a *Caenorhabditis elegans* guanylyl cyclase and the construction of a ligand-sensitive mammalian/nematode chimeric receptor. *J. Biol. Chem.* 272:16035–39

18. Yu S, Avery L, Baude E, Garbers DL. 1997. Guanylyl cyclase expression in specific sensory neurons: a new family of chemosensory receptors. *Proc. Natl. Acad. Sci. USA* 94:3384–87

19. Stults JT, O'Connell KL, Garcia C, Wong S, Engel AM, et al. 1994. The disulfide linkages and glycosylation sites of the human natriuretic peptide receptor-C homodimer. *Biochemistry* 33:11372–81

20. Fülle H-J, Vassar R, Foster DC, Yang R-B, Axel R, Garbers DL. 1995. A receptor guanylyl cyclase expressed specifically in olfactory sensory neurons. *Proc. Natl. Acad. Sci. USA* 92:3571–75

21. Julifs DM, Fülle H-J, Zhao AZ, Houslay MD, Garbers DL, Beavo JA. 1997. A subset of olfactory neurons that selectively express cGMP-stimulated phosphodiesterase (PDE2) and guanylyl cyclase-D define a unique olfactory signal transduction pathway. *Proc. Natl. Acad. Sci. USA* 94:3388–95

22. Laura RP, Dizhoor AM, Hurley JB. 1996. The membrane guanylyl cyclase, retinal guanylyl cyclase-1, is activated through its intracellular domain. *J. Biol. Chem.* 271:11646–51

23. Sokal I, Li N, Surgucheva I, Warren MJ, Payne AM, et al. 1998. GCAP1 (Y99C) mutant is constitutively active in autosomal dominant cone dystrophy. *Mol. Cell.* 2:129–33

24. Laura RP, Hurley JB. 1998. The kinase homology domain of retinal guanylyl cyclases 1 and 2 specifies the affinity and cooperativity of interaction with guanylyl cyclase activating protein-2. *Biochemistry* 37:11264–71

25. L'Etoile ND, Bargmann CI. 2000. Olfaction and odor discrimination are mediated by the *C. elegans* guanylyl cyclase ODR-1. *Neuron* 25:575–86

26. Linder JU, Engel P, Reimer A, Kruger T, Plattner H, et al. 1999. Guanylyl cyclases with the topology of mammalian adenylyl cyclases and an N-terminal P-type ATPase-like domain in *Paramecium, Tetrahymena* and *Plasmodium. EMBO J.* 18:4222–32

27. Linder JU, Hoffmann T, Kurz U, Schultz JE. 2000. A guanylyl cyclase from paramecium with 22 transmembrane spans. Expression of the catalytic domains and formation of chimeras with the catalytic domains of mammalian adenylyl cyclases. *J. Biol. Chem.* 275:11235–40

28. Carucci DJ, Witney AA, Muhia DK, Warhurst DC, Schaap P, et al. 2000. Guanylyl cyclase activity associated with putative bifunctional integral membrane proteins in *Plasmodium falciparum. J. Biol. Chem.* 275:22147–56

29. Zhang G, Liu Y, Ruoho AE, Hurley JH.

1997. Structure of the adenylyl cyclase catalytic core. *Nature* 386:247–53

30. Tesmer JJ, Sunahara RK, Gilman AG, Sprang SR. 1997. Crystal structure of the catalytic domains of adenylyl cyclase in a complex with Gsα GTPγS. *Science* 278:1907–16

31. Liu Y, Ruoho AE, Rao VD, Hurley JH. 1997. Catalytic mechanism of the adenylyl and guanylyl cyclases: modeling and mutational analysis. *Proc. Natl. Acad. Sci. USA* 94:13414–19

32. Sunahara RK, Beuve A, Tesmer JJ, Sprang SR, Garbers DL, Gilman AG. 1998. Exchange of substrate and inhibitor specificities between adenylyl and guanylyl cyclases. *J. Biol. Chem.* 273:16332–38

33. Harteneck C, Koesling D, Soling A, Schultz G, Böhme E. 1990. Expression of soluble guanylate cyclase: catalytic activity requires two enzyme subunits. *FEBS Lett.* 272:221–23

34. Buechler WA, Nakane M, Murad F. 1991. Expression of soluble guanylate cyclase activity requires both enzyme subunits. *Biochem. Biophys. Res. Commun.* 174:351–57

35. Hurley JH. 1999. Structure, mechanism, and regulation of mammalian adenylyl cyclase. *J. Biol. Chem.* 274:7599–602

36. Dessauer CW, Tesmer JJ, Sprang SR, Gilman AG. 1999. The interactions of adenylate cyclases with P-site inhibitors. *Trends Pharmacol. Sci.* 20:205–10

37. Beuve A. 1999. Conversion of a guanylyl cyclase to an adenylyl cyclase. *Methods* 19:545–50

38. Chrisman TD, Garbers DL, Parks MA, Hardman JG. 1975. Characterization of particulate and soluble guanylate cyclases from rat lung. *J. Biol. Chem.* 250:374–81

39. Lin MC, Salomon Y, Rendell M, Rodbell M. 1975. The hepatic adenylate cyclase system. II. Substrate binding and utilization and the effects of magnesium ion and pH. *J. Biol. Chem.* 250:4246–52

40. Tesmer JJ, Sunahara RK, Johnson RA,

Gosselin G, Gilman AG, Sprang SR. 1999. Two-metal-ion catalysis in adenylyl cyclase. *Science* 285:756–60

41. Garbers DL, Johnson RA. 1975. Metal and metal-ATP interactions with brain and cardiac adenylate cyclases. *J. Biol. Chem.* 250:8449–56

42. Tucker CL, Hurley JH, Miller TR, Hurley JB. 1998. Two amino acid substitutions convert a guanylyl cyclase, RetGC-1, into an adenylyl cyclase. *Proc. Natl. Acad. Sci. USA* 95:5993–97

43. Chinkers M, Garbers DL. 1989. The protein kinase domain of the ANP receptor is required for signaling. *Science* 245:1392–94

44. Aparicio JG, Applebury ML. 1996. The photoreceptor guanylate cyclase is an autophosphorylating protein kinase. *J. Biol. Chem.* 271:27083–89

45. Grant BD, Hemmer W, Tsigelny I, Adams JA, Taylor SS. 1998. Kinetic analyses of mutations in the glycine-rich loop of cAMP-dependent protein kinase. *Biochemistry* 37:7708–15

46. Leonard WJ, O'Shea JJ. 1998. Jaks and STATs: biological implications. *Annu. Rev. Immunol.* 16:293–322

47. Aringer M, Cheng A, Nelson JW, Chen M, Sudarshan C, et al. 1999. Janus kinases and their role in growth and disease. *Life Sci.* 64:2173–86

48. Cattaneo E, Conti L, De-Fraja C. 1999. Signalling through the JAK-STAT pathway in the developing brain. *Trends Neurosci.* 22:365–69

49. Saharinen P, Takaluoma K, Silvennoinen O. 2000. Regulation of the jak2 tyrosine kinase by its pseudokinase domain. *Mol. Cell. Biol.* 20:3387–95

50. Candotti F, Oakes SA, Johnston JA, Giliani S, Schumacher RF, et al. 1997. Structural and functional basis for JAK3-deficient severe combined immunodeficiency. *Blood* 90:3996–4003

51. Bentley JK, Garbers DL. 1986. Retention of the speract receptor by isolated

plasma membranes of sea urchin spermatozoa. *Biol. Reprod.* 34:413–21

52. Potter LR, Garbers DL. 1992. Dephosphorylation of the guanylyl cyclase-A receptor causes desensitization. *J. Biol. Chem.*
267:14531–34

53. Potter LR, Garbers DL. 1994. Protein kinase C-dependent desensitization of the
atrial natriuretic peptide receptor is mediated by dephosphorylation. *J. Biol. Chem.*
269:14636–42

54. Foster DC, Garbers DL. 1998. Dual role for
adenine nucleotides in the regulation of the
atrial natriuretic peptide receptor, guanylyl
cyclase-A. *J. Biol. Chem.* 273:16311–18

55. Potter LR, Hunter T. 1998. Phosphorylation of the kinase homology domain is
essential for activation of the A-type natriuretic peptide receptor. *Mol. Cell. Biol.*
18:2164–72

56. Potter LR, Hunter T. 1998. Identification
and characterization of the major phosphorylation sites of the B-type natriuretic peptide receptor. *J. Biol. Chem.* 273:15533–39

57. Potter LR, Hunter T. 1999. A constitutively
"phosphorylated" guanylyl cyclase-linked
atrial natriuretic peptide receptor mutant is
resistant to desensitization. *Mol. Biol. Cell*
10:1811–20

58. Chrisman TD, Garbers DL 1999. Reciprocal antagonism coordinates C-type
natriuretic peptide and mitogen-signaling
pathways in fibroblasts. *J. Biol. Chem.*
274:4293–99

59. Birnby DA, Link EM, Vowels JJ, Tian
H, Colacurcio PL, Thomas JH. 2000.
A transmembrane guanylyl cyclase (DAF-
11) and hsp90 (DAF-21) regulate a common set of chemosensory behaviors in
Caenorhabditis elegans. Genetics 155:85–
104

60. Buchner J. 1999. Hsp90 & Co.—a holding
for folding. *Trends Biochem. Sci.* 24:136–
41

61. Caplan AJ. 1999. Hsp90's secrets unfold:
new insights from structural and functional
studies. *Trends Cell. Biol.* 9:262–68

62. Chinkers M, Singh S, Garbers DL 1991.
Adenine nucleotides are required for activation of rat atrial natriuretic peptide
receptor/guanylyl cyclase expressed in
a baculovirus system. *J. Biol. Chem.*
266:4088–93

63. Vaandrager AB, van der Wiel E, de Jonge
HR. 1993. Heat-stable enterotoxin activa-
tion of immunopurified guanylyl cyclase
C. Modulation by adenine nucleotides.
J. Biol. Chem. 268:19598–603

64. Tucker CL, Laura RP, Hurley JB. 1997.
Domain-specific stabilization of photoreceptor membrane guanylyl cyclase by adenine nucleotides and guanylyl cyclase activating proteins (GCAPs). *Biochemistry*
36:11995–2000

65. Chinkers M. 1994. Targeting of a distinctive protein-serine phosphatase to the protein kinase-like domain of the atrial natriuretic peptide receptor. *Proc. Natl. Acad.
Sci USA* 91:11075–79

66. Russell LC, Whitt SR, Chen MS, Chinkers
M. 1999. Identification of conserved
residues required for the binding of a tetratricopeptide repeat domain to heat shock
protein 90. *J. Biol. Chem.* 274:20060–63

67. Ramsey AJ, Russell LC, Whitt SR,
Chinkers M. 2000. Overlapping sites of
tetratricopeptide repeat protein binding
and chaperone activity in heat shock protein 90. *J. Biol. Chem.* 275:17857–62

68. Tamura N, Ogawa Y, Chusho H, Nakamura
K, Nakao K, et al. 2000. Cardiac fibrosis
in mice lacking brain natriuretic peptide.
Proc. Natl. Acad. Sci. USA 97:4239–44

69. Garbers DL, Dubois S. 1999. The molecular basis of hypertension. *Annu. Rev.
Biochem.* 68:127–55

70. Lopez MJ, Wong SKF, Kishimoto I,
Dubois S, Mach V, et al. 1995. Salt-
resistant hypertension in mice lacking the
guanylyl cyclase-A receptor for atrial natriuretic peptide. *Nature* 378:65–68

71. Franco F, Dubois SK, Peshock RM, Shohet
RV. 1998. Magnetic resonance imaging accurately estimates LV mass in a transgenic

mouse model of cardiac hypertrophy. *Am. J. Physiol. Heart Circ. Physiol.* 274:H679–H83

72. Pandey KN, Oliver PM, Maeda N, Smithies O. 1999. Hypertension associated with decreased testosterone levels in natriuretic peptide receptor-A gene-knockout and gene-duplicated mutant mouse models. *Endocrinology* 140:5112–19

73. Kishimoto I, Dubois SK, Garbers DL. 1996. The heart communicates with the kidney exclusively through the guanylyl cyclase-A receptor: acute handling of sodium and water in response to volume expansion. *Proc. Natl. Acad. Sci. USA* 93:6215–19

74. Dubois SK, Kishimoto I, Lillis TO, Garbers DL. 2000. A genetic model defines the importance of the atrial natriuretic peptide receptor (guanylyl cyclase-A) in the regulation of kidney function. *Proc. Natl. Acad. Sci. USA* 97:4369–73

75. Gariepy J, Judd AK, Schoolnik GK. 1987. Importance of disulfide bridges in the structure and activity of *Escherichia coli* enterotoxin ST1b. *Proc. Natl. Acad. Sci. USA* 84:8907–11

76. Schulz S, Green CK, Yuen PST, Garbers DL. 1990. Guanylyl cyclase is a heat-stable enterotoxin receptor. *Cell* 63:941–48

77. Pfeifer A, Aszodi A, Seidler U, Ruth P, Hofmann F, Fassler R. 1996. Intestinal secretory defects and dwarfism in mice lacking cGMP-dependent protein kinase II. *Science* 274:2082–86

78. Schulz S, Lopez MJ, Kuhn M, Garbers DL. 1997. Disruption of the guanylyl cyclase-C gene leads to a paradoxical phenotype of viable but heat-stable enterotoxin-resistant mice. *J. Clin. Invest.* 100:1590–95

79. Mann EA, Jump ML, Wu J, Yee E, Giannella RA. 1997. Mice lacking the guanylyl cyclase C receptor are resistant to STa-induced intestinal secretion. *Biochem. Biophys. Res. Commun.* 239:463–66

80. Krause WJ, Freeman RH, Eber SL, Hamra FK, Currie MG, Forte LR. 1997. Guanylyl

cyclase receptors and guanylin-like peptides in reptilian intestine. *Gen. Comp. Endocrinol.* 107:229–39

81. White AA, Krause WJ, Turner JT, Forte LR. 1989. Opossum kidney contains a functional receptor for the *Escherichia coli* heat-stable enterotoxin. *Biochem. Biophys. Res. Commun.* 159:363–67

82. Yang RB, Foster DC, Garbers DL, Fulle HJ. 1995. Two membrane forms of guanylyl cyclase found in the eye. *Proc. Natl. Acad. Sci. USA* 92:602–6

83. Yang RB, Garbers DL. 1997. Two eye guanylyl cyclases are expressed in the same photoreceptor cells and form homomers in preference to heteromers. *J. Biol. Chem.* 272:13738–42

84. Yang RB, Robinson SW, Xiong WH, Yau KW, Birch DG, Garbers DL. 1999. Disruption of a retinal guanylyl cyclase gene leads to cone-specific dystrophy and paradoxical rod behavior. *J. Neurosci.* 19:5889–97

85. Perrault I, Rozet JM, Gerber S, Ghazi I, Leowski C, et al. 1999. Leber congenital amaurosis. *Mol. Genet. Metab.* 68:200–8

86. Perrault I, Rozet JM, Calvas P, Gerber S, Camuzat A, et al. 1996. Retinal-specific guanylate cyclase gene mutations in Leber's congenital amaurosis. *Nat. Genet.* 14:461–64

87. Semple-Rowland SL, Lee NR, Van Hooser JP, Palczewski K, Baehr W. 1998. A null mutation in the photoreceptor guanylate cyclase gene causes the retinal degeneration chicken phenotype. *Proc. Natl. Acad. Sci. USA* 95:1271–76

88. Kelsell RE, Gregory-Evans K, Payne AM, Perrault I, Kaplan J, et al. 1998. Mutations in the retinal guanylate cyclase (RETGC-1) gene in dominant cone-rod dystrophy. *Hum. Mol. Genet.* 7:1179–84

89. Perrault I, Rozet JM, Gerber S, Kelsell RE, Souied E, et al. 1998. A retGC-1 mutation in autosomal dominant cone-rod dystrophy. *Am. J. Hum. Genet.* 63:651–54

90. Gregory-Evans K, Kelsell RE, Gregory-Evans CY, Downes SM, Fitzke FW, et al. 2000. Autosomal dominant cone-rod retinal dystrophy (CORD6) from heterozygous mutation of GUCY2D, which encodes retinal guanylate cyclase. *Ophthalmology* 107:55–61

91. Duda T, Krishnan A, Venkataraman V, Lange C, Koch KW, Sharma RK. 1999. Mutations in the rod outer segment membrane guanylate cyclase in a cone-rod dystrophy cause defects in calcium signaling. *Biochemistry* 38:13912–19

92. Tucker CL, Woodcock SC, Kelsell RE, Ramamurthy V, Hunt DM, Hurley JB. 1999. Biochemical analysis of a dimerization domain mutation in RetGC-1 associated with dominant cone-rod dystrophy. *Proc. Natl. Acad. Sci. USA* 96:9039–44

93. Payne AM, Downes SM, Bessant DA, Taylor R, Holder GE, et al. 1998. A mutation in guanylate cyclase activator 1A (GUCA1A) in an autosomal dominant cone dystrophy pedigree mapping to a new locus on chromosome 6p21.1. *Hum. Mol. Genet.* 7:273–77

94. Dizhoor AM, Boikov SG, Olshevskaya EV. 1998. Constitutive activation of photoreceptor guanylate cyclase by Y99C mutant of GCAP-1. Possible role in causing human autosomal dominant cone degeneration. *J. Biol. Chem.* 273:17311–14

95. Huang PL, Dawson TM, Bredt DS, Snyder SH, Fishman MC. 1993. Targeted disruption of the neuronal nitric oxide synthase gene. *Cell* 75:1273–86

96. Nelson RJ, Demas GE, Huang PL, Fishman MC, Dawson VL, et al. 1995. Behavioural abnormalities in male mice lacking neuronal nitric oxide synthase. *Nature* 378:383–86

97. Huang PL. 1999. Neuronal and endothelial nitric oxide synthase gene knockout mice. *Braz. J. Med. Biol. Res.* 32:1353–59

98. Rai RM, Lee FY, Rosen A, Yang SQ, Lin HZ, et al. 1998. Impaired liver regeneration in inducible nitric oxide synthase deficient mice. *Proc. Natl. Acad. Sci. USA* 95:13829–34

99. Huang PL, Huang Z, Mashimo H, Bloch KD, Moskowitz MA, et al. 1995. Hypertension in mice lacking the gene for endothelial nitric oxide synthase. *Nature* 377:239–42

100. Shesely EG, Maeda N, Kim HS, Desai KM, Krege JH, et al. 1996. Elevated blood pressures in mice lacking endothelial nitric oxide synthase. *Proc. Natl. Acad. Sci. USA* 93:13176–81

101. Steudel W, Scherrer-Crosbie M, Bloch KD, Weimann J, Huang PL, et al. 1998. Sustained pulmonary hypertension and right ventricular hypertrophy after chronic hypoxia in mice with congenital deficiency of nitric oxide synthase 3. *J. Clin. Invest.* 101:2468–77

102. Rudic RD, Shesely EG, Maeda N, Smithies O, Segal SS, Sessa WC. 1998. Direct evidence for the importance of endothelium-derived nitric oxide in vascular remodeling. *J. Clin. Invest.* 101:731–36

103. Moroi M, Zhang L, Yasuda T, Virmani R, Gold HK, et al. 1998. Interaction of genetic deficiency of endothelial nitric oxide, gender, and pregnancy in vascular response to injury in mice. *J. Clin. Invest.* 101:1225–32

104. Kojda G, Laursen JB, Ramasamy S, Kent JD, Kurz S, et al. 1999. Protein expression, vascular reactivity and soluble guanylate cyclase activity in mice lacking the endothelial cell nitric oxide synthase: contributions of NOS isoforms to blood pressure and heart rate control. *Cardiovasc. Res.* 42:206–13

105. Ohashi Y, Kawashima S, Hirata K, Yamashita T, Ishida T, et al. 1998. Hypotension and reduced nitric oxide-elicited vasorelaxation in transgenic mice overexpressing endothelial nitric oxide synthase. *J. Clin. Invest.* 102:2061–71

106. John SW, Krege JH, Oliver PM, Hagaman JR, Hodgin JB, et al. 1995.

Genetic decreases in atrial natriuretic peptide and salt-sensitive hypertension. *Science* 267:679–81

107. John SWM, Veress AT, Honrath U, Chong CK, Peng L, et al. 1996. Blood pressure and fluid-electrolyte balance in mice with reduced or absent ANP. *Am. J. Physiol. Regulatory Integrative Comp. Physiol.* 271:R109–R14

108. Melo LG, Veress AT, Chong CK, Pang SC, Flynn TG, Sonnenberg H. 1998. Salt-sensitive hypertension in ANP knockout mice: potential role of abnormal plasma renin activity. *Am. J. Physiol. Regulatory Integrative Comp. Physiol.* 274:R255–R61

109. Melo LG, Veress AT, Ackermann U, Pang SC, Flynn TG, Sonnenberg H. 1999. Chronic hypertension in ANP knockout mice: contribution of peripheral resistance. *Regul. Pept.* 79:109–15

110. Klinger JR, Warburton RR, Pietras LA, Smithies O, Swift R, Hill NS. 1999. Genetic disruption of atrial natriuretic peptide causes pulmonary hypertension in normoxic and hypoxic mice. *Am. J. Physiol. Lung Cell Mol. Physiol.* 276:L868–L74

111. Steinhelper ME, Cochrane KL, Field LJ. 1990. Hypotension in transgenic mice expressing atrial natriuretic factor fusion genes. *Hypertension* 16:301–7

112. Barbee RW, Perry BD, Re RN, Murgo JP, Field LJ. 1994. Hemodynamics in transgenic mice with overexpression of atrial natriuretic factor. *Circ. Res.* 74:747–51

113. Ku DD, Guo L, Dai J, Acuff CG, Steinhelper ME. 1996. Coronary vascular and endothelial reactivity changes in transgenic mice overexpressing atrial natriuretic factor. *Am. J. Physiol. Heart Circ. Physiol.* 271:H2368–H76

114. Suda M, Ogawa Y, Tanaka K, Tamura N, Yasoda A, et al. 1998. Skeletal overgrowth in transgenic mice that overexpress brain natriuretic peptide. *Proc. Natl. Acad. Sci. USA* 95:2337–42

115. Matsukawa N, Grzesik WJ, Takahashi N, Pandey KN, Pang S, et al. 1999. The natriuretic peptide clearance receptor locally modulates the physiological effects of the natriuretic peptide system. *Proc. Natl. Acad. Sci. USA* 96:7403–8

116. Lopez MJ, Garbers DL, Kuhn M. 1997. The guanylyl cyclase-deficient mouse defines differential pathways of natriuretic peptide signaling. *J. Biol. Chem.* 272:23064–68

117. Oliver PM, Fox JE, Kim R, Rockman HA, Kim HS, et al. 1997. Hypertension, cardiac hypertrophy, and sudden death in mice lacking natriuretic peptide receptor A. *Proc. Natl. Acad. Sci. USA* 94:14730–35

118. Oliver PM, John SW, Purdy KE, Kim R, Maeda N, et al. 1998. Natriuretic peptide receptor 1 expression influences blood pressures of mice in a dose-dependent manner. *Proc. Natl. Acad. Sci. USA* 95:2547–51

119. Pfeifer A, Klatt P, Massberg S, Ny L, Sausbier M, et al. 1998. Defective smooth muscle regulation in cGMP kinase I-deficient mice. *EMBO J.* 17:3045–51

120. Hedlund P, Aszodi A, Pfeifer A, Alm P, Hofmann F, et al. 2000. Erectile dysfunction in cyclic GMP-dependent kinase I-deficient mice. *Proc. Natl. Acad. Sci. USA* 97:2349–54

121. Duda T, Venkataraman V, Goraczniak R, Lange C, Koch KW, Sharma RK. 1999. Functional consequences of a rod outer segment membrane guanylate cyclase (ROS-GC1) gene mutation linked with Leber's congenital amaurosis. *Biochemistry* 38:509–15

122. El-Shanti H, Al-Salem M, El-Najjar M, Ajlouni K, Beck J, et al. 1999. A nonsense mutation in the retinal specific guanylate cyclase gene is the cause of Leber congenital amaurosis in a large inbred kindred from Jordan. *J. Med. Genet.* 36:862–865

Annu. Rev. Physiol. 2001. 63:235–57

MOLECULAR DIVERSITY OF PACEMAKER ION CHANNELS

U Benjamin Kaupp and Reinhard Seifert

Institut für Biologische Informationsverarbeitung, Forschungszentrum Jülich, D-52425 Jülich, Germany; e-mail: a.eckert@fz-juelich.de

Key Words hyperpolarization-activated current, pacemaker current, HCN channels, cyclic nucleotides

■ **Abstract** Ionic currents activated by hyperpolarization and regulated by cyclic nucleotides were first discovered more than 20 years ago. Recently the molecular identity of the underlying channels has been unveiled. The structural features of the protein sequences are discussed and related to the mechanisms of activation, selectivity for cyclic nucleotides, and ion permeation. Coverage includes a comparison of the biophysical properties of recombinant and native channels and their significance for the physiological functions of these channels.

INTRODUCTION

Pacemaker currents were discovered during the late 1970s and early 1980s in sino-atrial node cells (12, 13, 18, 19, 93), in hippocampal pyramidal cells (35, 50), and in photoreceptor cells (4–6, 28). At the time this current was discovered, its properties were deemed unique, in particular the characteristically slow activation upon hyperpolarization; it has, therefore, been termed I_h (h for hyperpolarization-activated), I_f (f for funny) or I_q (q for queer). Similar currents were later discovered in a wide variety of neuronal and non-neuronal cells, and today these currents are recognized as ubiquitous components of the nervous system. Besides "pacing" rhythmic activity these ion channels subserve other functions as well. In many neurons, I_h currents co-determine resting potential and membrane conductance and thereby play an important role in the integrative behavior of neurons and the sensitivity to synaptic input. Dendritic I_h currents, for example, influence the cable properties of the dendrite and shape the time course of the excitatory postsynaptic potential (EPSP) as it is propagated to the soma (52). In other neurons, I_h currents are involved in shaping the cell's response to hyperpolarization, such as during the arrival of inhibitory postsynaptic potentials (IPSPs) (reviewed in 62). In photoreceptors these currents curtail the hyperpolarizing response of the cell to bright light stimuli (4–6, 28). In addition, presynaptic I_h currents are possibly involved in the control of synaptic transmission via serotonin-mediated upregulation of cAMP levels (10).

Ion channels underlying I_h display some unusual properties: (a) The activity of the channels is dependent on membrane voltage but, unlike most other voltage-dependent channels, pacemaker channels are opened by hyperpolarization of the membrane rather than by depolarization. The voltage of half-maximal activation ($V_{1/2}$) varies among different cell types; values between -65 and -95 mV have been reported (reviewed in 62). (b) Channels are selective for K^+ ions, yet they lack the exquisite K^+ selectivity of other K^+ channels. As a consequence, pacemaker channels carry a Na^+ inward current, which slowly depolarizes the membrane. (c) The relative ion permeability P_{Na}/P_K of pacemaker channels depends on the extracellular K^+ concentration and varies between 0.2 and 0.4 (27, 37, 53, 76, 92). (d) Low concentrations of extracellular Cs^+ ions block the current (28). (e) The activity of the channels is directly enhanced by cAMP and cGMP (24). (f) Extra-cellular Cl^- ions modulate the permeation of cations (40, 55, 58, 83, 93).

THE ROLE OF PACEMAKER CHANNELS IN THE BEATING HEART

In vertebrates, cardiac pacemaker activity originates in restricted areas of the heart, the sinus venosus, and in a remnant of it called the sino-atrial node. The pacemaker consists of small, weakly contractile, specialized muscle cells that spontaneously generate action potentials. The electrical activity initiated in the pacemaker region then spreads to other areas of the heart, triggering the contraction of the cardiac muscle.

The myogenic heart contains many cells capable of pacemaker activity (e.g. in the sino-atrial node, the atrio-ventricular node, the bundle of His, and the Purkinje fibers), but because cardiac cells are electrically coupled by gap junctions, the cell (or group of cells) with the fastest intrinsic activity normally stimulates the contraction and thereby determines the heart rate.

Figure 1 illustrates the mechanisms producing the action potential in cells of the sino-atrial node. At least four different ion channels are involved in the generation of rhythmic beating: two different types of Ca^{2+} channels, a K^+ channel, and the pacemaker channel (21). First, T-type Ca^{2+} channels open, followed by L-type Ca^{2+} channels, which cause a large depolarization of the cell. Subsequently, the cell is repolarized by the opening of K^+ channels. At the end of each action potential, the membrane voltage approaches the K^+ equilibrium potential (about -80 mV) due to the open K^+ channels. At this hyperpolarized voltage, the pacemaker channels open and produce a Na^+ inward current that slowly depolarizes the membrane until the threshold for the generation of a new action potential is reached. This pacemaker depolarization determines the time elapsing between successive action potentials. Thus pacemaker channels are responsible for the initiation of rhythmic activity and are involved in the control of firing frequency. A characteristic feature of pacemaker channels is the modulation by cyclic

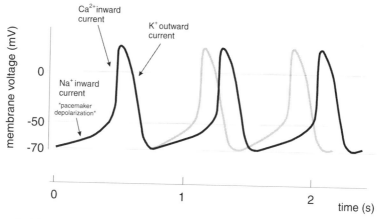

Figure 1 Rhythmic activity of sino-atrial node cells of the heart. Shown is the time course of potential changes during spontaneous action potential generation in sino-atrial node cells. The black trace depicts a succession of action potentials that is generated by three different ionic currents. The light trace illustrates the acceleration of the heartbeat during stimulation with agonists for β-adrenergic receptors.

nucleotides, i.e. cAMP and cGMP (24). Control of channel activity by intracellular levels of cAMP (or cGMP) is of utmost physiological importance as it underlies the acceleration of the heartbeat upon sympathetic stimulation. Stimulation of cardiac cells by agonists of β-adrenergic receptors gives rise to an increase of the intracellular level of cAMP via activation of an adenylyl cyclase. cAMP binds directly to the pacemaker channel thereby increasing its activity. As a result, the depolarization mediated by the pacemaker channels is accelerated, and the time interval between action potentials is shortened (11, 12). The opposite occurs during parasympathetic stimulation, i.e. with acetylcholine: cAMP levels decrease, pacemaker currents decline and, consequently, the heart rate is diminished (22, 34, 64). Recently another depolarizing background current (termed sustained inward current, I_{st}) has been described (reviewed in 59a). This current may also contribute to the pacemaker depolarization.

THE INVOLVEMENT OF PACEMAKER CHANNELS IN THE GENERATION OF RHYTHMIC ACTIVITY IN THE THALAMUS

Pacemaker channels play a fundamental role in shaping the autonomous rhythmic activity of single neurons and the periodicity of network oscillations (for review see 47). Among the best studied examples is the generation of rhythmic bursts of action potentials in the relay neurons of the thalamus (7–9, 17, 48, 49, 57). The thalamus is a major gateway for the flow of sensory information toward the cerebral cortex, and it is the first stage at which incoming signals can be blocked. During sleep, the rapid activity patterns characteristic of the aroused state are replaced by low-frequency, synchronized rhythms of neuronal activity. The physiological significance of oscillatory modes is uncertain, but they may play a role in controlling the flow of information through the thalamus. During early stages of quiescent sleep, thalamocortical neurons produce synchronized network oscillations of slow periodicity called spindle waves. The waves of electrical activity at 7–14 Hz wax and wane within a 1 to 3 s period and recur periodically once every 3–20 s (9, 79, 80). Spindle waves are produced by the reciprocal interaction between GABAergic neurons of the thalamic reticular nucleus and excitatory thalamic relay neurons (7, 8, 79, 80, 88). The barrages of IPSPs evoke Ca^{2+} rebounds by de-inactivation of T-type Ca^{2+} channels, which then, through the generation of trains of action potentials, re-excite the reticular cells (7–9). During the late stages of sleep, spindle waves are progressively replaced by oscillations with frequencies of 0.5–4 Hz. In contrast to the origin of spindle oscillations in synaptic networks, the slow-frequency rhythm can be generated in single cells (reviewed in 80). Pacemaker channels contribute to the different patterns of rhythmic activity of thalamocortical neurons in two ways. First, the interplay between low-threshold T-type Ca^{2+} channels and pacemaker channels confers the autonomous 0.5–4 Hz rhythm onto thalamocortical relay neurons (25, 56, 58, 77). Activation of Ca^{2+} channels results in Ca^{2+} spikes and often in a high-frequency burst of Na^+/K^+ action potentials. Inactivation of Ca^{2+} channels terminates the Ca^{2+} spike, followed by hyperpolarization of the neuron and activation of hyperpolarization-activated channels, which provide the depolarizing I_h current. Second, persistent activation of I_h during a spindle wave epoch shifts the membrane potential by up to 5 mV to more positive values (9). This after-depolarization stops oscillations probably by inactivation of the T-type Ca^{2+} channels (9). There is now good evidence that this after-depolarization results from an increase in pacemaker channel activity probably via Ca^{2+}-calmodulin stimulated adenylate cyclase activation and cAMP production (48, 49; but see also 14). The duration of the refractory period between spindle wave epochs (3–20 s) is probably determined by the time course of pacemaker channel deactivation (9).

MOLECULAR IDENTIFICATION OF PACEMAKER CHANNELS

Despite their obviously important physiological functions, it was not until recently that genes encoding pacemaker channels have been identified. Three different groups succeeded in cloning various pacemaker channel genes and identified the channels through heterologous expression (30, 45, 68, 69). In mice (45, 69) there are at least four different genes coding for pacemaker channels. Thus an entire family of ion channels is represented by the newly characterized genes. Gauss and colleagues (30) cloned an invertebrate channel gene from the testis of the sea urchin *Strongylocentrotus purpuratus*. In this species only a single gene was found.

Initially, the cloned genes received different designations and a common nomenclature was deemed necessary. Clapham (16) suggested the acronym HCN, which

TABLE 1   HCN channel subunits

Name	Original name	Species	References
HCN1	mBCNG-1/HAC2	Mouse	1, 2
	hBCNG-1[a]	Human	3
	HCN1	Rat	12
	HCN1[a]	Rabbit	7
HCN2	mBCNG-2/HAC1	Mouse	3, 2
	hBCNG-2[a]/hHCN2/hHCN2	Human	3–5
	HCN2[a]	Rat	7, 13
	HCN2[a]	Rabbit	7
HCN3	mBCNG-4[a]/HAC3	Mouse	3, 2
	HCN3	Rat	14
	HCN3[a]	Rabbit	7
HCN4	mBCNG-3[a]	Mouse	3
	hHCN4	Human	4, 6
	HCN4	Rat	15
	HCN4[b]/HCN4[a]	Rabbit	8, 7
SpHCN	SPIH	Sea urchin	9
HvHCN	HvCNG	Silkmoth	10
DmHCN	DMIH	Fruitfly	11

[a]Partial cDNA sequence.

[b]Probably represents a partial clone that is lacking part of the N-terminal region.

References and Genbank accession numbers: (1) Santoro et al 1997 (AF028737); (2) Ludwig et al 1998 (AF225122-AF225124); (3) Santoro et al 1998 (AF064873-AF064877); (4) Ludwig et al 1999 (AJ0112582, AJ132429); (5) Vaccari et al 1999 (AF065164); (6) Seifert et al 1999 (AJ238850); (7) Shi et al 1999 (AF155163-AF155170); (8) Ishii et al 1999 (AB022927); (9) Gauss et al 1998 (Y16880); (10) Krieger et al 1999 (AJ012664); (11) Marx et al 1999 (AF124300); (12) (AF247453); (13) (AF247451); (14) (AF247452); (15) (AF247450).

stands for hyperpolarization-activated and cyclic nucleotide-gated channels. Since the first reports, a number of full-length and partial nucleotide sequences for HCN channels from different vertebrates (mouse, rat, human, rabbit) and invertebrates (*Heliothes viscerens, Drosophila melanogaster*) have been identified (39, 43, 46, 54, 73, 74, 86). Table 1 summarizes the results of the cloning efforts and clarifies the initially confusing nomenclature.

STRUCTURAL FEATURES OF HCN CHANNEL SUBUNITS

HCN channels are cousins of the families of voltage-gated K^+ channels and cyclic nucleotide-gated (CNG) channels. The channels probably embody six transmembrane segments (S1–S6), a pore loop between the segments S5 and S6, and a cyclic nucleotide(cNMP)-binding domain in the C-terminal region of the polypeptide. The four different mammalian genes display high homology. The sequence

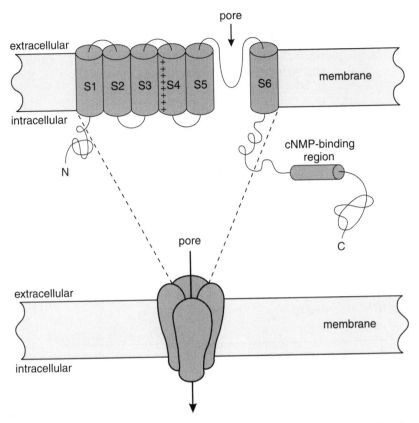

Figure 2 Transmembrane topology of HCN channel subunits with proposed functional sequence motifs (*upper*) and proposed homotetrameric structure of oligomeric channels (*lower*).

similarity is highest within the six transmembrane regions and the cNMP-binding domain (80–90%) and much lower within the N-and C-terminal regions. The transmembrane topology predicted from the primary structure is shown in Figure 2 (*upper part*). In analogy to *Shaker*-type K^+ channels and CNG channels, most likely four subunits assemble to form a functional channel (Figure 2, *lower part*).

The pore region is highly conserved among different HCN channels (Figure 3a) and shares with K^+ channels a GYG sequence motif. This motif is recognized as the signature sequence of K^+-selective channels (36). The amino acid triplet is known to form the narrowest part of the selectivity filter in K^+ channels (26). However, in contrast to K^+ channels, the HCN pore motif carries one or two positively charged residues and a histidine and lacks the cluster of threonine residues in the pore of K^+ and CNG channels. The amino acid position following the GYG motif is particularly interesting: In almost all known K^+ channels, this position is occupied by an Asp; however, in HCN channels, it is replaced by either a neutral amino acid (Ala in HCN1 and Gln in HCN3) or a positively charged amino acid (Arg in HCN2, HCN4 and Lys in SpHCN). Future work will show which of the pore residues are responsible for the differences in ion selectivity between K^+ channels and HCN channels.

The fourth transmembrane segment (S4) of HCN channels encompasses a typical voltage-sensor motif with eight to ten regularly spaced Arg or Lys residues at every third position. Similar sequence motifs have previously been identified in many voltage-dependent channels such as K^+, Na^+, and Ca^{2+} channels. In these channels, the S4 segment serves as a voltage sensor that, upon depolarization, moves toward the extracellular surface of the membrane and thus opens the channel (15, 32, 33, 61, 81). Different scenarios can be envisaged how this voltage sensor might activate the HCN channels upon hyperpolarization.

In HCN channels, depolarization of the membrane could stabilize the closed state of the channel. Hyperpolarization of the membrane would then destabilize the closed state and thereby open the channel. Alternatively, activation of HCN channels might be produced by a mechanism similar to that of the HERG K^+ channel. HERG channels are closed at rest and open upon depolarization. Because of rapid inactivation at positive voltages, channels shut off. Hyperpolarization of the membrane removes inactivation and the channels re-open (71, 75, 78).

Figure 3b compares the sequence of the S4 segments of several HCN channels with those of two well-known K^+ channels, the inwardly rectifying K^+ channel from *Arabidopsis thaliana*, KAT1 (3), and the *Shaker* K^+ channel of *D. melanogaster* (63). Interestingly, similar to the hyperpolarization-activated KAT1 channel, HCN channels possess a Ser residue in the center of the voltage sensor, thereby interrupting the regular spacing of Arg residues and dividing the motif into two domains. This feature sets HCN and KAT1 channels apart from the depolarization-activated *Shaker* K^+ channel. Perhaps these variations are responsible for activation upon hyperpolarization in HCN and KAT1 channels.

HCN channels carry in the C-terminal region a domain of approximately 80–100 amino acid residues that is highly homologous to the cNMP-binding domains of CNG channels, protein kinases A and G (PKA and PKG), and the catabolite gene activator protein (CAP) from *Escherichia coli*. The three-dimensional structure of CAP has been solved by X-ray crystallography and has become the template for cNMP-binding domains of other proteins (59, 89). The binding domain consists of three α helices A, B, and C, and eight β strands, $\beta 1$–$\beta 8$. The β strands form a flattened β-barrel consisting of two antiparallel β-sheets that are connected by four strands much like a jelly-roll topography. The three helices are located at the end of the β-barrel; the A-helix at the N-terminal end, and the B-helix followed by the C-helix at the C-terminal end. The cNMP-binding domains from CAP, PKA/PKG, and CNG channels are characterized by several invariant amino acid residues (42, 44, 84, 90). A set of highly conserved Gly residues located in the turns between several β strands is probably crucial for proper folding. Highly conserved Arg and Glu residues interact with the cyclic phosphodiester and the

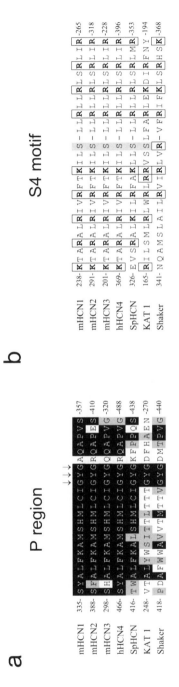

Figure 3 (*a*) Comparison of the P region of various HCN channels with that of K$^+$ channels. Residues identical or similar to the corresponding positions in mHCN1 are highlighted by black or grey backgrounds. KAT 1, hyperpolarization activated K$^+$ channel from *Arabidopsis thaliana* (3); Shaker, K$^+$ channel encoded by the *Drosophila Shaker b* gene (63). (*b*) Comparison of the voltage sensor (S4) motif of various HCN channels with that of K$^+$ channels. Arg or Lys residues are boxed. The Ser residue, which divides the S4 motif into two domains in HCN channels and in KAT 1 channels, is highlighted by a grey background. (*c*) Comparison of cNMP-binding domains: bCNGα1, α subunit of the CNG channel from bovine rod photoreceptors (41); PKA 1, cAMP-binding site 1 of protein kinase A (85); CAP, catabolite gene activator protein (1). Residues important for the structure of cNMP-binding domains and for the binding of the ligand are marked by arrows; residues that co-determine the ligand selectivity in bCNCα1 are marked by an asterisk. Secondary-structure predictions derived from CAP are shown below the sequences.

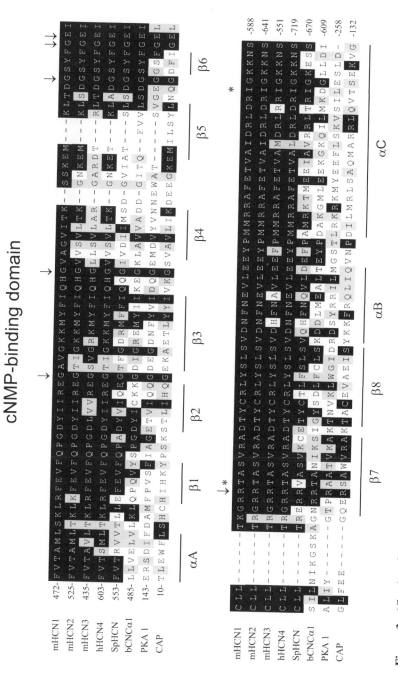

Figure 3 (*Continued*)

ribose moiety, respectively, as has been shown for CAP (59) and for the regulatory subunit of the PKA (82). Figure 3c compares the cNMP-binding domains of various HCN channels with that of a CNG channel subunit (bCNCα1), the regulatory subunit of PKA1, and CAP. Residues previously shown to be important for proper folding of the binding site and for contact with the ligand are also conserved in HCN channels (Figure 3c, arrows). Asterisks mark two residues that have been identified as important determinants of the ligand selectivity of CNG channels. The Thr residue, which co-determines the high cGMP selectivity of retinal CNG channels (2, 72), also exists in HCN1-4. However, as far as one can tell, HCN channels strongly select cAMP over cGMP. Therefore, other residues must contribute to the high cAMP selectivity of the HCN channels. It is interesting to note that SpHCN carries a Val at the corresponding position, which might explain this channel's much lower cGMP sensitivity compared with mammalian HCN channels (see below). The Ile in the C-helix of HCN channels is replaced by an Asp residue in the rod α1 subunit (D604). This Asp residue has been shown to be important for transmission of the ligand-binding event to an allosteric opening transition in the α subunit of CNG channels from retinal rods (31, 87). The negatively charged Asp undergoes an unfavorable electrostatic interaction with the free electron pair of N1 of cAMP, rendering cAMP a poor agonist for this CNG channel subtype. When the Asp is replaced by a neutral or hydrophobic amino acid, i.e. Gln or Met, cAMP becomes a much better agonist (in the D604M mutant even better than cGMP) (87). It will be interesting to see whether the Ile residue at this position is an important control element for the cAMP preference of HCN channels.

LOCALIZATION OF HCN CHANNEL SUBTYPES

The regional expression of the four mammalian HCN channel subtypes has been determined by Northern blotting, in situ hybridization, RNase protection assay (RPA), and by different PCR techniques. For some tissues, the results are controversial and require re-examination.

Expression Pattern of HCN1

The HCN1 message is abundantly expressed in brain (45, 68, 69, 74). In situ hybridization of mouse brain sections reveals that HCN1 is mainly expressed in the neocortex, the CA1 region of the hippocampus, the superior colliculus, and in the molecular cell layer of the cerebellum (45, 60). Whereas Northern blotting indicates no HCN1 message in the heart of human and mouse (45, 69), Shi and coworkers observed a substantial expression of HCN1 message in the sino-atrial node and detectable expression in the Purkinje fibers of the rabbit heart (74). The size of the sino-atrial node is small compared with other parts of the heart, which may explain the failure to detect HCN1 by Northern blotting. Neural innervation is most prominent in the sino-atrial node region, and contamination of the cardiac myocytes with parasympathetic neurons cannot be entirely excluded. However,

HCN1 message is also detected in Purkinje fibers, which contain few neurons (74).

Expression Pattern of HCN2

Expression of HCN2 was detected in brain (45, 69, 74) and in heart (45, 46, 69, 74, 86). In situ hybridization of mouse brain sections with radioactive probes shows widespread expression of HCN2 mRNA (45, 60). The highest expression level is observed in the olfactory bulb, the cerebral cortex, hippocampus, thalamus, amygdala, superior and inferior colliculi, cerebellum, and brainstem (60). These results have been confirmed using digoxigenin-labeled riboprobes (67). Within the heart, HCN2 was found in the ventricles and atrium (46). Shi and coworkers detected very low levels of HCN2 in the sino-atrial node and the left ventricle of the rabbit heart and moderate to abundant levels in the ventricle of neonatal and adult rat, respectively (74).

Expression Pattern of HCN3

HCN3 message was detected in brain although at significantly lower levels than the other three subtypes (45, 69, 74). In situ hybridization reveals very weak expression throughout the brain with somewhat higher expression in the olfactory bulb (60). Santoro and coworkers reported high amounts of mRNA in liver, lung, and kidney of mouse (69), in contrast to Ludwig and coworkers, who did not detect HCN3 mRNA in those tissues (45).

Expression Pattern of HCN4

The HCN4 message was detected in brain (45, 69, 73, 74). In situ hybridization identifies the olfactory bulb, the habenula, and the thalamus as the primary regions of expression (60). In addition to high expression levels in the thalamus, Seifert and coworkers reported significant levels of HCN4 message in the substantia nigra (73). HCN4 mRNA is also present at high levels in the heart (39, 45, 46, 69, 73, 74). Shi and colleagues describe strong expression of HCN4 in the sino-atrial node of rabbit and much less in the Purkinje fibers (74); this observation nicely agrees with the results of Ishii and coworkers (39). Moderate amounts of HCN4 message were detected in rat neonatal and adult ventricle (74), which agrees with the results obtained on human tissue (46).

Furthermore, HCN4 message reportedly exists in lung and skeletal muscle (69); however, others could not confirm this result (46, 73). Seifert and colleagues report HCN4 mRNA in human testis (73), which was not observed in mouse (69).

Expression of SpHCN

The sea urchin SpHCN mRNA is at high levels only in male gonads. No message was found in female tissue. Western blotting and immunocytochemical studies with an antibody against SpHCN located the channel protein specifically to the flagellum of sea urchin sperm (30).

Expression of HvHCN

The regional expression of the silkmoth HvHCN channel has been studied by Northern blotting and in situ hybridization (43). A high level of mRNA was found in the antennae; lower levels were detected in legs and in the head. In situ hybridization studies on longitudinal sections through the antenna of the insect showed labeled cells only in the vicinity of the sensillar hairs (43). It will be interesting to see whether the HvHCN channel is involved in chemoreception of the silkmoth and possibly other insects.

Expression of DmHCN

Tissue distribution of DmHCN was studied by Northern blotting, RT-PCR analysis, and in situ hybridization. Similar to the silkmoth HvHCN, DmHCN mRNA is strongly expressed within the region where chemoreception takes place. It is especially expressed in the third antennal segment, the funiculus, where cell bodies of olfactory receptor neurons are located. Additionally, DmHCN message was found in the maxillary palps, in the second antennal segment, in the compound eye, and in the whole head (54).

COMPARISON OF RECOMBINANT AND NATIVE HCN CHANNELS

So far, the vertebrate subtypes HCN1, HCN2, HCN4 and the invertebrate forms SpHCN and HvHCN have been expressed functionally. All channels produce currents with the hallmarks of pacemaker currents: Following hyperpolarization, inward currents develop with a typical sigmoidal waveform; channel activity is directly enhanced by cyclic nucleotides; channels are weakly K^+ selective; and external Cs^+ blocks the inward current at submillimolar concentrations in a voltage-dependent fashion. The molecular identification of HCN channels for the first time permitted studies on their functional properties in isolation and in comparison with native channels. The channel subtypes HCN1, HCN2, and HCN4 differ in their kinetics, in the voltage of half-maximal activation ($V_{1/2}$, also referred to as mid-point potential), and in the shift of $V_{1/2}$ by cAMP and cGMP.

Activation Kinetics

All HCN currents, whether native or recombinant, develop with a characteristic sigmoidal time course, which hints at a complex series of voltage-dependent activation steps. Figure 4a shows a whole-cell recording of the recombinant human HCN4 channel expressed in HEK293 cells, which illustrates the slowly developing

a   b

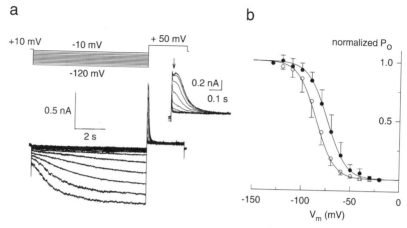

Figure 4 (*a*) Current responses of heterologously expressed hHCN4 channels to hyperpolarizing voltage steps from a holding voltage of 10 mV to test values between -10 and -120 mV. The voltage protocol is indicated above the current traces. The inset shows, on an expanded time scale, the tail currents (at $+50$ mV) that have been used for the determination of the normalized open probability. The arrow indicates the time at which the tail current amplitude was taken. (*b*) The normalized open probability P_o determined from tail currents was plotted versus voltage for experimental conditions in the absence (o) and in the presence (•) of cAMP (data from 73).

sigmoidal waveform. The normalized open probability of the channel in the absence and presence of cAMP is shown in Figure 4*b*.

A full quantitative account of the time course of HCN activation would require elaborate kinetic schemes. However, when the initial lag phase is excluded from the analysis, the activation kinetics is satisfactorily described by either a single or two exponential components. The distinction between a single and two kinetic components is not simply academic. Multiphasic kinetics may originate from (*a*) distinct populations of channels encoded by alternative genes (and various splice forms), (*b*) different post-translational modifications, or from (*c*) multiple gating processes within a channel.

HCN1 displays the fastest kinetics. The time constant of activation (τ) varies from 100 to 300 ms (at -130 to -100 mV) (67, 69). Activation of HCN2 proceeds somewhat slower (46, 67). Time constants range between 200 and 500 ms (at -140 to -100 mV). The activation kinetics of HCN4 is distinctively slower than that of HCN1 or HCN2 (39, 46, 73). Time constants range between a few hundred milliseconds (at -150 mV) up to 30 s (at -70 mV) (39, 46, 73).

In the past, comparison of the biophysical properties of native and recombinant channels has proven extremely fruitful in the discovery of novel subunits, auxiliary proteins, and modulatory actions of phosphorylation and Ca^{2+}-binding proteins. In principle, comparison of HCN activation kinetics could provide important clues as to the channel subtype(s) expressed in a given cell. However, the time course of HCN currents depends on the ionic milieu, cAMP concentration, voltage, and temperature. Unfortunately, the kinetics of HCN currents has been studied under vastly different conditions that prohibit definitive conclusions. Notwithstanding this complication, rapid activation of native currents correlates with the expression of subunits HCN1 and HCN2, and slower activation with the expression of HCN4 (39, 67, 74). Seifert and coworkers (73) determined the voltage dependence of the kinetics of recombinant HCN4 and compared it with the HCN currents from thalamocortical neurons (58). The kinetics of native and recombinant currents largely agree taking into account the different experimental temperatures and a Q_{10} of 6. A Q_{10} of 4.5 to 5 has been determined for native HCN channels (35, 51).

Mid-Point Potential

The voltage of half-maximal activation or mid-point potential $V_{1/2}$ is commonly determined from the amplitude of tail currents in a voltage pulse experiment. The $V_{1/2}$ is a measure of the voltage range within which the channel operates. The initial characterization of recombinant channels HCN1, HCN2, and HCN4 yielded $V_{1/2}$ values of ≤ -105 mV (45, 46, 69, 70), which raised questions as to the functional significance of the operational range of HCN channels. Seifert and coworkers (73) demonstrated that $V_{1/2}$ values critically depend on the length of the hyperpolarizing voltage pulses. Voltage pulses of short duration do not allow channel activation to come to completion and, therefore, the open probability P_o derived from tail current amplitudes is not in steady state. As a consequence, the open probability is seriously underestimated, and the apparent $V_{1/2}$ becomes shifted toward more negative values. The differences in estimated $V_{1/2}$ using different pulse protocols can be enormous (73). This effect is more pronounced for slow compared with fast HCN channels and low compared with high measuring temperatures. In the steady state, $V_{1/2}$ values for the human HCN4 are -75.2 mV, well within the operational range of most neurons. Subsequently, Santoro and coworkers (70) re-examined the $V_{1/2}$ values of HCN1 and HCN2, and for long pulses under two-electrode voltage clamp, report limiting $V_{1/2}$ values of -71.6 mV and -78.3 mV, respectively. Thus HCN1, HCN2, and HCN4 channels display similar $V_{1/2}$ constants that are consistent with values determined for most native HCN channels (-70 to -85 mV) (for compilation of data see 62, 70).

The HCN current in ventricular myocytes of the rat heart seems to be a remarkable exception. The HCN current in the ventricle of the neonatal rat begins to activate at potentials < -70 mV, whereas in the adult ventricle, HCN currents activate at potentials negative to about -115 mV ($V_{1/2}$ of roughly -140 mV) (65, 66, 94). The 40-mV negative shift in activation threshold is accompanied by slower kinetics in the adult (66, 74). Using RT-PCR, Shi and coworkers (74) showed that rat ventricles primarily express HCN2 and HCN4 transcripts at a ratio HCN2:HCN4 of 4.7 in the neonate that shifts to 13.7 in the adult. This result would argue that HCN2 is responsible for the negatively shifted $V_{1/2}$ in the adult and that switching of subunit types may account for the wide range of activation thresholds observed in cardiac tissue. As attractive as this idea is, it seems inconsistent with the slower kinetics in the adult ventricular myocytes, which speaks for enhanced expression of HCN4 rather than HCN2. Taking into account that $V_{1/2}$ values of HCN1, HCN2, and HCN4 do not differ much (67, 73), it may prove difficult to glean subunit composition from the $V_{1/2}$ values of activation.

A valid comparison of recombinant and native channels is confounded by yet another complication. The voltage dependence of activation seems to be regulated by intracellular factors. $V_{1/2}$ values change upon patch excision or during prolonged whole-cell recording. For example, the $V_{1/2}$ values determined for SpHCN in the whole-cell configuration and in excised patches are -50.8 and -84.7 mV, respectively (30). The variability of $V_{1/2}$ has been attributed to different cAMP levels and to endogenous factor(s) that are lost during whole-cell recordings or patch excision (23, 30, 45, 62). Activation thresholds of ventricular HCN currents are sensitive to treatment with phosphatase and kinase inhibitors (95), suggesting that post-translational modifications might be involved in this regulation.

Modulation by Cyclic Nucleotides

The cyclic nucleotides cAMP and cGMP modulate directly the activity of HCN channels without involving phosphorylation. This has been most convincingly shown in excised membrane patches for both native and recombinant channels (24, 30, 45) (Figure 5a, *middle panel*). HCN channels are set apart from each other by their ligand selectivity and the range of modulation. In mammalian HCN channels, cAMP shifts the activation curves to the right, i.e. $V_{1/2}$ values become more positive without changing the saturating current at very negative voltages (see Figure 4b for HCN4). The shift of $V_{1/2}$ by cAMP appears to be smallest in HCN1 ($\sim$2 mV) (69). HCN2 displays a shift of 12–14 mV (45, 46) and HCN4 of 11–23 mV (39, 46, 73) (see also Figure 4b).

The apparent ligand affinity and selectivity has been measured for HCN2 and SpHCN. Both channels are exquisitely sensitive to cAMP ($K_{1/2} = 0.5\ \mu$M for HCN2 and 0.7 μM for SpHCN) (30, 45). The binding curve can be described by a simple binding isotherm (i.e. Hill coefficient close to unity) (for SpHCN see Figure 5a, *right panel*). The HCN2 channel is approximately 10-fold less sensitive to cGMP than to cAMP ($K_{1/2} = 6\ \mu$M) (45), which agrees with the relative sensitivities of native channels from sino-atrial node myocytes ($K_{1/2}$ of 0.2 μM for cAMP and 7.8 μM for cGMP) (24). The SpHCN channel is almost 1000-fold less sensitive to cGMP than to cAMP ($K_{1/2}$ of roughly 500 μM), and the enlargement of the current by saturating cGMP concentrations is much smaller than by cAMP ($\sim$15 % of the cAMP response) (Figure 5a, *right panel*). To study the cAMP action in a single cell and to circumvent effects of slow cAMP-dependent phosphorylation that might occur during intracellular infusion with cAMP, the photorelease of cAMP from caged derivatives was used to rapidly

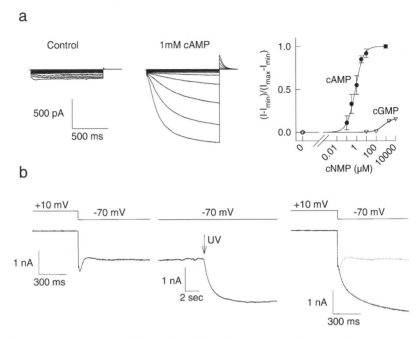

Figure 5 Modulation of SpHCN by cyclic nucleotides. (*a*) Hyperpolarization-activated currents in excised inside-out patches without cAMP (*left panel*) and with 1 mM cAMP (*middle panel*). Dose-response relations for cAMP and cGMP (*right panel*). Mean $K_{1/2}$ values are 0.75 μM (cAMP) and roughly 0.5 mM (cGMP). (*b*) Change in waveform of SpHCN activation upon rapid release of cAMP from a caged derivative. Waveform upon stepping from a holding voltage of +10 mV to −70 mV (*left panel*); change in current upon photolysis of caged cAMP at −70 mV (*middle panel*); comparison of activation waveforms upon a hyperpolarizing voltage step before (dotted line) and after three flashes of UV light (continuous line; *right panel*). For experimental details see Reference 30.

increase intracellular concentrations of cAMP (30, 73). Figure 5*b* illustrates the primary results for SpHCN. After the hyperpolarization-activated current reached a plateau (Figure 5*b*, *left panel*), the release of cAMP by a short flash of UV light further increased the current amplitude (Figure 5*b*, *middle panel*). The onset of current occurred rapidly with a time constant of ∼100 ms, supporting the concept that cAMP acts directly on HCN channels.

The waveform of the SpHCN-mediated current differs from that of the mammalian channels (30). Upon a hyperpolarizing step in the absence of cAMP, the current develops with a sigmoidal time course, reaches a peak, and then decays to a much lower plateau (Figure 5*a*, *left panel*) (30). In the presence of saturating cAMP, the currents are much larger and resemble the waveform of mammalian HCN currents (Figure 5*a*, *middle panel* and Figure 5*b*, *right panel*). The large augmentation of SpHCN currents by cAMP arises from an increase in the maximal open probability rather than from a positive shift in $V_{1/2}$, as observed for mammalian HCN channels (30).

Ion Selectivity

Although HCN channels preferentially conduct K^+ ions, other alkali cations can permeate as well. The K^+ selectivity is placed between those of the prototypical voltage-activated K^+ channels (P_{Na}/P_{Ka} = < 0.01–0.09) (38) and CNG channels ($P_{Na}/P_K \approx 1$) (see 29). Due to this peculiar ion selectivity, HCN currents, at physiological ion concentrations, reverse between -20 and -30 mV. As a consequence, HCN channels carry depolarizing inward Na^+ currents at rest (-65 mV). The P_{Na}/P_K selectivity depends on the extracellular K^+ concentration. For SpHCN it rises from 0.12 to 0.26 when the K^+ concentration is elevated from 1 to 20 mM (Figure 6a) (30). A similar K^+ dependence was observed in HCN2 (45), and in various native HCN channels (51, 91, 92). In the absence of extracellular K^+, the inward Na^+ current is abolished entirely (Figure 6b) (30). As a result of the strong K^+ dependence, currents become profoundly outwardly rectifying at low K^+ in the external medium (30). The dependence of the permeability ratios on ion concentration fits well with the idea that HCN channels are multi-ion pores and that Na^+ and K^+ ions do not pass independently from each other through the channel (38).

Single-Channel Conductance

The single-channel conductance g_i of mammalian HCN channels seems to be small compared with other channel types. DiFrancesco (20) determined a g_i value of

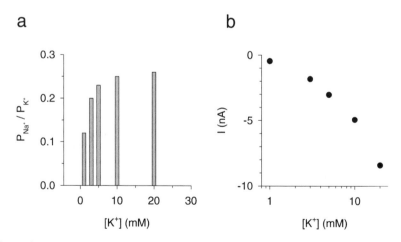

Figure 6 Ion selectivity of SpHCN. Dependence of inward current (a) and relative ion permeability P_{Na}/P_K (b) on the extracellular K^+ concentration. Data replotted from Reference 30.

~ 1 pS in isolated sino-atrial node cells. The HvHCN channel was also studied at the single-channel level. Krieger and coworkers (43) report a g_i of 30 pS (in 200 mM K^+ on both sides of the membrane). Single-channel events from recombinant mammalian HCN channels have not been reported.

SUMMARY

HCN channels, because of their unique properties, have intrigued physiologists for more than two decades. The molecular identification of the underlying proteins represents a major breakthrough that undoubtedly will greatly advance our knowledge about the cellular function of this novel class of channels and their regulation during normal and diseased states.

Now that the major subunits are identified, the answers to many pertinent questions should be revealed. Do HCN channels exist as homo- or heteromers? What is the molecular and stoichiometric subunit composition of native channels? If cells are furnished with more than one channel subtype, what is their subcellular distribution on the surface of highly polarized neurons? What is the nature of regulatory mechanisms? Is the modulation by cyclic nucleotides and other intracellular factors crucial for the generation of rhythmic activity?

ACKNOWLEDGMENT

This work was supported by the Deutsche Forschungsgemeinschaft Ka 545/9-1.

Visit the Annual Reviews home page at www.AnnualReviews.org

LITERATURE CITED

1. Aiba H, Fujimoto S, Ozaki N. 1982. Molecular cloning and nucleotide sequencing of the gene for *E. coli* cAMP receptor protein. *Nucleic Acid Res.* 10:1345–61
2. Altenhofen W, Ludwig J, Eismann E, Kraus W, Bönigk W. et al. 1991. Control of ligand specificity in cyclic nucleotide-gated channels from rod photoreceptors and olfactory epithelium. *Proc. Natl. Acad. Sci. USA* 88:9868–72
3. Anderson JA, Huprikar SS, Kochian LV, Lucas WJ, Gaber RF. 1992. Functional expression of a probable *Arabidopsis thaliana* potassium channel in *Saccharomyces cerevisiae*. *Proc. Natl. Acad. Sci. USA* 89:3736–40
4. Attwell D, Wilson M. 1980. Behaviour of the rod network in the tiger salamander retina mediated by membrane properties of individual rods. *J. Physiol.* 309:287–315
5. Bader CR, MacLeish PR, Schwartz EA. 1979. A voltage-clamp study of the light response in solitary rods of the tiger salamander. *J. Physiol.* 296:1–26
6. Bader CR, Bertrand D, Schwartz EA. 1982. Voltage-activated and calcium-activated currents studied in solitary rod inner segments from the salamander retina. *J. Physiol.* 331:253–84
7. Bal T, von Krosigk M, McCormick DA. 1995. Synaptic and membrane mechanisms underlying synchronized oscillations in the

ferret lateral geniculate nucleus in vitro. *J. Physiol.* 483:641–63

8. Bal T, von Krosigk M, McCormick DA. 1995. Role of the ferret perigeniculate nucleus in the generation of synchronized oscillations in vitro. *J. Physiol.* 483:665–85

9. Bal T, McCormick DA. 1996. What stops synchronized thalamocortical oscillations? *Neuron* 17:297–308

10. Beaumont V, Zucker RS. 2000. Enhancement of synaptic transmission by cyclic AMP modulation of presynaptic I_h channels. *Nat. Neurosci.* 3:133–41

11. Brown HF, DiFrancesco D, Noble SJ. 1979. Adrenaline action on rabbit sinoatrial node. *J. Physiol.* 290:31P–32

12. Brown HF, DiFrancesco D, Noble SJ. 1979. How does adrenaline accelerate the heart? *Nature* 280:235–36

13. Brown HF, DiFrancesco D. 1980. Voltage clamp investigations of currents underlying pacemaker activity in rabbit sino-atrial node. *J. Physiol.* 308:331–51

14. Budde T, Biella G, Munsch T, Pape HC. 1997. Lack of regulation by intracellular Ca^{2+} of the hyperpolarization-activated cation current in rat thalamic neurones. *J. Physiol.* 503:79–85

15. Catterall WA. 1986. Voltage-dependent gating of sodium channels: correlating structure and function. *Trends Neurosci.* 9:7–10

16. Clapham DE. 1998. Not so funny anymore: pacing channels are cloned. *Neuron* 21:5–7

17. Crunelli V, Kelly JS, Leresche N, Pirchio M. 1987. The ventral and dorsal lateral geniculate nucleus of the rat: intracellular recordings in vitro. *J. Physiol.* 384:587–601

18. DiFrancesco D. 1981. A new interpretation of the pace-maker current in calf Purkinje fibres. *J. Physiol.* 314:359–76

19. DiFrancesco D. 1981. A study of the ionic nature of the pace-maker current in calf Purkinje fibres. *J. Physiol.* 314:377–93

20. DiFrancesco D. 1986. Characterization of single pacemaker channels in cardiac sino-atrial node cells. *Nature* 324:470–73

21. DiFrancesco D. 1993. Pacemaker mechanisms in cardiac tissue. *Annu. Rev. Physiol.* 55:455–72

22. DiFrancesco D, Ducouret P, Robinson RB. 1998. Muscarinic modulation of cardiac rate at low acetylcholine concentrations. *Science* 243:669–71

23. DiFrancesco D, Mangoni M. 1994. Modulation of single hyperpolarization-activated channels (i_f) by cAMP in the rabbit sino-atrial node. *J. Physiol.* 474:473–82

24. DiFrancesco D, Tortora P. 1991. Direct activation of cardiac pacemaker channels by intracellular cyclic AMP. *Nature* 351:145–47

25. Dossi RC, Nunez A, Steriade M. 1992. Electrophysiology of a slow (0.5–4 Hz) intrinsic oscillation of cat thalamocortical neurones in vivo. *J. Physiol.* 447:215–34

26. Doyle DA, Morais Cabral J, Pfuetzner RA, Kuo A, et al. 1998. The structure of the potassium channel: molecular basis of K^+ conduction and selectivity. *Science* 280:69–77

27. Edman A, Gestrelius S, Grampp W. 1987. Current activation by membrane hyperpolarization in the slowly adapting lobster stretch receptor neurone. *J. Physiol.* 384:671–90

28. Fain GL, Quandt FN, Bastian BL. 1978. Contribution of a caesium-sensitive conductance increase to the rod photoresponse. *Nature* 272:467–69

29. Finn JT, Grunwald ME, Yau KW. 1996. Cyclic nucleotide-gated ion channels: an extended family with diverse functions. *Annu. Rev. Physiol.* 58:395–426

30. Gauss R, Seifert R, Kaupp UB. 1998. Molecular identification of a hyperpolarization-activated channel in sea urchin sperm. *Nature* 393:583–87

31. Gordon SE, Oakley JC, Varnum MD, Zagotta WN. 1996. Altered ligand specificity by protonation in the ligand binding

domain of cyclic nucleotide-gated channels. *Biochemistry* 35:3994–4001

32. Guy HR, Conti F. 1990. Pursuing the structure and function of voltage-gated channels. *Trends Neurosci.* 13:201–6

33. Guy HR, Seetharamulu P. 1986. Molecular model of the action potential sodium channel. *Proc. Natl. Acad. Sci. USA* 83:508–12

34. Hageman GR, Urthaler F, James TN. 1977. Differential sensitivity to neurotransmitters in denervated canine sinus node. *Am. J. Physiol. Heart Circ. Physiol.* 233:H211–H16

35. Halliwell JV, Adams PR. 1982. Voltage-clamp analysis of muscarine excitation in hippocampal neurons. *Brain Res.* 250:71–92

36. Heginbotham L, Lu Z, Abramson T, MacKinnon R. 1994. Mutations in the K^+ channel signature sequence. *Biophys. J.* 66:1061–67

37. Hestrin S. 1987. The properties and function of inward rectification in rod photoreceptors of the tiger salamander. *J. Physiol.* 390:319–33

38. Hille B. 1992. *Ionic Channels of Excitable Membranes.* Sunderland, MA: Sinauer

39. Ishii TM, Takano M, Xie L-H, Noma A, Ohmori H. 1999. Molecular characterization of the hyperpolarization-activated cation channel in rabbit heart sinoatrial node. *J. Biol. Chem.* 274:12835–39

40. Kamondi A, Reiner PB. 1991. Hyperpolarization-activated inward current in histaminergic tuberomammillary neurons of the rat hypothalamus. *J. Neurophysiol.* 66:1902–11

41. Kaupp UB, Niidome T, Tanabe T, Terada S, Bönigk W, et al. 1989. Primary structure and functional expression from complementary DNA of the rod photoreceptor cyclic GMP-gated channel. *Nature* 342:762–66

42. Kaupp UB. 1991. The cyclic nucleotide-gated channels of vertebrate photoreceptors and olfactory epithelium. *Trends Neurosci.* 14:150–57

43. Krieger J, Stobel J, Vogl A, Hanke W, Breer H. 1999. Identification of a cyclic nucleotide- and voltage-activated ion channel from insect antennae. *Insect. Biochem. Mol. Biol.* 29:225–67

44. Kumar VD, Weber IT. 1992. Molecular model of the cyclic GMP-binding domain of the cyclic GMP-gated ion channel. *Biochemistry* 31:4643–49

45. Ludwig A, Zong X, Jeglitsch M, Hofmann F, Biel M. 1998. A family of hyperpolarization-activated mammalian cation channels. *Nature* 393:587–91

46. Ludwig A, Zong X, Stieber J, Hullin R, Hofmann F, et al. 1999. Two pacemaker channels from human heart with profoundly different activation kinetics. *EMBO J.* 18:2323–29

47. Lüthi A, McCormick DA. 1998. H-current: properties of a neuronal and network pacemaker. *Neuron* 21:9–12

48. Lüthi A, McCormick DA. 1998. Periodicity of thalamic synchronized oscillations: the role of Ca^{2+}-mediated upregulation of I_h. *Neuron* 20:553–63

49. Lüthi A, McCormick DA. 1999. Modulation of a pacemaker current through Ca^{2+}-induced stimulation of cAMP production. *Nat. Neurosci.* 2:634–41

50. Maccaferri G, Mangoni M, Lazzari A, DiFrancesco D. 1993. Properties of the hyperpolarization-activated current in rat hippocampal CA1 pyramidal cells. *J. Neurophysiol.* 69:2129–36

51. Magee JC. 1998. Dendritic hyperpolarization-activated currents modify the integrative properties of hippocampal CA1 pyramidal neurons. *J. Neurosci.* 18:7613–24

52. Magee JC. 1999. Dendritic I_h normalizes temporal summation in hippocampal CA1 neurons. *Nat. Neurosci.* 2:508–14

53. Maricq AV, Korenbrot JI. 1990. Inward rectification in the inner segment of single

retinal cone photoreceptors. *J. Neurophysiol.* 64:1917–28

54. Marx T, Gisselmann G, Störtkuhl KF, Hovemann BT, Hatt H. 1999. Molecular cloning of a putative voltage- and cyclic nucleotide-gated ion channel present in the antennae and eyes of *Drosophila melanogaster. Invert. Neurosci.* 4:55–63

55. Mayer ML, Westbrook GL. 1983. A voltage-clamp analysis of inward (anomalous) rectification in mouse spinal sensory ganglion neurones. *J. Physiol.* 340:19–45

56. McCormick DA, Huguenard JR. 1992. A model of the electrophysiological properties of thalamocortical relay neurons. *J. Neurophysiol.* 68:1384–400

57. McCormick DA, Pape HC. 1988. Acetylcholine inhibits identified interneurons in the cat lateral geniculate nucleus. *Nature* 334:246–48

58. McCormick DA, Pape HC. 1990. Properties of a hyperpolarization-activated cation current and its role in rhythmic oscillation in thalamic relay neurones. *J. Physiol.* 431:291–318

59. McKay DB, Steitz TA. 1981. Structure of catabolite gene activator protein at 2.9 Å resolution suggests binding to left-handed B-DNA. *Nature* 290:744–49

59a. Mitsuiye T, Shinagawa Y, Noma A. 2000. Sustained inward current during pacemaker depolarization in mammalian sinoatrial node cells. *Circ. Res.* 87:88–91

60. Moosmang S, Biel M, Hofmann F, Ludwig A. 1999. Differential distribution of four hyperpolarization-activated cation channels in mouse brain. *Biol. Chem.* 380:975–80

61. Numa S. 1989. A molecular view of neurotransmitter receptors and ionic channels. In *The Harvey Lectures, Series 83*, ed. HR Kaback, MW Kirschner, S Numa, H Orkin, MG Rossmann, GM Rubin, H Varmus, pp. 121–65. New York: Liss

62. Pape HC. 1996. Queer current and pacemaker: the hyperpolarization-activated cation current in neurons. *Annu. Rev. Physiol.* 58:299–327

63. Pongs O, Kecskemethy N, Müller R, Krah-Jentgens I, Baumann A. et al. 1988. *Shaker* encodes a family of putative potassium channel proteins in the nervous system of *Drosophila. EMBO J.* 7:1087–96

64. Prystowsky EN, Grant AO, Wallace AG, Strauss HC. 1979. An analysis of the effects of acetylcholine on conduction and refractoriness in the rabbit sinus node. *Circ. Res.* 44:112–20

65. Ranjan R, Chiamvimonvat N, Thakor NV, Tomaselli GF, Marban E. 1998. Mechanism of anode break stimulation in the heart. *Biophys. J.* 74:1850–63

66. Robinson RB, Yu H, Chang F, Cohen IS. 1997. Developmental change in the voltage-dependence of the pacemaker current, i_f, in rat ventricle cells. *Pflügers Arch.* 433:533–35

67. Santoro B, Chen S, Lüthi A, Pavlidis P, Shumyatsky GP, et al. 2000. Molecular and functional heterogeneity of hyperpolarization-activated pacemaker channels in the mouse CNS. *J. Neurosci.* 20:5264–75

68. Santoro B, Grant SGN, Bartsch D, Kandel ER. 1997. Interactive cloning with the SH3 domain of N-src identifies a new brain specific ion channel protein, with homology to Eag and cyclic nucleotide-gated channels. *Proc. Natl. Acad. Sci. USA* 94:14815–20

69. Santoro B, Liu DT, Yao H, Bartsch D, Kandel ER, et al. 1998. Identification of a gene encoding a hyperpolarization-activated pacemaker channel of brain. *Cell* 93:717–29

70. Santoro B, Tibbs GR. 1999. The HCN gene family: molecular basis of the hyperpolarization-activated pacemaker channels. *Ann. NY Acad. Sci.* 868:741–64

71. Schönherr R, Heinemann SH. 1996. Molecular determinants for activation and inactivation of HERG, a human inward rectifier potassium channel. *J. Physiol.* 493:635–42

72. Scott SP, Harrison RW, Weber IT, Tanaka JC. 1996. Predicted ligand interactions of 3'5'-cyclic nucleotide-gated channel binding sites: comparison of retina and olfactory binding site models. *Protein Eng.* 4:333–44

73. Seifert R, Scholten A, Gauss R, Mincheva A, Lichter P, et al. 1999. Molecular characterization of a slowly gating human hyperpolarization-activated channel predominantly expressed in thalamus, heart, and testis. *Proc. Natl. Acad. Sci. USA* 96:9391–96

74. Shi W, Wymore R, Yu H, Wu J, Wymore RT, et al. 1999. Distribution and prevalence of hyperpolarization-activated cation channel (HCN) mRNA expression in cardiac tissues. *Circ. Res. (Online)* 85:e1–e6

75. Smith PL, Baukrowitz T, Yellen G. 1996. The inward rectification mechanism of the HERG cardiac potassium channel. *Nature* 379:833–36

76. Solomon JS, Nerbonne JM. 1993. Hyperpolarization-activated currents in isolated superior colliculus-projecting neurons from rat visual cortex. *J. Physiol.* 462:393–420

77. Soltesz I, Lightowler S, Leresche N, Jassik-Gerschenfeld D, Pollak CE, et al. 1991. Two inward currents and the transformation of low-frequency oscillations of rat and cat thalamocortical cells. *J. Physiol.* 441:175–97

78. Spector PS, Curran ME, Zou A, Keating MT, Sanguinetti MC. 1996. Fast inactivation causes rectification of the I_{Kr} channel. *J. Gen. Physiol.* 107:611–19

79. Steriade M, Deschênes M. 1984. The thalamus as a neuronal oscillator. *Brain Res.* 320:1–63

80. Steriade M, McCormick DA, Sejnowski TJ. 1993. Thalamocortical oscillations in the sleeping and aroused brain. *Science* 262:679–85

81. Stühmer W. 1991. Structure-function studies of voltage-gated ion channels. *Annu. Rev. Biophys. Biophys. Chem.* 20:65–78

82. Su Y, Dostmann WR, Herberg FW, Durick K, Xuon NH, et al. 1995. Regulatory subunit of protein kinase A: structure of deletion mutant with cAMP binding domains. *Science* 269:807–13

83. Takahashi T. 1990. Inward rectification in neonatal rat spinal motoneurones. *J. Physiol.* 423:47–62

84. Taylor SS, Buechler JA, Yonemoto W. 1990. cAMP-dependent protein kinase: framework for a diverse family of regulatory enzymes. *Annu. Rev. Biochem.* 59:971–1005

85. Titani K, Sasagawa T, Ericsson LH, Kumar S, Smith SB, et al. 1984. Amino acid sequence of the regulatory subunit of bovine type I adenosine cyclic 3',5'-phosphate dependent protein kinase. *Biochemistry* 23:4193–99

86. Vaccari T, Moroni A, Rocchi M, Gorza L, Bianchi ME, et al. 1999. The human gene coding for HCN2, a pacemaker channel of the heart. *Biochim. Biophys. Acta* 1446:419–25

87. Varnum MD, Black KD, Zagotta WN. 1995. Molecular mechanism for ligand discrimination of cyclic nucleotide-gated channels. *Neuron* 15:619–25

88. von Krosigk M, Bal T, McCormick DA. 1993. Cellular mechanisms of a synchronized oscillation in the thalamus. *Science* 261:361–64

89. Weber IT, Steitz TA. 1987. Structure of a complex of catabolite gene activator protein and cyclic AMP refined at 2.5 Å resolution. *J. Mol. Biol.* 198:311–26

90. Weber IT, Steitz TA, Bubis J, Taylor SS. 1987. Predicted structures of cAMP binding domains of type I and II regulatory subunits of cAMP-dependent protein kinase. *Biochemistry* 26:343–51

91. Wollmuth LP. 1995. Multiple ion binding sites in I_h channels of rod photoreceptors from tiger salamanders. *Pflügers Arch.* 430:34–43

92. Wollmuth LP, Hille B. 1992. Ionic

selectivity of I_h channels of rod photoreceptors in tiger salamanders. *J. Gen. Physiol.* 100:749–65

93. Yanagihara K, Irisawa H. 1980. Inward current activated during hyperpolarization in the rabbit sino atrial node cell. *Pflügers Arch.* 385:11–19

94. Yu H, Chang F, Cohen IS. 1993. Phosphatase inhibition by calyculin A increases i_f in canine Purkinje fibers and myocytes. *Pflügers Arch.* 422:614–16

95. Yu H, Chang F, Cohen IS. 1995. Pacemaker current i_f in adult canine cardiac ventricular myocytes. *J. Physiol.* 485:469–83

Annu. Rev. Physiol. 2001. 63:259–87

CELLULAR MECHANISMS OF OXYGEN SENSING

José López-Barneo, Ricardo Pardal,
and Patricia Ortega-Sáenz

Departamento de Fisiología, Facultad de Medicina y Hospital Universitario Virgen del Rocío, Universidad de Sevilla, E-41009, Sevilla, Spain; e-mail: lbarneo@cica.es

Key Words   hypoxia, ion channels, transcription factors, cell responses, gene induction

■ **Abstract** O_2 sensing is a fundamental biological process necessary for adaptation of living organisms to variable habitats and physiological situations. Cellular responses to hypoxia can be acute or chronic. Acute responses rely mainly on O_2-regulated ion channels, which mediate adaptive changes in cell excitability, contractility, and secretory activity. Chronic responses depend on the modulation of hypoxia-inducible transcription factors, which determine the expression of numerous genes encoding enzymes, transporters and growth factors. O_2-regulated ion channels and transcription factors are part of a widely operating signaling system that helps provide sufficient O_2 to the tissues and protect the cells against damage due to O_2 deficiency. Despite recent advances in the molecular characterization of O_2-regulated ion channels and hypoxia-inducible factors, several unanswered questions remain regarding the nature of the O_2 sensor molecules and the mechanisms of interaction between the sensors and the effectors. Current models of O_2 sensing are based on either a heme protein capable of reversibly binding O_2 or the production of oxygen reactive species by NAD(P)H oxidases and mitochondria. Complete molecular characterization of the hypoxia signaling pathways will help elucidate the differential sensitivity to hypoxia of the various cell types and the gradation of the cellular responses to variable levels of PO_2. A deeper understanding of the cellular mechanisms of O_2 sensing will facilitate the development of new pharmacological tools effective in the treatment of diseases such as stroke or myocardial ischemia caused by localized deficits of O_2.

INTRODUCTION

Oxygen is absolutely required for the survival of most life forms owing to its central role as an acceptor of the electrons in the mitochondrial respiratory chain, thus making possible the synthesis of adenosine triphosphate (ATP) by oxidative phosphorylation. The provision of sufficient O_2 to the tissues is a fundamental physiological challenge because even transient localized O_2 deficits can produce irreversible cellular damage. The lack of O_2 is critical in the pathogenesis of major causes of mortality such as stroke, myocardial infarction, and chronic lung disease,

0066-4278/01/0315-0259$14.00
259

TABLE 1   Representative fast and slow responses to hypoxia

Fast (acute) responses (s to min)	Slow (chronic) responses (hours to days)
Hyperventilation (arterial and airway chemoreceptors)	Activation of glucose metabolism and transport (most tissues)
Increase heart output (peripheral chemoreceptors, heart muscle)	Erythropoiesis (bone marrow)
Systemic arterial vasodilation (arterial endothelium and smooth muscle, irrigated tissues)	Angiogenesis and neovascularization (vascular endothelium, hypoxic or ischemic tissues)
Pulmonary vasoconstriction (vascular endothelium, resistance vessel pulmonary myocytes)	Tissue hypertrophy and remodeling (pulmonary arterial wall, myocardium, carotid body)
Relaxation of ductus arteriosus (ductus muscle)	Production of vasodilators (vascular endothelium and smooth muscle)
Activation of glucose uptake (cardiac and skeletal muscle, fat tissue)	

as well as reperfusion injury of transplanted organs. From bacteria to mammals there exists the capability of generating adaptive responses to hypoxia, which help minimize the deleterious effects of O_2 deficiency. Responses to hypoxia can be acute (occurring over a time scale of seconds to minutes) or chronic (with time course of hours to days) (Table 1). Protracted hypoxia induces the expression of genes encoding transporters, enzymes, and growth factors, which determine molecular and histological modifications to reduce the cellular need and dependence on O_2 and increase O_2 supply to the tissues. However, the survival of higher animals, and particularly of mammals, in acute hypoxia requires rapid respiratory and cardiovascular adjustments to ensure O_2 delivery to the most critical organs such as the brain or the heart.

The mechanisms of O_2 sensing and the signaling pathways that mediate the cellular adaptive responses to low O_2 tension (PO_2) constitute a field that has developed enormously in the last decade. Responsiveness to hypoxia, classically ascribed to specialized chemoreceptor organs such as the carotid body or kidney erythropoietin (EPO)-secreting cells, results from a widely operative molecular system represented in most tissues. Acute responses to hypoxia usually rely on the activity of excitable cells with O_2-sensitive ion channels in the plasmalemma, which mediate modifications in cell excitability, contractility, or secretory activity upon changes in PO_2. Similarly, specific O_2-dependent transcription factors are known to participate in mechanisms shared by most mammalian cells to regulate the expression of numerous genes. Although there are some recent interdisciplinary publications (1–3), research on the mechanisms of O_2 sensing has developed along two separate paths. On one are studies focusing on the O_2-dependent gene expression; on the other is the characterization of the cellular mechanisms underlying the respiratory and cardiovascular reflexes evoked by low PO_2. This review aims at reducing the gap between these two paths by presenting an updated and integrated view of the field. We describe the adaptive cellular responses to hypoxia and analyze recent advances in the O_2-sensing signaling pathways. Although much of the understanding of O_2 sensing has come from studies in bacteria and yeast, we focus here on the work done on mammalian cells. Detailed accounts on O_2 sensing in prokaryotic and lower eukaryotic organisms can be found elsewhere (4, 5).

PHYSIOLOGIC CELLULAR RESPONSES TO HYPOXIA

Physiologic responses to hypoxia include those mediated by ion channels, transporter regulation by O_2 tension, and regulation of gene expression and tissue remodeling.

Acute Responses to Hypoxia Mediated by Ion Channels

O_2-Sensitive Neurosecretory Cells   A well-studied acute cellular effect of hypoxia is the activation of transmitter release from O_2-sensitive neurosecretory cells. These are electrically excitable cells located in chemoreceptor organs capable of sensing global O_2 tension to produce cardiorespiratory adjustments upon exposure to environmental low PO_2. Chemoreceptor cells may have some tonic activity at the normal PO_2 levels of arterial blood ($\sim$90–100 mmHg), but they begin to be fully activated with moderate levels of hypoxia ($<$50–60 mmHg). The classical arterial chemoreceptors, the carotid and aortic bodies, contain clusters of sensory cells innervated by numerous afferent nerve fibers that activate the respiratory center during hypoxemia (6, 7). Clusters of innervated O_2-sensitive neurosecretory cells also exist in the neuroepithelial bodies of the lung where they detect PO_2 changes of the inspired air (8, 9). There is also clear evidence that, at least in the neonate, adrenal chromaffin cells are O_2 sensitive and capable of releasing catecholamines in response to low blood PO_2 (10–13). Sensitivity to hypoxia appears to be maintained in some subtypes of pheochromocytoma (PC-12) cells used as a model system to study the cellular responses to low O_2 tension (14).

Excitation of chemoreceptor cells by hypoxia depends on the presence of membrane K^+ channels whose activity is inhibited by low PO_2. These O_2-sensitive K^+ channels, initially discovered in glomus or type I cells of the rabbit carotid body, have been found in all the hypoxia-responsive neurosecretory cells studied so far (7, 8, 12, 15–22). Recordings illustrating the reversible inhibition by hypoxia of whole cell K^+ currents in several chemoreceptor cell types are shown in Figure 1A. Although the type of O_2-sensitive K^+ channel can differ among the

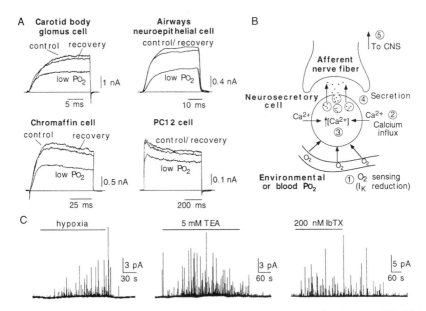

Figure 1   Responses to hypoxia of O_2-sensitive neurosecretory cells. *A.* Reversible inhibition of macroscopic K^+ currents by low PO_2 in four different cell types. *B.* Scheme of the membrane model of O_2 sensing in neurosecretory cells. *C.* Secretory responses of rat glomus cells in thin carotid body slices to hypoxia and K^+ channel blockers (modified from 8, 13–15, 25, 29).

various chemoreceptor cells or among cells in different animal species, electrophysiological studies give strong support to a unified "membrane model" of chemosensory transduction. This process is initiated with the closure of K^+ channels by low PO_2, which leads to membrane depolarization and Ca^{2+} influx, transmitter release to the extracellular milieu and, in the innervated organs, activation of afferent sensory fibers (Figure 1*B*) (8, 12, 17, 20, 23, 24).

The membrane model of chemotransduction has been tested in preparations of rat and rabbit carotid bodies (24–29). Exposure of dispersed glomus cells to moderate levels of hypoxia (20–30 mmHg) induces an increase of cytosolic $[Ca^{2+}]$ accompanied by quantal transmitter release. These responses are totally abolished by Ca^{2+} channel blockers or removal of extracellular Ca^{2+} (for review, see 30). Further support for the membrane model of chemotransduction comes from recent experiments on rat carotid body slices demonstrating that the neurosecretory response evoked by hypoxia in a glomus cell (Figure 1*C, left*) is mimicked by tetraethylammonium (Figure 1*C, middle*) or iberiotoxin (Figure 1*C, right*) (29), blockers of the O_2-sensitive Ca^{2+}-dependent maxi K^+ (K_{Ca}) channels present in these cells (17, 31).

O_2-Dependent Changes of Arterial Tone   The regional distribution of circulation in the body is determined in part by local variations in blood O_2 tension.

Although there are differences among the various vascular territories or between conduit and resistance arteries, the most common vascular responses to hypoxia are pulmonary vasoconstriction and dilation of systemic vessels (32–36). Hypoxia is known to cause the release of vasoactive substances from the endothelium and neighboring tissues; however, extensive work suggests that O_2-sensitive ion channels in vascular myocytes also participate in the O_2-dependent changes of arterial tone. Hypoxic pulmonary vasoconstriction (HPV) is a fast response that occurs in pulmonary arteries and veins but is greatest in small resistance arteries (Figure 2A, *left*). HPV is essential for fetal life as it helps maintain the high pulmonary vascular resistance that diverts blood through the ductus arteriosus. In adults, HPV reduces blood flow through poorly ventilated alveoli and thus contributes to matching perfusion to ventilation and preventing systemic hypoxemia when atelectasis is present. Several groups have shown that, as in the O_2-sensitive neurosecretory cells, the amplitude of macroscopic voltage-dependent K^+ currents of dispersed resistance vessel pulmonary myocytes is reversibly reduced by low PO_2 (Figure 2A, *middle*) (37–39). The membrane ionic events involved in HPV are summarized in Figure 2A (*right*). Hypoxia causes inhibition of one or several K^+ channels, leading to membrane depolarization, opening of voltage-gated Ca^{2+} channels, and myocyte contraction. Ca^{2+} released from ryanodine-sensitive stores in hypoxia could also contribute to contraction either directly or through blockade of K^+ channels (40, 41). In addition, hypoxia potentiates Ca^{2+} entry through L-type Ca^{2+} channels in a subset of resistance vessel myocytes (36, 42, 43).

Hypoxic vasodilation is another fast response (Figure 2A, *left*) that increases the perfusion of blood to the O_2-deprived tissues and is particularly well manifested in coronary and cerebral vessels. Vasodilation evoked by low PO_2 is important for the supply of sufficient O_2 to the working heart and for matching local perfusion to neuronal activity (and O_2 consumption) in the brain. A major component of hypoxic vasodilation is mediated by the K_{ATP} channels of vascular myocytes, which open in response to decrease of ATP production in hypoxia (44). However, there are other O_2-sensitive ionic mechanisms that cause myocyte relaxation because it occurs with PO_2 levels that do not compromise energy metabolism (32). K_{Ca} channels potentiated by low PO_2 have been described in isolated cerebral resistance vessel myocytes (45), where they possibly contribute to the hypoxic relaxation of precontracted arteries. A somewhat similar mechanism (inhibition of K^+ channels by normoxia) has been proposed to induce contraction of the ductus arteriosus at birth once the blood in the newborn is oxygenated (46). In addition to regulation of K^+ channels, evidence indicates that in arterial myocytes transmembrane Ca^{2+} influx is also directly inhibited by low PO_2. Relaxation by hypoxia is produced in arteries precontracted with high $[K^+]$ (a condition that prevents repolarization by opening of K_{ATP} or K_{Ca} channels) (47), and in isolated myocytes the elevation of cytosolic $[Ca^{2+}]$ induced by high $[K^+]$ is reversibly reduced by low PO_2 (36, 42, 43, 48). These observations (Figure 2B, *left* and *middle*) suggest direct inhibition of L-type Ca^{2+} channels by hypoxia, a phenomenon that has been demonstrated in patch-clamped conduit pulmonary and systemic arterial myocytes (Figure 2B, *right*) (36, 48–50)

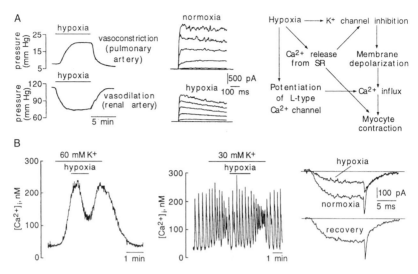

Figure 2   Responses of vascular smooth muscle cells to hypoxia. *A.* (*left*) Vasoconstriction and vasodilation of pulmonary and renal arterial rings, respectively, in response to hypoxia. (*Middle*) Inhibition by hypoxia of the macroscopic K^+ current in dispersed resistance pulmonary arterial myocytes. (*Right*) Scheme of the mechanisms involved in hypoxic pulmonary vasoconstriction in isolated pulmonary myocytes. *B.* Reversible inhibition by hypoxia of cytosolic $[Ca^{2+}]$ elevation induced by high extracellular $[K^+]$ in a silent coronary arterial myocyte (*left*) and in a conduit pulmonary arterial myocyte generating spontaneous calcium oscillations (*middle*). (*Right*) Inhibition of the Ca^{2+} current by hypoxia in a patch-clamped systemic arterial myocyte (modified from 34, 42, 48).

Modulation of Neuronal Excitability   Brain function is critically dependent on a proper O_2 supply. Cerebral hypoxia or ischemia produce, in a few seconds, slowing of electroencephalographic activity with subsequent depression of cortical-evoked potentials and loss of consciousness. Focal hypoxia is also known to produce rapid neuronal damage. Vulnerability of central neurons to O_2 deprivation results from a loss of ionic homeostasis and the abnormal release of excitatory neurotransmitters (51–54). In the early stages, neuronal responses to hypoxia are dependent on the modulation of ion channels. In most cortical and hippocampal neurons, hypoxia induces an immediate hyperpolarization by the activation of K_{Ca} channels (51, 52, 55). Reduction of the amplitude of Na^+ currents by hypoxia or metabolic intoxication also occurs in some neurons (56). These responses are viewed as protective because they prevent the dissipation of ionic gradients through activation of voltage-gated channels. However, after several minutes in extreme hypoxia, neurons undergo irreversible depolarization with massive Na^+ and Ca^{2+} uptake preceding cell death (53). At this stage, inhibition of K^+ channels or opening of non-inactivating Na^+ channels by low PO_2 may contribute to the neuronal response (57, 58). In contrast to this general cellular response to hypoxia, many brain stem neurons involved in respiratory and cardiovascular regulation or in sympatho-excitation by ischemia undergo a rapid depolarization (51, 59). This response may also have an adaptive role because it provides direct activation of neurohormonal reflexes independently of the peripheral chemoreceptors. The mechanisms underlying this early neuronal depolarization elicited by hypoxia are not well characterized, but inhibition of ATP- and/or Ca^{2+}-regulated K^+ channels and potentiation of Ca^{2+} channels could play a direct role (57, 59, 60).

Fast Regulation of Transporters by O_2 Tension

Alteration of O_2 tension can produce short-term modulation of some ion and glucose transporters. Regulation of ion transport by O_2 has been studied in red blood cells (RBCs) of several vertebrate species including humans. O_2 tension influences both the Na^+-H^+ exchanger (NHE) and the K^+-Cl^- cotransporter (KCC). NHE is stimulated by hypoxia and inhibited by high PO_2 values (61). In contrast, KCC is inhibited by hypoxia and potentiated by raising PO_2. KCC, a major regulator of volume in RBCs (62, 63), is also activated by cell swelling, concentrated urea, or acidification. When PO_2 is low, the transporter is refractory to activation by other stimuli. This regulation of KCC by O_2 may have an adaptive physiologic role in tissues with very low PO_2 such as the kidney medulla, to prevent shrinkage and alteration of erythrocytes (62, 64). Fast activation of glucose transport by hypoxia is important in tissues such as skeletal or cardiac muscle that have immediate energy demands in which glucose uptake is the rate-limiting step. Hypoxia, in minutes, can induce the translocation of GLUT-1 and GLUT-4 glucose transporters from intracellular vesicles to the plasma membrane and activate preexisting GLUT-1 in the membrane. Rotenone can also elicit translocation of GLUT-1 (65).

Hypoxia as Regulator of Gene Expression and Tissue Remodeling

It is long recognized that chronic hypoxia induces the expression of numerous genes whose products facilitate non-oxidative synthesis of ATP, increase the O_2-carrying capacity of blood, and multiply the number of vessels irrigating the hypoxic tissues (Table 2). Although there is no strict demarcation between physiologic and non-physiologic hypoxia, all these responses are considered to have an adaptive physiologic role because they are easily reversible and elicited with moderate levels of hypoxia (3–5 % O_2). These adaptive responses must be distinguished from the induction of genes in conditions of anoxia or extreme low PO_2, which contribute to the pathophysiology of tumor progression and cell apoptosis.

Glucose Metabolism   A universal adaptation to hypoxia is the increase in cellular utilization of glucose via routes other than mitochondrial aerobic metabolism. This phenomenon depends on up-regulated expression of glucose transporters and degradation enzymes (4, 65, 66). In most cells, and particularly in those with low

TABLE 2   Physiologically relevant genes induced by hypoxia

Glucose metabolism	Erythropoiesis, angiogenesis and tissue remodeling
Glucose transporters	Erythropoietin (EPO)
GLUT-1, GLUT-3	Transferrin
Glycolytic enzymes	Transferrin receptor
Aldolase A and C	Vascular endothelial growth factor (VEGF)
Hexokinase 1 and 3	Placental growth factor (PLGF)
Glyceraldehyde-3-phosphate dehydrogenase	Platelet-derived growth factor A and B
dehydrogenase	Insulin-like growth factor 2 (IGF-2)
Lactate dehydrogenase	Endothelin 1 (ET-1)
Phosphofructokinase	
Phosphoglycerate kinase	
Pyruvate kinase	
Triphosphate isomerase	

Vasomotor control	Carotid body function
Endothelin 1	Tyrosine hydroxylase (TH)
Nitric oxide synthase 2 (NOS-2)	
Heme oxygenase 1 (HO-1)	

levels of glucose such as fat or skeletal muscle, hypoxia induces the expression of transporters of the GLUT family. GLUT-1, the most widely represented glucose transporter, is regulated by cytokines, mitogens, or growth factors, as well as by low PO_2. Unlike other hypoxia-responsive genes, *GLUT-1* is also induced by inhibitors of mitochodrial respiration (rotenone, azide or antimycin A) or by the mitochondrial uncoupler dinitrophenol (67, 68). However, regulation of GLUT-1 by hypoxia and that by mitochondrial inhibitors depends on separate *cis*-acting elements and transcription factors. The GLUT-1 promoter contains a serum response element critical for induction by mitochondrial inhibitors. This element is different from the hypoxia-inducible factor (HIF) binding site, which determines the regulation by PO_2 (66, 67) (see below). Genes encoding glycolytic enzymes are also up-regulated by low PO_2, as well as by hormones and growth factors, but they are not influenced by mitochondrial inhibitors.

Erythropoiesis, Angiogenesis, and Cardiovascular Hypertrophy Erythropoietin (*EPO*) is the classical and best studied hypoxia-responsive gene. EPO, the major growth cytokine regulating erythopoiesis in mammals, is transcribed up to 100-fold the basal rate in response to anemia or hypobaric conditions (4). EPO is produced in peritubular cells of adult kidney or in hepatocytes during fetal life; however, much of the recent advance in EPO gene expression has come from studies in cell lines such as Hep 3B and Hep G2, which respond to hypoxia with pronounced EPO production (69). Hypoxia responsiveness of the *EPO* depends on an enhancer element located in the 3' flanking region. This 3' enhancer confers marked O_2 sensitivity to reporter genes transfected in cell lines (70–73). In addition to the HIF-binding region, the 3' enhancer also contains specific sites for binding of Zn-finger receptor proteins. *EPO* is induced by cobalt or the iron chelator desferrioxamine but is not affected by downstream mitochondrial inhibitors such as azide or cyanide (73–75). Interestingly, *EPO* induction by hypoxia is blocked by rotenone (66, 76). In addition to *EPO*, other genes, e.g. transferrin, important for iron transport and heme synthesis, are also up-regulated by hypoxia (Table 2).

Oxygen tension regulates angiogenesis in development and in adaptation and recovery from local ischemia. Angiogenesis results from interaction among several cytokines: vascular endothelial growth factor (VEGF), placental growth factor (PLGF), and platelet-derived growth factors A and B, all of which share sequence homology and are up-regulated by hypoxia (Table 2). VEGF, the best-characterized hypoxia-sensitive angiogenic factor, is produced in nearly all cells and tissues, but its receptor expression is restricted to endothelial cells (4, 66). Like EPO, VEGF is also induced by cobalt and desferrioxamine. In addition to polycytemia and angiogenesis, animals exposed to chronic hypoxia develop cardiac hypertrophy and pulmonary vascular remodeling, with increased thickness of the arteriolar muscle wall. Although increased cardiac output may have some adaptive role, pulmonary vascular hypertrophy can be the cause of chronic pulmonary hypertension and heart failure. In addition to VEGF, other factors (ET-1, IGF-II and NOS-2) are known to participate in hypoxia-dependent cardiovascular remodeling (Table 2).

Carotid Body Maturation and Plasticity   The carotid body, and possibly other peripheral chemoreceptors, mature after birth and undergo structural and functional changes in response to environmental modifications in PO_2. Well-known examples of carotid body plasticity include acclimation to chronic hypoxia in adults and blunted respiratory response to hypoxia in persons living at high altitudes (3). Carotid body adaptive changes in response to long-term hypoxia are the result of alterations in the expression of genes that regulate glomus cell growth, excitability, and sensitivity to low PO_2. Unlike its effect in other organs, hypoxia causes the carotid body to grow by increasing the number, size, and excitability of glomus cells (77). This "growth factor" effect of hypoxia could explain the remarkable long-term survival of glomus cells grafted into the striatum of Parkinsonian rats (78). Carotid body sensitivity to PO_2 increases after birth (79, 80), and this developmental adaptation disappears if animals are raised in hypoxia owing to reduction of K_{Ca} channel expression (81, 82). Expression of tyrosine hydroxylase (TH), the rate-limiting enzyme in the synthesis of dopamine, also depends on PO_2. The autoregulatory transmitter dopamine is highly concentrated in glomus cells (83). Induction of TH protein by hypoxia is seen in carotid body or PC-1_2 cells but not in other catecholamine-containing tissues such as adrenal gland or superior cervical ganglion (84, 85).

MECHANISMS OF OXYGEN SENSING

Although the cellular responses to hypoxia are relatively well characterized, the molecular mechanisms of O_2 sensing and how changes in environmental O_2 are translated into signals recognizable by the cell are just beginning to be understood. The components of the hypoxia signaling pathway are represented in Figure 3. Changes in PO_2 are detected by O_2 sensors that regulate the activity of the effectors which, in turn, determine the modifications of specific cellular functions. As described above, hypoxia can influence numerous cellular functions manifested over different time scales; nonetheless, the strategies used to sense O_2 appear to be similar in all O_2-sensitive cells. Below we discuss the hypoxia signal transduction mechanisms, beginning with a description of the effectors because they are far better characterized than the O_2 sensors or intermediate messenger molecules.

The Effectors

The most widely distributed molecules mediating the effects of changes in PO_2 are ion channels and transcription factors (Figure 3). O_2-regulated ion and glucose transporters or enzymes are less understood and their function is restricted to only a few cell types.

Distribution and Characteristics of O_2-Regulated Ion Channels O_2-regulated ion channels initially studied in carotid body glomus cells are found in a broad variety of cells, including several neurosecretory cells, smooth and heart muscle, and central neurons (86). Although the most numerous O_2-sensitive channels are K^+-selective, Ca^{2+} and Na^+ channels are also regulated by O_2. However, O_2 sensitivity is not a universal characteristic of ion channels (17, 21, 23, 31, 46, 87).

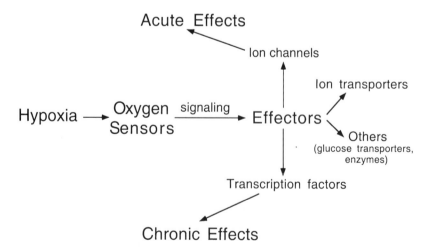

Figure 3   Components of the hypoxia signaling pathway.

TABLE 3 O_2-sensitive ionic conductances in mammalian cells. Effects of low PO_2[a]

Carotid body glomus cells	Vascular smooth muscle
Adult rabbit	Lung arterial tree
Delayed rectifier K^+ ($\downarrow$, *)	Delayed rectifier K^+, canine and cat
High voltage-activated Ca^{2+}	resistance myocytes ($\downarrow$, *)
($\downarrow$ at negative V_m)	L-type Ca^{2+}, rabbit resistance
Adult rat	myocytes ($\uparrow$ at negative V_m)
Calcium-activated K^+ ($\downarrow$, *)	L-type Ca^{2+}, rabbit conduit and
Delayed rectifier K^+ in chronically	resistance myocytes ($\downarrow$ at negative V_m)
hypoxic animals ($\downarrow$)	Calcium-activated K^+, sheep fetus,
Resting or leaky K^+ ($\downarrow$, *)	lung pulmonary artery ($\downarrow$)
Cat	Slowly activating K^+, adult rabbit ($\downarrow$)
Delayed rectifier K^+ ($\downarrow$)	Systemic myocytes
	L-type Ca^{2+}, rabbit ($\downarrow$ at negative V_m)
	Voltage-dependent Ca^{2+}, rat ($\downarrow$)
	Calcium-activated K^+, cat ($\uparrow$, *)
	Ductus arteriosus
	Delayed rectifier K^+, sheep fetus ($\uparrow$, *)

Central neurons	Chromaffin cells
Calcium- and ATP-dependent K^+, rat	Delayed rectifier K^+, fetal
neocortex and subs. nigra ($\downarrow$, *)	adrenal medulla ($\downarrow$)
Voltage-dependent Na^+, rat	Delayed rectifier K^+, newborn
neocortex ($\downarrow$)	and adult rat ($\downarrow$)
L-type Ca^{2+}, mouse inspiratory	Calcium and voltage-activated K^+,
neurons ($\uparrow$, *)	newborn rat ($\downarrow$)
Non-inactivating Na^+, rat	Delayed rectifier K^+,
hippocampal neurons ($\uparrow$, *)	PC12 cells ($\downarrow$, *)
Resting Ca^{2+} (non-selective	
conductance?), rat medulla ($\uparrow$)	

Cells in neuroepithelial bodies of lung	Heart muscle
Delayed rectifier K^+, rat ($\downarrow$)	Non-inactivating Na^+, rat ($\uparrow$, *)
Slow, non-inactivating K^+,	L-type Ca^{2+}, guinea pig
H-146 cells ($\downarrow$)	ventricular myocytes ($\downarrow$)

[a]Abbreviations: K^+, potassium current; Ca^{2+}, calcium current; Na^+, sodium current; V_m, membrane potential; $\downarrow$, inhibition of current; $\uparrow$, potentiation of current; *, studied with single-channel analysis.

A summary of the O_2-regulated ionic conductances described to date in mammalian cells is given in Table 3. Ion channels are considered O_2 sensitive because their modulation by PO_2 occurs without known modifications in cytosolic variables such as pH, $[Ca^{2+}]$, or ATP. Most O_2-sensitive ionic conductances have been studied in patch-clamped cells and in some cases are characterized at the single-channel level (Table 3). Some representative single-channel recordings of O_2-sensitive K^+

channels are shown in Figure 4*A*. PO_2 regulates channel open probability without changing the single-channel conductance, which indicates that O_2 tension influences specific gating properties of the channels without altering ion selectivity (19, 21, 35, 45, 57, 87–91).

O_2-sensitive ionic conductances can be either inhibited or potentiated by hypoxia, and this dual regulation is observed even in the same channel type expressed in different cells (Figure 4*A*). For example, maxi K_{Ca} channels are inhibited by low PO_2 in rat glomus cells or fetal ovine pulmonary vascular smooth muscle (17, 89, 92) but potentiated in cerebral arterial myocytes (45). Similarly, L-type Ca^{2+} channels are inhibited by hypoxia in rabbit systemic arterial myocytes but potentiated in resistance vessel pulmonary myocytes (36, 48, 49). This bidirectional regulation of channel activity is advantageous because it adds versatility to the biophysical mechanisms that the cells may use to adapt or respond to changes in PO_2. Other aspects of O_2-sensitive channels are their redundancy and variability in cells of different animal species. Several K^+ channel

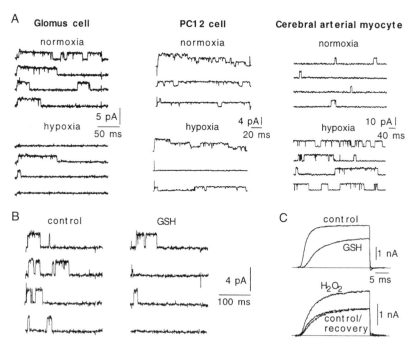

Figure 4 Modulation of K^+ channels by hypoxia and redox agents. *A.* Inhibition (*left* and *middle*) and potentiation (*right*) of single K^+ channel activity by hypoxia in three different cell types. *B.* Inhibition of the O_2-sensitive K^+ channel in rabbit glomus cells by reduced glutathione (GSH, 0.5 mM) added to the internal face of the membrane. *C.* Modulation of *Shaker* K^+ channels expressed in CHO cells by reduced glutathione (GSH, 2.5 mM) and H_2O_2 (0.1%) (modified from 21, 45, 94).

subtypes inhibited by low PO_2 coexist in rat and rabbit carotid body glomus cells (17, 20, 23, 31, 87) neonatal chromaffin cells (93), and resistance vessel pulmonary myocytes (35, 38, 39). Developmental changes affecting the kind and expression of O_2-sensitive channels are well documented in various cell types (80, 92).

Despite the growing number of known O_2-sensitive ion channels, the mechanisms underlying the O_2 interaction with the channels remain poorly understood. This is in part because O_2 sensitivity of ion channels is labile and easily altered by cell dissociation and other experimental maneuvers. Glomus cells enzymatically dispersed or in thin carotid body slices can lose their hypoxia responsiveness yet maintain normal electrophysiologic properties and secretory response to high extracellular [K^+] or K^+ channel blockers (29, 94). Thus it appears that the O_2-sensing apparatus can be destroyed or separated from the channels without altering their biophysical properties. The interaction of the O_2 sensors with the channels has been a subject of debate (86, 95). Since some channels retain the hypoxia responsiveness in excised membrane patches (19, 57), it was suggested that the O_2 sensor is closely associated with the channel oligomer, either attached to the pore-forming α-subunit or as part of an auxiliary subunit. Switching of the sensor between its deoxy and oxy conformations would alter channel gating either by direct allosteric interactions or by means of a mediator (86). Because reducing agents and hypoxia produce similar effects on several O_2-sensitive K^+ channels, (94, 96–98) (Figure 4*B*), a plausible explanation is that hypoxia modifies the balance of cellular redox couples and modifies the status of channel thiol groups, thus altering their gating properties. However, redox regulation of channel activity is nonspecific and occurs in many cloned K^+ channels (99–101). Recombinant *Shaker* K^+ channels, members of the Kv channel family, are, like the native O_2-sensitive K^+ channels, also regulated by reductants and oxidants (94) (Figure 4*C*). Therefore, it seems that O_2 sensitivity is not intrinsic to the ion channels but requires interaction between the O_2-sensing signaling mechanisms and the pore-forming channel subunits.

O_2 Sensitivity of Recombinant Ion Channels   Some heterologously expressed recombinant α-subunits of K^+ and Ca^{2+} channels are regulated by O_2. Although initial studies on the O_2 sensitivity of recombinant channels were promising (95, 102–105), advances to date are modest and the available data inconclusive. In addition to *Shaker* B channels (95, 102), several α-subunits of the Kv family of K^+ channels (Kv 1.2, 2.1, 3.1 and 4.2) are, like the native O_2-sensitive K^+ currents, modulated by changes of PO_2. Kv1.2, which mediates the O_2-sensitive K^+ current in PC12 cells (21, 106), is up-regulated by long-term hypoxia in these cells (106) but down-regulated in pulmonary myocytes (107). K^+ currents in mouse L cells transfected with Kv1.2 are also inhibited by low PO_2. In these cells, Kv1.5 currents are insensitive to hypoxia, but expression of a mixture of Kv1.2 and Kv1.5 cDNAs results in O_2-sensitive heteromeric channels with a lower activation threshold (108). Kv2.1 channels expressed in COS (105) and L cells (108) are inhibited by low PO_2. Co-expression of Kv2.1 with Kv9.3, a silent subunit that reduces the activation threshold of the heteromeric channels, results in channels that are more sensitive to hypoxia than the Kv2.1 homotetramers (105, 108). Recently, it was reported that in transfected L929 cells Kv3.1 channels are reversibly inhibited by low PO_2 (109).

Although these data indicate that the K^+ channels Kv1.2, Kv2.1, and Kv3.1 participate in O_2 sensing, such must be taken as preliminary because of the numerous unexplained contradictions and the variability among the different experimental preparations. For example, inhibition by hypoxia of *Shaker* B, Kv1.2, Kv2.1, and Kv3.3 α-subunits expressed in CHO cells was observed in our laboratory but, for unknown reasons, not in all batches of CHO cells used (95, 102). A similar phenomenon has been reported for COS cells expressing Kv2.1 channels (105). Moreover, Kv1.2 channels reported to be O_2 sensitive in PC12 cells (106) and in transfected L cells (108) are O_2 insensitive in B82 cells (109). Kv3.1 is O_2 sensitive in L929 cells, but other α-subunits have not been tested in the same cell type (109). This variability could reflect the changeable constitutive auxiliary subunits necessary for the channels to become O_2 sensitive. It has been reported that expression of the Kvβ1.2 subunit in HEK cells confers O_2 sensitivity to Kv4.2 but not to *Shaker* channels (110). However, Kvβ subunits do not seem to play the same role in all cell lines because co-expression of Kvβ1.1, 1.2 and 2 with either Kv1.2 or Kv4.2 in CHO cells fails to make the channels O_2 sensitive (J López-Barneo & P Ortega-Sáenz unpublished observations). Therefore, the essential element for making transfected K^+ channels O_2 sensitive is possibly the O_2 sensor itself or a specific form of interaction of the O_2 sensor with the channel oligomer.

Other recombinant channels have been shown to be regulated by O_2. HEK cells stably transfected with the α_{1C} L-type Ca^{2+} channel subunit express macroscopic Ca^{2+} currents that are, like the L-type Ca^{2+} channels of arterial myocytes, inhibited by low PO_2 (48, 49, 103). Recently, members of the TASK family of tandem-P-domain K^+ channels have been proposed to mediate the O_2-sensitive outward current of a human lung neuroepithelial-derived cell line (22) and the leaky O_2-sensitive K^+ current of rat carotid body cells (91).

Hypoxia-Inducible Transcription Factors   A major advance in the field of O_2 sensing has been the discovery of O_2-regulated transcription factors on which the expression of hypoxia-sensitive genes depends. Hypoxia-inducible factor 1 (HIF-1), the first O_2-regulated transcription factor identified, is ubiquitously expressed and participates in most of the chronic cellular responses to low PO_2 (66, 111–115). HIF-1 is a heterodimer composed of two subunits, HIF-1α and HIF-1β. HIF-1β is similar to ARNT (aryl hydrocarbon nuclear translocator), a previously known factor that dimerizes with the aryl hydrocarbon receptor (AHR) to activate transcription of genes encoding cytochrome P450 enzymes involved in metabolism of aryl hydrocarbon compounds. HIF-1β is expressed constitutively in many cells, but HIF-1α, almost absent in normoxia, is induced by hypoxia. Both HIF-1α and HIF-1β belong to a family of transcription factors with basic helix-loop-helix (bHLH) and PAS domains (116). Aside from HIF-1α, other hypoxia-regulated bHLH-PAS transcription factors, e.g. HIF-2α and HIF-3α, are homologous to HIF-1α but with a more limited tissue expression. Other β-subunits (HIF-2β and HIF-3β) have also been identified. HIF-1α is a protein of 826 amino acids whose N-terminal region, which includes the bHLH and PAS domains, is essential for dimerization and binding to DNA. The C-terminal half of the molecule contains two transactivation domains and one protein stability domain. The highly conserved transactivation domains interact with co-activators to regulate chromatin remodeling and the transcription of the target genes. Stabilization of HIF-1α in hypoxic conditions depends on the protein stability domain (66) (see below).

The role of HIF-1 in hypoxia signaling was discovered based on its binding to the hypoxia-responsive element (HRE) in the 3' enhancer of the EPO gene, but a similar HIF-binding region is present in all the genes up-regulated by low PO$_2$. The HRE of the *EPO* confers O$_2$ sensitivity and dependence on HIF-1 to reporter genes in all mammalian cells tested (111–113). Activation of HIF-1α by low PO$_2$ is detectable in less than 30 min, with peak response occurring in ~4 to 8 h. On return to normoxia, activity decays with a half-life under 5 min. HIF-1 DNA binding activity is modulated within physiologic PO$_2$ levels. It increases about twofold between 20 and 6% O$_2$ and tenfold between 6% and 0.5% O$_2$. Half-maximal activation is around 1.5% O$_2$ (PO$_2$ ~11 mmHg) (117).

Hypoxia increases HIF-1 activity at multiple levels. It potentiates HIF-1α transcriptional activation, mRNA stabilization, and nuclear translocation; however, the most powerful effect of low PO$_2$ is to prevent HIF-1α protein degradation (Figure 5). The low level of HIF-1α protein in normoxic cells is from permanent

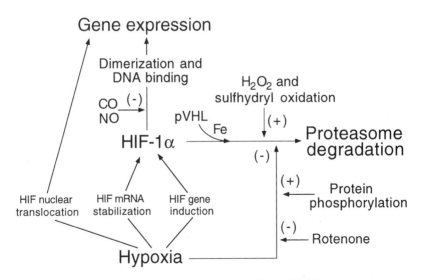

Figure 5 Scheme illustrating the turnover and regulation of HIF-1α protein.

ubiquitination and proteasome degradation, processes that, by unknown mechanisms, are blocked by low PO_2. The protein stability region between residues 401 and 603 is necessary and sufficient for regulation of HIF by PO_2 (118–122). HIF-1α protein stability is regulated by numerous factors besides O_2 tension, (Figure 5). Exogenous H_2O_2 inhibits the increase of HIF activity by hypoxia, and sulfhydryl oxidation reverses hypoxic activation (118, 120, 121); however, redox regulation of HIF is still debated (76) (see below). The von Hippel-Lindau (VHL) tumor suppressor gene product pVHL appears to participate in the ubiquitination and degradation of HIF-1α. In VHL-defective cells, HIF-1α is constitutively stabilized, which explains the angiogenic nature of the tumors in VHL syndrome (123, 124). Interaction of pVHL and HIF-1α seems to require iron and is inhibited by cobalt. This might explain why cobalt and the iron chelator desferrioxamine increase HIF DNA-binding activity and the expression of EPO or reporter genes (75, 113). Induction of HIF-1α activity by hypoxia is blocked by rotenone (an inhibitor of mitochondrial complex I) (66, 76).

Excitation-Transcription Coupling Whereas direct activation of HIF-1α provides most cells with a means to up-regulate hypoxia-inducible genes, in O_2-sensitive excitable cells, where hypoxia produces depolarization and elevation of cytosolic $[Ca^{2+}]$, gene expression is also regulated through the activation of immediate early genes. Depolarization (or excitation) -transcription coupling has been studied using the TH expression model in PC12 cells (14, 85, 125, 126). PC-12 cells do not have HIF-1α, but the *cis* element of the TH gene contains sites for the binding of activator protein-1 (AP-1) and HIF-2. Activation of AP-1 in hypoxia requires prior induction of the immediate early genes c-*fos* and *JunB*, which, as in other excitable cells, depends on the influx of extracellular Ca^{2+}. Depolarization-induced elevation of cytosolic $[Ca^{2+}]$ triggers a biochemical cascade mediated by Ca^{2+}/calmodulin, which determines c-*fos* and *JunB* expression, binding to AP1, and increased TH gene transcription. Interestingly, HIF-2α-dependent transactivation of transfected reporter genes is abolished in the absence of extracellular Ca^{2+} (126).

The Sensors and Signaling Pathways

Despite recent progress in the characterization of the cellular effectors of hypoxia, the mechanisms by which O_2 sensing is achieved remain elusive. It is generally believed that there are several O_2 sensors tuned to different O_2 levels and differentially distributed. However, the number of O_2-sensing mechanisms cannot be too large given the limited forms of physico-chemical interaction of O_2 with biomolecules. The interaction of O_2 with the putative O_2 sensors could be either as a reversible ligand, producing allosteric shifts of the sensor, or as a substrate, capable of direct oxidation of the sensor or enzymatically converted to reactive oxygen species (ROS) which, in turn, mediate the action on the effector molecules (Figure 6).

Ligand model

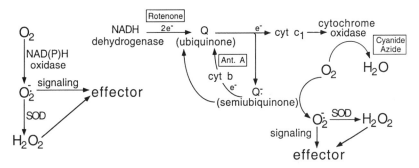

Redox models

Reactive oxygen species are mediators of O_2 sensing

Thiol-based direct O_2 sensor

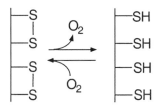

Figure 6 Models of O_2 sensing.

Ligand Model   The O_2 sensor can be viewed as a hemoprotein that in the deoxy conformation activates the effectors either directly or through a signaling cascade (Figure 6). The existence of a heme-based O_2 sensor is plausible because some heme proteins, such as hemoglobin, bind O_2 reversibly. Hemoglobin anchored to membrane proteins is likely involved in the O_2-dependent regulation of ion transporters in erythrocytes (61, 62), and in nitrogen-fixing bacteria, the O_2 sensor is a hemoprotein (FixL) with kinase activity in the deoxy state (4, 127). A heme-based O_2 sensor may exist in EPO-secreting cells because their response to hypoxia is reversed by CO which, like O_2, binds to heme groups and is mimicked by incubation of the cells with iron chelators or cobalt, treatments that interfere with heme synthesis or render heme unable to bind O_2 (75). These ideas are compatible with the findings on O_2-sensitive channels. Some native (19, 57) and recombinant (109, 110) channels retain O_2 sensitivity in excised membrane patches, which suggests a direct interaction between channels and O_2 sensor (86). Moreover, CO appears to reverse the effect of hypoxia on the O_2-sensitive K^+ channel of rabbit glomus cells (128).

However, a major problem of the heme model is its lack of direct experimental support. In addition, recent data indicate that CO can interact directly with HIF-1α and prevent its dimerization and that iron and cobalt have opposite effects on the interaction between pVHL and HIF-1α (see Figure 5). It has also been shown that inhibitors of heme synthesis fail to abolish the response of EPO-reporter genes to hypoxia (129). Although HIF-1α has a PAS domain that, as in FixL (5, 127), could bind a heme group, no direct interaction of HIF-1α with O_2 has been demonstrated. There are also ion channels with PAS domains (i.e. HERG), but their modulation by O_2 has not been documented (130). Another possible way to bind O_2 is by iron-sulfur centers. This mechanism of O_2 sensing is well represented in bacteria and yeast, but little is known about its function in mammalian cells (4).

Redox Models O_2 sensing could be done through enzymatic production of ROS to alter the redox status of signaling molecules and the function of the effectors. Although ROS can be produced at numerous cell sites and organelles, the two systems proposed as O_2 sensors are the NADPH oxidase and mitochondria (Figure 6). The NADPH oxidase can transduce O_2 levels by changing the rate of production of superoxide anion (O_2^-) (131, 132). Dismutation of O_2^- generates H_2O_2, which can oxidize transcription factors or ion channels and, at sites containing ferrous ion, can produce a hydroxyl radical ($\cdot OH$) by the Fenton reaction, thereby bringing about site-specific oxidation of regulatory proteins. The NADPH oxidase is a multisubunit assembly consisting of a membrane-bound catalytic complex formed by gp91^{phox} and p22^{phox} subunits, a b$_{558}$ cytochrome and several cytosolic regulatory subunits. The NADPH oxidase model predicts a decrease of H_2O_2 production and a shift of cytosolic redox pairs to the reduced state in response to hypoxia. This is compatible with some features of cellular O_2 sensing because sulfhydryl reduction activates HIF (Figure 5), and induction of hypoxia-responsive genes is inhibited by H_2O_2 (4, 66). Furthermore, hypoxia reduces ROS formation in the lung (96), and exogenous reductants mimic the effect of hypoxia on several types of O_2-sensitive K^+ (94, 97, 98, 100) and Ca^{2+} (133) channels (Figure 4C). Recent experiments provide direct evidence of NADPH oxidase participation in O_2 sensing in lung neuroepithelial body cells and the H-146 cell line. In these cells, the O_2-sensitive K^+ currents are potentiated by H_2O_2 or by activation of the oxidase with phorbol esters (134, 135), and regulation of K^+ channels by O_2 is abolished in the transgenic oxidase-deficient mouse with a null gp91^{phox} allele (136). However, several studies argue against a universal role of NADPH oxidase in O_2 sensing. The oxidase-deficient mouse has normal HPV and hypoxic inhibition of K^+ currents in its pulmonary myocytes (137). Moreover, patients with chronic granulomatous disease, with defects in one or several subunits of the oxidase, have normal EPO levels, and cell lines derived from these patients show normal VEGF and aldolase gene expression in response to low PO_2 (138). In the carotid body, a major source of b_{558} appears to be macrophages rather than the O_2-sensitive glomus cells (139). Finally, diphenyleneiodonium (DPI), an inhibitor of NADPH oxidase and other flavoproteins and nonselective blocker of ion channels, prevents the induction of some genes by low PO_2 but does not mimic the hypoxic response during normoxia. Therefore it is most likely that even if an NADPH oxidase participates as O_2 sensor in lung neuroepithelial cells, alternative O_2-sensing mechanisms must exist in other systems.

An obvious site of O_2 sensing is the mitochondrion because this organelle consumes almost all the available O_2 and is the major source of O_2^- owing to inefficient transfer of electrons in the respiratory chain. A model of O_2 sensing based on mitochondria (mitochondrial hypothesis) was postulated because mitochodrial inhibitors, such as cyanide or azide, which block cytochrome c oxidase, can stimulate the carotid body (3, 140). In many laboratories, mitochondrial inhibition (poisoning) was considered a form of hypoxia (histotoxic hypoxia). However, there is now no dispute that physiologic O_2 sensing in carotid body glomus cells depends on the inhibition of O_2-sensitive K^+ channels, which are modulated by O_2 tensions higher than those that depress metabolic function. Mitochondrial respiration is not limited by O_2 supply until extracellular PO_2 falls below 2 or 3 mmHg, whereas ion channels are regulated by PO_2 values below 80 mmHg. Unlike hypoxia (24–27), excitation of glomus cells by cyanide depends to a great extent on Ca^{2+} release from mitochondria. That physiologic O_2 sensing and mitochondrial inhibition are distinct phenomena is also evidenced by the lack of effect of cyanide or azide on the expression of hypoxia-sensitive genes (4, 66, 75). *GLUT-1* can be induced by both hypoxia and mitochodrial inhibitors but acting via separate *cis* sequences (67).

New insight into the possible role of mitochondria as O_2 sensors has come from recent work on cardiomyocytes suggesting that hypoxia induces a decrease of the cytochrome oxidase V_{max}, which results in accumulation of electrons in the reduced state and increased production of ROS (76, 141, 142). Radicals are produced preferentially at the semiubiquinone site, where an electron can be transferred to O_2 to produce O_2^- (Figure 6). It has been reported that in cardiomyocytes and Hep 3B cells hypoxia increases ROS production in parallel with the induction of hypoxia-responsive genes and that these effects disappear in mitochondrial-deficient cells (ρ^0 Hep 3B cells). However, in ρ^0 cells, gene induction by cobalt remains unaltered (76). Despite the appeal of these new data, the role of mitochondrial cytochrome oxidase as an O_2 sensor is challenged by unexplained or contradictory observations. In this model, both hypoxia and mitochondrial inhibitors that act downstream of the semiubiquinone site (i.e. cyanide or azide) should increase ROS production and shift redox pairs to the oxidized state. This is the opposite of the stabilizing effects of reductants on HIF-1α and the inhibition of HIF-dependent gene expression by exogenous H_2O_2 reported by several groups (4, 66, 119–122). The model also fails to explain why cyanide or azide has no effect on gene induction (4, 66, 75), the decrease of ROS production seen in hypoxic lungs (34), and the similarity of effects of hypoxia and reductants on most O_2-regulated ion channels (94, 97, 98, 100, 133). The shift of cytochrome oxidase V_{max} that develops during exposure to hypoxia for several minutes (142) is too slow to mediate the fast regulatory effect of O_2 on ion channels. Using carotid body slices, we observed differential effects of metabolic inhibitors on glomus cell secretion. Rotenone, but not antimycin A, blocks the effect of hypoxia, which suggests that a rotenone inhibitable molecule is involved in O_2 sensing (143). Interestingly, rotenone also blocks gene induction by hypoxia (4, 66) and the acute translocation of GLUT-1 transporter to the membrane (65). Therefore, involvement of some components of the mitochondrial electron transport chain in cellular O_2 sensing is plausible, but their identity and mode of interaction with the effectors remain to be elucidated.

A novel form of redox/O_2 sensing has been proposed based on the effects of PO_2 on the number of free-reduced cysteine residues present in the skeletal muscle ryanodine receptor/Ca^{2+} release channel (144). This protein does not contain heme, transition metals, or flavin domains but is unusually rich in free cysteines. Channels in the sarcoplasmic reticulum vesicles exposed to low PO_2 (between 10 and 20 mmHg) have several reduced cysteines susceptible to nitrosylation by NO. In ambient air ($\sim$150 mmHg), most of the cysteines are oxidized and thus regulation of the channels by NO is lost (144). These data suggest that PO_2 levels can be sensed through direct modification of the redox state of a thiol-rich molecule (Figure 6).

Cross-Talk Between Signaling Pathways   To place our discussion on O_2 sensing within the proper cell physiology context, it must be stressed that cellular responses to hypoxia not only depend on O_2 sensors and effectors but require integration of the hypoxia signaling pathway within the regulatory biochemical cascades. In addition to the HRE, hypoxia-inducible genes contain other *cis*-elements responsive to cytokines, hormones, and growth factors, and, like ion channels, HIF-1α is subjected to regulation by phosphorylation cascades involving several kinases and phosphatases (4, 66). For example, induction of HIF-1α protein and HIF-1α DNA binding is inhibited in hypoxic cells pretreated with genistein (a tyrosine kinase inhibitor), and cells transformed with oncogenes with intrinsic tyrosine kinase activity (like v-Src) overexpress HIF and have up-regulated responses to hypoxia (Figure 5). Moreover, blockade of the mitogen-activated protein kinase pathway prevents HIF-2α-dependent transactivation of the TH gene in PC-12 cells (125, 126). HIF-1α has reciprocal interactions with the function of NO and CO. Heme oxygenase and inducible nitric oxide synthase, which generate CO and NO, respectively, are induced by hypoxia through HIF-1α, and high levels of NO and CO inhibit HIF-1α dimerization and binding to DNA. Thus in tissues where these agents are produced they exert a feedback regulatory action on HIF activity (66). There are also important interrelations between HIF and genes regulating apoptotic cell death. Expression of the proapoptotic gene p53 induced by anoxia or extreme hypoxia in tumors or ischemic neuronal tissue requires intact HIF-1α activity (66, 145, 146). The central role of HIF-1α in the cross-talk between the various signaling pathways of the cells is clearly evidenced by the multiple pathological and lethal manifestations observed in HIF-1α-deficient mice (66, 145).

CONCLUSIONS AND FUTURE DIRECTIONS

O_2 sensing is a fundamental biological process required for adaptation of living organisms to variable habitats and physiologic situations with changes in the availability of O_2. Over the past decade we have witnessed rapid development and maturation of the field of cell O_2 sensing owing to the identification of O_2-regulated effector molecules, in particular ion channels and transcription factors. These molecules are part of a widely operating signaling system from bacteria to mammals that help provide sufficient O_2 to the tissues and protect the cells against damage caused by lack of O_2. Several unresolved pivotal questions remain regarding the nature of the O_2 sensor molecules and the mechanisms of interaction between sensors and effectors. However, recent experimental observations and current research promise rapid progress in the near future. Complete molecular characterization of the hypoxia-signaling pathways should elucidate the differential sensitivity to hypoxia of the various cell types or the gradation of the cellular responses to variable levels of PO_2. Much of the success of modern research on O_2 sensing is the result of reductionist experimental approaches using single-cell preparations and the combination of molecular biology and biophysical techniques. Knowledge in this field will be boosted by interdisciplinary analyses and comparative work in mammals and model animals, such as *Drosophila*, through the tools of molecular genetics. Research on the cellular mechanisms of O_2 sensing increasingly attracts growing medical attention, and developments in this field will surely have therapeutic impact. O_2-sensitive effectors are involved in vasomotor and cardiorespiratory control and focal O_2 deprivation is critical in the pathogenesis of major causes of mortality. Amplification or inhibition of adaptive responses to hypoxia are promising pharmacological strategies that may result in effective therapies for numerous diseases.

ACKNOWLEDGMENTS

We thank Dr. Elizabeth Pintado for comments on the manuscript. Research in the author's laboratory is supported by grants from the Spanish Ministerio de Educación, Fondo de Investigación Sanitaria, Fundación La Caixa, Fundación Ramón Areces, and Fundación Juan March.

Visit the Annual Reviews home page at www.AnnualReviews.org

LITERATURE CITED

1. Bauer C, Kutz A. 1997. *Forefronts in Nephrology: Oxygen Sensing on the Cellular and Molecular Levels.* Malden, MA: Blackwell

2. López-Barneo J, Weir EK. 1998. *Oxygen Regulation of Ion Channels and Gene Expression.* Armonk, NY: Futura

3. Lahiri S, Prabhakar NR, Forster RE. 2000. *Oxygen Sensing. Molecule to Man.* New York: Kluwer Academic/Plenum

4. Bunn HF, Poyton RO. 1996. Oxygen sensing and molecular adaptation to hypoxia. *Physiol. Rev.* 76:839–85

5. Taylor BL, Zhulin IB. 1999. PAS domains: internal sensors of oxygen, redox potential, and light. *Microbiol. Mol. Biol. Rev.* 63:479–506

6. Acker H. 1989. PO_2 chemoreception in arterial chemoreceptors. *Annu. Rev. Physiol.* 51:835–44

7. Ito S, Ohta T, Nakazato Y. 1999. Characteristics of 5-HT-containing chemoreceptor cells of the chicken aortic body. *J. Physiol.* 515:49–59

8. Youngson C, Nurse C, Yeger H, Cutz E. 1993. Oxygen sensing in airway chemoreceptors. *Nature* 365:153–55

9. Fu XW, Nurse CA, Wang YT, Cutz E. 1999. Selective modulation of membrane currents by hypoxia in intact airway chemoreceptors from neonatal rabbit. *J. Physiol.* 514:139–50

10. Mochizuki-Oda N, Takeuchi Y, Matsumara K, Oosawa Y, Watanabe Y. 1997. Hypoxia-induced catecholamine release and intracellular Ca^{2+} increase via suppression of K^+ channels in cultured rat adrenal chromaffin cells. *J. Neurochem.* 69:377–87

11. Mojet MH, Mills E, Duchen MR. 1997. Hypoxia-induced catecholamine secretion in isolated newborn rat adrenal chromaffin cells is mimicked by inhibition of mitochondrial respiration. *J. Physiol.* 504:175–89

12. Thompson RJ, Jackson A, Nurse CA. 1997. Developmental loss of hypoxic chemosensitivity in rat adrenomedullary chromaffin cells. *J. Physiol.* 498:503–10

13. Rychkov GY, Adams MB, McMillen IC, Roberts ML. 1998. Oxygen-sensing mechanisms are present in the chromaffin cells of the sheep adrenal medulla before birth. *J. Physiol.* 509:887–93

14. Zhu WH, Conforti L, Czyzyk-Krzeska MF, Millhorn DE. 1996. Membrane depolarization in PC12 cells during hypoxia is regulated by an O_2-sensitive K^+ current.

Am. J. Physiol. Cell Physiol. 271:C658–C65

15. López-Barneo J, López-López JR, Ureña J, González C. 1988. Chemotransduction in the carotid body: K^+ current modulated by PO_2 in type I chemoreceptor cells. *Science* 241:580–82

16. Delpiano MA, Hescheler J. 1989. Evidence for a pO_2-sensitive K^+ channel in the type-I cell of the rabbit carotid body. *FEBS Lett.* 249:195–98

17. Peers C. 1990. Hypoxic suppression of K^+ currents in type I carotid body cells: selective effect on the Ca^{2+}-activated K^+ current. *Neurosci. Lett.* 119:253–56

18. Stea A, Nurse CA. 1991. Whole-cell and perforated-patch recordings from O_2-sensitive rat carotid body cells grown in short- and long-term culture. *Pflügers Arch.* 418:93–101

19. Ganfornina MD, López-Barneo J. 1991. Single K^+ channels in membrane patches of arterial chemoreceptor cells are modulated by O_2 tension. *Proc. Natl. Acad. Sci. USA* 88:2927–30

20. Buckler KJ. 1997. A novel oxygen-sensitive potassium current in rat carotid body type I cells. *J. Physiol.* 498:649–62

21. Conforti L, Millhorn DE. 1997. Selective inhibition of a slow-inactivating voltage-dependent K^+ channel in rat PC12 cells by hypoxia. *J. Physiol.* 502:293–305

22. O'Kelly I, Stephens RH, Peers C, Kemp PJ. 1999. Potential identification of the O_2-sensitive K^+ current in a human neuroepithelial body-derived cell line. *Am. J. Physiol. Lung Cell Mol. Physiol.* 276:L96–L104

23. López-López J, González C, Ureña J, López-Barneo J. 1989. Low PO_2 selectively inhibits K channel activity in chemoreceptor cells of the mammalian carotid body. *J. Gen. Physiol.* 93:1001–15

24. Montoro RJ, Ureña J, Fernández-Chacón R, Álvarez de Toledo G, López-Barneo J. 1996. Oxygen sensing by ion channels and

chemotransduction in single glomus cells. *J. Gen. Physiol.* 107:133–43

25. López-Barneo J, Benot AR, Ureña J. 1993. Oxygen sensing and the electrophysiology of arterial chemoreceptor cells. *News Physiol. Sci.* 8:191–95

26. Buckler KJ, Vaughan-Jones RD. 1994. Effects of hypoxia on membrane potential and intracellular calcium in rat neonatal carotid body type I cells. *J. Physiol.* 476:423–28

27. Ureña J, Fernández-Chacón R, Benot AR, Álvarez de Toledo G, López-Barneo J. 1994. Hypoxia induces voltage-dependent Ca^{2+} entry and quantal dopamine secretion in carotid body glomus cells. *Proc. Natl. Acad. Sci. USA* 91: 10208–11

28. Carpenter E, Hatton CJ, Peers C. 2000. Effects of hypoxia and dithionite on catecholamine release from isolated type I cells of the rat carotid body. *J. Physiol.* 523:719–29

29. Pardal R, Ludewig U, García-Hirschfeld J, López-Barneo J. 2000. Secretory responses of intact glomus cells in thin slices of rat carotid body to hypoxia and tetraethylammonium. *Proc. Natl. Acad. Sci. USA* 97:2361–66

30. López-Barneo J. 1996. Oxygen-sensing by ion channels and the regulation of cellular functions. *Trends Neurosci.* 19:435–40

31. López-López JR, González C, Pérez-García MT. 1997. Properties of ionic currents from isolated adult rat carotid body chemoreceptor cells: effect of hypoxia. *J. Physiol.* 499:429–41

32. Detar R. 1980. Mechanism of physiological hypoxia-induced depression of vascular smooth muscle contraction. *Am. J. Physiol. Heart Circ. Physiol.* 238:H761–H69

33. Yuan XJ, Tod ML, Rubin LJ, Blaustein MP. 1990. Contrasting effects of hypoxia on tension in rat pulmonary and mesenteric arteries. *Am. J. Physiol. Heart Circ. Physiol* 259:H281–H89

34. Weir EK, Archer SL. 1995. The mechanism of acute hypoxic pulmonary vasoconstriction: the tale of two channels. *FASEB J.* 9:183–89

35. Archer SL, Huang JM, Reeve HL, Hampl V, Tolarova S, et al. 1996. Differential distribution of electrophysiologically distinct myocytes in conduit and resistance arteries determines their response to nitric oxide and hypoxia. *Circ. Res.* 78:431–42

36. Franco-Obregón A, López-Barneo J. 1996. Differential oxygen sensitivity of calcium channels in rabbit smooth muscle cells of conduit and resistance pulmonary arteries. *J. Physiol.* 491:511–18

37. Post JM, Hume JR, Archer SL, Weir EK. 1992. Direct role for potassium channel inhibition in hypoxic pulmonary vasoconstriction. *Am. J. Physiol. Cell Physiol.* 262:C882–C90

38. Yuan XJ, Goldman WF, Tod ML, Rubin LJ, Blaustein MP. 1993. Hypoxia reduces potassium currents in cultured rat pulmonary but not mesenteric arterial myocytes. *Am. J. Physiol. Lung Cell Mol. Physiol.* 264:L116–L23

39. Osipenko ON, Evans AM, Gurney AM. 1997. Regulation of the resting potential of rabbit pulmonary artery myocytes by a low threshold, O_2-sensing potassium current. *Br. J. Pharmacol.* 120:1461–70

40. Vadula MS, Kleinman JG, Madden JA. 1993. Effect of hypoxia and norepinephrine on cytoplasmic free Ca^{2+} in pulmonary and cerebral arterial myocytes. *Am. J. Physiol. Lung Cell Mol. Physiol.* 265:L591–L97

41. Post JM, Gelband CH, Hume JR. 1995. $[Ca^{2+}]_i$ inhibition of K^+ channels in canine pulmonary artery. Novel mechanism for hypoxia-induced membrane depolarization. *Circ. Res.* 77:131–39

42. Ureña J, Franco-Obregón A, López-Barneo J. 1996. Contrasting effects of hypoxia on cytosolic Ca^{2+} spikes in conduit and resistance myocytes of the rabbit pulmonary artery. *J. Physiol.* 496:103–9

43. Bakhramov A, Evans AM, Kozlowski RZ. 1998. Differential effects of hypoxia on the intracellular Ca^{2+} concentration of myocytes isolated from different regions of the rat pulmonary arterial tree. *Exp. Physiol.* 83:337–47

44. Dart C, Standen NB. 1995. Activation of ATP-dependent K^+ channels by hypoxia in smooth muscle cells isolated from the pig coronary artery. *J. Physiol.* 483:29–39

45. Gebremedhin D, Bonnet P, Greene AS, England SK, Rusch NJ, et al. 1994. Hypoxia increases the activity of Ca^{2+}-sensitive K^+ channels in cat cerebral arterial muscle cell membranes. *Pflügers Arch.* 428:621–30

46. Tristani-Firouzi M, Reeve HL, Tolarova S, Weir EK, Archer SL. 1996. Oxygen-induced constriction of rabbit ductus arteriosus occurs via inhibition of a 4-aminopyridine-, voltage-sensitive potassium channel. *J. Clin. Invest.* 98:1959–65

47. Marriott JF, Marshall JM. 1990. Differential effects of hypoxia upon contractions evoked by potassium and noradrenaline in rabbit arteries in vitro. *J. Physiol.* 422:1–13

48. Franco-Obregón A, López-Barneo J. 1996. Low PO_2 inhibits calcium channel activity in arterial smooth muscle cells. *Am. J. Physiol. Heart Circ. Physiol* 271:H2290–H99

49. Franco-Obregón A, Ureña J, López-Barneo J. 1995. Oxygen-sensitive calcium channels in vascular smooth muscle and their possible role in hypoxic arterial relaxation. *Proc. Natl. Acad. Sci. USA* 92:4715–19

50. Soloviev AI, Stefanov AV, Baziliyk OV, Rekalov VV, Pronchuk NF. 1996. Changes in plasma membrane ionic permeability and related contractile responses in vascular smooth muscle at hypoxia. *Pathophysiology* 3:11–20

51. Haddad GG, Jiang C. 1993. O_2 deprivation in the central nervous system: on mechanisms of neuronal response, differential sensitivity and injury. *Prog. Neurobiol.* 40:277–318

52. Martin RL, Lloyd HG, Cowan AI. 1994. The early events of oxygen and glucose deprivation: setting the scene for neuronal death? *Trends Neurosci.* 17:251–57

53. Lipton P. 1999. Ischemic cell death in brain neurons. *Physiol. Rev.* 79:1431–568

54. Haddad GG, Jiang C. 1997. O_2-sensing mechanisms in excitable cells: role of plasma membrane K^+ channels. *Annu. Rev. Physiol.* 59:23–42

55. Krnjevic K, Leblond J. 1989. Changes in membrane currents of hippocampal neurons evoked by brief anoxia. *J. Neurophysiol.* 62:15–30

56. Cummins TR, Jiang C, Haddad GG. 1993. Human neocortical excitability is decreased during anoxia via sodium channel modulation. *J. Clin. Invest.* 91:608–15

57. Jiang C, Haddad GG. 1994. A direct mechanism for sensing low oxygen levels by central neurons. *Proc. Natl. Acad. Sci. USA* 91:7198–201

58. Hammarstrom AK, Gage PW. 1998. Inhibition of oxidative metabolism increases persistent sodium current in rat CA1 hippocampal neurons. *J. Physiol.* 510:735–41

59. Sun MK, Reis DJ. 1994. Hypoxia-activated Ca^{2+} currents in pacemaker neurones of rat rostral ventrolateral medulla in vitro. *J. Physiol.* 476:101–16

60. Mironov SL, Richter DW. 1998. L-type Ca^{2+} channels in inspiratory neurones of mice and their modulation by hypoxia. *J. Physiol.* 512:75–87

61. Motais R, Garcia-Romeu F, Borgese F. 1987. The control of Na^+/H^+ exchange by molecular oxygen in trout erythrocytes. A possible role of hemoglobin as a transducer. *J. Gen. Physiol.* 90:197–207

62. Lauf PK. 1998. K^+-Cl^- cotransport: 'to be or not to be' oxygen sensitive. *J. Physiol.* 511:1

63. Berenbrink M, Volkel S, Heisler MN. 2000. O_2-dependent K^+ fluxes in trout red blood cells: the nature of O_2 sensing revealed by

the O_2 affinity, cooperativity and pH dependence of transport. *J. Physiol.* 526:69–80

64. Gibson JS, Speake PF, Ellory JC. 1998. Differential oxygen sensitivity of the K^+-Cl^- cotransporter in normal and sickle human red blood cells. *J. Physiol.* 511:225–34

65. Behrooz A, Ismail-Beigi F. 1999. Stimulation of glucose transport by hypoxia: signals and mechanisms. *News Physiol. Sci.* 14:105–10

66. Semenza GL. 1999. Regulation of mammalian O_2 homeostasis by hypoxia-inducible factor 1. *Annu. Rev. Cell Dev. Biol.* 15:551–78

67. Ebert BL, Firth JD, Ratcliffe PJ. 1995. Hypoxia and mitochondrial inhibitors regulate expression of glucose transporter-1 via distinct *cis*-acting sequences. *J. Biol. Chem.* 270:29083–89

68. Behrooz A, Ismail-Beigi F. 1997. Dual control of GLUT1 glucose transporter gene expression by hypoxia and by inhibition of oxidative phosphorylation. *J. Biol. Chem.* 272:5555–62

69. Goldberg MA, Glass GA, Cunningham JM, Bunn HF. 1987. The regulated expression of erythropoietin by two human hepatoma cell lines. *Proc. Natl. Acad. Sci. USA* 84:7972–76

70. Semenza GL, Dureza RC, Traystman MD, Gearhart JD, Antonarakis SE. 1990. Human erythropoietin gene expression in transgenic mice: multiple transcription initiation sites and *cis*-acting regulatory elements. *Mol. Cell. Biol.* 10:930–38

71. Semenza GL, Nejfelt MK, Chi SM, Antonarakis SE. 1991. Hypoxia-inducible nuclear factors bind to an enhancer element located 3′ to the human erythropoietin gene. *Proc. Natl. Acad. Sci. USA* 88:5680–84

72. Beck I, Ramirez S, Weinmann R, Caro J. 1991. Enhancer element at the 3′-flanking region controls transcriptional response to hypoxia in the human erythropoietin gene. *J. Biol. Chem.* 266:15563–66

73. Pugh CW, Tan CC, Jones RW, Ratcliffe PJ. 1991. Functional analysis of an oxygen-regulated transcriptional enhancer lying 3′ to the mouse erythropoietin gene. *Proc. Natl. Acad. Sci. USA* 88:10553–57

74. Necas E, Thorling EB. 1972. Unresponsiveness of erythropoietin-producing cells to cyanide. *Am. J. Physiol.* 222:1187–90

75. Goldberg MA, Dunning SP, Bunn HF. 1988. Regulation of the erythropoietin gene: evidence that the oxygen sensor is a heme protein. *Science* 242:1412–15

76. Chandel NS, Maltepe E, Goldwasser E, Mathieu CE, Simon MC, et al. 1998. Mitochondrial reactive oxygen species trigger hypoxia-induced transcription. *Proc. Natl. Acad. Sci. USA* 95:11715–20

77. Stea A, Jackson A, Nurse CA. 1992. Hypoxia and $N^6,O^{2'}$-dibutyryladenosine 3′,5′-cyclic monophosphate, but not nerve growth factor, induce Na^+ channels and hypertrophy in chromaffin-like arterial chemoreceptors. *Proc. Natl. Acad. Sci. USA* 89:9469–73

78. Espejo EF, Montoro RJ, Armengol JA, López-Barneo J. 1998. Cellular and functional recovery of Parkinsonian rats after intrastriatal transplantation of carotid body cell aggregates. *Neuron* 20:197–206

79. Donnelly DF, Doyle TP. 1994. Developmental changes in hypoxia-induced catecholamine release from rat carotid body, in vitro. *J. Physiol.* 475:267–75

80. Hatton CJ, Carpenter E, Pepper DR, Kumar P, Peers C. 1997. Developmental changes in isolated rat type I carotid body cell K^+ currents and their modulation by hypoxia. *J. Physiol.* 501:49–58

81. Wyatt CN, Wright C, Bee D, Peers C. 1995. O_2-sensitive K^+ currents in carotid body chemoreceptor cells from normoxic and chronically hypoxic rats and their roles in hypoxic chemotransduction. *Proc. Natl. Acad. Sci. USA* 92:295–99

82. Sterni LM, Bamford OS, Wasicko MJ, Carroll JL. 1999. Chronic hypoxia abolished the postnatal increase in carotid body type

I cell sensitivity to hypoxia. *Am. J. Physiol. Lung Cell Mol. Physiol.* 277:L645–L52

83. Benot AR, López-Barneo J. 1990. Feedback inhibition of Ca^{2+} currents by dopamine in glomus cells of the carotid body. *Eur. J. Neurosci.* 2:809–12

84. Czyzyk-Krzeska MF, Bayliss DA, Lawson EE, Millhorn DE. 1992. Regulation of tyrosine hydroxylase gene expression in the rat carotid body by hypoxia. *J. Neurochem.* 58:1538–46

85. Czyzyk-Krzeska MF, Beresh JE. 1996. Characterization of the hypoxia-inducible protein binding site within the pyrimidine-rich tract in the 3′-untranslated region of the tyrosine hydroxylase mRNA. *J. Biol. Chem.* 271:3293–99

86. López-Barneo J. 1994. Oxygen-sensitive ion channels: how ubiquitous are they? *Trends Neurosci.* 17:133–35

87. Ganfornina MD, López-Barneo J. 1992. Potassium channel types in arterial chemoreceptor cells and their selective modulation by oxygen. *J. Gen. Physiol.* 100:401–26

88. Ganfornina MD, López-Barneo J. 1992. Gating of O_2-sensitive K^+ channels of arterial chemoreceptor cells and kinetic modifications induced by low PO_2. *J. Gen. Physiol.* 100:427–55

89. Wyatt CN, Peers C. 1995. Ca^{2+}-activated K^+ channels in isolated type I cells of the neonatal rat carotid body. *J. Physiol.* 483:559–65

90. Ju YK, Saint DA, Gage PW. 1996. Hypoxia increases persistent sodium current in rat ventricular myocytes. *J. Physiol.* 497:337–47

91. Buckler KJ, Williams BA, Honoré E. 2000. An oxygen-, acid- and anaesthetic-sensitive TASK-like background potassium channel in rat arterial chemoreceptor cells. *J. Physiol.* 525:135–42

92. Cornfield DN, Reeve HL, Tolarova S, Weir EK, Archer S. 1996. Oxygen causes fetal pulmonary vasodilation through activation of a calcium-dependent potassium chan-nel. *Proc. Natl. Acad. Sci. USA* 93:8089–94

93. Thompson RJ, Nurse CA. 1998. Anoxia differentially modulates multiple K^+ currents and depolarizes neonatal rat adrenal chromaffin cells. *J. Physiol.* 512:421–34

94. López-Barneo J, Montoro R, Ortega-Sáenz P, Ureña J. 1998. Oxygen-regulated ion channels: functional roles and mechanisms. See Ref. 2, pp. 127–44

95. López-Barneo J, Ortega-Sáenz P, Molina A, Franco-Obregón A, Ureña J, Castellano A. 1997. Oxygen sensing by ion channels. *Kidney Int.* 51:454–61

96. Archer SL, Huang J, Henry T, Peterson D, Weir EK. 1993. A redox-based O_2 sensor in rat pulmonary vasculature. *Circ. Res.* 73:1100–12

97. Benot AR, Ganfornina MD, López-Barneo J. 1993. Potassium channel modulated by hypoxia and the redox status in glomus cells of the carotid body. In *Ion Flux in Pulmonary Vascular Control*, ed. EK Weir, JR Hume, JT Reeves, pp. 177–87. New York: Plenum

98. Yuan XJ, Tod ML, Rubin LJ, Blaustein MP. 1994. Deoxyglucose and reduced glutathione mimic effects of hypoxia on K^+ and Ca^{2+} conductances in pulmonary artery cells. *Am. J. Physiol. Lung Cell Mol. Physiol.* 267:L52–L63

99. Ruppersberg JP, Stocker M, Pongs O, Heinemann SH, Frank R, Koenen M. 1991. Regulation of fast inactivation of cloned mammalian IK(A) channels by cysteine oxidation. *Nature* 352:711–14

100. Vega-Sáenz de Miera E, Rudy B. 1992. Modulation of K^+ channels by hydrogen peroxide. *Biochem. Biophys. Res. Commun.* 186:1681–87

101. Duprat F, Guillemare E, Romey G, Fink M, Lesage F, et al. 1995. Susceptibility of cloned K^+ channels to reactive oxygen species. *Proc. Natl. Acad. Sci. USA* 92:11796–800

102. Ortega-Sáenz GP, Castellano A, Molina A, López-Barneo J. 1996. Regulation by

O_2 tension of recombinant K^+ channels. *Eur. J. Neurosci.* S9:14 (Abstr.)

103. Fearon IM, Palmer AC, Balmforth AJ, Ball SG, Mikala G, et al. 1997. Hypoxia inhibits the recombinant $\alpha 1C$ subunit of the human cardiac L-type Ca^{2+} channel. *J. Physiol.* 500:551–56

104. López-Barneo J. 1997. Perspectives on oxygen sensing: Recombinant Ca^{2+} channels get O_2 sensitive. *J. Physiol.* 500: 3

105. Patel AJ, Lazdunski M, Honoré E. 1997. Kv2.1/Kv9.3, a novel ATP-dependent delayed-rectifier K^+ channel in oxygen-sensitive pulmonary artery myocytes. *EMBO J.* 16:6615–25

106. Conforti L, Bodi I, Nisbet JW, Millhorn DE. 2000. O_2-sensitive K^+ channels: role of the Kv1.2 α-subunit in mediating the hypoxic response. *J. Physiol.* 524:783–93

107. Wang J, Juhaszova M, Rubin LJ, Yuan XJ. 1997. Hypoxia inhibits gene expression of voltage-gated K^+ channel α subunits in pulmonary artery smooth muscle cells. *J. Clin. Invest.* 100:2347–53

108. Hulme JT, Coppock EA, Felipe A, Martens JR, Tamkun MM. 1999. Oxygen sensitivity of cloned voltage-gated K^+ channels expressed in the pulmonary vasculature. *Circ. Res.* 85:489–97

109. Osipenko ON, Tate RJ, Gurney AM. 2000. Potential role for kv3.1b channels as oxygen sensors. *Circ. Res.* 86:534–40

110. Pérez-García MT, López-López JR, González C. 1999. Kvb1.2 subunit coexpression in HEK293 cells confers O_2 sensitivity to Kv4.2 but not to *Shaker* channels. *J. Gen. Physiol.* 113:897–907

111. Semenza GL, Wang GL. 1992. A nuclear factor induced by hypoxia via de novo protein synthesis binds to the human erythropoietin gene enhancer at a site required for transcriptional activation. *Mol. Cell. Biol.* 12:5447–54

112. Maxwell PH, Pugh CW, Ratcliffe PJ. 1993. Inducible operation of the erythropoietin $3'$ enhancer in multiple cell lines: evidence for a widespread oxygen-sensing mechanism. *Proc. Natl. Acad. Sci. USA* 90:2423–27

113. Wang GL, Semenza GL. 1993. Characterization of hypoxia-inducible factor 1 and regulation of DNA binding activity by hypoxia. *J. Biol. Chem.* 268:21513–18

114. Wang GL, Semenza GL. 1995. Purification and characterization of hypoxia-inducible factor 1. *J. Biol. Chem.* 270:1230–37

115. Semenza GL. 2000. HIF-1: mediator of physiological and pathophysiological responses to hypoxia. *J. Appl. Physiol.* 88:1474–80

116. Wang GL, Jiang BH, Rue EA, Semenza GL. 1995. Hypoxia-inducible factor 1 is a basic-helix-loop-helix-PAS heterodimer regulated by cellular O_2 tension. *Proc. Natl. Acad. Sci. USA* 92:5510–14

117. Jiang BH, Semenza GL, Bauer C, Marti HH. 1996. Hypoxia-inducible factor 1 levels vary exponentially over a physiologically relevant range of O_2 tension. *Am. J. Physiol. Cell Physiol.* 271:C1172–C80

118. Huang LE, Arany Z, Livingston DM, Bunn HF. 1996. Activation of hypoxia-inducible transcription factor depends primarily upon redox-sensitive stabilization of its α subunit. *J. Biol. Chem.* 271:32253–59

119. Huang LE, Gu J, Schau M, Bunn HF. 1998. Regulation of hypoxia-inducible factor 1α is mediated by an O_2-dependent degradation domain via the ubiquitin-proteasome pathway. *Proc. Natl. Acad. Sci. USA* 95:7987–92

120. Salceda S, Caro J. 1997. Hypoxia-inducible factor 1α (HIF-1α) protein is rapidly degraded by the ubiquitin-proteasome system under normoxic conditions. Its stabilization by hypoxia depends on redox-induced changes. *J. Biol. Chem.* 272:22642–47

121. Ema M, Hirota K, Mimura J, Abe H,

Yodoi J, et al. 1999. Molecular mechanisms of transcription activation by HLF and HIF1α in response to hypoxia: their stabilization and redox signal-induced interaction with CBP/p300. *EMBO J.* 18:1905–14

122. Kallio PJ, Wilson WJ, O'Brien S, Makino Y, Poellinger L. 1999. Regulation of the hypoxia-inducible transcription factor 1α by the ubiquitin-proteasome pathway. *J. Biol. Chem.* 274:6519–25

123. Kroll SL, Paulding WR, Schnell PO, Barton MC, Conaway JW, et al. 1999. von Hippel-Lindau protein induces hypoxia-regulated arrest of tyrosine hydroxylase transcript elongation in pheochromocytoma cells. *J. Biol. Chem.* 274:30109–14

124. Maxwell PH, Wiesener MS, Chang GW, Clifford SC, Vaux EC, et al. 1999. The tumour suppressor protein VHL targets hypoxia-inducible factors for oxygen-dependent proteolysis. *Nature* 399:271–75

125. Conrad PW, Freeman TL, Beitner-Johnson D, Millhorn DE. 1999. EPAS1 *trans*-activation during hypoxia requires p42/p44 MAPK. *J. Biol. Chem.* 274:33709–13

126. Millhorn DE, Beitner-Johnson D, Conforti L, Conrad PW, Kobayashi S, et al. 2000. Gene regulation during hypoxia in excitable oxygen-sensing cells: depolarization-transcription coupling. *Adv. Exp. Med. Biol.* 475:131–42

127. Gilles-González MA, Ditta GS, Helinski DR. 1991. A haemoprotein with kinase activity encoded by the oxygen sensor of *Rhizobium meliloti*. *Nature* 350:170–72

128. López-López JR, González C. 1992. Time course of K+ current inhibition by low oxygen in chemoreceptor cells of adult rabbit carotid body. Effects of carbon monoxide. *FEBS Lett.* 299:251–54

129. Srinivas V, Zhu X, Salceda S, Nakamura R, Caro J. 1998. Hypoxia-inducible factor 1α (HIF-1α) is a non-heme iron protein.

Implications for oxygen sensing. *J. Biol. Chem.* 273:18019–22

130. Overholt JL, Ficker E, Yang T, Shams H, Bright GR, et al. 2000. HERG-like potassium current regulates the resting membrane potential in glomus cells of the rabbit carotid body. *J. Neurophysiol.* 83:1150–57

131. Cross AR, Henderson L, Jones OT, Delpiano MA, Hentschel J, et al. 1990. Involvement of an NAD(P)H oxidase as a pO2 sensor protein in the rat carotid body. *Biochem. J.* 272:743–47

132. Acker H. 1994. Mechanisms and meaning of cellular oxygen sensing in the organism. *Respir. Physiol.* 95:1–10

133. Fearon IM, Palmer AC, Balmforth AJ, Ball SG, Varadi G, et al. 1999. Modulation of recombinant human cardiac L-type Ca2+ channel α1C subunits by redox agents and hypoxia. *J. Physiol.* 514:629–37

134. Wang D, Youngson C, Wong V, Yeger H, Dinauer MC, et al. 1996. NADPH-oxidase and a hydrogen peroxide-sensitive K+ channel may function as an oxygen sensor complex in airway chemoreceptors and small cell lung carcinoma cell lines. *Proc. Natl. Acad. Sci. USA* 93:13182–87

135. O'Kelly I, Lewis A, Peers C, Kemp PJ. 2000. O2 sensing by airway chemoreceptor-derived cells. Protein kinase C activation reveals functional evidence for involvement of NADPH oxidase. *J. Biol. Chem.* 275:7684–92

136. Fu XW, Wang D, Nurse CA, Dinauer MC, Cutz E. 2000. NADPH oxidase is an O2 sensor in airway chemoreceptors: evidence from K+ current modulation in wild-type and oxidase-deficient mice. *Proc. Natl. Acad. Sci. USA* 97:4374–79

137. Archer SL, Reeve HL, Michelakis E, Puttagunta L, Waite R, et al. 1999. O2 sensing is preserved in mice lacking the gp91 phox subunit of NADPH oxidase. *Proc. Natl. Acad. Sci. USA* 96:7944–49

138. Wenger RH, Marti HH, Schuerer-Maly CC, Kvietikova I, Bauer C, et al. 1996. Hypoxic induction of gene expression in chronic granulomatous disease-derived B-cell lines: oxygen sensing is independent of the cytochrome b558-containing nicotinamide adenine dinucleotide phosphate oxidase. *Blood* 87:756–61

139. Dvorakova M, Höhler B, Vollerthun R, Fischbach T, Kummer W. 2000. Macrophages: a major source of cytochrome b558 in the rat carotid body. *Brain Res.* 852:349–54

140. Duchen MR, Biscoe TJ. 1992. Relative mitochondrial membrane potential and $[Ca^{2+}]_i$ in type I cells isolated from the rabbit carotid body. *J. Physiol.* 450:33–61

141. Chandel NS, McClintock DS, Feliciano CE, Wood TM, Melendez JA, et al. 2000. Reactive oxygen species generated at mitochondrial complex III stabilize HIF-1α during hypoxia: a mechanism of O_2 sensing. *J. Biol. Chem.* 275:25130–38

142. Chandel NS, Schumacker PT. 2000. Cellular oxygen sensing by mitochondria: old questions, new insight. *J. Appl. Physiol.* 88:1880–89

143. Pardal R, López-Barneo J. 2000. Differential effects of mitochondrial inhibitors on the hypoxia sensitivity of glomus cells in slices of rat carotid body. *Eur. J. Neurosci.* 12(11):499 (Abstr.)

144. Eu JP, Sun J, Xu L, Stamler J, Meissner G. 2000. The skeletal muscle calcium release channel: coupled O_2 sensor and NO signaling function. *Cell* 102:499–509

145. Carmeliet P, Dor Y, Herbert JM, Fukumura D, Brusselmans K, et al. 1998. Role of HIF-1α in hypoxia-mediated apoptosis, cell proliferation and tumour angiogenesis. *Nature* 394:485–90

146. Halterman MW, Miller CC, Federoff HJ. 1999. Hypoxia-inducible factor-1α mediates hypoxia-induced delayed neuronal death that involves p53. *J. Neurosci.* 19:6818–24

Annu. Rev. Physiol. 2001. 63:289–325

EVOLUTION AND PHYSIOLOGICAL ROLES OF PHOSPHAGEN SYSTEMS

W Ross Ellington

Department of Biological Science and Institute of Molecular Biophysics, Florida State University, Tallahassee, Florida 32306-4370; e-mail: elling@bio.fsu.edu

Key Words   phosphagen kinases, ATP buffering, energy transport, intracellular targeting and compartmentation

■ **Abstract**   Phosphagens are phosphorylated guanidino compounds that are linked to energy state and ATP hydrolysis by corresponding phosphagen kinase reactions: phosphagen + MgADP + H$^+$ ↔ guanidine acceptor + MgATP. Eight different phosphagens (and corresponding phosphagen kinases) are found in the animal kingdom distributed along distinct phylogenetic lines. By far, the creatine phosphate/creatine kinase (CP/CK) system, which is found in the vertebrates and is widely distributed throughout the lower chordates and invertebrates, is the most extensively studied phosphagen system. Phosphagen kinase reactions function in temporal ATP buffering, in regulating inorganic phosphate (Pi) levels, which impacts glycogenolysis and proton buffering, and in intracellular energy transport. Phosphagen kinase reactions show differences in thermodynamic poise, and the phosphagens themselves differ in terms of certain physical properties including intrinsic diffusivity. This review evaluates the distribution of phosphagen systems and tissue-specific expression of certain phosphagens in an evolutionary and functional context. The role of phosphagens in regulation of intracellular Pi levels likely evolved early. Thermodynamic poise of the phosphagen kinase reaction profoundly impacts this capacity. Furthermore, it is hypothesized that the capacity for intracellular targeting of CK evolved early as a means of facilitating energy transport in highly polarized cells and was subsequently exploited for temporal ATP buffering and dynamic roles in metabolic regulation in cells displaying high and variable rates of aerobic energy production.

INTRODUCTION

Cells possess three major forms of so-called energy currency: the chemical potential of ATP hydrolysis and sodium and proton ionic gradients (1). The energy content of ATP is not fixed but rather is a function of how far the ATP hydrolysis reaction is displaced from equilibrium as expressed by the following equation (2–4):

$$\Delta G_{ATP} = \Delta G^{o'} + R \cdot T \cdot \ln \{(ATP) \cdot [(ADP)(Pi)]\}^{-1}$$

0066-4278/01/0315-0289$14.00

(where ΔG_{ATP} is the effective free energy change of hydrolysis and $\Delta G^{o'}$ is the free change of hydrolysis under standard conditions). Under normal physiological conditions, oxidative phosphorylation maintains the ATP hydrolysis reaction far displaced from equilibrium, thereby producing ΔG_{ATP} values exceeding -60 kJ/mole in certain cells (3).

The importance of ΔG_{ATP} levels in normal and pathophysiological processes is rather clear-cut (3). The supplementary roles of phosphagens are critical, especially in cells displaying high and variable rates of energy turnover such as muscles, neurons, and primitive-type spermatozoa. Phosphagens are phosphorylated guanidine compounds that are linked to ATP by way of a reversible reaction catalyzed by phosphagen (guanidino) kinases (phosphagen + MgADP + H^+ ↔ guanidine acceptor + MgATP). The traditional and conventional view is that phosphagens function as ATP buffers permitting maintenance of high ΔG_{ATP} values during periods in which there is a disequilibrium of ATP supply and demand (2, 3). Phosphagens also play a number of other roles, including regulation of glycogenolysis, proton buffering, and intracellular energy transport. A diverse array of different phosphagens and corresponding phosphagen kinases is present in the animal kingdom. The purpose of the present review is to highlight major advances in our understanding of the phosphagen systems and place these observations in a functional and evolutionary context.

PHOSPHAGEN SYSTEMS

Phosphagens and Phosphagen (Guanidino) Kinases

Eight phosphagens have been identified (Figure 1); all have the characteristic guanidino group but differ dramatically in terms of other chemical features. These compounds range from arginine phosphate (AP), an unmodified amino acid, to thalassemine phosphate (ThP), which is a highly modified guanidino compound (Figure 1). AP and ThP, as well as the other phosphagens [creatine phosphate (CP), glycocyamine phosphate (GP), taurocyamine phosphate (TP), hypotaurocyamine phosphate (HTP), lombricine phosphate (LP), and opheline phosphate (OP)] can be classified on the basis of similarities in terms of chemistry and biosynthetic pathway (discussed below). LP is unique in that contains a D-serine moiety in annelids and an L-serine moiety in echiuroids, a group of marine worms (5).

Each phosphagen has its own corresponding phosphagen kinase: arginine kinase (AK), thalassemine kinase (ThK), creatine kinase (CK), glycocyamine kinase (GK), taurocyamine kinase (TK), hypotaurocyamine kinase (HTK), lombricine kinase (LK) and opheline kinase (OK). CK, GK, and AK are rigidly specific for their respective substrates creatine/CP, glycocyamine/GP, and arginine/AP (6). In contrast, TK, HTK, LK, OK, and ThK are broadly specific and display varying degrees of activity when presented with taurocyamine/TP, hypotaurocyamine/HTP, lombricine/LP, opheline/OP, and/or thalassemine/ThP (6, 7). Phosphagen kinases

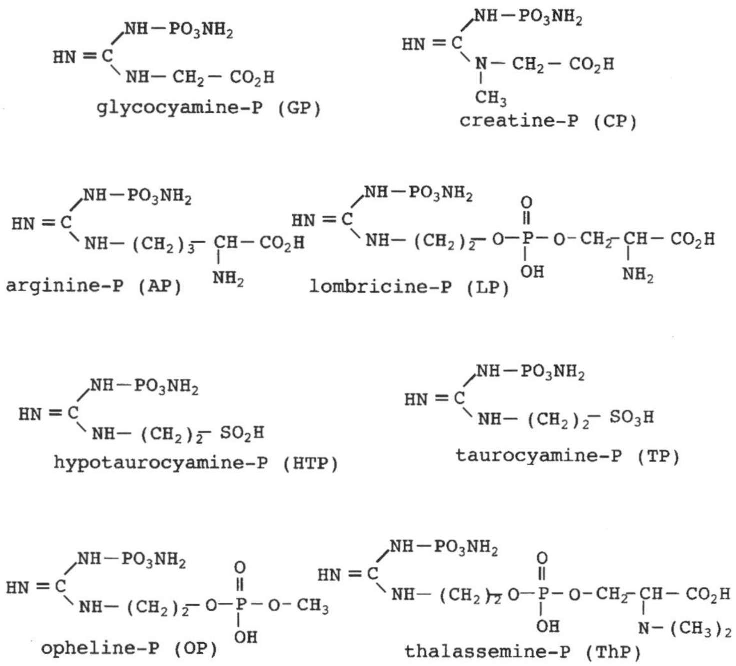

$$HN = C \begin{cases} NH-PO_3NH_2 \\ NH-CH_2-CO_2H \end{cases}$$
glycocyamine-P (GP)

$$HN = C \begin{cases} NH-PO_3NH_2 \\ N-CH_2-CO_2H \\ \quad CH_3 \end{cases}$$
creatine-P (CP)

$$HN = C \begin{cases} NH-PO_3NH_2 \\ NH-(CH_2)_3-CH-CO_2H \\ \qquad\qquad NH_2 \end{cases}$$
arginine-P (AP)

$$HN = C \begin{cases} NH-PO_3NH_2 \\ NH-(CH_2)_2-O-\overset{O}{\underset{OH}{P}}-O-CH_2-CH-CO_2H \\ \qquad\qquad\qquad\qquad\qquad NH_2 \end{cases}$$
lombricine-P (LP)

$$HN = C \begin{cases} NH-PO_3NH_2 \\ NH-(CH_2)_2-SO_2H \end{cases}$$
hypotaurocyamine-P (HTP)

$$HN = C \begin{cases} NH-PO_3NH_2 \\ NH-(CH_2)_2-SO_3H \end{cases}$$
taurocyamine-P (TP)

$$HN = C \begin{cases} NH-PO_3NH_2 \\ NH-(CH_2)_2-O-\overset{O}{\underset{OH}{P}}-O-CH_3 \end{cases}$$
opheline-P (OP)

$$HN = C \begin{cases} NH-PO_3NH_2 \\ NH-(CH_2)_2-O-\overset{O}{\underset{OH}{P}}-O-CH_2-CH-CO_2H \\ \qquad\qquad\qquad\qquad\qquad N-(CH_3)_2 \end{cases}$$
thalassemine-P (ThP)

Figure 1 Structures of the phosphagens.

constitute a highly conserved family of enzymes which, in addition to differences in guanidine specificity, also display major differences in quaternary structure, as well as capacity for intracellular targeting.

Distribution of Phosphagen Systems in the Animal Kingdom

CP and AP were first discovered in the late 1920s in vertebrate and crayfish muscle, respectively. CP was originally thought to be the vertebrate phosphagen, but this compound and CK were subsequently found in the tissues of higher and lower invertebrates, as well as a other chordates (reviewed extensively in 5, 8–12). AP and AK were also subsequently observed in other invertebrates and in some chordates (12). The remaining phosphagens and corresponding phosphagen kinases were discovered later, exclusively in the tissues of worm-like marine groups (5, 9).

Figure 2 maps the distribution of phosphagen systems on a phylogenetic tree of the major invertebrate and chordate groups. The AP system is widely distributed throughout. Surprisingly, sponges, which are at the base of the metazoan line, have been shown to contain CP/CK (13, 14). This observation has been recently confirmed via isolation and physico-chemical characterization of a sponge CK (15). Ecdysozoans, which contain the arthropods as the major group, have the AP/AK system only. Lophotrochozoans show a diversity of phosphagens

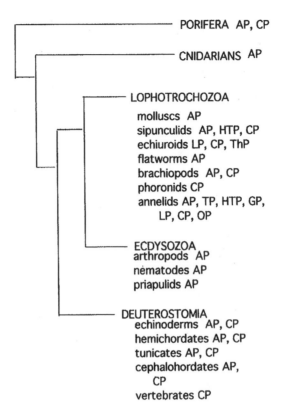

Figure 2 Distribution of phosphagen systems mapped on a well-accepted phylogenetic tree for the major metazoan groups. In this tree, the traditional protostomes are thought to have diverged into two clades: the lophotrochozoans and the ecdysozoans. Abbreviations for the phosphagen systems are as described in the text. The mapping was constructed on data from previous reviews (5–12). In most cases, phosphagen system was validated by presence of activity of the corresponding phosphagen kinase. Some data for sipunculids, echiuroids, and brachiopods are based on unpublished results (WR Ellington).

(Figure 2). Some groups such as mollusks and flatworms have been shown to contain only AP/AK, whereas others display a spectacular diversity. This is particularly true of the polychaetous annelids that as a group contain seven different phosphagen systems. As groups, lower chordates and the deuterostome invertebrates contain both the AP/AK and CP/CK systems, whereas CP/CK is the only phosphagen system present in the vertebrates (Figure 2).

There are some interesting patterns of tissue-specific expression of phosphagens in certain organisms. In a variety of groups (sipunculids, echiuroids, polychaetes, echinoderms, tunicates) regardless of which phosphagen system is expressed in somatic cells and/or eggs, the CP/CK system is virtually always present in the spermatozoa (16). This association with spermatozoa is discussed elsewhere in this review.

There are examples of multiple phosphagen systems being present in the same tissue. This phenomenon was first observed in echinoderm muscles, which appear to contain both the CP and AP systems (17). In recent studies, Ellington (18) has shown using ^{31}P-NMR methods, enzyme assays, enzyme-linked metabolite assays, and immunofluoresence microscopy techniques that the CP/CK and AP/AK systems are indeed present in sea urchin muscle and, possibly, coexist in the same fibers. This so-called pluriphosphagen phenomenon (9) is also widespread in polychaetes where as many as three different phosphagen systems may coexist in the same tissue (5, 9, 19). The physiological significance, if any, of pluriphosphagens remains to be elucidated (20).

Evolution of Phosphagen Kinases

The character mapping of phosphagen distribution in the metazoans reveals that the CP/CK and AP/AK systems are widespread. The remaining phosphagens have a much narrower distribution. Obviously, for a system to operate both the guanidine acceptor and the phosphagen kinase must be present. (Guanidine biosynthesis and transport is discussed below.) This section briefly reviews the current state of our understanding of the evolution of phosphagen kinases.

The recent development of rapid and efficient methods for the determination of cDNA and deduced amino acid sequences of phosphagen kinases has resulted in a robust sequence database that has shed some light on the evolution of phosphagen systems. Figure 3 is a phylogenetic tree constructed using sequences from 10 AKs, 14 CKs, an LK (from the earthworm *Eisenia*), a GK (from the polychaete *Neanthes*), and a contiguous dimeric phosphagen kinase of uncertain guanidine specificity (*Schistosoma* D1 and D2). Two superclusters are evident consisting of all AKs, excluding sea cucumber AK, and all CKs and LK and GK. AK from the sea cucumber *Stichopus*, a deuterostome invertebrate, is found within the CK/LK/GK clade (Figure 3), indicating that it likely evolved secondarily from a CK-like ancestor.

The above phylogenetic results provide historical insight into patterns of distribution of phosphagen systems in extant organisms. It is likely AK and CK evolved early in the course of metazoan evolution. These two distinct clades had different evolutionary trajectories. CK is present in the most primitive off all metazoans, the sponges (15). The CK gene underwent multiple gene duplication events ultimately resulting in the production of GK and LK, as well as the multiple isoforms characteristic of CKs (flagellar, M, B, and mitochondrial). Note that the mitochondrial isoform evolved very early.

Because LK, TK, HTK, OK, and ThK freely use each others respective guanidine substrates (6, 7), it seems likely that the latter four enzymes also evolved within the CK clade. The selective forces driving the evolution of these enzymes and GK remain obscure (5). It should be noted that GK, LK, TK, HTK, OK, and ThK are restricted to lophotrocozoan groups (Figure 2).

The AK clade is found in cnidarians and members of the two major protostome groups (Figures 2 and 3). Recently, a cDNA for AK from the eukaryotic protozoan

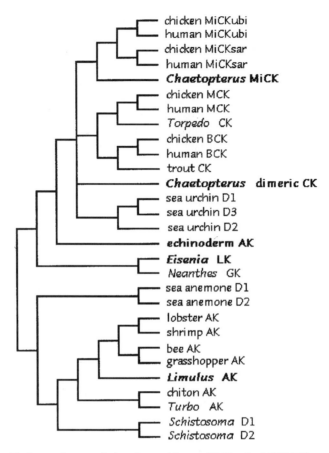

Figure 3 Phylogenetic tree of phosphagen kinases (G Pineda & WR Ellington, unpublished data). Sequence data are from (21, 22). Abbreviations: D1, domain 1 of two or three-domain phosphagen kinase; D2, domain 2; D3, domain 3; B, brain type; M, muscle type. Species identification where not obvious: *Limulus* (horseshoe crab), *C. elegans* (nematode), *Drosophila* (fruit fly), *Schistosoma* (flat worm), *Pseudocardium* (bivalve mollusk), and *Battilus* (gastropod mollusk). Note that guanidine specificity of *Schistosoma* phosphagen kinase (PK) is unclear.

Trypanosoma cruzi was cloned and sequenced (23). This AK clusters with arthropod AKs indicating that this is an ancient lineage, although it is possible that AK in *T. cruzi* was acquired by horizontal gene transfer (23). It is thought that arthropods were the earliest hosts of these parasites.

The independent evolution of echinoderm AK within the CK clade is of great interest as it clearly points to the possibility that AKs in lower chordates (Figure 2) also evolved from CK. Again, the factors underlying the secondary acquisition of the AP/AK system in the deuterostomes remain unclear but could potentially be related to functional factors. Interestingly, the major protostome groups, arthropods and mollusks, possess AK only. The lack of other phosphagen kinases is particularly perplexing in mollusks because most of the lophotrochozoans display a diversity of other phosphagen systems.

Suffice it to say, both the AP/AK and CP/CK systems evolved very early, at the dawn of the radiation of the metazoa. GK, LK, TK, HTK, OK, and ThK arose from a CK-like ancestor most likely after the divergence of the ecdysozoan and lophotrochozoan protostome groups. The traditional characterization of the evolutionary progression of phosphagen systems from primitive (AP/AK) to advanced (CP/CK) (11, 12) is not consistent with available data. These observations and conclusions lead to a fundamental question: Can the evolution, distribution in various animal groups, and selective expression in certain cell types of the various phosphagen systems be explained on the basis of unique differences in functional/physiological properties? To answer this question we address issues relating to biosynthesis/transport, physico-chemical properties, distribution/concentrations in various cells, and intracellular targeting of phosphagen kinases and view these issues in the context of the three, well-established physiological roles of phosphagen systems.

PROPERTIES OF PHOSPHAGEN SYSTEMS

Biosynthesis and Transport of Guanidine Acceptors

In addition to the presence of the phosphagen kinase, for a phosphagen system to exist there must be sufficient quantities of the respective guanidine acceptor present, as well as a mechanism for provisioning these compounds. With the exception of L-arginine, all other guanidine substrates of the phosphagen kinases exist as dead-end compounds in that they exist solely to be phosphorylated and dephosphorylated. As such, one can view the acquisition of both the substrate and the phosphagen kinase as coevolutionary events.

Arginine plays a special role in phosphagen systems, as a substrate of AK but also as an aid in the formation of other guanidine acceptors via transamidation reactions (24). Transamidation reactions are catalyzed by corresponding amidinotransferases (AMT) (Figure 4). AMT activities generally appear to be widely distributed, but the properties of these enzymes and their evolutionary relationships are poorly understood (19). However, arginine-glycine transamidase [forms glycocyamine (guanidinoacetate)] (Figure 4) appears to be absent in all invertebrates investigated thus far (19, 25).

Biosynthesis of creatine, thalassemine, and opheline also requires the participation of guanidine methyltransferases (GMT), as shown in Figure 4. GMTs for these latter two guanidine compounds have not been extensively investigated. Considerable effort has been made to determine whether glycocyamine methyltransferase (glycocyamine + S-adenosyl-methionine $\rightarrow$ creatine + S-adenosyl-homocysteine) is present in invertebrates possessing high tissue levels

Figure 4 Biosynthetic pathways for the guanidine acceptors.

Amidinotransferase (AMT):
Arginine + Acceptor --> Guanidine + Ornithine

Guanidine Methyltransferase (GMT):
S-Adenosyl-Methionine + Guanidine -->
    Methylguanidine + S-Adenosyl-Homocysteine

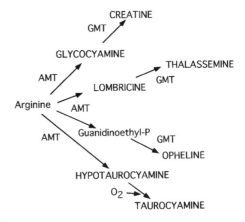

of creatine/CP. The available evidence indicates that invertebrates and all lower chordates, including the protochordate *Branchiostoma*, lack glycocyamine methyltransferase (19, 25). This observation, coupled with the absence of arginine-glycine amidotransferase activities, indicates that these organisms lack the capacity for creatine biosynthesis and thus must rely on dietary acquisition of this guanidine (25).

Vertebrates by and large are fully capable of creatine biosynthesis (25, 26). In humans, the biosynthetic enzymes are located in the liver and pancreas (26). Glycocyamine methyltransferase deficiency, a rare in-born error of metabolism, leads to a pathological state in which glycocyamine accumulates in the brain (27). In vertebrates, de novo creatine synthesis is supplemented by dietary uptake (26). In recent years, there has been considerable interest in and controversy over creatine loading in humans and the functional impact in terms of performance (or lack thereof) (28–33).

Regardless of the source of creatine in vertebrates, the compound must be transported into muscles, neurons, and other cells via a plasma membrane transporter (recently reviewed in 34). This Na^+: creatine transporter is present in fish (35) and higher vertebrates. It is a member of the large organic solute transporter family (35) and has been the subject of intensive molecular characterization in recent years (for instance see 35–40).

Creatine/CP pool sizes in certain invertebrates and lower chordates can be substantial. However, it is clear that these organisms are incapable of creatine biosynthesis and must obtain this material from exogenous sources. It has been shown that a variety of species ranging from sponges to protochordates are capable of taking up creatine from seawater (25, 41), presumably via a transporter system similar to the ones present in the vertebrates. The molecular characteristics of such putative transporters remain to be elucidated. Dietary sources of creatine are unique to particular species. Because creatine is non-enzymatically converted to creatinine (42), a cyclic derivative, there is a slow turnover of the creatine/CP pool in all organisms, for which there must be compensation. Given the absence of creatine biosynthetic capacity in invertebrates and lower chordates, the process of acquisition and transport becomes paramount and constitutes an interesting problem for future research.

Physico-Chemical Properties of Phosphagens

It has long been recognized that CP is more acid labile than the other phosphagens (43), owing to the methyl group in the guanidine region of creatine, which eliminates almost all resonance states thus producing an extremely labile phosphagen (44–47). This methyl group is replaced by a proton in all other phosphagens. This difference in stability impacts physico-chemical properties as these relate to the phosphoryl transfer reactions that utilize these compounds. Thus the apparent equilibrium constant for the CK reaction $[K' = (ATP) \cdot (creatine) \cdot (ADP) \cdot (CP)^{-1}]$ ranges from 80 to 160 under quasi-physiological conditions of pH and free Mg^{2+} (48), whereas the K' for the AK reaction is lower (49).

The relative thermodynamic poise of five major phosphagen kinase reactions has been determined by Ellington (20). The apparent K' values for these reactions as determined at pH 7.25, 35°C, and 1–2 mM free Mg^{2+} were as follows: $K'_{CK} = 100$ (48), $K'_{LK} = 32.3$, $K'_{TK} = 29.3$, $K'_{GK} = 29.0$, and $K'_{AK} = 13.2$ (20). Kamp et al (50) found a similar value for the K'_{TK}. These thermodynamic differences may have significant implications in terms of the ATP-buffering properties of phosphagen systems (see below).

K' values for phosphagen kinase are dependent on free Mg^{2+} concentrations, temperature, ionic strength, and pH. The above dependencies for the CK and AK reactions have recently been analyzed and characterized in great detail by Dobson and coworkers (51–54). Reductions in pH dramatically increase the K' for both reactions, but the physiological impact is much greater for CK because of the higher thermodynamic poise of this reaction.

An additional physico-chemical property is worth considering. Phosphagens are thought to play a major physiological role in intracellular energy transport. As such, differences in intrinsic diffusivity could impact such a physiological role. The various phosphagens differ considerably in terms of relative molecular mass (M_r) (Figure 1) and, as a consequence, molecular volume. This is reflected in differences in diffusion coefficients (D), which are inversely related to M_r (Figure 5). That is, the smallest phosphagens (GP and CP) have the highest diffusion coefficients. In the case of GP, the D value is nearly twice that of MgATP. It should be noted that the above D values for CP and ATP determined in vitro are roughly two times higher than values in living muscle fibers determined by pulsed gradient NMR spectroscopy (55, 56).

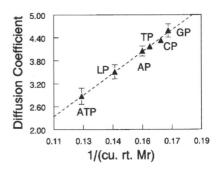

Figure 5 Relationship between the diffusion coefficient ($\times 10^{-6}$ cm^2/s) and the cubed root of the relative molecular mass for the various phosphagens and ATP. This figure is from Ellington & Kinsey (16).

CELLULAR DISTRIBUTION OF PHOSPHAGENS AND INTRACELLULAR TARGETING OF PHOSPHAGEN KINASES

Phosphagen Distribution in Relation to Cell Type

Typically, phosphagen systems are found in cell types that display high and variable rates of energy turnover. The most extensive database for cellular distribution is for the CP/CK system in vertebrates. In addition to being present in skeletal, cardiac and smooth muscle cells and neuronal tissues (57), CP/CK has been found in a variety of other vertebrate cells and tissues, including spermatozoa (58), electric organ cells (59), retina (60, 61), brush border epithelial cells (62), kidney (63, 64), stomach parietal cells (65), elasmobranch salt glands (66), and fish gills (67). The above distribution has been extensively reviewed (68). In the case of lower chordates and invertebrates, the CP/CK system has been observed in muscles (11, 12) and, as previously mentioned, in spermatozoa (16).

Of the other phosphagen systems, AP/AK has been the most intensively investigated in terms of distribution with respect to cell type. By and large, AP/AK is present in the musculature of all groups possessing this system (69, 70) and is present in neurons (for instance, see 71). Furthermore, this system is found in the spermatozoa of mollusks and arthropods (72, 73), arthropod photoreceptors (74, 75), and crab gills (76). The remaining phosphagen systems are typically found in muscles, although their presence in other cell types has not been extensively investigated.

Phosphagen Levels in Relation to Cell Type

Available data suggest that tissue levels of phosphagens are related to maximum potential rates of ATP turnover and oxidative capacity. In the case of muscle fibers, this is correlated with power output, as is shown in Table 1. In the case of both CP and AP, phosphagen levels in burst muscles are typically higher than corresponding levels in muscles that exhibit more sustained modes of contractile activity

TABLE 1   Representative phosphagen levels (expressed as $\mu M \cdot g$ wet weight^{-1}) in various cell/tissue systems[a]. In the case of muscles, the letter P designates phasic/burst muscles, T designates muscles that perform tonic, sustained contractile activities

Species	Cell/tissue	Phosphagen	Level	Source
Arenicola marina (polychaete)	Body wall muscle	TP	8.9	77
Glycera dibranchiata (polychaete)	Body wall muscle	CP	6.3	[b]
Sipunculus nudus (sipunculid)	Body wall muscle	PA	30.6	78
Argopecten irradians (scallop)	Snap adductor muscle, P	PA	18.5	79
Pecten maximus (scallop)	Snap adductor muscle, P	PA	52.2	70
Chlamys opercularis (scallop)	Snap adductor muscle, P	PA	20.4	80
Cardium tuberculatum (cockle)	Foot muscle, P	PA	22.0	81
Loligo vulgaris (squid)	Mantle muscle, P/T	PA	35.6	82
Busycon contrarium (whelk)	Ventricle, T	PA	10.3	83
Busycon contrarium (whelk)	Radula retractor, T	PA	12.5	84
Homarus vulgaris (lobster)	Abdominal muscle, P	PA	33.4	70
Crangon crangon (shrimp)	Abdominal muscle, P	PA	20.7	85
Calliphora vicinia (blowfly)	Flight muscle, T	PA	2.41	70
Apis mellifera (honey bee)	Flight muscle, T	PA	0.5	70
Lethocerus cordofanus (water bug)	Flight muscle, T	PA	4.4	70
Schistocerca gregaria (locust)	Flight muscle, T	PA	8.8	70
Schistocerca migratoria (locust)	Tibia muscle, P	PA	19.6	86
Arenicola marina (polychaete)	Spermatozoa	CP	6.1[c]	51
Branchiostoma florida (lancelet)	Muscle, T	CP	5.1	[b]
Flounder	Red muscle, T	CP	10.2	87
Flounder	White muscle, P	CP	13.7	87
Rana temporaria (frog)	Gastrocnemius, P	CP	19.9	70
Rat	Heart, T	CP	4.5	70
Rat	SO muscle, T	CP	11.7	88–90
Rat	FOG muscle, P	CP	16.8	88–90
Rat	FG muscle, P	CP	18.1	88–90
Mouse	Brain	CP	2.4	70

[a]In the case of muscles, P designates phasic burst muscles; T designates muscles that perform tonic, sustained contractile activities.

[b]N Graber and WR Ellington, unpublished observation.

[c]Calculated assuming that these cells are 75% water.

(Table 1). AP levels in scallop snap adductor and decapod crustacean (lobster, shrimp) abdominal muscles are among the highest observed in any system. It should be noted that these muscles effect powerful burst, escape responses that are very short in duration (79, 80, 85).

Metabolic rates of flying insects are 50–100 times higher than resting levels (91). However, the above correlation of phosphagens with power output is not evident in these organisms. AP levels are generally lower in insect flight muscles (Table 1). This is most likely related to the aerobic potential that relates to the high mitochondrial densities and efficiency of oxygen transfer via the tracheal system (92). Cells with minimal capacity for anaerobic metabolism, such as neurons and certain spermatozoa, typically have lower phosphagen levels (Table 1). The significance of the differences in phosphagen levels among cell types is discussed in a specific and functional context below.

Intracellular Targeting of Phosphagen Kinases

CK in higher vertebrates exists as two cytoplasmic isoforms (M, B), which form homodimeric (MM, BB) and heterodimeric (MB) isoenzymes (93). In addition to being freely soluble, a significant fraction of MM-CK is associated with the myofibril (94) and the SR and T-tubule systems (95, 96). Both BB-CK and MB-CK are not localized in this manner (97, 98). However, BB-CK is targeted to membrane ion transporters in gills (68), brain (99), salt glands (67), kidney (100), and stomach (66). It should be noted here that these instances involve association of CK with sites of significant ATP turnover (myosin ATPase, Ca^{2+} ATPase, Na^+:K^+ ATPase).

In addition to the cytoplasmic isoenzymes, CK in higher vertebrates is also present as two isoenzymes targeted to the mitochondrial intermembrane compartment (101). One of these mitochondrial CKs (MiCK) is restricted to muscles (sarcomeric MiCK), whereas the other is found in non-muscle tissues (ubiquitous MiCK) (101). These isoenzymes from chickens are termed basic (Mi_b-CK) and acidic (Mi_a-CK), respectively, owing to differences in pIs (101). MiCKs exist primarily as octamers (102), which have the capacity to bind electrostatically to both the inner and outer mitochondrial membranes (103). This interaction may facilitate CP formation from ATP exiting the adenine nucleotide translocase as well as its vectorial transport into the cytosol (101).

MiCKs are present in lower vertebrates, including amphibians and fish (101). In addition, octameric MiCKs have been found in the spermatozoa of sea urchins (104, 105) and the polychaete *Chaetopterus* (106). We have obtained the cDNA and deduced amino acid sequences for *Chaetopterus* MiCK (22); this enzyme displays as high as 71% identical amino acids to vertebrate MiCKs. Furthermore, *Chaetopterus* MiCK has a mitochondrial targeting leader peptide with features similar to intermembrane space-localized proteins (107, 108). Polychaetes such as *Chaetopterus* are lophotrochozoan invertebrates, which last shared common ancestor with deuterostomes at least 670 million years ago (109). Thus it is clear that the evolution of targeting of CK to the mitochondrial intermembrane compartment occurred rather early, at the dawn of the divergence of the major metazoan groups.

A final unique form of targeting of CK is worth considering. Spermatozoa of sea urchins have a CK isoenzyme localized in the flagellum (104). This isoenzyme is a large monomeric protein consisting of three contiguous CK domains (110). Recently, we have shown that this flagellar isoenzyme is present in *Chaetopterus* spermatozoa (106) and that this enzyme has a relative molecular mass on the order of the flagellar isoenzyme in sea urchins. Again, this points to an early origin of flagellar targeting of CK. The significance of the CP/K system in sperm motility is discussed below.

Intracellular targeting and localization of other phosphagen kinases has not been investigated extensively. However, activity of GK, TK, and LK appears to be lacking in body wall muscle mitochondria from annelids (111). Furthermore, mitochondria from mollusks (111) as well as flight muscle mitochondria from insects lack AK activity (86, 105, 111). Interestingly, there is good evidence for AK activity in mitochondria from the midgut of the tobacco horn worm (112). In addition, mitochondria from the chelicerate arthropod *Limulus polyphemus* (113, 114), and from a range of crustaceans (111, 115–118) contain significant AK activity. It was recently shown by immunogold transmission electron microscopy that this AK activity appears to be localized in the intermembrane compartment of cardiac mitochondria from *L. polyphemus* and the blue crab *Callinectes sapidus* (119).

AK in protostomes exists primarily as a monomer (6, 10). There is some evidence for intracellular localization in the cytosol of arthropods. Immunocytochemical techniques showed that AK is found in actin-containing regions of crayfish myofibrils (120), whereas in *Drosophila* AK is associated with the Z-line region of flight muscle and the A band in tubular muscle (121). Furthermore, it has been shown that scallop AK binds to F-actin in vitro (122). By far the most significant study of monomeric AK localization is recent work on migrating neuronal growth cones in the grasshopper (71). This study showed that AK is expressed throughout the developing nervous system, localizes with F-actin in the leading edges of glial lamellipodia and is present in high concentrations in growth cones and at the ends of filipodia (71). Wang et al (71) speculated that AK localization may serve to direct selective elaboration of specific growth cones. Intracellular localization may have important consequences with respect to the physiological roles of phosphagen systems.

PHYSIOLOGICAL ROLES OF PHOSPHAGEN SYSTEMS

Metabolic Capacitance

Phosphagens are typically found in cells that display high and variable rates of energy turnover. Phosphagen levels can be quite high in anaerobic, phasic muscles (Table 1). Furthermore, in these muscles there is a good correlation between maximum catalytic activities of the corresponding phosphagen kinases and maximum rates of ATP hydrolysis (87, 123). That is, in phasic muscles (such as vertebrate gastrocnemius, scallop snap adductor, or lobster abdominal muscles), CK or AK activities exceed calculated maximal rates of ATP turnover by over an order of magnitude (87). In contrast, in highly aerobic tonic muscles such as vertebrate heart and certain red muscles, as well as insect flight muscle, the ratios of phosphagen kinase activity over maximum ATP turnover rate approach or are even less than unity (87).

The above phasic versus tonic comparisons are indicative of tissue-specific differences in capacity for ATP (and ADP) buffering by phosphagen systems during shorts bursts of contractile activity. In spite of the long history of work on phosphagen systems, it was not until the early 1960s that Cain & Davies (124) proved by inhibition of CK that ATP hydrolysis was the direct driving force for muscle contraction. CK and other phosphagen kinases buffer ATP and ADP levels by the following reactions:

Phosphagen kinase:
$$\text{phosphagen} + \text{MgADP} + \text{H}^+ \rightarrow \text{guanidine acceptor} + \text{MgATP}$$

$$\text{ATPase}: \text{MgATP} \rightarrow \text{MgADP} + \text{Pi} + \text{H}^+$$

$$\text{NET}: \text{phosphagen} \rightarrow \text{guanidine acceptor} + \text{Pi}.$$

The above reactions delineate the traditional view of the physiological role of phosphagen systems, namely that of minimizing changes in ΔG_{ATP} values during periods in which there is a disequilibrium of ATP hydrolysis and ATP synthesis (by anaerobic glycolysis or mitochondrial oxidation). This physiological situation is best exemplified by phasic muscles. The above role of phosphagen reactions has been referred to as "temporal ATP buffering" by Meyer et al (125) and can be likened to the discharge of a capacitor (126, 127). This role is predicated on the general observation that in burst-type muscles, CK activities (and presumably other phosphagen kinase activities) are substantially higher than maximal rates of ATP turnover so as to maintain the phosphagen kinase reaction near equilibrium (125, 127–129).

The significance of maintenance of high ΔG_{ATP} values has long been recognized for vertebrates (2–4). Only recently has the importance of ΔG_{ATP} been appreciated in terms of invertebrate systems (130–133). The overall capacity of phosphagens for buffering of ΔG_{ATP} is dependent on a variety of factors, including total phosphagen pool size (relative to adenine nucleotides) and the thermodynamic properties of the particular phosphagen kinase reaction.

As noted above, the phosphagen kinase reactions differ in terms of thermodynamic poise. These differences are dramatically reflected in the free energy of hydrolysis values for high-energy phosphates versus the extent of hydrolysis of the total pool (Figure 6). Because of their instability, the phosphagen hydrolysis

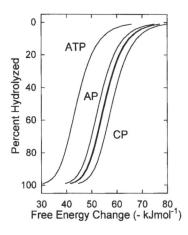

Figure 6 The relationship between the effective free energy change of hydrolysis and the extent of hydrolysis of the total pool size of ATP, AP, CP, TP, GP, and LP. Curves for TP, GP, and LP nearly superimpose on each other and fall intermediate between AP and CP. These data were recalculated and plotted as described in Ellington (20).

curves are displaced far to the right of ATP. For CP the range of free energy change values is much higher than for AP; for GP, TP, and LP, values lie between those for CP and AP.

The functional implications of the above differences in thermodynamic poise are manifold. Small changes in the extent of hydrolysis of ATP produce dramatic decreases in the ΔG_{ATP} (Figure 6) that could impact the functioning of ATP-requiring processes (2–4). However, if a phosphagen system is present and the phosphagen kinase reaction is near equilibrium with its substrates in vivo, then as pointed out by Kammermeier and coworkers (3, 4), the ΔG_{ATP} will be buffered at the expense of the phosphagen. This is illustrated by looking at the hydrolysis curve for CP in relation to that of ATP; with 50% of the CP discharged, the ΔG_{ATP} remains quite high (Figure 6). The extent of this buffering would be enhanced by increasing the total phosphagen pool size relative the adenine nucleotide pool.

Given the above relationships, it is clear that the phosphagen systems differ in terms of their capacity for ΔG_{ATP} buffering. The CP/CK system is able to buffer ATP over a higher range of ΔG_{ATP} values than the AP/AK system; the other phosphagen systems show intermediate ATP-buffering properties (Figure 6). I have argued that possession of the CP/CK system might be advantageous because of its capacity for buffering of ATP at a higher range of ΔG_{ATP} values (20). Furthermore, I argued that possession of the other phosphagen systems, especially that of AP/AK, might be advantageous in invertebrates that live in stressful environments where hypoxia and frequent intracellular acidosis prevail (70). These conditions might lead to a rapid dissipation of the CP pool through the high thermodynamic poise of the CK reaction, which would not be the case for the AP/AK system (20).

The above discussion clearly points to differences in the ATP-buffering properties of the phosphagen systems. These differences provide the opportunity for selection of the range of buffered ΔG_{ATP} values by choice of the phosphagen system expressed and elaborated. Does the distribution of phosphagens in the animal kingdom reflect some systematic pattern that correlates with these functional differences? The available data are not particularly supportive, at least with respect to CP/CK. The CP/CK system is widely distributed throughout the invertebrata and is found in certain species that live in very stressful environments. The selective expression of CP/CK in spermatozoa deserves additional consideration and is discussed below.

Inorganic Phosphate and Proton Buffering

Depending on the pool size and the prevailing ΔG_{ATP} value, cellular phosphagens trap considerable amounts of inorganic phosphate (Pi), which is liberated upon net phosphagen hydrolysis by the following reaction:

$$\text{Guanidine-PO}_3^{-2} + H_2O + H^+ \rightarrow \text{guanidine} + \beta Pi^{-1} + (1-\beta)Pi^{-2}.$$

β is a function of the prevailing pH; β increases as the prevailing pH approaches the pK_a for Pi. Liberation of Pi plays two critical roles: (*a*) providing substrate for the glycogen phophorylase reaction and (*b*) enhancing the intracellular nonbicarbonate H^+ buffering capacity

Pi^{-2} is the actual substrate of the glycogen phosphorylase reaction (134). Because prevailing Pi concentrations in resting vertebrate skeletal muscle are low, Griffiths (135) hypothesized that this is one of the factors that suppresses glycogenolysis under resting conditions and that liberation of Pi upon net CP hydrolysis is critical in promoting glycogen breakdown during muscle contraction. This is readily evident from data from Meyer et al (136) who effected a depletion of the CP pool in rat muscle by feeding animals β-guanidinopropionate. Lactate production was severely impaired during contraction presumably by limitations in availability of Pi, although there was evidence for increased aerobic capacity (136).

Davuliri et al (49) extended the perspective of Griffiths (135) to the AP/AK system by suggesting that the phosphorylation of creatine or arginine serves to reduce Pi to rate-limiting levels thereby controlling glycogenolysis. Presumably, this role in regulation of glycogen breakdown is applicable to the other phosphagen systems. Glycogenolysis leads to net H^+ accumulation (70). Pi is an effective H^+ buffer in the physiological pH range. Thus liberation of Pi during net phosphagen hydrolysis leads to a considerable increase in the intracellular nonbicarbonate H^+ buffering capacity (137, 138).

^{31}P-NMR studies of resting AP- (139–142), TP- (143), and LP- (144) containing muscles have shown that Pi levels are very low, presumably due to the lower K' values for the corresponding AK, TK, and LK reactions (20). Kamp (145) has pointed out the phosphagens likely play a significant role in regulation of glycogenolysis in marine invertebrates and has provided convincing evidence supporting this assertion. For instance, during burst contractions in the abdominal muscle of the shrimp *Crangon crangon*, Pi levels rise from 1 to 20 mM clearly leading to activation of glycogenolysis (146). Hypoxia results in nearly a threefold increase in body wall muscle Pi ($4.7 \rightarrow 12$ mM) in the polychaete *Arenicola marina*, which is coincident with activation of glycogenolysis (143). It should be noted in this context that the apparent K_m for Pi in *A. marina* glycogen phosphorylase is 13–16 mM (147), indicating that the observed physiological changes in Pi concentrations should dramatically impact enzyme activity in vivo.

It has been argued that possession of the AP/AK and other non-CP/CK phosphagens systems might be advantageous for organisms living in stressful environments (20). That is, because of their lower K' values relative to the CK reaction, these phosphagens more slowly discharge under conditions of environmental hypoxia. Thus, by slow release of Pi these phosphagen systems can more effectively regulate glycogenolysis than would be possible with the more labile phosphagen CP.

Intracellular Energy Transport

Without question, intracellular energy transport has been and most likely will continue to be heavily disputed and controversial. Below this subject is discussed in chronological order of the appearance of hypotheses/models describing the role of phosphagens in transport of high energy phosphate in cells. By and large, the bulk of work in this area has focused on the CP/CK system, but arguments apply to other phosphagens, especially where there is evidence for intracellular targeting of phosphagen kinase activities.

As indicated previously, significant activities of CK are found in mitochondria (148), and a fraction of MM-CK activity in skeletal (94, 149) and cardiac (150) muscle is associated with the myofibril. The presence of localized activities of CK at the ATP sink (myofibrillar-associated MM-CK) and the ATP source (MiCK in mitochondrial intermembrane compartment) prompted the development of a model for an additional role for the CK reaction as shown in Figure 7. In the earliest formulation of this model [the phosphorylcreatine shuttle of Bessman and coworkers (151, 152)], it was suggested that the bulk of cellular high-energy phosphate is transported in the form of CP rather than ATP. This is thought to circumvent the diffusive constraints of adenine nucleotide transport so as to maintain high ΔG_{ATP} values at the sites of ATP turnover (3, 153, 154).

Several key elements to the phosporylcreatine shuttle model are worth considering at this juncture. The so-called shuttle should operate at steady state during submaximal bouts of energy turnover; oxidative phosphorylation should be

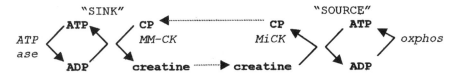

Figure 7 Transfer of high-energy phosphate between site of ATP synthesis and site of ATP utilization.

matched by CP turnover and resynthesis. Secondly, early proponents of the shuttle model suggested that separate pools of adenine nucleotides exist at source and sink (1, 51, 152, 155). Finally, a wealth of evidence indicated that MiCK may be coupled to oxidative phosphorylation and has privileged access to ATP exiting the adenine nucleotide translocase (ANT) (156–159). This potential coupling appears to involve a physical interaction of MiCK with the inner mitochondrial membrane on or near the ANT (160–162). The above issue have been reviewed extensively by Wyss et al (101).

The presence of mitochondrial AK in certain arthropods has prompted speculation that an analogous PA shuttle exists in these organisms (113, 114, 117, 118). However, total mitochondrial AK activities are quite low relative to cytoplasmic activity (113). Furthermore, it has been clearly demonstrated that no apparent functional coupling exists between mitochondrial AK and oxidative phosphorylation in cardiac mitochondria from the horseshoe crab, *L. polyphemus* (114). Doumen & Ellington (114) have suggested that mitochondrial AK serves to create a steeper ADP gradient in the mitochondrial intermembrane compartment.

Coincident with the appearance of the robust literature on the CP shuttle, an alternative perspective was published in 1984 by Meyer et al (125). According to this view, if one assumes that the CK reaction operates near equilibrium with its substrates in vivo, then transport of high-energy phosphate can be modeled as a form of facilitated diffusion. That is, the bulk of high-energy phosphate will be transported by CP owing to the fact that the CK reaction is near equilibrium, the total creatine/CP pool is typically higher than the adenine nucleotide pool, the CK reaction has a higher K' and, finally, CP has a somewhat higher diffusivity than ATP (125). Meyer et al (125) termed this process spatial ATP buffering, which can be viewed as a consequence of the metabolic capacitance (temporal ATP buffering) properties of the CK reaction.

The facilitated diffusion model has important implications with respect to energy transport. Meyer et al (125) argued that special compartmentation of CK isoenzymes is not necessary for spatial ATP buffering because the overall flux through CK is dominated by the cytosolic activity. They suggested that myofibrillar and mitochondrial targeting, and presumably targeting of CK to other sites, merely enhances local activities of CK where it is needed, thus achieving an overall economy of enzyme distribution throughout the cell. Furthermore, Meyer et al (125) suggested that energy transport of this sort is most important in cells in which there are large diffusion distances imposed by sparsely and non-uniformly distributed mitochondria. This prediction has been verified by modeling studies of red and white fish muscle, using in vivo values for diffusion coefficients for relevant chemical species (56).

The major determinants of capacity for energy transport by the spatial ATP buffering model are the K' for the phosphagen kinase reaction, the setpoint ATP/ADP ratio, the relative diffusivities of metabolites, and the relative sizes of the phosphagen and adenine nucleotide pools (125). According to the Meyer et al (125) model, intracellular compartmentation of phosphagen kinases is not

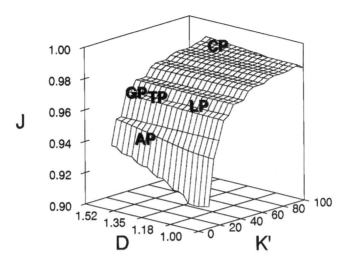

Figure 8 Impact of the ratio of phosphagen/ATP diffusivity (D) and apparent equilibrium constant (K′) on the fraction of total high-energy phosphate carried by phosphagens as calculated using the facilitated diffusion model of Meyer et al (125). [ATP]/[ADP] and total phosphagen pool/total adenine nucleotide pool ratios were set at 300 and 1, respectively. Specific values for CP, GP, TP, LP, and AP were calculated based on their respective D and K′ values and are denoted on the response surface. This figure is taken from Ellington & Kinsey (16).

necessary for facilitated transport. Thus spatial ATP buffering should be possible in all phosphagen systems regardless of whether intracellular targeting of phosphagen kinases exists. This perspective constitutes the most parsimonious way to view the transport role of phosphagens.

We have shown that there are thermodynamic differences between the phosphagen kinase reactions and that the phosphagens differ somewhat in intrinsic diffusivities (see above). Do the phosphagens differ in terms of potential for transport by facilitated diffusion? Using the Meyer et al (125) model, it is relatively easy to model the relative capacities of the different phosphagens in terms of spatial ATP buffering (Figure 8). The fraction of high-energy phosphate diffusive flux carried by the phosphagen is clearly a function of diffusion coefficient and K′ (Figure 8). Furthermore, CP carries the highest fraction of flux (high K′ and D value), AP the lowest, and GP, TP, and LP are intermediate (Figure 8). However, under these conditions the J values are all very high regardless of phosphagen type (>0.94). Furthermore, these small differences collapse as the size of the total phosphagen pool is increased (16). Thus there appears to be no major selective advantage for possession of a particular phosphagen in terms of spatial ATP buffering, at least according to the Meyer et al (125) model.

Work on the CP/CK system since the mid 1980s has introduced new results and perspectives that may confound the facilitated diffusion model for energy transport. These new results are manifold: (*a*) the underlying assumption that CK operates near equilibrium in vivo has been challenged, (*b*) additional restrictions to diffusion of ADP have been identified, and (*c*) apparent dynamic compartmentation of CK in mitochondrial contact sites has been hypothesized. These challenges to the facilitated diffusion model have prompted formulation of the CP circuit model (163, 164). The ensuing narrative addresses the new data and perspectives and describes the circuit model.

There is convincing spin transfer ^{31}P-NMR evidence for mammalian skeletal muscle that the CK reaction operates near equilibrium with its substrates at rest and during contractile activity. For instance, forward and reverse fluxes of CK were equal at rest, and over a 10-fold range of increased ATP-turnover rates during contractions in ex vivo preparations of cat soleus muscle (165). These results clearly suggest that CK operates near equilibrium with its substrates in vivo in this slow twitch muscle and are consistent with both temporal and spatial ATP buffering models (125). Recently, the validity of saturation transfer ^{31}P-NMR measurements of CK in muscle has been passionately challenged on the basis of the assertion that because of intracellular compartmenting of CK, a significant fraction of flux through this reaction is silent, presumably invalidating conclusions about the near-equilibrium nature of the reaction in vivo (166). For this perspective to be valid, a significant fraction of the total CP/creatine pool would have to be NMR invisible. Typically, NMR and chemical analyses of CP/creatine levels in muscle are in agreement (for instance, see 129). Furthermore, a recent review on studies of ^{31}P-NMR measured fluxes of CK in bioengineered mice concluded that CK flux is capable of matching ATP demand in skeletal muscle except, perhaps, at the onset of intense contractile activity (167).

In skeletal muscle the cytoplasm dominates other compartments in terms of CK activity and its reactants (125). For the facilitated diffusion model to operate, the bulk of the cell should exist as a freely mixing compartment in which CK has direct access to the entire pool of reactants. Experimental evidence using creatine analogs in mouse fast and slow twitch skeletal muscle suggests that this is the case (168, 169). However, a recent report suggests that a significant fraction of the creatine pool is not free to exchange with cytoplasmic creatine, which imposes a form of restriction to equilibration heretofore unrecognized (170).

The situation with respect to the equilibrium state of the CK reaction in cardiac muscle is more problematical. Available data suggest that the contribution of MiCK relative to M-CK in terms of total CK flux is much higher in heart cells (167, 171). This, of course, is likely because of the higher mitochondrial density in cardiac versus skeletal muscle. A recent series of mathematical models have appeared that take into account prevailing compartmentation of CK in cardiac muscle and energy turnover rates (172–174). These authors assert that the CK reaction in cardiac muscle is near equilibrium with its substrates only during diastole and only in the cytoplasmic compartment. Thus under all other conditions in the working heart, the CK reaction, regardless of compartment, is thought to be displaced from equilibrium (172–174), a state inconsistent with the facilitated diffusion model for energy transport (125). It is useful to point out in this context that cardiac muscle is the kind of tissue in which energy transport per se may not be as critical a problem owing to the higher mitochondrial density and short diffusion paths (125).

For global equilibrium of the CK reaction to exist, there should be no metabolite-specific restrictions to diffusion for any chemical species within the cytosol and into and out of the mitochondrial intermembrane compartment. There is convincing evidence that this is not the case for ADP because the outer mitochondrial membrane acts as a significant barrier to inward ADP diffusion (175–177). Thus relative ATP and ADP concentrations in the cytosol and in the mitochondrial intermembrane space may be quite different (178). This difference in concentrations is also thought to be related to the apparent unique micro-compartmentation of MiCK in the intermembrane space (178).

As indicated previously, MiCK in higher vertebrates binds to the inner mitochondrial membrane in close proximity to the ANT (160–162). Subsequent research uncovered what appears to be a form of dynamic metabolic compartmentation in which MiCK plays catalytic, regulatory, and quasi-structural roles in mitochondria. These new results and conclusions are as follows. (*a*) MiCK exists as an equilibrium of dimers and octamers with the octamer predominating under physiological circumstances (reviewed in 101). (*b*) The crystal structure of chicken sarcomeric MiCK shows that in the octameric state the top and bottom faces are identical, indicating that this enzyme is capable of binding electrostatically to both membrane surfaces (reviewed in 103). (*c*) MiCK octamers may bridge the formation of mitochondrial contact sites, regions in which the outer and inner membranes are in close apposition (reviewed in 179). (*d*) Contact sites are enriched with porin, ANT, and MiCK (reviewed in 180). (*e*) MiCK in contact sites functions in metabolic channeling by immediately phosphorylating creatine by using ATP exiting the ANT, thereby facilitating vectorial transport of CP out of the mitochondrion and enhancing the ADP gradient across the inner membrane (reviewed in 181).

The above observations and conclusions about MiCK, coupled with the new examples of CK targeting to a variety of other ATP sinks (discussed earlier), prompted the formulation by Wallimann and coworkers of the phosphocreatine circuit model (163, 164), which incorporates the temporal buffering, transport, and metabolic regulation roles of the CP/CK system. That is, the model embraces the metabolic capacitance role of the CP/CK system while at the same time recognizes the importance of the energy transport role of CP and creatine between ATP source and ATP sink. This latter function serves to maintain optimal ATP/ADP ratios at subcellular sites of ATP turnover (57).

It is the special role of MiCK in the phosphoryl creatine circuit that sets this model apart from other perspectives. The association of MiCK in the contact sites in proximity to porin and ANT is thought to produce a micro-compartment in which mitochondrial respiration becomes highly responsive to changes in energy turnover in the cytoplasmic compartment because of the near instantaneous phosphorylation of creatine entering the intermembrane space by ATP exiting the ANT (182, 183). Furthermore, it is thought that this coupling is dynamic to the extent that the dimer-octamer equilibrium and recruitment of octamers to contact sites may depend on physiologic and metabolic state of the cell (103, 181). Thus MiCK may play a dynamic role in long-term metabolic regulation and control (181).

Integrating Capacitance, Transport, and Regulation

It can be seen that the presence of intracellular targeting of CK in the cells of higher vertebrates can be viewed from two rather distinct perspectives. Meyer et al (125) argue that this targeting merely serves as a means of economizing enzyme protein, placing CK where it is needed most so as to maintain the reaction near equilibrium. The circuit model incorporates a very special role for restriction of diffusion of ADP into the mitochondrion, as well as channeling of substrates in an intermembrane space micro-compartment (181). Comparative results with lower animals may be helpful in placing the above differences in perspective. Insect flight muscles and the hearts of cephalopod muscles have among the highest aerobic power outputs in the invertebrata (91, 184), yet these tissues lack mitochondrial activity of AK (111). Certainly one can argue that if intracellular compartmentation of the phosphagen kinase activity is important in the energy transport role of phosphagens, then the lack of such compartmentation in insect and cephalopod muscles can be attributed to the fact that mitochondrial density is high and in close apposition to myofibrils (57). Thus energy transport per se is not constrained by short diffusion distances between source and sink. Due to the absence of mitochondrial AK, these muscles do lack the capacity for fine regulation and amplification of the energy state signal from cytoplasm, as is envisaged for MiCK-containing systems (181), yet these cells do not appear to be intrinsically compromised (111).

The transport role of phosphagens should be most important in highly aerobic cells in which there are large diffusion distances between source and sink (125). The next section deals with the role of phosphagens, in particular the CP/CK system, in energy metabolism of cells that aptly fit the above criteria, namely primitive-type spermatozoa.

PRIMITIVE-TYPE SPERMATOZOA

External fertilization in marine invertebrates is thought to be the primitive condition (185). That is, gametes are shed into the water column, and spermatozoa must spend considerable time swimming prior to fertilization (minutes to days). These spermatozoa typically have a specialized primitive-type morphology: head with nucleus and acrosomal apparatus, midpiece with one or more mitochondria, and a long flagellum ranging in size from 15 to as long as 100 μm (185). Furthermore, there may be specific metabolic adaptations such as reliance on lipid catabolism, which facilitates sustained aerobic energy production. In general, the spermatozoa of vertebrates are also of the primitive-type morphology (186), although internal fertilization is the norm in higher groups.

It has long been recognized that diffusion of ATP (and ADP) is likely a major restriction to motility in primitive-type spermatozoa owing to the long diffusion path from source to sink (187). As previously indicated, primitive-type spermatozoa of a broad range of lophotrocozoans (polychaetes, echiuroids, sipunculids), the deuterostome echinoderms, and lower chordates consistently express CK regardless of which phosphagen system is present in somatic tissues or eggs (5, 9, 16, 19, 50). The only exception to this case appears to be in spermatozoa of two sabellid polychaetes (*Sabella pavonia, Spirographis spallanzani*) where a unique dimeric AK has been observed but not extensively investigated (188). CK activity is found in spermatozoa of fish and birds, whereas the distribution in mammals is somewhat patchy and may be a function of the relative importance of glycolysis versus mitochondrial oxidation in terms of energy metabolism (186, 189). In groups lacking the potential for expression of CK such as mollusks, AK activities are quite high (72). The above association of the CP/CK and AP/AK systems with primitive-type spermatozoa clearly points to a potential role in energy transport.

This energy transport role has been elegantly dissected by Tombes & Shapiro, primarily using the spermatozoa of the sea urchin *Strongylocentrotus purpuratus*. These spermatozoa possess mitochondrial and flagellar isoforms of CK (104). As indicated previously, the flagellar CK is a unique contiguous trimer (110); a significant fraction of this CK activity is immobilized in the flagellar membrane (190). This association is mediated by myristoylation of the contiguous trimer (191, 192). Experimental studies and numerical simulations have shown that CK activity is absolutely essential for sustained motility in *S. purpuratus* spermatozoa (193). Titration of CK activity using fluorodinitrobeonzoic acid (FDNB) resulted in an attenuation of flagellar waves consistent with models of high-energy phosphate diffusion in these highly polarized cells (193). These observations were experimentally validated by spin transfer ^{31}P-NMR using sperm from another sea urchin species (194). Activation of motility resulted in a 10-fold increase in CK flux, which was accompanied by only minor changes in [ATP] and [CP]/[ATP] ratio, a condition consistent with a sustained, steady-state transport of high-energy phosphate by the CP/CK system (194).

The observation of significant CK activity in polychaetes (72) and the presence of both mitochondrial and flagellar CK in these lophotrochozoans (50, 106) indicate that intracellular targeting of CK and the energy transport role of this phosphagen system evolved rather early in the course of metazoan evolution. It is likely that the CP/CK system in polychaetes plays a similar role in motility as in sea urchin and other echinoderm spermatozoa. Unlike higher vertebrate MiCKs, which interact electrostatically with mitochondrial membrane surfaces (101), the octameric MiCKs of the spermatozoa of both polychaetes (106) and sea urchins (105) interact rather tightly with membranes and require detergents for initial solubilization. Furthermore, unlike their vertebrate counterparts, the octamers of these invertebrate MiCKs are highly stable and do not readily dissociate into dimers even when converted to the transition state analog complex (105, 106).

The above observations show that MiCKs from lower organisms differ from mammalian/avian octameric MiCKs in terms of the nature of membrane binding and stability of octamer. Some contemporary models of the role of MiCK in metabolic regulation and compartmentation in higher vertebrates envision that the dynamic nature of octamer-dimer association and consequent membrane interaction provide potential for long-term metabolic regulation and control (103, 181). This potential appears to be lacking in invertebrate MiCKs because of the high stability of octamers and membrane interaction. It is easy to hypothesize that the primitive condition for MiCK was that of a stable octamer, which bound fairly tightly to the inner mitochondrial membrane by hydrophobic interactions. Reliance on hydrophobic bonding may be related to the high ionic strength of the intracellular compartment, which would preclude weak polar interactions between octamer and membrane. Marine invertebrates are typically isosmotic with respect to sea water. Furthermore, sperm display two rates of energy turnover: (a) quiescence prior to release in which they are nearly ametabolic and (b) high rates of energy turnover during swimming; intermediate rates likely do not exist. In contrast, a broad range of rate states should exist in muscles that would be a function of power output. Expression of MiCK in these cells may have provided strong selective pressure for evolution of destabilization of the MiCK octamer and membrane interaction, thereby providing the capacity for fine tuning of regulation in these cells. As of yet, MiCKs have not been found in somatic tissues of invertebrates. Elucidation of the evolutionary transition of MiCK expression from spermatozoon to muscle constitutes an important avenue of future work.

In general, arthropod sperm are highly modified, which can be attributed to the fact that internal fertilization predominates (185). However, certain groups such as horseshoe crabs (*L. polyphemus*) and barnacles have primitive-type spermatozoa; AK activities in these cells are comparable to activities of CK in other primitive-type sperm (72, 73). Many mollusks, particularly bivalves, rely on external fertilization and have typical primitive-type sperm that contain high AK activities. Arthropods and mollusks have no alternative but to express AK in their primitive-type spermatozoa, yet these sperm do not appear to be inherently limited in terms of motility by possession of the AP/AK system.

The selective expression of the CP/CK system in the spermatozoa of vermiform lophotrocozoans and lower deuterostomes, even when the potential for expression of other phosphagen systems is present in their genomes, cannot be explained by a fundamental advantage of CP over the other phosphagens in terms of energy transport (16). There is no evidence for intracellular compartmentation in AK-containing sperm. The primitive-type spermatozoa of *L. polyphemus* do contain a sperm-specific AK isoform, a monomer, but this AK is distributed throughout the cell and is not present within the midpiece mitochondria (73). In contrast, intracellular targeting of CK to the mitochondrial intermembrane space and the flagella of sperm is widespread and evolved very early, prior to the radiation of the major metazoan groups (22, 106). We have argued that the selective expression of CK in spermatozoa is related to this intrinsic capacity for targeting, which is lacking in other phosphagen/phosphagen kinase systems (16; see discussion below).

EVOLUTIONARY PERSPECTIVES

Overwhelming evidence suggests that phosphagens play an important role in energy homeostasis in cells capable of high and variable rates of energy turnover. However, the available data also show that phosphagen systems are present in the simplest of organisms and in cell types that cannot be characterized as having high and variable rates of energy turnover. A good example is the well-documented demonstration of the AP/AK and CP/CK systems in the sponges (13–15), organisms that can hardly be described as having cells with such functional propensities. The activities of both AK and CK are quite low; these phosphagen systems may be present in only a few cells such as spermatozoa or the collared cells, which are flagellated and generate the water currents in these animals. If this is indeed the case, here would be yet another example of association of phosphagens with energy transport in highly polarized cells.

Phosphagen systems are widespread in the cells/tissues of other invertebrates that lack the capacity for high and variable rates of energy turnover. For instance, the basilar muscle of sea anemones secures the animal to the substratum under a variety of circumstances, including air exposure, and for intertidal species, severe wave action. Sea anemone basilar muscle contains significant AK activity (123), which most likely functions to regulate [Pi] and hence glycogenolytic flux during sustained stress events. Other examples in the invertebrates include catch muscles in mollusks and body wall muscles in many polychaetes, which are very low power output muscles capable of sustained glycogenolytic flux during hypoxic events. The importance of slow phosphagen discharge in this context is clear-cut and points to an early acquisition of this physiological role of phosphagens.

The above discussion suggests that selective pressures for regulation of glycogenolysis and possibly energy transport were early factors driving the evolution of phosphagen systems. This latter assertion is strongly supported by the near universal presence of either the AP/AK or the CP/CK systems in spermatozoa. Furthermore, there is rather old evidence that AK is present in ciliated protozoa such as *Stentor* and *Tetrahymena* (12). Because they have cilia, these organisms face energy transport problems similar to those of spermatozoa (195, 196). It is tempting to conclude that AP/AK and CP/CK systems evolved in response to energy transport constraints in these primitive, highly polarized cells.

The above point of view was addressed 25 years ago by Watts (12), who suggested that the CP/CK system first evolved "in association with a mobile gamete." In this context, it was argued that there is a selective advantage of CP over AP in spermatozoa because as a dead-end compound creatine is isolated from the mainstream of amino acid metabolism, whereas arginine is not. Arginine is required for histone biosynthesis, which Watts (12) argues is critical for sperm development.

However, this perspective fails to explain the lack of utilization of GP, TP, HTP, LP, and other phosphagens in sperm, even though these guanidine acceptors are also dead-end compounds (20). Furthermore, it is now clear that protein synthesis is nil in maturing sperm cells; all components are presynthesized and then packaged into developing spermatocytes.

The above conclusions, coupled with the apparent lack of functional differences in terms of energy transport among the phosphagens, suggest that the unique capacity for intracellular compartmentalization, which evolved early, is the major factor in the utilization of the CP/CK system in spermatozoa and subsequently in a variety of other cells. One can speculate that it is the intracellular targeting features of the CK isoforms, which are generally lacking in the other phosphagen kinases, that have dictated the expression of this system in spermatozoa and subsequently provided the basis for patterns of compartmentation seen in muscle and other cells in higher organisms.

The capacity for high rates of utilization of ATP, where the metabolic capacitance role of phosphagens is paramount, depended on the acquisition of burst-type muscles and organismal body forms and lifestyles where such muscles could be employed. Obviously, these developments occurred in the more advanced and complex metazoans. Furthermore, well-developed neuro-muscular systems display the capacity for graded levels of power output in which precise control of aerobic ATP production is necessary. It is under these conditions that one can envision the selective pressures that existed for the acquisition of the metabolic regulation role of the CP/CK system as espoused in the phosphocreatine circuit model. The inevitable, logical thread then suggests that the early role of phosphagen systems (particularly AP/AK, CP/CK) was energy transport in polarized cells and possibly regulation of Pi levels for controlling glycogenolytic flux. Of course, this perspective is highly speculative, but it is consistent with how phosphagen systems appear to be utilized in lower invertebrates.

ACKNOWLEDGMENTS

Supported by a research grant from the National Science Foundation (IBN-96-31907).

Visit the Annual Reviews home page at www.AnnualReviews.org

LITERATURE CITED

1. Skulachev VP. 1992. The laws of cell energetics. *Eur. J. Biochem.* 208:203–9
2. Kammermeier H. 1987. Why do cells need phosphocreatine and a phosphocreatine shuttle? *J. Mol. Cell. Cardiol.* 19: 115–18
3. Kammermeier H. 1993. Meaning of energetic parameters. *Basic Res. Cardiol.* 88:380–84
4. Kammermeier H, Schmidt P, Jungling E. 1982. Free energy change of ATP-hydrolysis: a causal factor of early hypoxic

failure of the myocardium. *J. Mol. Cell. Cardiol.* 14:267–77

5. Robin Y. 1974. Phosphagens and molecular evolution in worms. *BioSystems* 6:49–56

6. Van Thoai N. 1968. Homologous phosphagen kinases. In *Homologous Enzymes and Biochemical Evolution*, ed. N van Thoai, J Roche, pp. 199–229. New York: Gordon & Breach. 436 pp.

7. Van Thoai N, Robin Y, Guillou Y. 1972. A new phosphagen N' phosphoryl-guanidinoethylphospho-*O*-(α-N,N-dimethyl)serine (phosphothalassemine). *Biochemistry* 11:3890–95

8. Ennor AH, Morrison JF. 1958. Biochemistry of the phosphagens and related guanidines. *Physiol. Rev.* 38:631–74

9. Robin Y. 1964. Biological distribution of guanidines and phosphagens in marine annelida and related phyla with a note on pluriphosphagens. *Comp. Biochem. Physiol.* 12:347–67

10. Watts DC. 1968. The origin and evolution of the phosphagen phosphotransferases. In *Homologous Enzymes and Biochemical Evolution*, ed. N van Thoai, J Roche, 279–96. New York: Gordon & Breach. 436 pp.

11. Watts DC. 1971. Evolution of phosphagen kinases. In *Biochemical Evolution and the Origin of Life*, ed. E Schoffeniels, pp. 150–73. Amsterdam/London: North-Holland. 398 pp.

12. Watts DC. 1975. Evolution of phosphagen kinases in the chordate line. *Symp. Zool. Soc. London* 36:105–27

13. Roche J, Robin Y. 1954. Sur les phosphagenes des esponges. *C. R. Soc. Biol.* 48:1541–43

14. Robin Y, Guillou Y. 1980. Quelques aspects du metabolisme energetique chez les esponges. *C. R. Soc. Biol.* 174:121–26

15. Ellington WR. 2000. A dimeric creatine kinase from a sponge: implications in terms of phosphagen kinase evolution. *Comp. Biochem. Physiol. B* 126:1–7

16. Ellington WR, Kinsey ST. 1998. Functional and evolutionary implications of the distribution of phosphagens in primitive-type spermatozoa. *Biol. Bull.* 195:264–72

17. Needham DM, Needham J, Baldwin E, Yudkin Y. 1932. A comparative study of the phosphagens, with some remarks on the origin of the vertebrates. *Nature* 110:260–94

18. Ellington WR. 1991. Arginine kinase and creatine kinase appear to be present in the same same cells of an echinoderm muscle. *J. Exp. Biol.* 158:591–97

19. Van Thoai N, Robin Y. 1969. Guanidine compounds and phosphagens. In *Chemical Zoology*, ed. M Florkin, BT Scheer, pp. 163–203. New York: Academic. 548 pp.

20. Ellington WR. 1989. Phosphocreatine represents a thermodynamic and functional improvement over other muscle phosphagens. *J. Exp. Biol.* 143:177–94

21. Suzuki T, Kamidochi M, Inoue N, Kawamichi H, Yazawa Y, et al. 1999. Arginine kinase evolved twice: evidence that echinoderm arginine kinase originated from creatine kinase. *Biochem. J.* 340:671–75

22. Pineda AO, Ellington WR. 1999. Structural and functional implications of the amino acid sequences of dimeric, cytoplasmic and octameric, mitochondrial creatine kinase from a protostome invertebrate. *Eur. J. Biochem.* 264:67–73

23. Pereira CA, Alonso GD, Paveto MC, Iribarren A, Cabanas ML, et al. 2000. *Trypanosoma cruzi* arginine kinase characterization and cloning. A novel energetic pathway in protozoan parasites. *J. Biol. Chem.* 275:1495–501

24. Hird FJR. 1986. The importance of arginine in evolution. *Comp. Biochem. Physiol.* 85B:285–88

25. Van-Pilsum J, Stephens GC, Taylor D. 1972. Distribution of creatine, guanidinoacetate and the enzymes of their biosynthesis in the animal kingdom. *Biochem. J.* 126:325–45

26. Walker JB. 1979. Creatine: biosynthesis, regulation and function. *Adv. Enzymol.* 50:177–242

27. Stockler S, Isbrandt D, Hanefeld F, Schmidt B, von Figura K. 1996. Guanidinoacetate methyltransferase deficiency: the first inborn error of creatine metabolism in man. *Am. J. Hum. Genet.* 58: 914–22

28. Odland LM, MacDougall JD, Tarnopolsky MA, Elorriaga A, Borgmann A. 1997. Effect of oral creatine supplementation on muscle [PCr] and short-term maximum power output. *Med. Sci. Sports Exerc.* 29:216–19

29. Pulido SM, Passaquin AC, Leijendekker WJ, Challet C, Wallimann T, Ruegg UT. 1998. Creatine supplementation improves intracellular Ca^{2+} handling and survival in mdx skeletal muscle cells. *FEBS Lett.* 439:357–62

30. Williams MH, Branch JD. 1998. Creatine supplementation and exercise performance: an update. *J. Am. Coll. Nutr.* 17:216–34

31. Balestrino M, Rebaudo R, Lunardi G. 1999. Exogenous creatine delays anoxic depolarization and protects from hypoxic damage: dose-effect relationship. *Brain Res.* 816:124–30

32. Vandenberghe K, van Hecke P, van Leemputte, Vanstapel F, Hespel P. 1999. Phosphocreatine resynthesis is not affected by creatine loading. *Med. Sci. Sports Exerc.* 31:236–42

33. van Leemputte M, Vandenberghe K, Hespel P. 1999. Shortening of muscle relaxation time after creatine loading. *J. Appl. Physiol.* 86:840–44

34. Clark JF, Odoom J, Tracey I, Dunn J, Boehm EA, et al. 1996. Experimental observations of creatine phosphate and creatine metabolism. In *Creatine and Creatine Phosphate: Scientific and Clinical Perspectives*, ed. MA Conway, JF Clark, pp. 33–50. London/NewYork: Academic. 242 pp.

35. Guimbal C, Killimann MW. 1994. A creatine transporter cDNA from *Torpedo* illustrates structure/function relationships in the GABA/noradrenaline transporter family. *J. Mol. Biol.* 241:317–24

36. Guimbal C, Kilimann MW. 1993. A Na^+-dependent creatine transporter in rabbit brain, muscle, heart and kidney. *J. Biol. Chem.* 268:8418–21

37. Sora I, Richman J, Santoro G, Wei H, Wang Y, et al. 1994. Cloning and expression of a human creatine transporter. *Biochem. Biophys. Res. Commun.* 204:419–27

38. Dai W, Vinnakota S, Qian X, Kunze DL, Sarkar H. 1999. Molecular characterization of the human CRT-1 creatine transporter in *Xenopus* oocytes. *Arch. Biochem. Biophys.* 361:75–84

39. Dodd JR, Zheng T, Christie DL. 1999. Creatine accumulation and exchange by HEK293 cells stably expressing high levels of creatine transporter. *Biochim. Biophys. Acta* 1472:128–36

40. Guerro-Ontiveros ML, Wallimann T. 1998. Creatine supplementation in health and disease. Effects of chronic creatine ingestion in vivo: down regulation of the expression of creatine transporter isoforms in skeletal muscle. *Mol. Cell. Biochem.* 184:427–37

41. Van Pilsum JF, Taylor D, Bans L. 1975. Studies on the uptake of creatine from sea water by the marine annelid, *Glycera dibranchiata*. *Comp. Biochem. Physiol.* 51A:611–17

42. Hoberman HD, Sims EAH, Peters JH. 1948. Creatine and creatinine metabolism in the normal male adult studied with the aid of isotopic nitrogen. *J. Biol. Chem.* 172:45–48

43. Roche J, van-Thoai N, Robin Y. 1957. Sur la presence de creatine chez les invertebres et sa signification biologique. *Biochim. Biophys. Acta* 24:514–19

44. Kalkar HM. 1941. Nature of energetic coupling in biological synthesis. *Chem. Rev.* 28:71–178

45. Oesper P. 1950. Sources of the high energy content in energy-rich phosphates. *Arch. Biochem.* 27:255–70

46. Pullman B, Pullman A. 1959. Structure electronique des phosphates "riches en energie." *C.R. Seance Acad. Sci. Paris* 249:1827–28

47. Robin Y. 1980. Les phosphagenes des animaux marins. *Actual. Biochim. Mar.* 2:255–69

48. Lawson JWR, Veech RL. 1979. Effects of pH and free Mg^{2+} on the K_{eq} of the creatine kinase reaction and other phosphate hydrolyses and phosphate transfer reactions. *J. Biol. Chem.* 254:6528–37

49. Davuluri SP, Hird FJR, McClean RM. 1981. A re-appraisal of the function and synthesis of phosphoarginine and phosphocreatine in muscle. *Comp. Biochem. Physiol.* 69B:329–36

50. Kamp G, Englisch H, Müller R, Westhoff D. 1995. Comparison of two different phosphagen systems in the lugworm *Arenicola marina. J. Comp. Physiol.* 165:496–505

51. Teague WE Jr, Dobson GP. 1992. Effect of temperature on the creatine kinase equilibrium. *J. Biol. Chem.* 267:14084–93

52. Teague WE Jr, Golding EM, Dobson GP. 1996. Adjustment of the K' for the creatine kinase, adenylate kinase and ATP hydrolysis equilibria to varying temperature and ionic strength. *J. Exp. Biol.* 199:509–12

53. Teague WE Jr, Dobson GP. 1999. Thermodynamics of the arginine kinase reaction. *J. Biol. Chem.* 274:22459–63

54. Golding E, Teague WE Jr, Dobson GP. 1995. Adjustment of K' to varying pH and pMg for the creatine kinase, adenylate kinase and ATP hydrolysis equilibria permitting quantitative bioenergetic assessment. *J. Exp. Biol.* 198:1775–82

55. Hubley MJ, Rosanske RC, Moerland TS. 1995. Diffusion coefficients of ATP and creatine phosphate in isolated muscle: pulsed gradient ^{31}P-NMR of small biological samples. *NMR Biomed.* 8:72–78

56. Hubley MJ, Locke BR, Moerland TS. 1997. Reaction-diffusion analysis of the effects of temperature on high-energy phosphate dynamics in goldfish skeletal muscle. *J. Exp. Biol.* 200:975–88

57. Wallimann T, Wyss M, Brdicka D, Nicolay K, Eppenberger HM. 1992. Intracellular compartmentation, structure and function of creatine kinase isoenzymes in tissues with high and fluctuating energy demands: the "phosphocreatine" circuit for cellular energy homeostasis. *Biochem. J.* 281:21–40

58. Wallimann T, Moser H, Zurbriggen B, Wegmann G, Eppenberger HM. 1986. Creatine kinase isoenzymes in spermatozoa. *J. Muscle Res. Cell Motil.* 7:25–34

59. Carneiro LH, Hasson-Voloch A. 1983. Creatine kinase from the electric organ of *Electrophorus electricus:* isoenzyme analysis. *Int. J. Biochem.* 15:111–14

60. Hemmer W, Riesinger I, Wallimann T, Eppenberger HM, Quest AFG. 1993. Brain type creatine kinase in photoreceptor cell outer segments: role of the phosphocreatine circuit in outer segment energy metabolism and phototransduction. *J. Cell Sci.* 106:671–84

61. Wallimann T, Wegmann G, Moser H, Huber R, Eppenberger HM. 1986. High content of creatine kinase in chicken retina: compartmentalized localization of creatine kinase isoenzymes in photoreceptor cells. *Proc. Natl. Acad. Sci. USA* 83:3816–19

62. Keller TCS, Gordon PV. 1991. Functional coupling of a cytoplasmic and mitochondrial isoenzyme of creatine kinase in intestinal epithelial cells. *Cell Motil. Cytoskelet.* 19:38–45

63. Ikeda K. 1988. Localization of brain type creatine kinase in kidney epithelial cell populations in rat. *Experientia* 44:734–35

64. Friedman DL, Parryman MB. 1991. Compartmentation of multiple forms of creatine kinase in the distal nephron of the rat kidney. *J. Biol. Chem.* 266:22404–10

65. Sistermans EA, Klassen CHW, Peters W, Swarts HGP, Jap PHK, et al. 1995. Co-localization and functional coupling of creatine kinase B and gastric $H^+:K^+$-ATPase on the apical membrane and the tubovesicular system of parietal cells. *Biochem. J.* 311:445–51

66. Friedman DL, Roberts R. 1991. Purification and localization of brain-type creatine kinase in sodium chloride transporting epithelia of the spiny dogfish, *Squalus acanthias. J. Biol. Chem.* 267:4270–76

67. Kültz D, Somero GN. 1995. Ion transport in the gills of the euryhaline fish *Gillichthys mirabilis* is facilitated by the phosphocreatine circuit. *Am. J. Physiol. Regulatory Integrative Comp. Physiol.* 268:R1003–R12

68. Wallimann T, Hemmer W. 1994. Creatine kinase in non-muscle tissues and cells. *Mol. Cell. Biochem.* 133/134:193–220

69. Beis I, Newsholme EA. 1975. The contents of adenine nucleotides, phosphagens and some glycolytic intermediates in resting muscles from vertebrates and invertebrates. *Biochem. J.* 152:23–32

70. Grieshaber MK, Hardewig I, Kreutzer U, Pörtner H-O. 1994. Physiological and metabolic responses to hypoxia in invertebrates. *Rev. Physiol. Biochem. Pharmacol.* 125:43–147

71. Wang Y-ME, Esbensen P, Bentley D. 1998. Arginine kinase expression and localization in growth cone migration. *J. Neurosci.* 18:987–98

72. Tombes RM, Shapiro BM. 1989. Energy transport and cell polarity: relationship of phosphagen kinase activity to sperm function. *J. Exp. Zool.* 261:82–90

73. Strong SJ, Ellington WR. 1993. Horseshoe crab sperm contain a unique isoform of arginine kinase that is present in the midpiece and flagellum. *J. Exp. Zool.* 267:563–71

74. Langer H, Lues I, Rivera ME. 1976. Arginine phosphate in compound eyes. *J. Comp. Physiol.* 107:179–84

75. Kucharski R, Maleszka R. 1998. Arginine kinase is highly expressed in the compound eye of the honey bee, *Apis mellifera. Gene* 211:343–49

76. Kotlyar S, Weihrauch D, Paulsen R, Towle DW. 1999. Expression of arginine kinase mRNA and protein in gills of the green shore crab *Carcinus maenas. Comp. Biochem. Physiol.* 124A:S80.

77. Pörtner H-O, Surholt B, Grieshaber MK. 1979. Recovery from anaerobiosis of the lugworm *Arenicola marina*: changes of metabolite concentrations in the body wall musculature. *J. Comp. Physiol.* 133:227–31

78. Pörtner H-O, Kreutzer U, Siegmund B, Heisler N, Grieshaber MK. 1984. Metabolic adaptation of the intertidal worm *Sipunculus nudus* to functional and environmental hypoxia. *Mar. Biol.* 79:237–47

79. Chih CP, Ellington WR. 1983. Energy metabolism during contractile activity and environmental hypoxia in the bay scallop, *Argopecten irradians concentricus. Physiol. Zool.* 56:623–31

80. Grieshaber MK. 1978. Breakdown and formation of high energy phosphates and octopine in the adductor muscle of the scallop, *Chlamys opercularis* during escape swimming and recovery. *J. Comp. Physiol.* 126:269–76

81. Gäde G. 1980. The energy metabolism of the foot muscle of the jumping cockle, *Cardium tuberculatum*: sustained anoxia versus muscular activity. *J. Comp. Physiol.* 137:177–82

82. Grieshaber MK, Gäde G. 1976. The biological role of octopine in the squid, *Loligo vulgaris. J. Comp. Physiol.* 108:225–32

83. Ellington WR. 1981. Energy metabolism during hypoxia in the isolated, perfused ventricle of the whelk, *Busycon contrarium. J. Comp. Physiol.* 142:457–64

84. Ellington WR. 1982. Metabolism at the pyruvate branchpoint in the radula retractor

muscle of the whelk, *Busycon contrarium. Can. J. Zool.* 60:2973–77

85. Onnen T, Zebe E. 1983. Energy metabolism in the tail muscle of the shrimp *Crangon crangon* during work and subsequent recovery. *Comp. Biochem. Physiol.* 74A:883–38

86. Schneider A, Wiesner RJ, Grieshaber MK. 1989. On the role of arginine kinase in insect flight muscle. *Insect Biochem.* 19:471–80

87. Newsholme EA, Beis I, Leech AR, Zammit VA. 1978. The role of creatine kinase in muscle. *Biochem. J.* 172:533–37

88. Hultman E, Sjöholm H, Sahlin K, Edström L. 1980. The contents of adenine nucleotides and phosphagens in fast-twitch and slow-twitch muscles of rats and humans. *Muscle Nerve* 3:264

89. Rennie MJ, Holloszy JO. 1977. Inhibition of glucose uptake and glycogenolysis by availability of oleate in well-oxygenated perfused skeletal muscle. *Biochem. J.* 168:161–70

90. Saltin B, Gollnick PD. 1983. Skeletal muscle adaptability: significance for metabolism and performance. In *Handbook of Physiology*, ed. LD Peachy, RH Adrian, SR Geiger, 10:555–631. Bethesda: Am. Physiol. Soc. 688 pp.

91. Ellington CP. 1985. Power and efficiency of insect flight muscle. *J. Exp. Biol.* 115:293–304

92. Pennycuick CJ, Rezende MA. 1984. The specific power output of aerobic muscle, related to the power density of mitochondria. *J. Exp. Biol.* 108:377–92

93. Eppenberger HM, Dawson DM, Kaplan NO. 1967. The comparative enzymology of creatine kinases. I. Isolation and characterization from chicken and rabbit tissues. *J. Biol. Chem.* 242:204–9

94. Turner DC, Wallimann T, Eppenberger HM. 1973. A protein that binds specifically to the M-line of skeletal muscle is identified as the muscle form of creatine kinase. *Proc. Natl. Acad. Sci. USA* 70:702–5

95. Baskin RJ, Deamer DW. 1970. A membrane-bound creatine phosphokinase in fragmented sarcoplasmic reticulum. *J. Biol. Chem.* 245:1345–47

96. Rossi AM, Eppenberger HM, Volpe P, Cotruto R, Wallimann T. 1990. Muscle-type creatine kinase is specifically bound to sarcoplasmic reticulum and can support Ca^{2+} uptake and regulate local ATP/ADP ratios. *J. Biol. Chem.* 265:5258–66

97. Wallimann T, Moser H, Eppenberger HM. 1983. Isoenzyme specific localization of M-line bound creatine kinase in myogenic cells. *J. Muscle Res. Cell Motil.* 4:429–41

98. Shafer BW, Perriard J-C. 1988. Intracellular targeting of isoproteins in muscle cytoarchitecture. *J. Cell Biol.* 106:1161–70

99. Kaldis P, Hemmer W, Zanolla E, Holtzman D, Wallimann T. 1996. Hot spots of creatine kinase localization in brain: cerebellum, hippocampus and choroid plexus. *Dev. Neurosci.* 18:542–54

100. Guerrero LM, Beron J, Spindler B, Groscurth P, Wallimann T, Verrey F. 1997. Metabolic support of Na^+-pump in apically permeabilized A6 kidney cell epithelia: role of creatine kinase. *Am. J. Physiol. Cell Physiol.* 272:C697–C706

101. Wyss M, Smeitink J, Wevers RA, Wallimann T. 1992. Mitochondrial creatine kinase: a key enzyme of aerobic energy metabolism. *Biochim. Biophys. Acta* 1102:119–66

102. Wyss M, Schlegel J, James P, Eppenberger HM, Wallimann T. 1990. Mitochondrial creatine kinase from chicken brain: purification, biophysical characterization and generation of heterodimeric and heterooctameric molecules with subunits of other creatine kinase isoenzymes. *J. Biol. Chem.* 265:15900–8

103. Schlattner U, Forstner M, Eder M, Stachowiak O, Fritz-Wolf K, Wallimann T.

1998. Functional aspects of the X-ray structure of mitochondrial creatine kinase: a molecular physiology approach. *Mol. Cell. Biochem.* 184:125–40

104. Tombes RM, Shapiro BM. 1985. Metabolite channeling: a phosphorylcreatine shuttle to mediate high energy phosphate transport between sperm mitochondrion and tail. *Cell* 41:325–34

105. Wyss M, Maughan D, Wallimann T. 1995. Re-evaluation of the structure and function of guanidino kinases in fruit-fly (*Drosophila*), sea urchin (*Psammechinus miliaris*) and man. *Biochem. J.* 309: 255–61

106. Ellington WR, Roux K, Pineda AO. 1998. Origin of octameric creatine kinases. *FEBS Lett.* 425:75–78.

107. Mühlebach SM, Wirz T, Brandle U, Perriard J-C. 1996. Evolution of creatine kinases. The chicken acidic type mitochondrial creatine kinase gene as the first nonmammalian gene. *J. Biol. Chem.* 271:11920–29

108. Glick BS, Beasley EM, Schatz G. 1992. Protein sorting in mitochondria. *Trends Biochem. Sci.* 17:453–59

109. Doolittle RF, Feng D-F, Tsang S, Cho G, Little E. 1996. Determining divergence times of the major kingdoms of living organisms with a protein clock. *Science* 271:470–77

110. Wothe DD, Charbonneau H, Shapiro BM. 1990. The phosphocreatine shuttle of sea urchin sperm: flagellar creatine kinase resulted from a gene triplication. *Proc. Natl. Acad. Sci. USA* 87:5203–7

111. Ellington WR, Hines AC. 1991. Mitochondrial activities of phosphagen kinases are not widely distributed in the invertebrates. *Biol. Bull.* 180:505–7

112. Chamberlin M. 1997. Mitochondrial arginine kinase in the midgut of the tobacco horn worm. *J. Exp. Biol.* 200: 2789–96

113. Doumen C, Ellington WR. 1990. Mitochondrial arginine kinase from the horseshoe crab, *Limulus polyphemus.* I. Physicochemical properties and nature of interaction with the mitochondrion. *J. Comp. Physiol.* B 160:449–57

114. Doumen C, Ellington WR. 1990. Mitochondrial arginine kinase from the horseshoe crab, *Limulus polyphemus.* II. Catalytic properties and studies of potential coupling with oxidative phosphorylation. *J. Comp. Physiol.* B 160: 458–68

115. Chen C-H, Lehninger AL. 1973. Respiration and phosphorylation by mitochondria from the hepatopancreas of the blue crab *Callinectes sapidus. Arch. Biochem. Biophys.* 154:449–59

116. Skorkowski EF, Aleksandrowicz Z, Wrzolkowa T, Swierczyski J. 1976. Isolation and some properties of mitochondria from the abdomen of the crayfish *Orconectes limosus. Comp. Biochem. Physiol.* 80B:517–20

117. Hird FJR, McLean RM. 1983. Synthesis of phosphocreatine and phosphoarginine by mitochondria from various sources. *Comp. Biochem. Physiol.* 76B:41–46

118. Hird FJR, Robin Y. 1985. Studies on phosphagen synthesis by mitochondrial preparations. *Comp. Biochem. Physiol.* 80B:517–20

119. Pineda AO, Ellington WR. 1998. Immunogold transmission electron microscopy studies of arginine kinase localization in arthropod mitochondria. *J. Exp. Zool.* 281:73–79

120. Benzonana G, Gabbiani G. 1978. Immunofluorescent localization of some muscle proteins: a comparison between tissue sections and isolated myofibrils. *Histochemistry* 57:61–76

121. Lang AB, Wyss C, Eppenberger HM. 1980. Localization of arginine kinase in muscle fibers of *Drosophila melanogaster. J. Muscle Res. Cell Motil.* 1: 147–61

122. Reddy SRR, Houmeida A, Benyamin Y, Roustan C. 1992. Interaction in vitro of

scallop muscle arginine kinase with filamentous actin. *Eur. J. Biochem.* 206: 251–57

123. Zammit VA, Newsholme EA. 1976. The maximum activities of hexokinase, phosphofructokinase, phosphorylase, glycerol phosphate dehydrogenases, lactate dehydrogenase, octopine dehydrogenase, phosphoenolpyruvate carboxykinase, nucleoside diphosphatekinase, glutamate-oxaloacetate transaminase and arginine kinase in relation to carbohydrate utilization in muscle from marine invertebrates. *Biochem. J.* 160:447–62

124. Cain DF, Davies RE. 1962. Breakdown of adenosine triphosphate during a single contraction of working muscle. *Biochem. Biophys. Res. Commun.* 8:361–66

125. Meyer RA, Sweeney HL, Kushmerick MJ. 1984. A simple analysis of the "phosphocreatine shuttle." *Am. J. Physiol. Cell Physiol.* 246:C365–C77

126. Meyer RA. 1988. A linear model of muscle respiration explains monoexponential phosphocreatine changes. *Am. J. Physiol. Cell Physiol.* 254:C548–C53

127. Sweeney HL. 1994. The importance of the creatine kinase reaction: the concept of metabolic capacitance. *Med. Sci. Sports Exerc.* 26:30–36

128. McGilvery RW, Murray TW. 1974. Calculated equilibria of phosphocreatine and adenosine phosphates during the utilization of high energy phosphate by muscle. *J. Biol. Chem.* 249:5845–50

129. Meyer RA, Kushmerick MJ, Brown TR. 1982. Application of ^{31}P-NMR spectroscopy to the study of striated skeletal muscle metabolism. *Am. J. Physiol. Cell Physiol.* 242:C1–C11

130. Pörtner HO. 1993. Multicompartmental analyses of acid-base and metabolic homeostasis during anaerobiosis: invertebrate and lower vertebrate examples. In *Surviving Hypoxia: Mechanisms of Control and Adaptation*, ed. PW Hochachka, PL Lutz, T Sick, M Rosenthal, G van den Thillart, pp. 139–56. Boca Raton, FL: CRC Press. 570 pp.

131. Pörtner HO. 1993. Metabolism and energetics in squid (*Illex illecebrosus, Loligo pealei*) during muscular fatigue and recovery. *Am. J. Physiol. Regulatory Integrative Comp. Physiol.* 265:R157–R65

132. Pörtner HO. 1996. Metabolic and energy correlates of intracellular pH in progressive fatigue of squid (*Lolliguncola brevis*) mantle muscle. *Am. J. Physiol. Regulatory Integrative Comp. Physiol.* 271:R1403–R14

133. Combs CA, Ellington WR. 1996. Graded intracellular acidosis produces extensive and reversible reductions in the effective free energy change of ATP hydrolysis in a molluscan muscle. *J. Comp. Physiol.* 165B:203–12

134. Kasvinski PJ, Meyer WC. 1977. The effect of pH and temperature on the kinetics of native and altered glycogen phosphorylase. *Arch. Biochem. Biophys.* 181: 616–31

135. Griffiths JR. 1981. A fresh look at glycogenolysis in skeletal muscle. *Biosci. Rep.* 1:595–610

136. Meyer RA, Brown TR, Krilowicz, Kushmeric MJ. 1986. Phosphagen and intracellular pH changes during contraction of creatine depleted rat muscle. *Am. J. Physiol. Cell Physiol.* 250:C264–C74

137. Piiper J. 1980. Production of lactic acid in heavy exercise and acid-base balance. In *Lactate. Physiologic, Methodologic and Pathologic Approaches*, ed. PR Moret, J Weber, JC Haisly, H Denton, pp. 35–45. Berlin: Springer. 257 pp.

138. Pörtner HO. 1986. Proton balance of anaerobic and post-anaerobic metabolism-interrelations with pH regulation in marine invertebrates. *Zool. Beitr. NF* 30:23–247

139. Graham RA, Ellington WR, Chih CP. 1986. A saturation transfer phosphorus nuclear magnetic resonance study of

arginine phosphokinase in the muscle of a marine mollusc. *Biochim. Biophys. Acta* 887:157–63

140. Kinsey ST, Ellington WR. 1995. Interspecific comparisons of capacity for intracellular pH regulation in molluscan muscle. *Physiol. Zool.* 68:26–42

141. Kinsey ST, Ellington WR. 1996. [1]H and ^{31}P-nuclear magnetic resonance studies of L-lactate transport in isolated muscle fibers from the spiny lobster, *Panulirus argus. J. Exp. Biol.* 199:2225–34

142. Combs CA, Ellington WR. 1997. Intracellular sodium homeostasis in relation to the effective free energy change of ATP hydrolysis: studies of crayfish muscle fibers. *J. Comp. Physiol.* 167B:563–69

143. Kamp G, Juretschke H-P, Thiel U, Englisch H. 1995. In vivo magnetic resonance studies of the lugworm *Arenicola marina*. I. Free inorganic phosphate and free adenylmonophosphate concentrations in the body wall musculature and their dependence on hypoxia. *J. Comp. Physiol.* 165B:143–52

144. Van Waarde A, van den Thillart G, Verhagen M, Erkelens C, Addink A, Lugtenburg J. 1990. Direct observation of the phosphate acceptor and phosphagen pool sizes in vivo. *Am. J. Physiol. Regulatory Integrative Comp. Physiol.* 258:R1132–R39

145. Kamp G. 1993. Intracellular reactions controlling environmental anaerobiosis in the marine annelid *Arenicola marina*, a fresh look at old pathways. In *Surviving Hypoxia: Mechanisms of Control and Adaptation*, ed. PW Hochachka, PL Lutz, T Sick, M Rosenthal, G van den Thillart, pp. 5–17. Boca Raton, FL: CRC Press. 570 pp.

146. Kamp G, Juretschke HP. 1987. An in vivo ^{31}P-NMR study of the possible regulation of glycogen phosphorylase a by phosphagen via phosphate in the abdominal muscle of the shrimp *Crangon crangon. Biochim. Biophys. Acta* 929:121–27

147. Kamp G, Winnemöller M. 1992. Partially phosphorylated glycogen phosphorylase from the lugworm *A. marina*, its regulatory function during hypoxia. *Biol. Chem. Hoppe-Seyler* 373:1193–200

148. Jacobs H, Heldt HW, Klingenburg M. 1964. High activity of creatine kinase in mitochondria from muscle and brain. *Biochem. Biophys. Res. Commun.* 16:516–21

149. Wallimann T, Pelloni G, Turner DC, Eppenberger HM. 1978. Monovalent antibodies against MM-creatine kinase remove the M-line from myofibrils. *Proc. Natl. Acad. Sci. USA* 75:4296–300

150. Wallimann T. Kuhn HJ, Pelloni G, Turner DC, Eppenberger HM. 1977. Localization of creatine kinase isoenzymes in myofibrils. II. Chicken heart muscle. *J. Cell Biol.* 75:318–25

151. Bessman SP, Carpenter CL. 1985. The creatine-creatine phosphate energy shuttle. *Annu. Rev. Biochem.* 54:831–62

152. Bessman SP, Geiger PJ. 1981. Transport of energy in muscle: the phosphorylcreatine shuttle. *Science* 211:448–52

153. Mainwood GW, Rakusan K. 1982. A model for intracellular energy transport. *Can. J. Physiol. Pharmacol.* 60:98–102

154. Jacobus WE. 1985. Theoretical support for the heart phosphocreatine energy transport shuttle based on the intracellular diffusion limited mobility of ADP. *Biochem. Biophys. Res. Commun.* 133:1035–41

155. Erickson-Viitanen S, Viitanen P, Geiger PJ, Yang WTC, Bessman SP. 1982. Compartmentation of mitochondrial creatine kinase. I. Direct demonstration of compartmentation with the use of labeled precursors. *J. Biol. Chem.* 257:14395–404

156. Bessman SP, Fonyo A. 1966. The possible role of mitochondrial bound creatine

kinase in the regulation of mitochondrial respiration. *Biochem. Biophys. Res. Commun.* 22:597–602

157. Jacobus WE, Lehninger AL. 1973. Creatine kinase of rat heart mitochondria: coupling of creatine phosphorylation to electron transport. *J. Biol. Chem.* 248: 4803–10

158. Jacobus WE, Moreadith RW, Vandegaer KM. 1982. Mitochondrial respiratory control. Evidence against the regulation of respiration by extramitocondrial phosphorylation potentials or by [ATP]/[ADP] ratios. *J. Biol. Chem.* 257:2397–402

159. Jacobus WE, Saks VA. 1982. Creatine kinase of heart mitochondria: changes in its kinetic properties induced by coupling to oxidative phosphorylation. *Arch. Biochem. Biophys.* 219:167–78

160. Saks VA, Kupriyanov VV, Elizarova GV, Jacobus WE. 1980. Studies of energy transport in heart cells. The importance of creatine kinase localization for the coupling of mitochondrial phosphorylcreatine production to oxidative phosphorylation. *J. Biol. Chem.* 255: 755–63

161. Brooks SPJ, Suelter CH. 1987. Association of chicken mitochondrial creatine kinase with the inner mitochondrial membrane. *Arch. Biochem. Biophys.* 253: 122–32

162. Brooks SPJ, Suelter CH. 1987. Compartmented coupling of the chicken heart mitochondrial creatine kinase to the nucleotide translocase requires the outer mitochondrial membrane. *Arch. Biochem. Biophys.* 257:144–53

163. Wallimann T, Schnyder T, Schlegel J, Wyss M, Wegmann G, et al. 1989. Subcellular compartmentation of creatine kinase isoenzymes, regulation of CK and octameric structure of mitochondrial CK: important aspects of the phosphorylcreatine circuit. In *Muscle Energetics*, ed. RJ Paul, G Elzinga, K Yamada, 1 pp. 59–176. New York: Liss. 627 pp.

164. Wallimann T, Eppenberger HM. 1990. The subcellular compartmentation of creatine kinase isoenzymes as precondition for proposed phosphoryl-creatine circuit. In *Isozymes: Structure, Function and Use in Biology and Medicine*, ed. Z-I Ogita, CL Markert, pp. 877–89. New York: Wiley-Liss. 973 pp.

165. McFarland EW, Kushmerick MJ, Moerland TS. 1994. Activity of creatine kinase in a contracting mammalian muscle of uniform fiber type. *Biophys. J.* 67:1912–24

166. Wallimann T. 1996. ^{31}P-NMR-measured creatine kinase reaction flux in muscle: a caveat! *J. Muscle Res. Cell Motil.* 17: 177–81

167. Nicolay K, van Dorsten FA, Reese T, Kruiskamp MJ, Gellerich JF, van Echteld CJA. 1998. In situ measurements of creatine kinase flux by NMR. The lessons from bioengineered mice. *Mol. Cell. Biochem.* 184:195–208

168. Wiseman RW, Kushmerick MJ. 1995. Creatine kinase equilibration follows solution thermodynamics in skeletal muscle. ^{31}P-NMR studies using creatine analogs. *J. Biol. Chem.* 270:12428–38

169. Wiseman RW, Kushmerick MJ. 1997. Phosphorus metabolite distribution in skeletal muscle: quantitative bioenergetics using creatine analogs. *Mol. Cell. Biochem.* 174:23–28

170. Hochachka PW, Mossey MK. 1998. Does muscle creatine phosphokinase have access to the total pool of phosphocreatine plus creatine? *Am. J. Physiol. Regulatory Integrative Comp. Physiol.* 274:R868–R72

171. Van Dorsten FA, Nederhoff MG, Nicolay K, Van Echteld CJ. 1998. ^{31}P-NMR studies of creatine kinase flux in M-creatine kinase-deficient mouse heart. *Am. J. Physiol. Heart Circ. Physiol.* 275:H1191–H99

172. Saks VA, Aliev MK. 1996. Is there the creatine kinase equilibrium in working heart

cells? *Biochem. Biophys. Res. Commun.* 227:360–67

173. Aliev MK, van Dorsten FA, Nederhoff MG, van Echtfeld CJA, Veksler V, et al. 1998. Mathematical model of compartmentalized energy transfer: its use for analysis and interpretation of ^{31}P-NMR studies of isolated creatine kinase deficient mice. *Mol. Cell. Biochem.* 184: 209–29

174. Aliev MK, Saks VA. 1997. Compartmentalized energy transfer in cardiomyocytes: use of mathematical modelling for analysis of in vivo regulation of respiration. *Biophys. J.* 73:428–45

175. Gellerich FN, Khuchua ZA, Kuznetsov AV. 1993. Influence of the outer membrane and the binding of creatine kinase to the mitochondrial inner membrane on the compartmentation of adenine nucleotides in the intermembrane space of rat heart mitochondria. *Biochim. Biophys. Acta* 1140:327–34

176. Saks VA, Vasi'eva E, Belikova YO, Kuznetsov AV, Lyapina S, et al. 1993. Retarded diffusion of ADP in cardiomyocytes: a possible role of mitochondrial outer membrane and creatine kinase in cellular regulation of oxidative phosphorylation. *Biochim. Biophys. Acta* 1144:134–48

177. Brdiczka D, Wallimann T. 1994. The importance of the outer mitochondrial compartment in regulation of energy metabolism. *Mol. Cell. Biochem.* 133/134:69–84

178. Saks VA, Tiivel T, Kay L, Novel-Chate V, Daneshrad Z, et al. 1996. On the regulation of cellular energetics in health and disease. *Mol. Cell. Biochem.* 160/161:195–208

179. Stachiowiak O, Schlattner U, Dolder M, Wallimann T. 1998. Oligomeric state and membrane binding behavior of creatine kinase isoenzymes: implications for cellular function and mitochondrial structure. *Mol. Cell. Biochem.* 184:141–51

180. Brdiczka D, Beutner G, Rück A, Dolder M, Wallimann T. 1998. The molecular structure of mitochondrial contact sites. Their role in regulation of energy metabolism and permeability transition. *BioFactors* 8:235–42

181. Wallimann T, Dolder M, Schlattner U, Eder M, Hornemann T, et al. 1998. Some new aspects of creatine kinase (CK): compartmentation, structure, function and regulation for cellular bioenergetics and physiology. *BioFactors* 8: 229–34

182. Saks VA, Ventura-Clapier R, Aliev MK. 1996. Metabolic control and metabolic capacity: two aspects of creatine kinase functioning in the cells. *Biochim. Biophys. Acta* 1274:81–88

183. Saks VA, Dos Santos P, Gellerich FN, Diolez P. 1998. Quantitative studies of enzyme-substrate compartmentation, functional coupling and metabolic channeling in muscle cells. *Mol. Cell. Biochem.* 184:291–307

184. Houlihan DF, Agnisda C, Hamilton NM, Trara-Genoino I. 1985. Oxygen consumption of the isolated heart of *Octopus*: effects of power output and hypoxia. *J. Exp. Biol.* 131:137–57

185. Bacetti B, Afzelius BA. 1976. *The Biology of the Sperm Cell.* Basel: Karger. 254 pp.

186. Kaldis P, Kamp G, Piendl T, Wallimann T. 1997. Functions of creatine kinase isoenzymes in spermatozoa. *Adv. Dev. Biol.* 5:275–312

187. Nevo AC, Rickenspoel R. 1970. Diffusion of ATP in sperm flagella. *J. Theor. Biol.* 26:11–18

188. Robin Y, Klotz C, Guillou Y, Benyamin Y. 1975. A spermatozoa-specific isoenzyme of arginine kinase in sabellid worms. Biochemical and immunological comparison with muscle enzyme. *Comp. Biochem. Physiol.* 52B:387–92

189. Kamp G, Büsselmann G, Lauterwein J. 1996. Spermatozoa: models for studying

regulatory aspects of energy metabolism. *Experientia* 52:487–94

190. Quest AFG, Shapiro BM. 1991. Membrane association of flagellar creatine kinase in the sperm creatine phosphate shuttle. *J. Biol. Chem.* 266:19803–811

191. Quest AFG, Chadwick JK, Wothe DD, McIllhinney RHJ, Shapiro BM. 1992. Myristoylation of flagellar creatine kinase in the sperm phosphocreatine shuttle is linked to its membrane association properties. *J. Biol. Chem.* 267:15080–85

192. Quest AFG, Harvey DJ, McIllhinney RAJ. 1996. Identification of a nonmyristoylated pool of sea urchin flagellar creatine kinase: Myristolylation is necessary for efficient lipid association. *Biochemistry* 36:6993–7002

193. Tombes RM, Brokaw CJ, Shapiro BM. 1987. Creatine kinase-dependent energy transport in sea urchin spermatozoa. Flagellar wave attenuation and theoretical analysis of high energy phosphate diffusion. *Biophys. J.* 52:75–86

194. Van Dorsten FA, Wyss M, Wallimann T, Nicolay K. 1997. Activation of sea urchin sperm motility is accompanied by an increase in the creatine kinase exchange flux. *Biochem. J.* 325:411–16

195. Raff EC, Blum JJ. 1968. A possible role for adenylate kinase in cilia: concentration profiles in a geometrically constrained dual enzyme system. *J. Theor. Biol.* 18:53–71

196. Lin SH. 1972. Transient state analysis of dual enzyme reaction in cilia. *Biophysik* 8:264–70

Annu. Rev. Physiol. 2001. 63:327–57

ANTIFREEZE AND ICE NUCLEATOR PROTEINS IN TERRESTRIAL ARTHROPODS

John G Duman

Department of Biological Sciences, University of Notre Dame,
Notre Dame, Indiana 46556; e-mail: duman.1@nd.edu

Key Words   antifreeze proteins, insect cold tolerance, supercooling, freeze tolerance

■ **Abstract**   Terrestrial arthropods survive subzero temperatures by becoming either freeze tolerant (survive body fluid freezing) or freeze avoiding (prevent body fluid freezing). Protein ice nucleators (PINs), which limit supercooling and induce freezing, and antifreeze proteins (AFPs), which function to prevent freezing, can have roles in both freeze tolerance and avoidance. Many freeze-tolerant insects produce hemolymph PINs, which induce freezing at high subzero temperatures thereby inhibiting lethal intracellular freezing. Some freeze-tolerant species have AFPs that function as cryoprotectants to prevent freeze damage. Although the mechanism of this cryoprotection is not known, it may involve recrystallization inhibition and perhaps stabilization of the cell membrane. Freeze-avoiding species must prevent inoculative freezing initiated by external ice across the cuticle and extend supercooling abilities. Some insects remove PINs in the winter to promote supercooling, whereas others have selected against surfaces with ice-nucleating abilities on an evolutionary time scale. However, many freeze-avoiding species do have proteins with ice-nucleating activity, and these proteins must be masked in winter. In the beetle *Dendroides canadensis*, AFPs in the hemolymph and gut inhibit ice nucleators. Also, hemolymph AFPs and those associated with the layer of epidermal cells under the cuticle inhibit inoculative freezing. Two different insect AFPs have been characterized. One type from the beetles *D. canadensis* and *Tenebrio molitor* consists of 12- and 13-mer repeating units with disulfide bridges occurring at least every six residues. The spruce budworm AFP lacks regular repeat units. Both have much higher activities than any known AFPs.

INTRODUCTION

Insects and certain other terrestrial arthropods are arguably the most cold-tolerant animals known. This is especially true of species from polar, alpine, and continental subarctic regions such as the interior of Alaska, where these organisms routinely are exposed to temperatures of −50 to −70°C, or lower (1–5). Even in

0066-4278/01/0315-0327$14.00

more temperate environments less extreme subzero temperatures are common, and the frequent freeze-thaw cycles associated with these areas may be problematic. For some species, selection of a thermally buffered overwintering microhabitat is an important adaptation that usually removes the organism from exposure to the most extreme air temperatures (6). However, one of two basic physiological adaptations are still generally essential to overwintering success: freeze tolerance (the ability to survive body fluid freezing) and freeze avoidance (the ability to prevent freezing) (7–12). While each requires a certain suite of adaptations, antifreeze proteins and ice-nucleating proteins may be involved in both overwintering strategies. However, it is also important to recall that the tremendous adaptive radiation of insects ($\sim$75% of all known animal species) suggests that these organisms have evolved multiple means of achieving either freeze tolerance or freeze avoidance, and indeed this is the case.

Although it may seem odd to discuss protein ice nucleators (PINs) and antifreeze proteins (AFPs) in the same review, there are good reasons for doing so. In freeze-avoiding insects, the removal of ice nucleators or their masking by AFPs is often an important adaptation. Also, in the process of binding to and inactivating PINs, the freezing point depression activity of AFPs is often enhanced. In addition, although it may at first appear incongruous, extracellular PINs in freeze-tolerant insects function to prevent lethal intracellular ice and consequently, in a real sense, function as intracellular antifreezes in these species.

PROTEIN ICE NUCLEATORS

When small volumes of pure water are cooled, they typically do not freeze at their freezing point (0°C for pure water) but tend to supercool by as much as 40°C to a temperature (variously termed the supercooling point, nucleation temperature, crystallization temperature) where spontaneous nucleation occurs (13, 14, 14a). As the temperature decreases through this metastable supercooled state, small ice-like aggregations of water molecules (embryo crystals) temporarily form. As the temperature continues to drop, the size of the embryo crystals continues to increase until a critical radius is reached where the embryo crystals are large enough to nucleate or seed the supercooled water. This homogeneous nucleation temperature is near −40°C for small volumes of pure water. In biological systems this level of supercooling is unusual because of the presence of ice nucleators, sites with surfaces that organize water in an ice-like fashion such that the critical radius of embryo crystals is reached well above −40°C, which results in heterogeneous nucleation. The efficiency of ice nucleators varies considerably, but some ice-nucleating active bacteria can initiate nucleation at temperatures as high as −2°C (15). Actually, proteins in the outside membranes of the bacteria are responsible for their nucleation activity (16, 17). These ice-nucleation-active bacteria can initiate freezing in the gut when ingested by insects (18–20). Likewise, endogenous PINs inhibit supercooling in insects.

Structures of Insect PINs

The structure/function relationship of insect PINs is a ripe area for future research as information on this topic is limited. The first PIN to be purified was a 74-kDa hemolymph protein from overwintering freeze-tolerant queens of the hornet *Vespula maculata* (21). All that is known about the protein is its amino acid composition, which indicates that it is a hydrophilic protein containing ~20 mol % glutamate/glutamine. This suggests that the hydrogen-bonding abilities of the numerous hydrophilic sidechains may be important in organizing water into an embryo crystal on the surface of the PIN.

The freeze-tolerant larvae of the cranefly *Tipula trivittata* have a hemolymph lipoprotein and at least two other proteins with ice nucleation activity (22). Only the lipoprotein ice nucleator (LPIN) has been studied. The globular 800-kDa LPIN is 45% protein, 4% carbohydrate, and 51% lipid. The LPIN is present in all seasons and also functions as a typical hemolymph lipophorin to shuttle lipid. The apoproteins consist of a large Apo-I (265 kDa) and a smaller Apo-II (80 kDa). The lipid is ~40% neutral lipids and 12% phospholipids. The latter are of special interest because insect lipophorins are typically known to have a monolayer of phospholipid over the surface and thus are in position to interact with water. One of the phospholipids is phosphatidylinositol (PI). This was particularly interesting as PI had not previously been identified in insect lipophorins, and Warner (23) had suggested that inositol might order water in an ice-like fashion. In fact, various treatments that affect the head groups of PI inactivate the LPIN, suggesting that the hydroxyl groups of the inositol ring are especially important in nucleation. Both apoproteins are also needed for activity. The delipidated proteins are inactive, however, adding the lipids back to the apoproteins followed by appropriate sonication to produce proteoliposomes restored activity. By producing proteoliposomes made of various components of the native LPIN, it was determined that both of the apoproteins and PI were necessary and sufficient for activity.

These data suggest that the apoproteins orient the PI in an appropriate fashion so that the hydroxyl groups on the inositol rings form the active water-organizing site. Although this is likely to be true, other data indicate that the apoproteins, especially Apo-I, may play a more direct water-organizing role. Immunological studies identified common epitopes between the apoprotein and the bacterial ice nucleators (24). Polyclonal antibodies raised to the *Pseudomonas fluorescens* ice nucleator protein cross-react with the LPIN, and polyclonal antibodies to the LPIN cross-react to the bacterial protein. This is instructional because ~80% of the bacterial ice nucleator protein consists of a repeat structure (25, 26), and the cross-reactivity suggests that some level of this repeat is likely to be present in the LPIN apoprotein. In fact, antibodies prepared to a synthetic consensus octapeptide (L-T-A-G-Y-G-S-T) of the bacterial protein cross-reacted with the LPIN (24). An additional common feature of the bacterial protein and the *Tipula* LPIN is the requirement for lipid. While the exact mechanism of nucleation is not known, the bacterial protein itself is thought to provide the active water-organizing site (27).

However, the protein must be associated with lipid in the bacterial membrane to be active.

Another interesting feature common to the bacterial ice nucleator protein and the LPIN is the apparent requirement for aggregation of the individual proteins as an essential feature of ice-nucleating activity. In the case of the LPIN, a minimal concentration of 1×10^{-9} M is needed to produce a nucleation temperature higher than that of pure water in 1 μl droplets (28, 28a). Although intuition suggests that 1 molecule of LPIN should be enough to initiate nucleation, apparently 10^8 molecules are required in these 1 μl droplets. Similar requirements exist for the bacterial ice nucleators (26, 27). Either ice-nucleating ability is extremely rare in these molecules, or aggregation and cooperation are required. Scanning tunneling microscopy of the *Tipula* LPIN demonstrated that these LPINs are arranged into long chains, like pearls on a necklace, with two, or sometimes three, chains closely associated (29). *Manduca sexta* hemolymph lipoprotein, which lacks ice nucleator activity, also lacks this aggregation behavior. Proteoliposomes composed of *Tipula* apoproteins and PI have both aggregation behavior and ice-nucleating activity.

It is interesting that the adjacent chains of LPINs do not assume the most compact conformation (Figure 1*A*), but rather appear as shown in Figure 1*B*. It is likely that the active site constitutes only a small portion of the surface of the LPIN. (PI accounts for only 11% of the phospholipid in the native LPIN.) It may be that the appropriate arrangement of active sites on adjacent LPINs are necessary in order to allow organization of an embryo of sufficient size to induce nucleation (28). This cooperative arrangement of LPINs may occur in a stochastic fashion. It appears that both apoproteins are necessary for chain-forming behavior because proteoliposomes containing only Apo-I or Apo-II do not form chains. Also, proteoliposomes composed of Apo-I, Apo-II, and PIP2 form chains, but lack ice nucleator activity, presumably because the phosphorylated inositol rings cannot appropriately organize water. Thus Apo-I, Apo-II, and PI are required for nucleator activity, but the integrity of the inositol ring, while necessary for ice nucleator activity, is not required to form chains (28a). This indicates that the inositol hydroxyls organize the embryo crystal and the apoproteins function to appropriately position the PI, including the essential chain-forming behavior. However, this does not mean that the apoprotein may not also participate directly in organizing water at the active site. In fact, the immunological evidence sited above suggests that, like the bacterial protein, the LPIN apoprotein may also be directly involved in forming the embryo crystal. Sequence and higher order structural information on the LPIN apoproteins are badly needed.

Other Endogenous Ice Nucleators

The goldenrod gall fly, *Eurosta solidaginis*, overwinters as a freeze-tolerant larva within the goldenrod gall. Northern populations freeze at approximately $-8°C$, a temperature typical for a freeze-tolerant insect (30). However, the agent responsible

A   **B**

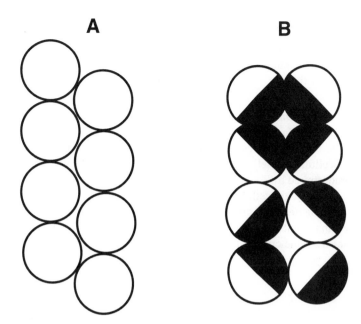

Figure 1   Representation of the chain-forming behavior of *Tipula trivittata* LPINs. (*A*) Although this pattern would provide the most efficient packing of the two LPIN chains as they lie side-by-side, this is not the pattern seen in scanning tunneling microscopy (29). (*B*) Scheme showing the organization of adjacent LPIN chains. The dark areas represent ice-nucleating surfaces of the individual spherical LPINs. Note that the organization of the top four LPINs permits cooperation of the water-organizing regions such that a larger embryo crystal is formed than is possible with the arrangement depicted in the bottom four LPINs.

for this high supercooling point has been somewhat controversial. Sömme (31) reported a hemolymph ice nucleator, but Bale (32) suggested that detrital contamination was responsible. However, calcium phosphate spherules that demonstrated ice nucleator activity were identified within the Malpiglian tubules (33). Other crystals commonly found in overwintering insects (potassium phosphate, potassium urate, sodium urate) also induced ice nucleation.

Ice-nucleating activity was also found to be associated with fat body cells in *Eurosta solidaginis* (33). Interestingly, these cells have the unique ability to survive intracellular ice (34, 35). The nucleating agent responsible was not identified, but considerable variability in nucleation temperature was noted. Storage excretion is a fairly common phenomenon in insects whereby materials are temporarily stored in certain cells, often as crystalloids (36, 37). Common among these storage cells are certain fat body cells, especially the so-called urate cells. Perhaps the variation seen in nucleation temperatures of *E. solidaginis* fat body cells is from storage of crystalloids.

The Roles of Protein Ice Nucleators

While it may be obvious that freeze-avoiding organisms must either select against or inhibit ice nucleators, it is much less obvious why many freeze-tolerant species select for them.

Freeze Tolerance   With few exceptions (e.g. fat body cells in the goldenrod gall insect *E. solidaginis*) (35), intracellular ice typically causes cell death, even in freeze-tolerant species. Extensive supercooling prior to nucleation often results in intracellular, as well as extracellular, ice formation (38, 39). Consequently, as first demonstrated by Zachariassen & Hammel (40), many freeze-tolerant insects have selected for extracellular ice nucleators, usually proteins, which initiate crystallization in the hemolymph at temperatures only a few degrees below the hemolymph freezing point (Figure 2). As extracellular ice is formed, the ice excludes solutes from the crystal lattice, thereby increasing the osmotic concentration in the

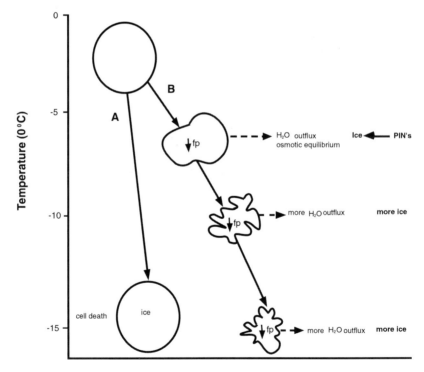

Figure 2   A comparison of extensive supercooling followed by freezing (path A) that results in lethal intracellular ice contrasted with the initiation of freezing with minimal supercooling by protein ice nucleators (PINs) in the extracellular fluid (path B). In path B, extracellular ice causes an outflux of water from the cell, which then lowers the freezing point of the intracellular fluid, thus preventing lethal intracellular ice (40).

unfrozen fraction of the extracellular water. This osmotic imbalance, along with the decreased vapor pressure resulting from the ice, causes an outflux of water from the cells, which depresses the freezing point and nucleation temperature of the intracellular fluid, thus helping to avert intracellular ice formation (39, 41). Thus as noted above, extracellular ice nucleators actually function to prevent intracellular ice. A functional, undamaged cell membrane generally prevents ice propagation from the extra—to the intracellular fluid. However, extensive dehydration of the cells can cause their death. An important function of the high concentrations of compatible solutes, such as glycerol, commonly present in freeze-tolerant insects, is to decrease the amount of extracellular ice present at any given temperature (thus reducing cellular dehydration) (7, 11), and to maintain appropriate hydration around membranes, proteins, and other macromolecules (43).

It is important to note that not all freeze-tolerant terrestrial arthropods have hemolymph PINs. The freeze-tolerant larvae of the moth *Cisseps fulvicolis* (44) and the centipede *Lithobius bifurcatus* (45) die upon freezing unless freezing is initiated by inoculation by external ice across the cuticle with virtually no supercooling. The arctic wooly bear caterpillar *Gynaephora groenlandica* nucleates at high temperatures (-6 to $-10°C$), but the ice nucleators are not present in the hemolymph (46). Also, there are exceptions to the rule that freeze-tolerant insects exhibit only minimal supercooling. Certain species of giant silkworm moths, which overwinter as freeze-tolerant pupae, lack potent ice nucleators and supercool to -17 to $-23°C$ (47). In addition there are a few insect species from the Canadian Rockies (48) and the interior of Alaska (3) that supercool from -50 to $-60°C$ and yet survive freezing. In spite of these exceptions, it appears that most freeze-tolerant insects have hemolymph PINs that initiate freezing, usually at -6 to $-10°C$.

Freeze Avoidance   For a freeze-avoiding organism to survive even the normal low winter temperatures encountered in a more temperate environment (-20 to $-30°C$ being common) generally requires that the organism (a) prevent inoculative freezing initiated by external ice across the cuticle and (b) extend its supercooling abilities beyond the lowest temperatures experienced. The lipid-coated cuticle of insects and certain other terrestrial arthropods may inhibit inoculative freezing (50), but colligative and/or protein antifreezes may also be required (discussed below). If inoculative freezing is controlled, then supercooling is a viable mechanism to extend the lower temperature range of the organism. Three mechanisms, the removal of ice nucleators and the production of colligative and/or protein antifreezes, or combinations of these three, are employed to extend supercooling. These latter two adaptations also inhibit inoculative freezing.

If all ice nucleators can be removed, small organisms such as terrestrial arthropods can theoretically supercool to nearly $-40°C$ (the homogeneous nucleation temperature for water) without the need for production of antifreeze. In fact, the removal of ice nucleators, especially the more potent ones, on either an evolutionary or seasonal time scale, appears to be a relatively common adaptation of freeze-avoiding species. The first demonstration of the seasonal removal of endogenous, in this case apparently intracellular, ice nucleators was by Zachariassen (51), who showed that upon warm acclimation, winter *Bolitophagus reticulatus* beetles that had not been fed raised their supercooling points 20°C, from −30 to −10°C, suggesting the production of endogenous ice nucleators in the summer and their elimination in the winter. Overwintering larvae of the stag beetle *Ceruchus piceus* lower the supercooling point from −7°C in summer to −26°C in winter without antifreeze production by clearing the gut and removing hemolymph LPINs (52). The normal lipid shuttle mechanism of the lipophorin is apparently not required in winter because the metabolism of the larvae is greatly reduced, and consequently the LPIN is not essential at this time. Larvae of the freeze-avoiding beetle *Dendroides canadensis* reduce, but do not eliminate, hemolymph LPINs and PINs in the winter. Because the hemolymph ice nucleators are not eliminated, antifreeze proteins are necessary to mask the ice nucleator activity, thereby permitting supercooling (53) (see below).

Some species seem to have selected against endogenous nucleators on an evolutionary time scale; apparently their evolving required proteins and other macromolecules that lack efficient ice-nucleating activity. Aphids seem not to have active ice nucleators and are therefore able to supercool to near −25°C even in the summer (54–56). Three species of willow gall insects from the interior of Alaska supercool to −25 to −30°C in summer and therefore lack active nucleators. Winter supercooling points reach nearly −60°C as a result of production of multimolar concentrations of polyols and, perhaps, removal of the inefficient ice nucleators present in the summer (3, 57). Likewise, Ring (4) has described insects from the Canadian Rockies that supercool to −50 to −60°C in winter.

In addition to endogenous ice nucleators (e.g. hemolymph PINs), many insects ingest ice nucleators, including bacteria and fungi, during feeding. Consequently, cessation of feeding and clearing the gut prior to the onset of winter is common in freeze-avoiding species (50, 58–61). For example, a 20°C lowering of the supercooling point in the solitary bee *Megachile rotundata* was attributed to gut evacuation (62). Experiments by Lee and colleagues in which insects were fed ice-nucleating bacteria have illustrated the importance of this strategy. When *Hippodamia convergens* lady beetles were fed ice-nucleating bacteria, the nucleation temperatures increased from −16 to −3°C (18). In fact, application of freeze-dried ice nucleation-active bacteria or fungi may be a useful means of killing insects that overwinter in stored grain (20, 63). Insects that feed on material which does not expose them to ingestion of ice nucleators, such as aphids feeding on plant phloem, often supercool to −25°C even in the summer (54–56).

ANTIFREEZE PROTEINS

Antifreeze proteins, also known as thermal hysteresis proteins, lower the non-equilibrium freezing point of water while not significantly affecting the melting point, thus producing a difference between the freezing and melting points, which has been termed thermal hysteresis (64). The magnitude of this characteristic thermal hysteresis activity is dependent upon the specific activity and concentration of the particular AFP and, in some cases, the presence of certain enhancers (65, 66). AFPs were first identified in Antarctic marine teleost fish where they function to lower the freezing point of the hypo-osmoregulating fish below that of the seawater (67). It soon became apparent that AFPs are common in teleost fish that inhabit ice-laden marine regions (68, 69, 69a; see Fletcher et al this volume).

Although AFPs were first discovered in fish, the phenomenon of thermal hysteresis was initially seen in larvae of the beetle *Tenebrio molitor* by Ramsay during his classic investigation of the physiology of the cryptonephridial rectal complex (70). Ramsay performed micropuncture in various regions of the cryptonephridial complex and in other fluid-containing sites and measured the melting points of the samples to determine the osmotic gradients present in the system. In a footnote he mentioned the presence of what would later be called thermal hysteresis, the unusual difference between the melting and freezing points in hemolymph and especially in perinephric space fluid. Later studies showed that protein was responsible for the activity, although the protein was not identified (71). Because activity was especially high in the perinephric space, Ramsay surmised that the protein was involved in the water reabsorption process of the complex (RA Ramsay, personal communication). Later studies identified AFPs in many other insects and indicated their antifreeze function (47, 72) in these and in *T. molitor* larvae (73). AFPs have also been identified in several other terrestrial arthropods including spiders (74, 75), mites (76), and centipedes (45). Recently, AFPs have been shown to be quite common in plants (77–81), fungi, and bacteria (82, 83). Most AFP-producing terrestrial arthropods are freeze avoiding, and the AFPs appear to function to prevent inoculative freezing across the cuticle and promote supercooling by inhibiting ice nucleators. However, some of the AFP-producing arthropods, and probably all the plants, are freeze tolerant, and the function of the AFPs in these organisms is less obvious, although the AFPs appear to function as cryoprotectants to inhibit freeze damage.

For a description of the non-colligative mechanism by which AFPs lower the freezing point of water see Fletcher et al (69a). However, a brief description of the most accepted theory, the adsorption-inhibition mechanism (84), follows. Although the structures of the various AFPs vary considerably, their freezing point depressing activity depends on the ability to adsorb onto the surface of potential seed ice crystals at preferred growth sites (84–86), probably by means of hydrogen bonding (69, 87). This forces crystal growth into highly curved, (and therefore high surface free energy) fronts rather than the preferred low curvature fronts (low surface free energy), and therefore temperature must be lowered before crystal growth proceeds. It has been suggested that van der Waals and hydrophobic interactions may also be involved in binding of winter flounder AFPs to ice (88, 89).

AFPs have been identified, often based on thermal hysteresis activity, in over 40 species of insects, 1 centipede (45), 1 oribatid mite (76), and 3 spiders (74, 75). Among the insects, 65% of the known AFP-producing species are beetles (Coleoptera). This predominance of beetles is not unexpected because ~45% of all the described species of insects are Coleoptera. The Collembola (springtails) are the only other insect group that has several (7) members known to use AFPs (90, 91). (Actually some taxonomists place Collembola in their own class, separate from the insects.) What is surprising is the relatively few known species of insects from orders other than the Collembola and beetles that are known to produce AFPs. This includes 1 stonefly (Plecoptera) (92), 1 wood roach (Orthoptera) (93), 2 true bugs (94; JG Duman & BM Barnes, unpublished data), 1 scorpionfly (Mecoptera) (75), 1 moth (Lepidoptera) (95), and 1 lacewing (Neuroptera) (JG Duman & BM Barnes, unpublished data). It is especially interesting that only one species of Lepidoptera (butterflies and moths), and no Diptera (flies) or Hymenoptera (ants, wasps, etc) are represented because these are, next to the beetles, the largest insect groups. It is most notable that AFPs have not yet been identified in Diptera since this group is the predominant insect group in the arctic, while beetles are under-represented there (1). These trends may to some extent result from the collecting tendencies of researchers. However, goodly numbers of Diptera, Hymenoptera, and Lepidoptera have been checked for thermal hysteresis activity, including arctic and subarctic species.

Structures of Insect AFPs

Currently, the sequences of AFPs from just three species of insects have been published, and structural information is not available for the AFPs of non-insect arthropods. Two of the insects are beetles (*D. canadensis* and *T. molitor*), and the AFPs from these are very similar. The third is a Lepidoptera, the spruce budworm *Choristoneura fumiferana*. All three have AFPs with significantly greater thermal hysteresis activity than do those of fishes, and none is similar to any known fish or plant AFPs.

The sequences of four AFPs from the larvae of the beetle *T. molitor*, obtained from fat body cDNAs, were the first insect AFP sequences published (96). Shortly thereafter, sequences of AFPs from overwintering larvae of the Pyrochroid beetle *D. canadensis*, based on cDNA and peptide sequencing, were also published (97). Recently additional sequences from both species were presented, so that sequences of 9 *Tenebrio* and 13 *Dendroides* AFPs are known (98, 99). With minor differences, these AFPs are very similar to one another, both within and between species. These AFPs consist of varying numbers of 12- or 13-mer repeats with molecular masses of $\sim$8.3 to 12.5. Throughout the lengths of the AFPs at least every sixth residues is a cysteine, which is disulfide bridged. Figure 3 shows the sequence of one of the mature *Dendroides* AFPs (DAFP-2) and one of the *Tenebrio* AFPs (YL1) arranged to illustrate the repeats. In DAFP-2 the blocked amino terminus was identified as pyroglutamate (97). The two amino-terminal repeats, A and B, and the carboxy-terminal repeat are somewhat different from the others (see below). The repeats exhibit some variation at certain positions; however, the repeats in the center of the protein have a number of highly conserved positions as shown in this consensus sequence.

$$-C-T-X_3-S-X_5-X_6-C-X_8-X_9-A-X_{11}-T-$$

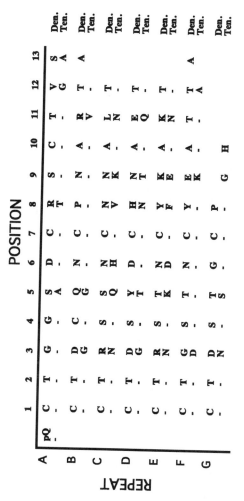

Figure 3 Sequences of *D. canadensis* DAFP-2 (97) and *T. molitor* YL1 (96) AFPs arranged to identify the 7 repeats (A-G) depicting the 12 or 13 positions in the repeats. Note how certain positions are highly conserved both between the two AFPs and between the various repeats.

Figure 4 shows the alignment of all 13 of the known DAFPs, again illustrating the repeating structure. Note that the above consensus sequence is maintained in the central repeats. This is likewise true of the *Tenebrio* AFPs (TAFPs).

Although the C_1 and C_6 residues are conserved, the amino-terminal repeat (A) is somewhat different from the above consensus sequence found in the central repeats, having the following consensus sequence (underlined residues identify those that are conserved in all 13 AFPs)

$$pQ\text{-}\underline{C}\text{-}\underline{T}\text{-}\underline{G}\text{-}G\text{-}S\text{-}D\text{-}\underline{C}\text{-}X_8\text{-}S\text{-}\underline{C}\text{-}\underline{T}\text{-}X_{12}\text{-}A\text{-}$$

Once again the TAFPs have the identical amino terminus with the exception of A for S at position 5, and T for X at position 8. Repeat B of the DAFPs has the consensus sequence

$$\underline{C}\text{-}\underline{T}\text{-}X_3\text{-}\underline{C}\text{-}X_5\text{-}\underline{N}\text{-}\underline{C}\text{-}\underline{P}\text{-}\underline{N}\text{-}\underline{A}\text{-}X_{11}\text{-}T\text{-}\underline{A},$$

with a strong tendency of X_3 toward D or N, X_5 toward Q, X_{11} toward R or L, and X_{12} to T. Once again, repeat B of the TAFPs is nearly identical except that X_5 is usually G, and the 13th position is missing.

The carboxyl terminals are likewise interesting and largely conserved through the first eight positions, which results in the consensus sequence

$$\underline{C}\text{-}T\text{-}X_3\text{-}S\text{-}T\text{-}\underline{G}\text{-}\underline{C}\text{-}\underline{P}.$$

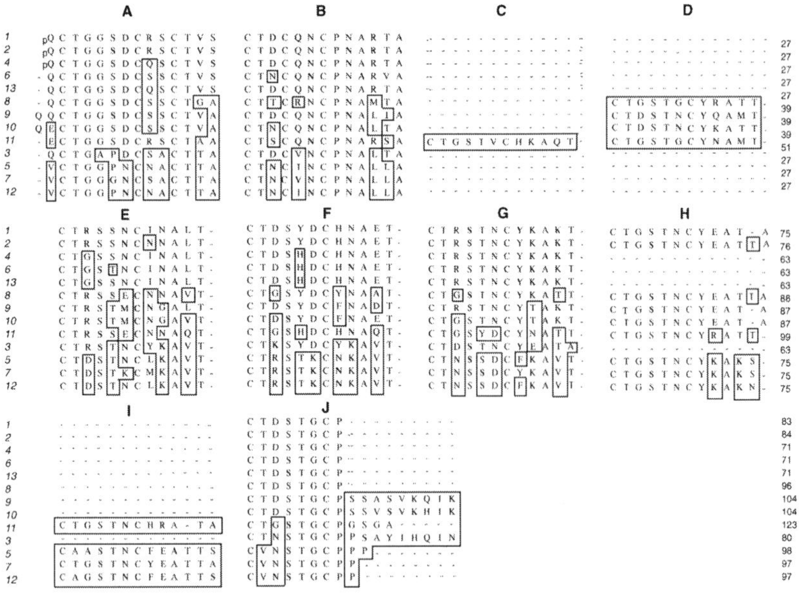

Figure 4 Sequences of the 13 known *D. canadensis* AFPs (99) showing the various 12- and 13-mer repeats (A-J). Residues that are different from DAFP-1 are outlined.

The TAFPs generally have a space at X_3 and G and H at positions 9 and 10 following the P. Most of the DAFPs end in a single, or in some cases multiple, Ps. The Ps protect the proteins from carboxypeptidases. Some of the DAFPs (3, 9, 10, 11) have additional residues beyond the P that do not follow the repeat sequence, which is conserved throughout the rest of the protein. Most TAFPs have an N at position 3 of the carboxyl-terminal repeat that may be glycosylated. However, these carbohydrate residues can be cleaved without loss of activity. Indeed, within *Tenebrio* hemolymph, both glycosylated and non-glycosylated forms of the same peptide exist. Most of the DAFPs lack this N-glycosylation site; however, DAFPs-3, 5, 7, and 12 do have the site and may also be glycosylated.

Note how certain DAFPs are more similar to one another than are others. Figure 4 was arranged to identify these sequence homologies. DAFPs-1, 2, 4, 6, and 13 form one such grouping, while DAFPs 8, 9, 10, and 11 form a second, and DAFPs 3, 5, 7, and 12 form a third. There is some overlap in certain characteristics between these groups, i.e. the groups are not unique. Size groupings also are apparent from Figure 4, and these do not always coincide with the sequence homology groups. Therefore, DAFP-11 is the largest DAFP, having repeat C. DAFPs -8, 9, and 10 are the next largest with repeat D. DAFPs 4, 6, 13, and 3 are the smallest. The TAFPs also exist in different size groups based on the presence or absence of repeats. The functional significance, if any, of these variations is not known. However, preliminary studies indicate that there may be tissue-specific forms of DAFPs. For example DAFPs 1, 2, and 4, plus a few others, are the predominant winter hemolymph DAFPs. In contrast, DAFPs 1, 2, and 4 are absent from midgut fluid, whereas DAFPs 3, 5, 7, and 12 are present (JG Duman, unpublished data).

Disulfide mapping of the DAFPs showed that all cysteines are disulfide bridged (100). In all but repeat A (amino terminus), C_1 is bridged to C_7 within the repeat (Figure 5). In repeat A, C_1 (position 2) is linked to C_{10} (position 11), and C_7 (position 8) of repeat A is linked to C_4 (position 18) of repeat B. This disulfide bridging imposes significant constraints on potential higher-order structures. Figure 5 illustrates the disulfide bridging and sequence of a generic AFP based on both *Dendroides* and *Tenebrio* AFPs. This structure does not reflect the variable number of repeats in these AFPs. Only residues that are identical through all 13 DAFPs and 9 TAFPs are identified. Some of the substitutions at the nonconserved positions are conservative substitutions, so that not any substitution is likely to be permitted at all of the non-identical sites. Because these conserved positions are found in all 22 of these beetle AFPs, it is possible that most of these are important for the activity of the AFPs. Over half of the residues are identical in all 22 AFPs. In particular, all the C residues are conserved. These act to stabilize the proteins and properly align the residues that hydrogen bond to ice or ice-nucleating sites. The hydroxyl groups of the highly conserved T and S residues are especially likely candidates for hydrogen bonding.

The crystal structure of *T. molitor* AFP was recently reported (101). The repetitive sequence forms an extremely regular β helix. On one side of the protein the

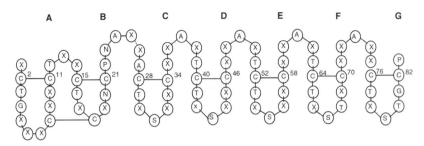

Figure 5 Generic beetle-type AFP sequence, based on the 13 known *D. canadensis* (97, 99) AFPs and the 9 known *T. molitor* (96, 98) AFPs, showing the disulfide bridge locations (100). Bold letters at the top identify repeat units. Only residues that are completely conserved through all these AFPs are identified. Position 14 is "missing" in the *T. molitor* AFPs.

conserved Thr-Cys-Thr motifs form a flat β sheet that is probably the ice-binding surface because the threonine sidechains form a near perfect match to the ice lattice on both the primary prism plane and the basal plane. The authors suggest that the hydroxyl sidechains of these threonines along with tightly bound co-planar external water form a two-dimensional array that mimics ice, which implies that the ordered water molecules may directly participate in the binding of the AFP to ice.

The 9-kDa spruce budworm AFP (Figure 6) has disulfide-bridged C residues, but these are much less numerous and less regularly arranged than in the beetle AFPs (102, 103). Also, in contrast to the beetle AFPs, there is no obvious repeat structure. However, NMR was recently used to determine the solution structure of the spruce budworm AFP (101a). Interestingly, in spite of the differences in sequences between the beetle and spruce budworm AFPs, the spruce budworm AFP also forms a β helix structure. It is triangular in cross section with rectangular sides that form parallel β sheets. One of these sides is apparently the ice-binding side because it contains several threonines arranges in a regular array of Thr-X-Thr motifs (X is an inward pointing amino acid) that match both the prism and basal planes of the ice lattice. AFPs with certain of these threonine residues mutated to leucine had 80–90% reduction in activity. Both ice etching and crystal habit studies indicated that this AFP binds to both the prism and basal planes. This apparent ability to bind to both the prism and basal planes of ice could account for the greater activities of the beetle and spruce budworm AFPs when compared with fish AFPs.

The only other insect species whose AFP has been purified is the milkweed bug, *Oncopeltus fasciatus* (94). This AFP, like the other insect AFPs, is highly hydrophilic, containing over 30 mol % serine. Sequence information on this interesting AFP is not available.

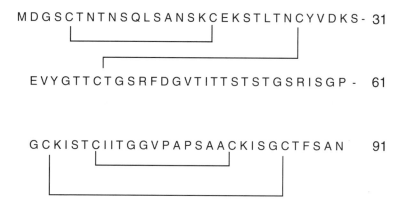

Figure 6   Sequence of the spruce budworm AFP showing the locations of disulfide bridges (103).

Thermal Hysteresis Activity

In marine fishes that produce AFPs, the average level of thermal hysteresis activity in the blood is approximately 0.7 to 1.5°C, a level sufficient to depress the freezing point of the body fluids below that of seawater, thereby protecting the freeze-avoiding fish. The average mid-winter thermal hysteresis activity of the hemolymph of AFP-producing terrestrial arthropods is generally 3 to 6°C, but, while this level of activity is greater than that of fishes, it does not appear to be sufficient to protect organisms that are routinely exposed to temperatures of −20°C or lower. In addition, while most AFP-producing terrestrial arthropods are freeze avoiding, some are freeze tolerant, and it is not apparent what value AFPs would be to these species, especially as many also have hemolymph PINs. Prior to discussing the physiological function of the AFPs, a treatment of thermal hysteresis activity and the technique for measuring this parameter may be useful.

To determine thermal hysteresis activity (64) the solution to be tested is partially frozen and the temperature then slowly raised to melt the ice until a very small ice crystal is just visible under the microscope. This is the melting point (equilibrium freezing point) of the sample. If the temperature is then lowered just 0.01–0.02°C, the crystal will immediately begin to grow if AFPs are not present (i.e. melting point = freezing point). However, if AFPs are present the crystal will not grow until the temperature has been lowered to the hysteretic freezing point (i.e. melting point ≠ freezing point) whereupon the crystal grows rapidly. Note that a seed crystal is present in the sample as the temperature is lowered, thus the temperature where the crystal grows (hysteretic freezing point) is not the nucleation temperature (supercooling point) of the sample. With certain insect AFPs the measured thermal hysteresis activity is inversely dependent on the size of the ice crystal present in the sample (104). This is important from the standpoint of comparing thermal hysteresis activities reported in the literature and also in understanding the relationship between the measured thermal hysteresis and level of protection provided to freeze-avoiding arthropods by AFPs. As regards measurement of thermal hysteresis activity, two related techniques based on the above description are generally used. In the capillary technique, a few (~2–6) microliters of sample are loaded into a sealed glass capillary tube and the measurement made with a crystal ~0.25 mm in diameter. The other technique employs a nanoliter (Clifton) osmometer, and although the general technique is the same, a smaller volume of sample and a smaller seed crystal are used. Consequently, the nanoliter osmometer may measure considerably higher levels of thermal hysteresis than the capillary technique on the same sample. For example, a sample of purified *D. canadensis* AFP, which had 1.4°C of thermal hysteresis activity with the capillary technique, had 5.5°C of activity with the nanoliter osmometer. Either technique is equally valid, but when making comparisons of activity the technique employed should be identified. (All values reported in this review are capillary measurements, unless otherwise stated.) The nanoliter osmometer may be best for samples with low levels of activity or for small volumes of sample. In contrast, the capillary technique may be better for samples with very high activities because the nanoliter osmometer cannot cool the sample beyond about −8°C, and insect hemolymph often has a lower freezing point than this.

There has been a perplexing problem in regard to the thermal hysteresis activity of *D. canadensis* AFPs in that the activity of the purified AFPs is considerably less than that seen in the hemolymph. Key insight into this problem was provided when addition of anti-DAFP polyclonal antibodies increased, rather than decreased, the thermal hysteresis activity by two to threefold (105). This suggests that the AFP-antibody complex, which is much larger than the AFP alone, blocks a larger surface of the ice crystal and also extends farther above the surface making it more difficult for the ice to overgrow the complex. Consequently, the hysteretic freezing point is decreased to lower temperatures. Based on this result, an endogenous 70-kDa enhancer protein was purified from *D. canadensis* (65). Addition of this protein enhancer to a DAFP solution with 1.6°C of activity increased the thermal hysteresis to over 5°C. Interestingly, this 70-kDa protein has ice nucleator activity, and the DAFP binds to the protein. Therefore, the mechanism by which the protein enhancer increases activity is likely to be similar to that proposed to explain the enhancing effect of antibodies described above. Ice nucleator proteins and lipoproteins from other species were also shown to produce the enhancer effect (66). Therefore, it seems that DAFPs can bind to certain PINs and LPINs, probably at the ice-nucleating site, and in the process of inhibiting the ice nucleator activity the thermal hysteresis can be enhanced. This may provide insight into the higher-order structure of the DAFPs since for the enhancement effect to occur the DAFP must be able to bind the larger enhancer protein and still bind to ice. This suggests that the DAFPs have binding surfaces in at least two planes, otherwise binding to the enhancer would sterically inhibit the DAFP from binding to ice.

More recently another type of enhancer of thermal hysteresis activity of DAFPs was identified (66). Certain low-molecular mass, generally organic, solutes were shown to enhance thermal hysteresis by threefold (glycerol, sorbitol, alanine, ammonium bicarbonate), fourfold (succinate, malate, aspartate, glutamate, ammonium sulfate), or as much as sixfold (citrate). Addition of citrate increased thermal hysteresis of a DAFP-4 solution from 1.2°C in its absence to 6.8°C. Very high (0.25–1 M) concentrations of these enhancers are generally required to produce such levels of enhancement. Glycerol is the only low-mass enhancer known to be present at these concentrations in winter hemolymph of *D. canadensis*, and consequently the physiological significance of many of these enhancers is unclear. The mechanism of this enhancement is unknown, but it must be different from that of the aforementioned protein enhancers.

Freeze Avoidance

Terrestrial arthropods, if they are to avoid freezing, must first prevent inoculative freezing initiated by external ice across the cuticle and then supercool to temperatures below those experienced over the course of the winter.

Prevention of Inoculative Freezing   Since most overwintering insects are, at least periodically, in contact with ice in their overwintering site, prevention of inoculative freezing is an essential first step in freeze avoidance. Three possible adaptations, or combinations thereof, may be used to provide protection: (*a*) a physical barrier, such as the waxy cuticle of insects, (*b*) colligative antifreezes, and (*c*) antifreeze proteins.

The wax-coated cuticle of insects is often thought to provide a physical barrier to inoculative freezing. Although this is true in some cases, ample evidence indicates that the insect cuticle can be crossed by inoculative freezing initiated by contact moisture (10, 44, 50, 107–111) or by the surface application of ice-nucleating bacterial suspensions (112, 111). A few insects have been shown to increase resistance to inoculative freezing with the onset of winter; however, the mechanisms involved are unknown (44, 111).

The osmolal freezing point constant for water is 1.86°C. Consequently, significant depression of the hemolymph melting point (equilibrium freezing point) using colligative antifreeze requires high concentrations of compatible solutes such as glycerol and/or sorbitol. Multimolar concentrations of polyols are fairly common in freeze-avoiding insects (2, 7, 10, 50), where they function not only to depress the melting point but also to extend supercooling. However, sufficient concentrations of polyols to lower the melting point to the temperatures required to protect from inoculative freezing (i.e. −20 to −30°C even in more temperate regions) is rarely seen. In spite of this, colligative antifreezes do assist in protection from inoculative freezing.

AFPs may also be important means of prevention from inoculative freezing in some species, and the level of protection provided may be well in excess of the 3 to 6°C of thermal hysteresis typically measured in the hemolymph. By manipulating temperature and photoperiodic cues to change the activity of hemolymph AFPs in two species of beetles (*Rhagium inquisitor* and *Ips acuminates*), Gehrken determined that hemolymph AFPs inhibited inoculative freezing (110). As the following indicates, AFPs along with cuticular changes help to prevent inoculative freezing in larvae of the beetle *D. canadensis* (113). In early September, the larvae are readily frozen by inoculative freezing at temperatures less than 1°C below the hemolymph freezing point. However, they gradually become resistant as the season progresses. Changes in epicuticular waxes contribute to this resistance; however, AFPs both in the hemolymph and in the epidermal layer underlying the cuticle play a major role in this resistance. Immunofluorescence using anti-DAFP antibodies shows that AFPs are present in the subcuticular epidermal layer in winter but not in summer. Also, as noted earlier, hemolymph thermal hysteresis activities typically range between 3 and 6°C in winter. A small plexiglass chamber was designed so that a patch of cuticle or integument (cuticle with underlying epidermis intact) could be located between ice on the exterior of the patch and a solution, the composition of which could be varied (plus or minus AFPs, etc), on the inside. The temperature was lowered until the inside solution (representing the hemolymph) was frozen either by inoculation across the patch or by spontaneous nucleation. Winter integument, with naturally occurring AFPs in the epidermis, provided more resistance to inoculative freezing than did summer integument. However, only when DAFPs were added to the physiological saline on the inside of the patch did the level of resistance to inoculative freezing match that seen in vivo in the larvae. Purified DAFP-4 at a concentration that produced 1.82°C of thermal hysteresis activity (capillary technique) was used in these experiments. Note that normal winter hemolymph thermal hysteresis activity is much higher (3–6°C) and that multiple DAFPs are present. More importantly, the level of protection provided by the DAFP was much greater than the hysteretic freezing point depression of the mock hemolymph solution would predict. It is likely that inoculative freezing across the cuticle proceeds through cuticular pores. Recall that the level of thermal hysteresis measured is inversely related to the size of the seed crystal used in the measurement (104), approximately 0.25 mm in diameter in the capillary technique. Because the cuticular pores are orders of magnitude smaller than this, the reduction in crystal size may explain the somewhat unexpectedly high level of inoculative freezing resistance provided by the AFPs in this experiment. It is interesting that while the 1.82°C of thermal hysteresis activity worked well in these experiments, a slightly lower activity (1.40°C) had no effect whatsoever, suggesting a threshold effect.

Supercooling If inoculative freezing can be prevented, then supercooling below the hemolymph freezing point becomes possible. As discussed above, if ice-nucleating surfaces are eliminated, supercooling to quite low temperatures can theoretically proceed without production of antifreezes. Although this does occur, more often colligative antifreezes and/or AFPs are required to extend supercooling.

Freeze-avoiding terrestrial arthropods often produce high, sometimes multi-molar, concentrations of colligative antifreezes such as glycerol, sorbitol, etc (7, 10, 51, 59, 60). The level of supercooling extension associated with these antifreezes seems to vary with different systems, but several studies have shown that the amount of increased supercooling resulting from colligative antifreezes ranges from one to three times the degree of melting point depression (see 114 for discussion). Therefore, a 1 M concentration of polyol, which depresses the melting point by $1.86°C$, might lower the supercooling point by 3.7 to $5.6°C$. It is not clear why this variation exists, but in some cases the extension in supercooling observed in the organism may not be totally the result of increased polyol concentration. Other factors such as variations in ice nucleator concentration may contribute. In any event, if colligative antifreeze is the only adaptation involved, it is obvious that quite high concentrations are required to significantly extend supercooling.

Production of hemolymph AFPs is often correlated with increased supercooling capacity of various terrestrial arthropods. However, as is often the case with colligative antifreezes, it is difficult to correlate the lower nucleation temperatures exclusively with AFPs as other factors (i.e. removal of ice nucleators, colligative antifreeze) may be contributing factors. However, *D. canadensis* AFPs are able to inactivate various ice nucleators. These include hemolymph LPINs and PINs (53) and also ice-nucleating active *Pseudomonas fluorescens* bacteria isolated from the gut (115). AFPs are present in the gut fluid of *D. canadensis* (116).

Freeze Tolerance

Although most known AFP-producing insects and all AFP-producing spiders and mites are freeze avoiding, there are a few insects (93) and the centipede *Lithobius forficatus* (45) that have AFPs but are freeze tolerant. This raises the question of function of these AFPs because it is not obvious why freeze-tolerant organisms, which typically have extracellular ice nucleators to prevent extensive supercooling, would benefit from the presence of hemolymph AFPs. One possibility is that the AFPs function as antifreezes during spring or autumn freezes when the animals are not fully cold-hardened and therefore not freeze tolerant. While this may be so, the AFPs also seem to be a component of the freeze-tolerance abilities of these species, functioning as cryoprotectants to protect from freeze damage.

A possible cryoprotective function of the AFPs in freeze-tolerant species is the ability of AFPs to prevent the potentially injurious process of recrystallization, even at very low concentrations (117, 118). Recrystallization proceeds by crystal growth within the frozen matrix. As temperature is held constant or raised after freezing some crystals grow as others shrink. The reasons for this are that the decrease in the total surface area to volume ratio of ice reduces the free energy of the system and that the original crystals formed may have greater internal free energy than the new ones. Freeze damage to tissue is often strongly dependent upon thawing rate, and recrystallization is a possible cause as mechanical disruption caused by growing crystals can be injurious (119, 120). Interestingly, recrystallization is especially fast at higher temperatures near the melting point. Therefore, the presence of hemolymph AFPs may be of value to freeze-tolerant organisms, both in more severe habitats with prolonged periods of freezing and in more temperate environments with less protracted bouts of freezing, but where the temperatures are less severe and therefore more conducive to promotion of recrystallization. As noted above, AFPs are extremely effective in preventing recrystallization, even when the AFP concentrations are much less than needed to produce thermal hysteresis. The mechanism by which AFPs inhibit recrystallization is similar to their mechanism of freezing point depression; however, because the driving force for crystal growth is less in the case of recrystallization, low AFP concentrations are effective (118).

The best studied of the freeze-tolerant AFP-producing terrestrial arthropods is the centipede *Lithobius forficatus* (45, 121). This centipede winters under large decomposing logs on the forest floor, sometimes burrowing into the underlying soil. Consequently it is thermally buffered, especially when there is snowcover. These centipedes are freeze tolerant, but survive only down to $\sim -6°C$, and only if supercooling is essentially eliminated by inoculative freezing. Recrystallization inhibition activity is present in the hemolymph of winter-collected individuals, but only occasional individuals have measurable thermal hysteresis. Based on immunoblots, the centipede AFP is immunologically similar to *D. canadensis* AFPs. Immunofluorescence studies showed that AFPs were not only present in the hemolymph, but were present either in or on the cell membranes of isolated cells from winter, but not summer, collected centipedes. Isolated midgut cells frozen in the presence of purified *D. canadensis* AFPs at a low concentration (0.02 mg/ml) in the bathing medium had significantly improved survivorship relative to cells frozen without AFPs. This included freezing protocols designed to produce recrystallization as well as other freezing regimes where recrystallization should not have been a problem even in the absence of AFPs. In addition, midgut cells from summer centipedes, which were incubated in medium containing AFPs, and then washed in buffer lacking AFPs to remove the AFPs from the medium prior to freezing, also had significantly improved survivorship after freezing. Immunofluorescence of these cells showed that the AFPs were in the cells and/or on the cell membrane, probably the latter. While this series of experiments suggests that AFPs are a component of the freeze-tolerance adaptations of the centipede, the mechanism(s) is not obvious. Recrystallization inhibition resulting from hemolymph AFPs is a possibility. Intracellular AFPs may be in a position to prevent lethal intracellular ice by inhibiting ice nucleators and/or seeding across the cell membrane by the extracellular ice. Another possible mechanism of protection involving hemolymph AFPs is suggested by the normal requirement for an optimal freezing rate for successful freeze preservation of biological materials (122). Freezing rates both slower or faster than optimal, which vary for different systems, can result in greatly increased mortality. By appropriate choice of overwintering microhabitat, terrestrial arthropods may have some control over freezing rates, but this control would generally not be very precise, and the organism would often be at the mercy of local weather conditions. However, by appropriate combinations of ice nucleators, colligative antifreeze, and AFPs the organism may be able to control the amount of supercooling that occurs prior to freezing and thereby control the critical rate of ice propagation following the initial freezing event.

It is interesting that while freeze tolerance is not prevalent in animals with AFPs, AFP-producing plants are typically freeze tolerant (77, 78, 82). In addition, the low thermal hysteresis activity present in these plants (generally $0.2-0.6°C$) is much less than that in AFP-producing arthropods, even most freeze-tolerant ones, except for the centipede.

Because of the low levels of thermal hysteresis present in both the centipede and plant systems perhaps these are comparable to one another. Recently, three AFPs from the bittersweet nightshade, *Solanum dulcamara*, were purified and characterized (123, 124). These plant AFPs, when added to the bathing medium, were able to provide cryoprotection to frozen protoplasts (cells from which the cell walls have been removed) at certain temperatures. Confocal microscopy showed that the AFPs were present on the protoplast cell membrane.

Under certain conditions some fish AFPs have been shown to provide cryoprotection to mammalian systems (125–128), but other studies have been unable to demonstrate a positive effect (129–133). In general, it appears that if recrystallization is potentially a problem, then fish AFPs provide protection (128). Also, the level of thermal hysteresis activity in the system may be important. Low activities may be beneficial, whereas high levels of activity may actually be detrimental probably because the fast-growing spear-like crystal growth common when freezing occurs in the presence of high thermal hysteresis activity may cause physical damage to cells. Fish glycoprotein AFPs provided protection to human platelets stored at low but above freezing temperatures for long periods and then rapidly rewarmed, apparently by preventing lateral phase separation in the membranes below the phase transition temperature (134). This result suggests that arthropod AFPs, especially if they contain a carbohydrate component, may function to prevent membrane damage in frozen systems. It is difficult to extrapolate these studies using AFPs from fish (which are not freeze tolerant) to cryoprotect tissues from non-freeze tolerant organisms (usually mammals). Further studies testing AFPs from freeze-tolerant organisms on cells and tissues from the same organisms may be instructive in determining the mechanism(s) of cryoprotection provided from these AFPs and suggest ways in which they may be applied to cryopreservation.

Control of AFP Concentrations and Activities

In some AFP-producing arthropods, hemolymph thermal hysteresis activity is present only during the colder months, but some species have low levels of activity (generally under $1°C$) in summer. This latter group includes both *D. canadensis* and *T. molitor* larvae. In *D. canadensis*, DAFP-1, -2, and -4 are the prevalent hemolymph AFPs in winter, but these are not present in the summer. However, DAFP-7 is present in the warm months. Northern blots showed that the DAFP-7 transcript is produced during the summer, while that of DAFP-1 is not (JG Duman, unpublished data).

In most years, thermal hysteresis activity of *D. canadensis* in the field began to increase in the early autumn, increased gradually through the autumn, peaked in early winter, and decreased gradually to summer values through the spring (135). Gut values lag behind those of the hemolymph by a few weeks in the autumn and are reduced earlier in the spring (116). The presence of AFPs, even at reduced levels, compared with winter levels, probably provides some protection during the autumn and spring when the larvae are active and feeding. AFP concentrations peak at ~20 mg/ml in mid-winter; however, enhancers may also contribute to increased thermal hysteresis activity in winter. Seasonal variations in protein enhancers have not been investigated. Hemolymph glycerol and sorbitol concentrations are high only during winter and, based on melting point determinations, other low-molecular mass solutes likewise only peak in the winter, suggesting that these enhancers are exclusively effective in winter (116, 135). Genomic Southern blots indicate that there are over 30 linked AFP genes in *T. molitor* (98). This may permit rapid synthesis of the AFPs.

Various environmental cues are used to initiate increases and decreases in thermal hysteresis at the appropriate times. Acclimation of warm-adapted larvae of the beetles *Meracantha contracta* (136) or *T. molitor* (73) to low temperatures, short photoperiods, or low relative humidity stimulated an increase in thermal hysteresis. In *D. canadensis*, temperature, photoperiod, and thermoperiod can be used to control thermal hysteresis (137, 138). Photoperiod is a more reliable cue than the notoriously variable environmental temperature. Photoperiod also permits the organism to anticipate the onset of seasonal temperature change, and thereby increase AFP activity prior to the arrival of cold temperatures. The photoperiodic response in *D. canadensis* is dependent on the entrainment of the circadian system by the light cycle (139, 140).

While cool temperature, short photoperiods, and thermoperiods definitely cue increases in AFP concentration and activity, various evidence (somewhat anecdotal) suggests that very cold (subzero) temperatures are required to stimulate the very high levels of thermal hysteresis activity normally present in the winter. Although average hemolymph thermal hysteresis in *D. canadensis* larvae is 3 to 6°C, the higher averages are associated with the colder winters and colder periods of winter. Also, the last three winters have been, in turn, the three warmest recorded winters in northern Indiana (United States), and these warm temperatures have allowed unusually low thermal hysteresis. For the winter of 1999–2000, the warmest winter on record in this area, hemolymph values were under 3°C for the entire season (JG Duman, unpublished observation). In addition, while various laboratory acclimations under AFP-inducing conditions result in increased thermal hysteresis, the level of activity is less than that seen in the field during normal winters. It is interesting that these laboratory acclimations also fail to induce a decrease in melting point to that of larvae in the field in winter, indicating that polyols are not induced by these laboratory conditions. This suggests that the absence of high levels of low-molecular mass enhancers may partially explain the low levels of thermal hysteresis.

In addition to the effects of the warming trend on thermal hysteresis, the warmer winters may have affected a change in overwintering strategy in *D. canadensis*, and another beetle larvae, *Cucujus clavipes*, from the same habitat. When these beetles were first studied in the 1970s, the winters were extreme and both were freeze tolerant (93, 135). However, by the early 1980s, after warmer winters, both beetles were freeze avoiding (141, 142) and have largely remained so since that time.

Information on environmental cues is integrated in the central nervous system, which then initiates release of juvenile hormone (JH), and possibly other hormonal signals. JH in turn stimulates the fat body to produce AFPs. Increases in AFPs and thermal hysteresis occur when JH is topically applied to *D. canadensis* larvae held under non-inducing environmental conditions (143). Also, *D. canadensis* acclimated to normally inducing conditions failed to increase thermal hysteresis if treated with the anti-JH drug precocene. Short photoperiod or low temperatures normally induce an increase in the hemolymph JH concentration in *T. molitor* (144). Also, JH treatment of cultured fat body from either *D. canadensis* or *T. molitor* induced AFP production (144, 145). However, addition of JH to the culture medium only stimulated AFP production in fat bodies taken from larvae that had been pre-treated with JH, suggesting that an additional hormone may be involved.

SUMMARY

Although AFPs and PINs have been discussed separately in this review, an effort has been made to integrate information as appropriate. However, it may be useful here to sum up the functional aspects of these proteins. Freeze-avoiding species must prevent inoculative freezing and promote supercooling. AFPs are often important components of both processes. Somewhat surprisingly, temperatures to which AFPs protect against inoculative freezing are far in excess of those predicted based on measured thermal hysteresis activities (113). Also, AFPs inhibit many ice nucleators, thereby extending the supercooling capabilities of the organism (53, 115). A few species, such as the willow cone gall fly (*Thabdophaga strobiloides*) larvae, in Alaska have selected against potent ice nucleators and thus, in conjunction with multimolar concentrations of colligative antifreezes, permit supercooling to $-56°C$ (3). Others, such as the beetle *Ceruchus piceus* from more temperate regions, remove LPINs in winter, which permits sufficient supercooling without the need for antifreezes (52). *D. canadensis* larvae decrease, but do not eliminate, PINs and therefore AFPs are needed to mask the nucleators (53, 115). Another beetle, *Ulona impressa*, has potent ice nucleators that its AFPs cannot mask, and consequently this necessitates AFPs and very high concentrations of polyols, which combine to lower the hemolymph freezing point to $-15°C$. In spite of this antifreeze, the beetle supercools only to $-21°C$ (93).

In contrast to freeze-avoiding species, many freeze-tolerant insects appear to have selected for hemolymph PINs, which induce ice at minimal levels of supercooling ($4-8°C$) and thus prevent lethal intracellular ice (22, 40). However, other freeze-tolerant species, such as many silk moth pupae (47), supercool by 15 to 20°C, while a few (*Pytho deplanatus*) supercool by 30 to 40°C prior to freezing (4). This begs the question of how intracellular freezing is prevented in these species. Another important question concerns the function of AFPs when they are occasionally found in freeze-tolerant insects (93) or in the centipede *Lithobius forficatus* (45). Recrystallization inhibition and/or other modifications of crystal habit are certainly possibilities; however, additional functions such as membrane stabilization are also possible (121).

Given the much greater levels of activity of insect AFPs relative to those of fish or plants, their potential value in any application where AFPs might be useful is great. Development of transgenic organisms such as freeze-susceptible plants, which produce high levels of insect antifreeze proteins, is an especially attractive possibility. In fact transgenic *Arabidopsis thaliana*, which express *D. canadensis* AFPs, freeze at lower temperatures than wild-type controls (124).

ACKNOWLEDGMENT

This work was partially supported by a National Science Foundation grant IBN98-08376.

Visit the Annual Reviews home page at www.AnnualReviews.org

LITERATURE CITED

1. Danks HV. 1981. *Arctic Arthropods*. Ottawa: Entomological Soc. Canada. 608 pp.
2. Lee RE, Denlinger DL, eds. 1991. *Insects at Low Temperature*. New York/London: Chapman & Hall. 513 pp.
2a. Sömme L, Block W. 1991. Adaptation to alpine and polar environments in insects and other terrestrial arthropods. See Ref. 2, pp. 318–59
3. Miller LK. 1982. Cold hardiness strategies of some adult and immature insects overwintering in interior Alaska. *Comp. Biochem. Physiol.* 73A:595–604
4. Ring JA. 1982. Freezing tolerant insects with low supercooling points. *Comp. Biochem. Physiol.* 73A:605–12
5. Kukal O. 1991. Behavioral and physiological adaptations to cold in a freeze tolerant arctic insect. See Ref. 2, pp. 276–300
6. Danks HV. 1991. Winter habits and ecological adaptations for winter survival. See Ref. 2, pp. 231–59
7. Lee RE. 1991. Principles of insect low temperature tolerance. See Ref. 2, pp. 17–46
8. Bale JS. 1987. Insect cold hardiness: freezing and supercooling—an ecological perspective. *J. Insect. Physiol.* 33:899–908
9. Block W. 1990. Cold tolerance of insects

and other arthropods. *Philos. Trans. R. Soc. London Ser. B* 326:613–33

10. Duman JG, Wu D, Xu L, Tursman D, Olsen TM. 1991. Adaptations of insects to subzero temperature. *Q. Rev. Biol.* 66:387–10

11. Storey KB, Storey JM. 1988. Freeze tolerance in animals. *Physiol. Rev.* 68:27–84

12. Zachariassen KE. 1985. Physiology of cold tolerance in insects. *Physiol. Rev.* 65:799–32

13. Knight CA. 1967. *The Freezing of Supercooled Liquids*. pp. 8–48. New York: Van Nostrand

14. Lee RE, Warren GJ, Gusta LV, eds. 1995. *Biological Ice Nucleation and Its Application*. St Paul, MN: Am. Phytopathol. Soc. 370 pp.

14a. Vali G. 1995. Principles of ice nucleation. See Ref. 14, pp. 1–28

15. Upper CD, Vali G. 1995. The discovery of bacterial ice nucleation and its role in the injury of plants by frost. See Ref. 14, pp. 29–40

16. Wolber PK, Deininger CA, Southworth MW, Vandekerckhove J, et al. 1986. Identification and purification of a bacterial ice nucleation protein. *Proc. Natl. Acad. Sci. USA* 83:7256–60

17. Wolber PK, Warren GJ. 1989. Bacterial ice nucleation proteins. *Trends Biochem. Sci.* 14:179–82

18. Strong-Gunderson JM, Lee RE, Lee MR, Riga TJ. 1990. Ingestion of ice-nucleating active bacteria increases the supercooling point of the lady beetle *Hippodamia convergens*. *J. Insect Physiol.* 36:153–57

19. Lee RE, Strong-Gunderson JM, Lee MR, Grove KS, Riga TJ. 1991. Isolation of ice nucleating active bacteria from insects. *J. Exp. Zool.* 257:124–27

20. Lee RE, Lee MR, Strong-Gunderson JM. 1995. Biological control of insect pests using ice-nucleating microorganisms. See Ref. 14, pp. 257–70

21. Duman JG, Patterson JL. 1978. The role of ice nucleators in the freeze toler-

ance of overwintering queens of the bald faced hornet *Vespula maculata*. *Comp. Biochem. Physiol.* 49A:69–72

22. Neven LG, Duman JG, Low MG, Sehl LC, Castellino FJ. 1989. Purification and characterization of an insect hemolymph lipoprotein ice nucleator: evidence for the importance of phosphatidylinositol and apolipoprotein in the ice nucleator activity. *J. Comp. Physiol.* 159:71–82

23. Warner DT. 1962. Some possible relationships of carbohydrates and other biological components with the water structure at 37°. *Nature* 196:1055–58

24. Duman JG, Wu DW, Wolber PI, Mueller GM, Neven LG. 1991. Further characterization of the lipoprotein ice nucleator from freeze tolerant larvae of the cranefly *Tipula trivittata*. *Comp. Biochem. Physiol.* 99B:599–07

25. Green RL, Warren GJ. 1985. Physical and functional repetition in a bacterial ice nucleation gene. *Nature* 317:645–48

26. Fall R, Wolber PK. 1995. Biochemistry of bacterial ice nuclei. See Ref. 14, pp. 63–84

27. Kajava AV. 1995. Molecular modeling of the three-dimensional structure of bacterial Ina proteins. See Ref. 14, pp. 101–14

28. Somero GN, Osmond CB, Bolis L. eds. 1992. *Water and Life: Comparative Analysis of Water Relationships at the Organismic, Cellular, and Molecular Level*. Berlin/Heidelberg: Springer-Verlag. 371 pp.

28a. Duman JG, Wu DW, Yeung KL. 1992. Hemolymph proteins involved in the cold tolerance of terrestrial arthropods: antifreeze and ice nucleator proteins. See Ref. 28, pp. 282–300

29. Yeung KL, Wolf EE, Duman JG. 1991. A scanning tunneling microscopy study of an insect lipoprotein ice nucleator. *J. Vac. Sci. Technol. B* 9:1197–201

30. Morrissey RE, Baust JG. 1976. The ontogeny of cold tolerance in the gall fly,

Eurosta solidaginis. J. Insect Physiol. 22:421–37

31. Sömme L. 1978. Nucleating agents in the haemolymph of the third instar larvae of *Eurosta solidaginis* (Fitch) (Diptera:Tephritidae). *Norw. J. Entomol.* 25:187–88

32. Bale JS, Hansen TN, Baust JG. 1989. Nucleators and sites of nucleation in the freeze tolerant larvae of the gallfly *Eurosta solidaginis* (Fitch). *J. Insect Physiol.* 35:291–98

33. Mugnano JA, Lee RE, Taylor RT. 1996. Fat body cells and calcium phosphate spherules induce ice nucleation in the freeze tolerant larvae of the gall fly *Eurosta solidaginis. J. Exp. Biol.* 199:465–71

34. Salt RW. 1962. Intracellular freezing in insects. *Nature* 193:1207–8

35. Lee RE, McGrath JJ, Morason RT, Taddeo RM. 1993. Survival of intracellular freezing, lipid coalescence and osmotic fragility in fat body cells of the freeze-tolerant gall fly *Eurosta solidaginis. J. Insect Physiol.* 39:445–50

36. Wiggesworth VB. *The Principles of Insect Physiology*, pp. 579–82. London: Chapman & Hall

37. Blum MS. 1985. *Fundamentals of Insect Physiology*. pp. 130–34. New York: Wiley & Sons

38. Mazur P. 1963. Kinetics of water loss from cells at subzero temperature and the likelihood of intracellular freezing. *J. Gen. Physiol.* 47:347–69

39. Fahy GM. 1995. The role of nucleation in cryopreservation. See Ref. 14, pp. 315–36

40. Zachariassen KE, Hammel HT. 1976. Nucleating agents in the haemolymph of insects tolerant to freezing. *Nature* 262:285–87

41. Zachariassen KE. 1992. Ice nucleating agents in cold-hardy insects. See Ref. 28, pp. 261–81

42. Deleted in proof

43. Timasheff SN. 1992. A physicochemical basis for the selection of osmolytes by nature. See Ref. 28, pp. 70–84

44. Fields PG, McNeil JN. 1986. Possible dual cold-hardiness strategies in *Cisseps fulvicollis* (Lepidoptera: Arctiidae). *Can. Entomol.* 118:1309–11

45. Tursman D, Duman JG, Knight CA. 1994. Freeze tolerance adaptations in the centipede *Lithobius forficatus. J. Exp. Zool.* 268:347–53

46. Kukal O, Serianni AS, Duman JG. 1988. Glycerol production in a freeze tolerant arctic insect, *Gynaephora groenlandica*: An in vivo $_{13}C$ NMR study. *J. Comp. Physiol.* 158:175–83

47. Duman JG, Xu L, Neven LG, Tursman D, Wu DW. 1991. Hemolymph proteins involved in insect subzero temperature tolerance: Ice nucleators and antifreeze proteins. See Ref. 2, pp. 94–130

48. Ring RA, Tesar D. 1980. Cold-hardiness of the arctic beetle, *Pytho americanus* Kirby Coleoptera, Pythidae (Salpingidae). *J. Insect Physiol.* 26:763–77

49. Deleted in proof

50. Sömme L. 1982. Supercooling and winter survival in terrestrial arthropods. *Comp. Biochem. Physiol.* 73A:519–43

51. Zachariassen KE. 1982. Nucleating agents in cold-hardy insects. *Comp. Biochem. Physiol.* 73A:557–62

52. Neven LG, Duman JG, Beals JM, Castellino FJ. 1986. Overwintering adaptations of the stag beetle, *Ceruchus piceus*: removal of ice nucleators in winter to promote supercooling. *J. Comp. Physiol.* 156:707–16

53. Olsen TM, Duman JG. 1997. Maintenance of the supercooled state in overwintering Pyrochroid beetle larvae *Dendroides canadensis*: role of hemolymph ice nucleators and antifreeze proteins. *J. Comp. Physiol.* B 167:105–13

54. O'Doherty R, Bale JS. 1985. Factors affecting cold hardiness of the peach-potato aphid *Myzus persicae. Ann. Appl. Biol.* 106:219–28

55. Knight JD, Bale JS. 1986. Cold hardiness and overwintering of the grain aphid *Sitobion avenae*. *Ecol. Entomol.* 11:189–970

56. O'Doherty R, Ring JS. 1987. Supercooling ability of aphid populations from British Columbia and the Canadian Arctic. *Can. J. Zool.* 65:763–65

57. Miller LK, Werner R. 1987. Extreme supercooling as an overwintering strategy in three species of willow gall insects from interior Alaska. *Oikos* 49:253–60

58. Salt RW. 1953. The influence of food on cold-hardiness in insects. *Can. Entomol.* 85:261–69

59. Lee RE, Costanzo JP, Mugnano JA. 1996. Regulation of supercooling and ice nucleation in insects. *Eur. J. Entomol.* 93:405–18

60. Zachariassen KE. 1985. Physiology of cold tolerance in insects. *Physiol. Rev.* 65:799–32

61. Cannon RJC, Block W. 1988. Cold tolerance of microarthropods. *Biol. Rev. Camb. Philos. Soc.* 63:23–77

62. Krunic M., Radovic L. 1974. The effect of gut content evacuation on the increase in cold-hardiness in *Megachile rotundata*. *Entomologia* 17:526–28

63. Lee RE, Costanzo JP, Lee MR. 1998. Reducing cold-hardiness of insect pests using ice nucleating active microbes. In *Temperature Sensitivity in Insects and Application in Integrated Pest Management*. pp. 99–124. Boulder/Oxford, UK: Westview

64. DeVries AL. 1986. Antifreeze glycopeptides and peptides: Interactions with ice and water. *Methods Enzymol.* 127:293–303

65. Wu DW, Duman JG. 1991. Activation of antifreeze proteins from the beetle *Dendroides canadensis*. *J. Comp. Physiol. B* 161:279–83

66. Li N, Andorfer CA, Duman JG. 1998. Enhancement of insect antifreeze protein activity by solutes of low molecular mass. *J. Exp. Biol.* 201:2243–51

67. DeVries AL. 1971. Glycoproteins as biological antifreeze agents in antarctic fishes. *Science* 172:1152–55

68. Davies PL, Hew CL. 1990. Biochemistry of fish antifreeze proteins. *FASEB J.* 4:2460–68

69. DeVries AL, Cheng C-HC. 1992. The role of antifreeze glycopeptides and peptides in the survival of cold-water fishes. See Ref. 28, pp. 301–15

69a. Fletcher GL, Hew CL, Davies PL. 2001. Antifreeze proteins of teleost fishes. *Annu. Rev. Physiol.* 63:359–90

70. Ramsay RA. 1964. The rectal complex of the mealworm, *Tenebrio molitor* L. Coleoptera, Tenebrionidae). *Philos. Trans. R. Soc. London Ser. B* 248:279–14

71. Grimstone AV, Mullinger AM, Ramsay JA. 1968. Further studies on the rectal complex of the mealworm, *Tenebrio molitor*. *Philos. Trans. R. Soc. London Ser. B* 253:343–82

72. Duman JG. 1977. The role of macromolecular antifreeze in the darkling beetle *Meracantha contracta*. *J. Comp. Physiol.* 115B:279–86

73. Patterson JL, Duman JG. 1978. The role of thermal hysteresis producing proteins in the low temperature tolerance and water balance of larvae of the mealworm, *Tenebrio molitor*. *J. Exp. Biol.* 74:37–45

74. Duman JG. 1979. Subzero temperature tolerance in spiders: the role of thermal hysteresis factors. *J. Comp. Physiol.* 131:347–52

75. Husby JA, Zachariassen ZE. 1980. Antifreeze agents in the body fluid of winter active insects and spiders. *Experientia* 36:963–64

76. Block W, Duman JG. 1989. Presence of thermal hysteresis producing antifreeze proteins in the Antarctic mite, *Alaskozetes antarcticus*. *J. Exp. Zool.* 250:229–31

77. Urrutia ME, Duman JG, Knight CA. 1992. Plant thermal hysteresis proteins. *Biochim. Biophys. Acta* 1121:199–206

78. Griffith M, Ala P, Yang DSC, Hon W-C, Moffatt BA. 1992. Antifreeze protein produced endogenously in winter rye leaves. *Plant Physiol.* 10:593–96

79. Hon WC, Griffith M, Mynarz A, Kwok YC, Yang DS. 1995. Antifreeze proteins in winter rye are similar to pathogenesis-related proteins. *Plant Physiol.* 109:879–89

80. Smallwood M, Worral D, Byass L, Elias L, Ashford D, et al. 1999. Isolation and characterization of a novel antifreeze protein from carrot (*Daucus carota*). *Biochem J.* 340:385–91

81. Wisniewski M, Webb R, Balsamo R, Close TJ, Yu XM, Griffith M. 1999. Purification, immunolocalization, cryoprotective, and antifreeze activity of PCA60: a dehydrin from peach (*Prunus persica*). *Physiol. Plant.* 105:600–8

82. Duman JG, Olsen TM. 1993. Thermal hysteresis protein activity in bacteria, fungi, and phylogenetically diverse plants. *Cryobiology* 30:322–28

83. Sun X, Griffith M, Pasternak JJ, Glick BR. 1995. Low temperature growth, freezing survival, and production of antifreeze protein by the plant growth promoting rhizobacterium *Pseudomonas putida* GR 12–2. *Can. J. Microbiol.* 41:776–84

84. Raymond JA, DeVries AL. 1977. Adsorption inhibition as a mechanism of freezing resistance in polar fishes. *Proc. Natl. Acad. Sci. USA* 74:2589–93

85. Raymond JA, Wilson PW, DeVries AL. 1989. Inhibition of growth on nonbasal planes in ice by fish antifreeze. *Proc. Natl. Acad. Sci. USA* 86(3):881–85

86. Knight CA, Cheng CC, DeVries AL. 1991. Adsorption of α-helical antifreeze peptides on specific ice crystal surface planes. *Biophys. J.* 59:409–18

87. Sicheri F, Yang DSC. 1995. Ice-binding structure and mechanism of an antifreeze protein from winter flounder. *Nature* 375:427–31

88. Cheng A, Merz KM. 1997. Ice-binding mechanism of winter flounder antifreeze proteins. *Biophys. J.* 73:2851–73

89. Chao H, Houston ME, Hodges RS, Kay CM, Sykes BD, et al. 1997. A diminished role for hydrogen bonds in antifreeze binding to ice. *Biochemistry* 36:14652–60

90. Zettel J. 1984. Cold hardiness strategies and thermal hysteresis in Collembola. *Rev. Ecol. Biol. Sol.* 21:189–03

91. Meier P, Zettel J. 1997. Cold hardiness in *Entomobrya nivalis* (Collembola, Entomobryidae): annual cycle of polyols and antifreeze proteins, and antifreeze triggering by temperature and photoperiod. *J. Comp. Physiol. B* 167:297–304

92. Gehrken U, Sömme L. 1987. Increased cold hardiness in eggs of *Arcynoptery compacta* (Plecoptera) by dehydration. *J. Insect Physiol.* 33:987–91

93. Duman JG. 1979. Thermal hysteresis factors in overwintering insects. *J. Insect Physiol.* 25:805–10

94. Patterson JL, Kelly TJ, Duman JG. 1981. Purification and composition of a thermal hysteresis producing protein from the milkweed bug *Oncopeltus fasciatus*. *J. Comp. Physiol.* 142B:539–42

95. Hew CL, Kao MH, So YP. 1983. Presence of cystine-containing antifreeze proteins in the spruce budworm, *Choristoneura fumiferana*. *Can. J. Zool.* 61:2324–28

96. Graham LA, Liow Y-C, Walker VK, Davies PL. 1997. Hyperactive antifreeze protein from beetles. *Nature* 388:727–28

97. Duman JG, Li N, Verleye D, Goetz FW, Wu DW. 1998. Molecular characterization and sequencing of antifreeze proteins from larvae of the beetle *Dendroides canadensis*. *J. Comp. Physiol. B* 168:225–32

98. Liou Y-C, Thibault P, Walker UK, Davies PL, Graham LA. 1999. A complex family of highly heterogeneous and internally repetitive hyperactive antifreeze proteins from the beetle *Tenebrio molitor*. *Biochemistry* 38:11415–24

99. Andorfer CA, Duman JG. 2000. Isolation and characterization of cDNA clones encoding antifreeze protein of the pyrochroid beetle *Dendroides canadensis*. *J. Insect Physiol.* 46:365–72

100. Li N, Chibber B, Castellino FJ,

Duman JG. 1998. Mapping of the disulfide bridges in antifreeze proteins from overwintering larvae of the beetle *Dendroides canadensis. Biochemistry* 37:6343–50

101. Liou Y-CL, Tocilj A, Davies PL, Jia X. 2000. Mimicry of ice structure by surface hydroxyls and water of a β-helix antifreeze protein. *Nature* 406:322–24

101a. Graether SP. Kulper MJ, Gagne SM, Walker VK, Jia Z, et al. 2000. β-helix structure and ice-binding properties of a hyperactive antifreeze protein from an insect. *Nature* 406:325–28

102. Tyshenko MG, Doucet D, Davies PL, Walker VK. 1997. The antifreeze potential of spruce budworm thermal hysteresis protein. *Nature Biotechnol.* 15:887–90

103. Gauthier SY, Kay CM, Sykes BD, Walker UK, Davies PL. 1998. Disulfide bond mapping and structural characterization of spruce budworm antifreeze protein. *Eur. J. Biochem.* 258:445–53

104. Zachariassen KE, Husby JA. 1982. Antifreeze effect of thermal hysteresis agents protects highly supercooled insects. *Nature* 298:865–67

105. Wu DW, Duman JG, Xu L. 1991. Enhancement of insect antifreeze protein activity by antibodies. *Biochim. Biophys. Acta* 1076:416–20

106. Deleted in proof

107. Salt RW. 1963. Delayed inoculative freezing of insects. *Can. Entomol.* 95:1190–202:

108. Humble LM, Ring RA. 1985. Inoculative freezing of a larval parasitoid within its host. *Cryo-Letters* 6:59–66

109. Gehrken U, Stromme A, Lundheim R, Zachariassen KE. 1991. Inoculative freezing in the overwintering Tenebrionid beetle, *Bolitophagus reticulatus* Panz. *J. Insect Physiol.* 37:683–87

110. Gehrken U. 1992. Inoculative freezing and thermal hysteresis in the adult bee-

tles *Ips acuminatus* and *Rhagin inquisitor. J. Insect Physiol.* 38:519–24

111. Rojas RR, Charlet LD, Leopold RA. 1992. A differential scanning calorimetric analysis of inoculative freezing in an insect. *Cryo-Letters* 13:355–62

112. Lee RE, Lee MR, Strong-Gunderson JM. 1993. Insect cold-hardiness and ice nucleating active microorganisms including their potential use for biological control. *J. Insect Physiol.* 39:1–12

113. Olsen TM, Sass SJ, Li N, Duman JG. 1998. Factors contributing to seasonal increases in inoculative freezing resistance in overwintering fire-colored beetle larvae *Dendroides canadensis* (Pyrochroidae). *J. Exp. Biol.* 201:1585–94

114. Duman JG, Olsen TM, Yeung KL, Jerva F. 1995. The roles of ice nucleators in cold tolerant invertebrates. See Ref. 14, pp. 201–19

115. Olsen TM, Duman JG. 1997/2. Maintenance of the supercooled state in the gut of overwintering Pyrochroid beetle larvae, *Dendroides canadensis*: role of gut ice nucleators and antifreeze proteins. *J. Comp. Physiol. B* 167:114–22

116. Duman JG. 1984. Thermal hysteresis antifreeze proteins in the midgut fluid of overwintering larvae of the beetle *Dendroides canadensis. J. Exp. Zool.* 230:355–61

117. Knight CA, DeVries AL, Oolman LD. 1984. Fish antifreeze protein and the freezing and recrystallization of ice. *Nature* 308:295–96

118. Knight CA, Duman JG. 1986. Inhibition of recrystallization of ice by insect thermal hysteresis proteins: a possible cryoprotective role. *Cryobiology* 23:256–62

119. Mazur P. 1970. Cryobiology: the freezing of biological systems. *Science* 168:939–49

120. Mazur P. 1984. Freezing of living cells: mechanisms and implications. *Am. J. Physiol. Cell Physiol.* 247:C125–C42

121. Tursman D, Duman JG. 1995. Cryoprotective effects of thermal hysteresis protein on survivorship of frozen gut cells from the freeze tolerant centipede *Lithobius forficatus*. *J. Exp. Zool.* 272:249–57

122. Farrant J. 1980. General observations on cell preservation. In *Low Temperature Preservation in Biology and Medicine*, ed. MJ Ashwood-Smith, J Farrant, pp. 1–8. Baltimore, MD: University Park Press

123. Sathyanesan S. 1999. *Purification and identification of thermal hysteresis and other cryoprotective proteins in the bittersweet nightshade* (Solanum dulcamara). PhD thesis, University of Notre Dame, Notre Dame, IN. 157 pp.

124. Huang T. 2000. *Expression of insect*, Dendroides canadensis, *antifreeze proteins in Arabidopsis and cloning of a thermal hysteresis (antifreeze) protein gene in* Solanum Dulcamara. PhD thesis, University of Notre Dame, Notre Dame, IN. 129 pp.

125. Rubinsky B, Arav A, Mattioli M, DeVries AL. 1990. The effect of antifreeze glycopeptides on membrane potential changes at hypothermic temperatures. *Biochem. Biophys. Acta* 173:1369–74

126. Rubinsky B, Arav A, DeVries AL. 1991. Cryopreservation of oocytes using directional cooling and antifreeze glycoproteins. *Cryo-Letters* 12:93–106

127. Rubinsky B, Arav A, Fletcher GL. 1991. Hypothermic protection—a fundamental property of "antifreeze" proteins. *Biochem. Biophys. Res. Commun.* 180:566–71

128. Carpenter JF, Hansen TN. 1992. Antifreeze protein modulates cell survival during cryopreservation: mediation through influence on ice crystal growth. *Proc. Natl. Acad. Sci. USA* 89:8953–57

129. DeVries AL. 1992. The use of antifreeze proteins in cryopreservation: facts and realities. *Cryobiology* 29:780–82

130. Sanford D, Young OA, Wilson P. 1992. Beef muscle frozen in the presence of antifreeze proteins. *Cryobiology* 29:30

131. Zhu Q, Yang X, Layne JR, DeVries AL, Wang T. 1992. Antifreeze glycoproteins from Antarctic Nototheniid fishes does not protect the cardiac explant during cryopreservation. *Cryobiology* 29:783–84

132. Hincha DK, DeVries AL, Schmitt JM. 1993. Cryotoxicity of antifreeze proteins and glycoproteins to spinach thylakoid membrane–comparison with cryotoxic sugar acids. *Biochem. Biophys. Acta* 1146:258–64

133. Ishiguro H, Rubinsky B. 1994. Mechanical interactions between ice crystals and red blood cells during directional solidification. *Cryobiology* 31:483–500

134. Tablin F, Oliver AE, Walker NJ, Crowe LM, Crowe JH. 1996. Membrane phase transition of intact human platelets. Correlation with cold-induced activation. *J. Cell Physiol.* 168:305–13

135. Duman JG. 1980. Factors involved in the overwintering survival of the freeze tolerant beetle *Dendroides canadensis*. *J. Comp. Physiol. B* 136:53–59

136. Duman JG. 1977. The effects of temperature, photoperiod and relative humidity on antifreeze protein production in larvae of the darkling beetle, *Meracantha contracta*. *J. Exp. Zool.* 201:233–37

137. Horwath KL, Duman JG. 1983. Photoperiodic and thermal regulation of antifreeze protein levels in the beetle *Dendroides canadensis*. *J. Insect Physiol.* 29:907–17

138. Horwath KL, Duman JG. 1986. Thermoperiodic involvement in antifreeze protein production in the cold hardy beetle *Dendroides canadensis*: implications for photoperiodic time measurement. *J. Insect Physiol.* 32:799–806

139. Horwath KL, Duman JG. 1982. Involvement of the circadian system in photoperiodic regulation of insect antifreeze proteins. *J. Exp. Zool.* 219:267–70

140. Horwath KL, Duman JG. 1984. Further studies on the involvement of the circadian system in photoperiodic control of antifreeze production in the beetle *Dendroides canadensis. J. Insect Physiol.* 30:947–55

141. Horwath KL, Duman JG. 1984. Yearly variations in the overwintering mechanism of the cold hardy beetle *Dendroides canadensis. Physiol. Zool.* 57:40–45

142. Duman JG. 1984. Change in overwintering mechanism in the Cucujid beetle, *Cucujus clavipes. J. Insect Physiol.* 30:235–39

143. Horwath KL, Duman JG. 1983a. Induction of antifreeze protein production by juvenile hormone in larvae of the beetle, *Dendroides canadensis. J. Comp. Physiol.* 151:233–40

144. Xu L, Duman JG, Goodman WG, Wu DW. 1992. A role for juvenile hormone in the induction of antifreeze protein production by the fat body in the beetle *Tenebrio molitor. Comp. Biochem. Physiol.* 101B:105–9

145. Xu L, Duman JG. 1991. Involvement of juvenile hormone in the induction of antifreeze protein production by the fat body of larvae of the beetle *Dendroides canadensis. J. Exp. Zool.* 258:288–93

Annu. Rev. Physiol. 2001. 63:359–90

ANTIFREEZE PROTEINS OF TELEOST FISHES

Garth L Fletcher[1], Choy L Hew[2], and Peter L Davies[3]

[1]Ocean Sciences Centre, Memorial University of Newfoundland, St. John's,
Newfoundland A1C 5S7, Canada; e-mail: fletcher@afprotein.com;
[2]Department of Biological Sciences, The National University of Singapore, 10 Kent Ridge
Cres., Singapore 119260; e-mail: choyhew9@hotmail.com;
[3]Department of Biochemistry, Queen's University, Kingston, Ontario K7L 3N6, Canada;
e-mail: daviesp@post.queensu.ca

Key Words   thermal hysteresis, ice, evolution, natural selection, gene expression

■ **Abstract**   Marine teleosts at high latitudes can encounter ice-laden seawater that
is approximately 1°C colder than the colligative freezing point of their body fluids.
They avoid freezing by producing small antifreeze proteins (AFPs) that adsorb to
ice and halt its growth, thereby producing an additional non-colligative lowering of
the freezing point. AFPs are typically secreted by the liver into the blood. Recently,
however, it has become clear that AFP isoforms are produced in the epidermis (skin,
scales, fin, and gills) and may serve as a first line of defense against ice propagation
into the fish. The basis for the adsorption of AFPs to ice is something of a mystery
and is complicated by the extreme structural diversity of the five antifreeze types.
Despite the recent acquisition of several AFP three-dimensional structures and the
definition of their ice-binding sites by mutagenesis, no common ice-binding motif or
even theme is apparent except that surface-surface complementarity is important for
binding. The remarkable diversity of antifreeze types and their seemingly haphazard
phylogenetic distribution suggest that these proteins might have evolved recently in
response to sea level glaciation occurring just 1–2 million years ago in the northern
hemisphere and 10–30 million years ago around Antarctica. Not surprisingly, the expression of AFP genes from different origins can also be quite dissimilar. The most
intensively studied system is that of the winter flounder, which has a built-in annual cycle of antifreeze expression controlled by growth hormone (GH) release from
the pituitary in tune with seasonal cues. The signal transduction pathway, transcription factors, and promoter elements involved in this process are just beginning to be
characterized.

INTRODUCTION

It has been thirty years since DeVries and colleagues (1, 2) first discovered antifreeze proteins (AFPs) in the blood plasma of Antarctic Nototheniids, thus establishing the paradigm that such proteins are essential to the survival of marine
teleosts inhabiting ice-laden waters. This discovery opened up a fascinating and

0066-4278/01/0315-0359$14.00

exciting field of research into the role such proteins play in preventing or reducing the damage caused by freezing to living organisms. AFPs have an appeal to scientists and lay-folk alike, for they can be found in many life forms—bacteria, fungi, plants, insects, and vertebrates—that encounter, or are in danger of encountering, freezing conditions in nature. AFPs are a subject of study in many disciplines; from ice physics to chemistry, from molecular biology to physiology, and from fisheries oceanography and ecology to evolutionary biology, and in recent years they have sparked the interest of the business community.

For over 20 years since their initial discovery, it was believed that AFPs were produced centrally by the liver and secreted into the blood to be distributed throughout the extracellular space. These proteins were thought to prevent the fish from freezing in ice-laden seawater, solely by reducing the freezing temperature of the extracellular fluids to safe levels. However, this line of thinking changed completely with the discovery that the winter flounder possesses two distinctly different antifreeze gene families, one of which is expressed in the liver to provide a central supply of antifreeze to the blood, and another that is expressed predominantly in gill and skin epithelia for the exclusive protection of the cells and tissues that come into direct contact with external ice (3). In addition to conferring freeze protection to the whole animal and to external epithelia, emerging evidence indicates that AFPs can interact with mammalian cell membranes and protect them from cold damage. This provocative information suggests that these proteins may also play a role in the cold acclimation process itself as reviewed by Fletcher et al (4). These recent discoveries, particularly the latter, have yet to stand the test of time. However, they have certainly prompted us to reexamine our thinking and views about the physiological functioning of AFPs in fish.

The topic of AFPs in fish was discussed in the *Annual Review of Physiology* 1983 (5), and there are a number of excellent recent reviews on AFPs to which the reader should refer (4, 6–10). Rather than try to present all aspects of AFPs in fish, the present review focuses on topics that are of current interest: (*a*) the enduring puzzle of how AFPs bind to ice; (*b*) the largely unexplored area of AFP gene expression, including tissue specificity, by which protection from freezing is afforded to the whole organism in a metabolically cost-effective manner; and (*c*) the remarkable examples AFPs provide of recent evolution in response to environmental change.

ANTIFREEZE PROTEINS AND ICE

It has been more than forty years since Scholander and colleagues traveled to the coast of Labrador to determine why marine teleosts do not freeze during the winter when the water temperature ($-1.9°C$) declined a full degree below the freezing point of their body fluids ($-0.7°C$) (11). They never found out why the fish did not freeze. However, they did discover that although some fish could survive in an undercooled state, if they were brought into contact with ice they immediately froze and died. This established the fundamentals of the problem for teleost fish: the combination of undercooling and ice contact is lethal.

Ten years later DeVries & Wohlschlag (1) found that the answer to Scholander's question resided with a family of plasma proteins that could lower the freezing temperature of the blood several hundred times better than any other known dissolved solute. This non-colligative lowering of the freezing point or thermal hysteresis (12) is entirely attributable to the structure of these unique proteins that enables them to bind to and prevent embryonic ice crystals from growing (13). These plasma proteins, collectively termed AFPs, are primarily synthesized in the liver and secreted into the blood stream to be distributed throughout the extracellular and interstitial space.

Antifreeze Activity Assays: Thermal Hysteresis

Thermal hysteresis is readily measured in vitro with the use of a Clifton nanoliter osmometer. Sub-microliter volumes of AFP solution are introduced into an oil droplet held by surface tension in a cylindrical well drilled into a metal plate, which is placed on a cooling stage and viewed under a microscope (32x magnification). Sample temperature is controlled by a Peltier device with a read-out in mOsmols, where 1000 mOsmols corresponds to 1.86°C. Observation through a microscope provides opportunities for still and video photography to record ice crystal morphology and monitor the absence of growth during the thermal hysteresis measurement.

One variable that can influence the thermal hysteresis reading is the rate of cooling. We lower the stage temperature by 10 mOsmol increments at 15 s intervals. When these parameters are followed, the readings are consistent and reproducible when compared both in-house and on nanoliter osmometers at other locations, and thermal hysteresis is not significantly increased by slower cooling. However, more rapid cooling can substantially decrease the non-equilibrium freezing point and hence the thermal hysteresis value. This is particularly noticeable when insect AFPs are being assayed. The latter may have thermal hysteresis values of 5–6°C (14), such that each measurement would take well over an hour to complete at this rate of cooling.

Another potential variable that is hard to control or even quantify is the size of the ice crystal present during the thermal hysteresis measurement. We note that larger ice crystals tend to burst at higher temperatures than do small crystals. This can be rationalized by considering that the surface area under containment by AFPs is a function of crystal size and that freezing can occur with the breakdown of that containment at any point of the crystal surface (Figure 1*B*). A complicating factor counterbalancing this effect is that starting crystal size is a reflection of AFP activity. The greater the AFP activity, the smaller the crystal formed in the melt.

Do AFPs Bind Irreversibly to Ice?

It has been argued by Knight & DeVries (15) that AFP binding to ice must be irreversible. Dissociation of an AFP from the ice at temperatures within the thermal

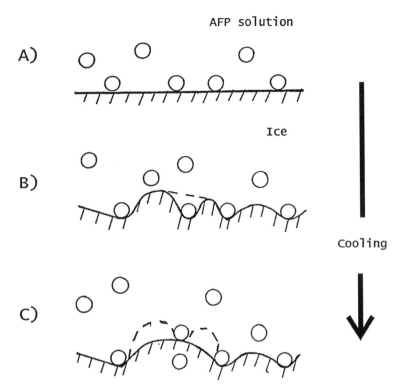

Figure 1 Inhibition of ice crystal growth following AFP adsorption. (*A*) AFP (open circles) in solution and in contact with the ice front (hatched line) at $0°C$. (*B*) The ice-water interface at an undercooling approaching the non-equilibrium freezing point, where the curvature between bound AFPs leads to ice growth inhibition by the Kelvin effect. The dotted line represents the overgrowth of a bound AFP. (*C*) Binding of an AFP from solution to the point of overgrowth in (*B*). Here the dotted line represents subsequent stabilization of the ice-water interface around the newly bound AFP. This figure is based on the two-dimensional representations of ice-growth inhibitions displayed in Knight & DeVries (15) and Knight (17).

hysteresis range would provide an opportunity for water to join the crystal lattice, particularly since water is present at 55M and AFPs at mM concentrations. Even if the AFPs rapidly rebound to the crystal, there would be some addition of water to the ice. Given that the ice crystals observed during thermal hysteresis measurements (~50 μm in length) might be bound by millions of AFPs, the net effect would be slow growth of the crystal. This would be lethal to fish unless they had a mechanism for removing or melting the ice. In practice, we have observed an ice crystal during thermal hysteresis readings for as long as five days without seeing any signs of growth.

The idea of irreversible binding between a ligand (ice) and receptor (AFP) without covalent bond formation is difficult to accept. Even the most avid binding interactions have a finite dissociation constant. However, unlike most ligand-receptor interactions, the contact site is potentially extensive and may involve multiple interactions—all of which must be broken simultaneously for the AFP to escape. We argue that this event has zero probability of occurring with wild-type AFPs. However, when the ice-binding site is modified by mutations, particularly those that spoil surface-surface complementarity, the altered AFP typically allows slow growth of the ice crystal (16). With mild mutants, growth is so slow that it is only detectable by video microscopy, in which case an end-point to the assay is observed as the ice crystal bursts at the non-equilibrium freezing point. Typically, however, this thermal hysteresis value is lower than that of the wild-type at all concentrations tested, and the activity of the mutant can be expressed as a percentage of the wild-type's thermal hysteresis value (Figure 2A). With more severe mutations, growth is obvious during the 15 s delay between cooling increments and, by definition, the non-equilibrium freezing point has been exceeded (e.g. A21L in Figure 2A,B). Indeed, growth can be so rapid that an obvious burst point is not reached before the ice crystal fills the aqueous compartment in the well. With the most severe mutations, affinity for ice is completely lost, as evidenced by the absence of ice crystal shaping, and the protein is no longer recognizable as an AFP (e.g. A17L in Figure 2B).

We can think of AFP binding to ice as having a threshold value above which it is irreversible, below which there is a gradation of affinities for ice that is reflected in how rapidly the ice crystal grows. Through natural selection, AFPs have evolved to bind irreversibly to ice, i.e. to be above the threshold value. But this leads to another quandary. If binding is irreversible, an ice crystal surface could be readily saturated in the presence of excess AFPs. Why then is thermal hysteresis dependent on AFP concentration (15, 17)? To some extent the local concentration of AFP may influence the surface density of AFPs because of diffusion effects. Note that various studies support the model of ice growth inhibition with incomplete coverage of the ice surface by AFPs (18). A further explanation might lie in events that occur immediately prior to the end-point of thermal hysteresis, i.e. at the new non-equilibrium freezing temperature. This end-point is likely to be triggered by the overgrowth of an AFP and the coalescence of the surrounding ice fronts (Figure 1B). This stochastic event could presumably occur at any point on the crystal as determined by the random spacing between millions of bound AFPs. There would be two possible outcomes. One would be uncontrolled addition of water to the ice. The other would be the re-establishment of control by binding of additional AFPs to the coalesced ice front (Figure 1C). In essence, there would be competition between water and AFP for binding to ice. The higher the local AFP concentration the more likely an antifreeze would bind. Because there would not be sufficient time for diffusion to bring AFPs to the site of growth, the lowering of the non-equilibrium freezing point would be related to local AFP concentration.

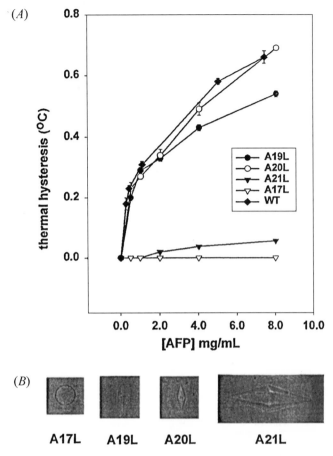

Figure 2 Effect of steric mutations on thermal hysteresis activity and ice crystal morphology produced by type I AFP. (*A*) Plot of thermal hysteresis (°C) as a function of AFP concentration (mg/mL) for the synthetic HPLC-6 isoform of type I AFP (WT) and variants where single Ala residues were replaced with Leu. WT (♦), A17L (∇), A19L (●), A20L (○), A21L (▾). (*B*) Ice crystal morphology obtained by the four different variants. Taken from Baardsnes et al (48) with permission.

AFP Diversity

Following discovery of antifreeze glycoproteins (AFGPs) in the blood plasma of Antarctic Nototheniids in the late 1960s and early 1970s, some very different AFPs were found in fishes of the northern hemisphere as more and more marine teleosts were surveyed for the presence of thermal hysteresis activity (Figure 3). Type I AFP was reported in winter flounder (19), type II in sea raven (20), type III in ocean pout (21), and most recently type IV in longhorn sculpin (22). A comparison of their properties can be found in several recent reviews (4, 6–10). Briefly, AFGPs are made up of 4 to more than 50 tandem repeats of Ala-Ala-Thr with a disaccharide (galactosyl-N-acetylgalactosamine) attached to each Thr OH. It is thought that AFGPs fold as an amphipathic polyproline type II helix. Type I AFPs are alanine-rich, amphipathic α-helices. Type II AFPs are globular proteins with mixed secondary structure. Type III AFP is made up of short β-strands and one helix turn that gives it a unique flat-faced globular fold. Based on homology to serum lipoproteins and partial proteolysis studies, type IV AFP is thought to be a helix-bundle protein (23). The classification scheme of Davies & Hew (24) has proved useful and durable. With the exception of type IV AFP, newly discovered AFPs from unrelated fishes have fitted into a pre-existing type (Figure 3). For example, AFGPs in the northern cods (25) are remarkably similar to the Nototheniid AFGPs in sequence and distribution of size classes based on the glycotripeptide repeat. The sculpin AFPs are alanine-rich, single α-helical peptides that clearly resemble the flounder type I AFPs. Type I AFPs have also been recently detected in liparids and the cunner (RP Evans, MH Kao & GL Fletcher, unpublished data). Also, lectin-like Type II AFPs have subsequently been found in smelt (26) and herring (27).

One explanation for AFP diversity is that ice can present many different surfaces for binding. Although ice is made up solely of oxygen and hydrogen, with the O atoms in a tetrahedral arrangement linked by hydrogen bonds, the spacing between these atoms and the resulting surface contours will typically be different on different planes. Binding to any nonbasal plane is sufficient to inhibit ice growth and shape its crystal into a hexagonal bipyramid. Different AFP types do indeed bind to different ice planes, as was established by Knight et al (28), who developed the technique of ice etching to determine the plane (and in some cases the direction) of binding of AFPs to ice. In this method, an oriented hemisphere of ice is allowed to continue growing in the presence of a dilute solution of the AFP. The AFP concentration is insufficient to halt growth of the hemisphere. Instead, the proteins bind to their preferred planes and are continuously overgrown. On removal of the hemisphere to a walk-in freezer, the binding surfaces are revealed during sublimation by the residue of AFP.

This technique has worked particularly well for the winter flounder (type I) AFP, which binds to the pyramidal plane {20–21}. This binding should produce hexagonal bipyramidal crystals with a c- to a-axis ratio of 3.3:1, which is close to that observed during thermal hysteresis measurements using the nanoliter osmometer (Figure 2). Other fish AFPs like the AFGPs and type III AFP have been shown to bind on or close to a prism plane (29). They also form hexagonal bipyramidal crystals, but with c- to a-axis ratios that are lower than expected and that vary slightly with AFP concentration. One explanation for this ice crystal morphology is that the pyramidal surfaces might be formed by step-growth inhibition on the molecular scale, where the AFP binds to a prism plane (riser) but covers part of the basal plane (step) (16, 30).

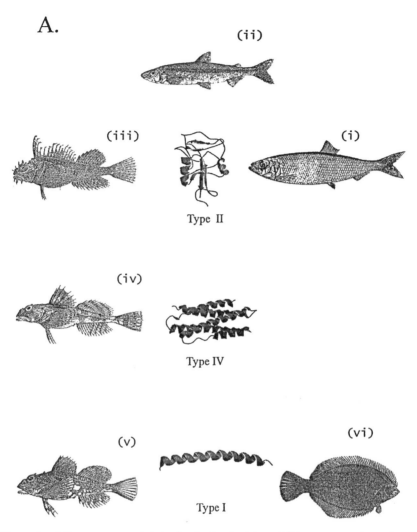

A.

(ii)

(iii)   Type II   (i)

(iv)

Type IV

(v)   Type I   (vi)

Figure 3 AFP structures and their distribution in fishes. Ribbon presentations of AFP structures from Davies & Sykes (7) are shown alongside fishes in which they occur. The AFGPs of cods and Nototheniids are represented by their glycotripeptide repeat. (*A*) (*i*) Atlantic herring (*Clupea harengus harengus*), (*ii*) American smelt (*Osmerus mordax*), (*iii*) sea raven (*Hemitripterus americanus*), (*iv*) longhorn sculpin (*Myoxocephalus octodec-imspinosus*), (*v*) shorthorn sculpin (*Myoxocephalus scorpius*), (*vi*) winter flounder (*Pleu-ronectes americanus*). (*B*) (*vii*) *Dissostichus mawsoni*, (*viii*) Arctic cod (*Boreogadus saida*), (*ix*) ocean pout (*Macrozoarces americanus*), (*x*) *Lycodichthys dearborni*. Fish pictures were reproduced from Leim & Scott (142) with the exception of *vii* and *x*, which came from Eastman (143). The figure is based on an earlier representation (9).

B.

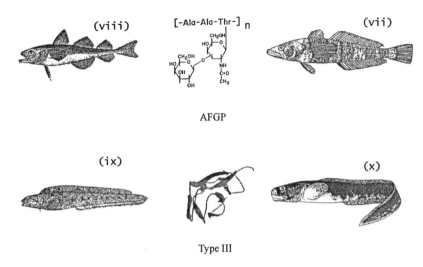

Figure 3 *(Continued)*

Structure-Function Relationships in the AFPs

Although the properties and amino acid sequences of the fish AFP support their classification into five nonhomologous types, this does not rule out the possibility that the AFPs might share a common three-dimensional ice-binding motif or principle. The drive to solve their three-dimensional structures has been largely fueled by the need to understand their structure-function relationships that are key to binding ice.

Type I AFP

Type I AFP from the winter flounder was the first AFP to have its three-dimensional structure determined. As anticipated by CD measurements and secondary structure predictions (31), it does indeed exist as a single, long, amphipathic, α-helix (32). The higher resolution X-ray structure revealed elaborate N- and C-terminal helix capping structures (33), which together with the internal salt bridge and high Ala content are the main reasons why such a long helix has stability, at least close to $0°C$ (31). The high-resolution structure also revealed the orientation of the putative ice-binding amino acid side chains, which was an issue for fitting the AFP to ice. When the first type I AFP amino acid sequence was determined by DeVries & Lin (34), these authors suggested a mechanism for AFP adsorption to ice whereby the regularly spaced hydrophilic Thr and Asx residues might hydrogen bond to oxygen atoms on the primary prism plane of ice. Subsequently, Knight et al (28) demonstrated that the adsorption surface was the {20–21} pyramidal plane of ice rather than a prism plane and that the helix was oriented in the ⟨01–12⟩ direction on this plane. In effect, the same mechanism was invoked, only with a different periodicity where the threonines, spaced 16.5 Å apart at the start of each 11-amino acid repeat on the same side of the helix, matched specific O atoms on the binding surface that repeated at 16.7 Å intervals. The first of many models was produced where the $i,i+3$ Asx also hydrogen bonded to ice with the same spacing, and the $i,i-1$ Leu were thought to provide some van der Waals interactions with the ice surface (35). This trinity of residues was dubbed an ice-binding motif, even though there was little if any experimental evidence that these residues contacted ice (33).

In the interim, concerns about the paucity of hydrogen bonds that could be involved in binding the AFP to ice were addressed by two imaginative proposals. Wen & Laursen suggested that type I AFPs might bind to ice as a patch of helices similarly oriented and stabilized by side-by-side protein-protein interactions (35). Only with cooperative binding of the helices to ice would the number of hydrogen bonds be sufficient for irreversible adsorption. An elegant test of this hypothesis was set up with the synthesis of an all D-amino acid type I enantiomer (36). This bound to the same {20–21} plane, but in the mirror image direction to the all L-amino acid enantiomer. The mixture of these two enantiomers was predicted to provide some interference to helix patch formation. This was not observed, as a 50:50 mixture of the two enantiomers was just as active as the all-D or all-L forms. A similar result was obtained with mixtures of three AFP types (I, II, and III) which, coming from different fishes, were intrinsically unlikely to form protein-protein interactions, but also bound to different planes of ice (37). Although the type I AFP results were rationalized in terms of helix sorting into patches of the same handedness (36), our interpretation was that each AFP bound singly and was independently active. This was proven for type III AFP by fusing this 7-kDa protein to proteins that were large enough to block side-by-side associations of the AFP (38).

The other proposal for bringing more hydrogen bonds to bear on AFP binding was the suggestion that functional groups such as the Thr hydroxyls might occupy an O atom site in the ice surface (39). In this instance, the O atom of the amino acid side chain would be hydrogen bonded to three ice oxygen atoms (and covalently linked to the AFP—thus having a tetrahedral arrangement). In a sense, the AFP would be frozen to the ice surface through its Thr side chains. However, the orientation of the Thr hydroxyl revealed by X-ray crystallography was toward the helix backbone, which is not suitable for penetration of the ice lattice (33). NMR studies showed that while the Thr side chain did occupy other rotameric conformations in solution, its most preferred conformation matched that seen in the crystal structure (40).

Although these data from the three-dimensional structures do not rule out a Thr side chain rearrangement on binding to ice, a more serious challenge to the hydrogen bonding hypothesis has come from amino acid replacement studies. When the central two of four Thr were replaced by Ser, there was a major decrease in thermal hysteresis activity (41). The Ser mutant had no activity below 2 mg/mL and had greatly reduced activity above this concentration. Similar results were obtained by Zhang & Laursen (42) and Haymet et al (43), who replaced all four Thr with Ser. This was surprising because the absence of the methyl group in the Ser side chain should have made it easier for the OH group to occupy an ice lattice O atom. Also surprising was the observation that Val was a relatively good substitute for the central two Thr, with only a 20% loss of thermal hysteresis activity (41). This result was confirmed and extended by Haymet who showed that a type I variant with all four Thr replaced by Val was functional, although less active than the wild-type (43). To keep this variant in solution it was necessary to add two more salt bridges (44). These results suggested that the Thr methyl group might have an important role in AFP binding which, together with the realization that fish AFPs are rather hydrophobic proteins (45, 46), has called into question the primacy of hydrogen bonds in fish AFP adsorption to ice (41).

Subsequent amino acid replacement studies indicated that Asx and Leu might be important for peptide solubility but failed to find a role for these two amino acids in ice binding (47). Indeed, a comparison of type I AFP isoforms from right-eye flounders shows that Asx and Leu are not well conserved. The region of the type I AFP that is perfectly well conserved is the Ala-rich face and the adjoining Thr residues. By substituting the bulky amino acid Leu for Ala at intervals around the helix at the mid-point of the molecule, we were able to establish the importance for ice binding of Ala 17 and Ala 21, the Ala residues immediately next to the Thr methyl group (48). Thus, although the nature of the binding forces are not established, it does appear that the hydrophobic face of the type I AFP helix is the ice-binding surface rather than the traditional ice-binding motifs defined by Sicheri & Yang (33).

Type III AFP

The type II AFP structure was determined by NMR methods and is of medium precision (49). Also, because of the difficulties of making and producing mutants of this AFP, its ice-binding site has not been pinpointed (50). The only other fish AFP for which there is a detailed structure and a finely mapped ice-binding site, is type III AFP. A high-resolution X-ray structure (to 1.25 Å) and a high precision NMR structure have been obtained for a recombinant QAE isoform (30, 46) and an X-ray structure for a natural SP isoform (51). The ice-binding site was identified by site-directed mutagenesis after targeting conserved, hydrophilic, solvent- exposed residues that were exposed on one face of the protein (52). In retrospect, the whole ice-binding surface is relatively hydrophobic, and the potential for the hydrophilic side chains to hydrogen bond to ice is limited. Tight packing of the side chains on this surface would not allow them to project into the ice surface or even to change orientations to adopt a more favorable conformation. Thus, there are notable similarities between AFP types I and III in the overall hydrophobicity of the ice-binding surface and the difficulty of modeling a large number of hydrogen bonds to ice. In marked contrast to these two fish AFPs, one (and possibly both) of the recently solved insect AFP structures has solvent-exposed Thr, which are oriented in such a position that their hydroxyls can occupy O atom positions in the ice lattice without steric hindrance (53, 54). It is not known if this structural distinction has any bearing on the higher thermal hysteresis activity shown by insect AFPs compared with fish AFPs.

In light of the known and predicted fish and insect AFP structures, it is possible to reclassify them as repetitive and nonrepetitive. The repetitive AFPs include the AFGPs, type I AFP with its underlying 11-amino-acid repeat, and the two insect AFPs, where each β-helix turn brings a Thr-Xaa-Thr (where Xaa is any amino acid) ice-binding motif into register on one side of the coil. These repetitive structures typically suggest a lattice match to ice. AFP types II and III show no signs of repeating elements in their amino acid sequences or three-dimensional structures, although there is evidence for a secondary structure repeat in type III AFP (51). Type IV is difficult to classify at this time. However, it has been pointed out that some of its homologs have an obvious 22-amino-acid repeat (8). Irrespective of how fish AFPs are classified, these diverse protein structures binding to different planes of ice have remarkably similar thermal hysteresis activities, approaching $1°C$ at mM AFP concentrations.

PHYSIOLOGICAL FUNCTION
OF ANTIFREEZE PROTEINS

As a general rule, cells are well protected from intracellular freezing at high freezing temperatures owing to the nature of the cell membrane and the spatial requirements for ice growth (55). Therefore freezing of intact tissues, organs, and whole organisms at high-freezing temperatures is, in the first instance, confined to the extracellular fluids. Thus it is evident that the addition of AFPs to the extracellular fluids of fish will not only protect these fluids from freezing, but also protect the entire animal. There is abundant evidence to demonstrate that the freezing temperature of blood plasma is a reasonable approximation of the freezing point of intact fish (56–58). In addition, intraperitoneal injections of purified AFP into rainbow trout improved their freezing resistance in direct proportion to the levels of AFP found in the blood (59).

In order for an undercooled fish to freeze, ice must propagate into it from the external environment. Several studies have shown that biological membranes can be effective at preventing ice propagation to undercooled fluids (55, 60, 61). Valerio et al (61) used a modified Ussing chamber to determine the temperature at which ice would propagate across isolated winter flounder and ocean pout skin, and ocean pout urinary and gall bladder epithelia. This study demonstrated that not only did these epithelial tissues act as effective barriers to ice propagation, but that the ice propagation temperatures were lower than the freezing point of seawater (4). In acute experiments, where fish that have had no prior exposure to ice are incrementally cooled below their freezing point prior to ice exposure, it is evident that the nucleating ice must enter the fish at a location other than the skin. Of the two possible routes, gills and gut, the most likely would be the gills where the epithelium consists of a single-cell layer (62).

Two indirect lines of evidence indicate that ice crystals do gain entry to fish inhabiting ice-laden seawater without the fish suffering lethal consequences. DeVries (63) reported on a number of experiments whereby fish that had been residing in or exposed to ice-laden seawater would freeze when exposed to ice-free water at temperatures well below the freezing point of seawater ($-2.7°$C). He concluded from these observations that fish inhabiting icy waters contain ice crystals. Another line of evidence comes from a study by Verdier et al (64) who used ice nucleation as an assay to detect the presence of anti-ice Igs in the blood sera of two marine fish species (ocean pout and Atlantic herring) that produce AFP and inhabit icy waters during winter. Anti-ice Igs were not found in rainbow trout, tilapia, and bighead carp, freshwater species that had no prior exposure to ice at temperatures below the colligative freezing points of their body fluids. The presence of circulating anti-ice Igs suggests that ice crystals do gain entry into the marine fish species and remain for a time sufficient to elicit an immune response.

The evidence that ice can enter and reside within fish that produce AFPs is consistent with our current understanding of the mode of antifreeze action. As ice crystals enter the extracellular fluids of fish, they are prevented from further growth by being bound up by AFPs. Only when the fish encounter temperatures that are too low for the AFPs to inhibit ice crystal growth will they suffer the lethal consequences of freezing.

Although the hypothesis that plasma AFPs function to prevent the growth of ice crystals that gain entry into the fish seems robust, it raises questions as to the mechanisms of freeze resistance availed by other fish that produce little or no plasma AFPs yet reside in the same icy environment. One such example is the cunner (*Tautogolabrus adspersus*), which inhabits Newfoundland waters. This marine species overwinters in relatively shallow areas where it can be exposed to ice at temperatures as low as -1.6 to $-1.8°$C each winter. Plasma freezing points approximate $-0.77°$C, and we have rarely seen any evidence for the presence of plasma AFPs. On the occasions that we have obtained some evidence, the levels have been low as judged by thermal hysteresis measurements ($<0.1°$C) (65; GL Fletcher & MH Kao, unpublished data). This species clearly overwinters in an undercooled state, and we speculate that it likely survives by entering a near-torpid state, finding refuge in rock crevices and relying on an epidermis fortified by antifreeze to provide a barrier to ice propagation that is only penetrated under extreme conditions.

REGULATION OF PLASMA ANTIFREEZE PROTEIN PRODUCTION

All the antifreeze-producing teleosts that inhabit the waters off the Northeastern coast of North America show a distinct seasonal cycle in the level of AFPs observed in the blood plasma. There is, however, considerable species variation in the timing of this cycle. Within the coastal waters of Newfoundland, where the water temperatures range from 16°C during summer to as low as −1.8°C during winter, shorthorn sculpin (*Myoxocephalus scorpius*) and winter flounder (*Pleuronectes americanus*) produce AFPs well before environmental freezing conditions occur (66, 67). Juvenile cod (*Gadus morhua*) also produce AFGP prior to the onset of winter, whereas adults synthesize them only in response to freezing conditions (66, 68). Ocean pout (*Macrozoarces americanus*) possess high concentrations of AFP year round, although winter levels are several-fold greater than those observed during summer (69).

There are also significant population differences in the levels of AFPs produced by ocean pout and juvenile cod (69–71), and in winter flounder, there are clear differences in the time of the onset of antifreeze production between geographically distant populations (72). At the molecular level there appears to be a strong positive correlation between antifreeze gene dosage, antifreeze protein levels, and the environmental freezing conditions to which the fish are exposed. Newfoundland winter flounder residing in shallow coastal waters produce high concentrations of plasma AFP (10–15 mg/ml) during the winter and have approximately 30–40 copies of the liver-specific AFP genes (73). The yellowtail flounder (*Pleuronectes ferrugenia*), a close relative of the winter flounder, can also be exposed to subzero temperatures. However by virtue of its deeper water habitat it faces little or no danger of freezing by ice contact. This species has only one third of the AFP gene copy number observed in winter flounder and produces considerably less plasma AFP (2–4 mg/ml) (74).

A more striking example of the relationship between gene dosage and plasma AFP levels comes from the ocean pout. Plasma AFP levels in Newfoundland populations of ocean pout are five to ten times higher than those found in ocean pout from a more southerly New Brunswick population, where subzero water temperatures and ice occur considerably less frequently than in Newfoundland (69). Genomic Southern blots reveal that the basis for these differences likely lies with AFP gene dosage. Newfoundland populations have approximately 150 AFP gene copies, whereas ocean pout from New Brunswick have 30–40 (75).

The distinct seasonal cycles of plasma AFP concentrations in these cold-temperate fish provides a unique opportunity to study environmental, physiological and molecular factors involved in AFP gene regulation. Most of our research into the regulation of AFP production has been carried out on the winter flounder. This is largely because of its year-round accessibility in Newfoundland coastal waters and because it was the first nonglycosylated AFP to be described.

The annual cycle of AFP production and secretion into the blood has been extensively studied in the winter flounder. All the flounder within a particular geographical location are highly synchronous in their annual cycle, with little year-to-year variation in timing (72, 76). In Newfoundland waters the annual cycle of plasma AFP levels correlates closely with the annual cycle of seawater temperatures. AFP appears in the plasma during November as the water temperature declines below 8°C, reaches peak levels of 10–15 mg/ml during winter, and clears from the plasma as the temperature rises above 0°C. Peak levels of AFP during winter reduce the plasma freezing temperature to approximately −1.7°C. Because plasma freezing temperatures are a good indicator of a fish's freezing temperature, it is evident that the AFP improves the flounder's freeze resistance to the freezing point of seawater (59).

The liver was found to be the source of the plasma AFP, and cDNA cloning demonstrated that the AFP was encoded in liver mRNAs as preproproteins. The pre-sequence is removed cotranslationally, and the proAFP is secreted into the blood where the pro-sequence is removed within 24 h to yield a 37-amino-acid mature AFP (77–81). With the use of these cDNA probes it was determined that AFP mRNA appears in the liver in October, approximately one month prior to the appearance of AFP in the plasma, and declines during March and April, when water temperatures are still less than 0°C (82, 83).

The environmental factors regulating this annual cycle have been reviewed in detail by Davies et al (84) and Chan et al (85). Water temperature does not appear to play a major role in initiating or preventing the initiation of AFP mRNA or AFP synthesis in the fall, nor does it appear to be involved in terminating AFP production in the spring. However, it is important that the temperature be sufficiently low (<8°C) for AFP mRNA to accumulate and direct the synthesis of winter levels of plasma AFP (86–88). Similar effects of temperature on the turnover of type I AFP and its mRNA have been observed in transgenic tobacco and *Drosophila*, where the mRNA is destabilized at room temperature (89, 90). Photoperiod appears to act as the zeitgeber for the onset of AFP production by the liver in the fall. Long day lengths (>14 h) result in delays of several months in the appearance of liver AFP mRNA and plasma AFP levels, and in some instances complete suppression. Short day lengths (4–8 h) did not have any effect on the onset of AFP appearance in the plasma, suggesting the possibility that it is the loss of long-day lengths in the fall that allows AFP synthesis to proceed on schedule (83, 86, 91).

This effect of photoperiod on the annual cycle of plasma antifreeze production likely acts through the central nervous system to control the release of GH from the pituitary. Hypophysectomy during the summer results in the induction of liver AFP synthesis and subsequent elevation of plasma AFP levels. Pituitary transplants or the administration of pituitary extracts or purified growth hormone (GH) represses AFP gene transcription, thereby preventing the synthesis of AFP and its subsequent accumulation in the plasma (91–95).

Precisely how GH controls the annual cycle of antifreeze synthesis by the liver is unknown. It is assumed that there is an annual cycle of GH release from the pituitary gland that regulates the synthesis of insulin-like growth factor (IGF-1) by the liver, as has been observed for other teleosts (96–98). Recent experiments have demonstrated that IGF-1 can inhibit liver-type AFP gene enhancer activity in transient expression assays in cell culture. This inhibition was reversed by the use of wortomanin, a P13-kinase inhibitor believed to be one of the downstream factors for IGF-1 signaling. These results suggest that the GH/IGF-1 signaling pathways are important for liver AFP gene regulation (M Miao, SL Chan, GL Fletcher & CL Hew, unpublished data).

The hypothesis that growth hormone is responsible for regulating the annual cycle of plasma AFP levels by repressing AFP gene transcription during the summer is consistent with what is known about the annual life cycle of the winter flounder. Newfoundland winter flounder do not feed or grow during the winter months, a time when liver AFP mRNA and plasma AFP levels are at their peak. They resume feeding in April, when liver AFP mRNA has declined to background levels and cease feeding during October when AFP mRNA first appears in the liver (91, 99).

SKIN ANTIFREEZE PROTEINS

Until the 1990s it was generally accepted that the synthesis of AFPs was confined to the liver from where they were secreted into the blood. The significance of a report by Schneppenheim & Theede (100) on the isolation of AFP from the skin of European shorthorn sculpin, where none was evident in the plasma, went unrecognized. Subsequently, Valerio et al found evidence for antifreeze activity in the skin of cunner, another species that appeared to have no AFP in the plasma (65). However, the importance of these findings was not fully realized until Gong et al (101) demonstrated the presence of AFP mRNA transcripts in a variety of tissues in winter flounder and ocean pout, indicating that AFP synthesis was widespread in these fish. Gong et al (3) solidified this concept when, upon a detailed examination of a skin cDNA library from the winter flounder, they discovered that there were two distinct antifreeze gene families: the already well-known liver-type (wflAFP) whose expression is highly liver specific, and a skin-type (wfsAFP) that is expressed in many tissues, but most abundantly in the external epithelia (Table 1). Another observation made in this seminal paper was that the skin-type AFPs differed from the liver-type AFPs in that they lacked the pre- and pro-sequences. This lack of a secretory signal sequence (pre-sequence) suggests that these skin-type AFPs might remain and function intracellularly. Recently, skin-type AFPs have been discovered in shorthorn and longhorn sculpins (102; WK Low, Q Lin, C Stathakis, M Miao, GL Fletcher & CL Hew, unpublished data), suggesting that the production of AFP in external epithelia is a widespread phenomenon.

The functional significance of these skin-type AFPs remains an interesting question. The abundance of skin-type AFP mRNA found in gills and skin suggests that

TABLE 1 General features of liver-type (wflAFPs) and skin-type (wfsAFPs) AFPs

	Liver-type (wflAFP)	Skin-type (wfsAFP)
Tissue and cellular localization	Liver-specific; synthesized as preproAFP extracellular secretory proteins	Widely distributed in peripheral tissues; synthesized as mature AFP intracellular proteins?
Gene structure and organization	40 copies, primarily as tandem repeats; 2A-7b, a representative gene contains two exons and one intron	40 copies, primarily linked but irregularly spaced; F2, 11-3 as examples contain two exons and a larger intron
Seasonal and hormonal regulation	500–700-fold seasonal variations; inhibited by GH	6–10 fold seasonal variation; not affected by GH
Transcriptional control	Intron as liver-specific enhancer, contains DNA motifs for C/EBPα and AEP	Intron as ubiquitous enhancer, contains AEP and other DNA binding motifs; C/EBPα site destroyed by TA insertion

substantial amounts of AFP are produced in these tissues. Because external epithelia would come into intimate contact with ice crystals in an ice-laden environment, it may be that these tissues have a requirement for additional freeze protection over and above that conferred by AFP produced and secreted by the liver into the circulatory system. Although the absence of a pre-sequence suggests that the skin-type AFP might be retained to function within the cell, recent studies indicate that this may not be the case in all tissues. Through the use of immunohistochemistry, HM Murray, K Kao, CL Hew & GL Fletcher (manuscript in preparation) found in winter flounder that the skin-type AFP was, as expected, restricted to the cytoplasm of the gill epithelial cells. However, in the skin these AFPs could be located only outside of the cells in the interstitial space. Therefore, despite the lack of a secretory signal sequence, the skin-type AFPs appear to have been exported from these cells. Alternative pathways for protein export that bypass the Golgi apparatus have been described by Mignatti et al (103).

The localization of the skin-type AFP within the extracellular space of the skin is consistent with the idea that the AFP would assist in blocking ice propagation into and through the skin. In this case, localized concentrations of AFP could serve two functions: The first and possibly most important role would be to prevent the damaging effects of freezing within the epidermis itself, and the second would be the deterrence of ice propagation through the epidermis and into the blood.

A primary function of the gills is to facilitate the rapid diffusion of respiratory gasses between the fish and its aqueous environment. Therefore, the diffusion distance between water and blood is kept to a minimum by limiting the epithelium directly involved in gas exchange to a single-cell layer a few microns in thickness

(62). The consequence of this is that gill epithelia may be more susceptible to ice propagation and damage than any other external tissue. This risk would be exacerbated by the fish actively pumping ice water across the gills in order to meet its respiratory requirements. The presence of AFP within the gill epithelial cells implies that there is a need to lower the freezing temperature of the cytoplasm in order to prevent it from freezing. This would suggest that there is a danger of ice forming within or being propagated into these cells when ice-laden sea water is pumped across the gills. Given the role that this epithelium plays in ion regulation and gas exchange, it seems unlikely that the cell membrane on the apical face of the epithelial cell would be any more permeable to ice propagation than any other cell. However, the relatively delicate structure of the gill lamellae does render it susceptible to structural damage.

The inability to detect AFP in the intercellular space between the gill epithelial cells may be related to the tightness of the junctions that exist within this cell layer. The intercellular space between the skin epithelial cells is considerably greater than it is between the gill epithelial cells. Therefore, intercellular AFP may be detected more readily in the skin than it would be in the gill tissue. Consequently, it is possible that AFPs find their way out of gill cells in the same manner as the skin epithelial cells and remain undetected by the immunohistochemical methods used in this study (HM Murray, K Kao, CL Hew & GL Fletcher, manuscript in preparation). Quite apart from protecting the cytoplasm from ice damage, any AFP that is present in the interstitial space would serve to inhibit ice propagation through this cell layer.

In contrast to the liver-type AFP genes, the skin-type genes appear to be expressed constitutively. Although the levels of AFP mRNA observed in the non-liver tissues peak during winter, they are only several-fold greater than those observed during summer. This contrasts to the several-hundred-fold seasonal change that occurs with the liver-type AFP mRNA. In addition, the skin-type AFP mRNA levels do not appear to be influenced by hypophysectomy. Taken together these results indicate that the two sets of genes are not regulated by the same mechanisms (104).

REGULATION OF ANTIFREEZE PROTEIN GENE EXPRESSION

The recent discovery of two different gene families encoding liver-type and skin-type AFPs makes the winter flounder an interesting model in which to study environmental, hormonal, and tissue-specific AFP gene regulation. Extensive studies have been conducted on the DNA elements controlling winter flounder liver-type AFP gene transcription. The gene investigated (clone 2A-7b) codes one of the most abundant AFP isoforms found in the plasma. It is less than 1 kb in length and consists of two exons and a single intron of 0.5 kb.

Promoter analysis of the 2 kb 5′ upstream sequences of clone 2A-7b did not reveal any presumptive *cis*-acting sequences important for the liver-type AFP gene transcription (105). Instead, the enhancer was located within the intron and, with the use of transient expression assays, was found to be liver specific (106, 107). The liver specificity of this gene was confirmed in transgenic salmon in which the 2A-7b gene was integrated into their genome (108). Biochemical studies, including deletion, mutagenesis, foot-printing, and mobility shift assays, defined the core enhancer as a 19 bp fragment designated Element B (106). An examination of Element B indicated that it contained presumptive DNA-binding motifs for the C/EBPα transcription factor and a novel AP-1 binding complex termed antifreeze enhancer-binding protein (AEP).

The use of C/EBP oligonucleotides and specific antibodies for the C/EBP family of proteins established evidence for C/EBPα binding to the intron enhancer. C/EBPα is a transcription factor with limited tissue specificity (109, 110), which raises the possibility that interactions between C/EBPα and the enhancer may be part of the basis for the tissue specificity of the liver-type AFP genes. In addition it has been demonstrated that treatment of adipocytes with IGF-1 causes dephosphorylation of C/EBPα, an effect that was correlated with the down-regulation of the glucose transporter gene GLUT4 (111). The demonstration that IGF-1 can significantly reduce the enhancer activity of liver-type AFP in expression assays suggests the possibility that IGF-1 may prevent the expression of the liver-type AFP genes in winter flounder during summer (M Miao, SL Chan, GL Fletcher & CL Hew, unpublished data).

The presence of a presumptive AEP and evidence for its interaction with Element B of the liver-type AFP gene were demonstrated using mammalian and flounder hepatocyte nuclear extracts (106, 107). The identity of the AEP analog was revealed by screening a rat liver cDNA expression library using Element B as a probe (M Miao, SL Chan, GL Fletcher & CL Hew, submitted) and found to belong to an AEP family of proteins that appear to be expressed in a wide variety of tissues (112–115).

In contrast to the liver-type AFP gene intron, the skin-type intron was found to function as an enhancer in a variety of cell types. An examination of the C/EBPα-binding site revealed that the skin-type AFP enhancer is disrupted by the central insertion of a TA dinucleotide. This lack of a functional C/EBPα-binding site may, in part, be responsible for the more ubiquitous tissue expression of the skin-type AFP genes. It may also help explain why the skin-type AFP genes are largely unaffected by season or hormones.

A working model of our current hypotheses regarding the various environmental, physiological, and molecular factors regulating the annual cycle of AFP production by the liver is illustrated in Figure 4. During the summer months, the release of pituitary GH stimulates the production of IGF-1, which in turn results in dephosphorylation and deactivation of C/EBPα and/or alters the level of AEP expression, resulting in transcriptional inhibition of the liver-type AFP genes. With the loss of long-day length in the fall, the production of GH is inhibited by the CNS. C/EBPα and AEP are left active to enable AFP gene expression.

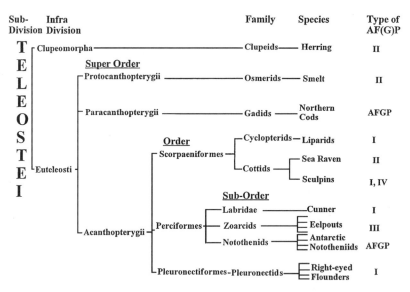

Figure 4   Seasonal regulation of AFP gene expression in winter flounder. Abbreviations: CNS, central nervous system; GHRH, growth hormone-releasing hormone; GH growth hormone; IGF-1, insulin-like growth factor-1; C/EBPα, CCAAT/enhancer-binding protein a; AEP, antifreeze enhancer-binding protein.

RECENT EVOLUTION OF AFPs

A perplexing feature of the distribution of AFP types in the teleosts is that it does not match taxonomic relationships. Rather than having one type confined to one branch of the teleost radiation, AFP types appear to be almost randomly distributed (Figure 5). Especially puzzling is the occurrence of different types in closely related species, a good example of which is the shorthorn sculpin producing type I AFP and the sea raven producing type II AFP (Figure 3). Both species are Northern hemisphere cottids belonging to different genera of the same family. Even more striking is the occurrence of type IV AFP in the longhorn sculpin, a species in the same genus as shorthorn sculpin.

The remarkable diversity in AFP structure in closely related cottids suggested that the need for an antifreeze occurred very recently in geological time, in some cases after the present speciation had been established. A search of the literature on climate change revealed that the first geological evidence for ice in seawater dates back ~10–30 million years ago in the southern hemisphere (116–118), but only 1–2 million years ago in the northern hemisphere (119). Both recent cooling events were the consequences of continental drift, the isolation of Antarctica by a circumpolar current, and the pinching off of the Bering Sea, respectively. Thus all but the very latest stages of the teleost radiation that began 175 million years ago took place in the absence of the threat of freezing. The sea-level glaciation

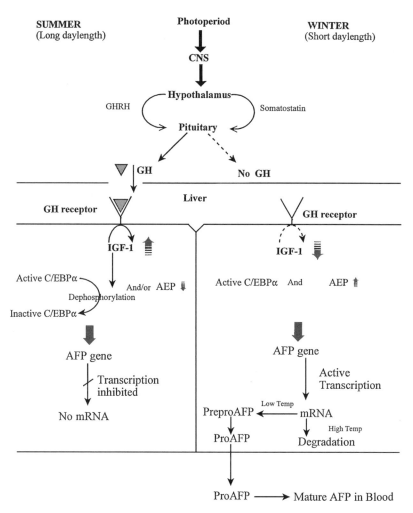

Figure 5 Phylogenetic tree of AFP evolution in fishes. This simplified scheme has been adapted from that shown in Davies et al (1993) and the original version of Scott et al (1986). The relationship of AFP-producing fishes within the teleost radiation was based on Greenwood et al (144) and Nelson (145).

hypothesis, first put forward by Scott et al (120) and reiterated in subsequent review articles (84, 121), states that AFPs were evolved (or elaborated from pre-existing proteins) as a direct response to the recent appearance of ice in seawater. The lateness of this selective pressure meant that some present day species developed radically different AFPs to bind and control the growth of ice. It appears that the same conclusions were arrived at autonomously by Cheng (8). Her evolutionary tree of AFP origins has many similarities to the original design and especially its later refinement (120, 121). The plausibility of the sea-level glaciation hypothesis can only be enhanced by this convergence of opinion from two independent studies.

As noted above, a second contributing factor to the evolution of novel AFP types is the fact that ice can present a variety of binding surfaces. This is a very unusual situation where the ligand (ice) can present many different faces for recognition by different receptors (AFPs). Consequently, any protein with an affinity for an ice surface (other than the basal plane alone) has the potential to be an antifreeze. If binding were strong enough to produce a thermal hysteresis activity, the host species should be able to survive or invade this newly formed niche. Natural selection has presumably improved the ice-binding capabilities of AFP through mutation and ensured through gene amplification that there is an adequate quantity of the AFPs.

Convergent Evolution

One potentially confounding observation to the hypothesis of recent AFP evolution is the occurrence of similar AFPs in unrelated fishes. In some cases these fishes inhabit different hemispheres. For example, the AFGPs in the Nototheniids of the Antarctic Ocean bear a remarkable resemblance to AFGPs in the cods of the northern hemisphere. Did these AFPs evolve much earlier on in the teleost radiation, before the division into superorders (Figure 4)? If so, are they present in a wide range of fishes but without being expressed? Or are they the product of recent convergent evolution?

Evidence from the Cheng laboratory supports the latter scenario. An AFGP gene was first isolated and characterized from *Notothenia coriiceps neglecta* and shown to encode the AFGP peptide backbone as a polyprotein that contained over 40 units of the smaller AFGPs separated by tripeptide spacers (122). Processing would require excision of the flanking spacers by a presumed chymotryptic-like proteinase, as well as glycosylation on the threonines. A gene homolog was subsequently isolated from another Nototheniid, *Dissostichus mawsoni*, but this was embedded in a trypsinogen gene with most of the trypsinogen-coding region exons removed (123, 124). It appears that the fundamental tripeptide repeat Ala-Ala-Thr might have arisen from a 9 bp sequence at the first intron-exon boundary that underwent repeated duplication and unequal crossing over events to produce the large polyprotein sequence. When an AFGP gene was cloned from a cod (*Boreogadus saida*) it was also found to encode a polyprotein version of the antifreeze (125). Despite this remarkable coincidence (polyproteins being rare in eukaryotes) and the fact that the cod AFGP gene was isolated using the Nototheniid AFGP-coding region as a hybridization probe, the two genes appeared to be unrelated (126). They have different intron-exon structures and different signal sequences, use different codon sets for the Ala-Ala-Thr repeats, and the AFGP units in the polyprotein precursor are flanked by different sequences. In place of the hydrophobic tripeptide spacers (e.g. Leu-Ile-Phe and Phe-Asn-Phe) in the Nototheniid polyprotein, the cod sequence is punctuated by arginine. Cleavage of the cod polyprotein by a trypsin-like proteinase would account for the presence of this basic amino acid at the C terminus of the cod AFGPs. Although the precursor of the cod AFGP gene has not been identified, it does not appear to be a trypsinogen gene (125).

Convergence in Parallel?

A variation of convergent evolution of AFPs may account for the presence of the type II AFPs found in sea raven, herring, and smelt (Figure 3). All three AFPs show sequence and structural homology to the carbohydrate recognition domain (CRD) of C-type lectins, proteins that bind to sugars in a Ca^{2+}-dependent manner (45). It seems very unlikely that the three type II AFPs are related by direct descent, that is by the conversion of a C-type lectin to an AFP at a time before all three fishes diverged from their common ancestor. If this were so, type II AFP would pre-exist in a large section of the teleost radiation (Figure 4), a section including species that have subsequently produced totally different AFP types. Why would they have evolved other AFPs when they already had one that would do the job? A more parsimonious explanation is that type II AFPs have evolved from C-type lectins on separate occasions (convergence in parallel). The C-type lectins are present in all fishes as a protein superfamily related by descent. Only in isolated cases would there have been the chance conversion of a lectin family member into an AFP that has given the host fish a selective advantage in resisting freezing.

Like the C-type lectin CRDs, from which they have evolved, the type II AFPs from herring and smelt are dependent on Ca^{2+} for their activity. The AFPs show no thermal hysteresis activity if Ca^{2+} is absent or chelated by EDTA (127). In the lectins, X-ray crystallography has shown that Ca^{2+} is directly involved in binding to the sugars (128), and there is evidence this metal is required at the ice-binding site of the AFPs. For example, although the herring and smelt AFPs are only 30% identical to some of the well-characterized CRDs (from mammalian lectins), they have retained the key amino acids that coordinate Ca^{2+}. Replacement of Ca^{2+} by other divalent metal ions has noticeable effects on both thermal hysteresis activity and ice crystal morphology (127). Also, two amino acid replacements at the putative ice-binding site of the herring AFP eliminated ice binding (129). These replacements were equivalent to those that changed the sugar specificity of a CRD from galactose-binding to mannose-binding (130, 131).

The herring and smelt AFPs share a surprising degree of identity (80%). This fact alone led Ewart et al (10) to question the classification scheme that places herring and smelt into different orders of fish, the Clupeiformes and Osmeriformes. Nevertheless, it is conceivable that the two AFPs have been derived independently from the same CRD, one that has been well conserved during the long separation of these orders. A third member of the group, type II AFP from sea raven, is only 40% identical to the herring and smelt AFPs. It lacks the requisite amino acids for Ca^{2+} chelation and does not require Ca^{2+} for activity, yet its NMR structure clearly shows that it has the same fold as the C-type lectins (49). Site-directed mutagenesis studies indicate the sea raven AFP's ice-binding site is quite distinct from that of the Ca^{2+}-dependent type II AFPs (50). The sea raven AFP has presumably been derived from a different member of the C-type lectin protein superfamily. It will be interesting to survey the new databases emerging from the genome sequencing projects for clues to the identity of the type II AFP ancestors.

The appearance of type I AFPs in right-eye flounders and some sculpin species again raises the same question of similarity by descent or by convergent evolution from a common non-antifreeze precursor. Convergence from two unrelated sources has all but been ruled out by the following tenuous connections. The skin and serum AFPs in winter flounder appear to be extreme isoforms encoded by their own multigene families (3). They share appreciable amino acid and DNA sequence identity, and their relationship by descent is established by the isolation of a genomic clone showing physical linkage of the skin and serum isoform genes (132, 133). Although the serum AFPs in the shorthorn sculpin have not yet been viewed at the DNA level, they bear a striking resemblance to the type I AFP isoforms found in winter flounder skin, even beginning with the same N-terminal sequence Met-Asp-Ala-Pro-Ala (3, 32). The recent discovery (GL Fletcher, RP Evans & MH Kao, unpublished data) of type I AFPs in a liparid (from the same order as sculpins) and in the cunner (a perciforme species) makes it even more likely that type I AFPs have been derived from a common lineage on more than one occasion. There are other small alanine-rich sequences in the databases, such as the kin-encoded proteins in plants (134, 135). However, they have no antifreeze activity, and there is no indication of homology other than their high content of alanine.

Type III AFPs are unique (so far) to zoarcid species and their relatives and are presumably all related. There is one interesting evolutionary issue that has to do with the zoogeography of this suborder. These are the only AFP-containing fishes found in both polar oceans, and it is not at all clear how species containing the same AFPs have ended up literally poles apart. The similarity of some type III isoforms shared by northern and southern hemisphere zoarcids is greater than the most diverse isoforms within one species (24). Therefore, we presume that type III AFPs predate the present dispersion of zoarcid species. If type III AFP evolved in response to sea level glaciation, it would be logical for it to have emerged in the south with subsequent dissemination to the northern hemisphere. There is no indication yet of a progenitor from which type III AFP might have been derived.

AFP Gene Amplification

While AFP diversity provides one of the best examples of natural selection in action, one of the hallmarks of this rapid response to environmental cooling is gene amplification (136). In those fishes (and insects) that show significant thermal hysteresis activity, and for which an AFP gene probe is available, the AFPs are invariably encoded by large gene families. Estimates range from ~10 AFP genes in yellowtail flounder (74), 30–50 copies in winter flounder (73, 137), 80 copies in the wolffish (138), to 150 copies in a population of ocean pout from Newfoundland waters (75). Where extensive sequencing has been done at the protein, cDNA, and/or genomic levels in fish or insects, there is evidence for multiple isoforms, many of which differ by only a few conservative amino acid replacements. It is unlikely that these very similar isoforms have specialized functions because they are typically not well conserved from species to species (compare, for example, serum AFPs in the yellowtail flounder and winter flounder, or the wolffish and ocean pout). These small differences might be the result of genetic drift. There are, however, some isoforms that display greater divergence (50% identity) and even tissue specificity, such as the flounder skin AFP isoforms (mentioned above), which is an indicator of functional divergence. The skin isoforms in flounder are themselves encoded as a multigene family that is as extensive as the liver-specific serum isoforms (3). Another indicator of the rapidity of this evolutionary event is the tandem amplification of certain genes that accounts for the dominance of a specific isoform or sets of isoforms such as the HPLC-6 and -8 isoforms of type I AFP in flounder serum (73). These abundant isoforms are encoded by 1 kb genes in 7–8 kb tandem-direct repeats that may be kept relatively homogeneous by gene conversion and/or unequal crossing over (139). Gene amplification has been seen in many artificial systems where there is intense selective pressure to overcome an environmental insult, such as the treatment of mosquitoes with insecticide (140) and the poisoning of cells with methotrexate (141).

ACKNOWLEDGMENTS

This work was supported by grants from the Canadian Institutes for Health Research (formerly Medical Research Council) to PLD and CLH, and from the Natural Sciences Engineering Research Council to GLF. We are extremely grateful to Dr. Margaret Shears and Sherry Gauthier for help in the preparation of this manuscript, and to the many research assistants, postdoctoral fellows and graduate students who have made valuable contributions to the research on AFPs in our laboratories over the past 25 years.

Visit the Annual Reviews home page at www.AnnualReviews.org

LITERATURE CITED

1. DeVries AL, Wohlschlag DE. 1969. Freezing resistance in some Antarctic fishes. *Science* 163:1074–75
2. DeVries AL, Komatsu SK, Feeney RE. 1970. Chemical and physical properties of freezing point-depression glycoproteins from Antarctic fishes. *J. Biol. Chem.* 245:2901–13
3. Gong Z, Ewart KV, Hu Z, Fletcher GL, Hew CL. 1996. Skin antifreeze protein genes of the winter flounder, *Pleuronectes ameri-*

canus, encode distinct and active polypeptides without the secretory signal and prosequences. *J. Biol. Chem.* 271:4106–12
4. Fletcher GL, Goddard SV, Davies PL, Gong Z, Ewart KV, Hew CL. 1998. New insights into fish antifreeze proteins: physiological significance and molecular regulation. In *Cold Ocean Physiology*, ed. HO Portner, R Playle, pp. 239–65. New York: Cambridge Univ. Press
5. DeVries AL. 1983. Antifreeze peptides and

glycopeptides in cold-water fishes. *Annu. Rev. Physiol.* 45:245–60

6. Yeh Y, Feeney RE. 1996. Antifreeze proteins: structures and mechanisms of function. *Chem. Rev.* 96:601–17

7. Davies PL, Sykes BD. 1997. Antifreeze proteins. *Curr. Opin. Struct. Biol.* 7:828–34

8. Cheng C-HC. 1998. Evolution of the diverse antifreeze proteins. *Curr. Opin. Genet. Dev.* 8:715–20

9. Davies PL, Fletcher GL, Hew CL. 1999. Freeze-resistance strategies based on antifreeze proteins. In *Environmental Stress and Gene Regulation*, ed. KB Storey, pp. 61–80. Oxford: BIOS Sci.

10. Ewart KV, Lin Q, Hew CL. 1999. Structure, function and evolution of antifreeze proteins. *Cell. Mol. Life Sci.* 55:271–83

11. Scholander PF, VanDam L, Kanwisher JW, Hammel HT, Gordon MS. 1957. Supercooling and osmoregulation in Arctic fish. *J. Cell. Comp. Physiol.* 49:5–24

12. Ramsay JA. 1964. The rectal complex of the mealworm *Tenebrio molitor* L. *Philos. Trans. R. Soc. London* 248:279–314

13. Raymond JA, DeVries AL. 1977. Adsorption inhibition as a mechanism of freezing resistance in polar fishes. *Proc. Natl. Acad. Sci. USA* 74:2589–93

14. Graham LA, Liou L-C, Walker VK, Davies PL. 1997. Hyperactive antifreeze protein from beetles. *Nature* 388:727–28

15. Knight CA, DeVries AL. 1994. Effects of a polymeric, nonequilibrium "antifreeze" upon ice growth from water. *J. Cryst. Growth* 143:301–10

16. DeLuca CI, Chao H, Sönnichsen FD, Sykes BD, Davies PL. 1996. Effect of type III antifreeze protein dilution and mutation on the growth inhibition of ice. *Biophys. J.* 71:2346–55

17. Knight CA. 2000. Adding to the antifreeze agenda. *Nature* 406:249–50

18. Wilson PW, Beaglehole D, DeVries AL. 1993. Antifreeze glycopeptide adsorption on single crystal ice surfaces using ellip-

sometry. *Biophys. J.* 64:1878–84

19. Duman JG, DeVries AL. 1974. Freezing resistance in winter flounder, *Pseudopleuronectes americanus. Nature* 247:237–38

20. Slaughter D, Fletcher GL, Ananthanarayanan VS, Hew CL. 1981. Antifreeze proteins from the sea raven, *Hemitripterus americanus.* Further evidence for diversity among fish polypeptide antifreezes. *J. Biol. Chem.* 256:2022–26

21. Hew CL, Slaughter D, Joshi S, Fletcher GL, Ananthanarayanan VS. 1984. Antifreeze polypeptides from the Newfoundland ocean pout, *Macrozoarces americanus*: presence of multiple and compositionally diverse components. *J. Comp. Physiol. B* 155:81–88

22. Deng G, Andrews DW, Laursen RA. 1997. Amino acid sequence of a new type of antifreeze protein, from the longhorn sculpin *Myoxocephalus octodecimspinosis. FEBS Lett.* 402:17–20

23. Deng G, Laursen RA. 1998. Isolation and characterization of an antifreeze protein from the longhorn sculpin, *Myoxocephalus octodecimspinosis. Biochim. Biophys. Acta* 1388:305–14

24. Davies PL, Hew CL. 1990. Biochemistry of fish antifreeze proteins. *FASEB J.* 4:2460–68

25. Osuga DT, Feeney RE. 1978. Antifreeze glycoproteins from Arctic fish. *J. Biol. Chem.* 253:5338–43

26. Ewart KV, Rubinsky B, Fletcher GL. 1992. Structural and functional similarity between fish antifreeze proteins and calcium-dependent lectins. *Biochem. Biophys. Res. Commun.* 185:335–40

27. Ewart KV, Fletcher GL. 1993. Herring antifreeze protein: primary structure and evidence for a C-type lectin evolutionary origin. *Mol. Mar. Biol. Biotechnol.* 2:20–27

28. Knight CA, Cheng CC, DeVries AL. 1991. Adsorption of alpha-helical antifreeze peptides on specific ice crystal surface planes. *Biophys. J.* 59:409–18

29. Cheng CC, DeVries AL. 1991. The role

of antifreeze glycopeptides and peptides in the freezing avoidance of cold-water fish. In *Life Under Extreme Conditions*, ed. G di Prisco, pp. 1–14. Berlin: Springer-Verlag

30. Jia Z, DeLuca CI, Chao H, Davies PL. 1996. Structural basis for the binding of a globular antifreeze protein to ice. *Nature* 384:285–88. Erratum. 1997. *Nature* 385(6616):555

31. Ananthanarayanan VS, Hew CL. 1977. Structural studies on the freezing point-depressing protein of the winter flounder *Pseudopleuronectes americanus. Biochem. Biophys. Res. Commun.* 74:685–89

32. Yang DS, Sax M, Chakrabartty A, Hew CL. 1988. Crystal structure of an antifreeze polypeptide and its mechanistic implications. *Nature* 333:232–37

33. Sicheri F, Yang DS. 1995. Ice-binding structure and mechanism of an antifreeze protein from winter flounder. *Nature* 375:427–31

34. DeVries AL, Lin Y. 1977. Structure of a peptide antifreeze and mechanism of adsorption to ice. *Biochim. Biophys. Acta* 495:388–92

35. Wen D, Laursen RA. 1992. A model for binding of an antifreeze polypeptide to ice. *Biophys. J.* 63:1659–62

36. Wen D, Laursen RA. 1993. A D-antifreeze polypeptide displays the same activity as its natural L-enantiomer. *FEBS Lett.* 317:31–34

37. Chao H, DeLuca CI, Davies PL. 1995. Mixing antifreeze protein types changes ice crystal morphology without affecting antifreeze activity. *FEBS Lett.* 357:183–86

38. DeLuca CI, Comley R, Davies PL. 1998. Antifreeze proteins bind independently to ice. *Biophys. J.* 74:1502–8

39. Knight CA, Driggers E, DeVries AL. 1993. Adsorption to ice of fish antifreeze glycopeptides 7 and 8. *Biophys. J.* 64:252–59

40. Gronwald W, Chao H, Reddy DV, Davies PL, Sykes BD, Sonnichsen FD. 1996. NMR characterization of side chain flex-

ibility and backbone structure in the type I antifreeze protein at near freezing temperatures. *Biochemistry* 35:16698–704

41. Chao H, Houston ME Jr, Hodges RS, Kay CM, Sykes BD, et al. 1997. A diminished role for hydrogen bonds in antifreeze protein binding to ice. *Biochemistry* 36:14652–60

42. Zhang W, Laursen RA. 1998. Structure-function relationships in a type I antifreeze polypeptide. The role of threonine methyl and hydroxyl groups in antifreeze activity. *J. Biol. Chem.* 273:34806–12

43. Haymet AD, Ward LG, Harding MM, Knight CA. 1998. Valine substituted winter flounder 'antifreeze': preservation of ice growth hysteresis. *FEBS Lett.* 430:301–6

44. Chakrabartty A, Hew CL. 1991. The effect of enhanced alpha-helicity on the activity of a winter flounder antifreeze polypeptide. *Eur. J. Biochem.* 202:1057–63

45. Sönnichsen FD, Sykes BD, Davies PL. 1995. Comparative modeling of the three-dimensional structure of type II antifreeze protein. *Protein Sci.* 4:460–71

46. Sönnichsen FD, DeLuca CI, Davies PL, Sykes BD. 1996. Refined solution structure of type III antifreeze protein: hydrophobic groups may be involved in the energetics of the protein-ice interaction. *Structure* 4:1325–37

47. Loewen MC, Chao H, Houston ME Jr, Baardsnes J, Hodges RS, et al. 1999. Alternative roles for putative ice-binding residues in type I antifreeze protein. *Biochemistry* 38:4743–49

48. Baardsnes J, Kondejewski LH, Hodges RS, Chao H, Kay C, Davies PL. 1999. New ice-binding face for type I antifreeze protein. *FEBS Lett.* 463:87–91

49. Gronwald W, Loewen MC, Lix B, Daugulis AJ, Sönnichsen FD, et al. 1998. The solution structure of type II antifreeze protein reveals a new member of the lectin family. *Biochemistry* 37:4712–21

50. Loewen MC, Gronwald W, Sönnichsen

FD, Sykes BD, Davies PL. 1998. The ice-binding site of sea raven antifreeze protein is distinct from the carbohydrate-binding site of the homologous C-type lectin. *Biochemistry* 37:17745–53

51. Yang DS, Hon WC, Bubanko S, Xue Y, Seetharaman J, et al. 1998. Identification of the ice-binding surface on a type III antifreeze protein with a "flatness function" algorithm. *Biophys. J.* 74:2142–51

52. Chao H, Sönnichsen FD, DeLuca CI, Sykes BD, Davies PL. 1994. Structure-function relationship in the globular type III antifreeze protein: identification of a cluster of surface residues required for binding to ice. *Protein Sci.* 3:1760–69

53. Liou Y-C, Tocilj A, Davies PL, Jia Z. 2000. Mimicry of ice structure by surface hydroxyls and water of a ß-helix antifreeze protein. *Nature* 406:322–24

54. Graether SP, Kuiper MJ, Gagné SM, Walker VK, Jia Z, et al. 2000. ß-Helix structure and ice-binding properties of a hyperactive insect antifreeze protein. *Nature* 406:325–28

55. Valerio PF, Kao MH, Fletcher GL. 1992. Fish skin: an effective barrier to ice crystal propagation. *J. Exp.Biol.* 164:135–51

56. DeVries AL, Lin Y. 1977. The role of glycoprotein antifreezes in the survival of Antarctic fishes. In *Adaptations Within Antarctic Ecosystems*, ed. GA Liano, pp. 439–57. Washington, DC: Smithson. Inst.

57. Fletcher GL, Kao MH, Dempson JB. 1988. Lethal freezing temperatures of Arctic Char and other salmonoids in the presence of ice. *Aquaculture* 71:369–78

58. Goddard SV, Fletcher GL. 1994. Antifreeze proteins: their role in cod survival and distribution from egg to adult. *ICES Mar. Sci. Symp.* 198:676–83

59. Fletcher GL, Kao MH, Fourney RM. 1986. Antifreeze peptides confer freezing resistance to fish. *Can. J. Zool.* 64:1897–1901

60. Turner JD, Schrag JD, DeVries AL. 1985. Ocular freezing avoidance in Antarctic fish. *J. Exp. Biol.* 118:121–31

61. Valerio PF, Goddard SV, Kao MH, Fletcher GL. 1992. Survival of Northern Atlantic cod (*Gadus morhua*) eggs and larvae when exposed to ice and low temperature. *Can. J. Fish. Aquat. Sci.* 49:1–8

62. Randall DJ. 1970. Gas exchange in fish. In *Fish Physiology*, ed. WS Hoar, DJ Randall, 4:253–92. New York: Academic

63. DeVries AL. 1988. The role of antifreeze glycopeptides and peptides in the freezing avoidance of Antarctic fishes. *Comp. Biochem. Physiol.* 90:611–21

64. Verdier J-M, Ewart KV, Griffith M, Hew CL. 1996. An immune response to ice crystals in North Atlantic fishes. *Eur. J. Biochem.* 241:740–43

65. Valerio PF, Kao MH, Fletcher GL. 1990. Thermal hysteresis activity in the skin of the cunner, *Tautogolabrus adspersus. Can. J. Zool.* 68:1065–67

66. Fletcher GL, King MJ, Kao MH. 1987. Low temperature regulation of antifreeze glycopeptide levels in Atlantic cod (*Gadus morhua*). *Can. J. Zool.* 65:227–33

67. Hew CL, Fletcher GL, Ananthanarayanan VS. 1980. Antifreeze proteins from the shorthorn sculpin, *Myoxocephalus scorpius*: isolation and characterization. *Can. J. Biochem.* 58:377–83

68. Goddard SV, Kao MH, Fletcher GL. 1992. Antifreeze production, freeze resistance, and overwintering of juvenile Northern Atlantic cod (*Gadus morhua*). *Can. J. Fish. Aquat. Sci.* 49:516–22

69. Fletcher GL, Hew CL, Li X, Haya K, Kao MH. 1985. Year-round presence of high levels of plasma antifreeze peptides in a temperate fish, ocean pout (*Macrozoarces americanus*). *Can. J. Zool.* 63:488–93

70. Goddard SV, Kao MH, Fletcher GL. 1999. Population differences in antifreeze production cycles of juvenile Atlantic cod (*Gadus morhua*) reflect adaptations to overwintering environment. *Can. J. Fish. Aquat. Sci.* 56:1991–99

71. Rose GA, de Young B, Kulka DW, Goddard SV, Fletcher GL. 2000. Distributional

shifts and overfishing the Northern cod (*Gadus morhua*): a view from the ocean. *Can. J. Fish. Aquat. Sci.* 57:644–64

72. Fletcher GL, Haya K, King MJ, Reisman HM. 1985. Annual antifreeze cycles in Newfoundland, New Brunswick and Long Island winter flounder, *Pseudopleuronectes americanus. Mar. Ecol. Prog. Ser.* 21:205–12

73. Scott GK, Hew CL, Davies PL. 1985. Antifreeze protein genes are tandemly linked and clustered in the genome of the winter flounder. *Proc. Natl. Acad. Sci. USA* 82:2613–17

74. Scott GK, Davies PL, Kao MH, Fletcher GL. 1988. Differential amplification of antifreeze protein genes in the pleuronectinae. *J. Mol. Evol.* 27:29–35

75. Hew CL, Wang NC, Joshi S, Fletcher GL, Scott GK, et al. 1988. Multiple genes provide the basis for antifreeze protein diversity and dosage in the ocean pout, *Macrozoarces americanus. J. Biol. Chem.* 263:12049–55

76. Fletcher GL. 1977. Circannual cycles of blood plasma freezing point and Na^+ and Cl^- concentrations in Newfoundland winter flounder (*Pseudopleuronectes americanus*): correlation with water temperature and photoperiod. *Can. J. Zool.* 55:789–95

77. Hew CL, Yip C. 1976. The synthesis of freezing-point-depressing protein of the winter flounder *Pseudopleuronectus americanus* in *Xenopus laevis* oocytes. *Biochem. Biophys. Res. Commun.* 71:845–49

78. Hew CL, Liunardo N, Fletcher GL. 1978. In vivo biosynthesis of the antifreeze protein in the winter flounder—evidence for a larger precursor. *Biochem. Biophys. Res. Commun.* 85:421–27

79. Davies PL, Roach AH, Hew CL. 1982. DNA sequence coding for an antifreeze protein precursor from winter flounder. *Proc. Natl. Acad. Sci. USA* 79:335–39

80. Pickett M, Scott G, Davies PL, Wang N, Joshi S, Hew CL. 1984. Sequence of an an-

tifreeze protein precursor. *Eur. J. Biochem.* 143:35–38

81. Gourlie BB, Lin Y, Price JL, DeVries AL, Powers DA, Huang RCC. 1984. Winter flounder antifreeze proteins: a multigene family. *J. Biol. Chem.* 259:14960–65

82. Pickett MH, Hew CL, Davies PL. 1983. Seasonal variation in the level of antifreeze protein mRNA from the winter flounder. *Biochim. Biophys. Acta* 739:97–104

83. Fourney RM, Fletcher GL, Hew CL. 1984. The effects of long day length on liver antifreeze mRNA in the winter flounder, *Pseudopleuronectes americanus. Can. J. Zool.* 62:1456–60

84. Davies PL, Hew CL, Fletcher GL. 1988. Fish antifreeze proteins: physiology and evolutionary biology. *Can. J. Zool.* 66:2611–17

85. Chan SL, Fletcher GL, Hew CL. 1993. Control of antifreeze protein gene expression in winter flounder. See Ref. 146, pp. 293–305

86. Fletcher GL. 1981. Effects of temperature and photoperiod on the plasma freezing point depression, Cl^- concentration, and protein "antifreeze" in winter flounder. *Can. J. Zool.* 59:193–201

87. Price JL, Gourlie BB, Lin Y, Huang RCC. 1986. Induction of winter flounder antifreeze protein messenger RNA at 4°C in vivo and in vitro. *Physiol. Zool.* 59:679–95

88. Vaisius A, Martin-Kearley J, Fletcher GL. 1989. Antifreeze protein gene transcription in winter flounder is not responsive to temperature. *Cell. Mol. Biol.* 35:547–54

89. Kenward KD, Altschuler M, Hildebrand D, Davies PL. 1993. Accumulation of type I fish antifreeze protein in transgenic tobacco is cold-specific. *Plant Mol. Biol.* 23:377–85

90. Duncker BP, Koops MD, Walker VK, Davies PL. 1995. Low temperature persistence of type I antifreeze protein is mediated by cold-specific mRNA stability. *FEBS Lett.* 377:185–88

91. Fletcher GL, Idler DR, Vaisius A, Hew CL.

1989. Hormonal regulation of antifreeze protein gene expression in winter flounder. *Fish Physiol. Biochem.* 7:387–93

92. Hew CL, Fletcher GL. 1979. The role of pituitary in regulating antifreeze protein synthesis in the winter flounder. *FEBS Lett.* 99:337–39

93. Fletcher GL, King MJ, Hew CL. 1984. How does the brain control the pituitary's release of antifreeze synthesis inhibitor? *Can. J. Zool.* 62:839–44

94. Fourney RM, Fletcher GL, Hew CL. 1984. Accumulation of winter flounder antifreeze messenger RNA after hypophysectomy. *Gen. Comp. Endocrinol.* 54:392–401

95. Idler DR, Fletcher GL, Belkhode S, King MJ, Hwang SJ. 1989. Regulation of antifreeze protein production in winter flounder: a unique function for growth hormone. *Gen. Comp. Endocrinol.* 74:327–34

96. Duguay SJ, Swanson P, Dickhoff WW. 1994. Differential expression and hormonal regulation of alternatively spliced IGF-I mRNA transcripts in salmon. *J. Mol. Endocrinol.* 12:25–37

97. Shamblott MJ, Cheng CM, Bolt D, Chen TT. 1995. Appearance of insulin-like growth factor mRNA in the liver and pyloric ceca of a teleost in response to exogenous growth hormone. *Proc. Natl. Acad. Sci. USA* 92:6943–46

98. Shepherd BS, Sakamoto T, Nishioka RS, Richman 'NH 3rd,' Mori I, et al. 1997. Somatotropic actions of the homologous growth hormone and prolactins in the euryhaline teleost, the tilapia, *Oreochromis mossambicus. Proc. Natl. Acad. Sci. USA* 94:2068–72

99. Fletcher GL, King MJ. 1978. Seasonal dynamics of Cu^{2+}, Zn^{2+}, Ca^{2+}, and Mg^{2+} in gonads and liver of winter flounder (*Pseudopleuronectes americanus*): evidence for summer storage of Zn^{2+} for winter gonad development in females. *Can. J. Zool.* 56:284–90

100. Schneppenheim R, Theede H. 1982. Freezing-point depressing peptides and glycoproteins from Arctic-boreal and Antarctic fishes. *Polar Biol.* 1:115–23

101. Gong Z, Fletcher GL, Hew CL. 1992. Tissue distribution of fish antifreeze protein mRNAs. *Can. J. Zool.* 70:810–14

102. Low WK, Miao M, Ewart KV, Yang DS, Fletcher GL, Hew CL. 1998. Skin-type antifreeze protein from the shorthorn sculpin, *Myoxocephalus scorpius.* Expression and characterization of a M_r 9700 recombinant protein. *J. Biol. Chem.* 273:23098–103

103. Mignatti P, Morimoto T, Rifkin DB. 1992. Basic fibroblast growth factor; a protein devoid of a secretory signal sequence is released from cells via a pathway independent of the endoplasmic reticulum-Golgi complex. *J. Cell. Physiol. C* 263:1310–13

104. Gong Z, King MJ, Fletcher GL, Hew CL. 1995. The antifreeze protein genes of the winter flounder, *Pleuronectes americanus*, are differentially regulated in liver and non-liver tissues. *Biochem. Biophys. Res. Commun.* 206:387–92

105. Gong Z, Hew CL. 1993. Promoter analysis of fish antifreeze protein genes. See Ref. 146, pp. 307–24

106. Chan SL, Miao M, Fletcher GL, Hew CL. 1997. The role of CCAAT/enhancer-binding protein alpha and a protein that binds to the activator-protein-1 site in the regulation of liver-specific expression of the winter flounder antifreeze protein gene. *Eur. J. Biochem.* 247:44–51

107. Miao M, Chan SL, Hew CL, Fletcher GL. 1998. Identification of nuclear proteins interacting with the liver-specific enhancer B element of the antifreeze protein gene in winter flounder. *Mol. Mar. Biol. Biotechnol.* 7:197–203

108. Hew C, Poon R, Xiong F, Gauthier S, Shears M, et al. 1999. Liver-specific and seasonal expression of transgenic Atlantic salmon harboring the winter flounder

antifreeze protein gene. *Transgenic Res.* 8:405–14

109. Landschulz WH, Johnson PF, Adashi EY, Graves BJ, McKnight SL. 1988. Isolation of a recombinant copy of the gene encoding C/EBP. *Genes Dev.* 2:786–800. Erratum. 1994. *Genes Dev.* 8(9):1131

110. Takiguchi M. 1998. The C/EBP family of transcription factors in the liver and other organs. *Int. J. Exp. Pathol.* 79:369–91

111. Hemati N, Ross SE, Erickson RL, Groblewski GE, MacDougald OA. 1997. Signaling pathways through which insulin regulates CCAAT/enhancer binding protein alpha (C/EBPalpha) phosphorylation and gene expression in 3T3-L1 adipocytes. Correlation with GLUT4 gene expression. *J. Biol. Chem.* 272:25913–19

112. Kerr D, Khalili K. 1991. A recombinant cDNA derived from human brain encodes a DNA binding protein that stimulates transcription of the human neurotropic virus JCV. *J. Biol. Chem.* 266:15876–81

113. Fukita Y, Mizuta TR, Shirozu M, Ozawa K, Shimizu A, Honjo T. 1993. The human S mu bp-2, a DNA-binding protein specific to the single-stranded guanine-rich sequence related to the immunoglobulin mu chain switch region. *J. Biol. Chem.* 268:17463–70

114. Mizuta TR, Fukita Y, Miyoshi T, Shimizu A, Honjo T. 1993. Isolation of cDNA encoding a binding protein specific to 5′-phosphorylated single-stranded DNA with G-rich sequences. *Nucleic Acids Res.* 21:1761–66

115. Shieh SY, Stellrecht CM, Tsai MJ. 1995. Molecular characterization of the rat insulin enhancer-binding complex 3b2. Cloning of a binding factor with putative helicase motifs. *J. Biol. Chem.* 270:21503–8

116. Denton GH, Armstrong RL, Stuiver M. 1980. The late Cenozoic glacial history of Antarctica. In *The Late Cenozoic Glacial*

Ages, ed. KK Turekian, pp. 267–306. New Haven, CT: Yale Univ. Press

117. Kennet JP, Shackleton NJ. 1976. Oxygen isotopic evidence for the development of the psychrosphere 38 Myr ago. *Nature* 260:513–15

118. Kerr RA. 1984. Ice cap of 30 million years ago detected. *Science* 224:141–42

119. Shackleton NJ, Backman J, Zimmerman H, Kent DV, Hall MA, et al. 1984. Oxygen isotope calibration of the onset of ice-rafting and history of glaciation in the North Atlantic region. *Nature* 307:620–22

120. Scott GK, Fletcher GL, Davies PL. 1986. Fish antifreeze proteins: recent evolution. *Can. J. Fish. Aquat. Sci.* 43:1028–34

121. Davies PL, Ewart KV, Fletcher GL. 1993. The diversity and distribution of fish antifreeze proteins: new insights into their origins. See Ref. 146, pp. 279–91

122. Hsiao KC, Cheng CH, Fernandes IE, Detrich HW, DeVries AL. 1990. An antifreeze glycopeptide gene from the Antarctic cod *Notothenia coriiceps neglecta* encodes a polyprotein of high peptide copy number. *Proc. Natl. Acad. Sci. USA* 87:9265–69

123. Chen L, DeVries AL, Cheng CH. 1997. Evolution of antifreeze glycoprotein gene from a trypsinogen gene in Antarctic notothenioid fish. *Proc. Natl. Acad. Sci. USA* 94:3811–16

124. Cheng CH, Chen L. 1999. Evolution of an antifreeze glycoprotein. *Nature* 401:443–44

125. Chen L, DeVries AL, Cheng CH. 1997. Convergent evolution of antifreeze glycoproteins in Antarctic notothenioid fish and Arctic cod. *Proc. Natl. Acad. Sci. USA* 94:3817–22

126. Logsdon JM Jr, Doolittle WF. 1997. Origin of antifreeze protein genes: a cool tale in molecular evolution. *Proc. Natl. Acad. Sci. USA* 94:3485–87

127. Ewart KV, Yang DS, Ananthanarayanan VS, Fletcher GL, Hew CL. 1996. Ca^{2+}-

dependent antifreeze proteins. Modulation of conformation and activity by divalent metal ions. *J. Biol. Chem.* 271:16627–32

128. Weis WT, Drickamer K, Hendrickson WA. 1992. Structure of a C-type mannose-binding protein complexed with an oligosaccharide. *Nature* 360:127–34

129. Ewart KV, Li Z, Yang DS, Fletcher GL, Hew CL. 1998. The ice-binding site of Atlantic herring antifreeze protein corresponds to the carbohydrate-binding site of C-type lectins. *Biochemistry* 37:4080–85

130. Drickamer K. 1992. Engineering galactose-binding activity into a C-type mannose-binding protein. *Nature* 360:183–86

131. Iobst ST, Drickamer K. 1994. Binding of sugar ligands to Ca^{2+}-dependent animal lectins. *J. Biol. Chem.* 269:15512–19

132. Davies PL, Hough C, Scott GK, Ng N, White BN, Hew CL. 1984. Antifreeze protein genes of the winter flounder. *J. Biol. Chem.* 259:9241–47

133. Davies PL, Gauthier SY. 1992. Antifreeze protein pseudogenes. *Gene* 112:171–78

134. Kurkela S, Borg-Franck M. 1992. Structure and expression of *kin2*, one of two cold- and ABA-induced genes of *Arabidopsis thaliana*. *Plant Mol. Biol.* 19:689–92

135. Boothe JG, Sönnichsen FD, de Beus MD, Johnson-Flanagan AM. 1997. Purification, characterization, and structural analysis of a plant low-temperature-induced protein. *Plant Physiol.* 113:367–76

136. Davies PL, Fletcher GL, Hew CL. 1989. Fish antifreeze protein genes and their use in transgenic studies. *Oxford Surv. Eukaryot. Genes* 6:85–109

137. Gourlie B, Lin Y, Price J, DeVries AL,

Powers D, Huang RC. 1984. Winter flounder antifreeze proteins: a multigene family. *J. Biol. Chem.* 259:14960–65

138. Scott GK, Hayes PH, Fletcher GL, Davies PL. 1988. Wolffish antifreeze protein genes are primarily organized as tandem repeats that each contain two genes in inverted orientation. *Mol. Cell. Biol.* 8:3670–75

139. Davies PL. 1992. Conservation of antifreeze protein-encoding genes in tandem repeats. *Gene* 112:163–70

140. Mouches C, Pasteur N, Berge JB, Hyrien O, Raymond M, et al. 1986. Amplification of an esterase gene is responsible for insecticide resistance in a California *Culex* mosquito. *Science* 233:778–80

141. Alt F, Kellems RE, Bertino JR, Schimke RT. 1978. Selective multiplication of dihydrofolate reductase genes in methotrexate-resistant variants of cultured murine cells. *J. Biol. Chem.* 253:1357–70

142. Leim AH, Scott WB. 1966. Fishes of the Atlantic coast of Canada. *Bull. Fish. Res. Board Can. 155.* Ottawa: Fish. Res. Board Can.

143. Eastman JT. 1993. *Antartic Fish Biology: Evolution in a Unique Environment.* San Diego, CA: Academic

144. Greenwood PH, Rosen DE, Weitzman SH, Myers GS. 1966. Phyletic studies of Teleostean fishes, with a provisional classification of living forms. *Bull. Am. Mus. Nat. Hist.* 131:339–456

145. Nelson JS. 1984. *Fishes of the World.* New York: Wiley Intersci.

146. Hochachka PW, Mommsen TP, eds. 1993. *Biochemistry and Molecular Biology of Fishes*, Vol. 2. Amsterdam: Elsevier Sci.

Annu. Rev. Physiol. 2001. 63:391–426

Cytoplasmic Signaling Pathways That Regulate Cardiac Hypertrophy

Jeffery D Molkentin[1] and Gerald W Dorn II[2]

[1]*Department of Pediatrics, University of Cincinnati, Division of Molecular Cardiovascular Biology, Children's Hospital Medical Center, Cincinnati, Ohio 45229-3039; e-mail: jeff.molkentin@chmcc.org;* [2]*Department of Medicine, University of Cincinnati, Division of Cardiology, Cincinnati, Ohio 45267-0590; e-mail: Dorngw@ucmail.uc.edu*

Key Words heart failure, cardiomyocytes, signaling, kinase, phosphatase

■ **Abstract** This review discusses the rapidly progressing field of cardiomyocyte signal transduction and the regulation of the hypertrophic response. When stimulated by a wide array of neurohumoral factors or when faced with an increase in ventricular-wall tension, individual cardiomyocytes undergo hypertrophic growth as an adaptive response. However, sustained cardiac hypertrophy is a leading predictor of future heart failure. A growing number of intracellular signaling pathways have been characterized as important transducers of the hypertrophic response, including specific G protein isoforms, low-molecular-weight GTPases (Ras, RhoA, and Rac), mitogen-activated protein kinase cascades, protein kinase C, calcineurin, gp130-signal transducer and activator of transcription, insulin-like growth factor I receptor pathway, fibroblast growth factor and transforming growth factor β receptor pathways, and many others. Each of these signaling pathways has been implicated as a hypertrophic transducer, which collectively suggests an emerging paradigm whereby multiple pathways operate in concert to orchestrate a hypertrophic response

INTRODUCTION

Because heart disease remains one of the leading causes of death in all industrialized nations of the world (1–3), much effort has centered on characterizing the intracellular signal transduction cascades that are associated with hypertrophy and cardiomyopathy. Given that adult cardiomyocytes are resistant to cell cycle reentry, many of the same intracellular signaling pathways that regulate proliferation in cancer cells or immune cells instead regulate hypertrophic growth of cardiomyocytes. The hypertrophic growth of cardiomyocytes is initiated by endocrine, paracrine, and autocrine factors that stimulate a wide array of membrane-bound receptors. Their activation results in the triggering of multiple cytoplasmic signal transduction cascades, which ultimately affects nuclear factors and the regulation of gene expression. In this review, we focus on the intermediate signal transduction cascades that reside within the cytoplasm downstream of membrane-bound receptors and upstream of transcription factors. From this discussion it becomes obvious that no single intracellular transduction cascade regulates cardiomyocyte hypertrophy in isolation, but instead each pathway operates as an integrated component of an orchestrated response between interdependent and cross-talking networks. In this manner, blockade of specific intracellular signaling pathways in the heart can dramatically affect the orchestration of the entire hypertrophic response and effectively diminish heart enlargement. This model predicts that specific activation of any of a number of discrete signal transduction pathways will be sufficient to activate the entire hypertrophic response through effects on other cross-talking signaling networks.

G PROTEINS AND CARDIAC HYPERTROPHY

Heterotrimeric GTP-binding proteins transduce stimulatory or inhibitory signals from agonist-occupied seven-transmembrane-spanning-domain receptors of the rhodopsin superfamily. Within the cardiovascular system, three functional classes of G protein–coupled receptors are of primary importance owing to their acute hemodynamic and chronic myotrophic effects. The functional classes of cardiovascular receptors correspond to the three major classes of G proteins (Figure 1). Thus, β-adrenergic receptors (βAR), which couple primarily to $G_{\alpha s}$, mediate acute enhancement of heart rate and myocardial contractility in response to epinephrine and norepinephrine stimulation (reviewed in 4, 5). The second class of myocardial receptors are the cholinergic receptors, typically coupled to $G_{\alpha i}$, which are activated by acetylcholine. The third class of receptors, coupled primarily to $G_{\alpha q}$, includes angiotensin II, endothelin, and α-adrenergic (αAR) receptors. Activation of these pathways is less important in modulating minute-by-minute cardiac function, but it is likely to play a major role in cardiac hypertrophic responses to pathological stimuli.

All heterotrimeric G proteins consist of separate G_α and $G_{\beta \gamma}$ subunits. Agonist occupation of a membrane-bound receptor catalyzes GDP to GTP exchange on the G_α subunit and subsequent dissociation of G_α from $G_{\beta \gamma}$. Both subunits are then free to modulate the activity of downstream signaling effectors, typically adenylyl cyclase (AC) (modulated by $G_{\alpha s}$ and $G_{\alpha i}$) or phospholipase C (PLC; activated by $G_{\alpha q/11}$) (6). In addition, free $G_{\beta \gamma}$ subunits can directly enhance mitogen-activated protein kinase (MAPK) signaling, phosphatidylinositol 3-kinase (PI3K) activity, and Ras signaling in the heart (7–9; Figure 1). Although multiple G_α, $_\beta$, and $_\gamma$ proteins have been identified, we focus on the function of the three major classes of G_α subunits that mediate most receptor-effector coupling pathways in the heart.

$G_{\alpha i}$ in Cardiac Disease

Receptor-mediated activation of the $G_{\alpha i}$ subunit results in the direct attenuation of AC in the heart. AC catalyzes the formation of cyclic AMP, which augments

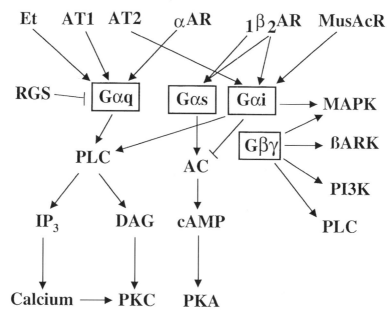

Figure 1 G protein–mediated signaling pathways. Multiple seven-transmembrane-spanning receptors directly couple to G proteins resulting in GDP-GTP exchange, disassociation of the G_α subunit from the $G_{\beta\gamma}$, and activation of effector proteins by both subunits. Abbreviations: Et, endothelin receptor; AT1 and AT2, angiotensin receptors, AR, adrenergic receptor; MusAcR, muscarinic acetylcholine receptor; AC, adenylyl cyclase; PLC, phospholipase C; PKC, protein kinase C; PKA, protein kinase A; MAPK, mitogen-activated protein kinase; βARK, β-adrenergic receptor kinase; PI3K, phosphatidylinositol 3-kinase; IP_3, inositol 3-phosphate; DAG, diacylglycerol.

myocardial contractility, in part, through a protein kinase A-signaling pathway, which directly inhibits phospholamban, promoting increased SERCA2 ATPase activity and augmented calcium handling in the heart (reviewed in 10). Because $G_{\alpha i}$ inhibits AC activity, increased expression of $G_{\alpha i}$ has been predicted to contribute to the pathology of cardiac hypertrophy and heart failure. The first convincing evidence that up-regulation of $G_{\alpha i}$ occurred in human heart failure was published by Neumann et al in 1988 (11). In this small clinical study, three patients with idiopathic dilated cardiomyopathy showed increased $G_{\alpha i}$ and impaired responsiveness to isoprenaline. The hypothesis that increased expression of $G_{\alpha i}$ might be involved in heart failure was subsequently confirmed and extended by Bristow and colleagues in 1991, through a comparative study of myocardial tissue from 12 pairs of failing and nonfailing human ventricles (12). $G_{\alpha i}$ content was increased by ~30% in failing hearts, and basal AC activity was depressed by ~70%.

Multiple studies have now confirmed that $G_{\alpha i}$ is up-regulated in different heart failure models from numerous species (13–18). Increased $G_{\alpha i}$ content and impaired AC activity are not limited to failing hearts but have also been demonstrated in experimental and genetic hypertension characterized by cardiac hypertrophy (14, 15). Up-regulation of $G_{\alpha i}$ and the resulting blunting of AC signaling may thus represent a primary event in cardiac hypertrophy, which can contribute to the transition from compensated hypertrophy to decompensated heart failure. Up-regulation of $G_{\alpha i}$ in cardiac hypertrophy suggests regulation of $G_{\alpha i}$ expression at the molecular level, a notion that is supported by most but not all published studies. Feldman and coworkers were the first to examine $G_{\alpha i}$ mRNA expression in failing human hearts by Northern blot analysis, and they reported increased $G_{\alpha i}$ and $G_{\alpha s}$ gene expression (19). This observation was supported by a subsequent study reporting increased $G_{\alpha i}$ mRNA in heart failure (20). In addition, elevated cyclic-AMP levels were shown to augment $G_{\alpha i2}$ promoter activity, suggesting a plausible mechanism for up-regulation of $G_{\alpha i}$ in heart disease (21). Finally, mice genetically engineered to express a conditional $G_{\alpha i}$-coupled receptor demonstrated a profound decrease in heart rate upon stimulation (22).

$G_{\alpha s}$ in Cardiac Disease

Whereas increased expression of inhibitory $G_{\alpha i}$ is generally accepted as contributing to βAR unresponsiveness in cardiac hypertrophy and heart failure, a role for altered $G_{\alpha s}$ content is less clear because the published data are in conflict over this issue (19, 23–29). Thus, it is not possible to conclude that regulation of $G_{\alpha s}$ occurs or contributes in a meaningful way to the pathophysiology of human heart failure. However, the functional and pathological consequences of increased cardiac $G_{\alpha s}$ expression have been explored in a series of studies using transgenic mice that over-express $G_{\alpha s}$. In these mice, wild-type $G_{\alpha s}$ was expressed at approximately threefold the endogenous levels, resulting in an increase in $G_{\alpha s}$ activity of 88% without any significant effect on AC activity (30). The major measurable consequence of this level of $G_{\alpha s}$ overexpression on signaling in the heart was an increase in the proportion of βAR coupled to $G_{\alpha s}$. At the functional level, $G_{\alpha s}$ overexpression enhanced isoproterenol-stimulated contractility, but not basal left-ventricular contractility, as measured by echocardiography (31). However, $G_{\alpha s}$ overexpression also increased myocardial collagen content and fibrosis with variable cardiomyocyte atrophy or hypertrophy associated with increased apoptosis (31, 32).

The phenotype of $G_{\alpha s}$-transgenic mice resembles the alterations in cardiac function and pathology associated with exogenously administered catecholamines or catecholamine cardiomyopathies reported in humans (33–36). Deleterious consequences of unregulated cardiac βAR signaling have also been observed in transgenic models of β_1AR and β_2AR overexpression (37–39). It is not clear at this time whether the mechanisms for the deleterious effects of $G_{\alpha s}$ and βAR are mediated through AC or through other signaling pathways.

$G_{\alpha q}$ in Heart Disease

A compelling case supporting a critical role for $G_{\alpha q}$ signaling in cardiac hypertrophy has been established from in vitro and in vivo experimental models and from inferential clinical data. Most mechanistic information is derived from studies in which cultured neonatal rat cardiac myocytes are stimulated with $G_{\alpha q}$-activating agonists or in which the alpha subunit of $G_{\alpha q}$ is overexpressed. Initial studies by Simpson and colleagues, showed that the αAR agonist norepinephrine, but not the βAR agonist isoproterenol, increased cultured neonatal-rat cardiomyocyte cell size in a dose-dependent manner (40, 41). Using variations of this tissue culture model, hypertrophic effects of phenylephrine, angiotensin II, endothelin, and prostaglandin $F_2\alpha$ have all since been demonstrated (42–45). Each of these structurally diverse hypertrophic agonists stimulates a membrane receptor that activates PLC via the Gq class of GTP-binding proteins, which suggests that Gq and PLC could be hypertrophy-signaling effectors (45–50).

More direct evidence was obtained by the observation that overexpression of Gq-coupled receptors or an activated $G_{\alpha q}$ in cardiomyocytes promotes cellular hypertrophy (51–53). Conversely, inhibition of $G_{\alpha q}$ signaling with microinjected neutralizing antibodies prevents αAR-mediated cardiomyocyte hypertrophy (53). Thus, these studies support an obligatory role for $G_{\alpha q}$ signaling in cardiomyocyte hypertrophy.

Although the studies noted above have demonstrated that cardiomyocyte receptors coupled to $G_{\alpha q}$ can be important transducers of hypertrophy in cultured cardiomyocytes (40–45), there has not, until recently, been general acceptance for the notion that $G_{\alpha q}$-coupled signaling pathways play an important pathophysiological role in vivo. However, indirect evidence for a pathophysiological role of the $G_{\alpha q}$-coupled angiotensin receptor system in heart failure is provided by the favorable results of angiotensin-converting-enzyme inhibitors in modifying the course of heart failure and in regressing cardiac hypertrophy (54–57). In support of this notion, $G_{\alpha q}$ and PLC were shown to be up-regulated in the perinfarct myocardium of experimentally infarcted rats (58).

The necessity for and sufficiency of $G_{\alpha q}$ signaling to stimulate in vivo myocardial growth have been compellingly demonstrated in a series of studies from several laboratories, using genetically manipulated mouse models. $G_{\alpha q}$-overexpressing transgenic mice exhibited a hypertrophy phenotype similar to pressure overload hypertrophy in terms of the extent of cardiac hypertrophy, the pattern of fetal gene expression, and the increase in cardiomyocyte cross-sectional area (59, 60). However, $G_{\alpha q}$ over-expressers also exhibited features distinct from compensated pressure overload hypertrophy, such as eccentric ventricular remodeling, resting sinus bradycardia, and left-ventricular contractile depression (60). This phenotype of hypertrophy and contractile depression in independent lines of $G_{\alpha q}$ over-expressers indicates that signaling events downstream of $G_{\alpha q}$ are sufficient to cause maladaptive cardiac hypertrophy. To evaluate the effects of intrinsic $G_{\alpha q}$ signaling on cardiac responses to pressure overload, $G_{\alpha q}$ over-expressers were subjected to transverse aortic banding (60). Whereas aortic-banded nontransgenic mice developed compensated, concentric, left-ventricular hypertrophy, $G_{\alpha q}$ over-expressers developed eccentric hypertrophy with progressively declining ventricular function, eventually resulting in overt functional decompensation and pulmonary edema.

In support of these findings, overexpression of an activated mutant of $G_{\alpha q}$ also promotes a cardiomyopathic phenotype associated with progressive ventricular dilation (61).

That G_q-mediated signaling induces a cardiomyopathic phenotype was also demonstrated in peripartum $G_{\alpha q}$-transgenic mice (52). In the terminal period of pregnancy or immediately after delivery, these animals rapidly progressed into heart failure characterized by massive biventricular and biatrial-ventricular dilation with pulmonary congestion, pleural effusions, and ascites. Histologically, these hearts exhibited cardiomyocyte apoptosis, but without the inflammatory reaction normally accompanying a necrotic process.

The studies discussed above demonstrate that $G_{\alpha q}$ signaling is sufficient to induce cardiac hypertrophy that makes a transition into heart failure. However, the necessity of $G_{\alpha q}$ signaling in physiologic or pathophysiologic forms of hypertrophy was not, until recently, characterized. Akhter et al demonstrated that transgenic overexpression of a dominant-negative $G_{\alpha q}$ peptide in the heart rendered mice resistant to pressure overload hypertrophy stimulated by acute aortic banding (62). Further supporting evidence was obtained by overexpression of RGS4 in the heart. RGS (regulator of G protein signaling) proteins are GTPase-activating proteins (GAPs) that increase $G\alpha$ inactivation by promoting GTP hydrolysis. Transgenic overexpression of RGS4 in the heart reduced cardiac hypertrophy in response to pressure overload stimulation (63). Collectively, the above studies demonstrate that $G_{\alpha q}$-coupled signaling responses are both necessary and sufficient for mediating cardiac hypertrophy.

LOW-MOLECULAR-WEIGHT GTPASES IN CARDIAC HYPERTROPHY (RAS, RHOA, AND RAC1)

A number of in vitro and in vivo studies have implicated a Ras-dependent signaling pathway in the regulation of cardiac hypertrophy. Microinjection of activated Ras protein into cultured cardiomyocytes increased both cell size and atrial natriuretic factor (ANF) expression (64). Transgenic mice that overexpress a constitutively active form of *Ras* in the mouse heart show cardiac hypertrophy and diastolic dysfunction (65). Transfection of expression vectors encoding activated *Raf-1* or *Ras* increased myocyte cell dimensions and augmented expression of hypertrophy-responsive promoters (66). In addition, adenoviral-mediated gene transfer of dominant-negative *Ras* (17N Ras) inhibited the upregulation of protein and mRNA production in response to phenylephrine (PE) treatment in cultured cardiomyocytes (67). However, using the same adenoviral construct, another group concluded that endothelin-1-stimulated cardiomyocyte hypertrophy was not attenuated by dominant-negative 17N Ras (68). Whereas the general consensus is that Ras activation is associated with cardiac hypertrophy, the downstream signaling events that mediate hypertrophy are less defined.

Ras is a low-molecular-weight GTPase and, like the canonical G proteins discussed above, is activated by GDP-to-GTP exchange initiated by membrane-bound receptors. Ras activation can promote activation of Raf-1, PI3K, small GTPase Ral proteins, p120GAP, and p190GAP, leading to Rho activation (reviewed in 69). In addition, Ras activity is known to result in activation of all three MAPK signaling branches [extracellular-signal-regulated kinases 1 and 2 (ERK1 and 2), c-Jun NH$_2$-terminal kinases (JNKs), and p38], whereas Raf-1 activation is associated only with ERK 1 and 2 activation (Figure 2). Indeed, transgenic mice expressing activated Ras have significant JNK activation in the heart, suggesting that Ras activation may have a broad influence in MAPK signaling responses in the heart (70).

More recently, overexpression approaches in transgenic mice have been used to examine the role of other low-molecular-weight GTPases in cardiac hypertrophy. Overexpression of *RhoA* in the mouse heart caused atrial enlargement and conduction defects, without stimulating ventricular hypertrophy (71). It is unlikely that Rho regulates the actin cytoskeleton in cardiac myocytes, as demonstrated in

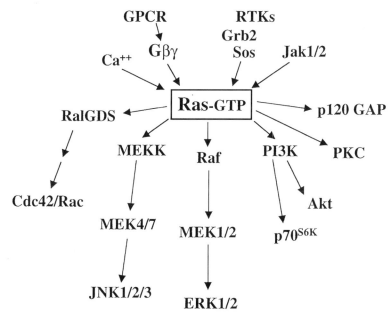

Figure 2   Ras signaling pathways. Ras is activated through G protein–coupled receptors (GPCR), receptor tyrosine kinases (RTK), Janus kinase 1 (Jak), or increases in intracellular calcium resulting in GDP-GTP exchange and the activation of numerous effector proteins. Abbreviations: PKC, protein kinase C; PI3K, phosphatidylinositol 3-kinase; MEK, mitogen-activated protein kinase kinase; MEKK, mitogen-activated protein kinase kinase kinase; JNK, c-Jun NH$_2$ terminal kinase; ERK, extracellular signal-regulated kinase; GAP, GTPase-activating protein.

other cell types, given that transfection of a Rho inhibitor did not disrupt actin muscle fiber morphology (72). However, angiotensin-II-stimulated RhoA activation in cardiac myocytes did result in the formation of premyofibrils, a function consistent with cytoskeletal organizing capacity (73).

Adenovirus-mediated gene transfer of an activated V12rac1 factor in cultured cardiomyocytes potently induced hypertrophy in a manner indistinguishable from agonist stimulation (74). In addition, adenovirus-mediated gene transfer of a dominant-negative N17rac1 factor attenuated PE-induced morphological hypertrophy in culture (74). More recently, transgenic mice overexpressing an activated V12rac1 factor in the heart produced profound cardiac hypertrophy and ventricular dilation (75). Collectively, these studies indicate that Ras and Rac GTPases are prohypertrophic, whereas RhoA may play only a limited role in the hypertrophic program of cardiomyocytes.

MEK1 AND 2 EXTRACELLULAR SIGNAL-REGULATED KINASE1 AND 2 PATHWAY AND CARDIAC HYPERTROPHY

Two separate ERK isoforms have been described, ERK1 and ERK2, that are coordinately phosphorylated and activated by a wide array of mitogenic stimuli (reviewed in 76). The major upstream activators of ERK1 and 2 MAPKs are two MAPK kinases (MAPKKs), MEK1 and MEK2, which directly phosphorylate the dual site in ERK1 and 2 (Thr-Glu-Tyr) (Figure 3). Directly upstream of MEK1 and 2 in the MAPK-signaling cascade are the MAPKK kinase (MAPKKK) Raf-1, A-Raf, B-Raf, and MEKK1–3 (reviewed in 76).

In response to agonist stimulation or cell stretching, ERK1 and 2 become activated both in cultured cardiac myocytes and in isolated perfused hearts (77–83). These observations have implicated ERK1- and 2-signaling factors as regulators of the hypertrophic response. In support of this notion, transfection of a constitutively active MEK1-encoding construct (immediate upstream activator of ERK1 and 2) augmented ANF promoter activity in cultured cardiomyocytes, whereas a dominant-negative MEK1-encoding construct attenuated activity (84). Using antisense oligonucleotides, Glennon et al demonstrated that ERK signaling is necessary for PE-induced cardiomyocyte hypertrophy in culture (85). Similarly, using the MEK1 inhibitor PD98059, Clerk et al reported that the ERKs were required for sarcomeric organization induced by hypertrophic agonists (83). However, this same study also concluded that PD98059 did not prevent cellular hypertrophy in response to agonist stimulation, suggesting that ERKs play a more specialized role in cardiomyocyte hypertrophy.

Although the Ras-Raf-1-MEK1/2-ERK1/2-signaling pathway may regulate certain intracellular responses to a hypertrophic agonist, a large number of studies have disputed the importance of this pathway in the regulation of cardiac hypertrophy.

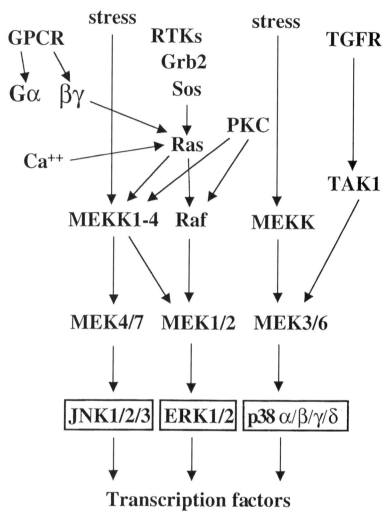

Figure 3   Mitogen-activated protein kinase signaling pathways (MAPK). MAPK signaling pathways are activated in cardiomyocytes by G protein–coupled receptors (GPCRs), receptor tyrosine kinases (RTKs), transforming growth factor β receptor (TGFR), protein kinase C (PKC), calcium, or stress stimuli. These upstream events result in the activation of mitogen-activated protein kinase kinase kinase (MEKK) factors, which leads to the activation of mitogen-activated protein kinase kinase (MEK) factors, and in turn leads to activation of the three terminal MAPK effectors, c-Jun NH_2 terminal kinases (JNK1/2/3), extracellular signal-regulated kinases (ERK1/2), and p38. Abbreviations: TAK1, TGFβ-activated kinase.

Thorburn et al demonstrated that, although Ras-Raf-1-ERK activation was sufficient to augment c-Fos and ANF promoter activity in cardiomyocytes, inhibition of these signaling factors did not antagonize hypertrophic morphology or cytoskeletal organization in response to the agonist (86, 87). However, Post et al reported that neither dominant-negative ERK1 and 2 nor PD98059 were sufficient to block PE-induced ANF promoter activity in cultured cardiomyocytes, suggesting that ERKs are not even important for inducible gene expression. In a subsequent study, transfection of an activated MEK1 encoding expression plasmid was shown to induce c-Fos, but not ANF or myosin light-chain-2V promoter activity in cultured cardiomyocytes (88). More recent studies with the MEK1 inhibitor PD98059 also suggest a minimal role for ERKs in cardiac hypertrophy (70, 89, 90). Intriguingly, one study has even suggested that ERK activation in response to ANF treatment was associated with prevention of cardiomyocyte hypertrophy (91). Although there is clearly a lack of consensus regarding the necessity of ERK signaling as a hypertrophic mediator, overwhelming evidence implicates ERKs as immediate downstream effectors of the hypertrophic response. However, the effector functions of activated ERKs have yet to be fully explored in cultured cardiomyocytes, nor have conclusive genetic or in vivo approaches been used to date. In the future, it will be interesting to examine the association between ERK signaling and cardiac hypertrophy using transgenic or knockout model systems in the mouse.

p38 AND CARDIAC HYPERTROPHY

Four separate p38 MAPK isoforms have been described including p38α, p38β, p38γ, and p38δ (reviewed in 76). p38 MAPKs are activated by a wide array of stress stimuli including chemical stress, physical stress, osmolar stress, radiation stress, and G protein–coupled receptor (GPCR) activation (reviewed in 92). The major upstream activators of p38 MAPKs are two MAPKKs, MKK3 and MKK6, which directly phosphorylate the dual site in p38 MAPKs (Thr-Gly-Tyr) (Figure 3). Less is known of the MAPKKK factors, which lie upstream of MKK3 and MKK6 in cardiomyocytes, although PAK, TAK1, and MLK3 are potential activators (reviewed in 76).

In cardiac myocytes, mechanical deformation, GPCR ligands (angiotensin II, endothelin-1, and PE), and mitogens are potent activators of p38 (reviewed in 93). Activated p38 MAPKs directly phosphorylate serine and threonine residues in a wide array of cytoplasmic proteins and transcription factors to mediate stress-responsive signaling, including MEF2, MAPKAPK2 and 3, ATF-2, ELK-1, Chop, and Max (reviewed in 76). p38α and p38β are thought to be the most important isoforms of p38 expressed in the human heart, whereas p38γ and p38δ are undetectable (94).

The association between p38 MAPKs and the regulation of cardiac hypertrophy has primarily been investigated in cultured neonatal-rat cardiomyocytes. The GPCR agonists PE and endothelin-1 are potent activators of p38 MAPKs in cardiomyocytes (83). In vivo, p38 MAPK activity is elevated by pressure over-load hypertrophy in aortic-banded mice (95) and in human hearts with failure secondary to advanced coronary artery disease (96). Further evidence for p38 as a hypertrophic factor came from the observation that overexpression of an activated MKK3 or MKK6 factor in neonatal cardiomyocytes was sufficient to induce hypertrophy and ANF expression (89, 95, 97). Although there are data supporting a role for p38 activation as a regulator of cardiomyocyte hypertrophy in vitro, its sufficiency and necessity in vivo have not been evaluated.

Investigators have used both the pharmacologic inhibitors SB203580 and SB202190 and dominant-negative constructs to assess the necessity of p38 signaling in cardiac hypertrophy. Pharmacologic inhibition of p38 kinase activity blocked agonist-stimulated cardiomyocyte hypertrophy in culture (83, 89, 97). In addition, adenovirus-mediated gene transfer of a dominant-negative p38β MAPK blunted the hypertrophic response of neonatal cardiomyocytes (95), and pharmacologic or dominant-negative inhibition of p38 signaling significantly reduced agonist-induced b-type natriuretic peptide promoter activity in vitro (98, 99). In contrast, two recent studies have reported that p38 inhibition is not sufficient to attenuate agonist-induced cardiomyocyte hypertrophy under certain conditions, suggesting a more specialized role for p38 MAPK signaling (90, 100). Consistent with this interpretation, inhibition of p38 activity with SB203580 did not affect phenotypic myocyte hypertrophy in response to PE or endothelin-1 within 24 h, yet attenuation was observed by 48 h (83).

c-JUN NH$_2$ TERMINAL KINASE AND CARDIAC HYPERTROPHY

Three distinct *JNK* or *SAPK* (stress-activated protein kinase) genes have been identified in mammalian cells. Each is activated by the upstream MAPK kinases MKK4 and MKK7, which is turn are activated by MEKK1 or MEKK2 (reviewed in 76). The MKKKKs upstream of MEKK1 and 2 include GLK, HPK1, NIK, MST1, and members of the low-molecular-weight G proteins (Ras), and even Grb2 (reviewed in 76). JNK factors are directly phosphorylated by MKK4 or MKK7 on a dual site consisting of the amino acids Thr-Pro-Tyr (Figure 3). JNK1 and JNK2 have each been shown to be expressed in the heart, whereas JNK3 expression is mostly restricted to the brain (101).

In cultured cardiomyocytes, JNK isoforms become phosphorylated in response to stress stimuli (stretching) or GPCR activation (90, 102, 103). JNK activation has also been associated with load-induced cardiac hypertrophy in the rat, myocardial infarction, and human heart failure (96, 104, 105).

A number of studies have shown that JNK1 and 2 are critical regulators of cardiac hypertrophy in vitro and in vivo. In transfection experiments, an activated MEKK1 or MKK4 induced promoter expression of certain hypertrophy-associated genes and transfection of a dominant-negative MEKK1-encoding expression vector-attenuated ANF promoter activity (70, 72, 82). In contrast, transfection of MEKK1 was actually reported to attenuate PE-induced sarcomeric organization, suggesting an antihypertrophic effect of the JNK signaling pathway (72). In addition, Nemoto and others demonstrated that MEKK1 and JNK activation blocked ANF expression in cultured cardiomyocytes (97). Although these differing accounts are confusing, they demonstrate both the complexity of MAPK signaling in cardiac myocytes and the variability that is intrinsic to cultured cardiomyocyte hypertrophy assays. Another influencing factor is the cross-regulation between MAPK-signaling pathways because MEKK1 also activates MEK1 and 2 and ERK in addition to JNK (72, 89).

More recently, evidence has accumulated that strongly implicates JNK activation as a necessary molecular event in the cardiac hypertrophic response, both in vitro and in vivo. Adenovirus-mediated gene transfer of a dominant-negative MKK4 (SEK1) factor significantly attenuated agonist-induced cardiomyocyte hypertrophy in vitro. These observations were extended in vivo by dominant-negative MKK4 adenoviral delivery to the hearts of aortic-banded rats, resulting in reduced cardiac hypertrophy in response to pressure overload (105). Collectively, these studies implicate JNKs as necessary regulators of cardiac hypertrophy in culture and in the adult heart.

PROTEIN KINASE C AND CARDIAC HYPERTROPHY

The protein kinase C (PKC) isoforms, a family of ubiquitous lipid-binding serine-threonine kinases, act downstream of virtually all membrane-associated signal transduction pathways (106). The PKC family consists of ≥ 10 isoenzymes encoded by different genes; each exhibits distinct patterns of tissue-specific expression and agonist-mediated activation. Based on enzymatic properties, PKC isoforms are classified as being conventional (cPKC) or calcium dependent; novel (nPKC) or calcium independent; and atypical (aPKC), which are activated by lipids other than diacylglycerol. An important feature of PKC isoforms is that, when activated, they translocate to distinct subcellular sites.

In cardiac tissue, PKC enzymatic activity is increased after ischemia and acute or chronic pressure overload where it is postulated to mediate ischemic preconditioning and to transduce hypertrophy signaling, respectively (107–110). However, the heterogeneity of PKC isoform expression and differences in PKC isoform regulation and activation in the heart have complicated attempts to precisely define the role of PKC in adaptive cardiac responses and related maladaptive sequelae.

αAR stimulation of cultured rat cardiac myocytes is associated with translocation of PKCβ1 from cytosol to nucleus, PKCβII from fibrillar structures to perinucleus and sarcolemma, PKCε from nucleus and cytosol to myofibrils, and PKCδ to the perinuclear region (110, 111). This differential subcellular compartmentalization of activated PKC isoforms implies distinct substrates and therefore unique cellular functions for each isoform (112, 113). The mechanism for subcellular translocation and activation of PKC isoforms involves binding to anchoring proteins termed RACKs (receptors for activated C kinases) (111, 114). Each PKC isoform or group of related isoforms binds to a specific RACK through unique binding domains, and interference of PKC-RACK binding with peptide analogs of the RACK-binding domain can inhibit translocation of PKC isoforms (Figure 4).

Unstimulated PKC exists in a folded conformation so that the pseudo-substrate domain occupies the substrate-binding site, rendering the enzyme catalytically inactive. In the presence of phospholipid or calcium (depending on the PKC isoform), the PKC protein unfolds and exposes the substrate and RACK-binding sites, facilitating activation. Biochemically, overexpression of small peptides corresponding to the RACK-binding domain competitively inhibit PKC activity by preventing translocation (109, 115). Conversely, overexpression of pseudo-RACK peptides stimulates unfolding of inactivated PKC isoforms, exposing the catalytic site and RACK association site (116).

The described mechanism of activation of PKC isoforms in cardiomyocytes has been largely pioneered by Mochly-Rosen. Accordingly, a PKCβ C$_2$ domain peptide was shown to inhibit phorbol ester attenuation of isoproterenol-stimulated calcium channel activity, suggesting that a cPKC (PKCα or β) mediates phorbol 12-myristate 13-acetate (PMA) -induced inhibition of this channel (117). A PKCε V$_1$ fragment (144 amino acids) or the eight-amino-acid PKCε RACK-binding-site peptide was shown to attenuate PMA or norepinephrine-dependent negative chronotropy and prevented ischemic preconditioning in cultured neonatal cardiac myocytes (109, 115). Finally, specific activation of cardiomyocyte PKCε with an octapeptide pseudo-RACK peptide protected cardiac myocytes from ischemic damage (118).

Whereas associations between PKC isoform activation and specific cardiomyocyte responses are beginning to emerge from in vitro studies, as mentioned above, most in vivo observations of PKC isoform effects have tended to be strictly correlative. For instance, it has been observed that PKCε is selectively translocated to the particulate ventricular fractions during acute or chronic pressure overload (107, 119, 120) and after angiotensin-II stimulation (108). An interesting recent report also noted an association between PKCε activation by chronic ethanol consumption in guinea pigs and ethanol-induced cardioprotection from ischemic reperfusion injury (121). PKCε activation and PKCα up-regulation are two of many cell-signaling events to be described in the genetic G$_{\alpha q}$-mediated hypertrophy model (122). While these associations between PKC activity and different pathological cardiac responses clearly suggest that PKC signaling can contribute mechanistically to these events, gain- and loss-of-function studies are necessary for causality to be established.

Conventional and inducible cardiac-specific transgenesis has been used to explore the direct effects of PKCβ signaling in vivo. Although there is controversy over whether PKCβ is expressed in the adult mouse heart, (123, 124), Wakasaki et al expressed PKCβII under control of a truncated α-myosin heavy-chain promoter and observed a phenotype of hypertrophy, fibrosis, and systolic dysfunction (125). In a follow-up study, PKCβ-mediated phosphorylation of troponin

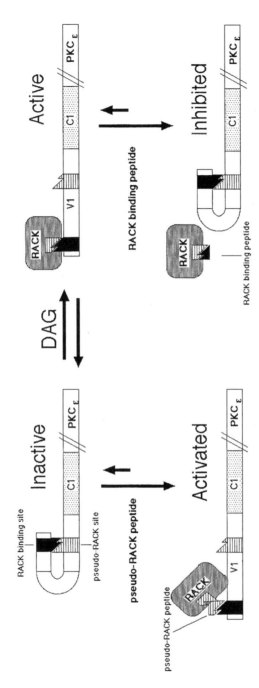

Figure 4 Mechanism of protein kinase C (PKC) activation. The pseudo-RACK binding site normally holds PKC factors in an inactive conformation unless stimulated. Once stimulated by diacylglycerol (DAG) or calcium, PKC factors change conformations, allowing interaction with RACK domain-containing proteins and exposure of the active site.

I was suggested as a mechanism for contractile dysfunction in these mice (126). Using inducible expression of a mutationally activated PKCβ, Bowman and colleagues found hypertrophy when the transgene was induced in the adult heart but a lethal effect of expression in the neonatal mouse (127).

Recent studies are focusing on the more abundant adult cardiac PKC isoforms, such as PKCε. Mochly-Rosen & Dorn have used transgenic techniques to express PKCε-activating and -inhibiting peptides in the mouse heart. The initial description of this model demonstrated that increasing basal translocation of PKCε by approximately 20% was sufficient to exert a powerful protective effect on cardiac contractile function and myocyte integrity in isolated hearts subjected to global ischemia with reperfusion (118). Subsequent studies using the complementary approaches of PKC isoform inhibition and activation demonstrated that PKCϵ activation causes a physiologic form of hypertrophy, whereas inhibition of PKCε translocation with a RACK-binding peptide (εV1) caused the opposite response, that is, thinning of the ventricular walls and lethal heart failure from a dilated cardiomyopathy (128). These studies begin to suggest that PKCε activation is a necessary component of normal trophic growth of cardiomyocytes during postnatal development. It is likely that the approach of in vivo PKC translocation modulation will, in the future, yield similarly useful information about the roles of other naturally occurring myocardial PKC isoforms.

CALCINEURIN AND CARDIAC HYPERTROPHY

Although a great deal of attention has been focused on the elucidation of kinase-signaling pathways as mediators of reactive signaling, the reciprocal pathways of dephosphorylation are less well characterized. Recently, the intracellular phosphatase calcineurin has been implicated as a regulator of the hypertrophic response in conjunction with the transcription factors nuclear factor of activated T cells (NFAT). Calcineurin is a serine-threonine phosphatase that is uniquely activated by calcium-calmodulin (Figure 5). The calcineurin enzyme consists of a 59- to 61-kDa catalytic subunit termed calcineurin A and a 19-kDa calcium-binding EF-hand domain containing protein. The catalytic subunit is encoded by three genes, *calcineurin Aα*, *calcineurin Aβ*, and *calcineurin Aγ*. In the adult human, rat, or mouse heart, both *calcineurin Aα* and *calcineurin Aβ* gene products can be detected, but not *calcineurin Aγ* (129; JD Molkentin, unpublished results).

The paradigm of calcineurin as a regulator of reactive intracellular signaling through NFAT transcription factors has been firmly established in T cells (130). Activation of the T-cell receptor ultimately results in elevated concentrations of intracellular calcium, which binds calmodulin, resulting in calcineurin activation. Once activated, calcineurin directly dephosphorylates members of the NFAT transcription factor family in the cytoplasm, resulting in their nuclear translocation and the activation of immune response genes (Figure 5). The immunosuppressive drugs cyclosporine A and FK506 are thought to act by inhibiting calcineurin and preventing NFAT nuclear translocation (129).

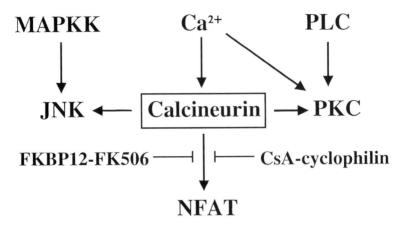

Figure 5 Calcineurin-signaling pathway in cardiomyocytes. Calcineurin is activated by calcium bound to calmodulin, which in turn leads to nuclear factor of activated T cell (NFAT) dephosphorylation and its nuclear translocation. Activated calcineurin has also been shown to promote c-Jun NH_2 terminal kinase (JNK) activation, and certain protein kinase C (PKC) isoforms (120). Abbreviations: CsA, cyclosporine A; MAPKK, mitogen-activated protein kinase kinase; FKBP12, FK506-binding protein.

A conserved role for calcineurin-NFAT signaling was recently identified in the heart (131). The notion of a calcium-activated signal transduction pathway in the myocardium was particularly attractive given the long-standing notion that altered intracellular calcium handling is associated with cardiac hypertrophy and heart failure (reviewed in 132). Overexpression of activated calcineurin in the heart of transgenic mice resulted in profound cardiac hypertrophy that underwent a transition to dilated-heart failure within 2 months (131). Calcineurin was subsequently shown to operate through NFAT3 in the heart because transgenic mice expressing a constitutively nuclear mutant of NFAT3 also demonstrated cardiac hypertrophy. The specificity of the transgenes was demonstrated by the observation that cyclosporine A inhibited cardiac hypertrophy in calcineurin-transgenic mice, but not in NFAT3-transgenic mice (131, 133).

Because cyclosporine A and FK506 are effective inhibitors of calcineurin, many groups pursued pharmacologic approaches to evaluate the necessity of this pathway in various rodent disease models. Pharmacologic calcineurin inhibition attenuated dilated and hypertrophic cardiomyopathy in three different mouse models of heart disease owing to alterations in sarcomeric proteins, and calcineurin also inhibited the development of pressure overload hypertrophy in aortic-banded rats (134). However, immediately after this initial report, four separate studies concluded that calcineurin inhibitors had no effect in blocking pressure overload hypertrophy in rodents (135–138). In contrast, seven additional rodent-based studies have reached the opposite conclusion that calcineurin inhibitors are effective agents for preventing or attenuating cardiac hypertrophy in vivo (61, 133, 139–143). The reason for these conflicting data is unknown, but factors such as effective drug dosage, differences in the surgical preparations and aortic-banding procedures, or age and sex of animals may underlie the disparities.

Because both cyclosporine A and FK506 have multiple intracellular targets, the mechanism whereby these drugs attenuate cardiac hypertrophy is uncertain. To explore the issue of specificity, a recent report demonstrated that adenovirus-mediated gene transfer of noncompetitive calcineurin-inhibitory-protein domains into cultured cardiomyocytes significantly attenuated agonist-induced hypertrophy (144). These data suggest that cyclosporine A and FK506 mediate their inhibitory effects on cultured cardiomyocytes through a calcineurin-specific mechanism.

In response to hypertrophic stimuli, calcineurin protein content and enzymatic activity are increased (140, 141, 144). However, two other studies reported no change in calcineurin activity in response to pressure overload hypertrophy in the heart (137, 139), whereas a third study reported dramatic down-regulation (138). Once again, the reasons behind these divergent conclusions are uncertain. However, assessment of calcineurin enzymatic activity in cardiac protein extracts is technically difficult given the relatively low calcineurin content in the heart (145), its labile nature and sensitivity to oxidation (146), and the background of other phosphatases that act on the RII peptide substrate.

A lack of consensus also surrounds the studies that have examined calcineurin in failed human hearts. Calcineurin A activity was suggested to be significantly elevated in failed human hearts through the use of a calmodulin co-immunoprecipitation assay (147). More recently, these results were extended by the observation that calcineurin $A\beta$ protein levels and total calcineurin enzymatic activity are each significantly elevated in both hypertrophied and failed human hearts (148; HW Lim & JD Molkentin, unpublished results). In contrast, another group reported that calcineurin A protein content was elevated with one commercial source of antibody but not with another (149). Although it is attractive to suggest that calcineurin may be a disease-predisposing pathway in the human heart, the utility of calcineurin inhibitory agents as potential therapeutics for human heart disease is uncertain given the known deleterious side effects of these drugs, including hypertension (150).

Because calcineurin-NFAT represents a newly appreciated regulatory pathway in heart, a number of critical questions remain to be addressed. The relative importance of NFAT transcription factors as necessary downstream mediators of calcineurin activity is uncertain. Northern blot analysis has demonstrated that at least four different *NFAT* genes are expressed on the heart, suggesting that knock-out strategies might not be effective (151–153). Dominant-negative approaches that could globally inhibit NFAT factors or calcineurin in the hearts of transgenic animals will be necessary and are, in fact, in progress.

gp130-SIGNAL TRANSDUCER AND ACTIVATOR OF TRANSCRIPTION AND CARDIAC HYPERTROPHY

Recently, a series of seminal studies have elucidated the role that the interleukin-6 (IL-6) family of cytokines plays in cardiac myocyte maturation and hypertrophy (reviewed in 154). Cardiotrophin-1 is an important member of the IL-6 cytokine family that interacts with the dimerized membrane receptors gp130 and low-affinity leukemia inhibitor factor receptor (LIFR) (155). Ligand binding to the gp130-LIFR complex results in phosphorylation of Janus kinase (Jak) signaling factors, which in turn phosphorylates gp130, generating a docking site for SH2 domain-containing proteins (156–158; Figure 6). The family of signal transducer and activator of transcription (STAT) are SH2 domain-containing factors that are

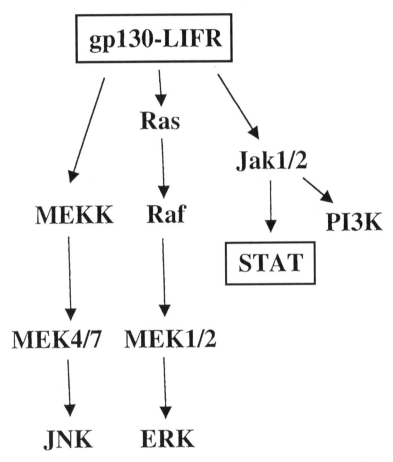

Figure 6   gp130-signal transducer and activator of transcription (STAT) signaling pathway. The gp130 transmembrane receptor associated with the leukemia inhibitory factor receptor (LIFR) is activated by LIF, cardiotrophin, and other members of the interleukin-6 cytokine family. Once activated, this receptor interacts with Janus kinase 1 (Jak1) causing its activation, which in turn leads to STAT phosphorylation promoting dimerization and nuclear entry. This receptor also promotes activation of, phosphatidylinositol 3-kinase (PI3K), Ras, and mitogen-activated protein kinase kinase kinases (MEKK).

recruited to phosphorylated gp130, resulting in their subsequent phosphorylation and homo- and heterodimerization and nuclear translocation (157, 159). In addition, activation of gp130 and/or LIFR has also been shown to lead to MAPK activation through activated Ras (160–162). Finally, the addition of leukemia inhibitor factor (LIF) to cardiomyocytes leads to gp130 activation, which can also lead to PI3K activation by a mechanism involving Jak1-mediated phosphorylation (163). Addition of wortmannin, a PI3K inhibitor, diminished LIF-induced MAPK activation, suggesting that gp130-Jak are interconnected with MAPK signaling pathways through PI3K or enhanced calcium signaling (163, 164).

Cardiotrophin-1–gp130-Jak activity is increased in cardiomyocytes in response to hypertrophic stimulation such as stretching or in response to pressure overload in vivo (165, 166). Cardiotrophin-1 and other members of the IL-6 cytokine family are potent inducers of neonatal cardiomyocyte hypertrophy in culture through gp130-LIFR activation (155, 167, 168). In addition, continuous activation of the gp130-STAT pathway causes cardiac hypertrophy in mice (169), and targeted disruption of *gp130* in the mouse results in embryonic lethality associated with hypoplastic ventricular development (170). Recently, cardiac-specific disruption of *gp130* revealed a critical role for this receptor in cardiac homeostasis and survival after aortic banding. Cardiac-specific *gp130* knockout mice were viable, but they quickly underwent a transition into heart failure after pressure overload stimulation, which was associated with profound apoptosis (171). Downstream, adenovirus-mediated gene transfer of either wild-type or dominant-negative STAT3 was shown to either stimulate or attenuate LIF-induced cardiomyocyte hypertrophy, respectively (172). In addition, transgenic overexpression of STAT3 in the heart induced cardiac hypertrophy (173). These results establish the IL-6 family of ligands, together with gp130-Jak-STAT signaling factors, as sufficient regulators of cardiac development, hypertrophy, and survival.

IGF-1 TRANSDUCTION PATHWAY
AND CARDIAC HYPERTROPHY

Insulin-like growth factors (IGFs) I and II (IGF-I and IGF-II) are peptides that convey growth-factor-like signals which promote cellular proliferation and/or differentiation through binding to a specific heterotetrameric receptor with intrinsic tyrosine kinase activity (reviewed in 174). The activated IGF receptor phosphorylates the insulin receptor substrates (IRSs) 1 and 2 (IRS-1 and IRS-2) leading to signal transduction through Crk and Shc and resulting in Grb-2, Sos, and Ras activation (Figure 7). The regulatory subunit of PI3K contains an SH2 domain that interacts with IRS-1, resulting in PI3K activation (175). PI3K then leads to Akt (protein kinase B) activation and p70/p85 S6K through PDK1, which affect diverse intracellular processes such as translational regulation and cell survival (Figure 7).

Numerous studies have implicated IGF signaling in the regulation of cardiac homeostasis and maturation (reviewed in 174). We attempt to briefly review only

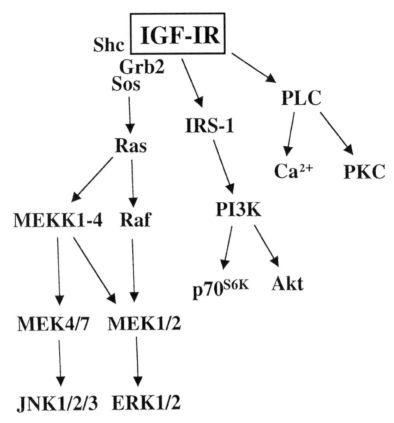

Figure 7   Insulin-like growth factor I receptor (IGF-IR) signaling pathway. IGF-IR activation leads to activation of Ras, phospholipase C (PLC), and insulin receptor substrates (IRS-1) proteins. Abbreviations: MEKK, mitogen-activated protein kinase kinase kinases; MEK, mitogen-activated protein kinase kinases; JNK1/2/3, c-Jun NH_2 terminal kinases; ERK1/2, extracellular signal-regulated kinases; PI3K, phosphatidylinositol 3-kinase; PKC, protein kinase C.

the data that have implicated IGF-signaling pathways in the control of cardiac hypertrophy. Transgenic mice overexpressing IGF-1 in the myocardium were reported to have increased numbers of total myocytes without hypertrophy of individual muscle fibers (176, 177). In contrast, a recent study reported that overexpression of the local form of IGF-1 in the hearts of transgenic mice was sufficient to induce a hypertrophic phenotype that eventually led to reduced systolic performance (178). There is also a lack of consensus concerning the cardiac phenotype associated with IGF-1 deficiency. Growth hormone and IGF-1 deficiency in humans has been associated with cardiac atrophy and reduced function (179, 180). In contrast, IGF-1-deficient mice were reported to have elevated blood pressure and enhanced cardiac contractility (181).

Signaling components downstream of the IGF receptor have been implicated in cardiac hypertrophy. Angiotensin-II-induced cardiomyocyte hypertrophy in vitro was shown to induce p70S6K, resulting in greater protein translation (182). Selective inhibition of p70S6K with rapamycin blocked the augmentation of agonist-induced protein synthesis and the ensuing hypertrophic growth of cultured cardiomyocytes (182–184). In vivo, pressure overload stimulation activated both p70S6K and p85S6K, suggesting a role in physiologic hypertrophy (185). More recently, PI3K was also shown to regulate cardiac myocyte hypertrophy in transgenic mice. Overexpression of an activated form of the PI3K catalytic subunit resulted in cardiac hypertrophy, whereas transgenic overexpression of a dominant-negative PI3K produced smaller hearts and individual fibers (186). Finally, Akt activation was also shown to promote cardiomyocyte viability, although its role in hypertrophy was not reported (187). Collectively, these studies indicate that the IGF-PI3K-Akt-p70S6K signaling pathway plays an important role in regulating cardiac hypertrophy, viability, and homeostasis.

FIBROBLAST GROWTH FACTOR 2
AND TRANSFORMING GROWTH FACTOR β
IN CARDIAC HYPERTROPHY

Fibroblast growth factor 2 (FGF-2) (also called basic FGF) and transforming growth factor β (TGFβ) are peptide growth factors that can each induce a fetal-like gene program in cultured rat neonatal ventricular myocytes, consistent with induction of the hypertrophic program (188). Since this original description, a number of additional studies have demonstrated the importance of FGF-2 and TGFβ signaling responses as mediators of the hypertrophic program. Both FGF-2 and TGFβ are produced by cardiomyocytes or non-myocytes within the heart, acting as autocrine or paracrine growth factors (reviewed in 189). FGF-2 and TGFβ each bind separate membrane receptors that have intracellular tyrosine kinase activity (FGF) or serine-threonine kinase activity (TGFβ) to elicit further signaling.

In adult cardiac myocytes, pacing induced FGF-2 release from cardiomyocytes, which then acted in an autocrine fashion to stimulate a hypertrophic phenotype and phenylalanine incorporation (190). In vivo, FGF-2 infusion stimulated cardiac hypertrophy in adult rats after myocardial infarction (191), but in a different study by the same group this was not confirmed (192). To definitively examine the role of FGF-2 in cardiac hypertrophy, Schultz et al characterized *FGF-2*-null mice after aortic banding (193). *FGF-2*-null mice demonstrated a significant attenuation of the hypertrophic response after pressure overload stimulation, indicating that this signaling pathway was a necessary regulator of cardiac hypertrophy (193). Although Schultz et al did not examine the downstream consequences on intracellular signaling in *FGF-2*-null mice, another study demonstrated that FGF-2 and its receptor signal, in part, through the MAPK cascade to elicit myocyte hypertrophy (194).

Significantly less is known concerning a role for TGFβ in the hypertrophic response. Although TGFβ1 mRNA is increased in response to pressure overload or norepinephrine infusion in the rat heart, a functional role as a hypertrophic regulator has not been established (195). In vitro, adenovirus-mediated overexpression of TGFβ1 in cultured neonatal cardiomyocytes increased sarcomeric actin, suggesting a growth response (196). In addition, angiotensin-II-induced neonatal myocyte hypertrophy required paracrine TGFβ1 release from non-myocytes in culture (197). Downstream of TGFβ receptor activation (type-I and type-II receptors), two main intracellular-signaling branches involving Smad proteins or TGFβ-activated kinase (TAK1) have been documented (198). Whereas Smad proteins are not known to regulate cardiomyocyte hypertrophy, TAK1 can directly activate MAPKK factors, leading to JNK and/or p38 activation (198). Indeed, TGFβ1 was reported to cause TAK1 activation, leading to p38 phosphorylation and up-regulation of the skeletal α-actin promoter in cultured neonatal cardiomyocytes (199).

OTHER INTRACELLULAR REGULATORS OF CARDIAC HYPERTROPHY

Additional hypertrophic mediators have been implicated, and undoubtedly countless others have yet to be described. For example, Src is activated in pressure-loaded hearts (200), and overexpression of activated Src in neonatal cardiomyocytes induced hypertrophy through a Ras- and Raf-dependent pathway (201). Focal adhesion kinase another nonreceptor tyrosine kinase, was also reported to induce cardiac hypertrophy when overexpressed in transgenic mouse hearts (202). Neuregulin signaling through the ErbB2 or ErbB4 receptors (member of the epidermal growth factor receptor family) can induce neonatal cardiomyocyte hypertrophy in culture through an ERK MAPK signaling pathway (203). In vivo, ErbB2 and ErbB4 mRNA levels were reported to be down-regulated in early-stage heart failure induced by pressure overload, suggesting that lowered ErbB receptor signaling plays a role in loss of hypertrophy and decompensation (204). Signaling through the epidermal-growth-factor-like tyrosine kinase receptor can also induce cardiomyocyte hypertrophy in culture (205).

A number of other less typical signaling pathways may also play a role in cardiac hypertrophy. Thyroid hormone induces cardiac hypertrophy in vitro and in vivo through binding to its intracellular receptor, which then acts as a transcription factor to directly induce expression of cardiac genes (reviewed in 206). More recently, the myosin light-chain kinase was shown to directly regulate sarcomeric organization in cardiac myocytes, a characteristic associated with hypertrophy (207). The cytokine tumor necrosis factor α is also expressed by cardiac myocytes and can activate the tumor necrosis factor receptor, resulting in hypertrophy of cultured cardiomyocytes (208). In addition, transgenic mice overexpressing tumor necrosis factor α specifically in the heart develop dilated cardiomyopathy and heart failure (209, 210).

CONCLUSIONS: Integrated Model
of Intracellular Signal Transduction

Estimates derived from the number of kinase and phosphatase genes identified in *Caenorhabditis elegans* predict that, of ~50,000 human genes, ~1100 are kinases and 300 are phosphatases (211). These figures suggest an almost overwhelming complexity in mammalian signal transduction cascades and underscore the potential difficulty in designing pharmacologic agents with both specificity and efficacy in treating various forms of cardiomyopathy. However, lessons from past studies actually suggest an opposite interpretation, that is, that most strategies used today are effective. Numerous studies have demonstrated that inhibition of specific central-signaling pathways can attenuate the hypertrophic response. Indeed, hypertrophy secondary to hypertension in humans can be partially reversed with pleiotropic drugs such as angiotensin-converting enzyme inhibitors, βAR blockers, and calcium channel blockers (212, 213).

In this review, we have discussed a number of studies in animal models of pressure overload hypertrophy, each of which demonstrated attenuation of hypertrophy by inhibiting divergent intracellular signaling pathways. For example, a dominant-negative $G_{\alpha q}$ peptide or a dominant-negative (MKK4) SEK factor each has an impact on the ability of the heart to mount a hypertrophic response in vivo. Furthermore, FGF-2 knockout mice or treatment of rodents with a calcineurin inhibitor (cyclosporine) also attenuates the hypertrophic response in vivo. These seemingly contradictory studies actually support an integrated model of signal transduction in the heart such that multiple pathways are necessary for timely and effective hypertrophy. Specific inhibition of central regulatory pathways likely diminishes the activation of other interdependent signal transduction pathways. Indeed, cyclosporine A-mediated attenuation of hypertrophy was not only associated with inhibition of calcineurin but was also found to lead to inhibition of JNK, PKCα, and PKCθ in pressure-loaded rat hearts (120). Collectively, this model emphasizes the potential for specific inhibition of any of a number of central regulatory pathways as an effective strategy for treating certain forms of hypertrophic disease.

Visit the Annual Reviews home page at www.AnnualReviews.org

LITERATURE CITED

1. Levy D, Garrison RJ, Savage DD, Kannel WB, Castelli WP. 1990. Prognostic implications of echocardiographically determined left ventricular mass in the Framingham heart study. *N. Engl. J. Med.* 322:1561–66

2. Ho KK, Levy D, Kannel WB, Pinsky JL. 1993. The epidemiology of heart failure: the Framingham study. *J. Am. Coll. Cardiol.* 22:6–13

3. Dominguez LJ, Parrinello G, Amato P, Licata G. 1999. Trends of congestive heart failure epidemiology: contrast with clinical trial results. *Cardiologia* 44:801–8

4. Lefkowitz RJ, Koch WJ, Rockman HA. 2000. Functional consequences of altering

myocardial adrenergic receptor signaling. *Annu. Rev. Physiol.* 62:237–60

5. Lefkowitz RJ, Rockman HA, Koch WJ. 2000. Catecholamines, cardiac beta-adrenergic receptors, and heart failure. *Circulation* 101:1634–37

6. Simon MI, Strathmann MP, Gautam N. 1991. Diversity of G proteins in signal transduction. *Science* 252:802–8

7. Crespo P, Xu N, Simonds WF, Gutkind JS. 1994. Ras-dependent activation of MAP kinase pathway mediated by G-protein beta gamma subunits. *Nature* 369:418–20

8. Pumiglia KM, LeVine H, Haske T, Habib T, Jove R, Decker SJ. 1995. A direct interaction between G-protein beta gamma subunits and the Raf-1 protein kinase. *J. Biol. Chem.* 270:14251–54

9. Sathyamangla V, Prasad N, Esposito G, Mao L, Koch WJ, et al. 2000. G-beta gamma-dependent phosphoinositide 3-kinase activation in hearts with in vivo pressure overload hypertrophy. *J. Biol. Chem.* 275:4693–98

10. Kadambi VJ, Kranias EG. 1998. Genetically engineered mice: model systems for left ventricular failure. *J. Card. Fail.* 4:349–61

11. Neumann J, Schmitz W, Scholz H, von Meyerinck L, Doring V, Kalmar P. 1988. Increase in myocardial Gi-proteins in heart failure. *Lancet* 2:936–37

12. Hershberger RE, Feldman AM, Bristow MR. 1991. A1-adenosine receptor inhibition of adenylate cyclase in failing and nonfailing human ventricular myocardium. *Circulation* 83:1343–51

13. Marzo KP, Frey MJ, Wilson JR, Liang BT, Manning DR, et al. 1991. Beta-adrenergic receptor-G protein-adenylate cyclase complex in experimental canine congestive heart failure produced by rapid ventricular pacing. *Circ. Res.* 69:1546–56

14. Böhm M, Gierschik P, Knorr A, Larisch K, Weismann K, Erdmann E. 1992. Desensitization of adenylate cyclase and increase of Gi alpha in cardiac hypertrophy

due to acquired hypertension. *Hypertension* 20:103–12

15. Böhm M, Gierschik P, Knorr A, Larisch K, Weismann K, Erdmann E. 1992. Role of altered G-protein expression in the regulation of myocardial adenylate cyclase activity and force of contraction in spontaneous hypertensive cardiomyopathy in rats. *J. Hypertens.* 10:1115–28

16. Kawamoto H, Ohyanagi M, Nakamura K, Yamamoto J, Iwasaki T. 1994. Increased levels of inhibitory G protein in myocardium with heart failure. *Jpn. Circ. J.* 58:913–24

17. Böhm M, Kirchmayr R, Erdmann E. 1995. Myocardial Gi alpha-protein levels in patients with hypertensive cardiac hypertrophy, ischemic heart disease and cardiogenic shock. *Cardiovasc. Res.* 30:611–18

18. Vatner DE, Sato N, Galper JB, Vatner SF. 1996. Physiological and biochemical evidence for coordinate increases in muscarinic receptors and Gi during pacing-induced heart failure. *Circulation* 94:102–7

19. Feldman AM, Cates AE, Bristow MR, Van Dop C. 1989. Altered expression of alpha-subunits of G proteins in failing human hearts. *J. Mol. Cell. Cardiol.* 21:359–65

20. Eschenhagen T, Mende U, Nose M, Schmitz W, Scholz H, et al. 1992. Increased messenger RNA level of the inhibitory G protein alpha subunit Gi alpha-2 in human end-stage heart failure. *Circ. Res.* 70:688–96

21. Eschenhagen T, Friedrichsen M, Gsell S, Hollman A, Mittmann C, et al. 1996. Regulation of the human Gi alpha-2 gene promoter activity in embryonic chicken cardiomyocytes. *Basic Res. Cardiol.* 91:41–46

22. Redfern CH, Coward P, Degtyarev MY, Lee EK, Kwa AT, et al. 1999. Conditional expression and signaling of a specifically designed Gi-coupled receptor in transgenic mice. *Nat. Biotechnol.* 17:165–69

23. Chen LA, Vatner DE, Vatner SF, Hittinger L, Homcy CJ. 1991. Decreased Gs alpha mRNA levels accompany the fall in Gs and adenylyl cyclase activities in compensated left ventricular hypertrophy. In heart failure, only the impairment in adenylyl cyclase activation progresses. *J. Clin. Invest.* 87:293–98

24. Longabaugh JP, Vatner DE, Vatner SF, Homcy CJ. 1988. Decreased stimulatory guanosine triphosphate binding protein in dogs with pressure-overload left ventricular failure. *J. Clin. Invest.* 81:420–24

25. Sethi R, Elimban V, Chapman D, Dixon IM, Dhalla NS. 1998. Differential alterations in left and right ventricular G-proteins in congestive heart failure due to myocardial infarction. *J. Mol. Cell. Cardiol.* 30:2153–63

26. Roth DA, Urasawa K, Helmer GA, Hammond HK. 1993. Downregulation of cardiac guanosine 5′-triphosphate-binding proteins in right atrium and left ventricle in pacing-induced congestive heart failure. *J. Clin. Invest.* 91:939–49

27. Bohm M, Gierschik P, Knorr A, Schmidt U, Weismann K, Erdmann E. 1993. Cardiac adenylyl cyclase, beta-adrenergic receptors, and G proteins in salt-sensitive hypertension. *Hypertension* 22:715–27

28. Brodde OE, Vogelsang M, Broede A, Michel-Reher M, Beisenbusch-Schafer E, et al. 1998. Diminished responsiveness of Gs-coupled receptors in severely failing human hearts: no difference in dilated versus ischemic cardiomyopathy. *J. Cardiovasc. Pharmacol.* 4:585–94

29. Sethi R, Bector N, Takeda N, Nagano M, Jasmin G, Dhalla NS. 1994. Alterations in G-proteins in congestive heart failure in cardiomyopathic (UM-X7.1) hamsters. *Mol. Cell. Biochem.* 140:163–70

30. Gaudin C, Ishikawa Y, Wight DC, Mahdavi V, Nadal-Ginard B, et al. 1995. Overexpression of Gs alpha protein in the hearts of transgenic mice. *J. Clin. Invest.* 95:1676–83

31. Iwase M, Bishop SP, Uechi M, Vatner DE, Shannon RP, et al. 1996. Adverse effects of chronic endogenous sympathetic drive induced by cardiac $G_{s\alpha}$ overexpression. *Circ. Res.* 78:517–24

32. Geng YJ, Ishikawa Y, Vatner DE, Wagner TE, Bishop SP, et al. 1999. Apoptosis of cardiac myocytes in $G_{s\alpha}$ transgenic mice. *Circ. Res.* 84:34–42

33. Behrana AJ, Hasleton P, Leen CLS, Ashleigh RS, Gholkar A. 1989. Multiple extra-adrenal paragangliomas associated with catecholamine cardiomyopathy. *Eur. Heart J.* 10:182–85

34. Imperato-McGinley J, Gautier T, Ehlers K, Zullo MA, Goldstein DS, Vaughn ED Jr. 1987. Reversibility of catecholamine-induced dilated cardiomyopathy in a child with a pheochromocytoma. *N. Engl. J. Med.* 316:793–97

35. Van Vliet PD, Burchell HB, Titus JL. 1966. Focal myocarditis associated with pheochromocytoma. *N. Engl. J. Med.* 274:1102–8

36. Sardesai SH, Mourant AJ, Sivathandon Y, Farrow R, Gibbons DO. 1990. Phaeochromocytoma and catecholamine induced cardiomyopathy presenting as heart failure. *Br. Heart J.* 63:234–37

37. Liggett SB, Tepe NM, Lorenz JN, Canning AM, Jantz TD, et al. 2000. Early and delayed consequences of β_2 adrenergic receptor overexpression in mouse hearts: critical role for expression level. *Circulation* 101:1707–14

38. Dorn GW II, Tepe NM, Lorenz JN, Koch WJ, Liggett SB. 1999. Low- and high-level transgenic expression of β_2-adrenergic receptors differentially affects cardiac hypertrophy and function in Gαq overexpressing mice. *Proc. Natl. Acad. Sci. USA* 96:6400–5

39. Engelhardt S, Hein L, Wiesmann F, Lohse MJ. 1999. Progressive hypertrophy and heart failure in beta1-adrenergic receptor transgenic mice. *Proc. Natl. Acad. Sci. USA* 96:7059–64

40. Simpson P. 1983. Norepinephrine-stimulated hypertrophy of cultured rat myocardial cells is an alpha1 adrenergic response. *J. Clin. Invest.* 72:732–38

41. Simpson P, McGrath A, Savion S. 1982. Myocyte hypertrophy in neonatal rat heart cultures and its regulation by serum and by catecholamines. *Circ. Res.* 51:787–801

42. Adams JW, Migita DS, Yu MK, Young R, Hellickson MS, et al. 1996. Prostaglandin $F_{2\alpha}$ stimulates hypertrophic growth of cultured neonatal rat ventricular myocytes. *J. Biol. Chem.* 271:1179–86

43. Knowlton KU, Michel MC, Itani M, Schubeita HE, Ishihara K, et al. 1993. The α_1-adrenergic receptor subtype mediates biochemical, molecular, and morphologic features of cultured myocardial cell hypertrophy. *J. Biol. Chem.* 268:15374–80

44. Sadoshima J-I, Xu Y, Slayer HS, Izumo S. 1993. Autocrine release of angiotensin II mediates stretch-induced hypertrophy of cardiac myocytes in vitro. *Cell* 75:977–84

45. Shubeita HE, McDonough PM, Harris AN, Knowlton KU, Glembotwski CC, et al. 1990. Endothelin induction of inositol phospholipid hydrolysis, sarcomere assembly and cardiac gene expression in ventricular myocytes: a paracrine mechanism for myocardial cell hypertrophy. *J. Biol. Chem.* 265:20555–62

46. Adams JW, Sah VP, Henderson SA, Brown JH. 1998. Prostaglandin $F_{2\alpha}$-stimulated hypertrophic growth in neonatal rat cardiac myocytes is mediated by action of tyrosine kinases and Jun N-terminal kinase. *Circ. Res.* 83:167–78

47. Brown JH, Martinson EA. 1992. Phosphoinositide-generated second messengers in cardiac signal transduction. *Trends Cardiovasc. Med.* 2:209–14

48. Clerk A, Sugden PH. 1997. Regulation of phospholipases C and D in rat ventricular myocytes: stimulation by endothelin-1, bradykinin and phenylephrine. *J. Mol. Cell. Cardiol.* 29:1593–604

49. McDonough PM, Brown JH, Glembotski CC. 1987. Phenylephrine and endothelin differentially stimulate cardiac PI hydrolysis and ANF expression. *Am. J. Physiol. Heart Circ. Physiol.* 264:H625–H30

50. Sadoshima J-I, Izumo S. 1993. Signal transduction pathways of angiotensin II-induced c-fos gene expression in cardiac myocytes in vitro: roles of phospholipid-derived second messengers. *Circ. Res.* 73:424–38

51. Ramirez MT, Post GR, Sulakhe PV, Brown JH. 1995. M_1 muscarinic receptors heterologously expressed in cardiac myocytes mediates Ras-dependent changes in gene expression. *J. Biol. Chem.* 270:8446–51

52. Adams JW, Sakata Y, Davis MG, Sah VP, Wang Y, et al. 1998. Enhanced $G\alpha q$ signaling: A common pathway mediates cardiac hypertrophy and heart failure. *Proc. Natl. Acad. Sci. USA* 95:10140–45

53. LaMorte VJ, Thorburn J, Absher D, Spiegel A, Brown JH, et al. 1994. Gq- and/Ras-dependent pathways mediate hypertrophy of neonatal rat ventricular myocytes following alpha$_1$-adrenergic stimulation. *J. Biol. Chem.* 269:13490–96

54. The SOLVD Investigators. 1991. Effect of enalapril on survival in patients with reduced left ventricular ejection fractions and congestive heart failure. *N. Engl. J. Med.* 325:293–302

55. Dunn FG, Oigman W, Ventura HO, Messeri FH, Kobrin I, Frolich ED. 1984. Enalapril improves systemic and renal hemodynamics and allows regression of left ventricular mass in essential hypertension. *Am. J. Cardiol.* 53:105–8

56. Garavaglia GE, Messeri FH, Nunez BD, Schmieder RE, Frohlich ED. 1988. Immediate and short-term cardiovascular effects of a new converting enzyme inhibitor (Lisinopril) in essential hypertension. *Am. J. Cardiol.* 62:912–16

57. Nakashima Y, Fouad FM, Tarazi RC. 1984. Regression of left ventricular hypertrophy from systemic hypertension by enalapril. *Am. J. Cardiol.* 53:1044–49

58. Ju H, Zhao S, Tappia PS, Panagia V, Dixon IMC. 1998. Expression of $G_{q\alpha}$ and PLC-β in scar and border tissue in heart failure due to myocardial infarction. *Circulation* 97:892–99

59. D'Angelo DD, Sakata Y, Lorenz JN, Boivin GP, Walsh RA, et al. 1997. Transgenic Gαq overexpression induces cardiac contractile function in mice. *Proc. Natl. Acad. Sci. USA* 94:8121–26

60. Sakata Y, Hoit BD, Liggett SB, Walsh RA, Dorn GW II. 1998. Decompensation of pressure overload hypertrophy in Gαq overexpressing mice. *Circulation* 97:1488–95

61. Mende U, Kagen A, Cohen A, Aramburu J, Schoen FJ, Neer EJ. 1998. Transient cardiac expression of constitutively active Gαq leads to hypertrophy and dilated cardiomyopathy by calcineurin-dependent and independent pathways. *Proc. Natl. Acad. Sci. USA* 95:13893–98

62. Akhter SA, Luttrell LM, Rockman HA, Iaccarino G, Lefkowitz RJ, Koch WJ. 1998. Targeting the receptor-Gq interface to inhibit in vivo pressure overload myocardial hypertrophy. *Science* 280:574–77

63. Rogers JH, Tamirisa P, Kovacs A, Weinheimer C, Courtois M, et al. 1999. RGS4 causes increased mortality and reduced cardiac hypertrophy in response to pressure overload. *J. Clin. Invest.* 104:567–76

64. Thorburn A, Thorburn J, Chen SY, Powers S, Shubeita HE, et al. 1993. HRas-dependent pathways can activate morphological and genetic markers of cardiac muscle cell hypertrophy. *J. Biol. Chem.* 268:2244–49

65. Hunter JJ, Tanaka N, Rockman HA, Ross J Jr, Chien KR. 1995. Ventricular expression of a MLC-2v-ras fusion gene induces cardiac hypertrophy and selective diastolic dysfunction in transgenic mice. *J. Biol. Chem.* 270:23173–78

66. Fuller SJ, Gillespie-Brown J, Sugden PH. 1998. Oncogenic src, raf, and ras stimulate a hypertrophic pattern of gene expression and increase cell size in neonatal rat ventricular myocytes. *J. Biol. Chem.* 273:18146–52

67. Abdellatif M, Packer SE, Michael LH, Zhang D, Charng MJ, Schneider MD. 1998. A Ras-dependent pathway regulates RNA polymerase II phosphorylation in cardiac myocytes: implications for cardiac hypertrophy. *Mol. Cell. Biol.* 11:6729–36

68. Pracyk JB, Hegland DD, Tanaka K. 1997. Effect of a dominant negative ras on myocardial hypertrophy by using adenoviral-mediated gene transfer. *Surgery* 122:404–11

69. Vojtek AB, Der CJ. 1998. Increasing complexity of the Ras signaling pathway. *J. Biol. Chem.* 273:19925–28

70. Ramirez MT, Sah VP, Zhao XL, Hunter JJ, Chien KR, Brown JH. 1997. The MEKK-JNK pathway is stimulated by alpha1-adrenergic receptor and ras activation and is associated with in vitro and in vivo cardiac hypertrophy. *J. Biol. Chem.* 272:14057–61

71. Sah VP, Minamisawa S, Tam SP, Wu TH, Dorn GW 2nd, et al. 1999. Cardiac-specific overexpression of RhoA results in sinus and atrioventricular nodal dysfunction and contractile failure. *J. Clin. Invest.* 103:1627–34

72. Thorburn J, Xu S, Thorburn A. 1997. MAP kinase- and Rho-dependent signals interact to regulate gene expression but not actin morphology in cardiac muscle cells. *EMBO J.* 16:1888–900

73. Aoki H, Izumo S, Sadoshima J. 1998. Angiotensin II activates RhoA in cardiac myocytes: a critical role of RhoA in angiotensin II-induced premyofibril formation. *Circ. Res.* 82:666–76

74. Pracyk JB, Tanaka K, Hegland DD, Kim KS, Sethi R, et al. 1998. A requirement for the rac1 GTPase in the signal transduction pathway leading to cardiac myocyte hypertrophy. *J. Clin. Invest.* 102:929–37

75. Sussman MA, Welch S, Walker A, Klevitsky R, Hewett TE, et al. 2000. Altered

focal adhesion regulation correlates with cardiomyopathy in mice expressing constitutively active rac1. *J. Clin. Invest.* 105: 875–86

76. Garrington TP, Johnson GL. 1999. Organization and regulation of mitogen-activated protein kinase signaling pathways. *Curr. Opin. Cell. Biol.* 11:211–18

77. Yamazaki T, Tobe K, Hoh E, Maemura K, Kaida T, et al. 1993. Mechanical loading activates mitogen-activated protein kinase and S6 peptide kinase in cultured rat cardiac myocytes. *J. Biol. Chem.* 268:12069–76

78. Bogoyevitch MA, Glennon PE, Andersson MB, Clerk A, Lazou A, et al. 1994. Endothelin-1 and fibroblast growth factors stimulate the mitogen-activated protein kinase signaling cascade in cardiac myocytes: the potential role of the cascade in the integration of two signaling pathways leading to myocyte hypertrophy. *J. Biol. Chem.* 269:1110–19

79. Clerk A, Bogoyevitch MA, Anderson MB, Sugden PH. 1994. Differential activation of protein kinase C isoforms by endothelin-1 and phenylephrine and subsequent stimulation of p42 and p44 mitogen-activated protein kinases in ventricular myocytes cultured from neonatal rat hearts. *J. Biol. Chem.* 269:32848–57

80. Post GR, Goldstein D, Thuerauf DJ, Glembotski CC, Brown JH. 1996. Dissociation of p44 and p42 mitogen-activated protein kinase activation from receptor-induced hypertrophy in neonatal rat ventricular myocytes. *J. Biol. Chem.* 271:8452–57

81. Zou Y, Komuro I, Yamazaki T, Aikawa R, Kudoh S, et al. 1996. Protein kinase C, but not tyrosine kinases or Ras, plays a critical role in angiotensin II-induced activation of Raf-1 kinase and extracellular signal-regulated protein kinases in cardiac myocytes. *J. Biol. Chem.* 271:33592–97

82. Bogoyevitch MA, Gillespie-Brown J, Ketterman AJ, Fuller SJ, Ben-Levy R, et al. 1996. Stimulation of the stress-activated mitogen-activated protein kinase subfamilies in perfused heart. p38/RK mitogen-activated protein kinases and c-Jun N-terminal kinases are activated by ischemia/reperfusion. *Circ. Res.* 79:162–73

83. Clerk A, Michael A, Sugden PH. 1998. Stimulation of the p38 mitogen-activated protein kinase pathway in neonatal rat ventricular myocytes by the G protein-coupled receptor agonists, endothelin-1 and phenylephrine: A role in cardiac myocyte hypertrophy? *J. Cell. Biol.* 142:523–35

84. Gillespie-Brown J, Fuller SJ, Bogoyevitch MA, Cowley S, Sugden PH. 1995. The mitogen-activated protein kinase kinase MEK1 stimulates a pattern of gene expression typical of the hypertrophic phenotype in rat ventricular cardiomyocytes. *J. Biol. Chem.* 270:28092–96

85. Glennon PE, Kaddoura S, Sale EM, Sale GJ, Fuller SJ, Sugden PH. 1996. Depletion of mitogen-activated protein kinase using an antisense oligodeoxynucleotide approach downregulates the phenylephrine-induced hypertrophic response in rat cardiac myocytes. *Circ. Res.* 78:954–61

86. Thorburn J, Frost JA, Thorburn A. 1994. Mitogen-activated protein kinases mediate changes in gene expression, but not cytoskeletal organization associated with cardiac muscle cell hypertrophy. *J. Cell. Biol.* 126:1565–72

87. Thorburn J, McMahon M, Thorburn A. 1994. Raf-1 kinase activity is necessary and sufficient for gene expression changes but not sufficient for cellular morphology changes associated with cardiac myocyte hypertrophy. *J. Biol. Chem.* 269:30580–86

88. Thorburn J, Carlson M, Mansour SJ, Chien KR, Ahn NG, Thorburn A. 1995. Inhibition of a signaling pathway in cardiac muscle cells by active mitogen-activated protein kinase kinase. *Mol. Biol. Cell* 6:1479–90

89. Zechner D, Thuerauf DJ, Hanford DS,

McDonough PM, Glembotski CC. 1997. A role for the p38 mitogen-activated protein kinase pathway in myocardial cell growth, sarcomeric organization, and cardiac-specific gene expression. *J. Cell. Biol.* 139:115–27

90. Choukroun G, Hajjar R, Kyriakis JM, Bonventre JV, Rosenzweig A, Force T. 1998. Role of the stress-activated protein kinases in endothelin-induced cardiomyocyte hypertrophy. *J. Clin. Invest.* 102:1311–20

91. Silberbach M, Gorenc T, Hershberger RE, Stork PJ, Steyger PS, Robert CT Jr. 1999. Extracellular signal-regulated protein kinase activation is required for the antihypertrophic effect of atrial natriuretic factor in neonatal rat ventricular myocytes. *J. Biol. Chem.* 274:24858–64

92. Paul A, Wilson S, Belham CM, Robinson CJ, Scott PH, et al. 1997. Stress-activated protein kinases: activation, regulation and function. *Cell Signal.* 9:403–10

93. Sugden PH, Clerk A. 1998. "Stress-responsive" mitogen-activated protein kinases (c-Jun N-terminal kinases and p38 mitogen-activated protein kinases) in the myocardium. *Circ. Res.* 24:345–52

94. Jiang Y, Gram H, Zhao M, New L, Gu J, et al. 1997. Characterization of the structure and function of the fourth member of p38 group mitogen-activated protein kinases, p38delta. *J. Biol. Chem.* 272:30122–28

95. Wang Y, Huanf S, Sah VP, Ross J, Heller-Brown J, et al. 1998. Cardiac muscle cell hypertrophy and apoptosis induced by distinct members of the p38 mitogen-activated protein kinase family. *J. Biol. Chem.* 273:2161–68

96. Cook SA, Sugden PH, Clerk A. 1999. Activation of c-Jun N-terminal kinases and p38-mitogen-activated protein kinases in human heart failure secondary to ischaemic heart disease. *J. Mol. Cell. Cardiol.* 31:1429–34

97. Nemoto S, Sheng Z, Lin A. 1998. Opposing effects of Jun kinase and p38 mitogen activated protein kinases on cardiomyocyte hypertrophy. *Mol. Cell. Biol.* 18:3518–26

98. Liang F, Gardner DG. 1999. Mechanical strain activates BNP gene transcription through a p38/NF-kappaB-dependent mechanism. *J. Clin. Invest.* 104:1603–12

99. Liang F, Lu S, Gardner DG. 2000. Endothelin-dependent and -independent components of strain-activated brain natriuretic peptide gene transcription require extracellular signal regulated kinase and p38 mitogen-activated protein kinase. *Hypertension* 35(1, Pt 2):188–92

100. Hines WA, Thorburn J, Thorburn A. 1999. Cell density and contraction regulate p38 MAP kinase-dependent responses in neonatal rat cardiac myocytes. *Am. J. Physiol. Heart Circ. Physiol.* 277:H331–H41

101. Ito M, Yoshioka K, Akechi M, Yamashita S, Takamatsu N, et al. 1999. JSAP1, a novel jun N-terminal protein kinase (JNK)-binding protein that functions as a Scaffold factor in the JNK signaling pathway. *Mol. Cell. Biol.* 19:7539–48

102. Komuro I, Kudo S, Yamazaki T, Zou Y, Shiojima I, Yazaki Y. 1996. Mechanical stretch activates the stress-activated protein kinases in cardiac myocytes. *FASEB J.* 10:631–36

103. Yano M, Kim S, Izumi Y, Yamanaka S, Iwao H. 1998. Differential activation of cardiac c-jun amino-terminal kinase and extracellular signal-regulated kinase in angiotensin II-mediated hypertension. *Circ. Res.* 83:752–60

104. Li WG, Zaheer A, Coppey L, Oskarsson HJ. 1998. Activation of JNK in the remote myocardium after large myocardial infarction in rats. *Biochem. Biophys. Res. Commun.* 246:816–20

105. Choukroun G, Hajjar R, Fry S, del Monte F, Haq S, et al. 1999. Regulation of cardiac hypertrophy in vivo by

the stress-activated protein kinases/c-Jun NH$_2$-terminal kinases. *J. Clin. Invest.* 104:391–98

106. Nishizuka Y. 1986. Studies and perspectives of protein kinase C. *Science* 233:305–12

107. Gu X, Bishop SP. 1994. Increased protein kinase C and isozyme redistribution in pressure-overload cardiac hypertrophy in the rat. *Circ. Res.* 75:926–31

108. Schunkert H, Sadoshima J-I, Cornelius T, Kagaya Y, Weinberg EO, et al. 1995. Angiotensin II-induced growth responses in isolated adult rat hearts: evidence for load-independent induction of cardiac protein synthesis by angiotensin II. *Circ. Res.* 76:489–97

109. Gray MO, Karliner JS, Mochly-Rosen D. 1997. A selective ε-protein kinase C antagonist inhibits protection of cardiac myocytes from hypoxia-induced cell death. *J. Biol. Chem.* 272:30945–51

110. Disatnik MH, Jones SN, Mochly-Rosen D. 1995. Stimulus-dependent subcellular localization of activated protein kinase C; a study with acidic fibroblast growth factor and transforming growth factor-beta 1 in cardiac myocytes. *J. Mol. Cell. Cardiol.* 27:2473–81

111. Disatnik MH, Buraggi G, Mochly-Rosen D. 1994. Localization of protein kinase C isozymes in cardiac myocytes. *Exp. Cell. Res.* 210:287–97

112. Hug H, Sasse J. 1993. Protein kinase C isoenzymes: divergence in signal transduction? *Biochem. J.* 291:329–43

113. Steinberg SF, Goldberg M, Rybin VO. 1995. Protein kinase C isoform diversity in the heart. *J. Mol. Cell. Cardiol.* 27:141–53

114. Mochly-Rosen D. 1995. Localization of protein kinases by anchoring proteins: a theme in signal transduction. *Science* 268:247–51

115. Johnson JA, Gray MO, Chen C-H, Mochly-Rosen D. 1996. A protein kinase C translocation inhibitor as an isozyme-selective antagonist of cardiac function. *J. Biol. Chem.* 271:24962–66

116. Ron D, Mochly-Rosen D. 1995. An autoregulatory region in protein kinase C: the pseudoanchoring site. *Proc. Natl. Acad. Sci. USA* 92:492–96

117. Zhang Z-H, Johnson JA, Chen L, El-Sherif N, Mochly-Rosen D, Boutjdir M. 1997. C2 region-derived peptides of β-protein kinase C regulate cardiac Ca^{2+} channels. *Circ. Res.* 80:720–29

118. Dorn GW 2nd, Souroujon MC, Liron T, Chen CH, Gray MO, et al. 1999. Sustained in vivo cardiac protection by a rationally designed peptide that causes epsilon protein kinase C translocation. *Proc. Natl. Acad. Sci. USA* 96:12798–803

119. Paul K, Ball NA, Dorn GW II, Walsh RA. 1997. Left ventricular stretch stimulates angiotensin II mediated phosphatidylinositol hydrolysis and protein kinase Cε isoform translocation in adult guinea pig hearts. *Circ. Res.* 81:643–50

120. De Windt LJ, Lim HW, Force T, Molkentin JD. 2000. Calcineurin promotes protein kinase C and c-Jun NH$_2$-terminal kinase activation in the heart: evidence of crosstalk between cardiac hypertrophic signaling pathways. *J. Biol. Chem.* 275:13571–79

121. Miyamae M, Rodriguez MM, Camacho SA, Diamond I, Mochly-Rosen D, Figueredo VM. 1998. Activation of epsilon protein kinase C correlates with a cardioprotective effect of regular ethanol consumption. *Proc. Natl. Acad. Sci. USA* 95:8262–67

122. Dorn GW II, Tepe NM, Wu G, Yatani A, Liggett SB. 2000 Mechanisms of impaired beta-adrenergic receptor signaling in G(alphaq)-mediated cardiac hypertrophy and ventricular dysfunction. *Mol. Pharmacol.* 57:278–87

123. Rybin VO, Steinberg SF. 1994. Protein kinase C isoform expression and regulation in the developing rat heart. *Circ. Res.* 74:299–309

124. Kohout TA, Rogers TB. 1993. Use of PCR-based method to characterize protein kinase C isoform expression in cardiac cells. *Am. J. Physiol. Cell Physiol.* 264:C1350–C59

125. Wakasaki H, Koya D, Schoen FJ, Jirousek MR, Ways DK, et al. 1997. Targeted overexpression of protein kinase Cβ2 isoform in myocardium causes cardiomyopathy. *Proc. Natl. Acad. Sci. USA* 94:9320–25

126. Takeishi Y, Chu G, Kirkpatrick DM, Li Z, Wakasaki H, et al. 1998. In vivo phosphorylation of cardiac troponin I by protein kinase C beta 2 decreases cardiomyocyte calcium responsiveness and contractility in transgenic mouse hearts. *J. Clin. Invest.* 102:72–78

127. Bowman JC, Steinberg SF, Jiang T, Geenen DL, Fishman GI, et al. 1997. Expression of protein kinase Cβ in the heart causes hypertrophy in adult mice and sudden death in neonates. *J. Clin. Invest.* 100:2189–95

128. Mochly-Rosen D, Wu G, Hahn H, Osinska H, Liron T, et al. 2000. Cardiotrophic effects of εprotein kinase C: analysis by in vivo modulation of εPKC translocation. *Circ. Res.* 86:1173–79

129. Klee CB, Ren H, Wang X. 1998. Regulation of the calmodulin-stimulated protein phosphatase, calcineurin. *J. Biol. Chem.* 273:13367–70

130. Crabtree GR. 1999. Generic signals and specific outcomes: signaling through calcium, calcineurin, and NF-AT. *Cell* 96:611–14

131. Molkentin JD, Lu JR, Antos CL, Markham B, Richardson J, et al. 1998. A calcineurin-dependent transcriptional pathway for cardiac hypertrophy. *Cell* 93:215–28

132. Balke CW, Shorofsky SR. 1998. Alterations in calcium handling in cardiac hypertrophy and heart failure. *Cardiovasc. Res.* 37:290–99

133. Lim HW, De Windt LJ, Mante J, Kimball TR, Witt SA, et al. 2000. Reversal of cardiac hypertrophy in transgenic disease models by calcineurin inhibition. *J. Mol. Cell. Cardiol.* 32:697–709

134. Sussman MA, Lim HW, Gude N, Taigen T, Olson EN, et al. 1998. Prevention of cardiac hypertrophy in mice by calcineurin inhibition. *Science* 281:1690–93

135. Luo Z, Shyu KG, Gualberto A, Walsh K. 1998. Calcineurin and cardiac hypertrophy. *Nat. Med.* 10:1092–93

136. Müller JG, Nemoto S, Laser M, Carabello BA, Menick DR. 1998 Calcineurin inhibition and cardiac hypertrophy. *Science* 282:1007

137. Zhang W, Kowal RC, Rusnak F, Sikkink RA, Olson EN, Victor RG. 1999. Failure of calcineurin inhibitors to prevent pressure-overload left ventricular hypertrophy in rats. *Circ. Res.* 84:722–28

138. Ding B, Price RL, Borg TK, Weinberg EO, Halloran PF, Lorell BH. 1999. Pressure overload induces severe hypertrophy in mice treated with cyclosporine, an inhibitor of calcineurin. *Circ. Res.* 84:729–34

139. Meguro T, Hong C, Asai K, Takagi G, McKinsey TA, et al. 1999. Cyclosporine attenuates pressure overload hypertrophy in mice while enhancing susceptibility to decompensation and heart failure. *Circ. Res.* 84:735–40

140. Shimoyama M, Hayashi D, Takimoto E, Zou Y, Oka T, et al. 1999. Calcineurin plays a critical role in pressure overload-induced cardiac hypertrophy. *Circulation* 100:2449–54

141. Lim HW, De Windt LJ, Steinberg L, Taigen T, Witt SA, et al. 2000. Calcineurin expression, activation, and function in cardiac pressure overload hypertrophy. *Circulation* 101:2431–37

142. Hill JA, Karimi M, Kutschke W, Davisson RL, Zimmerman K, et al. 2000. Cardiac hypertrophy is not a required compensatory response to short-term

pressure overload, Hill LV function following calcineurin inhibition. *Circulation* 101:2863–69

143. Mervaala E, Muller DN, Park JK, Dechend R, Schmidt F, et al. 2000. Cyclosporin A protects against angiotensin II-induced end-organ damage in double transgenic rats harboring human renin and angiotensinogen genes. *Hypertension* 35(1, Pt 2):360–66

144. Taigen T, De Windt LJ, Lim HW, Molkentin JD. 2000. Targeted inhibition of calcineurin prevents agonist-induced cardiomyocyte hypertrophy. *Proc. Natl. Acad. Sci. USA* 97:1196–201

145. Mitsuhashi S, Shima H, Kikuchi K, Igarashi K, Hatsuse R, et al. 2000. Development of an assay method for activities of serine/threonine protein phosphatase type 2B (calcineurin) in crude extracts. *Anal. Biochem.* 278:192–97

146. Wang X, Culotta VC, Klee CB. 1996. Superoxide dismutase protects calcineurin from inactivation. *Nature* 383:434–37

147. Lim HW, Molkentin JD. 1999. Calcineurin and human heart failure. *Nat. Med.* 5:246–47

148. Lim HW, Molkentin JD. 2000. Reply to revisiting calcineurin and human heart failure. *Nat. Med.* 6:3

149. Tsao L, Neville C, Musaro A, McCullagh KJ, Rosenthal N. 2000. Revisiting calcineurin and human heart failure. *Nat. Med.* 6:2–3

150. Ventura HO, Malik FS, Mehra MR, Stapelton DD, Smart FW. 1997. Mechanisms of hypertension in cardiac transplantation and the role of cyclosporine. *Curr. Opin. Cardiol.* 12:375–81

151. Hoey T, Sun YL, Williamson K, Xu X. 1995. Isolation of two new members of the NF-AT gene family and functional characterization of the NF-AT proteins. *Immunity* 2:461–72

152. Liu J, Koyano-Nakagawa N, Amasaki Y, Saito-Ohara F, Ikeuchi T, et al. 1997. Calcineurin-dependent nuclear translo-

cation of a murine transcription factor NFATx: molecular cloning and functional characterization. *Mol. Biol. Cell.* 8:157–70

153. Masuda ES, Naito Y, Tokumitsu H, Campbell D, Saito F, et al. 1995. NFATx, a novel member of the nuclear factor of activated T cells family that is expressed predominantly in the thymus. *Mol. Cell. Biol.* 15:2697–706

154. Wollert KC, Chien KR. 1997. Cardiotrophin-1 and the role of gp130-dependent signaling pathways in cardiac growth and development. *J. Mol. Med.* 75:492–501

155. Wollert KC, Taga T, Saito M, Narazaki M, Kishimoto T, et al. 1996. Cardiotrophin-1 activates a distinct form of cardiac muscle cell hypertrophy: assembly of sarcomeric units in series VIA gp130/leukemia inhibitory factor receptor-dependent pathways. *J. Biol. Chem.* 271:9535–45

156. Narazaki M, Witthuhn BA, Yoshida K, Silvennoinen O, Yasukawa K, et al. 1994. Activation of JAK2 kinase mediated by the interleukin 6 signal transducer gp130. *Proc. Natl. Acad. Sci. USA* 91:2285–89

157. Lutticken C, Wegenka UM, Yuan J, Buschmann J, Schindler C, et al. 1994. Association of transcription factor APRF and protein kinase Jak1 with the interleukin-6 signal transducer gp130. *Science* 263:89–92

158. Stahl N, Boulton TG, Farruggella T, Ip NY, Davis S, et al. 1994. Association and activation of Jak-Tyk kinases by CNTF-LIF-OSM-IL-6 beta receptor components. *Science* 263:92–95

159. Zhong Z, Wen Z, Darnell JE Jr. 1994. Stat3: a STAT family member activated by tyrosine phosphorylation in response to epidermal growth factor and interleukin-6. *Science* 264:95–98

160. Nakafuku M, Satoh T, Kaziro Y. 1992. Differentiation factors, including nerve growth factor, fibroblast growth factor, and interleukin-6, induce an

accumulation of an active Ras GTP complex in rat pheochromocytoma PC12 cells. *J. Biol. Chem.* 267:19448–54

161. Kumar G, Gupta S, Wang S, Nel AE. 1994. Involvement of Janus kinases, p52shc, Raf-1, and MEK-1 in the IL-6-induced mitogen-activated protein kinase cascade of a growth-responsive B cell line. *J. Immunol.* 153:4436–47

162. Kunisada K, Hirota H, Fujio Y, Matsui H, Tani Y, et al. 1996. Activation of JAK-STAT and MAP kinases by leukemia inhibitory factor through gp130 in cardiac myocytes. *Circulation* 94:2626–32

163. Oh H, Fujio Y, Kunisada K, Hirota H, Matsui H, et al. 1998. Activation of phosphatidylinositol 3-kinase through glycoprotein 130 induces protein kinase B and p70 S6 kinase phosphorylation in cardiac myocytes. *J. Biol. Chem.* 273:9703–10

164. Murata M, Fukuda K, Ishida H, Miyoshi S, Koura T, et al. 1999. Leukemia inhibitory factor, a potent cardiac hypertrophic cytokine, enhances L-type Ca^{2+} current and $[Ca^{2+}]_i$ transient in cardiomyocytes. *J. Mol. Cell. Cardiol.* 31:237–45

165. Pan J, Fukuda K, Kodama H, Makino S, Takahashi T, et al. 1997. Role of angiotensin II in activation of the JAK/STAT pathway induced by acute pressure overload in the rat heart. *Circ. Res.* 81:611–17

166. Nyui N, Tamura K, Mizuno K, Ishigami T, Kihara M, et al. 1998. gp130 is involved in stretch-induced MAP kinase activation in cardiac myocytes. *Biochem. Biophys. Res. Commun.* 245:928–32

167. Pennica D, King KL, Shaw KJ, Luis E, Rullamas J, et al. 1995. Expression cloning of cardiotrophin 1, a cytokine that induces cardiac myocyte hypertrophy. *Proc. Natl. Acad. Sci. USA* 92:1142–46

168. Kodama H, Fukuda K, Pan J, Makino S, Baba A, et al. 1997. Leukemia inhibitory factor, a potent cardiac hypertrophic cy-

tokine, activates the JAK/STAT pathway in rat cardiomyocytes. *Circ. Res.* 81:656–63

169. Hirota H, Yoshida K, Kishimoto T, Taga T. 1995. Continuous activation of gp130, a signal-transducing receptor component for interleukin 6-related cytokines, causes myocardial hypertrophy in mice. *Proc. Natl. Acad. Sci. USA* 92:4862–66

170. Yoshida K, Taga T, Saito M, Suematsu S, Kumanogoh A, et al. 1996. Targeted disruption of gp130, a common signal transducer for the interleukin 6 family of cytokines, leads to myocardial and hematological disorders. *Proc. Natl. Acad. Sci. USA* 93:407–11

171. Hirota H, Chen J, Betz UA, Rajewsky K, Gu Y, et al. 1999. Loss of a gp130 cardiac muscle cell survival pathway is a critical event in the onset of heart failure during biomechanical stress. *Cell* 97:189–98

172. Kunisada K, Tone E, Fujio Y, Matsui H, Yamauchi-Takihara K, Kishimoto T. 1998. Activation of gp130 transduces hypertrophic signals via STAT3 in cardiac myocytes. *Circulation* 98:346–52

173. Kunisada K, Negoro S, Tone E, Funamoto M, Osugi T, et al. 2000. Signal transducer and activator of transcription 3 in the heart transduces not only a hypertrophic signal but a protective signal against doxorubicin-induced cardiomyopathy. *Proc. Natl. Acad. Sci. USA* 97:315–19

174. Ren J, Samson WK, Sowers JR. 1999. Insulin-like growth factor I as a cardiac hormone: physiological and pathophysiological implications in heart disease. *J. Mol. Cell. Cardiol.* 31:2049–61

175. Dhand R, Hara K, Hiles I, Bax B, Gout I, et al. 1994. PI 3-kinase: structural and functional analysis of intersubunit interactions. *EMBO J.* 13:511–21

176. Reiss K, Cheng W, Ferber A, Kajstura J, Li P, et al. 1996. Overexpression of insulin-like growth factor-1 in the heart

is coupled with myocyte proliferation in transgenic mice. *Proc. Natl. Acad. Sci. USA* 93:8630–35

177. Redaelli G, Malhotra A, Li B, Li P, Sonnenblick EH, et al. 1998. Effects of constitutive overexpression of insulin-like growth factor-1 on the mechanical characteristics and molecular properties of ventricular myocytes. *Circ. Res.* 82:594–603

178. Delaughter MC, Taffet GE, Fiorotto ML, Entman ML, Schwartz RJ. 1999. Local insulin-like growth factor I expression induces physiologic, then pathologic, cardiac hypertrophy in transgenic mice. *FASEB J.* 13:1923–29

179. Merola B, Cittadini A, Colao A, Longobardi S, Fazio S, et al. 1993. Cardiac structural and functional abnormalities in adult patients with growth hormone deficiency. *J. Clin. Endocrinol. Metab.* 77:1658–61

180. Amato G, Carella C, Fazio S, La Montagna G, Cittadini A, et al. 1993. Body composition, bone metabolism, and heart structure and function in growth hormone (GH)-deficient adults before and after GH replacement therapy at low doses. *J. Clin. Endocrinol. Metab.* 77:1671–76

181. Lembo G, Rockman HA, Hunter JJ, Steinmetz H, Koch WJ, et al. 1996. Elevated blood pressure and enhanced myocardial contractility in mice with severe IGF-1 deficiency. *J. Clin. Invest.* 98:2648–55

182. Sadoshima J, Izumo S. 1995. Rapamycin selectively inhibits angiotensin II-induced increase in protein synthesis in cardiac myocytes in vitro: potential role of 70-kD S6 kinase in angiotensin II-induced cardiac hypertrophy. *Circ. Res.* 77:1040–52

183. Takano H, Komuro I, Zou Y, Kudoh S, Yamazaki T, Yazaki Y. 1996. Activation of p70 S6 protein kinase is necessary for angiotensin II-induced hypertrophy in neonatal rat cardiac myocytes. *FEBS Lett.* 379:255–59

184. Boluyt MO, Zheng JS, Younes A, Long X, O'Neill L, et al. 1997. Rapamycin inhibits alpha 1-adrenergic receptor-stimulated cardiac myocyte hypertrophy but not activation of hypertrophy-associated genes: evidence for involvement of p70 S6 kinase. *Circ. Res.* 81:176–86

185. Laser M, Kasi VS, Hamawaki M, Cooper G 4th, Kerr CM, Kuppuswamy D. 1998. Differential activation of p70 and p85 S6 kinase isoforms during cardiac hypertrophy in the adult mammal. *J. Biol. Chem.* 273:24610–19

186. Shioi T, Kang PM, Douglas PS, Yballe CM, Cantley LC, et al. 1999. Phosphoinositide 3-kinase selectively regulates cell size and specific gene expression in the adult mouse heart. *Circulation* 200:1032 (Abstr.)

187. Fujio Y, Nguyen T, Wencker D, Kitsis RN, Walsh K. 2000. Akt promotes survival of cardiomyocytes in vitro and protects against ischemia-reperfusion injury in mouse heart. *Circulation* 101:660–67

188. Parker TG, Packer SE, Schneider MD. 1990. Peptide growth factors can provoke "fetal" contractile protein gene expression in rat cardiac myocytes. *J. Clin. Invest.* 85:507–14

189. Hefti MA, Harder BA, Eppenberger HM, Schaub MC. 1997. Signaling pathways in cardiac myocyte hypertrophy. *J. Mol. Cell. Cardiol.* 29:2873–92

190. Kaye D, Pimental D, Prasad S, Maki T, Berger HJ, et al. 1996. Role of transiently altered sarcolemmal membrane permeability and basic fibroblast growth factor release in the hypertrophic response of adult rat ventricular myocytes to increased mechanical activity in vitro. *J. Clin. Invest.* 97:281–91

191. Scheinowitz M, Kotlyar A, Zimand S, Ohad D, Leibovitz I, et al. 1998. Basic fibroblast growth factor induces myocardial hypertrophy following acute infarction in rats. *Exp. Physiol.* 83:585–93

192. Scheinowitz M, Abranov D, Kotlyar A,

Savion N, Eldar M. 1998. Continous administration of insulin-like growth factor-1 and basic fibroblast growth factor does not affect left ventricular geometry after acute myocardial infarction in rats. *Int. J. Cardiol.* 63:217–21

193. Schultz JE, Witt SA, Nieman ML, Reiser PJ, Engle SJ, et al. 1999. Fibroblast growth factor-2 mediates pressure-induced hypertrophic response. *J. Clin. Invest.* 104:709–19

194. Bogoyevitch MA, Glennon PE, Andersson MB, Clerk A, Lazou A, et al. 1994. Endothelin-1 and fibroblast growth factors stimulate the mitogen-activated protein kinase signaling cascade in cardiac myocytes: the potential role of the cascade in the integration of two signaling pathways leading to myocyte hypertrophy. *J. Biol. Chem.* 269:1110–19

195. Takahashi N, Calderone A, Izzo NJ Jr, Maki TM, Marsh JD, Colucci WS. 1994. Hypertrophic stimuli induce transforming growth factor-beta 1 expression in rat ventricular myocytes. *J. Clin. Invest.* 94:1470–76

196. Villarreal FJ, Lee AA, Dillmann WH, Giordano FJ. 1996. Adenovirus-mediated overexpression of human transforming growth factor-beta 1 in rat cardiac fibroblasts, myocytes and smooth muscle cells. *J. Mol. Cell. Cardiol.* 28:735–42

197. Gray MO, Long CS, Kalinyak JE, Li HT. 1998. Karliner JS Angiotensin II stimulates cardiac myocyte hypertrophy via paracrine release of TGF-beta 1 and endothelin-1 from fibroblasts. *Cardiovasc. Res.* 40:352–63

198. Piek E, Heldin CH, Ten Dijke P. 1999. Specificity, diversity, and regulation in TGF-beta superfamily signaling. *FASEB J.* 13:2105–24

199. Zhang D, Narasimhaswamy S, Schwartz RJ, Schneider MD. 1999. The SRF coactivator, ATF6, is a nuclear target of the TAK1 pathway in TGFβ signal transduction. *Circulation.* 352:1850 (Abstr.)

200. Kuppuswamy D, Kerr C, Narishige T, Kasi VS, Menick DR, Cooper G 4th. 1997. Association of tyrosine-phosphorylated c-Src with the cytoskeleton of hypertrophying myocardium. *J. Biol. Chem.* 272:4500–8

201. Fuller SJ, Gillespie-Brown J, Sugden PH. 1998. Oncogenic src, raf, and ras stimulate a hypertrophic pattern of gene expression and increase cell size in neonatal rat ventricular myocytes. *J. Biol. Chem.* 273:18146–52

202. Shioi T, Douglas PS, Izumo S. 1999. Cardiac-specific overexpression of focal adhesion kinase induces cardiac hypertrophy. *Circulation* 52:264. (Abstr.)

203. Baliga RR, Pimental DR, Zhao YY, Simmons WW, Marchionni MA, et al. 1999. NRG-1-induced cardiomyocyte hypertrophy: role of PI-3-kinase, p70(S6K), and MEK-MAPK-RSK. *Am. J. Physiol. Heart Circ. Physiol.* 277:H2026–H37

204. Rohrbach S, Yan X, Weinberg EO, Hasan F, Bartunek J, et al. 1999. Neuregulin in cardiac hypertrophy in rats with aortic stenosis: differential expression of erbB2 and erbB4 receptors. *Circulation* 100:407–12

205. Perrella MA, Maki T, Prasad S, Pimental D, Singh K, et al. 1994. Regulation of heparin-binding epidermal growth factor-like growth factor mRNA levels by hypertrophic stimuli in neonatal and adult rat cardiac myocytes. *J. Biol. Chem.* 269:27045–50

206. Polikar R, Burger AG, Scherrer U, Nicod P. 1993. The thyroid and the heart. *Circulation* 87:1435–41

207. Aoki H, Sadoshima J, Izumo S. 2000. Myosin light chain kinase mediates sarcomere organization during cardiac hypertrophy in vitro. *Nat. Med.* 6:183–88

208. Yokoyama T, Nakano M, Bednarczyk JL, McIntyre BW, Entman M, Mann DL. 1997. Tumor necrosis factor-alpha provokes a hypertrophic growth response

in adult cardiac myocytes *Circulation* 95:1247–52

209. Kubota T, McTiernan CF, Frye CS, Slawson SE, Lemster BH, et al. 1997. Dilated cardiomyopathy in transgenic mice with cardiac-specific overexpression of tumor necrosis factor-alpha. *Circ. Res.* 81:627–35

210. Bryant D, Becker L, Richardson J, Shelton J, Franco F, et al. 1998. Cardiac failure in transgenic mice with myocardial expression of tumor necrosis factor-alpha. *Circulation* 97:1375–81

211. Plowman GD, Sudarsanam S, Bingham J, Whyte D, Hunter T. 1999. The protein kinases of *Caenorhabditis elegans*: a model for signal transduction in multicellular organisms. *Proc. Natl. Acad. Sci. USA.* 96:13603–10

212. Dahlof B, Pennert K, Hansson L. 1992. Reversal of left ventricular hypertrophy in hypertensive patients: a meta-analysis of 109 treatment studies. *Am. J. Hypertens.* 5:95–110

213. Susic D, Nunez E, Frohlich ED. 1995. Reversal of hypertrophy: an active biologic process. *Curr. Opin. Cardiol.* 10:466–72

Annu. Rev. Physiol. 2001. 63:427–50

SOMATIC GENE THERAPY IN THE CARDIOVASCULAR SYSTEM

I Baumgartner[1] and JM Isner[2]

[1]Swiss Cardiovascular Center, Division Angiology, University Hospital, 3010 Bern, Switzerland; e-mail: iris.baumgartner@insel.ch; [2]Tufts University School of Medicine, Department of Medicine (Vascular Medicine) and Biomedical Research, St. Elizabeth's Medical Center, Boston, Massachusetts 02135;e-mail: VeJeff@aol.com

Key Words angiogenesis, intra-arterial gene transfer, intramuscular gene transfer, restenosis, vascular endothelial growth factor

■ **Abstract** This review surveys a range of approaches using plasmid DNA encoding the 165-amino-acid isoform of vascular endothelial growth factor ($phVEGF_{165}$) to therapeutically modulate micro- or macrovascular endothelial cells, focusing on strategies to augment postnatal collateral circulation in arterial insufficiency or to accelerate re-endothelialization after balloon angioplasty to prevent restenosis. We focus on intra-arterial and intramuscular/intramyocardial gene transfer of the $VEGF_{165}$ gene, the options that have been most thoroughly studied to date in patients. We review developmental and postnatal significance of the endothelial-cell-specific mitogen VEGF that has stimulated these studies and present limitations of current knowledge as well as challenges for the future.

INTRODUCTION

Somatic gene therapy in the cardiovascular system has been an active area of investigation since the first report by Nabel et al in 1989 (1, 2). Two general approaches to introduce genes into the vessel wall have been studied. Initial attempts isolated endothelial cells from experimental animals, grew and infected the cells with recombinant retrovirus in culture, and then reseeded them into the donor (1). The option to use putative, bone marrow-derived endothelial progenitor cells as potential autologous vectors for ex vivo gene transfer was more recently considered by Asahara et al (3). Indirect or ex vivo gene transfer is based on the concept that target cells that express the recombinant gene product in vitro are selected and then transplanted to the host vessel wall (1, 4–6). In a second approach, genes were directly transferred to cells within the vessel wall by using percutaneous delivery devices (2, 7–9). The advantage of such direct in vivo gene transfer is that it obviates removal of cells from a patient.

In either case, the success of gene transfer is ultimately determined by transfection efficiency, which is defined as the percentage of cells within the segment of an artery exposed to a given transgene that expresses the transgene. Investigations of intra-arterial gene transfer suggest that the relatively low transfection efficiency that is characteristic of direct intravascular gene transfer may, nevertheless, be sufficient to generate meaningful biological effects when the transgene encodes a secreted protein compared with transgenes encoding proteins that remain inside the cell (10–13). The first application of this principle in human subjects involved the transfer of naked plasmid DNA encoding vascular endothelial growth factor (VEGF; a secreted endothelial-cell-specific mitogen) (14–17) to the arterial wall by using a hydrogel-coated balloon catheter.

To increase transfection efficiency of intra-arterial gene transfer, viral vectors have been utilized [for review of arterial gene delivery in vivo with viral and nonviral vectors, see Mulligan (18) and Nabel (19)]. Viral vectors exploit highly efficient natural mechanisms to transfer their genetic material to target cells. By deleting portions of the viral genome required to reconstitute the infectious viral particle, viral vectors are rendered unable to replicate (i.e. become replication deficient), and the risk of systemic or local infection for treated patients is presumably minimal. The extent to which adenoviral vectors will be ultimately used in clinical protocols for direct intravascular gene transfer depends on the resolution of concerns about safety and immunogenicity (20); other viral vectors, including adeno-associated virus and lentivirus, are under investigation for potential use in clinical applications. Covalently bound plasmid DNA (i.e. DNA unassociated with viral or other adjunctive vectors) represents what is perhaps the minimum vector with which to transfer a therapeutic gene into a living cell. The first published report that naked-DNA gene transfer could be successfully used to achieve a clinically apparent biological outcome in human subjects demonstrated the process in a patient with critical limb ischemia who received intra-arterial gene transfer of the 165-amino-acid isoform of VEGF ($phVEGF_{165}$) (21) to the popliteal artery. Angiographic and histologic evidence of enhanced collateral vessel development by 4-weeks post-transfection was documented (21, 22). Technical limitations of the trans-arterial approach led to studies demonstrating that intramuscular gene transfer of $phVEGF_{165}$ is an alternative to promote collateral angiogenesis in a rabbit ischemic hindlimb model (23), in patients with critical limb ischemia (24, 25), and in patients with myocardial ischemia (26, 27).

Our review focuses on the endothelial cell as the target for phenotypic modulation using VEGF complementary DNA. This strategy is based on the rationale that stimulation of the endothelial cells may augment collateral vessel development or accelerate reconstitution of endothelial integrity after balloon-mediated injury, a concept that was initially proven in animal models and more recently has been tested in humans.

THE ENDOTHELIAL CELL AS THERAPEUTIC TARGET

The endothelium plays a central role in vessel wall homeostasis by affecting smooth muscle cells (28), in vascularization of ischemic and neoplastic tissues (29), in regulation of fibrinolysis and coagulation, in blood-tissue exchange, in vasomotor regulation, and in control of leukocyte adhesion. Given the crucial role of the endothelial cell, its modulation represents a tempting therapeutic goal. Below, the endothelial cell–specific mitogen VEGF, its biological effect on the endothelial cell, and the rationale to use the *VEGF* gene for modulation of the endothelial cell are illustrated.

Vasculogenesis and Angiogenesis

The first molecule known to be expressed on mesodermal cells giving rise to endothelial progenitor cells is the VEGF receptor VEGFR-2 (also called flk-1/KDR). Formation of primitive blood vessels by in situ differentiation of endothelial progenitor cells (i.e. vasculogenesis) is dependent on the presence of VEGFR-2 and its ligand VEGF, secreted by the adjacent endoderm layer (30, 31). The mesoderm and endoderm represent an early paracrine system in which the ligand VEGF stimulates expression of its receptor VEGFR-2 and in which a critical threshold concentration of the ligand is necessary to sustain receptor expression. The requirement of endodermal signaling is supported by the observation that no endothelial (progenitor) cells are formed in the mesoderm in the absence of endoderm (32). The key function of VEGF and its receptors VEGFR-2 and VEGFR-1 (also called flt-1) during early embryogenesis was finally established by gene-targeting experiments in mice. Disruption of the genes for VEGFR-2 or VEGFR-1 interfered with differentiation of endothelial progenitor cells and vasculogenesis, respectively, leading to death of embryos between days 8.5 and 9.5 (33, 34).

After the formation of a primary vascular plexus by in situ differentiation of endothelial progenitor cells, more endothelial cells are generated, which form new capillaries by sprouting or by splitting from their vessel of origin in a process called angiogenesis. Proteolytic degradation of the extracellular matrix is followed by chemotactic migration and proliferation of endothelial cells and by formation of a new lumen [for review, see Risau et al (35)]. This process, in which endothelial cells are activated and undergo rapid proliferation, can be initiated by a variety of angiogenic cytokines (36–38). Although there is probably a redundant assembly of angiogenesis-inducing factors during embryogenesis, VEGF seems to be crucial. Gene-targeting experiments demonstrated that loss of even a single allele of the *VEGF* gene leads to embryonic lethality at days 8.5 through 9, with impairment of both vasculogenesis and angiogenesis (39, 40). Even selective inactivation of larger-sized heparin-binding VEGF isoforms has been shown to be insufficient for proper development of the cardiovascular system, thus resulting in myocardial ischemia and early lethality (41). Later in vessel formation, the endothelial tyrosine kinase ligands angiopoietin (42, 43) and ephrin (44, 45) have important functions in the formation and maintenance of the vascular system, as do endothelial cell–specific members of the transforming growth factor β receptor and Notch families (46, 47; for review see 48).

Postnatal Neovascularization   Endothelial-cell proliferation, which is high during embryonic and early postnatal development, ceases or is very low in adults. The endothelium in the normal adult is considered quiescent, with a turnover of thousands of days (49). Exceptions to this rule exist in association with the female reproductive cycles or disruption of vascular endothelial integrity.

Postnatal neovascularization starts with reactivation of stationary, nonproliferative endothelial cells, which enter the developmental cycle of de novo vessel formation; extracellular proteinases (50), which are necessary for endothelial-cell invasion into tissues, are up-regulated (51, 52), and endothelial cells migrate, reattach, and proliferate beyond the vessel of origin to form new capillary networks. Capillary sprouting is followed by smooth muscle cell and pericyte recruitment to the vascular wall by factors derived from the endothelium (29), and larger vessels become established and mature (53–55). Corresponding to embryonic neovascularization, VEGF is involved and possibly primarily responsible for the postnatal neovascularization that occurs in the female reproductive system and during a variety of pathologic states, including wound healing, diabetic retinopathy, solid tumor growth, and arterial obstructive disease (56–60). More recent data indicate that bone marrow–derived, circulating endothelial progenitor cells also contribute to postnatal neovascularization (61, 62) and that angiopoietins act in concert with VEGF (63).

Whereas activation phenomena such as proteolytic activity, migration, and proliferation of endothelial cells/endothelial progenitor cells occur mainly in the microvascular bed, large-vessel endothelium differs from the microvascular endothelium in that it is not directly involved in tissue neovascularization (64, 65). In situ proliferation of smooth muscle and endothelial cells in preexisting stem arteries (i.e. remodeling) or collateral arteries (i.e. adaptive arteriogenesis) contributes to large-vessel growth with shear stress considered an important mediator. The role of monocytes/macrophages in adaptive arteriogenesis was suggested by Schaper and colleagues, who demonstrated monocyte adhesion to the intima of coronary collaterals followed by rapid growth of these vessels (66–68). Activated monocytes are known to produce a variety of cytokines stimulating smooth muscle and endothelial cell proliferation/migration [e.g. basic fibroblast growth factor (FGF), platelet-derived growth factor, and transforming growth factor β). Exogenously administered VEGF also promotes collateral vessel growth in animal models of peripheral and myocardial ischemia [for review, see Isner (69, 70)]. Whether VEGF-related arteriogenesis occurs as a direct result of growth factor modulation, as a flow-mediated response to downstream capacitance caused by the augmented tissue neovascularization, or as a chemoattractant effect on monocytes expressing VEGFR-1 remains to be clarified.

Vascular Endothelial Growth Factor

Four homodimeric species resulting from alternative splicing of the *VEGF-1* (*VEGF-A*) gene have been identified (71, 72). The secretion patterns of the four amino acid isoforms ($VEGF_{121}$, $VEGF_{165}$, $VEGF_{189}$, and $VEGF_{201}$) differ markedly. $VEGF_{121}$ is a weakly acidic polypeptide that does not bind to heparin and is freely soluble. The heparin-binding capacities of the remaining three isoforms are progressively augmented as a result of a stepwise enrichment in basic residues. The predominant isoform, $VEFG_{165}$, is a basic heparin-binding glycoprotein with an isoelectric point of 8.5; although it is secreted, a significant portion remains bound to the cell surface or extracellular membrane. The $VEGF_{189}$ isoform includes 24 additional amino acids and is not freely secreted but instead remains nearly completely bound to the cell surface and extracellular matrix, respectively (73). Other members of the VEGF family have been reviewed recently (74–77).

Endothelial cell–specific mitogenesis has been regarded as an important therapeutic advantage of VEGF because endothelial cells represent the critical cell type responsible for new vessel formation and vessel wall homeostasis. Given the limited two- to fourfold increase of endothelial-cell proliferation in vitro, VEGF-enhanced endothelial-cell survival likely contributes to a net increase in the number of viable endothelial cells (78–81).

GENE THERAPY

Basics

Intra-arterial gene transfer has the potential to alter the biological response of vascular cells that may contribute to the development of cardiovascular disease. Techniques that directly introduce genes into the vessel wall to change the biological behavior of the primary target cell are compromised by the fact that only a low percentage of cells will become transfected with the DNA regardless of the site, species, gene construct, or delivery device (2, 7–9, 18, 82). Although adenoviral vectors have proven effectiveness in animal models, the ability to achieve comparable gene transfer with nonviral vectors would provide potentially desirable safety and toxicity features for clinical studies (83, 84).

Secreted Transgene Product   Nabel and colleagues documented evidence of extensive vasculitis in arteries transfected with the gene for the foreign class I major histocompatibility complex HLA-B7 (85), development of intimal thickening in arteries transfected with the gene for platelet-derived growth factor β, intimal hyperplasia and abundant vasa vasorum in arteries transfected with the secreted form of the *FGF-1* gene (11), and intimal hyperplasia with substantial extracellular matrix production in arteries transduced with an expression vector for secreted active transforming growth factor β (86) despite the fact that, in all cases, successful transfection appeared limited to <1% of cells. Evidence of biological efficacy was based on the fact that all transgenes encoded a secreted gene product that caused phenotypic modulation of a multiplicity of cells via a paracrine loop. Accordingly, Losordo and colleagues demonstrated that site-specific transfection of rabbit ear arteries with plasmid DNA encoding the gene for human growth hormone yields circulating levels of the protein in the physiological range, despite immunohistochemical evidence of gene expression among <1% of cells in the transfected arterial segment (12).

Primary Target Cell for Transfection   With intra-arterial gene transfer, the transfected cell type and location vary depending on the delivery system used. The endothelium, but almost no medial cells, is transfected by isolating a vessel segment and injecting the transgene via a double-balloon catheter (2, 7), thereby leaving the endothelial layer intact (84). Endothelial removal appears to be critical for successful medial transfection (87, 88); the endothelium and/or the internal elastic laminae seem to represent the physical barrier to medial transfection. Endothelial denudation is implicit using a hydrogel-coated balloon catheter. The transgene is pipetted onto the balloon surface ex vivo, followed by percutaneous positioning of the transgene-impregnated balloon to the desired segment of the target vessel. After percutaneous removal of the protection sheath, the transgene is transferred to smooth muscle cells by balloon inflation. Steg demonstrated that adenovirus-mediated gene transfer (*Ad-RSVβgal*) using a hydrogel-coated balloon was associated with 9.6% of medial smooth muscle cell transfection (whole thickness) [84; for plasmid DNA, see Riessen et al (89); for plasmid DNA/liposome complex, see Leclerc (9)].

Percutaneous transfer via double balloon thus appears to represent a satisfactory means of performing site-specific arterial gene transfer for disorders in which the endothelium represents the primary target (e.g. thrombin inhibitor); delivery from a hydrogel-coated balloon catheter appears more appropriate for application of arterial gene transfer targeted to smooth muscle cells (e.g. restenosis).

Proliferation Rate of Target Cells   Human smooth muscle cells from normal arteries, primary atherosclerotic plaques, and restenotic lesions were shown to be successfully transfected by using plasmid DNA-liposome complexes (e.g. *pRSVLuc* and *pGSVLacZ*) in vitro with preferential expression of the transgene in a subpopulation of cells with a high rate of mitosis and with a relatively high proportion of cells coexpressing various transgenes (e.g. *pGSVLacZ* or *pXGH5* human growth hormone) (90). This suggests that not all cells in a given culture have the same probability of being successfully transfected. Similar observations of double-transfected cells after lipofection have been noted in *Xenopus* brain organ culture experiments (91). The effect of prior endothelial denudation on lipofection (*pRSVLuc* or *pGSVLacZ*) was shown by Takeshita et al (92). In rabbit iliac artery segments that had been transfected in vivo with or without antecedent endothelial denudation, liposome-mediated arterial gene transfer was augmented by ongoing cell proliferation in denuded arteries. Depending on the technique of assessment, <0.1 to <1% of total cells were found to be transfected. Highest transgene activity was found with gene transfer between days 3 and 7 after denudation. Although results suggest that proliferating restenotic lesions may be more amenable to intra-arterial gene transfer, it remains unclear whether these results in normal or endothelium-denuded arteries can be extended to more extensively diseased arteries in vivo.

Atherosclerotic Lesions   Atherosclerosis attenuates transfection efficiency achievable with adenoviral vectors (e.g. *Ad-RSVβgal* or *Ad-RSVapoA1*-apolipoprotein A1) and thus constitutes a potential limitation to intra-arterial gene transfer as shown by Feldman in experimental animals (93). In a hypercholesterolemia/injury model, transfection efficiency was ≤10-fold lower compared with non-hypercholesterolemic rabbits, whereas transgene expression remained the same. Atherosclerotic lesions did not increase the rate of undesired extra-arterial transfection.

Adenoviral Vector Systems   To increase intra-arterial transfection efficiency, replication-deficient adenoviral vectors represent the most efficient system (87, 94, 95). These vectors have the E1a region deleted so they can replicate only in 293 cells, a kidney embryonic cell line that has been stably transfected with E1a. These vectors are potentially useful for gene transfer because host cell proliferation is not required; most cells possess adenovirus receptors, the viral genome can be manipulated to accept foreign genes of ≤7.5 kb, and recombinations are rare. Regardless of variations in catheter design used, the resulting transfection efficiencies have been typically higher with adenoviral vectors compared with retroviral vectors (96, 97), plasmid DNA-liposome complexes (2, 7, 9, 90, 98), or plasmid DNA (82, 99), with ≤100-fold-higher levels of gene expression compared with nonviral gene transfer. However, with adenoviral vector systems, concerns related to host immune response (100) may limit dosing and repeated administration for human use. Most studies suggest that transgene expression does not exceed 3 weeks and that repeated adenovirus administration leads to antibody-mediated reduction in gene expression.

Naked Plasmid DNA   Wolff and colleagues (101–103) showed that intramuscular injection of naked plasmid DNA was feasible, and they suggested that muscle might be a suitable tissue for heterologous transgene expression. It obviates immunological concerns associated with viral vectors (100, 104), and, because plasmid DNA remains in a nonreplicative, unintegrated, circular form (101), this strategy is also unlikely to be complicated by insertional mutagenesis. Since the first report of plasmid DNA injections into skeletal muscle using a *Rous sarcoma virus (RSV)*-based plasmid (101), improvements in the expression vectors have led to a 1000-fold increase in luciferase recovery from injected muscle [105; for review, see Felgner (106)].

Quantification of Intramuscular Gene Transfer   Wolff established that injection of plasmid DNA (*pRSVCAT*-chloramphenicol acetyl transferase) gave 12% of chloramphenicol acetyl transferase activity 48 h after gene transfer compared with direct CAT-RNA injection, with maximum protein activity after 18 h. Using a *β-galactosidase* reporter gene (*pRSVLacZ*), ~60 (1.5%) of the 4000 muscle cells that make up the entire quadriceps and 10 to 30% of the cells within the injection area were stained blue. The dose response effect using the *firefly luciferase* reporter gene (*pRSVLuc*) gave 4.6 pg of luciferase/μg of DNA in muscle compared with 6.0 pg of luciferase/μg of DNA in fibroblasts transfected under optimized conditions in vitro. Similar results have been obtained in adult and neonatal rats (102), primate skeletal muscle (107), and cardiac muscle (108, 109). Plasmid expression by differentiated muscle cells persisted up to 19 months in mice (103, 110), a result that was rather unexpected compared with the transient plasmid expression in cultured fibroblasts. No specific sequences were required for persistent expression with *pCMVLuc*, *pUC19*, or *pRSVLuc* giving similar results, which suggest that the postmitotic state of the myofiber nuclei and the multinucleated nature of muscle cells may enable persistence of plasmid DNA. It is unclear whether the limited plasmid persistence described by others is based on techniques of assessment or on the gene constructs used (111).

Variability of Reporter Gene Expression   Transgene expression is described to vary substantially after intramuscular injection (SE, 25–60%). Variable degradation of the injected plasmid DNA is suggested to play an important role in causing variable expression, whereas inherent differences among muscles (102), injection volumes (102, 112), injection techniques (113), and augmented expression in ischemic or regenerating muscle (114–116) and in younger animals (117) were also considered.

After intramuscular injection, plasmid DNA appears to enter the blood stream at early times; however, its level drops below the detection limit by 24 h after injection. Lew et al (118) found that intact plasmid DNA in blood has a half-life of <5 min and is undetectable by polymerase chain reaction (PCR) at 1 h after intravenous injection. There is no evidence that plasmid DNA is taken up by germ line cells in testes or ovaries after intramuscular application (111, 118, 119).

Robust vascularity and long-term stability of extrachromosomal DNA in striated muscle cells indicate that the muscle is an attractive alternative target tissue for introducing transgenes that encode a secreted protein. The limited persistence of transgene expression after plasmid DNA-mediated gene transfer and the undefined clearance mechanisms responsible for it remain important challenges to be clarified to define the clinical usefulness of this approach.

Therapeutic Angiogenesis: Animal Models

Several angiogenic moieties, including FGF-1 (120), FGF-5 (121), VEGF$_{165}$ (13, 122, 123), VEGF-C (124), VEGF$_{121}$ (125), angiopoietin-1 (126), and hyoxia-inducible factor-1 (127), can expedite perfusion and collateral artery development in animal models of hindlimb or myocardial ischemia after gene transfer. Among these, plasmid DNA encoding $phVEGF_{165}$ transcriptionally regulated by a 736-bp cytomegalovirus (CMV) promoter/enhancer has been best-studied.

Intra-Arterial phVEGF$_{165}$ Gene Transfer   The *VEGF* gene is particularly appealing for accomplishing therapeutic angiogenesis because the first exon of the *VEGF* gene includes a signal sequence that permits the protein to be naturally secreted from intact cells (15, 71). Initially, 400 μg of $phVEGF_{165}$ was applied to the hydrogel-polymer coating of an angioplasty balloon (99, 128). The balloon was delivered to the iliac artery of rabbits in which the femoral artery had been excised to cause severe hindlimb ischemia. Site-specific transfection was confirmed by using reverse transcription-polymerase chain reaction (RT-PCR), with transient gene expression up to day 21. Neither neoangiogenesis nor inflammatory cell infiltration was seen at remote sites such as brain, heart, liver, lung, spleen, testes, or the contralateral limb, indicating that VEGF-induced neovascularization was not indiscriminate or widespread but was instead restricted to sites of ischemia. Intra-arterial $phVEGF_{165}$ gene transfer led to an augmented collateral circulation, documented by serial angiograms (ischemic limb), amelioration of the hemodynamic deficit demonstrated by improved calf blood pressure ratio (ischemic/nonischemic limb), and increased capillary density at necropsy (ischemic limb). Comparison with gene transfer of the three isoforms, $VEGF_{121}$, $VEGF_{165}$, and $VEGF_{189}$, showed biological equivalency with regard to collateral development. Morphometric analysis documented that enriched vascularity encompasses a whole range of vessel calibers. The medium range of new vessel growth, however, appeared to skew toward smaller-caliber arteries of <200 μm in diameter (69, 129). It is likely that a portion of newly recognized medium-sized arteries develops as a result of adaptive arteriogenesis, that is, in situ proliferation of preexisting arteriolar connections into larger collateral vessels (68). Whether such adaptive arteriogenesis occurs as a direct result of VEGF modulation or as a flow-mediated response to augmented downstream capacitance remains to be determined.

Intramuscular phVEGF$_{165}$ Gene Transfer   Intramuscular gene transfer combines the biological rationale of VEGF-augmented angiogenesis with the previously demonstrated efficacy of plasmid DNA-mediated gene transfer to skeletal muscle (101) to achieve local expression of the *VEGF* gene. Protein secreted by the genetically modified muscle is expected to readily enter the capillary network because muscle is a highly vascularized tissue (130). In the rabbit ischemic hindlimb model, a dose of 5 $\times$ 100 μg of $phVEGF_{165}$/0.5 ml of 0.9% saline was directly injected into ischemic muscles (122). Augmented collateral development compared with that of animals treated with a reporter gene (*pCMVLacZ*) was demonstrated by selective angiography, calf blood pressure, capillary density, and regional blood flow using colored microspheres. The transfection efficiency, evaluated morphometrically using *pCMVβgal*, and chemiluminescent analysis of luciferase activity, using *pCMVLuc*, demonstrated that $2.2 \pm 1.2\%$ of ischemic skeletal myocytes and $0.3 \pm 0.2\%$ of non-ischemic myocytes expressed the transgene. Expression at the mRNA level was limited to 14 days and was undetectable at day 30 by non-quantitative RT-PCR. Light microscopic evidence of angiogenesis was limited and targeted to the ischemic hindlimb.

Improvement of myocardial perfusion and function in the ischemic porcine heart model was demonstrated with intramyocardial injection of a replication-deficient adenovirus vector encoding $VEGF_{121}$ (125). A less invasive alternative of direct intramyocardial *pCMVLacZ* gene transfer was shown by Vale, using a catheter-based system that is also under clinical investigation (131).

Accelerated Re-Endothelialization: Animal Models

Previous studies in a variety of animal species demonstrated that extensive endothelial denudation of the arterial wall invariably leads to a proliferative response in smooth muscle cells (132–134). These experimental studies support the notion that certain functions of the endothelium, including its barrier function, antithrombogenicity, and prevention of leukocyte adherence, as well as production of growth inhibitory molecules, are critical to prevent luminal narrowing by neointimal thickening after vessel wall injury. The capability of certain cytokines to serve as mitogens for endothelial cells in vitro suggests that growth-stimulatory molecules might be exploited to accelerate re-endothelialization (4, 135–139). Evidence that accelerated re-endothelialization can be achieved and is sufficiently potent to reduce intimal proliferation by direct intra-arterial gene therapy using *phVEGF*$_{165}$ was shown by Asahara et al (140) and shortly thereafter by Van Belle et al (141). The concept is based on the inherent ability of vascular smooth muscle cells to spontaneously take up plasmid DNA and express extrachromosomal DNA. Experimentally, simultaneous balloon injury and site-specific *phVEGF*$_{165}$ transfection of the femoral artery in rabbits disclosed near complete re-endothelialization by day 7, whereas the extent was < 50% by day 7, and remained nearly 20% incomplete at week 4 in control animals transfected with a *pCMVLacZ* reporter gene. Furthermore, *phVEGF*$_{165}$ transfection was associated with a concomitant reduction in proliferative activity (i.e. of proliferating cell nuclear antigen and bromodeoxyuridine activity) of smooth muscle cells in both the media and neointima. Potentially contributory and beyond its mitogenic effect was the potential for VEGF to stimulate endothelium-dependent vasomotor reactivity (142, 143).

CLINICAL IMPLICATIONS

The extent to which the use of *phVEGF*$_{165}$ gene transfer may be affected by specific risk factors in patients with vascular disease is not known. Impaired angiogenesis in the ischemic hindlimb model associated with reduced VEGF expression was shown in non-obese diabetic mice, which develop a form of diabetes with clinical features similar to those of human type-I, insulin-dependent diabetes. The pivotal role of VEGF in diabetes-related impairment of angiogenesis was confirmed by replacement of this growth factor by intramuscular application of a replication-deficient adenovirus encoding the murine VEGF gene.

Coronary artery disease in patients with diabetes mellitus indicates the likelihood of a less favorable outcome compared with the same disease in those without diabetes, including a three- to fourfold increased risk of mortality (144). Diffuse endothelial dysfunction is likely one of the important elements (145) and impaired collateral artery formation another (146, 147). Inter-individual differences in the degree of collateral blood vessel formation seem to correlate with the increase of VEGF production in monocytes harvested from patients with coronary artery stenosis (147).

These findings may also have implications for the high incidence of restenosis (148, 149) reported for diabetic patients treated by percutaneous revascularization. If VEGF is compromised to the extent observed in skeletal muscle of the non-obese diabetic mice and in patients with insufficient collateral artery formation, the consequent disruption of the endothelial integrity by balloon angioplasty may promote recurrent luminal narrowing in patients with insufficient local VEGF production.

Endothelial cell dysfunction and impaired angiogenesis were also described to be dependent on insufficient VEGF up-regulation in experimental models using older animals and in experimental hypercholesterolemia (apoE-/- mice), both mimicking a common clinical situation in patients with advanced cardiovascular disease (150, 151). Cytokine supplementation to individuals who, because of advanced age, diabetes, hypercholesterolemia, and/or other yet undefined circumstances, are unable to appropriately up-regulate cytokine expression in response to tissue ischemia may become a treatment option analogous to insulin administration in patients with diabetes.

Therapeutic Angiogenesis

Why adaptive collateral-vessel development in patients does not usually increase to the point that it can restore normal flow is not clear; it may result from a combination of time lag of collateral development in the case of rapid progression of the occlusive process and either insufficient local generation of necessary cytokines or other factors needed for angiogenesis to occur or perhaps a decreased responsiveness of endothelial cells to growth factors involved in neovascularization (152, 153). Even under the best circumstances, collateral development usually remains incomplete, and only ~30% of the maximal blood flow capacity is restored (154). Bypass surgery or catheter-based revascularization is not suitable for ~10–15% of patients with severe end-stage peripheral or coronary artery disease, which is associated with a grim prognosis with regard to limb salvage and survival. Therefore, it seems logical to substitute angiogenic growth factors to boost the physiologically insufficient system of collateral development.

Intra-Arterial Gene Transfer for Therapeutic Angiogenesis   Proof of the concept that therapeutic angiogenesis could be successfully extended to human subjects was first demonstrated with intra-arterial gene transfer of $phVEGF_{165}$ for the treatment of critical limb ischemia (21, 22). Using a dose-escalating design, treatment was initiated with 100 μg of $phVEGF_{165}$. Three patients with rest pain but no gangrene and treated with 1000 μg of $phVEGF_{165}$ were subsequently shown, at one-year follow-up, to have improved blood flow to the ischemic limb, as well as no rest pain. With the increase in dose of $phVEGF_{165}$ to 2000 μg, angiographic and histologic evidence of new blood vessel formation became apparent (21). The strategy of intra-arterial gene delivery to achieve a clinically significant effect on collateral artery development, however, was limited by the fact that, in many patients, access to the lower-extremity circulation was limited by occlusive atherosclerosis.

Intramuscular/Intramyocardial Gene Transfer for Therapeutic Angiogenesis

In patients for whom atherosclerosis is too extensive to permit an intra-arterial approach, $phVEGF_{165}$ is injected intramuscularly. In a phase-I trial involving nine consecutive patients with 10 critically ischemic limbs, the clinical effects included significant improvement in the ankle- or toe-brachial index, improved collateral flow, as shown by contrast or magnetic resonance angiography, symptomatic improvement, including healed ischemic ulcers in four of seven limbs, and limb salvage in three patients recommended for below-knee amputation (24). Gene expression at the protein level was shown by a transient increase of VEGF serum levels. Evidence of bioactivity included development of peripheral edema temporally related to increased VEGF serum levels in six patients, consistent with augmented vascular permeability owing to VEGF (155). Transgene expression disclosed a slow increase, which peaked between weeks 1 and 2 and declined after week 3. Southern blot analysis indicated that intact plasmid DNA was still present within the muscle for ≥ 10 weeks, although there was no more measurable increase in circulating VEGF protein. Improvement of ischemic neuropathy was documented by a neurological examination score and electrophysiological testing (156), consistent with direct as well as indirect effects of VEGF on neural elements (157). Younger patients with critical limb ischemia caused by Buerger's disease (thrombangiitis obliterans) appeared to respond most consistently (25), in agreement with the finding of age-dependent angiogenesis in animals (150)

The first successful direct intramyocardial injection of $phVEGF_{165}$ as sole therapy for myocardial ischemia in patients with medically intractable angina who were not candidates for further conventional revascularization procedures was reported in 1998 (26, 158). The first 10 patients received a total of 125 μg of $phVEGF_{165}$, whereas the second group of 10 patients received a total of 250 μg according to the dose-escalating protocol. Preliminary results for the 20 patients treated in a phase-I, non-placebo-controlled trial designed to determine safety and bioactivity showed that, by day 60, most patients had experienced a reduction in angina frequency, and 70% of patients monitored for ≤ 180 days were completely angina free. The use of nitroglycerin tablets decreased from a mean ($\pm$ SE) of 60 $\pm$ 5 per week before gene therapy to 7.0 $\pm$ 2.5 per week on day 60. Stress dobutamine or persantine single-photon-emission computerized tomography sestamibi studies documented an improvement between baseline and day 60 in 13 of 17 patients analyzed (7 out of 8 in the group with a 250-μg dose); the improvement is consistent with resolution of hibernating myocardium, a finding that has been recently confirmed using catheter-based electromechanical mapping (123). The surgical procedure was performed under general anesthesia, with a left anterior thoracotomy incision for $phVEGF_{165}$ injection in 2-ml aliquots at four separate sites. There was one late death in this series unrelated to the transgene, which occurred at 4 months post-gene transfer. Diagnostic coronary angiography performed before and 60 days after gene transfer showed evidence of improved collateral filling, based on the Rentrop score (159), in most patients.

In a second phase-I gene therapy trial that included 21 patients, a replication-deficient adenoviral vector expressing human $VEGF_{121}$ ($Ad_{GV}VEGF1_{21}$) was administered to an area of reversible myocardial ischemia as an adjunct to conventional coronary artery bypass graft surgery or through a mini-thoracotomy as sole therapy (27). Five dose groups with total doses between 4×10^8 and 4×10^{10} plaque-forming units of $Ad_{GV}VEGF_{121}$ were evaluated. In both groups, coronary angiography and stress sestamibi scans performed 30 days after therapy suggested improvement in the area of vector administration. All patients reported improvement in angina at day 30 after therapy, including the six patients receiving $Ad_{GV}VEGF_{121}$ alone. Myocardial administration of $Ad_{GV}VEGF_{121}$ induced an increase in anti-Ad-neutralizing antibodies in most of the study population; nevertheless, there was no evidence of systemic immune-related toxicity in any patient, including no immediate anaphylactic-type reaction, vasculitis, or renal damage.

Intramuscular gene transfer appears well suited for promoting therapeutic angiogenesis in patients with severe peripheral or myocardial ischemic disease. First, striated skeletal muscle and cardiac muscle cells are relatively permissive to transfection with naked DNA. Second, naked plasmid DNA reduces the risk of immunological toxicity or insertional mutagenesis associated with viral vectors. Third, in contrast to hereditary diseases, therapeutic angiogenesis does not require ongoing genetic modulation; short-term expression appears sufficient to boost physiologic neovascularization, after which collateral-vessel patency persists indefinitely. Fourth, intramuscular gene transfer is an inherently simple application. Finally, in contrast to the negative clinical outcomes obtained using recombinant protein to achieve therapeutic angiogenesis in patients with myocardial ischemia and to the questions raised about discrepancies between the considerable efficacy in animal models of coronary or limb ischemia (160, 161), gene transfer achieves transiently sustained, high-local (and low-systemic) concentrations of angiogenic growth factor. The influence of host diversity, including the extent of native VEGF and VEGF receptor expression among patients with peripheral and/or myocardial ischemia, remains undetermined. Whether a single treatment is sufficient to induce functional blood vessels for prolonged periods of time or re-administration is needed also remain to be investigated.

Accelerated Re-Endothelialization to Prevent Restenosis

The term restenosis denotes recurrent narrowing of a blood vessel after successful revascularization, such as by percutaneous transluminal angioplasty. Despite the advent of endovascular prostheses (stents) and promising applications of brachytherapy, restenosis continues to be a vexing and expensive complication of this otherwise efficient intervention. Superficial femoral-artery stenosis represents one of the most common sites of peripheral vascular obstruction. The acute procedural success for percutaneous revascularization using conventional guide wires and standard percutaneous transluminal angioplasty is well over 90%. On the other hand, as reported by Adar, who reviewed 12 selected clinical reports (162), 3-year patency was 62% for patients with intermittent claudication and 43% for patients undergoing revascularization for limb salvage, with the largest decline in patency occurring during the first 6–12 months. Multiple strategies have been used to inhibit recurrent intimal thickening (i.e. restenosis). These include antiproliferative strategies designed to interfere with smooth muscle cell proliferation; anti-platelet or anti-coagulant therapies designed to prevent development of a platelet-fibrin scaffold; anti-inflammatory drugs, spasmolytic drug therapy; and lipid-lowering agents. None of the clinical studies published to date has demonstrated, even for selected subgroups, significant reduction in restenosis.

In February 1994, the first human trial of anti-restenosis gene therapy, involving percutaneous arterial gene transfer of $phVEGF_{165}$, consisted of a nonrandomized, open-label phase-I trial for patients with intermittent claudication caused by femoropopliteal obstructions (163). Gene transfer was performed using a hydrogel-coated balloon catheter to deliver a single application of $phVEGF_{165}$ (10 patients received 1000 μg and 9 patients received 2000 μg of plasmid DNA) to the site of preceding balloon angioplasty. No restenosis or only minimal neointimal hyperplasia was observed in 14 patients (75%), and revascularization was required for clinical restenosis in only 4 patients (22%), with an average follow-up of 9 months. These results may be cautiously interpreted to indicate that gene therapy designed to accelerate re-endothelialization at the site of percutaneous-transluminal-angioplasty-induced endothelial disruption is safe; further study will be required to establish the value of this strategy for inhibition of restenosis (164).

CONCLUSION

Somatic gene therapy implements the concept that human disease can be attacked at the genetic level and that it can be an adjunct to traditional therapies or a definitive therapy of its own. However, for each potential application, careful consideration of the appropriate target cell, delivery technique, gene, vector, and timing is required. For example, direct intravascular gene transfer still has several shortcomings, including low expression using plasmid DNA, generation of an immune inflammatory response with viral vectors, and potential risk of undesired vascular injury, depending on the delivery device used. Moreover, effects of gene transfer in animal models may not be applicable to diseased human arteries. Despite these imperfections, gene therapy for vascular disease in humans has begun, and preliminary results collectively suggest that skeletal and cardiac myocytes can be used as secretory organs that are sufficiently potent to achieve biologically meaningful results for transgenes that encode a secreted gene product.

Visit the Annual Reviews home page at www.AnnualReviews.org

LITERATURE CITED

1. Nabel EG, Plautz G, Boyce FM, Stanley JC, Nabel GJ. 1989. Recombinant gene expression in vivo within the endothelial cells of the arterial wall. *Science* 244:1342–44
2. Nabel EG, Plautz G, Nabel GJ. 1990. Site-specific gene expression in vivo by direct gene transfer into arterial wall. *Science* 249:1285–88
3. Asahara T, Murohara T, Sullivan A, Silver M, Van der Zee R, et al. 1997. Isolation of putative progenitor endothelial cells for angiogenesis. *Science* 275:964–67
4. Dichek DA, Neville RF, Zwiebel JA, Freeman SM, Leon MB, et al. 1989. Seeding of intravascular stents with genetically engineered endothelial cells. *Circulation* 80:1347–53
5. Plautz G, Nabel EG, Nabel GJ. 1991. Introduction of vascular smooth muscle cells expressing recombinant genes in vivo. *Circulation* 83:578–83
6. Lynch CM, Clowes MM, Osborne WRA, Clowes AW, Miller AD. 1992. Long-term expression of human adenosine deaminase in vascular smooth muscle cells of rats: a model for gene therapy. *Proc. Natl. Acad. Sci. USA* 89:1138–42
7. Lim CS, Chapman GD, Gammon RS, Muhlestein JB, Bauman RP, et al. 1991. Direct in vivo gene transfer into the coronary and peripheral vasculatures of intact dog. *Circulation* 83:2007–11
8. Flugelman MY, Jaklitsch MT, Newman KD, Cascells W, Bratthauer GL, et al. 1992. Low level in vivo gene transfer into the arterial wall through a perforated balloon catheter. *Circulation* 85:1110–17
9. Leclerc G, Gal D, Takeshita S, Nikol S, Weir L, et al. 1992. Percutaneous arterial gene transfer in a rabbit model: efficiency in normal and balloon-dilated atherosclerotic arteries. *J. Clin. Invest.* 90:936–44
10. Nabel EG, Yang Z, Liptay S, San H, Gordon D, et al. 1993. Recombinant platelet-derived growth factor B gene expression in porcine arteries induces intimal hyperplasia in vivo. *J. Clin. Invest.* 91:1822–29
11. Nabel EG, Yang Z, Plautz G, Forough R, Zhan X, et al. 1993. Recombinant fibroblast growth factor-1 promotes intimal hyperplasia and angiogenesis in arteries in vivo. *Nature* 362:844–46
12. Losordo DW, Pickering JG, Takeshita S, Leclerc G, Gal D, et al. 1994. Use of the rabbit ear artery to serially assess foreign protein secretion after site specific arterial gene transfer in vivo: evidence that anatomic identification of successful gene transfer may underestimate the potential magnitude of transgene expression. *Circulation* 89:785–92
13. Takeshita S, Weir L, Chen D, Zheng LP, Riessen R, et al. 1996. Therapeutic angiogenesis following arterial gene transfer of vascular endothelial growth factor in a rabbit model of hindlimb ischemia. *Biochem. Biophys. Res. Commun.* 227:628–35
14. Keck PJ, Hauser SD, Krivi G, Sanzo K, Warren T, et al. 1989. Vascular permeability factor, an endothelial cell mitogen related to PDGF. *Science* 246:1309–12

15. Leung DW, Cachianes G, Kuang WJ, Goeddel DV, Ferrara N. 1989. Vascular endothelial growth factor is a secreted angiogenic mitogen. *Science* 246:1306–9

16. Ferrara N, Henzel WJ. 1989. Pituitary follicular cells secrete a novel heparin-binding growth factor specific for vascular endothelial cells. *Biochem. Biophys. Res. Commun.* 161:851–55

17. Plouet J, Schilling J, Gospodarowicz D. 1989. Isolation and characterization of a newly identified endothelial cell mitogen produced by AtT-20 cells. *EMBO J.* 8:3801–6

18. Mulligan RC. 1993. The basic science of gene therapy. *Science* 260:926–31

19. Nabel EG. 1995. Gene therapy for cardiovascular disease. *Circulation* 91:541–48

20. March KL. 1997. *Gene Transfer in the Cardiovascular System. Experimental Approaches and Therapeutic Implications.* Boston: Kluwer Academic

21. Isner JM, Pieczek A, Schainfeld R, Blair R, Haley L, et al. 1996. Clinical evidence of angiogenesis following arterial gene transfer of phVEGF165 in a patient with ischemic limb. *Lancet* 348:370–74

22. Isner JM. 1998. Arterial gene transfer of naked DNA for therapeutic angiogenesis: early clinical results. *Adv. Drug Deliv. Rev.* 30:185–97

23. Pu LQ, Sniderman AD, Brassard R, Lachapelle KJ, Graham AM, et al. 1993. Enhanced revascularization of the ischemic limb by means of angiogenic therapy. *Circulation* 88:208–15

24. Baumgartner I, Pieczek A, Manor O, Blair R, Kearney M, et al. 1998. Constitutive expression of phVEGF165 following intramuscular gene transfer promotes collateral vessel development in patients with critical limb ischemia. *Circulation* 97:1114–23

25. Isner JM, Baumgartner I, Rauh G, Schainfeld R, Blair R, et al. 1998. Treatment of thrombangiitis obliterans (Buerger's disease) by intramuscular gene transfer of vascular endothelial growth factor: preliminary clinical results. *J. Vasc. Surg.* 28:964–75

26. Losordo DW, Vale PR, Symes JF, Dunnington CH, Esakof DD, et al. 1998. Gene therapy for myocardial angiogenesis. Initial clinical results with direct myocardial injection of phVEGF165 as sole therapy for myocardial ischemia. *Circulation* 98:2800–4

27. Rosengart TK, Lee LY, Patel SR, Sanborn TA, Parikh M, et al. 1999. Angiogenesis gene therapy. Phase I assessment of direct intramyocardial administration of an adenovirus vector expressing VEGF121 cDNA to individuals with clinically significant severe coronary artery disease. *Circulation* 100:468–74

28. Ross R. 1993. Atherosclerosis: a defense mechanism gone awry. *Am. J. Pathol.* 143:985–1002

29. Folkman J, D'Amore PA. 1996. Blood vessel formation: what is its molecular basis? *Cell* 87:1153–55

30. Risau W, Sariola H, Zerwes H-G, Sasse J, Ekblom P, et al. 1988. Vasculogenesis and angiogenesis in embryonic stem cell-derived embryoid bodies. *Development* 102:471–78

31. Flamme I, Risau W. 1992. Induction of vasculogenesis and hematopoiesis in vitro. *Development* 116:435–39

32. Wilt FH. 1965. Erythropoiesis in the chick embryo: the role of endoderm. *Science* 147:1588–90

33. Shalaby F, Rossant J, Yamaguchi TP, Gertsenstein M, Wu XF, et al. 1995. Failure of blood-island formation and vasculogenesis in flk-1-deficient mice. *Nature* 376:62–66

34. Fong GH, Rossant J, Gertsenstein M, Breitman ML. 1995. Role of the Flt-1 receptor tyrosine kinase in regulating the assembly of vascular endothelium. *Nature* 376:66–70

35. Risau W. 1997. Mechanisms of angiogenesis. *Nature* 386:671–74

36. Klagsbrun M, D'Amore PA. 1991. Regulators of angiogenesis. *Annu. Rev. Physiol.* 53:217–39

37. Folkman J, Shing Y. 1992. Angiogenesis. *J. Biol. Chem.* 267:10931–34

38. Pepper MS, Ferrara N, Orci L, Montesano R. 1992. Potent synergism between vascular endothelial growth factor and basic fibroblast growth factor in the induction of angiogenesis in vitro. *Biochem. Biophys. Res. Commun.* 3:211–20

39. Carmeliet P, Ferriera V, Brier G, Pollefeyt S, Kieckens L, et al. 1996. Abnormal blood vessel development and lethality in embryos lacking a single VEGF allele. *Nature* 380:435–44

40. Ferrara N, Carver-Moore K, Chen H, Dowd M, Lu L, et al. 1996. Heterozygous embryonic lethality induced by targeted inactivation of the VEGF gene. *Nature* 380:439–42

41. Carmeliet P, Ng YS, Nuyens D, Theilmeier G, Brusselmans K, et al. 1999. Impaired myocardial angiogenesis and ischemic cardiomyopathy in mice lacking the vascular endothelial growth factor isoforms VEGF164 and VEGF188. *Nat. Med.* 5:495–502

42. Suri C, Jones PF, Patan S, Bartunkova S, Maisonpierre PC, et al. 1996. Requisite role of angiopoietin-1, a ligand for the TIE2 receptor, during embryonic angiogenesis. *Cell* 87:1171–80

43. Maisonpierre PC, Suri C, Jones PF, Bartunkova S, Wiegand SJ, et al. 1997. Angiopoietin-2, a natural antagonist for Tie2 that disrupts in vivo angiogenesis. *Science* 277:55–60

44. Wang HU, Chen ZF, Anderson DJ. 1998. Molecular distinction and angiogenic interaction between embryonic arteries and veins revealed by ephrin-B2 and its receptor Eph-B4. *Cell* 93:741–53

45. Adams RH, Wilkinson GA, Weiss C, Diella F, Gale NW, et al. 1999. Roles of ephrinB ligands and EphB receptors in cardiovascular development: demarcation of arterial/venous domains, vascular morphogenesis, and sprouting angiogenesis. *Genes Dev.* 13:295–306

46. Uyttendaele H, Marazzi G, Wu G, Yan Q, Sassoon D, et al. 1996. Notch4/int-3, a mammary proto-oncogene, is an endothelial cell-specific mammalian Notch gene. *Development* 122:2251–59

47. Johnson DW, Berg JN, Baldwin MA, Gallione CJ, Marondel I, et al. 1996. Mutations in the activin receptor-like kinase 1 gene in hereditary haemorrhagic telangiectasia type 2. *Nat. Genet.* 13:189–95

48. Gale NW, Yancopoulos GD. 1999. Growth factors acting via endothelial cell specific receptor tyrosine kinases: VEGFs, angiopoietins, and ephrins in vascular development. *Genes Dev.* 13:1055–66

49. Engerman RL, Pfaffenbach D, Davis MD. 1967. Cell turnover of capillaries. *Lab. Invest.* 17:738–43

50. Pepper MS, Ferrara N, Orci L, Montesano R. 1991. Vascular endothelial growth factor (VEGF) induces plasminogen activators and plasminogen activator inhibitor-1 in microvascular endothelial cells. *Biochem. Biophys. Res. Commun.* 181:902–6

51. Pepper MS, Montesano R. 1990. Proteolytic balance and capillary morphogenesis. *Cell Diff. Dev.* 32:319–28

52. Carmeliet P, Collen D. 1995. Gene targeting and gene transfer of the plasminogen/plasmin system: implications in thrombosis, hemostasis, neointima formation, and atherosclerosis. *FASEB J.* 9:934–38

53. Orlidge A, D'Amore PA. 1987. Inhibition of capillary endothelial cell growth by pericytes and smooth muscle cells. *J. Cell. Biol.* 105:1455–62

54. Sato Y, Rifkin DB. 1989. Inhibition of endothelial cell movement by pericytes and smooth muscle cells: activation of a latent transforming growth factor-beta 1-like molecule by plasmin during co-culture. *J. Cell. Biol.* 109:309–15

55. Mandriota SJ, Menoud P-A, Pepper MS. 1996. Transforming growth factor beta

1 down-regulates vascular endothelial growth factor receptor 2/flk-1 expression in vascular endothelial cells. *J. Biol. Chem.* 271:11500–5

56. Plate KH, Breier G, Weich HA, Risau W. 1992. Vascular endothelial growth factor is a potential tumor angiogenesis factor in vivo. *Nature* 359:845–47

57. Shweiki D, Itin A, Soffer D, Keshet E. 1992. Vascular endothelial growth factor induced by hypoxia may mediate hypoxia-induced angiogenesis. *Nature* 359:843–45

58. Banai S, Shweiki D, Pinson A, Chandra M, Lazarovici G, et al. 1994. Upregulation of vascular endothelial growth factor expression induced by myocardial ischemia: implications for coronary angiogenesis. *Cardiovasc. Res.* 28:1176–79

59. Aiello LP, Avery RL, Arrigg PG, Keyt BA, Jampel HD, et al. 1994. Vascular endothelial growth factor in ocular fluids of patients with diabetic retinopathy and other retinal disorders. *N. Engl. J. Med.* 331:1480–87

60. Folkman J. 1995. Clinical applications of research on angiogenesis. *N. Engl. J. Med.* 333:1757–63

61. Asahara T, Takahashi T, Masuda H, Kalka C, Chen D, et al. 1999. VEGF contributes to postnatal neovascularization by mobilizing bone-marrow derived endothelial progenitor cells. *EMBO J.* 18:3964–72

62. Takahashi T, Kalka C, Masuda H, Chen D, Silver M, et al. 1999. Ischemia- and cytokine-induced mobilization of bone-marrow-derived endothelial progenitor cells for neovascularization. *Nat. Med.* 5:434–38

63. Asahara T, Chen D, Takahashi T, Fujikawa K, Kearney M, et al. 1998. Tie2 receptor ligands, angiopoietin-1 and angiopoietin-2, modulate VEGF-induced postnatal neovascularization. *Circ. Res.* 83:233–40

64. Kumar I, West DC, Ager A. 1987. Heterogeneity in endothelial cells from large vessels and microvessels. *Differentiation* 36:57–70

65. Peters KG, Werner S, Chen G, Williams LT. 1992. Two FGF-receptor genes are differentially expressed in epithelial and mesenchymal tissues during limb formation and organogenesis in the mouse. *Development* 114:233–43

66. Schaper J, Koenig R, Franz D, Schaper W. 1976. The endothelial surface of growing coronary collateral arteries. Intimal margination and diapedesis of monocytes. A combined SEM and TEM study. *Virchows Arch. A Pathol. Anat. Histopathol.* 370:193–205

67. Ito WD, Arras M, Winkler B, Scholz D, Schaper J, et al. 1997. Monocyte chemotactic protein-1 increases collateral and peripheral conductance after femoral artery occlusion. *Circ. Res.* 80:829–37

68. Arras M, Ito WD, Scholz D, Winkler B, Schaper J, et al. 1997. Monocyte activation in angiogenesis and collateral growth in the rabbit hindlimb. *J. Clin. Invest.* 101:40–50

69. Isner JM. 1996. The role of angiogenic cytokines in cardiovascular disease. *Clin. Immunol. Immunopathol.* 80:S82–91

70. Isner JM, Asahara T. 1999. Angiogenesis and vasculogenesis as therapeutic strategies for postnatal neovascularization. *J. Clin. Invest.* 103:1231–36

71. Tischer E, Mitchell R, Hartmann T, Silva M, Gospodarowicz D, et al. 1991. The human gene for vascular endothelial growth factor: multiple protein forms are encoded through alternative exon splicing. *J. Biol. Chem.* 266:11947–54

72. Senger DR, Van De Water L, Brown LF, Nagy JA, Yeo K-T, et al. 1993. Vascular permeability factor (VPF, VEGF) in tumor biology. *Cancer Metastasis Rev.* 12:303–24

73. Houck KA, Leung DW, Rowland AM, Winer J, Ferrara N. 1992. Dual regulation of vascular endothelial growth factor bioavailability by genetic and proteolytic mechanisms. *J. Biol. Chem.* 267:26031–37

74. Carmeliet P, Collen D. 1999. Role of vascular endothelial growth factor and vascular

endothelial growth factor receptor in vascular development. *Curr. Top. Microbiol. Immunol.* 237:133–58

75. Eriksson U, Alitalo K. 1999. Structure, expression and receptor-binding properties of novel vascular endothelial growth factors. *Curr. Top. Microbiol. Immunol.* 237:41–57

76. Neufeld G, Cohen T, Gengrinovitch S, Poltorak Z. 1999. Vascular endothelial growth factor (VEGF) and its receptors. *FASEB J.* 13:9–22

77. Clauss MM, Lepple-Wienhues A, Waltenberger J, Augustin HG, Ziche M, et al. 1999. A novel vascular endothelial growth factor encoded by Orf virus, VEGF-E, mediated angiogenesis by signaling through VEGF-2 (KDR) but not VEGFR-1 (Flt-1) receptor tyrosine kinase. *EMBO J.* 18:363–74

78. Brook PC, Montgomery AMP, Rossenfeld M, Reisfeld RA, Hu T, et al. 1994. Integrin alpha-v-beta-3 antagonist promote tumor regression by inducing apoptosis of angiogenic blood vessels. *Cell* 79:1157–64

79. Spyridopoulos I, Brogi E, Kearney M, Sullivan AB, Cetrulo C, et al. 1997. Vascular endothelial growth factor inhibits endothelial cell apoptosis induced by tumor necrosis factor-alpha: balance between growth and death signals. *J. Mol. Cell. Cardiol.* 29:1321–30

80. Gerber HP, McMurtrey A, Kowalski J, Yan M, Keyt BA, et al. 1998. Vascular endothelial growth factor regulates endothelial cell survival through the phosphatidylinositol 3'-kinase/Akt signal transduction pathway. Requirement for Flk-1/KDR activation. *J. Biol. Chem.* 273:303336–43

81. Fujio Y, Walsh K. 1999. Akt mediates cytoprotection of endothelial cells by vascular endothelial growth factor in an anchorage-dependent manner. *J. Biol. Chem.* 274:16349–54

82. Chapman GD, Lim CS, Gammon RS, Culp SC, Desper JS, et al. 1992. Gene transfer into coronary arteries of intact animals with a percutaneous balloon catheter. *Circ. Res.* 71:27–33

83. Barr E, Tripathy SK, Kozarsky K, Wilson JM, Carroll JD, et al. 1993. Efficient catheter-mediated gene transfer into the heart using replication-defective adenovirus. *Circulation* 88(Suppl.):I-475

84. Steg PG, Feldman LJ, Scoazec J-Y, Tahlil O, Barry JJ, et al. 1994. Arterial gene transfer to rabbit endothelial and smooth muscle cells using percutaneous delivery of an adenoviral vector. *Circulation* 90:1648–56

85. Nabel EG, Plautz G, Nabel GJ. 1992. Transduction of a foreign histocompatibility gene into the arterial wall induces vasculitis. *Proc. Natl. Acad. Sci. USA* 89:5157–61

86. Nabel EG, Shum L, Pompili VJ, Yang ZY, San H, et al. 1993. Direct gene transfer of transforming growth factor β1 into arteries stimulates fibrocellular hyperplasia. *Proc. Natl. Acad. Sci. USA* 90:11307–11

87. Lemarchand P, Jones M, Yamada I, Crystal RG. 1993. In vivo gene transfer and expression in normal uninjured blood vessels using replication-deficient adenovirus vectors. *Circ. Res.* 72:1132–38

88. Rome JJ, Shayani V, Flugelman MY, Newman KD, Farb A, et al. 1994. Anatomic barriers influence the distribution of in vivo gene transfer into the arterial wall: modeling with microscopic tracer particles and verification with a recombinant adenoviral vector. *Arterioscler. Thromb.* 14:148–61

89. Riessen R, Rahimizadeh H, Takeshita S, Gal D, Barry JJ, et al. 1993. Successful vascular gene transfer using a hydrogel coated balloon angioplasty catheter. *Hum. Gene. Ther.* 4:749–58

90. Pickering JG, Jekanowski J, Weir L, Takeshita S, Losordo DW, et al. 1994. Liposome-mediated gene transfer into human vascular smooth muscle cells. *Circulation* 89:13–21

91. Holt CE, Garlick N, Cornel E. 1990. Lipofection of cDNA in the embryonic vertebrate central nervous system. *Neuron* 4:203–14

92. Takeshita S, Gal D, Leclerc G, Pickering JG, Riessen R, et al. 1994. Increased gene expression after liposome-mediated arterial gene transfer associated with intimal smooth muscle cell proliferation: in vitro and in vivo findings in a rabbit model of vascular injury. *J. Clin. Invest.* 93:652–61

93. Feldman LJ, Steg PG, Zheng LP, Chen D, Kearney M, et al. 1995. Low-efficiency of percutaneous adenovirus-mediated arterial gene transfer in the atherosclerotic rabbit. *J. Clin. Invest.* 95:2662–71

94. Lee SW, Trapnell BC, Rade JJ, Virmani R, Dichek DA, et al. 1993. In vivo adenoviral vector-mediated gene transfer into balloon-injured rat carotid arteries. *Circ. Res.* 73:797–807

95. Guzman RJ, Lemarchand P, Crystal RG, Epstein SE, Finkel T. 1993. Efficient and selective adenovirus-mediated gene transfer into vascular neointima. *Circulation* 88:2838–48

96. Miller DG, Adam MA, Miller AD. 1990. Gene transfer by retrovirus vectors occurs only in cells that are actively replicating at the time of infection. *Mol. Cell. Biol.* 10:4239–42

97. Kahn ML, Lee SW, Dichek DA. 1992. Optimization of retroviral vector-mediated gene transfer into endothelial cells in vitro. *Circ. Res.* 71:1508–17

98. Felgner PL, Gadek TR, Holm M, Roman R, Chan HW, et al. 1987. Lipofection: a highly efficient, lipid-mediated DNA-transfection procedure. *Proc. Natl. Acad. Sci. USA* 84:7413–17

99. Riessen R, Rahimizadeh H, Blessing E, Takeshita S, Barry JJ, et al. 1993. Arterial gene transfer using pure DNA applied directly to a hydrogel-coated angioplasty balloon. *Hum. Gene. Ther.* 4:749–58

100. Yang Y, Nunes FA, Berencsi K, Furth EE, Gonczol E, et al. 1994. Cellular immunity to viral antigens limits E1-deleted adenoviruses for gene therapy. *Proc. Natl. Acad. Sci. USA* 91:4407–11

101. Wolff JA, Malone RW, Williams P, Chong W, Acsadi G, et al. 1990. Direct gene transfer into mouse muscle in vivo. *Science* 247:1465–68

102. Wolff JA, Williams P, Acsadi G, Jiao S, Jani A, et al. 1991. Conditions affecting direct gene transfer into rodent muscle in vivo. *Biotechniques* 11:474–85

103. Wolff JA, Ludtke JJ, Acsadi G, Williams P, Jani A. 1992. Long-term persistence of plasmid DNA and foreign gene expression in mouse muscle. *Hum. Mol. Genet.* 1:363–69

104. Nabel GJ, Nabel EG, Yang ZY, Fox BA, Plautz GE, et al. 1993. Direct gene transfer with DNA-liposome complexes in melanoma: expression, biologic activity, and lack of toxicity in humans. *Proc. Natl. Acad. Sci. USA* 90:11307–11

105. Hartikka J, Sawdey M, Cornefert-Jensen F, Margalith M, Barnhart K, et al. 1996. An improved plasmid DNA expression vector for direct injection into skeletal muscle. *Hum. Gene. Ther.* 7:1205–17

106. Felgner PL. 1996. Improvements in cationic liposomes for in vivo gene transfer. *Hum. Gene. Ther.* 7:1791–93

107. Jiao S, Williams P, Berg RK, Hodgeman BA, Liu L, et al. 1992. Direct gene transfer into nonhuman primate myofibers in vivo. *Hum. Gene. Ther.* 3:21–33

108. Lin H, Parmacek MS, Morle G, Boling S, Leiden JM. 1990. Expression of recombinant genes in myocardium in vivo after direct injection of DNA. *Circulation* 82:2217–21

109. Acsadi G, Jiao S, Jani A, Duke D, Williams P, et al. 1991. Direct gene transfer and expression into rat heart in vivo. *New Biol.* 3:71–81

110. Ascadi G, Dickson G, Love DR, Jani A, Walsh FS, et al. 1991. Human dystrophin

expression in mdx mice after intramuscular injection of DNA constructs. *Nat. Med.* 352:815–18

111. Winegar RA, Monforte JA, Suing KD, O'Loughlin KG, Rudd CJ, et al. 1996. Determination of tissue distribution of an intramuscular plasmid vaccine using PCR and in situ DNA hybridisation. *Hum. Gene. Ther.* 7:2185–94

112. Davis HL, Whalen RG, Demeneix BA. 1993. Direct gene transfer into skeletal muscle in vivo: factors affecting efficiency of transfer and stability of expression. *Hum. Gene. Ther.* 4:151–59

113. Levy MY, Barron LG, Meyer KB, Szoka FC Jr. 1996. Characterization of plasmid DNA transfer into mouse skeletal muscle: evaluation of uptake mechanism, expression and secretion of gene products into blood. *Gene Ther.* 3:201–11

114. Vitadello M, Schiaffino M, Picard A, Scarpa M, Schiaffino S. 1994. Gene transfer in regenerating muscle. *Hum. Gene Ther.* 5:11–18

115. Danko I, Fritz JD, Jiao S, Hogan K, Latendresse JS, et al. 1994. Pharmacological enhancement of in vivo foreign gene expression in muscle. *Gene Ther.* 1:114–21

116. Takeshita S, Isshiki T, Sato T. 1996. Increased expression of direct gene transfer into skeletal muscles observed following acute ischemic injury in rats. *Lab. Invest.* 74:1061–65

117. Danko I, Williams P, Herweijer H, Zhang G, Latendresse JS, et al. 1997. High expression of naked plasmid DNA in muscles of young rodents. *Hum. Mol. Genet.* 6:1435–43

118. Lew D, Parker SE, Latimer T, Abai AM, Kuwahara-Rundell A, et al. 1995. Cancer gene therapy using plasmid DNA: pharmakokinetic study of DNA following injection in mice. *Hum. Gene. Ther.* 6:553–64

119. Nabel EG, Gordon D, Yang Z-Y, Xu L, San H, et al. 1992. Gene transfer in vivo with DNA-liposome complexes: lack of autoimmunity and gonadal localization. *Hum. Gene. Ther.* 3:649–56

120. Tabata H, Silver M, Insner JM. 1997. Arterial gene transfer of acidic fibroblast growth factor for therapeutic angiogenesis in vivo: critical role of secretion signal in use of naked DNA. *Cardiovasc. Res.* 35:470–79

121. Giordano FJ, Ping P, McKirnan D, Nozaki S, De Maria AN, et al. 1996. Intracoronary gene transfer of fibroblast growth factor-5 increases blood flow and contractile function in an ischemic region of the heart. *Nat. Med.* 2:534–39

122. Tsurumi Y, Takeshita S, Chen D, Kearney M, Rossow ST, et al. 1996. Direct intramuscular gene transfer of naked DNA encoding vascular endothelial growth factor augments collateral development and tissue perfusion. *Circulation* 94:3281–90

123. Vale PR, Milliken CE, Tkebuchava T, Chen D, Iwaguro H, et al. 1999. Catheter-based gene transfer of VEGF utilizing electromechanical LV mapping accomplishes therapeutic angiogenesis: preclinical studies in swine. *Circulation* 100(Suppl.):I-512

124. Witzenbichler B, Asahara T, Murohara M, Silver M, Spyridopoulos J, et al. 1998. Post-natal overexpression of vascular endothelial growth factor-C (VEGF-C/VEGF-2) promotes angiogenesis in the setting of tissue ischemia. *Am. J. Pathol.* 153:381–94

125. Mack CA, Patel SR, Schwarz EA, Zanzonico P, Hahn RT, et al. 1998. Biologic bypass with the use of adenovirus-mediated gene transfer of the complementary deoxyribonucleic acid for vascular endothelial growth factor 121 improves myocardial perfusion and function in the ischemic porcine heart. *Thorac. Cardiovasc. Surg.* 115:168–76

126. Shyu KG, Manor O, Magner M, Yancopoulos GD, Isner JM. 1999. Direct intramuscular injection of plasmid DNA encoding angiopoietin-1 but not

angiopoietin-2 augments revascularization in the rabbit ischemic hindlimb. *Circulation* 98:2081–87

127. Iwaguro H, Asahara T, Akita GY, Masuda H, Kalka C, et al. 1999. Angiogenesis induced by adenovirus-mediated gene transfer of a hypoxia-inducible factor-1 alpha/VP16 hybrid in rabbit hindlimb ischemia. *Circulation* 100(Suppl.):I-47

128. Takeshita S, Zheng LP, Brogi E, Kearney M, Pu LQ, et al. 1994. Therapeutic angiogenesis: A single intra-arterial bolus of vascular endothelial growth factor augments revascularisation in a rabbit ischemic hindlimb model. *J. Clin. Invest.* 93:662–70

129. Schaper W, de Brabander M, Lewi P. 1971. DNA synthesis and mitoses in coronary collateral vessels of the dog. *Circ. Res.* 28:671–79

130. Browning J, Hogg N, Gobe G, Cross R. 1996. Capillary density in skeletal muscle of Wistar rats as a function of muscle weight and body weight. *Microvasc. Res.* 52:281–87

131. Vale PR, Losordo DW, Tkebuchava T, Chen D, Milliken CE, et al. 1999. Catheter-based myocardial gene transfer utilizing nonfluoroscopic electromechanical left ventricular mapping. *J. Am. Coll. Cardiol.* 34:246–54

132. Reidy MA, Schwartz SM. 1981. Endothelial regeneration: III. Time course of intimal changes after small defined injury to rat aortic endothelium. *Lab. Invest.* 44:301–8

133. Clowes AW, Reidy MA, Clowes MM. 1983. Kinetics of cellular proliferation after arterial injury. I. Smooth muscle growth in the absence of endothelium. *Lab. Invest.* 49:327–33

134. Scott-Burden T, Vanhoutte PM. 1993. The endothelium as a regulator of vascular smooth muscle proliferation. *Circulation* 87(Suppl.):V51–55

135. Wilson JM, Birinyi LK, Salomon RN, Libby P, Callow A, et al. 1989. Implantation of vascular grafts lined with genetically modified endothelial cells. *Science* 244:1344–46

136. Dunn PF, Kurt ND, Jones M, Yamada I, Shayani V, et al. 1996. Seeding of vascular grafts with genetically modified endothelial cells: secretion of recombinant TPA results in decreased seeded cell retention in vitro and in vivo. *Circulation* 93:1439–46

137. Lindner V, Majack RA, Reidy MA. 1990. Basic fibroblast growth factor stimulates endothelial regrowth and proliferation in denuded arteries. *J. Clin. Invest.* 85:2004–8

138. Laitinen M, Zachary I, Breier G, Pakkanen T, Hakkinen T, et al. 1997. VEGF gene transfer reduces intimal thickening via increased production of nitric oxide in carotid arteries. *Hum. Gene. Ther.* 8:1737–44

139. Hiltunen MO. 2000. Intravascular adenovirus-mediated VEGF-C gene transfer inhibits neointima formation in balloon-denuded rabbit aorta. *Circulation.* In press

140. Asahara T, Bauters C, Pastore CJ, Kearney M, Rossow S, et al. 1995. Local delivery of vascular endothelial growth factor accelerates re-endothelialization and attenuates intimal hyperplasia in balloon-injured rat carotid artery. *Circulation* 91:2793–801

141. Van Belle E, Tio FO, Chen D, Maillard L, Kearney M, et al. 1997. Passivation of metallic stents following arterial gene transfer of phVEGF165 inhibits thrombus formation and intimal thickening. *J. Am. Coll. Cardiol.* 29:1371–79

142. McBride W, Lange RA, Hillis LD. 1988. Restenosis after successful coronary angioplasty: pathophysiology and prevention. *N. Engl. J. Med.* 318:1734–37

143. Takeshita S, Isshiki T, Ochiai M, Eto K, Mori H, et al. 1998. Endothelium-dependent relaxation of collateral microvessels after intramuscular gene transfer of

vascular endothelial growth factor in a rat model of hindlimb ischemia. *Circulation* 98:1261–63

144. Abbott RD, Donahue RP, Kannel WB, Wilson PF. 1988. The impact of diabetes on survival following myocardial infarction in men vs. women: the Framingham study. *J. Am. Med. Assoc.* 260:3456–60

145. Cohen RA. 1993. Dysfunction of vascular endothelium in diabetes mellitus. *Circulation* 87(Suppl.):V67–76

146. Abaci A, Adburrahman O, Kahraman S, Eryol NK, Uenal S, et al. 1999. Effect of diabetes mellitus on formation of coronary collateral vessels. *Circulation* 99:2239–42

147. Schultz A, Lavie L, Hochberg I, Beyar R, Stone T, et al. 1999. Interindividual heterogeneity in the hypoxic regulation of VEGF. Significance for the development of the coronary artery collateral circulation. *Circulation* 547:547–52

148. Rensing BJ, Hermans WRM, Vos J, Tijssen JGP, Rutch W, et al. 1993. Luminal narrowing after percutaneous transluminal coronary angioplasty: a study of clinical procedural and lesional factors to long-term angiographic outcome. *Circulation* 88:975–85

149. Alderman EL, Andrews K, Bost J, Bourassa M, Chaitma BR, et al. 1996. Comparison of coronary bypass surgery with angioplasty in patients with multivessel disease. *N. Engl. J. Med.* 335:217–25

150. Rivard A, Fabre JE, Silver M, Chen D, Murohara T, et al. 1999. Age-dependent impairment of angiogenesis. *Circulation* 99:111–20

151. Couffinhal T, Silver M, Kearney M, Sullivan A, Witzenbichler B, et al. 1999. Impaired collateral vessel development associated with reduced expression of vascular endothelial growth factor in ApoE -/- mice. *Circulation* 99:3188–98

152. Schaper W, Ito WD. 1996. Molecular mechanisms of coronary collateral vessel growth. *Circ. Res.* 79:911–19

153. Ware JA, Simons M. 1997. Angiogenesis in ischemic heart disease. *Nat. Med.* 3:158–64

154. Schaper W, Piek JJ, Munoz-Chapuli R, Wolf C, Ito W. 1999. Collateral circulation of the heart. In *Angiogenesis and Cardiovascular Disease.*, ed. JA Ware, M Simons, pp. 159–98. New York: Oxford Univ. Press

155. Baumgartner I, Rauh G, Pieczek A, Wuensch D, Magner M, et al. 2000. Lower-extremity edema associated with gene transfer of naked DNA encoding vascular endothelial growth factor. *Ann. Intern. Med.* 132:880–84

156. Simovic D, Ropper AH, Isner JM, Weinberg DH. 1999. Improvement in ischemic limb neuropathy after VEGF gene transfer. *Circulation* 100(Suppl.):I-770

157. Schratzberger P, Schratzberger G, Silver M, Curry C, Kearney M, et al. 2000. Favorable effect of VEGF gene transfer on ischemic peripheral neuropathy. *Nat. Med.* 6:405–13

158. Symes JF, Losordo DW, Vale PR, Lahti K, Esakof DD, et al. 1999. Gene therapy with vascular endothelial growth factor for inoperable coronary artery disease. *Ann. Thor. Surg.* 68:830–36

159. Rentrop KP, Feit F, Sherman W, Thornton JC. 1989. Serial angiographic assessment of coronary artery obstruction and collateral flow in acute myocardial infarction: report from the second Mount Sinai–New York University Reperfusion Trial. *Circulation* 80:1166–75

160. Henry TD, Annex BH, Azrin MA, McKendall GR, Willerson JT, et al. 1999. Final results of the VIVA trial of rhVEGF for human therapeutic angiogenesis. *Circulation* 100(Suppl.):I-476

161. Laham RJ, Chronos NA, Leimbach M, Pearlman JD, Pettigrew R, et al. 2000. Results of a phase I open label dose escalating study of intracoronary and

intravenous basic fibroblast growth factor (rhFGF-2) in patients with severe ischemic heart disease: 6 months followup. *J. Am. Coll.Cardiol.* 35(Suppl.):73A

162. Adar R, Critchfield GC, Eddy DM. 1989. A confidence profile analysis of the results of femoropopliteal percutaneous transluminal angioplasty in the treatment of lower-extremity ischemia. *J. Vasc. Surg.* 10:57–67

163. Isner JM, Walsh K, Rosenfield K, Schainfeld R, Asahara T, et al. 1996. Arterial gene therapy for restenosis. *Hum. Gene. Ther.* 7:989–1011

164. Vale PR, Wuensch DI, Rauh GF, Rosenfield KM, Schainfeld RM, et al. 1998. Arterial gene therapy for inhibition restenosis in patients with claudication undergoing superficial femoral artery angioplasty. *Circulation* 98(Suppl.):I-66

Annu. Rev. Physiol. 2001. 63:451–69

GENETIC ASSEMBLY OF THE HEART:
Implications for Congenital Heart Disease

Deepak Srivastava

Department of Pediatrics and Molecular Biology, University of Texas Southwestern
Medical Center, Dallas, Texas 75390-9148; e-mail: dsriva@mednet.swmed.edu

Key Words   cardiac development, transcription factors, signaling pathways, left-right asymmetry, human genetics

■ **Abstract**   More children die from congenital heart defects (CHD) each year than are diagnosed with childhood cancer, yet the causes remain unknown. The remarkable conservation of genetic pathways regulating cardiac development in species ranging from flies to humans provides an opportunity to experimentally dissect the role of critical cardiogenic factors. Utilization of model biological systems has resulted in a molecular framework in which to consider the etiology of CHD. As whole genome sequencing and single nucleotide polymorphism data become available, identification of genetic mutations predisposing to CHD may allow preventive measures by modulation of secondary genetic or environmental factors. In this review, genetic pathways regulating cardiogenesis revealed by cross-species studies are reviewed and correlated with human CHD.

INTRODUCTION

The heart has captured the imagination of mankind for centuries because of its elegant simplicity yet relentless capacity to support a living organsim. As the organ most essential for life, the heart is the first organ to form in an embryo and must function to support the rapidly growing embryo before it has the opportunity to shape itself into a four-chambered organ. The combination of complex morphogenetic events necessary for cardiogenesis and the superimposed hemodynamic influences may contribute to the exquisite sensitivity of the heart to perturbations. This phenomenon is reflected in the estimated 10% incidence of severe cardiac malformations observed in early miscarriages. The fraction of congenital heart malformations that are hemodynamically compatible with the intrauterine circulation compose the spectrum of congenital heart defects (CHD) that is observed clinically.

The anatomic features of most CHD in humans have been carefully catalogued. Although CHD was classified in the 18th and 19th centuries based upon

0066-4278/01/0315-0451$14.00

embryologic considerations, the advent of palliative procedures and clinical management led to a descriptive nomenclature founded on anatomic and physiologic features that governed surgical and medical therapy. However, seemingly unrelated CHD could be argued to share common embryologic origins from a mechanistic standpoint, suggesting that the etiology of CHD may be better understood by considering their developmental bases. Recent advances in genetics and molecular biology have stimulated a renaissance in seeking an embryologic framework for understanding CHD as genetically based alterations. Null mutations in genes that function during cardiac development established that abnormalities in cardiovascular ontogeny can be a primary cause of embryonic demise. The ability to go beyond descriptions of the anatomical defects to developing an understanding of the genes responsible for distinct steps of cardiac morphogenesis is necessary for more directed therapeutic and preventive measures.

Although human genetic approaches have been important in understanding CHD, detailed molecular analysis of cardiac development in humans has been difficult. The recognition that cardiac genetic pathways are highly conserved across vastly diverse species from flies to humans has resulted in an explosion of information from studies in more tractable and accessible biological models. The fruit fly (*Drosophila*) has been a source of discovery for genes involved in early cardiac determination events. Although no biological system is ideal for studying human disease, *Drosophila* has several advantages. It has a simple genome and usually has a single copy of genes that often have three or four orthologues in vertebrates; genetic studies are facilitated by rapid breeding times; and, most importantly, its DNA can be chemically mutated in a random fashion followed by phenotypic analysis and reverse genetics to identify the DNA mutation associated with distinct developmental defects. Similar chemical mutagenesis efforts have been successful in another model system, the zebrafish. Zebrafish have the added advantages of being vertebrates. They have a more complex two-chambered heart, and because the embryos grow in water, they have a heart that is easily visible and not necessary for survival during the period of cardiac development. Although genetic approaches are not feasible in chick embryos, they have four-chambered hearts, and the embryos are easily accessible within the egg for surgical and molecular manipulation during cardiogenesis. The chick has thus been useful in cell fate analyses and defining the role of populations of cells during development. Finally, use of the laboratory mouse, a mammal with a cardiovascular system nearly identical to humans, has been invaluable in understanding the mechanisms underlying human disease through direct gene targeting. Thus each biological system offers unique opportunities to develop a deeper understanding of cardiogenesis.

Despite the diversity of body plans adopted by different species, a genetic program for the early formation of a circulatory system has remained of central importance. The essential conservation of these programs is reflected in their repeated use of core elements like the *tinman/Nkx2.5/Csx* homeobox gene, whose expression first specifies the precardiac lineage in *Drosophila*, zebrafish, *Xenopus*, chick, mouse, and human (1). The cardiovascular systems of these organisms have evolved with increasing complexity in order to adapt to specific environments. In a simplified view, it appears that higher organisms have retained the morphologic steps utilized by lower organisms and have built complexity into the heart in a modular fashion (2–4). In particular, the specification of chamber structures and the advent of a parallel circulation through chamber duplication and outflow tract division by neural crest derivatives have facilitated the development of larger, air-breathing organisms utilizing complex circulatory systems.

In this review, anatomic, molecular, and clinical aspects of cardiac embryology are interwoven to develop a framework in which to consider the etiology of human congenital cardiac defects. Clinical lessons combined with experimental studies in mice, chick, fish, and flies have led to a model suggesting that unique regions and segments of the heart have been added in a modular fashion during evolution. In this model, defects in particular regions of the heart may arise from unique genetic and environmental effects during specific developmental windows of time. To simplify the complex events of cardiogenesis, unique regions of the developing heart are considered individually in the context described above.

Cardiomyocyte Differentiation and Heart Tube Formation

The heart is the first organ to form in vertebrates, and it arises through a complex series of morphogenetic interactions involving cells from several embryonic origins (5) (Figure 1, see color insert). Beginning soon after gastrulation (about embryonic day 18 in humans), progenitor cells within the anterior lateral plate mesoderm become committed to a cardiogenic fate in response to an inducing signal thought to emanate from the adjacent endoderm (6). The specific signaling molecule(s) responsible for cardiogenic commitment remains to be identified, although members of the transforming growth factor β (TGF-β) family, including bone morphogenetic protein-2 (BMP-2), appear to be critical for this step (6). Cardiac precursors form a bilaterally symmetric cardiogenic "field" that develops further into parallel cardiac primordia, which fuse at the midline to form the primitive cardiac tube (7). This straight heart tube contains an outer myocardium and an inner endocardium separated by an extracellular matrix (ECM) known as the cardiac jelly. The tubular heart initiates rhythmic contractions at about day 21 in humans.

Fruitflies have a primitive heart-like structure known as the dorsal vessel that is analogous to the straight heart tube of the vertebrate embryo. It contracts rhythmically and pumps hemolymph through an open circulatory system. In flies, a member of the TGF-β family, decapentaplegic (dpp), is essential for the initial determination of a cardioblast (8). Formation of the dorsal vessel in flies is dependent on a protein, Tinman, whose name is based on the Wizard of Oz character that lacks a heart (9, 10). Tinman belongs to the homeodomain family of proteins that was initially described to play a role in establishing regional identity of cells and organs during embryogenesis. Tinman is necessary for specification of the cardiac lineage and directly activates transcription of the *Mef2* gene, encoding a transcription factor that controls myocyte differentiation (11). Tinman and Nkx2.5, its mammalian orthologue, directly interact with zinc-finger transcription factors of the GATA family to activate cardiac gene expression (12, 13).

In mice, Nkx2.5 is not required for initial cardiac specification, suggesting that some degree of genetic redundancy exists for the early but not later functions of Nkx2.5 (14, 15). This hypothesis is supported by the observations that dominant-negative versions of Nkx2.5 and its relative, Nkx2.3, are able to prevent early cardiogenesis in frog and zebrafish embryos (16, 17).

Bilaterally symmetric cardiac primordia converge along the ventral midline of the embryo to form a beating linear heart tube composed of distinct myocardial and endocardial layers (Figure 1). Mutations of GATA proteins in mice and zebrafish have demonstrated a critical role for this family of transcription factors in midline fusion of the heart tube (18–20). In an example of the power of zebrafish genetics, positional cloning of a gene responsible for a cardiac bifida phenotype, *miles apart*, has revealed a role for lysophospholipids in vertebrate development (21). The *miles apart* gene encodes a novel sphingosine 1-phosphate receptor that may be mediating a midline signal to attract cardiomyocytes from the lateral aspect of the early embryo, although the mechanisms of cell movement and fusion are yet to be determined.

As the straight heart tube takes shape, five distinct tubular segments form in a temporal sequence, along the anterior-posterior (AP) axis (7). The primitive right and left ventricles are the first to be distinguished, followed by the atrioventricular canal segment. The sino-atrial segment forms most caudally and has distinct left-right (LR) asymmetry with the right and left limbs of this segment later contributing to the right and left atria, respectively. The conotruncus is the last segment to form and lies in the most anterior portion of the heart tube. As the heart tube loops to the right, the cardiac chambers begin to become distinguished morphologically (Figure 1).

In addition to the AP segmentation, a discrete dorsal-ventral (DV) polarity is present in the primitive heart tube. As the heart tube loops to the right, the ventral surface of the tube rotates, becoming the outer curvature of the looped heart with the dorsal surface forming the inner curvature. The outer curvature becomes the site of active growth while remodeling of the inner curvature is essential for ultimate alignment of the inflow and outflow tracts of the heart. A model in which individual chambers "balloon" from the outer curvature in a segmental fashion has been proposed (22). Consistent with this model, numerous genes are expressed specifically on the ventral and outer curvature of the heart (22, 23). Remodeling of the inner curvature allows migration of the inflow tract to the right and outflow tract to the left, facilitating proper alignment and separation of right and left-sided circulations.

Cardiac Looping and Left-Right Asymmetry

The pathways that control the direction of cardiac looping along the LR axis have recently been elucidated (Figure 2, see color insert) (reviewed in 24). The heart is the first organ to break the bilateral symmetry present in the early embryo, and

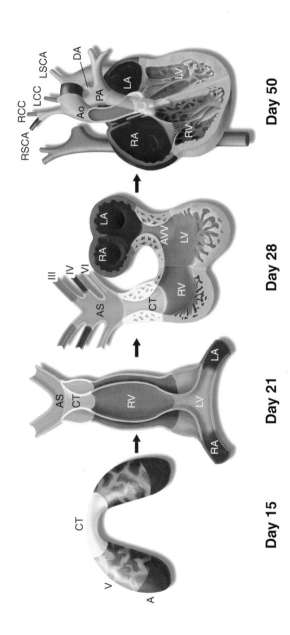

Figure 1 Schematic of cardiac morphogenesis. Illustrations depict cardiac development with color coding of morphologically related regions, seen from a ventral view. Cardiogenic precursors form a crescent (*far-left panel*) that is specified to form specific segments of the linear heart tube, which is patterned along the AP axis to form the various regions and chambers of the looped and mature heart. Each cardiac chamber balloons out from the outer curvature of the looped heart tube in a segmental fashion. Neural crest cells populate the bilaterally symmetric aortic arch arteries (III, IV, and VI) and aortic sac (AS) that together contribute to specific segments of the mature aortic arch (color-coded). Mesenchymal cells form the cardiac valves from the contruncal (CT) and atrioventricular valve (AVV) segments. Corresponding days of human embryonic development are indicated. RV, right ventricle; LV left ventricle; RA, right atrium; LA, left atrium; PA, pulmonary artery; Ao, aorta; DA, ductus arteriosus; RSCA, right subclavian artery; LSCA, left subclavian artery; RCC, right common carotid; LCC, left common carotid. (Reproduced with permission from Reference 2.)

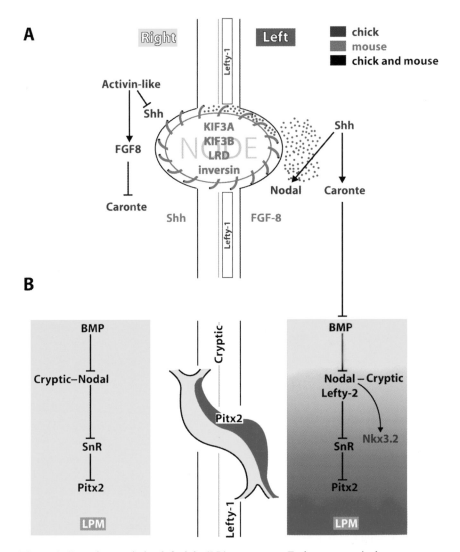

Figure 2 Cascades regulating left-right (LR) asymmetry. Early asymmetrical gene expression around the node (*A*) results in activation or repression of sonic hedgehog (Shh) or fibroblast growth factor (FGF) 8-dependent pathways on the right or left (ventral view). Early roles of Shh and FGF8 are reversed in mouse and chick, as indicated by color. Leftward flow of morphogens (green dots) by nodal cilia establishes the asymmetric gradient around the node in mice. Expression of Lefty-1 near the midline may serve as a barrier to maintain left-sided asymmetry of morphogens. At later stages of organogenesis, the nodal LR asymmetric information is transferred to the lateral plate mesoderm (LPM) by caronte. Caronte relieves BMP inhibition of the left, initiating a cascade of events culminating in expression of Pitx2 in the left LPM and in the left side of the heart tube (*B*).

the rightward direction of its looping reflects a more global establishment of LR asymmetry that affects the lungs, liver, spleen, and gut. Defects in establishment of LR asymmetry in humans are associated with a wide range of cardiac alignment defects, suggesting that pathways regulating LR asymmetry dramatically affect cardiac development.

A cascade of signaling molecules regulating the establishment of embryonic LR asymmetry has been revealed from recent studies of chick embryonic development. Before the formation of organs in the developing embryo, asymmetric expression of the morphogen, Sonic hedgehog (Shh), on the left side of Hensen's node leads to left lateral mesoderm expression of nodal and lefty, members of the TGF-β family (25). Transfer of this signal from the node to the lateral mesoderm is mediated by the secreted molecule, caronte (26, 27). Caronte inhibits BMP on the left side, relieving BMP-mediated repression of nodal in the left lateral plate mesoderm. Left-sided expression of nodal induces rightward looping of the midline heart tube. Fibroblast growth factor and activin receptor-mediated pathways suppress caronte expression on the right side, and the resulting activity of BMP signaling results in suppression of right-sided nodal expression. Conversely, the snail-related (cSnR-1) zinc finger transcription factor is expressed in the right lateral mesoderm and is repressed by Shh on the left (28). The above signaling pathways are active in the lateral plate mesoderm but not in the heart or other organs that actually display LR asymmetry. Ultimately, the nodal-dependent pathways result in expression of a homoedomain protein, Pitx2, on the left side of visceral organs and repression of Pitx2 on the right (29–31). Asymmetric expression of Pitx2 is sufficient for establishing the LR asymmetry of the heart, lungs, and gut.

The mechanisms that control directionality of cardiac looping have also been explored by genetic analysis of mouse mutants with abnormalities in LR asymmetry. Mice homozygous for mutation in the *left-right dynein* gene (*iv/iv*) display randomization of left-right orientation of the heart and viscera (32). In the situs inversus (*inv*) mouse model, there is a nearly 100% reversal of LR asymmetry, although the function of the *inv* gene remains unknown (33, 34). *Inv* mice express nodal and Pitx2 along the right lateral mesoderm rather than the left, displaying complete reversal of the LR signals (35, 36). In contrast, *iv/iv* mice display bilaterally symmetric, absent, or randomization of nodal and Pitx2 expression. Confirming a critical role for Pitx2 in LR asymmetry, *Pitx2* mutant mice have abnormal LR pulmonary asymmetry (37, 38). Oddly, the initial LR asymmetry and roles of fg8 and shh are opposite in mice and chicks; however, the LR sidedness of later events involving nodal and Pitx2 are conserved in all species studied (39).

Although the necessity of LR asymmetric gene expression is intuitive, how the early asymmetry of molecules is established remains in question. Initial clues came from studies of immotile cilia syndrome, also known as Kartagener's syndrome, in which individuals had situs inversus totalis, with mirror-image reversal of all organs (40). It was recently found that, prior to organ formation, Hensen's node contains ciliary processes that beat in a vortical fashion (41). It is currently believed that a combination of ciliary beating that moves morphogens to the left side of the embryo and establishment of a midline barrier, possibly by *lefty* gene expression along the left midline, are responsible for subsequent asymmetric gene expression. Mice lacking ciliary movement in the node display abnormal LR patterning, consistent with this model.

It has been proposed that abnormalities in the process of cardiac looping underlie a number of CHD. Folding of the heart tube positions the inflow cushions adjacent to the outflow cushions and involves extensive remodeling of the inner curvature of the looped heart tube. In the primitive looped heart, the segments of the heart are still in a linear pattern and must be repositioned considerably for alignment of the atrial chambers with the appropriate ventricles and the ventricles with the aorta and pulmonary arteries. The atrioventricular septum (AVS) begins to divide the common atrio-ventricular canal (AVC) into a right and left AVC that subsequently shifts to the right to position the AVS over the ventricular septum. This allows the right AVC and the left AVC to be aligned with the right and left ventricles, respectively. Simultaneously, the conotruncal region becomes septated into the aorta and pulmonary trunks as the conotruncus moves toward the left side of the heart such that the conotruncal septum is positioned over the AVS. The rightward shift of the AVS and leftward shift of the conotruncus converts the single-inlet, single-outlet heart into a four-chambered heart that has separate atrial inlets and ventricular outlets (42).

Arrest or incomplete movement of the AVS or conotruncus might result in malalignment of the inflow and outflow tracts. A scenario in which the AVS fails to shift to the right would result in communication of the right and left AVCs with the left ventricle, a condition known as double-inlet left ventricle (DILV). Incomplete shifting may be the basis for unbalanced AVC defects where the right AVC only partly communicates with the right ventricle. Similarly, if the conotruncal septum fails to shift to the left, both the aorta and pulmonary artery would arise from the right ventricle causing a double-outlet right ventricle (DORV). Thus any abnormality in cardiac looping can be associated with DILV or DORV, along with other manifestations of improper alignment of specific regions of the heart.

It is likely that patients with situs inversus totalis have a well-coordinated reversal of LR asymmetry and thus have a lower incidence of defects in visceral organogenesis. However the majority of patients with LR defects have viscero-atrial heterotaxy and thus have randomization of cardiac, pulmonary, and gastrointestinal situs, similar to the *iv/iv* mouse in which coordinated signaling is absent. Such patients can have defects in almost all aspects of cardiogenesis. Often either the right or left side predominates with patients having either bilateral right-sidedness (asplenia syndrome) or bilateral left-sidedness (polysplenia syndrome). In such cases, features of the right or left side of the lungs, heart, and gut are duplicated. Disruption of cascades determining either the left or right side of the embryo might result in asplenia or polysplenia syndromes, respectively. For example, targeted deletion of the activin receptor IIb in a mouse model results in randomization of heart, lung, and gut placement with a predominance of right-sidedness (43). Indeed, mutations in LR pathway members are found in some patients with heterotaxy (44). Familial cases of heterotaxy have also led to identification of mutations in a zinc-finger transcription factor, ZIC3, that results in LR axis abnormalities (45).

Patterning of the Developing Heart Tube

Recent studies in numerous model organisms have begun to reveal the genetic basis of a segmental ballooning model of cardiogenesis. Separable regulatory regions of genes such as *Nkx2.5, GATA-5,6, myosin light chain 2V*, and *myosin light chain 1F* direct expression to specific chambers of the heart (reviewed in 46). Correspondingly, numerous transcription factors are expressed in a chamber-specific fashion, providing a possible mechanism to explain how distinct segments of the heart adopt their respective fates.

dHAND and eHAND are related basic helix-loop-helix (bHLH) transcription factors expressed predominantly in the primitive right and left ventricle segments, respectively, during mouse heart development (47, 48). Deletion of dHAND in mice results in hypoplasia of the right ventricular segment from a cell survival defect (49). Mice lacking eHAND die early from placental defects precluding detailed analysis of its role in left ventricular development (50, 51). However, eHAND is down-regulated in Nkx2.5-deficient mice, which die around the stage of cardiac looping (52). Disruption of both dHAND and Nkx2.5 results in absence of the right and left ventricle, suggesting that the combined function of dHAND and Nkx2.5, possibly through its regulation of eHAND, is necessary for ventricular formation (H Yamagishi & D Srivastava, unpublished observations). In zebrafish, which has a single ventricle, only one *HAND* gene has been identified (dHAND) (53), deletion of which results in lack of a ventricular segment of the heart (54), similar to that seen in the absence of dHAND and Nkx2.5. Expression of the ventricular-specific homeobox gene of the Iroquois family, *Irx4*, is dependent upon both dHAND and Nkx2.5, and misexpression of *Irx4* in the atria is sufficient to activate ventricle-specific gene expression (55, 56). These findings suggest that HAND and Nkx2.5 proteins may cooperate in early ventricle-specific decisions. Interestingly, deletion of MEF2C, one of the four MEF2 factors in mice, results in hypoplasia of the right and left ventricles but not of the atria (57). The chamber-specific role of MEF2C, in spite of its homogenous expression in the heart, suggests that it might be a necessary co-factor for one or more of the other ventricular-restricted regulatory proteins.

In contrast to the ventricle-specific transcription factors, the orphan nuclear receptor, COUP-TFII, is expressed specifically in the atrial precursors and is required for atrial but not ventricular growth (58). How the segmental pattern of gene expression is established remains unclear; however, retinoid signaling has been implicated in atrial specification and regulation of the atrioventricular (AV) border along the AP axis of the heart tube (59). The recent discovery of a novel class of hairy-related transcription factors (HRT1, HRT2, HRT3) may also provide some insight (60). Hairy proteins often function downstream of the transmembrane receptor, Notch, in establishing boundaries of gene expression. Interestingly, HRT1 and HRT2, are expressed in a complementary fashion in the atria and ventricles, respectively. How the many transcription factors function in a coordinated manner to regulate chamber specification and differentiation remains to be determined.

Myocardial Growth

Mutations of a wide variety of genes in mice result in hypoplasia of the muscular wall of the heart (61). Mice homozygous for a null mutation in the *retinoid X receptor-α* (*RXRα*) gene display ventricular chamber hypoplasia and have a defect in compaction of the myocardium, although this may not be a cell-autonomous effect (62). A similar phenotype is seen in mice carrying mutations in the N-*myc*, *TEF-1* and *neurofibromatosis* (*NF-1*) genes (63–65). Deficiencies of the cell adhesion molecules alpha-4 integrin, VCAM, and Wilm's tumor (*WT-1*) genes result in epicardial dissolution and subsequent myocardial thinning (66, 67). The diversity of genes affecting myocardial growth suggests that this aspect of cardiac development is particularly sensitive to perturbations.

Signaling between the endocardium and the myocardium also appears to be important for ventricular growth. Neuregulin growth factors are expressed in the endocardium and are required for the development of trabeculae, the finger-like projections of the ventricular myocardium. In mice deficient in neuregulin or its receptors, erbB2 and erbB4, the ventricular trabeculae fail to form, possibly as a result of decreased endocardial signals (68–70). Similar defects in ventricular trabeculation have been observed in mice lacking angiogenic factors that are also expressed in the endocardium (71, 72). Defects in myocardial formation and contractility are also observed in the *cloche* zebrafish mutant, which lacks endocardial cells, consistent with an important role for endocardial-myocardial interactions (73).

Cardiac Valvulogenesis

Formation of cardiac valves allows for chamber septation and for coordinated flow of blood from the inflow to the outflow segments of the heart. During early heart tube formation, "cushions" of extracellular matrix between the endocardium and myocardium presage valve formation at each end of the heart tube. Reciprocal signaling, mediated in part by TGF-β family members, between the myocardium and endocardium in the cushion region induces a transformation of endocardial cells into mesenchymal cells that migrate into the cushion ECM (74). These mesenchymal cells differentiate into the fibrous tissue of the valves and are involved in septation of the common atrioventricular canal into right- and left-sided orifices.

Recent studies in mice have provided an entry to understand the transcriptional mechanisms of valvulogenesis. The transcription factor, NFATc, is expressed specifically in the forming embryonic valves, and targeted deletion of *NFATc* in mice results in absence of cardiac valve formation (75, 76). In contrast, a transcription factor that mediates TGF-β signaling, Smad6, is also expressed specifically in the cardiac valve precursors, but mutation of *Smad6* in mice leads to abnormally thickened, gelatinous valves, similar to those seen in some human valvular disease (77). Trisomy 21 (Down syndrome) in humans is commonly associated with incomplete septation of the atrioventricular valves; however, the gene(s) on chromosome 21 responsible for valve development remains unknown. Further genetic analysis of NFATc and Smad6 and use of the Trisomy 16 mouse model of Trisomy 21 may provide insight into the molecular mechanisms of valve septation.

Conotruncal and Aortic Arch Development

Congenital cardiac defects involving the cardiac outflow tract, aortic arch, ductus arteriosus, and proximal pulmonary arteries account for 20–30% of all CHD. This region of the heart undergoes extensive and rather complex morphogenetic changes. The cardiac outflow tract can be divided into the muscularized conus and the adjacent truncus arteriosus, collectively termed the conotruncus, as it arises from the primitive right ventricle. The conotruncus normally shifts to the left to override the forming ventricular septum. The truncus arteriosus then becomes septated by mesenchymal cells into the aorta and pulmonary arteries, with a muscular ridge forming between the two vessels known as the conotruncal septum. However, at this stage, the aorta communicates with the right ventricle and the pulmonary artery with the left ventricle. Subsequent rotation of the two vessels in a spiraling fashion places the aorta in a more dorsal and leftward position and the pulmonary artery in a more ventral and rightward location (Figure 1). This spiraling event achieves the normal alignment of the aorta and pulmonary artery to the left and right ventricles, respectively. Abnormalities in septation or incomplete spiraling of the conotruncus result in many CHD. For example, the conotruncal septum between the aorta and pulmonary artery forms in tetralogy of Fallot (TOF), but because of mal-alignment of the great vessels, the conotruncal septum and aorta are shifted to the right. This results in an aorta that overrides the ventricular septum and failure of the conotruncal septum to connect to the muscular ventricular septum, and consequently a ventricular septal defect. Similarly, any mal-alignment of the conotruncus results in an obligatory ventricular septal defect that, unlike muscular VSDs, does not have the potential to close spontaneously after birth.

A structure referred to as the aortic sac lies rostral to the conotruncus and gives rise to six bilaterally symmetric vessels known as aortic arch arteries. The aortic arch arteries arise sequentially along the AP axis, each traversing a pharyngeal arch before joining the paired dorsal aortae. The first and second arch arteries involute and the fifth arch artery never fully forms. The third, fourth, and six arch arteries undergo extensive remodeling to ultimately form distinct regions of the mature aortic arch and proximal pulmonary arteries (Figure 1). The majority of the right-sided dorsal aorta and aortic arch arteries undergo programmed cell death leading to a left-sided aortic arch. The third aortic arch artery contributes to the proximal carotid arteries. The left fourth aortic arch artery forms the transverse aortic arch between the left common carotid and left subclavian arteries. Finally, the sixth arch artery contributes to the proximal pulmonary artery and the ductus arteriosus (78). Extrapolating from their embryologic origins, it is believed that aberrant subclavian arteries and other subtle arch anomalies are the result of third or fourth aortic arch defects; interrupted aortic arch from fourth arch defects; and patent ductus arteriosus and proximal pulmonary artery hypoplasia/discontinuity from defects in sixth arch artery development.

Contribution of the Cardiac Neural Crest to Cardiogenesis

A unique population of cells along the crest of the neural folds (neural crest cells) migrate away from the neural folds and retain the ability to differentiate into multiple cell types and are therefore pluripotent. Their migratory path and ultimate cell fates are dependent upon their relative position of origin along the anterior-posterior axis. Neural crest cells differentiate and contribute to diverse embryonic structures, including the cranial ganglia, peripheral nervous system, adrenal glands, and melanocytes. Neural crest cells that arise from the otic placode to the third somite migrate through the developing pharyngeal arches and populate the mesenchyme of each of the pharyngeal and aortic arch arteries, the conotruncus, and conotruncal septum. Because of their migratory path this segment of the neural crest is often referred to as the cardiac neural crest (79).

Surgical, and more recently laser, ablation of the cardiac neural crest prior to migration away from the neural folds in chick embryos demonstrated a critical role for neural crest cells during cardiogenesis (80). Embryos deficient in cardiac neural crest cells displayed a variety of cardiac outflow tract and aortic arch defects similar to those seen in humans. These included tetralogy of Fallot (TOF), persistent truncus arteriosus, double-outlet right ventricle, and conotruncal ventricular septal defects. Within the aortic arch, a broad spectrum of aortic arch anomalies were observed including interruption of the aortic arch, aberrant origins of the right subclavian artery, and persistence of the right aortic arch rather than the left aortic arch. Thus defects in neural crest migration or differentiation likely underlie the many conotruncal and aortic arch defects seen in children.

Insight into the genes that regulate cardiac neural crest development has come from studies in other vertebrate models. Mice lacking endothelin-1 (ET-1) or its G protein-coupled receptor, ET_A, have post-migratory cardiac neural crest defects including cleft palate and other craniofacial anomalies reminiscent of 22q11 deletion syndrome in humans (81, 82). dHAND and eHAND are normally expressed in the neural crest-derived pharyngeal and aortic arches, but are down-regulated in *ET-1*- and *ET_A*-deficient mice, although low levels of expression are detectable. These data suggest that enhancement of *HAND* expression is regulated by ET-1 signaling (83). Complete absence of dHAND as observed in *dHAND* null mice results in a severe survival defect of pharyngeal and aortic arch mesenchyme (83), consistent with a critical role for dHAND. In a screen for genes downstream of dHAND, neuropilin-1, a semaphorin and VEGF receptor, was found to be down-regulated in *dHAND* mutants. Interestingly, targeted mutation of *neuropilin-1* results in conotruncal and aortic arch defects similar to that of *ET-1* mutants, suggesting that ET-1, dHAND and neuropilin-1 may function in a common pathway regulating the cardiac neural crest (84, 85).

The aortic arch undergoes a tremendous amount of remodeling in a segmental fashion, much like the heart, and each segment of the mature aortic arch develops relatively independently. Disruption of Mfh1, a forkhead transcription factor, specifically affects the fourth aortic arch artery in mice and results in absence of the transverse aortic arch (86), a phenotype resembling interruption of the aortic arch seen in humans. Mice harboring mutations in the homeodomain protein, pax3, or mutations in retinoic acid receptors also have a variety of outflow tract and aortic arch defects (87, 88). A zebrafish mutant, *gridlock*, has been described in which coarctation (narrowing) of a discrete region of the aorta is observed. Recent positional cloning efforts have demonstrated that the *gridlock* phenotype is the result of a point mutation in a gene encoding the zebrafish orthologue of the bHLH transcription factor, Hesr2/HRT2b/Hey2 (89). How these hairy-related transcription factors mediate Notch signaling during aortic arch patterning will be an important area for future study. Finally, evidence for independent regulation of the sixth aortic arch artery comes from the third most common CHD in which the ductus arteriosus, an embryonic vessel connecting the aorta and pulmonary artery, fails to close after birth. Heterozygous mutations of the trancription factor, TFAP2B, can result in familial patent ductus arteriosus, suggesting a role for TFAP2B in governing patency or closure of this vessel (90).

Human Genetic Studies

The study of chromosomal disorders and autosomal dominant syndromes in the setting of CHD and genetic linkage analysis of rare pedigrees with milder forms of CHD have been informative, particularly in conjunction with functional studies in model organisms. Although few CHD have known genetic etiologies, monoallelic microdeletion of chromosome 22q11 is commonly associated with a variety of cardiac neural crest anomalies (91). The 22q11 deletion, typically 3 million base pairs (Mb) in size, is the most common human gene deletion and is the second most common known genetic cause of CHD, after Trisomy 21. Patients with this deletion often have other neural crest-derived defects, including cleft palate and other typical facial features, thymic hypoplasia, and hypoparathyroidism. The phenotypic spectrum is often referred to as DiGeorge, velocardiofacial, or Shprintzen syndrome, all of which are associated with the same 22q11 deletion (92–94). Thus it is likely that one or more genes involved in neural crest development lie in the 22q11 locus.

Sequencing of the commonly deleted 22q11 region revealed nearly 30 genes, of which several are expressed in developing neural crest cells (95). However, the genetic complexity and heterogeneity of this syndrome has precluded definitive determination of the critical gene(s) in this region. Attempts to model this deletion in a mouse model have met with limited success. A large heterozygous deletion of the syntenic region of 22q11 in mice (chromosome 16) encompassing 15 genes resulted in a partial penetrance of fourth aortic arch anomalies, including interruption of the aortic arch and aberrant right subclavian artery (96). Unfortunately, none of the other cardiac or extracardiac manifestations of 22q11 deletion in humans were observed in these mice with significant frequency.

Within the commonly deleted region, *UFD1, TBX1,* and *HIRA* are expressed in neural crest-derived cells and may play some role in the 22q11 deletion phenotype. Ufd1, involved in ubiquitin-dependent degradation of short-lived cellular proteins in yeast (97, 98), is down-regulated in *dHAND*-null mice and was specifically deleted, along with a neighboring cell cycle regulator, *CDC45*, in a patient with the typical features of 22q11 deletion (99). However, heterozygous mutation of *ufd1* alone does not cause any apparent defects in mice whereas homozygosity is embryonic lethal (96). HIRA, a transcriptional co-repressor in yeast, physically interacts with Pax3 and may thus play a role in Pax3 regulation of the cardiac neural crest (100, 101). However, similar to *ufd1*, mice heterozygous for mutation in HIRA are normal and homozygous deletions are embryonic lethal. Finally, TBX1, a transcription factor expressed in the pharyngeal arches, was specifically deleted along with COMT (catechol-*O*-methyltransferase), in a patient with DiGeorge-like features (102). However, heterozygosity of Tbx1 in mice does not result in any aortic arch deformity. Thus it appears that heterozygosity of a single gene in the 22q11 locus may not be sufficient for the aortic arch phenotype, although heterozygosity of a dominant gene may be necessary.

Genetic linkage analysis of several families with atrial septal defects (ASD) and conduction defects revealed a previously unrecognized role for the homeodomain-containing transcription factor, NKX2.5, in later phases of cardiac development and function. Numerous point mutations, clustered in the homeodomain region, have been identified in patients with ASD, providing a genetic etiology for a subset of one of the most common CHD (103). Sporadic mutations of *NKX2.5* have also been found in patients with TOF and tricuspid valve anomalies (104), suggesting that *NKX2.5* plays multiple roles during cardiogenesis that may be impacted upon by genetic background and/or environmental effects.

Holt-Oram syndrome, an autosomal dominant disease characterized by cardiac (atrial and ventricular septal defects) and limb anomalies, is caused by mutations in *TBX5* (105, 106). The heart and limbs are derived from lateral mesoderm precursors that may share common developmental regulatory pathways. Interestingly, mutations in distinct regions of TBX5 can result in families that have predominance of either cardiac or limb defects. This observation suggests that TBX5 may be regulating different genetic pathways in specific tissues based on interactions with unique cofactors (107). In fact, zebrafish mutations in the *dHAND* gene result in the absence of a ventricular chamber, fin abnormalities, and a failure of Tbx5 expression (54), raising the possibility that dHAND functions upstream of a Tbx5-dependent pathway regulating limb and heart development. Accordingly, dHAND is required for expression of sonic hedgehog in the zone of polarizing activity of the developing limb and misexpression of dHAND is sufficient to induce ectopic Shh expression and mirror image duplications of posterior skeletal elements in limbs of mice and chicks (108, 109).

Alagille syndrome, another autosomal dominant disorder characterized by biliary atresia and cardiac defects, typically pulmonary artery stenosis and TOF, is caused by mutations in *JAGGED-1*, a ligand for the Notch receptor (110, 111). Isolated pulmonary stenosis or TOF has also been associated with *JAGGED-1* mutations (112). The Notch signaling pathway is involved in cell fate and differentiation decisions throughout the embryo but has only recently been implicated in cardiovascular development. How Notch-related pathways function to establish the vascular connections to the heart remains to be determined.

SUMMARY

Complementary studies utilizing model organisms and those primarily involving human genetics have revealed some of the complex molecular steps necessary for formation of the heart. The preliminary outlines of the mechanisms underlying cardiogenesis will provide a foundation for further dissection of the molecular pathways governing development of individual regions of the heart. This effort should be greatly facilitated by emerging technologies that capitalize on high throughput strategies in the area of genomics and proteomics. Complete sequencing of the human genome will allow for identification of single nucleotide differences in critical genes in those with or without heart disease. The combination of such approaches may ultimately identify those individuals or their progeny who have increased genetic risk for heart disease.

Discovery of the causes of complex genetic traits, such as CHD, has been difficult. However, the observation that secondary factors, be they genetic or environmental, contribute to CHD provides hope for the treatment and prevention of CHD. While prospects for gene therapy remains in the distant future, knowledge of the genetic pathways regulating cardiogenesis should lead to some of the secondary factors that may be modulated during the period of embryonic heart development. Given the rapid pace of discovery and the ever-increasing tools available to scientists and clinicians, the hope of translating genetic information regarding heart formation into tangible benefits for families with CHD has never been brighter.

Visit the Annual Reviews home page at www.AnnualReviews.org

LITERATURE CITED

1. Harvey RP. 1996. NK-2 homeobox genes and heart development. *Dev. Biol.* 178:203–16

2. Srivastava D, Olson EN. 2000. A genetic blueprint for cardiac development. *Nature* 407:221–26

3. Fishman MC, Olson EN. 1997. Parsing the heart: genetic modules for organ assembly. *Cell.* 91(2):153–56

4. Fishman MC, Chien KR. 1997. Fashioning the vertebrate heart: earliest embryonic decisions. *Development* 124:2099–117

5. Harvey R, Rosenthal N. 1999. *Heart Development*. San Diego: Academic. 530 pp.
6. Schulthesis TM, Xydas S, Lassar AB. 1995. Induction of avian cardiac myogenesis by anterior endoderm. *Development* 121:4203–14
7. DeHaan RL. 1965. Morphogenesis of the vertebrate heart. In *Organogenesis*, ed. RL DeHaan, H Ursprung, pp. 377–420. New York: Holt, Reinhart & Winston
8. Frasch M. 1995. Induction of visceral and cardiac mesoderm by ectodermal Dpp in the early Drosophila embryo. *Nature* 374(6521):464–67
9. Bodmer R. 1993. The gene *tinman* is required for specification of the heart and visceral muscles in Drosophila. *Development* 118:719–29
10. Azpiazu N, Frasch M. 1993. *Tinman* and *bagpipe*: two homeo box genes that determine cell fates in the dorsal mesoderm of Drosophila. *Genes Dev.* 7:1325–40
11. Gajewski K, Kim Y, Lee YM, Olson EN, Schulz RA. 1997. D-mef2 is a target for *Tinman* activation during Drosophila heart development. *EMBO J.* 16:515–22
12. Gajewski K, Fossett N, Molkentin JD, Schultz RA. 1999. The zinc finger proteins Pannier and GATA4 function as cardiogenic factors in Drosophila. *Development* 126:5679–88
13. Durocher D, Charron F, Warren R, Schwartz RJ, Nemer M. 1997. The cardiac transcription factors Nkx2-5 and GATA-4 are mutual cofactors. *EMBO J.* 16:5687–96
14. Lyons I, Parsons LM, Hartley L. 1995. Myogenic and morphogenetic defects in the heart tubes of murine embryos lacking the homeobox gene Nkx2-5. *Genes Dev.* 9:1654–66
15. Tanaka M, Chen Z, Bartunkova S, Yamasaki N, Izumo S. 1999. The cardiac homeobox gene Csx/Nkx2.5 lies genetically upstream of multiple genes essential for heart development. *Development* 126(6):1269–80
16. Fu Y, Yan W, Mohun TJ, Evans SM. 1998. Vertebrate tinman homologues XNkx2-3 and XNkx2-5 are required for heart formation in a functionally redundant manner. *Development* 125:4439–49
17. Grow MW, Kreig PA. 1998. Tinman function is essential for vertebrate heart development: elimination of cardiac differentiation by dominant inhibitory mutants of the tinman-related genes, XNkx2-3 and XNkx2-5. *Dev. Biol.* 204:187–96
18. Molkentin J, Lin Q, Duncan SA, Olson EN. 1997. Requirement of the GATA4 transcription factor for heart tube formation and ventral morphogenesis. *Genes Dev.* 11:1061–72
19. Kuo CT, Morrisey EE, Anandappa R, Sigrist K, Lu MM, et al. 1997. GATA4 transcription factor is required for ventral morphogenesis and heart tube formation. *Genes Dev.* 11:1048–60
20. Reiter JF, Alexander J, Rodaway A, Yelon D, Patient R, et al. 1999. Gata5 is required for the development of the heart and endoderm in zebrafish. *Genes Dev.* 13:2983–95
21. Kupperman E, An S, Osborne N, Waldron S, Stainier DY. 2000. A sphingosine-1–phosphate receptor regulates cell migration during vertebrate heart development. *Nature* 406(6792):192–95
22. Christoffels VM, Habets PEMH, Franco D, Campione M, de Jong F, et al. 2000. Chamber formation and morphogenesis in the developing mammalian heart. *Dev. Biol.* 223:266–78
23. Thomas T, Yamagishi H, Overbeek PA, Olson EN, Srivastava D. 1998. The bHLH factors, dHAND and eHAND, specify pulmonary and systemic cardiac ventricles independent of left-right sidedness. *Dev. Biol.* 196(2):228–36
24. Capdevila J, Vogan KJ, Tabin CJ, Belmonte JC. 2000. Mechanisms of left-right determination in vertebrates. *Cell* 101:9–21
25. Levin M, Johnson RL, Stern CD, Kuehn M, Tabin CJ. 1995. A molecular pathway

determining left-right asymmetry in chick embryogenesis. *Cell* 82:803–14

26. Yokouchi Y, Vogan KJ, Pearse RV II, Tabin CJ. 1999. Antagonistic signaling by Caronte, a novel Cerberus-related gene, establishes left-right asymmetric gene expression. *Cell* 98:573–83

27. Rodriguez-Esteban C, Capdevila J, Economides AN, Pascual J, Ortiz A, Izpisúa-Belmonte JC. 1999. The novel Cer-like protein Caronte mediates the establishment of embryonic left-right asymmetry. *Nature* 401:243–51

28. Isaac A, Sargant MG, Cooke J. 1997. Control of vertebrate left-right asymmetry by a snail-related zinc finger gene. *Science* 275:1301–4

29. Piedra ME, Icardo JM, Albajar M, Rodriguez-Rey JC, Ros MA. 1998. Pitx2 participates in the late phase of the pathway controlling left-right asymmetry. *Cell* 94(3):319–24

30. Logan M, Pagan-Westphal SM, Smith DM, Paganessi L, Tabin CJ. 1998. The transcription factor Pitx2 mediates site-specific morphogenesis in response to left-right asymmetric signals. *Cell* 94:307–17

31. Ryan AK, Blumberg B, Rodriguez-Esteban C, Yonei-Tamura S, Tamura K, et al. 1998. Pitx2 determines left-right asymmetry of internal organs in vertebrates. *Nature* 394:545–51

32. Supp DM, Witte DP, Potter SS, Brueckner M. 1997. Mutation of an axonemal dyenin in the left-right asymmetry mouse mutant inversus viscerum. *Nature* 389:963–99

33. Mochizuki T, Saijoh Y, Tsuchiya K, Shirayoshi Y, Takai S, et al. 1998. Cloning of *inv*, a gene that controls left/right asymmetry and kidney development. *Nature* 395:177–81

34. Morgan D, Turnpenny L, Goodship J, Dai W, Majumder K, et al. 1998. *Inversin*, a novel gene in the vertebrate left-right axis pathway, is partially deleted in the *inv* mouse. *Nat. Genet.* 20:149–56

35. Campione M, Steinbeisser H, Schweickert A, Deissler K, van Bebber F, et al. 1999. The homeobox gene Pitx2: mediator of asymmetric left-right signaling in vertebrate heart and gut looping. *Development* 126:1225–34

36. Yoshioka H, Meno C, Koshiba K, Sugihara M, Itoh H, et al. 1998. Pitx2, a bicoid-type homeobox gene, is involved in a left-signaling pathway in determination of left-right asymmetry. *Cell* 94:299–305

37. Lin CR, Kioussi C, OConnell S, Briata P, Szeto D, et al. 1999. Pitx2 regulates lung asymmetry, cardiac positioning and pituitary and tooth morphogenesis. *Nature* 401:279–82

38. Lu MF, Pressman C, Dyer R, Johnson RL, Martin, JF. 1999. Function of Rieger syndrome gene in left-right asymmetry and craniofacial development. *Nature* 401:276–78

39. Meyers EN, Martin GR. 1999. Differences in left-right axis pathways in mouse and chick: functions of FGF8 and SHH. *Science* 285:403–6

40. Ajzelius BA. 1976. A human syndrome caused by immotile cilia. *Science* 193:317–19

41. Nonaka S, Tanaka Y, Okada Y, Takeda S, Harada A, et al. 1998. Randomization of left-right asymmetry due to loss of nodal cilia generating leftward flow of extraembryonic fluid in mice lacking KIF3B motor protein. *Cell* 95(6):829–37

42. Mjaatvedt CH, Yamamura H, Wessels A, Ramsdell A, Turner D, Markwald RR. 1999. Mechanisms of segmentation, septation, and remodeling of the tubular heart: endocardial cushion fate and cardiac looping. In *Heart Development*, ed. RP Harvey, N Rosenthal. San Diego: Academic. 530 pp.

43. Oh SP, Li E. 1997. The signaling pathway mediated by the type IIB activin receptor controls axial patterning and lateral asymmetry in the mouse. *Genes Dev.* 11:1812–26

44. Kosaki R, Gebbia M, Kosaki K, Lewin

M, Bowers P, et al. 1999. Left-right
axis malformations associated with mutations in ACVR2B, the gene for human activin receptor type IIB. *Am. J. Med. Genet.*
82(1):70–76

45. Gebbia M, Ferrero GB, Pilia G, Bassi MT,
Aylsworth A, et al. 1997. X-linked situs
inversus and situs ambiguous result from
mutations in the zinc-finger transcription
factor ZIC3. *Nat. Genet.* 17:305–8

46. Schwartz RJ, Olson EN. 1999. Building the
heart piece by piece: modularity of *cis*-
elements regulating Nkx2.5 transcription.
Development 126:4187–92

47. Srivastava D, Cserjesi P, Olson EN. 1995.
A new subclass of bHLH proteins required for cardiac morphogenesis. *Science*
270:1995–99

48. Srivastava D. 1999. HAND proteins:
molecular mediators of cardiac development and congenital heart disease. *Trends
Cardiovasc. Med.* 9(1–2):11–18

49. Srivastava D, Thomas T, Lin Q, Kirby
ML, Brown D, Olson EN. 1997. Regulation of cardiac mesodermal and neural
crest development by the bHLH transcription factor, dHAND. *Nat. Genet.* 16:154–
60

50. Firulli AB, McFadden DG, Lin Q, Srivastava D, Olson EN. 1998. Heart and extraembryonic mesodermal defects in mouse
embryos lacking the bHLH transcription
factor Hand1. *Nat. Genet.* 18(3):266–
70

51. Riley P, Anson-Cartwright L, Cross JC.
1998. The Hand1 bHLH transcription factor is essential for placentation and cardiac
morphogenesis. *Nat. Genet.* 18:271–75

52. Biben C, Harvey RP. 1997. Homeodomain factor Nkx2-5 controls left/right
asymmetric expression of bHLH gene
eHand during murine heart development.
Genes Dev. 11:1357–69

53. Angelo S, Lohr J, Lee KH, Ticho BS,
Breitbart RE, Hill S, et al. 2000. Con-
servation of sequence and expression of
Xenopus and Zebrafish dHAND during

cardiac, branchial arch and lateral mesoderm development. *Mech. Dev.* 95:231–37

54. Yelon D, Ticho B, Halpern ME, Ruvin-
sky I, Ho RK, et al. 2000. Parallel roles
for the bHLH transcription factor HAND2
in xebrafish and pectoral fin development.
Development 127:2573–82

55. Bruneau BG, Bao ZZ, Tanaka M, Schott
JJ, Izumo S, et al. 2000. Cardiac expression of the ventricle-specific homeobox gene Irx4 is modulated by Nkx2-5 and
dHand. *Dev. Biol.* 217:266–77

56. Bao Z, Bruneau BG, Seidman JG, Seidman CE, Cepko CL. 1999. Regulation
of chamber-specific gene expression in
the developing heart by Irx4. *Science*
283:1161–64

57. Lin Q, Schwarz J, Bucana C, Olson EN.
1997. Control of mouse cardiac morphogenesis and myogenesis by transcription
factor MEF2C. *Science* 276:1404–7

58. Pereira FA, Qui Y, Zhou G, Tsai M,
Tsai S. 1999. The orphan nuclear receptor COUP TFII is required for angiogenesis and heart development. *Genes Dev.*
13:1037–49

59. Dyson E, Sucov HM, Kubalak SW,
Schmid-Schonbein GW, DeLano FA,
et al. 1995. Atrial-like phenotype is associated with embryonic ventricular failure
in retinoid X receptor alpha -/- mice. *Proc.
Natl. Acad. Sci. USA* 92:7386–90

60. Nakagawa O, Nakagawa M, Richardson JA, Olson EN, Srivastava D. 1999.
HRT1, HRT2, and HRT3: a new subclass
of bHLH transcription factors marking specific cardiac, somitic, and pharyngeal arch
segments. *Dev. Biol.* 216(1):72–84

61. Rossant J. 1996. Mouse mutants and cardiac development: new molecular insights
into cardiogenesis. *Circ. Res.* 78(3):349–
53

62. Sucov HM, Dyson E, Gumeringer CL,
Price J, Chien KR, et al. 1994. RXRα mutant mice establish a genetic basis for vitamin A signaling in heart morphogenesis.
Genes Dev. 8:1007–18

63. Charron J, Malynn BA, Fisher P, Stewart V, Jeannotte L, et al. 1992. Embryonic lethality in mice homozygous for a targeted disruption of the N-myc gene. *Genes Dev.* 6:2248–57

64. Chen Z, Friedrich GA, Soriano P. 1994. Transcriptional enhancer factor 1 disruption by a retroviral gene trap leads to heart defects and embryonic lethality in mice. *Genes Dev.* 8:2293–301

65. Brannan CI, Perkins AS, Vogel KS, Ratner N, Nordlund ML, et al. 1994. Targeted disruption of the neurofibromatosis type-1 gene leads to developmental abnormalities in heart and various neural crest-derived tissues. *Genes Dev.* 8:1019–29

66. Kwee L, Baldwin HS, Shen HM, Stewart CL, Buck C, et al. 1995. Defective development of the embryonic and extraembryonic circulatory systems in vascular cell adhesion molecule (VCAM1) deficient mice. *Development* 121:489–503

67. Kreidberg JA, Sariola H, Loring JM, Maeda M, et al. 1993. WT-1 is required for early kidney development. *Cell* 74:679–91

68. Meyer D, Birchmeier C. 1995. Multiple essential functions of neuregulin in development. *Nature* 378:386–90

69. Lee KF, Simon H, Chen H, Bates B, Hung MC, Hauser C. 1995. Requirement for neuregulin receptor erbB2 in neural and cardiac development. *Nature* 378:394–98

70. Gassmann M, Casagranda F, Orioli D, Simon H, Lai C, et al. 1995. Aberrant neural and cardiac development in mice lacking the ErbB4 neuregulin receptor. *Nature* 378:390–94

71. Carmeliet P, Ferreira V, Breier G, Pollefeyt S, Kieckens L, et al. 1996. Abnormal blood vessel development and lethality in embryos lacking a single VEGF allele. *Nature* 380:435–39

72. Suri C, Jones PF, Patan S, Bartunkova S, Maisonpierre PC, et al. 1996. Requisite role of angiopoietin-1, a ligand for the TIE2 receptor, during embryonic angiogenesis. *Cell* 87:1171–80

73. Parker L, Stainier DY. 1999. Cell-autonomous and non-autonomous requirements for the zebrafish gene cloche in hematopoiesis. *Development* 126(12): 2643–51

74. Brown CB, Boyer AS, Runyan RB, Barnett JV. 1999. Requirement of type III TGF beta receptor for endocardial cell transformation in the heart. *Science* 283:2080–82

75. Ranger AM, Grusby MJ, Hodge MR, Gravallese EM, de la Brousse FC, et al. 1998. The transcription factor NF-ATc is essential for cardiac valve formation. *Nature* 392:186–90

76. De la Pompa JL, Timmerman LA, Takimoto H, Yoshida H, Elia AJ, et al. 1998. Role of the NF-ATc transcription factor in morphogenesis of cardiac valves and septum. *Nature* 392:182–86

77. Galvin KM, Donovan MJ, Lynch CA, Meyer RI, Paul RJ, et al. 2000. A role for smad6 in development and homeostasis of the cardiovascular system. *Nat. Genet.* 24:171–74

78. Sadler TW. 2000. Cardiovascular system. In *Langman's Medical Embryology*, ed. TW Sadler, pp. 208–59. *Baltimore*, MD: Williams & Wilkins

79. Kirby ML, Waldo KL. 1990. Role of neural crest in congenital heart disease. *Circulation* 82:332–40

80. Kirby ML, Waldo KL. 1995. Neural crest and cardiovascular patterning. *Circ. Res.* 77:211–15

81. Kurihara Y, Kurihara H, Oda H, Maemura K, Nagai R, et al. 1995. Aortic arch malformations and ventricular septal defect in mice deficient in endothelin-1. *J. Clin. Invest.* 96:293–300

82. Clouthier DE, Hosoda K, Richardson JA, Williams SC, Yanagisawa H, et al. 1998. Cranial and cardiac neural crest defects in endothelin-A receptor-deficient mice. *Development* 125:813–24

83. Thomas T, Kurihara H, Yamagishi H, Kurihara Y, Yazaki Y, et al. 1998. A signaling cascade involving endothelin-1, dHAND

and Msx1 regulates development of neural crest-derived branchial arch mesenchyme. *Development* 125:3005–14

84. Yamagishi H, Olson EN, Srivastava D. 2000. The bHLH transcription factor, dHAND, is required for vascular development. *J. Clin. Invest.* 105:261–70

85. Kawasaki T, Kitsukawa T, Bekku Y, Matsuda Y, Sanbo M, et al. 1999. A requirement for neuropilin-1 in embryonic vessel formation. *Development* 126:4854–902

86. Iida K, Koseki H, Kakinuma H, Kato N, Mizutani-Koseki Y, et al. 1997. Essential roles of the winged helix transcription factor MFH-1 in aortic arch patterning and skeletogenesis. *Development* 124:4627–38

87. Li J, Liu KC, Jin F, Lu MM, Epstein JA. 1999. Transgenic rescue of congenital heart disease and spina bifida in Splotch mice. *Development* 126:2495–503

88. Gruber PJ, Kubalak SW, Pexieder T, Sucov HM, Evans RM, et al. 1996 RXRα deficiency confers genetic susceptibility for aortic sac, conotruncal, atrioventricular cushion, and ventricular muscle defects in mice. *J. Clin. Invest.* 98:1332–43

89. Zhong TP, Rosenberg M, Mohideen MA, Weinstein B, Fishman MC. 2000. Gridlock, an HLH gene required for assembly of the aorta in zebrafish. *Science* 287:1820–24

90. Satoda M, Zhao F, Diaz GA, Burn J, Goodship J, et al. 2000. Mutations in TFAP2B cause Char syndrome, a familial form of patent ductus arteriosus. *Nat. Genet.* 25:42–46

91. Goldmuntz E, Clark BJ, Mitchell LE, Jawad AF, Cuneo BF, et al. 1998. Frequency of 22q11 deletions in patients with conotruncal defects. *J. Am. Coll. Cardiol.* 32(2):492–98

92. Wilson DI, Burn J, Scambler P, Goodship J. 1993. DiGeorge syndrome: part of CATCH 22. *J. Med. Genet.* 30:852–56

93. Driscoll DA, Salvin J, Sellinger B. 1993. Prevalence of 22q11 microdeletions in DiGeorge and velocardiofacial syndromes:

implications for genetic counseling and prenatal diagnosis. *J. Med. Genet.* 30:813–56

94. Burn J, Takao A, Wilson D. 1993. Conotruncal anomaly face syndrome is associated with a deletion within chromosome 22q11. *J. Med. Genet.* 30:822–24

95. Emanuel BS, Budarf ML, Scambler PJ. 1998. The genetic basis of conotruncal cardiac defects: the chromosome 22q11.2 deletion. In *Heart Development*, ed. RP Harvey, N Rosenthal, pp. 463–78. New York: Academic

96. Lindsay EA, Botta A, Jurecic V, Carattini-Rivera S, Cheah YC, et al. 1999. Congenital heart disease in mice deficient for the DiGeorge syndrome region. *Nature* 401:379–83

97. Johnson ES, Ma PC, Ota IM, Varshavsky A. 1995. A proteolytic pathway that recognizes ubiquitin as a degradation signal. *J. Biol. Chem.* 270:17442–56

98. Pizzuti A, Novelli G, Ratti A, Amati F, Mari A, et al. 1997. UFD1L, a developmentally expressed ubiquitination gene, is deleted in CATCH 22 syndrome. *Hum. Mol. Genet.* 6:259–65

99. Yamagishi H, Garg V, Matsuoka R, Thomas T, Srivastava D. 1999. A molecular pathway revealing a genetic basis for human cardiac and craniofacial defects. *Science* 283(5405):1158–61

100. Magnaghi P, Roberts C, Lorain S, Lipinski M, Scambler P J. 1998. HIRA, a mammalian homologue of *Saccharomyces cerevisiae* transcriptional co-repressors, interacts with Pax3. *Nat. Genet.* 20:74–77

101. Farrell MJ, Stadt H, Wallis KT, Scambler P, Hixon RL, et al. 1999. HIRA, a DiGeorge syndrome candidate gene, is required for cardiac outflow tract septation. *Circ. Res.* 84(2):127–35

102. McQuade L, Christodoulou J, Budarf M, Sachdev R, Wilson M, et al. 1999. Patient with a 22q11.2 deletion with no overlap of the minimal DiGeorge syndrome

critical region (MDGCR). *Am. J. Med. Genet.* 86(1):27–33

103. Schott J-J, Benson DW, Basson CT, Pease W, Silberbach GM, et al. 1998. Congenital heart disease caused by mutations in the transcription factor NKX2-5. *Science.* 281:108–11

104. Benson DW, Silberbach GM, Kavanaugh-McHugh A, Cottrill C, Zhang Y, et al. 1999. Mutations in the cardiac transcription factor NKX2.5 affect diverse cardiac developmental pathways. *J. Clin. Invest.* 104:1567–73

105. Basson CT, Bachinsky DR, Lin RC, Levi T, Elkins JA, et al. 1997. Mutations in human TBX5 cause limb and cardiac malformation in Holt-Oram syndrome. *Nat. Genet.* 15:30–35

106. Li QY, Newbury-Ecob RA, Terrett JA, Wilson DI, Curtis AR, et al. 1997. Holt-Oram syndrome is caused by mutations in TBX5, a member of the Brachyury (T) gene family. *Nat. Genet.* 15:21–29

107. Basson CT, Huang T, Lin RC, Bachinsky DR, Weremowicz S, et al. 1999. Different TBX5 interactions in heart and limb defined by Holt-Oram syndrome mutations. *Proc. Natl. Acad. Sci. USA* 96:2919–24

108. Fernandez-Teran M, Piedra MD, Kathiriya I, Srivastava D, Rodriguez-Rey JC, Ros MA. 2000. Role of dHAND in anterior-posterior polarity during limb development: implications for the Sonic hedgehog pathway. *Development* 127:2133–42

109. Charite J, McFadden DG, Olson EN. 2000. The bHLH transcription factor dHAND controls Sonic hedgehog expression and establishment of the zone of polarizing activity during limb development. *Development* 127(11):2461–70

110. Li L, Krantz ID, Deng Y, Genin A, Banta AB, et al. 1997. Alagille syndrome is caused by mutations in human Jagged1, which encodes a ligand for Notch1. *Nat. Genet.* 16:243–51

111. Oda T, Elkahloun AG, Pike BL. 1997. Mutations in the human Jagged1 gene are responsible for Alagille syndrome. *Nat. Genet.* 16:235–42

112. Krantz ID, Colliton RP, Genin A, Rand EB, Li L, et al. 1999. Jagged1 mutations in patients ascertained with isolated congenital heart defects. *Am. J. Hum. Genet.* 84:56–60

Annu. Rev. Physiol. 2001. 63:471–94

Molecular Regulation
of Lung Development

Wellington V Cardoso

Pulmonary Center, Boston University School of Medicine, Boston,
Massachusetts 02118; e-mail: wcardoso@bupula.bu.edu

Key Words   organogenesis, branching morphogenesis, fibroblast growth factors, pattern formation, retinoids

■ **Abstract**   There is increasing evidence suggesting that formation of the tracheo-bronchial tree and alveoli results from heterogeneity of the epithelial-mesenchymal interactions along the developing respiratory tract. Recent genetic data support this idea and show that this heterogeneity is likely the result of activation of distinct networks of signaling molecules along the proximal-distal axis. Among these signals, fibroblast growth factors, retinoids, Sonic hedgehog, and transforming growth factors appear to play prominent roles. We discuss how these and other pattern regulators may be involved in initiation, branching, and differentiation of the respiratory system.

INTRODUCTION

The mammalian lung evolved as a system of branched conduits for air and blood coupled to a vast network of honeycomb-like alveolar structures designed for gas exchange. In the developing respiratory system, while airway branching is eminently a prenatal event, formation of the alveoli spans pre- and postnatal life, and in many species such as the rat and mouse occurs only postnatally (93, 109).

Primordial lung buds originate as outpouchings of the primitive foregut endoderm, and the airway tree is generated by reiterated budding and branching of these tubules. Blood vessels are formed in situ from mesodermal cells around the tips of the branching tubules (vasculogenesis), or migrate to the lung by sprouting from the pulmonary artery (angiogenesis). As the lung develops, vascular and airway components intermingle at the distal end of this tree to form the future alveolar-capillary barrier. The complex branching pattern of the airways ensures that during postnatal life air is properly cleared of particulates, humidified, and distributed evenly to all alveolar units.

The questions of how lung morphogenesis occurs and which molecules direct lung development have attracted the interest of developmental biologists for

0066-4278/01/0315-0471$14.00   **471** decades and recently have been much explored. We review these aspects from the events that precede lung formation to late developmental stages. Because the vast majority of the genetic studies have been performed in the mouse, this species is used as the model system throughout most of the text.

BEFORE LUNG MORPHOGENESIS

Formation of the Foregut

In the mouse, gut morphogenesis is initiated around gestational day 7.5, when a single sheet of endodermal cells located in the external surface of the embryo undergoes anterior-posterior (A-P) specification and expresses specific A-P marker genes (reviewed in 118). Fate map analysis has shown that anterior endodermal cells generate the ventral foregut that will subsequently form lungs, liver, ventral pancreas, and stomach (52). From day 7.5–8.5, complex morphogenetic movements of the endodermal layer and looping of the embryo lead to invagination and closure of this layer to form the primitive gut tube. Endodermal cells form the epithelial lining of the tube. Lateral plate mesodermal cells migrate and condense around the endoderm to form the mesenchyme (splanchnic mesoderm) and the serosa (somatic mesoderm) of the gut. Mesothelial cells (serosa) surrounding the gut in contact with the coelomic cavity form pleural, pericardial, and peritoneal membranes.

Among the earliest endodermal signals essential for gut morphogenesis are the GATA (zinc finger proteins that recognize GATA DNA sequences) and hepatocyte nuclear factors (HNF) transcription factors. Targeted deletion of *GATA-4* in mice is lethal by day 7–9.5, resulting in impaired folding of the embryo and disruption of endoderm morphogenesis (50). $GATA-6^{-/-}$ mice die even earlier (at day 6.5–7.5) from disruption of endodermal differentiation, with down-regulation of *GATA-4* and *HNF-4* (75). Interestingly, once the lung forms, *GATA-6* but not *GATA-4* continues to be expressed in the lung epithelium. There is genetic evidence suggesting that *GATA-6* may be required for activation of the lung developmental program in the foregut endoderm (75).

Expression of *HNF3α* and *β* is also found in the foregut endoderm and is maintained in the lung epithelium throughout embryonic to adult life (16, 74). *HNF3β* null mutant mice die by day 7–9.5, with multiple defects that include failure of the foregut endoderm to invaginate and form a closed tube. This results in severe disruption of gut morphogenesis (1, 119). In these mutants, preserved expression of *HNF3β* suggests that endodermal differentiation has been initiated. However, the increasing number of dying cells in embryos that survive until day 9.5 suggests that HNF3β is a survival factor for the endoderm (119). Several studies implicate HNF3β in lung differentiation and regulation of surfactant protein gene expression (reviewed in 89).

Formation of Foregut Derivatives: The Role of Local and Diffusible Signals

Thyroid and liver buds are first seen at day 8.5; lung and pancreatic buds form one day later. Several transcription factors are locally expressed in overlapping domains along the endoderm in a pattern that suggests that they may be responsible for induction of organ-specific developmental programs. For example, *Nkx 2.1* (or thyroid transcription factor 1, *TTF-1*) is found in the anterior endoderm near the prospective sites of thyroid and lung bud formation (48), whereas *Pdx-1* is expressed at a more posterior location, in the area of the prospective pancreatic buds (83). Nevertheless, genetic studies have shown that these factors individually are not necessarily critical for initiation of organ-specific morphogenesis. *Nkx 2.1*$^{-/-}$ mice do not have thyroid; however, they form lungs that are highly abnormal (48, 72). Although pancreas development is dramatically disrupted in *Pdx-1*$^{-/-}$ mice, the initial steps of pancreas morphogenesis and expression of glucagon and insulin do take place (83).

While expressing their own repertoire of pattern regulators, endodermal cells are also exposed to signals that diffuse from developing structures that neighbor the gut. For example, posterior endoderm is exposed to retinoic acid (RA) from the node and to fibroblast growth factor (FGF)-4 from the posterior mesoderm (118). Importantly, FGFs secreted from the adjacent cardiac mesoderm activate signaling by FGFR-1 and -4 in the ventral foregut endoderm to induce the initial steps of hepatogenesis and liver-specific gene expression (43). During pancreatic development, the day 7.5 endoderm receives patterning signals from the neighboring notochord. The notochord secretes activin-βB and FGF-2, which in turn inhibit Sonic hedgehog (Shh) signaling in the pre-pancreatic dorsal endoderm, and initiate a program of pancreatic gene expression (35). Surgical deletion of the notochord in chicks at a stage when this structure still touches the foregut endoderm prevents expression of pancreatic genes (47). Whether notochord deletion also affects lung bud morphogenesis has not been reported. Interestingly, delayed separation of the notochord from the gut endoderm has been associated with disruption of tracheal development leading to tracheoesophageal fistula and tracheal atresia in rats (70).

Prespecification of Patterns in Lung Morphogenesis

The genetic programs that determine axis and branching patterns are defined at an early developmental stage. For example, the left-right (L-R) axis of the lung appears to be specified well before there is any sign of lung. L-R differences in pattern are first seen when secondary buds form; these differences continue to develop as airways undergo branching and are assembled into lobes by the visceral pleura (lobation), which result in more lobes in the right lung (mouse, four; human, three) than in the left (mouse, one; human, two).

The basis for L-R asymmetry in viscera lies in genes such as *Lefty-1* and *-2*, *nodal*, and *Pitx-2*, whose inactivation in mice reveals striking lung phenotypes (67). *Lefty-1*$^{-/-}$ mice show left pulmonary isomerism, a condition where single-lobed lungs are found bilaterally (67). In these mice, the lobation pattern typically seen on the right side (four lobes) is substituted for left-side pattern (one lobe). Interestingly, *Lefty-1, -2*, and *nodal* are only transiently expressed in the embryo at around day 8–8.5, on the left side of the prospective floor plate and lateral plate mesoderm, and are no longer detected at later stages (67 and references therein). Thus specification of the branching pattern and of lobation of the lung is linked to the general body plan and has started at least 24–36 h prior to the appearance of the primordial lung bud (day 9.5).

L-R-determining genes are targets of RA. Expression of *Lefty, nodal*, and *Pitx* genes occurs at a stage when RA synthesis and utilization are highly active in the foregut and its surroundings (discussed further below). Experiments where RA signaling is antagonized in whole-embryo cultures show that RA is necessary for expression of genes such as *Lefty-1* and its targets (14). Although no L-R asymmetry in retinoid receptor distribution has been reported in the lung (21, 22), compound *RAR α/β2* knockout mice do not have the left lung (65). The requirement of RA signaling activation for expression of L-R genes, or for a gene that is asymmetrically distributed in the embryo prior to lung development, may be one of the reasons for this defect.

LUNG BUD INITIATION

The molecular mechanisms responsible for primary lung bud induction are little understood. Lung buds originate from the ventral foregut endoderm, which fuse in the midline as they grow to form the lung and the tracheal primordia (104). This process is fully blocked in mice that lack both *Gli2 and Gli3* zinc-finger transcription factors. Gli 1, 2, and 3 (vertebrate homologs of the *Drosophila* gene *cubitus interruptus*) are expressed in the foregut mesoderm and have been identified as downstream components of the Shh signaling cascade (38). *Gli2*$^{-/-}$; *Gli3*$^{-/-}$ embryos have multiple defects in endodermal derivatives, including agenesis of lung and trachea, and do not survive beyond day 10.5 (77). However, it is unclear how the effects of mesenchymal Gli expression are transduced to the foregut endoderm at the sites of lung bud initiation. In this process, Gli 2 and 3 seem to act independently of Shh because lung agenesis is not a feature of Shh knock-out mice (88). Glis may ultimately be necessary to maintain expression of genes that promote endodermal survival such as hepatocyte nuclear factor, *HNF3β* (1, 119). *Gli2*$^{-/-}$; *Gli3*$^{-/-}$ mice have decreased levels of *HNF3β* compared with that of wild-type animals (77).

Results from genetically altered mice and vitamin A-deprived rats have implicated signaling by FGF and RA in lung bud initiation. These regulators are discussed in greater detail in subsequent sections.

Foregut cells likely start to acquire specialized lung features before lung bud formation is initiated. Perhaps the first sign of lung differentiation is expression of the lung-specific surfactant protein gene *SP-C*. Expression of *SP-C* mRNA has been reported at the tips of epithelial tubules from embryonic day 11 and localizes to type II alveolar cells in the adult lung (120). However, studies in a transgenic mouse bearing a reporter *CAT* (chloramphenicol acetyl transferase) gene driven by 3.7-kb human *SP-C* promoter suggest that endogenous *SP-C* might start at least one day earlier and become restricted to the tips of secondary buds at day 11 (120). Other surfactant protein genes, *SP-A, SP-B*, and *SP-D*, appear later, and their expression in the adult is restricted to the distal lung in alveolar type II and bronchiolar epithelial cells (66).

LUNG MORPHOGENESIS: Role of Fibroblast Growth Factors

The FGF family of polypeptides currently consists of 23 members. FGF signaling is transduced by four transmembrane tyrosine kinase receptors (FGFRs). FGF-FGFR interactions are modulated by heparan sulfate proteoglycans (HSPG), such as syndecans and perlecan. Upon ligand binding, receptors dimerize and autophosphorylate, leading to activation of a variety of intracellular pathways that are fundamental to control cell proliferation, differentiation, and pattern formation (reviewed in 107).

FGFs are widely expressed throughout animal phyla and are found in species as diverse as worms, insects, and humans. A remarkable feature of FGF signaling is its conserved functional role in branching morphogenesis during evolution (reviewed in 68). The branching pattern of the *Drosophila* trachea is established by expression of the FGF *branchless (Bnl)* in clustered cells near tracheal epithelial tubules at prospective sites of budding. Bnl activates an FGFR, breathless (btl), in the epithelium. This results in epithelial bud migration and elongation toward the Bnl-expressing cells (106). Thus *Drosophila* FGF acts as a chemotactic factor for the epithelium. Homogeneous expression of the *FGFR* may ensure that all epithelial cells are capable of responding to the local chemotactic stimulus by budding.

FGF-10 and Budding

In the developing mouse lung, a mechanism involving FGF-10 and FGFR-2, reminiscent of that described above in flies, regulates airway branching. *FGFR-2* is expressed throughout the respiratory tract epithelium from the earliest stages of lung development (embryonic day 9.5) and during branching morphogenesis (12, 90). The mesenchyme expresses *FGF-10* in a localized fashion in close association with distal epithelial tubules. In situ hybridization analysis of day 11–12 embryonic lungs has shown that local expression of *FGF-10* is dynamic; it appears to precede distal bud formation, and signals are down-regulated once the bud is formed (6).

Interestingly, in day 11.5 lung epithelial explants growing in the absence of mesenchyme, recombinant FGF-10 can substitute for the mesenchyme and induce generalized budding when dissolved in the culture medium (6, 85). Moreover, a gradient of FGF-10 protein can be established in these cultures by implanting a heparin bead soaked in FGF-10 near the explant. Under this condition, epithelial buds grow toward the FGF-10 source and engulf the bead within 48 h (85, 117). This is also seen when FGF-10 beads are grafted onto intact day 11.5 mouse lungs and grown in culture, simulating a situation where high levels of FGF-10 are artificially fixed in time and space (85). By overriding the dynamic pattern of endogenous *FGF-10*, the FGF bead appears to redirect airway growth to an ectopic position and distorts the normal pattern of branching. Results from these assays also show that, when compared with another FGF such as FGF-7, FGF-10 acts at relatively short-range distances in the developing lung. In explants cultured in the absence of mesenchyme, the chemotactic effect is observed in epithelial buds located as far as 150 μm from an FGF-10 bead (117), and within 50 to 75 μm distant from the FGF-10 bead when it is grafted onto intact lung explants (85). This difference could be accounted for by FGF-10 binding to matrix components in the mesenchyme such as HSPGs (40), which may locally restrict the FGF-10 effects in intact lungs in vitro or in vivo. This effect and the mechanisms that transcriptionally regulate *FGF-10* expression (see below) contribute to fine tuning of the patterning effects of FGF-10 in the developing lung.

In addition to being a source of FGF-10, the mesenchyme also modulates the response of the epithelium to FGF-10. When FGF-10 beads are grafted onto proximal and distal sites of day 11.5 lungs, effects are elicited only in distal epithelium. Since at this time proximal and distal epithelia express *FGFR-2* at apparently similar levels (12, 90), the lack of effects in proximal airways suggests that the mesenchyme contains factors that interfere with FGF-10 activation and cellular activities in the epithelium. Indeed, epithelial explants isolated from proximal airways cultured in the absence of mesenchyme are able to migrate toward an FGF-10 bead (117)

Collectively the data are compatible with the idea that FGF-10 locally induces and guides bud outgrowths to proper positions during lung branching morphogenesis. The critical role that FGF-10 plays in lung pattern formation has been confirmed by genetic studies. In *FGF-10* knock-out mice, induction of primary lung buds is disrupted. As a result, lungs do not form and mice have a blunt-ended tracheal tube (71, 96). There is also genetic evidence that the chemotactic response and lung bud induction elicited in the epithelium by FGF-10 result from local activation of FGFR-2. Lung agenesis is similarly found when *FGFR-2* is inactivated either by excision of the *IIIb* exon (19) or by disruption of the *IIIc* exon and the transmembrane domain (2). Thus signaling by FGF-10-FGFR-2 is prototypical of epithelial-mesenchymal interactions classically described in grafting experiments, where mesenchymal FGF-10 is an inducer of distal epithelial buds.

FGF-10 Effects: Similarities and Differences with Other FGFs

Because FGFR-2 is also a high-affinity binding receptor for FGF-1 and FGF-7 (107), these ligands could theoretically have the same bud-inducing potential as FGF-10. In reality only FGF-1 has this potential. FGF-1 can mimic the FGF-10 effects (6, 81, 85) likely because of its ability to bind to all FGFR, including FGFR-2. Nevertheless, experiments using FGF-1 beads show that its chemotactic effect is less marked than that elicited by FGF-10 (85). Furthermore, the late onset of expression and spatial distribution of endogenous FGF-1 do not seem to be relevant for early branching (see below).

Although FGF-7 does not show chemotactic properties when applied to lung explants, it has a potent effect on epithelial cell proliferation. Mesenchyme-free lung epithelial explants treated with FGF-7 show generalized growth that results in formation of cyst-like structures instead of budding (12). This effect is also see in lungs of transgenic mice carrying an *SP-C* or *CC10* promoter-driven *FGF-7* transgene (101, 112). FGF-7, in contrast to FGF-10, appears to act as a long-range signal in the developing lung. When grafted onto day 11.5 embryonic lungs and cultured, the effect of FGF-7-loaded beads in the epithelium is seen over 500 μm from the source (85). It is intriguing that *FGF-7* and *FGF-10* share a high degree of homology and have high-affinity binding to FGFR-2 but exert very different effects in the developing lung epithelium.

How does FGF signaling exert its effects on budding? The studies in *Drosophila* have shown that *branchless* acts purely as a chemotactic factor (106). By contrast, lung bud induction by FGF-10 involves both chemotaxis and epithelial proliferation, although FGF-10 is less potent than FGF-7 as a mitogen in lung epithelial cells (85, 117). Interestingly, at least in keratinocytes, heparin enhances the mitogenic activity of FGF-10 while inhibiting that of FGF-7 (40).

Whether proliferation is the primary driving force for lung epithelial budding has been debated. Experiments using mesenchyme-free lung epithelial cultures suggest that the appearance of differential cell proliferation within the epithelium is not the initial event that triggers lung bud induction. In these cultures, FGF-1 induces budding within 18 h in culture, but regional differences in BrDU incorporation are evident only after budding has initiated (82). Alternatively, FGF signaling could initially induce changes in cell-cell adhesion and cell motility, thus leading to cell rearrangement and trigger budding, as shown in other systems (reviewed in 31).

FGFs as Differentiation Signals

Studies in organ cultures have shown that grafting distal lung mesenchyme onto trachea results in induction of tracheal epithelial buds with cellular features of lung type II cells, such as lamellar bodies (organelles that store surfactant), and *SP-C* expression (98, 104). Interestingly, a mixture of soluble factors that includes FGF-7 and FGF-1 can substitute for distal mesenchyme inducing type II cell differentiation in tracheal epithelial cultures (*trans*-differentiation). By deleting individual components of this mixture, Shannon and collaborators (99) show that FGF-7 and FGF-1 are necessary in the medium for *trans*-differentiation; however, none of the factors in the mixture can individually induce *SP-C* expression in trachea. In contrast, there is evidence that in lung epithelial cultures, exogenous FGF-7 by itself is able to induce at least a partial program of type II cell differentiation. In the absence of mesenchyme and serum, FGF-7 induces precocious expression of high levels of the differentiation markers *SP-A* and *-B* and lamellar body formation. This effect cannot be reproduced by FGF-1 or FGF-10 treatment at any concentration, even though both factors also bind the FGF-7 receptor (FGFR2-IIIb) with high affinity (12). FGF-7 likely continues to be a proliferation and differentiation factor for the distal lung throughout life; in the adult lung, FGF-7 acts as an alveolar type II cell mitogen and increases *SP-A* and *-B* mRNA expression (105, 114). Surprisingly, lungs from *FGF-7$^{-/-}$* mice appear normal, suggesting that the role of FGF-7 in the lung overlaps with that of other growth factors (32). In fetal rat lung epithelial cells cultured in EHS matrix, expression of *SP-A, -B,* and *-C* has been shown to be induced by FGF-2 through a MAPK-independent pathway (62).

Modulation of FGF Signaling: FGF Interactions

An important observation from the studies above is that uncontrolled availability of FGF-10 (recombinant protein in beads) leads to distortions of the branching pattern. Thus fine-tuning of branching might require that FGF-10 levels in time and space be precisely controlled by other pattern regulators expressed in both mesenchyme and the epithelium. Dynamic expression of *FGF-10* might result from a combination of local induction and restriction of expression by inhibitors.

Although inhibitors of *FGF-10* gene expression have been identified (see below), to date *FGF-10* inducers have not yet been reported in the lung. Interestingly, if embryonic lung mesenchymal cells are cultured in the absence of the epithelium, *FGF-10* mRNA levels markedly increase within 24 to 48 h. This contrasts with the decrease in levels of FGF-7 mRNA, assessed within the same period (53, 92). The data suggest that the developing lung epithelium has diffusible factors that are inhibitory for *FGF-10* and stimulatory for *FGF-7*. There is evidence that mesenchymal factors also influence *FGF-10* expression and its effects in the epithelium.

The subsequent section reviews information about a selected number of pattern regulators that have been shown to interact with FGFs during lung morphogenesis.

Sonic hedgehog (Shh)   Shh regulates pattern formation of a variety of developing structures including the lung (24). At day 9.5, when primary lung buds are forming, *Shh* is already expressed in the ventral foregut endoderm (55). *Shh* is subsequently expressed in the developing lung epithelium in a gradient fashion, with the highest levels in cells at the tips. In turn, most components of the Shh pathway, including Shh target genes and its receptor Ptc1, are found in the mesenchyme (5, 30). Although another receptor, Ptc2, has been identified in the epithelium (78), its role in transducing Shh signaling in the lung is unknown.

Shh signaling is initiated upon binding to Ptc1 (from now on referred to as Ptc) and results in activation of Shh target genes by Gli transcription factors (reviewed in 41). *Ptc* expression in the lung follows the proximal-distal gradient of *Shh* (5). *Glis* (*1, 2, 3*) are expressed in overlapping but distinct domains in the lung mesenchyme. The proximal-distal gradient is evident in *Gli1*, which together with *Ptc*, is transcriptionally up-regulated by Shh and is expressed in the subepithelial mesenchyme (30). The distinct phenotypes observed when *Gli* genes are inactivated individually or in combinations suggest that there are complex interactions between *Gli* members in regulating lung growth and pattern formation (30, 77, 86).

Shh knockout mice show that, while Shh is essential for branching morphogenesis, it is not required for primary bud induction as are Gli 2 and 3. Lungs from *Shh*[-/-] mice develop as rudimentary sacs by failure of the epithelial tubules to branch properly. The defect seems to be primarily in the mesenchyme, as shown by an increase in mesenchymal cell death; decreased cell proliferation is also reported. Branching, but not proximal-distal differentiation, is affected (55, 88).

A paramount feature of *Shh*[-/-] lungs is the widespread distribution of *FGF-10* signals in the mesenchyme, contrasting with the local pattern present in wild type (88). This supports the idea that, not only the presence of FGF-10, but its correct spatial distribution is necessary for patterning. If *FGF-10* signals are diffuse rather than localized, directional clues are lost and branching is disrupted. Importantly, data also suggest that under normal conditions Shh plays a role on controlling *FGF-10* expression in the distal lung. Two other models support this statement. When Shh is over-expressed in the lungs of transgenic mice, increased mesenchymal cell proliferation and down-regulation of *FGF-10* gene expression are observed (5, 6). Moreover, treatment of embryonic lung mesenchymal cells with recombinant Shh protein prevents the increase in *FGF-10* expression observed within 48 h when these cells are grown in control conditions (53). Thus Shh is part of an epithelial network of regulators that restricts *FGF-10* expression. Shh-FGF-10 interaction supports a model proposed by Bellusci and coworkers (6) in which the growing epithelial bud, which expresses high levels of Shh, interacts with a chemotactic source (FGF-10) in the distal mesenchyme to extinguish it (Figure 1).

Expression of *Shh* and *Ptc* do not seem to be influenced by FGF-10; however, both genes are down-regulated by FGF-7 in lung explant cultures (53). Interestingly, at early stages of lung development, high levels of *Shh* and *Ptc* but low *FGF-7* levels are found in the embryonic lung. Conversely, prior to birth, high levels of *FGF-7* and low levels of *Shh* and *Ptc* are detected (5, 6, 11, 85). Whether FGF-7 functions as an inhibitory factor of Shh signaling in vivo remains to be determined.

Bone Morphogenetic Protein-4 (BMP-4)   BMPs belong to the TGFβ superfamily of growth factors, with at least three members (BMP-4, -5, and -7) present in the developing lung (4, 49). BMP-4 is an important regulator of epithelial proliferation and proximal-distal cell fate during lung morphogenesis. Studies using a *BMP-4*[lacZ] reporter mouse show mesenchymal signals as early as gestation day

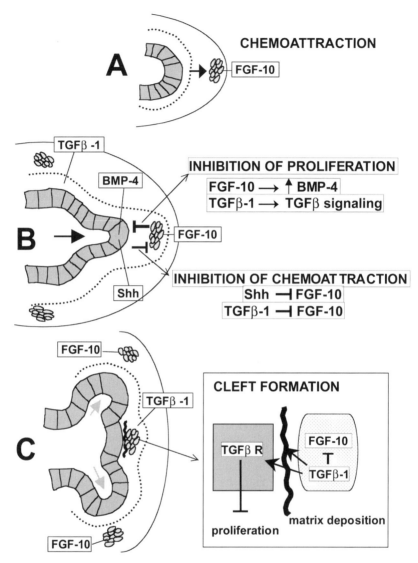

Figure 1 Control of bud formation during branching morphogenesis. Diagram incorporates models proposed by Bellusci and coworkers (6) and Lebeche and coworkers (53). (*A*) Local expression of FGF-10 in the mesenchyme induces chemo-attraction and epithelial growth. (*B*) As the bud is induced, FGF-10 is inhibited by Shh expressed at the tips and by TGFβ-1 expressed throughout the subepithelial region. Concomitantly, proliferation is inhibited at the tips by FGF-10-mediated up-regulation of BMP-4. (*C*) These mechanisms limit bud outgrowth and expansion, resulting in cleft formation. FGF-10-expressing cells appear at other sites to induce a new generation of buds. At the cleft, low levels of FGF-10 are maintained by subepithelial TGFβ-1, which also induces synthesis of extracellular matrix components deposited in the epithelial-mesenchymal interface and prevents local budding (modified from 53).

9–9.5 in the ventral foregut, in the domains of the nascent right and left lung bud (116). Although this suggests a role for BMP-4 in establishing the initial lung field in the foregut mesenchyme, evidence from genetic studies is not currently available.

During branching morphogenesis, BMP-4 is dynamically expressed in the distal epithelium of branching airways. The *BMP-4^{lacZ}* reporter gene mouse shows that when buds are forming, signals appear after bud initiation and levels increase at the tips during the period of bud extension (117). Thus BMP-4 appears to be unnecessary for bud induction. Type I and type II serine-threonine kinase receptors and Smad transcription factors transduce BMP-4 signaling (reviewed in 58). Disruption of BMP-4 signaling in the lung of transgenic mice disrupts the proximal-distal pattern of growth and differentiation of the lung. Mice expressing either a dominant-negative type I BMP receptor (*Alk6*) or a secreted BMP-4 inhibitor *Xenopus noggin* (*Xnoggin*) under the control of the *SP-C* promoter do not properly form distal lung. In these mice, proximal cell types, such as ciliated cells, and expression of the proximal genes *HFH-4, CC-10* are ectopically found in the periphery of the lung (116). Conversely, over-expression of *BMP-4* in the distal lung results in small lungs with large distal sacs lined by epithelial cells whose morphology is reminiscent of that of alveolar type I cells (4). The concomitant decrease in the number of type II cells (*SP-C* positive) in these mice led the authors to propose that high levels of BMP-4 stimulate distal lung formation but might preferentially induce alveolar type I cell fate. Conversely, cells located far from the tips and exposed to low levels of BMP-4 assume a proximal character (116). Collectively, the data suggest that BMP-4 is part of a distal signaling center that controls proliferation and regulates proximal-distal differentiation.

Levels of *BMP-4* expression at the tips of the growing epithelial buds are influenced by gradients of *FGF-10* in neighboring mesenchymal cells. Recombinant FGF-10 in beads up-regulates *BMP-4* expression in the distal epithelium and induces ectopic expression of *BMP-4* in proximal epithelial explants (53, 117). Moreover, recombinant BMP-4 inhibits epithelial cell proliferation and prevents budding, thus antagonizing the effect of FGF-10 in epithelial explants (117). Presumably, FGF-10 -BMP-4 interaction serves to limit bud outgrowth during budding (Figure 1).

TGFβ-1   TGFβ-1 is a member of a subfamily of peptides having at least two other members, all expressed in the developing lung. TGFβ signaling is mediated by serine-threonine kinase receptors (type I and II) and Smad transcription factors (reviewed in 58). Activation of TGFβ signaling is inhibitory for epithelial branching; expression of a dominant-negative TGFβ RII in lung organ cultures stimulates branching morphogenesis (127). In the day 11–12 embryonic lung, *TGFβ-1* transcripts are uniformly expressed in the subepithelial mesenchyme. TGFβ-1 protein accumulates later at sites of cleft formation and along proximal airways. TGFβ-1 promotes synthesis of extracellular matrix that, when deposited in the epithelial-mesenchymal interface, is thought to prevent local branching (36). TGFβ-1 has also been identified as a potent negative regulator of epithelial cell proliferation and differentiation in vitro and in vivo. Recombinant TGFβ-1 inhibits branching morphogenesis in cultured lung explants (97). When *TGFβ-1* is mis-expressed in the distal lung epithelium of transgenic mice, lungs do not develop beyond the late pseudoglandular period and show decreased levels of *SP-C* expression. Furthermore, blood vessel formation is impaired in these animals, presumably because of decreased levels of VEGF (129). In contrast, lung abnormalities have not been reported in *TGFβ-1* knockout mice; it is unclear, however, whether this may have resulted from maternal transfer of this peptide rescuing the phenotype (54).

TGFβ-1 may control levels of *FGF-10* expression in the developing lung mesenchyme. In the day 11–13 embryonic lung, *TGFβ-1* signals are present in the subepithelial mesenchyme, a site where *FGF-10* is normally not expressed. Furthermore, recombinant TGFβ-1 markedly inhibits *FGF-10* expression, both in lung embryonic mesenchymal cell and in lung organ cultures (53). Therefore, TGFβ-1 potentially exerts its effect on lung morphogenesis by at least three mechanisms: limiting epithelial bud proliferation, inhibiting FGF-10-mediated chemoattraction, and synthesizing extracellular matrix components that stabilize clefts (Figure 1).

Sprouty (Spry)   *Spry* genes encode a family of cysteine-rich proteins that antagonize FGF signaling. In *Drosophila, Spry* is induced by FGF signaling at the tips of branching tracheal tubules and inhibits lateral budding by a mechanism currently not well understood (34). At least three related murine genes, *mSpry 1, 2,* and *4,* have been identified in specific cell types of different organs at late stages of development. In vertebrates, not all FGFs induce *Spry* expression, perhaps reflecting differences in sensitivity of these genes to individual FGFs or a requirement for additional cooperative factors (73). *Spry 2* and *Spry 4* are expressed in the developing distal lung in the epithelium and mesenchyme, respectively (18, 108). Antisense oligonucleotide inactivation of *Spry 2* has an stimulatory effect on distal branching and differentiation in organ cultures (108).

FGFs   Studies in other developing structures such as the limb bud have shown that FGFs regulate expression of other FGF family members (reviewed in 57). The possibility that this may also be true in the lung is suggested by the sequential pattern of induction of individual FGFs during lung development and by data from FGF-treated lung cultures (see below).

FGF-9 and *FGF-10* are the first of all FGFs to be detected in the embryonic lung by in situ hybridization (6, 17). At day 9.5–10 lung, *FGF-9* is expressed in pleural and epithelial cells. At around day 11.5, low levels of *FGF-7* and *FGF-2* transcripts are detected by RT-PCR; however, transcripts are found in the mesenchyme by in situ hybridization only by day 13–14. At this stage, when expression of these FGFs is well established, *FGF-1* signals first appear in the lung epithelium and mesenchyme (6, 53, 85). In embryonic lung mesenchymal cell and organ cultures, treatment with recombinant FGF-1 or FGF-2 has been shown to up-regulate *FGF-7* gene expression, whereas recombinant FGF-7 up-regulates *FGF-1*. Based on these observations, it has been proposed that at early stages, FGF-2 induces *FGF-7*, which in turn induces *FGF-1*; at later stages, FGF-1 may maintain *FGF-7* expression (53). *FGF-10* expression does not seem to be influenced by FGF-1, 2, or 7. Although it remains to be demonstrated, FGF-9 has been suggested as a potential regulator of *FGF-10* expression, via activation of FGFR-1 signaling in the early lung (2).

RETINOIC ACID SIGNALING AND LUNG MORPHOGENESIS

Retinoids are fundamental for normal development and homeostasis of a number of biological systems including the lung. RA (all-*trans*, 9-*cis*, 13-*cis*) is considered to be the active form of the retinoids in most systems. RA results from sequential oxidation of vitamin A from retinol to retinaldehyde and to the acid form (reviewed in 13). Among the several enzymes involved in this pathway, retinaldehyde dehydrogenase-2 (RALDH-2) plays a prominent role in generating RA during organogenesis (79, 80, 115, 128). Expression of *RALDH-2* is developmentally regulated and represents one of the mechanisms that controls RA availability to target cells. RA metabolism represents another way of regulating ligand availability by generating products that are inactive or that differentially affect morphogenesis or regeneration. P450RAI (CYP26) is an RA-inducible, RA-metabolizing enzyme of the cytochrome P450 family, which specifically converts RA into hydroxylated products (26, 121). P450RAI can serve as a mechanism to protect RA-sensitive tissues from high RA levels (42, 76). Recently, another related metabolizing enzyme, P450RAI-2, has been identified in adult human tissues, with highest levels in cerebellum (122).

RA signaling is mediated by nuclear receptors from the steroid hormone superfamily RAR (α, β, γ) and retinoid RXR (α, β, γ), each having multiple isoforms (13). RAR/RXR heterodimers have been shown to transduce RA signaling in vivo (46). These receptors are widely expressed in the embryo, and their genetic inactivation in mice results in abnormalities that resemble those found in vitamin A–deficient animals (65, 123). RA signaling is modulated by a variety of factors that serve as coactivators or corepressors (13). In some systems, nuclear factors such as COUP-TFs (chicken ovalbumin upstream promoter-transcription factors) interfere with RA-mediated transactivation by mechanisms that include sequestration of RXRs (reviewed 113). Retinoid-binding proteins (CRBPs and CRABPs) have been also identified in the embryo, but they do not seem to play a role in morphogenesis, as assessed by genetic studies (29, 51).

RA in the Embryonic Lung

Despite the large number of studies showing teratogenic effects of excess or deficiency of vitamin A during organogenesis, the role or retinoids in lung development is still not clearly defined. There is evidence that RA signaling is required for lung bud initiation. Acute vitamin A deprivation in pregnant rats at the onset of lung development results in blunt-end tracheae and lung agenesis in some embryos, a phenotype similar to that described in *FGF-10*[-/-] mice (20, 96). Day 8.0 whole embryos cultured in the presence of a pan-RAR antagonist show disruption of lung bud formation (73a). Furthermore, disruption of RA signaling in *RAR α/β2* knockout mice leads to agenesis of the left lung and right lung hypoplasia (65).

A recent analysis of the ontogeny of the RA pathway in the embryonic mouse lung shows that, when primary buds are forming (day 9.5), RA signaling is locally active. As suggested by *RALDH-2* expression, RA is synthesized by pleural and tracheal mesenchymal cells (56). Sites where RARs are being activated can be mapped using a reporter mouse carrying a RA-responsive element-driven *lacZ* (*RARE-lacZ*) transgene (95). Ubiquitous distribution of RARE-lacZ signals in the lung primordia suggests that RARs are activated in all layers (56).

Interestingly, subsequent branching morphogenesis is characterized by a dramatic down-regulation of RA signaling in the lung. There is evidence that despite-continued expression of *RARs* and *RALDH-2*, *RARE-lacZ* signals are not detected in the epithelium and in most of the mesenchyme (21, 56). This appears to result from activation of mechanisms that antagonize RA signaling, such as increased RA degradation in the epithelium via P450RAI-mediated metabolism and inhibition of RA signaling in the mesenchyme presumably by COUPTF-II expression (56) (Figure 2). The efficiency of these mechanisms may be critical for distal lung morphogenesis. Preventing down-regulation of RA signaling by treating embryonic lung explants with high concentrations of RA (10^{-6} -10^{-5}M) results in dramatic disruption of distal budding and formation of proximal-like immature airways (10, 56). In these cultures, RA inhibits expression and alters distribution of *FGF-10* and *BMP-4*, pattern-related genes that are involved in distal lung morphogenesis. It is also noteworthy that during early stages of branching (day 11–12.5), *RALDH-2* expression is concentrated in trachea (mesenchyme) and proximal lung (mesothelium) at sites of low branching activity. The *RALDH-2* pattern is non-overlapping with that of *FGF-10*, supporting the idea that RA signaling restricts *FGF-10* expression and may have to be inhibited to allow proper distal lung morphogenesis.

The mechanism involved in RA-induced inhibition of *FGF-10* may be mediated by up-regulation of Shh, although there are data suggesting a Shh-independent pathway (6, 11, 56). The RA effect on pattern formation appears to involve signaling by RARβ; the inhibitory effect of exogenous RA on distal bud formation in vitro is reduced in lungs of RARβ knockout mice. RA also alters expression of *Hox* genes in the lung (7, 11, 84), but how these changes influence the lung phenotype remains to be determined. Hox proteins regulate anterior-posterior specification of the body axis during development. Several Hox genes are expressed in the lung (reviewed in 9, 45); however, to date, only *Hoxa-5* has shown a lung phenotype (laryngotracheal malformation and lung immaturity) when inactivated in mutant mice (3).

Reports on the effects of RA on surfactant protein gene expression have been conflicting, possibly because of differences in methodologies or choice of species in the studies. For instance, in one study in cultured rat explants in which all-*trans*

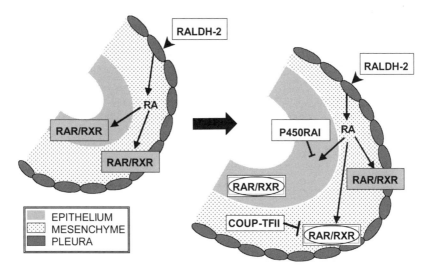

Figure 2 Regulation of RA signaling at the onset of lung development (*left*) and during branching morphogenesis (*right*) based on data from Malpel and coworkers (56). At an initial stage, mesothelial cells expressing RALDH-2 synthesize RA, which diffuses and activates RA signaling ubiquitously (RAR/RXR in gray boxes represents activated RA signaling; RAR/RXR encircled in white boxes represents suppressed RA signaling). During branching, RA signaling is suppressed in the epithelium by P450RAI-mediated RA metabolism and by COUP-TFII inhibition of RAR/RXR activation of target genes (modified from 56).

RA disrupted distal lung formation, *SP-A, -B*, and *-C* genes were down-regulated (10). In another study using human fetal lung explants, *SP-A* and *-C* were also down-regulated, but *SP-B* was up-regulated (69).

At late gestation, although *RALDH-2* continues to be expressed in the pleura, data from *RARE-lacZ* mice show little evidence of RA utilization in the lung (56). Whether this implies that RA signaling does not play a role in late developmental events remains to be determined. Paradoxically, data from fetal rat lungs suggest that there is an increase in retinoid availability toward birth. A lipid-rich mesenchymal cell (lipofibroblast or lipid interstitial cell) containing high levels of retinyl esters, the storage form of retinoids, has been identified in embryonic rat lungs (64). Biochemical analysis shows that from late gestation to early postnatal life there is a decline in the retinyl ester content of these cells that coincides with an increase in the levels of retinol and RA (63, 64). Lung lipofibroblasts have been also reported in other species, including humans, hamsters, and mice (44).

RA in Alveolar Formation

The process by which saccules transform into alveolar units involves formation of secondary septae from the pre-existing walls and represents the final major morphogenetic event of the developing lung (126). Some data suggest that RA signaling is involved in alveolization. Low plasma levels of vitamin A have been reported in premature neonates who develop bronchopulmonary dysplasia, a condition in which alveolization is impaired (100). RA treatment of neonatal rats during the period of alveolization increases the number of alveoli and partially rescues a block in alveolar formation induced by dexamethasone (59, 61). In adult rats, RA has been reported to reverse the anatomical features of elastase-induced emphysema (60). Furthermore, RA treatment also partially rescues the lung defect of the adult *Tight-skin* mouse, a mutant bearing a tandem duplication within the *fibrillin-1* gene with impaired alveolization (103). The mechanisms by which *RA* exert these effects are still poorly understood.

DEVELOPMENT OF PROXIMAL AIRWAYS

In mice, the primitive trachea emerges once primary lung buds form and the tracheo-esophageal septum separates the digestive tract from the respiratory system (104). The origin and role of this septum in tracheal development is controversial. (125). There is evidence that trachea and lung require different signals to form and that during morphogenesis they can develop independently from each other. This is best exemplified in $FGF-10^{-/-}$ mice, in which tracheal morphogenesis and differentiation occur normally, but primary lung buds never form (71, 96).

Proximal epithelial features of differentiation include those of ciliated, mucous, serous, and Clara cells. At around embryonic day 14.5, expression of *HFH-4* (HNF3/forkhead homologue-4) in areas that do not overlap with *SP-C* domains represents initial evidence of proximal epithelial differentiation (33). By day 16, proximal airways also start expressing *Clara cell 10-kDa protein (CC10)* mRNA, which marks non-mucous and non-serous secretory cells from trachea to terminal bronchioles (91, 102, 120). Development of ciliated cells is regulated by HFH-4; in the absence of this transcription factor, cilia are not formed in any cell type, and $HFH-4^{-/-}$ mice display random determination of L-R asymmetry of internal organs (15). Conversely, targeted expression of high levels of *HFH-4* to the distal epithelium of transgenic mice results in the ectopic appearance of ciliated cells, *β-tubulin IV* mRNA, and suppression *SP-B* and *SP-C* signals (111). Also, transgenic lungs do not express the proximal marker *CC10*. It has been proposed that *HFH-4* may be part of a mechanism that restricts Clara cell and distal alveolar development and promotes columnar and ciliated cell differentiation.

An important developmental aspect of proximal respiratory tract is the appearance of submucosal glands in the trachea and in bronchi of some species. These structures are formed by mucous, serous, and ciliated cells and produce the secretions that line the airway lumen. In humans, they develop mostly during intrauterine life. Nevertheless, pluripotent progenitor cells have been identified in the respiratory epithelium of adults with the capacity to recapitulate gland development (25). Submucosal glands originate from invagination of the airway epithelium into the interstitium (submucosa), where buds subsequently undergo lateral expansion (110). Invasion of the mesenchyme by the epithelial bud is mediated by epidermal growth factor (EGF) and TGFα signaling and is inhibited by TGFβ-1, presumably by stimulation of matrix synthesis and deposition at the epithelial-mesenchymal interface (27, 36). The transcription factor LEF1 (lymphoid enhancer binding factor 1) is found in the epithelium of gland progenitor cells and is essential for gland formation. Although gland development in *LEF-1* knockout mice is impaired, transgenic mice overexpressing *LEF-1* show no significant effect in airways, suggesting that additional factors may be required (23). These observations and the fact that LEF/TCF is a downstream component of the Wnt pathway (39) possibly implicate Wnt signaling in proximal airway development.

CONCLUDING REMARKS

Several important issues such as the role of extracellular matrix components in lung morphogenesis, regulation of epithelial differentiation (surfactant protein and airway secretory product expression), and embryonic lung neovascularization have not been addressed in this review. A dedicated chapter could be written for each of them.

Despite the fact that many of the classical questions about regulation of lung morphogenesis remain unanswered, increasing information from genetic studies and in vitro systems is enlightening. The identification of signaling molecules that regulate pattern formation in species such as *Drosophila* and the evolutionary conservation of their function have helped characterize the molecular mechanisms of the epithelial-mesenchymal interactions in the developing lung. Nothing is known about how territories of the primitive foregut endoderm are demarcated and fated to become lung. The observation that branching patterns are specified before the onset of lung development and that inactivation of a single gene such as *Lefty-1* can modify these programs raises the question about how hierarchies are established within the regulatory network of genes that governs lung pattern formation.

Variable levels of *FGFs, Shh, TGFβ, EGF,* retinoid receptors, and other signals that play a role in lung morphogenesis have been reported in the adult lung (8, 24, 28, 87, 94, 124). It is unclear whether and to what extent these regulators are recruited during adult life to mediate cellular activities in processes such as post-injury repair, compensatory lung growth, or asthma. Recent studies implicate EGF and TGFβ signaling as mediators of epithelial-mesenchymal interactions during airway remodeling in asthma (reviewed in 37). Exploring these areas will open an array of possibilities to understand the role of these signaling molecules in the above processes and to approach new therapeutic strategies in lung disease.

ACKNOWLEDGMENTS

I thank Mark Krasnow, Hiroyuki Nogawa, Jose Xavier Neto, Cathy Mendelsohn, Jerry Brody, and Mary Williams for many helpful discussions. I also thank Mary Williams for critical reading of the manuscript. I am grateful to former and present members of my lab, Sarah Malpel, Djamel Lebeche, William Park, Renee Anderson, and Barbara Miranda, who generated some of the results and discussions presented here. I am also grateful to Julie Gorestein for help in the organization of the manuscript. This work was supported by a grant from NIH/NHLBI (PO1HL47049).

Visit the Annual Reviews home page at www.AnnualReviews.org

LITERATURE CITED

1. Ang S-L, Rossant J. 1994. HNF-3β is essential for node and notochord formation in mouse development. *Cell* 78:561–74
2. Arman E, Haffner-Krausz R, Gorivodsky M, Lonai P. 1999. Fgfr2 is required for limb outgrowth and lung branching morphogenesis. *Proc. Natl. Acad. Sci. USA* 96:11895–99
3. Aubin J, Lemieux M, Tremblay M, Berard J, Jeanotte L. 1997. Early postnatal lethality in *Hoxa-5* mutant mice is attributable to respiratory tract defects. *Dev. Biol.* 192:432–45
4. Bellusci S, Henderson R, Winnier G, Oikawa T, Hogan B. 1996. Evidence from normal expression and targeted misexpression that Bone Morphogenetic Protein-4 (Bmp-4) plays a role in mouse embryonic lung morphogenesis. *Development* 122: 1693–702
5. Bellusci S, Furuta Y, Rush MG, Henderson R, Winnier G, Hogan BL. 1997. Involvement of Sonic Hedgehog (Shh) in mouse embryonic lung growth and morphogenesis. *Development* 124:53–63
6. Bellusci S, Grindley J, Emoto H, Itoh N, Hogan BL. 1997. Fibroblast growth factor 10 (FGF10) and branching morphogenesis in the embryonic mouse lung. *Development* 124:4867–78
7. Bogue CW, Gross I, Vasavada H, Dynia DW, Wilson CM, Jacobs HC. 1994. Identification of Hox genes in newborn lung and effects of gestational age and retinoic acid on their expression. *Am. J. Physiol. Lung Cell Mol. Physiol.* 266:L448–L54
8. Buch S, Han RNN, Liu J, Moore A, Edelson JD, et al. 1995. Basic fibroblast growth factor and growth expression in 85%

O$_2$-exposed rat lung. *Am. J. Physiol. Lung Cell Mol. Physiol.* 268:L455–L64
9. Cardoso WV. 1995. Transcription factors and pattern formation in the developing lung. *Am. J. Physiol. Lung Cell Mol. Physiol.* 269:L429–L42
10. Cardoso WV, Williams MC, Mitsialis SA, Joyce-Brady M, Rishi AK, Brody JS. 1995. Retinoic acid induces changes in the pattern of airway branching and alters epithelial cell differentiation in the developing lung in vitro. *Am. J. Respir. Cell. Mol. Biol.* 12:464–76
11. Cardoso WV, Mitsialis SA, Brody JS, Williams MC. 1996. Retinoic acid alters the expression of pattern-related genes in the developing rat lung. *Dev. Dyn.* 207:47–59
12. Cardoso WV, Ito A, Nogawa H, Mason I, Brody JS. 1997. FGF-1 and FGF-7 induce distinct patterns of growth and differentiation in embryonic lung epithelium. *Dev. Dyn.* 208:398–405
13. Chambon P. 1996. A decade of molecular biology of retinoic acid receptors. *FASEB J.* 10:940–54
14. Chazaud C, Chambon P, Dolle P. 1999. Retinoic acid is required in the mouse embryo for left-right asymmetry determination and heart morphogenesis. *Development* 126:2589–96
15. Chen J, Knowles HJ, Hebert JL, Hackett BP. 1998. Mutation of the mouse hepatocyte nuclear factor/forkhead homologue 4 gene results in an absence of cilia and random left-right asymmetry. *J. Clin. Invest.* 102:1077–82

factor-beta 1 null mice. *Science.* 264:1936–38

55. Litingtung Y, Lei L, Westphal H, Chiang C. 1998. Sonic hedgehog is essential to foregut development. *Nat. Genet.* 20:58–61

56. Malpel SM, Mendelsohn C, Cardoso WV. 2000. Regulation of retinoic acid signaling during lung morphogenesis. *Development* 127:3057–67

57. Martin GR. 1998. The roles of FGFs in the early development of vertebrate limbs. *Genes Dev.* 12:1571–86

58. Massagué J. 1998. TGFβ signal transduction. *Annu. Rev. Biochem.* 67:753–91

59. Massaro GD, Massaro D. 1996. Postnatal treatment with retinoic acid increases the number of pulmonary alveoli in rats. *Am. J. Physiol. Lung Cell Mol. Physiol.* 270:L305–L10

60. Massaro GD, Massaro D. 1997. Retinoic acid treatment abrogates elastase-induced pulmonary emphysema in rats. *Nat. Med.* 3:675–77

61. Massaro GD, Massaro D. 2000. Retinoic acid treatment partially rescues failed septation in rats and in mice. *Am. J. Physiol. Lung Cell Mol. Physiol.* 278:L955–L60

62. Matsui R, Brody JS, Yu Q. 1999. FGF-2 induces surfactant protein gene expression in fetal rat lung epithelial cells through a MAPK-independent pathway. *Cell Signal.* 11:221–28

63. McGowan SE, Harvey CS, Jackson SK. 1995. Retinoids, retinoic acid receptors, and cytoplasmic retinoid binding proteins in perinatal rat lung fibroblasts. *Am. J. Physiol. Lung Cell Mol. Physiol.* 269:L463–L72

64. McGowan SE, Torday JS. 1997. The pulmonary lipofibroblast (lipid interstitial cell) and its contributions to alveolar development. *Annu. Rev. Physiol.* 59:43–62

65. Mendelsohn C, Lohnes D, Decimo D, Lufkin T, LeMeur M, et al. 1994. Function of the retinoic acid receptors (RARs) during development (II). Multiple abnormalities at various stages of organogenesis in RAR double mutants. *Development* 120:2749–71

66. Mendelson CR. 2000. Role of transcription factors in fetal lung development and surfactant protein gene expression. *Annu. Rev. Physiol.* 62:875–915

67. Meno C, Shimono A, Saijoh Y, Yashiro K, Mochida K, et al. 1998. Lefty-1 is required for left-right determination as a regulator of lefty-2 and nodal. *Cell* 94:287–97

68. Metzger RJ, Krasnow MA. 1999. Genetic control of branching morphogenesis. *Science* 284:1635–39

69. Metzler MD, Snyder JM. 1993. Retinoic acid differentially regulates expression of surfactant-associated proteins in human fetal lung. *Endocrinology* 133:1990–98

70. Merei JM, Hasthorpe S, Farmer P, Hutson JM. 1998. Embryogenesis of tracheal atresia. *Anat. Rec.* 52:271–75

71. Min H, Danilenko DM, Scully SA, Bolon B, Ring BD, et al. 1998. Fgf-10 is required for both limb and lung development and exhibits striking functional similarity to *Drosophila* branche less. *Genes Dev.* 12:3156–61

72. Minoo P, Su G, Drum H, Bringas P, Kimura S. 1999. Defects in tracheoesophageal and lung morphogenesis in Nkx2.1 (-/-) mouse embryos. *Dev. Biol.* 209:60–71

73. Minowada G, Jarvis LA, Candace L, Neubuser A, Sun X, et al. 1999. Vertebrate *sprouty* genes are induced by FGF signaling and can cause chondrodysplasia when overexpressed. *Development* 126:4465–75

73a. Mollard R, Ghyselinck NB, Wendling O, Chambon P, Mark M. 2000. Stage-dependent responses of the developing lung to retinoic acid signaling. *Int. J. Dev. Biol.* 44:457–62

74. Monaghan AP, Kaestner KH, Grau E, Schutz G. 1993. Postimplantation expression patterns indicate a role for the

mouse forkhead/HNF-3 α, β, and γ genes in determination of the definitive endoderm, chordamesoderm and neuroectoderm. *Development.* 119:567–78

75. Morrisey EE, Tang Z, Sigrist K, Lu MM, Jiang F, et al. 1998. GATA6 regulates HNF4 and is required for differentiation of visceral endoderm in the mouse embryo. *Genes Dev.* 12:3579–90

76. Moss JB, Neto JX, Shapiro MD, Nayeem SM, McCaffery P, et al. 1998. Dynamic pattern of retinoic acid synthesis and response in the developing mammalian heart. *Dev. Biol.* 199:55–71

77. Motoyama J, Liu J, Mo R, Ding Q, Post M, Hui C-C. 1998. Essential function of Gli2 and Gli3 in the formation of lung, trachea and oesophagus. *Nat. Genet.* 20:54–57

78. Motoyama J, Takabatake T, Takeshima K, Hui C-C. 1998. Ptch 2, a second mouse Patched gene is co-expressed with Sonic hedgehog. *Nat. Genet.* 18:104–6

79. Niederreither K, McCaffery P, Drager U, Chambon P, Dolle P. 1997. Restricted expression and retinoic-induced down-regulation of the retinaldehyde dehydrogenase type 2 (RALDH-2) gene during mouse development. *Mech. Dev.* 62:67–78

80. Niederreither K, Subbarayan V, Dolle P, Chambon P. 1999. Embryonic retinoic acid synthesis is essential for early mouse post-implantation development. *Nat. Genet.* 21:444–48

81. Nogawa H, Ito T. 1995. Branching morphogenesis of embryonic mouse lung epithelium in mesenchyme-free culture. *Development* 121:1015–22

82. Nogawa H, Morita K, Cardoso WV. 1998. Bud formation precedes the appearance of differential cell proliferation during branching morphogenesis of mouse lung epithelium in vitro. *Dev. Dyn.* 213:228–35

83. Offield MF, Jetton TL, Labosky RA, Ray M, Stein R, et al. PDX-1 is required for pancreatic outgrowth and differentiation of the rostral duodenum. *Development* 122:983–95

84. Packer AI, Mailutha KG, Ambrozevicz LA, Wolgemuth DJ. 2000. Regulation of Hoxa4 and Hoxa5 genes in the embryonic mouse lung by retinoic acid and TGF-β1: implications for lung development and patterning. *Dev. Dyn.* 217:62–74

85. Park WY, Miranda B, Lebeche D, Hashimoto G, Cardoso WV. 1998. FGF-10 is a chemotactic factor for distal epithelial buds during lung development. *Dev. Biol.* 201:125–34

86. Park HL, Bai C, Platt KA, Matise MP, Beeghly A, et al. 2000. Mouse Gli1 mutants are viable but have defects in SHH signaling in combination with Gli2 mutation. *Development* 127:1593–605

87. Pelton RW, Dickinson ME, Moses HL, Hogan BLM. 1990. In situ hybridization analysis of TGF-β 3 RNA expression during mouse development: comparative studies with TGF-β1 and 2. *Development* 110:609–20

88. Pepicelli CV, Lewis P, McMahon A. 1998. Sonic hedgehog regulates branching morphogenesis in the mammalian lung. *Curr. Biol.* 8:1083–86

89. Perl A-KT, Whitsett JA. 1999. Molecular mechanisms controlling lung morphogenesis. *Clin. Genet.* 56:14–27

90. Peters KG, Chen WG, Williams LT. 1992. Two FGF receptors are differentially expressed in epithelial and mesenchymal tissues during limb formation and organogenesis. *Development* 114:233–43

91. Plopper CG, Hyde DM, Buckpitt AR. 1997. Clara cells. In *The Lung: Scientific Foundations*, ed. RG Crystal, JB West, ER Weibel, PJ Barnes, pp. 517–33. Philadelphia: Lippincott-Raven

92. Post M, Souza P, Liu J, Tseu I, Wang J, et al. 1996. Keratinocyte growth factor and its receptor are involved in regulating early lung branching. *Development* 122:3107–15

93. Pringle KC. 1986. Human fetal lung development and related animal models. *Clin. Obstet. Gynecol.* 29:502–13

94. Rall LB, Scott J, Bell GI, Craqford RJ,

Penschow JD, et al. 1985. Mouse prepro-epidermal growth factor synthesis by the kidney and other tissues. *Nature* 321:228–31

95. Rossant J, Zirngibl R, Cado D, Giguere V. 1991. Expression of a retinoic acid response element-hsp *LacZ* transgene defines specific domains of transcriptional activity during mouse embryogenesis. *Genes Dev.* 5:1333–44

96. Sekine K, Ohuchi H, Fujiwara M, Yamasaki M, Yoshizawa T, et al. 1999. Fgf-10 is essential for limb and lung formation, *Nat. Genet.* 21:138–41

97. Serra R, Moses HL. 1995. pRb is necessary for inhibition of N-*myc* expression by TGFβ-1 in embryonic lung organ cultures. *Development* 121:3057–66

98. Shannon JM. 1994. Induction of alveolar type II cell differentiation in fetal tracheal epithelium by grafted distal lung mesenchyme. *Dev. Biol.* 166:600–14

99. Shannon JM, Gebb S, Nielsen LD. 1999. Induction of alveolar type II cell differentiation in embryonic tracheal epithelium in mesenchyme-free culture. *Development* 126:1675–88

100. Shenai JP, Chytil F, Stahlman MT. 1985. Vitamin A status of neonates with bronchopulmonary dysplasia. *Pediatr. Res.* 19:185–89

101. Simonet WS, DeRose M, Bucay N, Nguyen HQ, Wert S, et al. 1995. Pulmonary malformation in transgenic mice expressing human keratinocyte growth factor in the lung. *Proc. Natl. Acad. Sci. USA* 92:12461–65

102. Singh G, Singh J, Katyal SJ, Brown WE, PacPherson JA, Squeglia N. 1988. Identification, cellular localization, isolation and characterization of human Clara cell-specific 10 kD protein. *J. Histochem. Cytochem.* 36:73–80

103. Siracusa LD, McGrath R, Ma Q, Moskow JJ, Manne J, et al. 1996. A tandem duplication within the fibrillin-1 gene is associated with the mouse tight skin syndrome. *Genome Res.* 6:300–13

104. Spooner BS, Wessels NK. 1970. Mammalian lung development: interactions in primordium formation and bronchial morphogenesis. *J. Exp. Zool.* 175:445–54

105. Sugahara K, Rubin JS, Mason RJ, Aronsen EL, Shannon J. 1995. Keratinocyte growth factor increases mRNAs for SP-A and SP-B in adult rat alveolar type II cells in culture. *Am. J. Physiol. Lung Cell Mol. Physiol.* 269:L344–L50

106. Sutherland D, Samakovlis C, Krasnow MA. 1996. Breathless encodes a Drosophila FGF homolog that controls tracheal cell migration and the pattern of branching. *Cell* 87:1091–101

107. Szebenyi G, Fallon JF. 1999. Fibroblast growth factors as multifunctional signaling factors. *Int. Rev. Cytol.* 185:45–106

108. Tefft DT, Lee M, Smith S, Leinwand M, Zhao J, et al. 1999. Conserved function of mSpry-2, a murine homolog of Drosophila sprouty, which negatively modulates respiratory organogenesis. *Curr. Biol.* 9:219–22

109. Ten Have-Opbroek AAW. 1981. The development of lung in mammals: an analysis of concepts and findings. *Am. J. Anat.* 162:201–19

110. Thurlbeck WM, Benjamin B, Reid L. 1961. Development and distribution of mucous glands in the fetal human trachea. *Br. J. Dis. Chest.* 55:54–64

111. Tichelaar JW, Lim L, Costa RH, Whitsett JA. 1999. HNF3/forkhead homologue-4 influences lung morphogenesis and respiratory epithelial cell differentiation in vivo. *Dev. Biol.* 213:405–17

112. Tichelaar JW, Lu W, Whitsett JA. 2000. Conditional expression of fibroblast growth factor-7 in the developing and mature lung. *J. Biol. Chem.* 275:11858–64

113. Tsai SY, Tsai MJ. 1997. Chick ovalbumin upstream promoter-transcription

factors (COUP-TFs): coming of age. *Endocr. Rev.* 18:229–40

114. Ulich TR, Yi ES, Longmuir K, Yin S, Biltz R, et al. 1994. Keratinocyte growth factor is a growth factor for type II pneumocytes in vivo. *J. Clin. Invest.* 93:1298–306

115. Ulven SM, Gundersen TE, Weedon MS, Landaas VO, Sakhi AK, et al. 2000. Identification of endogenous retinoids, enzymes, binding proteins, and receptors during early postimplantation development in mouse: important role of retinal dehydrogenase type 2 in synthesis of all-*trans*-retinoic acid. *Dev. Biol.* 220: 379–91

116. Weaver M, Yingling JM, Dunn NR, Bellusci S, Hogan BL. 1999. Bmp signaling regulates proximal-distal differentiation of endoderm in mouse lung development. *Development* 126:4005–15

117. Weaver M, Dunn NR, Hogan BL. 2000. Bmp-4 and fgf10 play opposing roles during lung bud morphogenesis. *Development* 127:2695–704

118. Wells JM, Melton DA. 1999. Vertebrate endoderm development *Annu. Rev. Cell Dev. Biol.* 15:393–410

119. Weinstein D, Ruiz i Altaba A, Chen WS, Hoodless P, Prezioso WR, et al. 1994. The winged-helix transcription factor HNF-3β is required for notochord development in the mouse embryo. *Cell* 78:575–88

120. Wert S, Glasser SW, Korfhagen TR, Whitsett JA. 1993. Transcriptional elements from the human SP-C gene direct expression in the primordial respiratory epithelium of transgenic mice. *Dev. Biol.* 156:426–43

121. White JA, Guo YD, Baetz K, Beckett-Jones B, Bonasoro J, et al. 1996. Identification of the retinoic acid-inducible

all-*trans*-retinoic acid 4-hydroxylase. *J. Biol. Chem.* 271:29922–27

122. White JA, Ramshaw H, Taimi M, Stangle W, Zhang A, et al. 2000. Identification of the human cytochrome P450, P450RAI-2, which is predominantly expressed in the adult cerebellum and is responsible for all-*trans*-retinoic acid metabolism. *Proc. Natl. Acad. Sci. USA* 97:6403–8

123. Wilson JG, Roth CB, Warkany J. 1953. An analysis of the syndrome of malformation induced by maternal vitamin A deficiency. Effects of restoration of vitamin A at various times during gestation. *Am. J. Anat.* 92:189–217

124. Yamasaki M, Miyake A, Tagashira S, Itoh N. 1996. Structure and expression of the rat mRNA encoding a novel member of the fibroblast growth factor family *J. Biol. Chem.* 271:15918–21

125. Zaw-Tun HA. 1982. The tracheoesophageal septum—Fact or fantasy? *Acta Anat.* 114:1–21

126. Zeltner TB, Burri PH. 1987. The postnatal development and growth of the human lung: II. Morphology. *Respir. Physiol.* 67:269–82

127. Zhao J, Bu D, Lee M, Slavkin HC, Hall FL, Warburton D. 1996. Abrogation of transforming growth factor beta type II receptor stimulates embryonic mouse lung branching morphogenesis in culture. *Dev. Biol.* 180:242–57

128. Zhao D, McCaffery P, Ivins KJ, Neve RL, Hogan P, et al. 1996. Molecular identification of a major retinoic acid synthesizing enzyme: a retinaldehyde-specific dehydrogenase. *Eur. J. Biochem.* 240:15–22

129. Zhou LJ, Dey C, Wert SE, Whitsett JA. 1996. Arrested lung morphogenesis in transgenic mice bearing an SP-C-TGF-β 1 chimeric gene. *Dev . Biol.* 175:227–38

Annu. Rev. Physiol. 2001. 63:495–519

THE PULMONARY COLLECTINS AND SURFACTANT METABOLISM

Samuel Hawgood and Francis R Poulain

Cardiovascular Research Institute and Department of Pediatrics,
University of California San Francisco, San Francisco, California 94143-0734;
e-mail: hawgood@itsa.ucsf.edu; poulain@itsa.ucsf.edu

Key Words   SP-A, SP-D, surfactant homeostasis, mouse models

■ **Abstract**   Lung surfactant covers and stabilizes a large, delicate surface at the interface between the host and the environment. The surfactant system is placed at risk by a number of environmental challenges such as inflammation, infection, or oxidant stress, and perhaps not surprisingly, it demonstrates adaptive changes in metabolism in response to alterations in the alveolar microenvironment. Recent experiments have shown that certain components of the surfactant system are active participants in the regulation of the alveolar response to a wide variety of environmental challenges. These components are capable not only of maintaining a low interfacial surface tension but also of amplifying or dampening inflammatory responses. These observations suggest that regulatory molecules are capable of both sensing the environment of the alveolus and providing feedback to the cells regulating surfactant synthesis, secretion, alveolar conversion, and clearance. In this review we examine the evidence from in vitro systems and gene-targeted mice that two surfactant-associated collectins (SP-A and SP-D) may serve in these roles and help modify surfactant homeostasis as part of a coordinated host response to environmental challenges.

INTRODUCTION

Collectins are proteins defined by the presence of two discrete structural modules—a fibrillar collagen-like module and a globular carbohydrate-recognition module (1). Two members of the collectin family, surfactant proteins A and D (SP-A and SP-D), are expressed in the lung. SP-A was named a surfactant protein initially on the basis of its association with surfactant in the lung. Subsequently, a substantial body of experimental work supported a role for SP-A in regulating pulmonary surfactant structure, function, and metabolism. SP-D was named a surfactant protein on the basis of primary sequence similarities with SP-A and co-expression of both proteins in surfactant-producing type II epithelial cells. Subsequent to this nomenclature, scientists recognized that SP-A shared quaternary structural features with the first component of complement C1q (2) and that other members of

0066-4278/01/0315/0495$14.00

the collectin family participate in the innate immune response (3, 4). These observations quickly led to experiments confirming that both SP-A and SP-D have immunomodulatory functions in vitro. These observations also contributed to the alternate hypothesis that SP-A and SP-D respond to a range of environmental challenges within the overall host (5). The relative importance of the surfactant-related and immunomodulatory activities ascribed to SP-A and SP-D remains to be established. Such distinctions may, in fact, be unnecessary as it is now apparent that these activities significantly overlap. Recent work suggests the surfactant and immune systems may be more closely related than researchers previously believed, i.e. perturbations in pulmonary immune defenses lead to inflammation and altered surfactant homeostasis and vice versa. We first focus on the organization of the collectin protein subfamily of C-type lectins with the goal of providing adequate structural information about SP-A and SP-D for the subsequent discussion of the roles of SP-A and SP-D in surfactant metabolism. Although we recognize the analysis of gene-targeted and transgenic mice is not complete, we have attempted to synthesize recent information derived from these model mice with the larger body of in vitro studies. The related review by Crouch & Wright (5a) in this volume covers the contributions of SP-A and SP-D to pulmonary innate immunity.

THE COLLECTIN PROTEIN FAMILY

Members of the collectin family are found in many vertebrate species, from birds to humans. Related secreted C-type lectins, lacking a collagen-like sequence, are also found in invertebrates. There are currently six members of the vertebrate collectin family. Mannose-binding proteins (MBP-A and MBP-C), SP-A, and SP-D (6) are present in several species including mice, rats, nonhuman primates, and humans. The other three members of the collectin family have been reported in only a single species to date. Conglutinin (7) and CL-43 (8) are both bovine serum collectins. Liver collectin-1 (CL-L1) (9) is a human cytosolic protein and the only member of the collectin family apparently not secreted into the extracellular space. The function of CL-L1 is unknown. Accumulating evidence suggests that the other five secreted collectins all have roles in antibody-independent pathogen recognition and clearance (6, 10). These collectins also may have additional and discrete non-host defense functions, including direct effects on pulmonary surfactant activity and metabolism. The probable functional plasticity of the C-type lectin domain, which defines the collectin family, is highlighted by the identification of at least 125 proteins in the *Caenorhabditis elegans* genome containing protein modules related to the C-type carbohydrate recognition domains of vertebrate lectins (11).

Genomic Organization and the Collectin Locus

The genomic organization of the collectins closely reflects the domain structure of the encoded proteins. The collectin collagen-like sequences are encoded by several short exons (3, 12, 13, 14) with the overall length of the protein domain in each specific collectin determined by the number of tandem exon duplications (see gene structures in Figure 1; see color insert). The regular size and intron-exon boundaries of the collagen-like exons imply a close evolutionary relationship to the nonfibrillar collagens (3). The noncollagen regions of the collectins, composed of a helical-coiled coil domain and the carbohydrate recognition domain (CRD), are each encoded by single discrete exons (3, 12, 13, 14). The similar organization of each of the collectin genes suggests they evolved by duplication from a common ancestral gene, itself probably formed by exon shuffling between genes encoding nonfibrillar collagens and a primordial lectin.

Three of the collectin genes (MBP-A, SP-A, and SP-D) are closely linked on mouse chromosome 14 (15) and reside contiguously within a 55-kb region (Figure 1A). In the human, a more dispersed collectin gene cluster containing two SP-A structural genes (SP-A1 and SP-A2), an SP-A pseudogene, structural genes for SP-D and MBP-A, and an MBP-A pseudogene is found on the syntenic region of chromosome 10 (16). Not all collectins lie within these loci as MBP-C (17) and CL-L1 (9) map outside the main collectin locus on chromosomes 19 and 8 in mouse and human, respectively.

Protein Organization

All collectins are large oligomeric proteins assembled from multiple copies (3–18) of a single polypeptide chain consisting of four structural domains. An amino-terminal disulfide-rich domain of 7 (SP-A) to 25 (SP-D) amino acids contributes to interchain covalent interactions; scientists believe this helps to stabilize the basic trimeric organization imposed on each collectin by the triple helix of the collagen-like domains. The second domain consists of this collagen-like sequence and forms an extended fibrillar triple helix 20 (SP-A) (18) to 46 (SP-D) nm long (19). MBP and SP-A have a single interruption in the Gly-X-Y tripeptide repeat pattern leading to a kink in the fibrillar domain, whereas SP-D and conglutinin have uninterrupted repeats throughout the fibrillar domain. Domain three forms a short trimeric helical-coiled coil (20) that bridges the collagen-like arm to the globular CRD (21), which forms the carboxy-terminal domain of the collectins.

CRD Structure

The CRDs are held in trimeric array at the end of each collagenous stalk. Progress in our understanding of CRD structure and function, including the dependence on calcium of most collectin functions, has been greatly assisted by the solutions of the crystal structure of the MBP (22–24) and of the SP-D CRDs (25). The two solutions show a highly conserved overall folding topology for the collectin CRDs with minor differences in the orientation of the CRD to the helical-coiled coil trimerization domain and the structures of the surface loops. Researchers assume but have not yet shown that the CRD of SP-A has a similar structure. The basic CRD structure consists of a structural core made up of alpha helical and beta strands. Attached to this conserved core is a region that has no regular secondary structure and consists of four loops interconnected by extended structure. The CRD structure is stabilized by two disulfide bridges and by binding calcium to two conserved sites.

Ligand and Receptor Binding

The crystal structure of an oligosaccharide complex of MBP has also revealed the direct involvement of bound calcium in sugar binding and surprisingly few direct interactions between the bound sugar and the MBP backbone (26). The collectins display relatively broad sugar-binding specificity based on stereochemistry with a preference for sugars with an equatorial orientation of the 3- and 4-hydroxyl groups such as mannose, glucosamine, glucose, and fucose (21, 26). Each collectin displays some differences in sugar selectivity in vitro. SP-A binds preferentially to mannose and fucose (27), whereas SP-D has a relatively greater selectivity toward glucose and maltose (28). The collectin-binding sites do not as readily accommodate galactose and sialic acid, sugars commonly terminating mammalian glycoconjugates.

The arrangement of each individual low-affinity sugar-binding site into trimeric arrays suggests that multivalent ligands require a matching ligand topology bridging a distance of 45–53 Å to achieve high-affinity binding (29). This kind of modeling has been used to explain the preference of collectins for the type and macropattern of sugars displayed on the surface of a diverse array of microorganisms in the form of lipopolysaccharide, lipoteichoic acid, and mannan over the less suitable terminal monosaccharides and macropatterns of mammalian glycoconjugates (30). The collectins therefore have structures compatible with their proposed role as pattern recognition molecules in an ante-antibody host defense response (4).

The CRDs of SP-A and SP-D bind selected lipids and proteins in addition to sugars. SP-A binds phosphatidylcholine and galactoslyceramide (31–33). SP-D binds phosphatidylinositol (PI) and glucosylceramide (34–36) and may also interact with phosphatidylcholine under some circumstances (37, 38). The binding of SP-D to PI is strictly calcium dependent and can be inhibited by inositol, which indicates binding via the sugar-binding site (34). The binding of SP-A to liposomal dipalymitoylphosphatidylcholine (DPPC) is calcium independent (31). Based on results obtained from experiments with a series of chimeric SP-A/SP-D constructs, researchers conclude that the binding site on SP-A for DPPC is spatially distinct from the sugar-binding site and probably involves the region between Cys[204] and Cys[218] (39–43). Both SP-A and SP-D also bind specifically to the surface of type II cells (44–48) and alveolar macrophages (49–52). The molecular basis of this binding has not been established with certainty, but it has many of the characteristics associated with specific receptors. A number of candidate collectin receptors (53), both soluble and surface bound, have been identified. In vitro, SP-A interacts with the C1q receptor calreticulin (54), the C1q phagocytic receptor (C1q$_{RP}$,) (55),

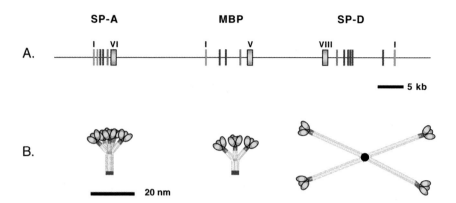

Figure 1 Organization of the mouse collectin gene locus and protein structure. The SP-A, MBP, and SP-D genes are all located on mouse chromosome 14 in a locus extending over 55-60 kb. The colors show the relationship between gene organization and protein domains. The untranslated exons are colored green, the exons encoding the amino-terminal dimerization domains and collagen-like sequences are blue, the exons encoding the helical coiled-coil neck red, and the exons encoding the carbohydrate-recognition domain and the 3' untranslated region yellow. The exon number indicating the direction of translation is given above each gene. The relative size and shape of the oligomeric proteins are modeled after published rotary shadowed electron micrographs (18, 66).

Figure 3 Lungs of one year old SP-D deficient (-/-) and littermate control (+/+) mice fixed at 20 cm H_2O pressure with intratracheal liquid fixative. The -/- lungs are larger and have patchy areas of pale discolortaion beneath the pleura corresponding to regions of the most pronounced lipidosis, airspace enlargement and macrophage accumulation.

cellular myosin (56), the soluble form of a novel scavenger receptor gp340 (57), annexin (58), and unidentified proteins of 210 kDa (59) and ~55 kDa (60–62). SP-D binds soluble gp340 (63, 64) and microfibril-associated protein 4 (65), but SP-D does not bind $C1q_{RP}$ or calreticulin. At present, the biological significance of these multiple interactions is unknown.

Oligomeric Structure

The fibrillar collagen-like stalks of the collectins orient the CRDs in one of two geometries. MBP and SP-A assemble with a bouquet-like shape (18); SP-D and conglutinin assemble as a tetramer with fibrillar spokes radiating from a central covalently linked hub (66) (Figure 1*B*). Higher and lower order oligomers of SP-D have been also isolated. The final multivalent molecules are large with diameters of 20–100 nm. Scientists believe this geometry allows for both the flexible orientation of the collectin-binding sites to fit diverse ligand assemblies (macropatterns) and the cross-linking or agglutination of bound membranes or particles including allergens and microbes. The fibrillar stalks may have additional properties including receptor or cofactor binding sites, as observed in the collagen-like C1q (67). Like C1q, MBP interacts with specific MBP-associated proteases (MASPs) to activate complement via the alternate pathway (68). There is as yet no evidence that SP-A and SP-D bind MASPs or activate complement.

Tissue Distribution

In the lung both SP-A and SP-D are expressed in alveolar epithelial type II cells, nonciliated respiratory epithelial (Clara) cells, and serous cells of tracheo-bronchial glands (69–72). In humans, Clara cells are confined to the respiratory bronchioles, whereas in mice, Clara cells expressing SP-D are found throughout the large and small airways. The extrapulmonary expression of both SP-A and SP-D appears to be species specific. In rats, SP-A may be expressed in the small and large intestine (73), but extra-pulmonary expression of SP-A has not been confirmed in other species.

SP-D appears to be expressed more widely with mRNA for SP-D detected by RT-PCR. Although SP-D may be expressed in many human tissues including heart, prostate gland, salivary gland, small intestine, kidney, and pancreas, it does so at significantly lower levels than in the distal lung (74). By immunohistochemistry, SP-D is detected in many mucosal surfaces. Lining cells of the parotid duct, sweat glands, salivary glands, lachrymal glands, gall bladder ducts, intrahepatic bile ducts, pancreatic ducts, and collecting tubules of the kidney, as well as epithelial cells of the skin, urinary tract, esophagus, and small intestine stain positive with anti-SP-D monoclonal antibodies (74). In rats, SP-D has been detected in the lung and gastric mucosa but not, in other sites (75). SP-D has also been localized to the eustachian tube in the pig (76). This wide tissue and cell distribution suggests SP-D and possibly SP-A have functions that are not restricted to the lung surfactant system but are generally applicable to a broad range of mucosal surfaces. The tissue and cell distribution of SP-A and SP-D is consistent with a role in innate mucosal immunity, but additional functions at specific sites are also possible.

OVERVIEW OF SURFACTANT METABOLISM

For optimal gas exchange, the alveolus must remain in an inflated state throughout the respiratory cycle. For this to occur the strong surface forces acting at the air-water interface in the alveolar lumen must be reduced by the presence of a functioning surface-active material referred to as surfactant (77). Surfactant in the air spaces of the lung proceeds through an orderly metabolic cycle that begins when surfactant is secreted into the alveolus from type II epithelial cells and ends when it is cleared from the air space by type II cells or alveolar macrophages (78). Between these two points, surfactant stabilizes lung volume against collapse, keeps the alveolus from flooding with fluid, and perhaps contributes to the clearance of invading pathogens (5, 79).

Surfactant Composition

The composition of surfactant is dominated by the phospholipid, DPPC, which makes up about 40–45% of the total surfactant mass. Other lipids, including unsaturated phosphatidylcholines, phosphatidylglycerol, phosphatidylinositol, and cholesterol, make up most of the remaining surfactant mass as surfactant is assembled in the type II epithelial cell prior to secretion (80). At least two proteins with pronounced biophysical effects on surfactant function, SP-B (81) and SP-C (82), are co-assembled with the surfactant lipids in the type II cell (83–85). Additional proteins, including SP-A and possibly SP-D, are predominantly secreted by different pathways (86, 87). After these proteins have been secreted into the alveolar lumen, they then associate with the surfactant lipids. DPPC has surface properties consistent with those we would expect the primary surfactant component responsible for lowering the alveolar surface tension (88) to have. The other surfactant components have variable roles in the metabolic cycle and are responsible for delivering DPPC to the air-liquid interface and maintaining a stable and adequate pool size.

Surfactant Metabolism

The metabolic pathway is characterized morphologically by the sequential conversions of surfactant into distinct structural forms (89). First, surfactant secreted from type II cells in lamellar bodies unravels, coalesces, and converts to the lattice-like tubular myelin (90, 91). Then, the tubular myelin is disaggregated and disassembled; this probably occurs during the process of surface film formation. Finally, in a process that is dependent on ventilation of the air-filled lung, vesicles of various sizes (92) are formed from precursor structures; these structures could include the surface film, remnants of tubular myelin, or remnants of lamellar bodies.

Each structure has a markedly different protein content (93) and surface property (89) and is cleared from the alveolus at different rates and possibly by different pathways (94). DPPC turnover time in the lung is approximately 5 h (95). Two primary surfactant clearance pathways have been described. The first appears to be a recycling pathway into type II cells (96). In this pathway, surfactant components are taken back into the type II cell and continue into a minor lysosomal degradation pathway (97, 98) or major reutilization pathway (89, 96, 99). In the second clearance pathway, surfactant components are removed from the cycle by phagocytosis and degradation within alveolar macrophages (100, 101). Although some surfactant is degraded by the type II cell, the alveolar macrophage is the more significant site for surfactant degradation in the lung. In newborn animals, the recycling pathway accounts for approximately 80% of the total clearance of surfactant (102). In the mature animal, the recycling pathway accounts for about 50% of the total surfactant clearance from the alveolar space (103).

Because respiratory demands vary rapidly over a wide range, with changing levels of activity and in various disease states, the surfactant system must be capable of quickly responding to such changes by adjustments in rates of secretion and clearance and possibly composition and physicochemical properties. These responses imply multiple levels of regulation. Therefore, the surfactant system must contain molecules (typically proteins) that both encode regulatory signals and respond to them, as well as molecules (typically lipids) that primarily alter surface tension. This complex metabolism is required to precisely match the surface forces in the alveolus to the wide range of ventilation patterns experienced in rest and exercise while maintaining the normal balance between surfactant secretion and clearance (104–107).

SURFACTANT PROTEINS A AND D AND SURFACTANT HOMEOSTASIS IN VITRO

A substantial body of experimental work suggests SP-A, and perhaps SP-D under certain circumstances, contributes to the regulation of surfactant metabolism in the alveolus. Based on in vitro studies, possible functions for SP-A include a role in the formation and maintenance of the tubular myelin structure (108, 109); a synergistic effect with SP-B on the adsorption of phospholipids to surface film (81); and a role in regulating the alveolar surfactant pool size by influencing surfactant secretion (110, 111), alveolar subfraction conversion from tubular myelin to vesicular forms (112), and surfactant clearance (113). Fewer in vitro studies suggest a role for SP-D in surfactant metabolism, but SP-D does promote the formation of alternate tubular structures and surface film formation in the presence of PI (114). SP-D also binds to the surface of both type II cells (48) and alveolar macrophages (115). Some of these observations are briefly summarized here. As we discuss below, recent findings in transgenic mice have raised unresolved questions about the significance of several of these in vitro observations.

Surfactant Secretion

Appropriately regulated surfactant secretion is a critical step in the maintenance of the alveolar surface film and overall surfactant homeostasis (116). Surfactant phospholipids are stored in lamellar bodies within type II cells. Lamellar body contents are released into the alveolar lining fluid by regulated exocytosis at an estimated rate of about 10% of the intracellular surfactant pool per hour (78). Considerable effort has been invested into defining both physiologic and pharmacologic agonists and inhibitors of surfactant secretion (116). Several independent laboratories have demonstrated that purified, delipidated SP-A inhibits surfactant secretion from isolated type II cells (110, 111, 117). SP-D has no direct effect on surfactant secretion from type II cells in vitro (118). Inhibition is dependent on SP-A cell surface binding, presumably to a specific, as yet undefined, receptor (46, 119). All forms of stimulated secretion are inhibited, which suggests either a very proximal or very distal interruption common to all of the signaling cascades that result in exocytosis (111). One potentially important caveat to this interpretation is the observation that the inhibition of secretion by purified SP-A is almost totally lost in the presence of surfactant phospholipids (111). The availability of SP-A that is free to interact with type II cell receptors in the intact lung is unknown.

Tubular Myelin Formation

Morphologic studies have shown that tubular myelin forms directly from the contents of secreted lamellar bodies (90). The rapid association of SP-A with secreted lamellar body (120) contents probably contributes to the dramatic rearrangements of lipid structure from lamellar bodies to tubular myelin. Both simple reconstitution studies in vitro (108, 109) and ultrastructural examination of the surfactant in SP-A (121) and SP-B (122) gene-targeted mice show that both proteins are needed to form tubular myelin. Although tubular myelin is present in all mammals, the functional significance of this complex form of surfactant remains a mystery. In vitro, tubular myelin is the most active of all surfactant subfractions (89), and morphological studies of the alveolus show tubular myelin in close proximity to the surface layer of the alveolar fluid (123). These findings suggest a specific precursor-product relationship between the two surfactant forms (88), but the actual function of tubular myelin is unknown.

Surface Film Formation

The surfactant apoproteins have marked effects on the kinetics of surface film formation in vitro. Optimal surface activity in vitro depends on functional cooperativity between three surfactant apoproteins (SP-A, SP-B, and SP-C) (81, 124–126), but both SP-B and SP-C are independently capable of promoting the adsorption of phospholipids to an air-water interface in a concentration-dependent manner (84, 127, 128). When taken together with the fatal consequences of a genetic deficiency of SP-B (or the disruption of normal SP-C metabolism) in humans (129) and mice (122), the in vitro results most consistently attribute a primary role for SP-B, and perhaps SP-C, in surfactant surface activity and a secondary synergistic or regulatory role for SP-A in these phenomena. The synergy between SP-A and SP-B in the processes of surfactant film formation is particularly pronounced in experiments that model surfactant dysfunction caused by high concentrations of serum proteins (130, 131). Under these conditions, in vitro SP-A preserves surfactant activity.

SP-D also enhances SP-B-mediated surface film formation from phospholipid membranes containing PI (114). Unusual, but nevertheless highly ordered, tubular structures with surface activity similar to authentic tubular myelin are generated from such mixtures. These findings suggest that SP-D might compensate for SP-A deficiency and form surface active tubular structures in intact animals if the appropriate lipid ligand (PI) is present. Elevations of PI are commonly reported in many forms of lung injury and repair. Although such collectin redundancy has not been shown in any physiologic or pathologic state (132), structures similar to the SP-D-dependent tubules are seen in the secretions of type II cells in long-term culture (114) and in some patients with alveolar proteinosis (133).

Surfactant Conversion

The major change in surfactant structure from lamellar body contents to tubular myelin to the surface layer implies the possible generation of remnant particles, depleted of the components that selectively enter and remain in the surface layer. A large number of heterogeneous small vesicles (SV) are present in alveolar fluid in situ (92). Their abundance varies as a function of respiratory pattern (134). Vesicular forms can be isolated from lavage fluid by differential (89) or sucrose density gradient centrifugation (135) and are called the light surfactant subfraction to distinguish from the tubular myelin-rich or heavy subfraction. This binary classification is an oversimplification, but it has proven useful in clinical and mechanistic studies. The light vesicular forms could represent remnants of secreted lamellar body contents, remnants of adsorbed tubular myelin, or desorbed surface layer components. Heavy, protein-dense particles are also present (136). Vesicles are not seen in the fluid-filled fetal lung and can only be generated in vitro with exposure to a cyclically expanding and contracting surface layer (137). This implies that physicochemical factors associated with adsorption to and desorption from the air-water interface are essential in the generation of these remnant particles. The inclusion of SP-A slows the conversion of active forms into inactive forms in vitro, which suggests SP-A may protect surfactant from this kind of inactivation and may be an important component of surfactant during certain forms of lung injury (112).

Surfactant Clearance

The metabolic fate of the SVs is not known, but they may be the form of surfactant that is recycled into type II cells. SP-A may play a role in this recycling process.

In vitro, SP-A enhances the uptake of phospholipids into both type II cells (138) and alveolar macrophages (139). Lipid turnover studies in rabbits suggest that some of the phospholipid recycled into type II cells is degraded while the majority is re-utilized intact (140). Phospholipid taken up by type II cells in the presence of SP-A largely escapes degradation, whereas the majority is degraded in the absence of SP-A (138).

SP-D co-isolates with SVs isolated from broncho-alveolar lavage by differential centrifugation, and some lipid is closely associated with SP-D in this light fraction of surfactant (37). SP-D also binds to and is taken up by isolated type II cells (48) and alveolar macrophages (115), but no evidence exists that directly links SP-D with secretion, recycling, or clearance of major surfactant components in vitro. The available results do not exclude the possibility that SP-D may affect the clearance of minor surfactant lipid components, such as the anionic phospholipids, cholesterol, or perhaps oxidized or otherwise altered surfactant components.

SURFACTANT HOMEOSTASIS IN THE SP-A-DEFICIENT MOUSE

In light of the several effects SP-A has on surfactant structure, function, and metabolism in vitro, researchers were surprised to discover that mice that completely lacked SP-A as a result of gene targeting had normal postnatal survival with no detectable alteration in pulmonary function (141).

SP-A-Deficient Surfactant

As researchers expected to discover based on in vitro studies, surfactant isolated from the SP-A-deficient mice completely lacked tubular myelin. Despite this marked change in surfactant structure, the measured surface activity of the SP-A-deficient surfactant did not differ significantly from control surfactant except at high dilutions in the absence of calcium (121, 141). The significance of this difference is uncertain because surfactant is normally present in the alveolus at very high concentrations, and the SP-A-deficient mouse has no detectable abnormalities in histology, lung wet weight, lung volume, or compliance. Researchers noted two significant differences in the in vitro behavior of the SP-A-deficient surfactant that might be relevant to responses to certain forms of lung injury. One, SP-A-deficient mouse surfactant is significantly more sensitive to plasma inactivation, and two, it converts more rapidly to inactive SVs in a cycling assay (121). Although both observations are consistent with results from reconstitution studies using purified components, the biological significance of the findings remains to be established. SP-A-deficient mice and control mice respond similarly to exercise and to *N*-nitroso-*N*-methylurethane-induced lung injury (121), but additional models of stress on the surfactant system are necessary before we can conclude the wealth of in vitro data is invalid.

Surfactant Metabolism in the SP-A-Deficient Mouse

In vitro studies also suggest a role for SP-A in the regulation of surfactant metabolism by inhibiting secretion from type II cells (110, 111, 117) and enhancing surfactant uptake into type II cells and alveolar macrophages (138, 139). In the SP-A-deficient mouse, there is a modest 50% increase in alveolar DPPC pool size and a 35% increase in the size of the total lung DPPC pool compared with strain- and age-matched controls (142). With currently available techniques, investigators have difficulty precisely determining the mechanisms behind this small change in pool size, but in clearance studies they consistently find a small decrease in surfactant uptake by the lung in the absence of SP-A (142). This finding agrees well with in vitro studies, but other regulatory pathways, either those normally present or those specifically induced in the SP-A-deficient mouse, are able to modulate surfactant metabolism to an almost normal state in the absence of SP-A.

Other forms of stress, inflammation, or injury may create a physiologic correlate for the lack of SP-A. Another possibility is either that the importance of SP-A to the biophysical properties and metabolism of surfactant may have been overestimated on the basis of in vitro tests or that the compensatory adaptations effectively negate the lack of SP-A in the living animal. Based on in vitro studies, two possible adaptations with the potential to compensate for the lack of SP-A are (*a*) an upregulation of PI synthesis with SP-D that then substitutes for SP-A activity (114) or (*b*) an increase in the relative amount of SP-B in the active surfactant forms (143). It is unfortunate that for our current understanding neither of these two adaptations is evident; therefore we currently are unable to explain the minimally unperturbed surfactant phenotype in the SP-A-deficient mouse (S Hawgood & F Poulain, unpublished observations).

SURFACTANT HOMEOSTASIS IN THE SP-D-DEFICIENT MOUSE

In vitro studies had revealed potential interactions between SP-D and the PI (34) and possibly other lipids (37, 38) present in surfactant. These studies had also revealed the potential for delipidated SP-D to bind the surface of type II cells (48) and alveolar macrophages (115). However, a compelling hypothesis giving SP-D a role in surfactant homeostasis had not been developed prior to the analysis of two independently derived gene-targeted mice lines (144, 145). Despite having grossly normal lung function, growth, fertility, and longevity, these mice display several significant perturbations of surfactant homeostasis, including increased surfactant pool size and abnormalities in type II cells, alveolar macrophages, pulmonary-associated lymphoid tissue, and lung structure (Figure 2). Whether these changes reflect a primary role of SP-D in normal surfactant metabolism or these changes are a secondary perturbation resulting from an altered state of lung inflammation remains unclear. The available data seem to favor the latter hypothesis.

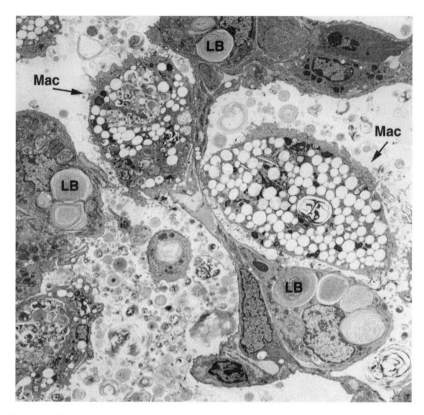

Figure 2   Electron micrograph of the alveolar region of a SP-D-deficient mouse at 18 weeks of age. The enlarged lamellar bodies within hyperplastic type II cells are labeled LB. The arrows point to enlarged alveolar macrophages (Mac) with numerous phagolysosomes, intracytoplasmic oil droplets, and rod-like crystals. The alveolar spaces are filled with an abnormal amount of secretions, most of which resemble lamellar body contents.

Altered Surfactant Pool Sizes

Alveolar surfactant DPPC pool size is increased four- to tenfold in SP-D-deficient mice (144, 145). Although both SP-D-deficient mice lines display an increased surfactant lipid pool size, investigators observed a large difference in the magnitude of the increase. Variances in the genetic background of the mice might account for the observed difference, but the modifiers responsible for these variances are unknown. The surfactant lipid composition is not significantly altered in SP-D-deficient mice, so there is a comparable increase in pool size of all phospholipid species and cholesterol (144, 145). Total protein content and the concentration of the other surfactant apoproteins in the alveolar lavage are also increased in SP-D-deficient mice, although these increases are less than the increase of lipid. SP-A levels in alveolar lavage from SP-D-deficient mice are increased approximately twofold, (144) but as most of this SP-A is associated with the macrophage cell pellet, cell-free lavage levels are 50% or less than control values (145). Consistent with the decrease in cell-free lavage SP-A, the amount of tubular myelin seen by investigators is qualitatively decreased; and the amount of surfactant in a heavy, easily sedimentable form is decreased. Despite these alterations in surfactant density and form, no significant differences in in vitro surface activity have been found in SP-D-deficient surfactant (144).

Late-term fetal tissue DPPC pools are no different than control, but tissue DPPC pools are increased in SP-D-deficient mice as early as 2 days after birth. Alveolar pool sizes increase in both control mice and SP-D-deficient mice until about 8 weeks after birth, but the maximum four- to tenfold difference in pool size between control mice and SP-D-deficient mice is established by 3 to 4 weeks and remains stable throughout life. The accumulation in both type II cells and alveolar air spaces is patchy and most pronounced in subpleural and peribronchial regions. Even at 1 year of age, some alveoli remain histologically uninvolved near regions of extensive lipid and macrophage accumulation.

The cause of the lipid accumulation is unknown. By 1 month of age a new equilibrium seems to be established with increased but stable tissue and alveolar surfactant pools. Despite stable pool sizes, SP-D-deficient mice might have altered surfactant turnover, but the problems of sampling precursor pools and the almost tenfold differences in pool sizes make detailed comparisons of surfactant turnover times difficult. Total precursor incorporation measured as ^{3}H-choline incorporation into DPPC is increased in the SP-D-deficient mouse proportionate to the increase in tissue and alveolar lavage pool size, so that specific activity is not significantly changed. The time to peak-specific activity is delayed, as we expected, from the larger pool sizes; but the slopes of the curves that describe label disappearance from the lavage fraction are not different. The calculated secretion rates at early time points after labeling are also similar (146). These results suggest no differences in synthesis, secretion, or clearance of surfactant lipids in the SP-D-deficient mice at 8 to 10 weeks of age when six- to eightfold increases in the tissue and lavage pool sizes are noted over wild-type values. It is likely that by 8 to 10 weeks of age, the mouse's system has compensated for the primary disturbance to surfactant metabolism. Unfortunately, studies of mice conducted when their pool sizes are changing, i.e. between the time of birth and 3 to 4 weeks of age, are not feasible using current techniques. However, the metabolic results are in clear contrast to the almost negligible clearance researchers reported in the granulocyte-macrophage colony–stimulating factor (GM-CSF)-deficient mouse (147). This finding suggests the lipidosis in SP-D-deficient mice is not the result of a block in macrophage-dependent surfactant clearance. Studies with isolated type II cells will likely be required to further sort out the underlying metabolic disturbances.

Changes in Type II Cells

Other prominent features of the SP-D-deficient mouse are a striking hypertrophy of alveolar epithelial type II cells and a marked enlargement of some intracellular lamellar bodies (144). Researchers have not performed the appropriate morphometry to assess whether the type II cell hypertrophy is associated with hyperplasia or whether the change in lamellar body size is accompanied by an overall decrease in lamellar body number per cell. Like the lipid accumulation, the lamellar body changes appear early in the mouse, within 3 weeks of birth, and they are patchy throughout the lung at all ages. Giant lamellar bodies have been described in other rodent models, including rats after endotoxin exposure (148), the Chediak-Higashi model mouse (149), and with expression of truncated forms of proSP-B in the SP-B null background (150). In the first of these examples, there is evidence the giant lamellar bodies form as a result of intracellular fusion, which suggests disturbed exocytosis. Hypertrophied (and hyperplastic) type II cells are reported in a number of models of cytokine or growth factor overexpression in the alveolar region. Specific examples, such as the overexpression of GM-CSF (151) or keratinocyte growth factor (152), may provide clues to the basis of the cellular changes in the SP-D-deficient mouse. Again, isolated cell studies will likely be required to ascertain the cause of the lamellar body and type II cell responses in the SP-D-deficient mouse.

Changes in Alveolar Macrophages

The number of alveolar macrophages progressively increases after birth in the SP-D-deficient mouse. By 2 months, there is a tenfold increase in alveolar macrophage number (144, 145). The macrophages progressively enlarge and accumulate intracellular lipid, both phospholipids in membrane-bound phagolysosomes and cytoplasmic oil droplets characteristic of foam cells. Clear rod-like crystals probably containing free cholesterol also accumulate in the cytoplasm of the macrophages. The metabolic activity of the macrophages in the SP-D-deficient mouse has not been characterized, but the foamy transformation is consistent with increased surfactant uptake and degradation with upregulated triglyceride and/or cholesterol-ester synthesis as a means of handling the toxic fatty acids generated. Researchers have not reported what effects this massive lipid accumulation has on macrophage function at baseline or in response to stimulation.

Changes in Lung Structure and the Alveolar Microenvironment

The lungs of SP-D-deficient mice appear structurally normal at birth but become progressively enlarged with age (Figure 3; see color insert). The lung dry weight is almost doubled (1.5 ± 0.2 cf 2.7 ± 0.9 g, $x \pm$ sd), and total lung DNA and protein are both 30% greater in SP-D-deficient mice compared with wild-type mice by 8 to 12 weeks after birth (S Hawgood & F Poulain, unpublished observations). The type II cell and macrophage changes previously described contribute partially to the larger, heavier, and more cellular lungs. The alveolar walls are also more cellular in the SP-D-deficient mouse, and there is a notable expansion of the bronchial-associated lymphoid tissue (144). Progressive emphysematous changes also contribute significantly to the increased lung size. The emphysema seems to be destructive rather than developmental and may in part be secondary to the release of proteases, which include several matrix metalloproteinases and reactive oxygen species from activated alveolar macrophages (153).

It is reasonable to expect that the marked ultrastructural changes in the type II cells and alveolar macrophages, as well as the expansion of the lymphoid compartment, will be associated with altered alveolar concentrations of growth factors, chemokines, cytokines, and reactive species. Preliminary experiments suggest significant changes in several chemokines and cytokines, as well as an increase in reactive oxygen (153) and nitrogen species, but a great deal more work will be required to ascertain the source and significance of these changes.

Overexpression of SP-D in the Distal Lung

Fisher and colleagues recently reported the consequences of overexpressing SP-D in the distal mouse lung. Using the SP-C promoter to drive a transgene, they achieved SP-D levels approximately 30–50 fold greater than control levels in BAL (154). They observed no obvious effects of this level of overexpression of the SP-D transgene in the wild-type mouse. However, the SP-D transgene successfully rescued all phenotypic features of the SP-D deficiency in the SP-D-deficient mouse. Although the transgenic expression of SP-D was driven by a type II cell-specific promoter, SP-D appeared to be restricted to the distal respiratory bronchiole without detectable expression in type II cells in these mice (154). This result implies either that the alveolar phenotype can be rescued by relatively distant expression of SP-D or that very low levels of local alveolar expression are needed to reverse the phenotype. The SP-D transgenic mouse will be a valuable resource for the further definition of the role of SP-D in the regulation of lung host defense and immune homeostasis.

OTHER MOUSE MODELS OF DISTURBED SURFACTANT HOMEOSTASIS

Several mouse lines displaying disturbed surfactant homeostasis qualitatively similar in some respects to the changes seen with SP-D deficiency have been described. In addition to their valuable work characterizing SP-A- and SP-D-deficient mice, Ikegami and colleagues have systematically studied surfactant homeostasis in several of these models. Their results suggest that several pathways can lead to similar increases in surfactant lipid and protein pool sizes, depending on the relative changes in synthesis, secretion, and clearance that occur. In situations where inflammation is increased, e.g. the overexpression of IL-4 in Clara cells (155) or after silica instillation (156, 157), the increased surfactant pool results from both increased surfactant lipid synthesis and its clearance. These changes appear to most closely resemble those defined in the SP-D-deficient mouse, which reinforces the hypothesis that the changes in surfactant homeostasis observed in SP-D deficiency may be secondary to a shift toward a pro-inflammatory state in the lung. Overexpression of GM-CSF in the distal lung, another example of a pro-inflammatory environment, also results in increased surfactant lipid synthesis and clearance and increased surfactant tissue pools; but in this example there is no alteration in alveolar lipid pools (158). Despite years of work, researchers have not discovered the factors establishing the set point for tissue and alveolar pool sizes in normal and inflamed states.

Large changes in surfactant lipid and protein pools can also result from a disturbance in normal alveolar macrophage function. Mice deficient in GM-CSF or in GM-CSF receptor develop increased tissue and alveolar surfactant lipid and proteins pools (159, 160). The rate of surfactant catabolism in these mice is below the level of detection (147). Restoring GM-CSF signaling in the alveolar macrophage by marrow transplant in GM-CSF-receptor-deficient mice corrects the alveolar lipidosis and proteinosis (161). This result confirms the critical role the alveolar macrophage has in surfactant homeostasis, and it also suggests that changes in macrophage function, as a result of injury, inflammation, or infection, may have major consequences for surfactant homeostasis.

SUMMARY

Predictions about the respective roles of SP-A and SP-D in surfactant metabolism and the host's response to inflammatory or infectious challenge have been brought into question by the phenotypes of mice deficient in these two collectins. Perhaps one of the most exciting lessons learned to date is that surfactant metabolism and the inflammatory response are intimately linked. The complex redundant and counter-regulatory pathways, as well as the adaptations within the intact animal, make simple interpretations of the phenotypes extremely difficult, but the new questions raised by these model mice have already been helpful in the development of testable hypotheses. The precise roles of SP-A and SP-D in the intact animal are not known. Given our current knowledge, we believe their designation as surfactant proteins should remain until we have a better understanding of their functions. The processes of more precisely teasing out the functional overlap between SP-A and SP-D and characterizing the complex host adaptations initiated in response to the absence or excess of the collectins and other molecules involved in surfactant homeostasis will be difficult but exciting and rewarding.

ACKNOWLEDGMENTS

Grants HL-24075 and HL-58047 from the National Heart Lung and Blood Institute of the National Institutes of Health and a grant from the Howard Hughes Medical Institute supported this work.

LITERATURE CITED

1. Hoppe HJ, Reid KB. 1994. Collectins—soluble proteins containing collagenous regions and lectin domains—and their roles in innate immunity. *Protein Sci.* 3:1143–58

2. Tenner AJ, Robinson SL, Borchelt J, Wright JR. 1989. Human pulmonary surfactant protein (SP-A), a protein structurally homologous to C1q, can enhance FcR- and CR1-mediated phagocytosis. *J. Biol. Chem.* 264:13923–28

3. Drickamer K, McCreary V. 1987. Exon structure of a mannose-binding protein gene reflects its evolutionary relationship to the asialoglycoprotein receptor and nonfibrillar collagens. *J. Biol. Chem.* 262:2582–89

4. Ezekowitz AB. 1991. Anti-antibody immunity. *Curr. Biol.* 1:60–62

5. Wright JR. 1997. Immunomodulatory functions of surfactant. *Physiol. Rev.* 77:931–62

5a. Crouch EC, Wright JR. 2001. Surfactant proteins A and D and pulmonary host defense. *Annu. Rev. Physiol.* 63:521–54

6. Crouch E, Hartshorn K, Ofek I. 2000. Collectins and pulmonary innate immunity. *Immunol. Rev.* 173:52–65

7. Lu J, Laursen SB, Thiel S, Jensenius JC, Reid KB. 1993. The cDNA cloning of conglutinin and identification of liver as a primary site of synthesis of conglutinin in members of the Bovidae. *Biochem. J.* 292:157–62

8. Holmskov U, Teisner B, Willis AC, Reid KB, Jensenius JC. 1993. Purification and characterization of a bovine serum lectin (CL-43) with structural homology to conglutinin and SP-D and carbohydrate specificity similar to mannan-binding protein. *J. Biol. Chem.* 268:10120–25

9. Ohtani K, Suzuki Y, Eda S, Kawai T, Kase T, et al. 1999. Molecular cloning of a novel human collectin from liver (CL-L1). *J. Biol. Chem.* 274:13681–89

10. Holmskov U. 1999. Lung surfactant proteins (SP-A and SP-D) in non-adaptive host responses to infection. *J. Leukoc. Biol.* 66:747–52

11. Drickamer K, Dodd RB. 1999. C-Type lectin-like domains in *Caenorhabditis elegans*: predictions from the complete genome sequence. *Glycobiology* 9:1357–69

12. White RT, Damm D, Miller J, Spratt K, Schilling J, et al. 1985. Isolation and characterization of the human pulmonary surfactant apoprotein gene. *Nature* 317:361–63

13. Lawson PR, Perkins VC, Holmskov U, Reid KB. 1999. Genomic organization of the mouse gene for lung surfactant protein D. *Am. J. Respir. Cell Mol. Biol.* 20:953–63

14. Rust K, Grosso L, Zhang V, Chang D, Persson A, et al. 1991. Human surfactant protein D: SP-D contains a C-type lectin carbohydrate recognition domain. *Arch. Biochem. Biophys.* 290:116–26

15. Akiyama J, Volik SV, Plajzer-Frick I, Prince A, Sago H, et al. 1999. Characterization of the mouse collectin gene locus. *Am. J. Respir. Cell Mol. Biol.* 21:193–99

16. Hoover RR, Floros J. 1998. Organization of the human SP-A and SP-D loci at 10q22–q23. Physical and radiation hybrid mapping reveal gene order and orientation. *Am. J. Respir. Cell Mol. Biol.* 18:353–62

17. Motwani M, White RA, Guo N, Dowler LL, Tauber AI, et al. 1995. Mouse surfactant protein-D. cDNA cloning, characterization, and gene localization to chromosome 14. *J. Immunol.* 155:5671–77

18. Voss T, Eistetter H, Schäfer KP, Engel J. 1988. Macromolecular organization of natural and recombinant lung surfactant protein SP 28–36. Structural homology with

the complement factor C1q. *J. Mol. Biol.* 201:219–27

19. Crouch EC. 1998. Structure, biologic properties, and expression of surfactant protein D (SP-D). *Biochim. Biophys. Acta* 1408:278–89

20. Hoppe HJ, Barlow PN, Reid KB. 1994. A parallel three stranded alpha-helical bundle at the nucleation site of collagen triple-helix formation. *FEBS Lett.* 344:191–95

21. Drickamer K. 1999. C-type lectin-like domains. *Curr. Opin. Struct. Biol.* 9:585–90

22. Weis WI, Kahn R, Fourme R, Drickamer K, Hendrickson WA. 1991. Structure of the calcium-dependent lectin domain from a rat mannose-binding protein determined by MAD phasing. *Science* 254:1608–15

23. Weis WI, Drickamer K. 1994. Trimeric structure of a C-type mannose-binding protein. *Structure* 2:1227–40

24. Sheriff S, Chang CY, Ezekowitz RA. 1994. Human mannose-binding protein carbohydrate recognition domain trimerizes through a triple alpha-helical coiled-coil. *Nat. Struct. Biol.* 1:789–94. Erratum. 1996. *Nat. Struct. Biol.* 1:103

25. Hakansson K, Lim NK, Hoppe HJ, Reid KB. 1999. Crystal structure of the trimeric alpha-helical coiled-coil and the three lectin domains of human lung surfactant protein D. *Struct. Fold. Des.* 7:255–64

26. Weis WI, Drickamer K. 1996. Structural basis of lectin-carbohydrate recognition. *Annu. Rev. Biochem.* 65:441–73

27. Haagsman HP, Hawgood S, Sargeant T, Buckley D, White RT, et al. 1987. The major lung surfactant protein, SP 28–36, is a calcium-dependent, carbohydrate-binding protein. *J. Biol. Chem.* 262:13877–80

28. Persson A, Chang D, Crouch E. 1990. Surfactant protein D is a divalent cation-dependent carbohydrate-binding protein. *J. Biol. Chem.* 265:5755–60

29. Weis WI, Drickamer K, Hendrickson WA. 1992. Structure of a C-type mannose-binding protein complexed with an oligosaccharide. *Nature* 360:127–34

30. Hoffmann JA, Kafatos FC, Janeway CA, Ezekowitz RA. 1999. Phylogenetic perspectives in innate immunity. *Science* 284:1313–18

31. King RJ, Phillips MC, Horowitz MC, Dang S-C. 1986. Interaction between the 35 kDa apolipoprotein of pulmonary surfactant and saturated phosphatidylcholines. Effects of temperature. *Biochim. Biophys. Acta* 879:1–13

32. Kuroki Y, Akino T. 1991. Pulmonary surfactant protein A (SP-A) specifically binds dipalmitoylphosphatidylcholine. *J. Biol. Chem.* 266:3068–73

33. Kuroki Y, Gasa S, Ogasawara Y, Makita A, Akino T. 1992. Binding of pulmonary surfactant protein A to galactosylceramide and asialo-GM2. *Arch. Biochem. Biophys.* 299:261–67

34. Persson AV, Gibbons BJ, Shoemaker JD, Moxley MA, Longmore WJ. 1992. The major glycolipid recognized by SP-D in surfactant is phosphatidylinositol. *J. Biol. Chem.* 267:19846–53

35. Ogasawara Y, Kuroki Y, Akino T. 1992. Pulmonary surfactant protein D specifically binds to phosphatidylinositol. *J. Biol. Chem.* 1992:21244–49

36. Kuroki Y, Gasa S, Ogasawara Y, Shiratori M, Makita A, et al. 1992. Binding specificity of lung surfactant protein SP-D for glucosylceramide. *Biochem. Biophys. Res. Commun.* 187:963–99

37. Kuroki Y, Shiratori M, Ogasawara Y, Tsuzuki A, Akino T. 1991. Characterization of pulmonary surfactant protein D: its copurification with lipids. *Biochim. Biophys. Acta* 1086:185–90

38. Taneva S, Voelker DR, Keough KM. 1997. Adsorption of pulmonary surfactant protein D to phospholipid monolayers at the air-water interface. *Biochemistry* 36:8173–79

39. Chiba H, Sano H, Saitoh M, Sohma H, Voelker DR, et al. 1999. Introduction of mannose binding protein-type phosphatidylinositol recognition into pulmonary

surfactant protein A. *Biochemistry* 38: 7321–31

40. Honma T, Kuroki Y, Tsunezawa W, Ogasawara Y, Sohma H, et al. 1997. The mannose-binding protein A region of glutamic acid185–alanine221 can functionally replace the surfactant protein A region of glutamic acid195–phenylalanine228 without loss of interaction with lipids and alveolar type II cells. *Biochemistry* 36:7176–84

41. Kuroki Y, McCormack FX, Ogasawara Y, Mason RJ, Voelker DR. 1994. Epitope mapping for monoclonal antibodies identifies functional domains of pulmonary surfactant protein A that interact with lipids. *J. Biol. Chem.* 269:29793–800

42. Saitoh M, Sano H, Chiba H, Murakami S, Iwaki D, et al. 2000. Importance of the carboxy-terminal 25 amino acid residues of lung collectins in interactions with lipids and alveolar type II cells. *Biochemistry* 39:1059–66

43. Tsunezawa W, Sano H, Sohma H, McCormack FX, Voelker DR, et al. 1998. Site-directed mutagenesis of surfactant protein A reveals dissociation of lipid aggregation and lipid uptake by alveolar type II cells. *Biochim. Biophys. Acta* 1387:433–46

44. Murata Y, Kuroki Y, Akino T. 1993. Role of the C-terminal domain of pulmonary surfactant protein A in binding to alveolar type II cells and regulation of phospholipid secretion. *Biochem. J.* 291:71–76

45. McCormack FX, Kuroki Y, Stewart JJ, Mason RJ, Voelker DR. 1994. Surfactant protein A amino acids Glu195 and Arg197 are essential for receptor binding, phospholipid aggregation, regulation of secretion, and the facilitated uptake of phospholipid by type II cells. *J. Biol. Chem.* 269:29801–7

46. Kuroki Y, Mason RJ, Voelker DR. 1988. Alveolar type II cells express a high-affinity receptor for pulmonary surfactant protein A. *Proc. Natl. Acad. Sci. USA* 85:5566–70

47. Wright JR, Borchelt JD, Hawgood S. 1989.

Lung surfactant apoprotein SP-A (26–36 kDa) binds with high affinity to isolated alveolar type II cells. *Proc. Natl. Acad. Sci. USA* 86:5410–14

48. Herbein JF, Savov J, Wright JR. 2000. Binding and uptake of surfactant protein D by freshly isolated rat alveolar type II cells. *Am. J. Physiol. Lung Cell. Mol. Physiol.* 278:L830–L39

49. Deleted in proof

50. Pison U, Wright JR, Hawgood S. 1992. Specific binding of surfactant apoprotein SP-A to rat alveolar macrophages. *Am. J. Physiol. Lung Cell Mol. Physiol.* 262: L412–L17

51. Dong Q, Wright JR. 1998. Degradation of surfactant protein D by alveolar macro- GR62 phages. *Am. J. Physiol. Lung Cell Mol. Physiol.* 274:L97–L105

52. Miyamura K, Leigh LE, Lu J, Hopkin J, Lopez Bernal A, et al. 1994. Surfactant protein D binding to alveolar macrophages. *Biochem. J.* 300:237–42

53. Tenner AJ. 1999. Membrane receptors for soluble defense collagens. *Curr. Opin. Immunol.* 11:34–41

54. Malhotra R, Haurum J, Thiel S, Sim RB. 1992. Interaction of C1q receptor with lung surfactant protein A. *Eur. J. Immunol.* 22:1437–45

55. Nepomuceno RR, Henschen-Edman AH, Burgess WH, Tenner AJ. 1997. cDNA cloning and primary structure analysis of C1qR(P), the human C1q/MBL/SPA receptor that mediates enhanced phagocytosis in vitro. *Immunity* 6:119–29

56. Michelis D, Kounnas MZ, Argraves WS, Sanford ED, Borchelt JD, et al. 1994. Interaction of surfactant protein A with cellular myosin. *Am. J. Respir. Cell Mol. Biol.* 11:692–700

57. Tino MJ, Wright JR. 1999. Glycoprotein-340 binds surfactant protein-A (SP-A) and stimulates alveolar macrophage migration in an SP-A-independent manner. *Am. J. Respir. Cell Mol. Biol.* 20:759–68

58. Sohma H, Matsushima N, Watanabe T,

Hattori A, Kuroki Y, et al. 1995. Ca(2+)-dependent binding of annexin IV to surfactant protein A and lamellar bodies in alveolar type II cells. *Biochem. J.* 312:175–81

59. Chroneos ZC, Abdolrasulnia R, Whitsett JA, Rice WR, Shepherd VL. 1996. Purification of a cell-surface receptor for surfactant protein A. *J. Biol. Chem.* 271:16375–83

60. Kresch MJ, Christian C, Lu H. 1998. Isolation and partial characterization of a receptor to surfactant protein A expressed by rat type II pneumocytes. *Am. J. Respir. Cell Mol. Biol.* 19:216–25

61. Strayer DS, Yang S, Jerng HH. 1993. Surfactant protein A-binding proteins. Characterization and structures. *J. Biol. Chem.* 268:18679–84

62. Stevens PA, Wissel H, Sieger D, Meienreis-Sudau V, Rustow B. 1995. Identification of a new surfactant protein A binding protein at the cell membrane of rat type II pneumocytes. *Biochem. J.* 308:77–81

63. Holmskov U, Mollenhauer J, Madsen J, Vitved L, Gronlund J, et al. 1999. Cloning of gp-340, a putative opsonin receptor for lung surfactant protein D. *Proc. Natl. Acad. Sci. USA* 96:10794–99

64. Holmskov U, Lawson P, Teisner B, Tornoe I, Willis AC, et al. 1997. Isolation and characterization of a new member of the scavenger receptor superfamily, glycoprotein-340 (gp-340), as a lung surfactant protein-D binding molecule. *J. Biol. Chem.* 272:13743–49

65. Lausen M, Lynch N, Schlosser A, Tornoe I, Saekmose SG, et al. 1999. Microfibril-associated protein 4 is present in lung washings and binds to the collagen region of lung surfactant protein D. *J. Biol. Chem.* 274:32234–40

66. Crouch E, Persson A, Chang D, Heuser J. 1994. Molecular structure of pulmonary surfactant protein D (SP-D). *J. Biol. Chem.* 269:17311–19

67. Reid KB. 1989. Chemistry and molecular genetics of C1q. *Behring. Inst. Mitt.* 84:8–19

68. Matsushita M, Endo Y, Fujita T. 2000. Cutting edge: complement-activating complex of ficolin and mannose-binding lectin-associated serine protease. *J. Immunol.* 164:2281–84

69. Wong CJ, Akiyama J, Allen L, Hawgood S. 1996. Localization and developmental expression of surfactant proteins D and A in the respiratory tract of the mouse. *Pediatr. Res.* 39:930–37

70. Crouch E, Parghi D, Kuan SF, Persson A. 1992. Surfactant protein D: subcellular localization in nonciliated bronchiolar epithelial cells. *Am. J. Physiol. Lung Cell Mol. Physiol.* 263:L60–L66

71. Williams MC, Benson B. 1981. Immunocytochemical localization and identification of the major surfactant protein in adult rat lung. *J. Histochem. Cytochem.* 29:291–305

72. Voorhout WF, Veenendaal T, Kuroki Y, Ogasawara Y, van Golde LMG, et al. 1992. Immunocytochemical localization of surfactant protein D (SP-D) in type II cells, clara cells, and alveolar macrophages of rat lung. *J. Histochem. Cytochem.* 40:1589–97

73. Rubio S, Lacaze-Masmonteil T, Chailley-Heu B, Kahn A, Bourbon JR, et al. 1995. Pulmonary surfactant protein A (SP-A) is expressed by epithelial cells of small and large intestine. *J. Biol. Chem.* 270:12162–69

74. Madsen J, Kliem A, Tornoe I, Skjodt K, Koch C, et al. 2000. Localization of lung surfactant protein D on mucosal surfaces in human tissues. *J. Immunol.* 164:5866–70

75. Fisher JH, Mason R. 1995. Expression of pulmonary surfactant protein D in rat gastric mucosa. *Am. J. Respir. Cell Mol. Biol.* 12:13–18

76. Paananen R, Glumoff V, Hallman M. 1999. Surfactant protein A and D expression in the porcine Eustachian tube. *FEBS Lett.* 452:141–44

77. Clements JA, Hustead RF, Johnson RP,

Gribetz I. 1961. Pulmonary surface tension and alveolar stability. *J. Appl. Physiol.* 16:444–50

78. Wright JR, Hawgood S. 1989. Pulmonary surfactant metabolism. *Clin. Chest. Med.* 10:83–93

79. Clements JA. 1977. Functions of the alveolar lining. *Am. Rev. Respir. Dis.* 115:67–71

80. King RJ, Clements JA. 1972. Surface active materials from dog lung. II. Composition and physiological correlations. *Am. J. Physiol.* 223:715–26

81. Hawgood S, Benson BJ, Schilling J, Damm D, Clements JA, et al. 1987. Nucleotide and amino acid sequences of pulmonary surfactant protein SP 18 and evidence for cooperation between SP 18 and SP 28–36 in surfactant lipid adsorption. *Proc. Natl. Acad. Sci. USA* 84:66–70

82. Warr RG, Hawgood S, Buckley DI, Crisp TM, Schilling J, et al. 1987. Low molecular weight human pulmonary surfactant protein (SP5): isolation, characterization, and cDNA and amino acid sequences. *Proc. Natl. Acad. Sci. USA* 84:7915–19

83. Phizackerley PJR, Town M-H, Newman GE. 1979. Hydrophobic proteins of lamellated osmiophilic bodies isolated from pig lung. *Biochem. J.* 183:731–36

84. Curstedt T, Jörnvall H, Robertson B, Bergman T, Berggren P. 1987. Two hydrophobic low-molecular-mass protein fractions of pulmonary surfactant. Characterization and biophysical activity. *Eur. J. Biochem.* 168:255–62

85. Oosterlaken-Dijksterhuis MA, van Eijk M, van Buel BL, van Golde LM, Haagsman HP. 1991. Surfactant protein composition of lamellar bodies isolated from rat lung. *Biochem. J.* 274:115–19

86. Froh D, Ballard PL, Williams MC, Gonzales J, Goerke J, et al. 1990. Lamellar bodies of cultured human fetal lung: content of surfactant protein A (SP-A), surface film formation and structural transformation in vitro. *Biochim. Biophys. Acta* 1052:78–89

87. Osanai K, Mason RJ, Voelker DR. 1998. Trafficking of newly synthesized surfactant protein A in isolated rat alveolar type II cells. *Am. J. Respir. Cell Mol. Biol.* 19:929–35

88. Goerke J. 1974. Lung surfactant. *Biochim. Biophys. Acta* 344:241–61

89. Magoon MW, Wright JR, Baritussio A, Williams MC, Goerke J, et al. 1983. Subfractionation of lung surfactant. Implications for metabolism and surface activity. *Biochim. Biophys. Acta* 750:18–31

90. Williams MC. 1977. Conversion of lamellar body membranes into tubular myelin in alveoli of fetal rat lungs. *J. Cell Biol.* 72:260–77

91. Gil J, Reiss OK. 1973. Isolation and characterization of lamellar bodies and tubular myelin from rat lung homogenates. *J. Cell Biol.* 58:152–71

92. Manabe T. 1979. Freeze-fracture study of alveolar lining layer in adult rat lungs. *J. Ultrastruct. Res.* 69:86–97

93. Wright JR, Benson BJ, Williams MC, Goerke J, Clements JA. 1984. Protein composition of rabbit alveolar surfactant subfractions. *Biochim. Biophys. Acta* 791:320–32

94. Wright JR, Wager RE, Hamilton RL, Huang M, Clements JA. 1986. Uptake of lung surfactant subfractions into lamellar bodies of adult rabbit lungs. *J. Appl. Physiol.* 60:817–25

95. Baritussio AG, Magoon MW, Goerke J, Clements JA. 1981. Precursor-product relationship between rabbit type II cell lamellar bodies and alveolar surface-active material. Surfactant turnover time. *Biochim. Biophys. Acta* 666:382–93

96. Hallman M, Epstein BL, Gluck L. 1981. Analysis of labeling and clearance of lung surfactant phospholipids in rabbit. Evidence of bidirectional surfactant flux between lamellar bodies and alveolar lavage. *J. Clin. Invest.* 68:742–51

97. Rider ED, Ikegami M, Jobe AH. 1992. Localization of alveolar surfactant clearance in rabbit lung cells. *Am. J. Physiol. Lung Cell Mol. Physiol.* 263:L201–L9

98. Chander A, Reicherter J, Fisher AB. 1987. Degradation of dipalmitoyl phosphatidylcholine by isolated rat granular pneumocytes and reutilization for surfactant synthesis. *J. Clin. Invest.* 79:1133–38

99. Jacobs H, Jobe A, Ikegami M, Miller D, Jones S. 1984. Reutilization of phosphatidylcholine analogues by the pulmonary surfactant system. The lack of specificity. *Biochim. Biophys. Acta* 793:300–9

100. Grabner R, Meerbach W. 1991. Phagocytosis of surfactant by alveolar macrophages in vitro. *Am. J. Physiol. Lung Cell Mol. Physiol.* 261:L472–L77

101. Miles PR, Ma YC, Bowman L. 1988. Degradation of pulmonary surfactant disaturated phosphatidylcholines by alveolar macrophages. *J. Appl. Physiol.* 64:2474–81

102. Jacobs H, Jobe A, Ikegami M, Jones S. 1982. Surfactant phosphatidylcholine source, fluxes, and turnover times in 3-day-old, 10-day-old, and adult rabbits. *J. Biol. Chem.* 257:1805–10

103. Jacobs HC, Ikegami M, Jobe AH, Berry DD, Jones S. 1985. Reutilization of surfactant phosphatidylcholine in adult rabbits. *Biochim. Biophys. Acta* 837:77–84

104. Nicholas TE, Power JHT, Barr HA. 1982. Surfactant homeostasis in the rat lung during swimming exercise. *J. Appl. Physiol.: Respir. Environ. Exerc. Physiol.* 53:1521–28

105. Nicholas TE, Power JHT, Barr HA. 1982. The pulmonary consequences of a deep breath. *Respir. Physiol.* 49:315–24

106. Nicholas TE, Barr HA. 1983. The release of surfactant in rat lung by brief periods of hyperventilation. *Respir. Physiol.* 52:69–83

107. Fisher AB, Dodia C, Chander A. 1989. Secretagogues for lung surfactant increase lung uptake of alveolar phospholipids. *Am. J. Physiol. Lung Cell Mol. Physiol.* 257:L248–L52

108. Suzuki Y, Fujita Y, Kogishi K. 1989. Reconstitution of tubular myelin from synthetic lipids and proteins associated with pig pulmonary surfactant. *Am. Rev. Respir. Dis.* 140:75–81

109. Williams MC, Hawgood S, Hamilton RL. 1991. Changes in lipid structure produced by surfactant proteins SP-A, SP-B, and SP-C. *Am. J. Respir. Cell Mol. Biol.* 5:41–50

110. Rice WR, Ross GF, Singleton FM, Dingle S, Whitsett JA. 1987. Surfactant-associated protein inhibits phospholipid secretion from type II cells. *J. Appl. Physiol.* 63:692–98

111. Dobbs LG, Wright JR, Hawgood S, Gonzalez R, Venstrom K, et al. 1987. Pulmonary surfactant and its components inhibit secretion of phosphatidylcholine from cultured rat alveolar type II cells. *Proc. Natl. Acad. Sci. USA* 84:1010–14

112. Veldhuizen RA, Yao LJ, Hearn SA, Possmayer F, Lewis JF. 1996. Surfactant-associated protein A is important for maintaining surfactant large-aggregate forms during surface-area cycling. *Biochem. J.* 313:835–40

113. Wright JR. 1990. Clearance and recycling of pulmonary surfactant. *Am. J. Physiol. Lung Cell Mol. Physiol.* 259:L1–L12

114. Poulain FR, Akiyama J, Allen L, Brown C, Chang R, et al. 1999. Ultrastructure of phospholipid mixtures reconstituted with surfactant proteins B and D. *Am. J. Respir. Cell Mol. Biol.* 20:1049–58

115. Kuan SF, Persson A, Parghi D, Crouch E. 1994. Lectin-mediated interactions of surfactant protein D with alveolar macrophages. *Am. J. Respir. Cell Mol. Biol.* 10:430–36

116. Mason RJ, Voelker DR. 1998. Regulatory mechanisms of surfactant secretion. *Biochim. Biophys. Acta* 1408:226–40

117. Kuroki Y, Mason RJ, Voelker DR. 1988. Pulmonary surfactant apoprotein A structure and modulation of surfactant secretion by rat alveolar type II cells. *J. Biol. Chem.* 263:3388–94

118. Kuroki Y, Shiratori M, Murata Y, Akino T. 1991. Surfactant protein D (SP-D) counteracts the inhibitory effect of surfactant protein A (SP-A) on phospholipid secretion by alveolar type II cells. Interaction of native SP-D with SP-A. *Biochem. J.* 279:115–19

119. Kuroki Y, Mason RJ, Voelker DR. 1988. Chemical modification of surfactant protein A alters high affinity binding to rat alveolar type II cells and regulation of phospholipid secretion. *J. Biol. Chem.* 263:17596–602

120. Voorhout WF, Veenendaal T, Haagsman HP, Verkkleij AJ, van Golde LM, et al. 1991. Surfactant protein A is localized at the corners of the pulmonary tubular myelin lattice. *J. Histochem. Cytochem.* 39:1331–36

121. Ikegami M, Korfhagen TR, Whitsett JA, Bruno MD, Wert SE, et al. 1998. Characteristics of surfactant from SP-A-deficient mice. *Am. J. Physiol. Lung Cell Mol. Physiol.* 275:L247–L54

122. Clark JC, Wert SE, Bachurski CJ, Stahlman MT, Stripp BR, et al. 1995. Targeted disruption of the surfactant protein B gene disrupts surfactant homeostasis, causing respiratory failure in newborn mice. *Proc. Natl. Acad. Sci. USA* 92:7794–98

123. Weibel ER. 1973. Morphological basis of alveolar-capillary gas exchange. *Physiol. Rev.* 53:419–95

124. Notter RH, Penney DP, Finkelstein JN, Shapiro DL. 1986. Adsorption of natural lung surfactant and phospholipid extracts related to tubular myelin formation. *Pediatr. Res.* 20:97–101

125. Notter RH, Shapiro DL, Ohning B, Whitsett JA. 1987. Biophysical activity of synthetic phospholipids combined with purified lung surfactant 6000 dalton apoprotein. *Chem. Phys. Lipids* 44:1–17

126. Yu SH, Possmayer F. 1990. Role of bovine pulmonary surfactant-associated proteins in the surface-active property of phospho-lipid mixtures. *Biochim. Biophys. Acta* 1046:233–41

127. Curstedt T, Johansson J, Barros-Söderling J, Robertson B, Nilsson G, et al. 1988. Low-molecular mass surfactant protein type 1. The primary structure of a hydrophobic 8–kDa polypeptide with eight half-cystine residues. *Eur. J. Biochem.* 172:521–25

128. Curstedt T, Johansson J, Persson P, Eklund A, Robertson B, et al. 1990. Hydrophobic surfactant-associated polypeptides; SP-C is a lipopeptide with two palmitoylated cisteine residues whereas SP-B lacks covalently linked fatty acyl groups. *Proc. Natl. Acad. Sci. USA* 87:2985–89

129. Nogee LM, de Mello DE, Dehner LP, Colten HR. 1993. Brief report: deficiency of pulmonary surfactant protein B in congenital alveolar proteinosis. *N. Engl. J. Med.* 328:406–10

130. Cockshutt AM, Weitz J, Possmayer F. 1990. Pulmonary surfactant-associated protein A enhances the surface activity of lipid extract surfactant and reverses inhibition by blood proteins in vitro. *Biochemistry* 29:8425–29

131. Yukitake K, Brown CL, Schlueter MA, Clements JA, Hawgood S. 1995. Surfactant apoprotein A modifies the inhibitory effect of plasma proteins on surfactant activity in vivo. *Pediatr. Res.* 37:21–25

132. Honda Y, Kataoka K, Hayashi H, Takahashi H, Suzuki A, et al. 1989. Alterations of acidic phospholipids in bronchoalveolar lavage fluids of patients with pulmonary alveolar proteinosis. *Clin. Chim. Acta* 181:11–18

133. Takemura T, Fukuda Y, Harrison M, Ferrans VJ. 1987. Ultrastructural, histochemical, and freeze-fracture evaluation of multilamellated structures in human pulmonary alveolar proteinosis. *Am. J. Anat.* 179:258–68

134. Savov J, Silbajoris R, Young SL. 1999. Mechanical ventilation of rat lung: effect

on surfactant forms. *Am. J. Physiol. Lung Cell Mol. Physiol.* 277:L320–L26

135. Gross NJ, Narine KR. 1989. Surfactant subtypes in mice: characterization and quantitation. *J. Appl. Physiol.* 66:342–49

136. Baritussio A, Alberti A, Quaglino D, Pettenazzo A, Dalzoppo D, et al. 1994. SP-A, SP-B, and SP-C in surfactant subtypes around birth: reexamination of alveolar life cycle of surfactant. *Am. J. Physiol. Lung Cell Mol. Physiol.* 266:L436–L47

137. Gross NJ, Narine KR. 1989. Surfactant subtypes of mice: metabolic relationships and conversion in vitro. *J. Appl. Physiol.* 67:414–21

138. Wright JR, Wager RE, Hawgood S, Dobbs L, Clements JA. 1987. Surfactant apoprotein $M_r = 26,000–36,000$ enhances uptake of liposomes by type II cells. *J. Biol. Chem.* 262:2888–94

139. Wright JR, Youmans DC. 1995. Degradation of surfactant lipids and surfactant protein A by alveolar macrophages in vitro. *Am. J. Physiol. Lung Cell Mol. Physiol.* 268:L772–L80

140. Jacobs H, Jobe A, Ikegami M, Conaway D. 1983. The significance of reutilization of surfactant phosphatidylcholine. *J. Biol. Chem.* 258:4159–65

141. Korfhagen TR, LeVine AM, Whitsett JA. 1998. Surfactant protein A (SP-A) gene targeted mice. *Biochim. Biophys. Acta* 1408:296–302

142. Ikegami M, Korfhagen TR, Bruno MD, Whitsett JA, Jobe AH. 1997. Surfactant metabolism in surfactant protein A-deficient mice. *Am. J. Physiol. Lung Cell Mol. Physiol.* 272:L479–L85

143. Mizuno K, Ikegami M, Chen CM, Ueda T, Jobe AH. 1995. Surfactant protein-B supplementation improves in vivo function of a modified natural surfactant. *Pediatr. Res.* 37:271–76

144. Botas C, Poulain F, Akiyama J, Brown C, Allen L, et al. 1998. Altered surfactant homeostasis and alveolar type II cell morphology in mice lacking surfactant

protein D. *Proc. Natl. Acad. Sci. USA* 95:11869–74

145. Korfhagen TR, Sheftelyevich V, Burhans MS, Bruno MD, Ross GF, et al. 1998. Surfactant protein-D regulates surfactant phospholipid homeostasis in vivo. *J. Biol. Chem.* 273:28438–43

146. Pramanik A, Brown C, Poulain F, Hawgood S. 1999. Altered surfactant metabolism in the SP-D deficient mouse. *Pediatr. Res.* 45:316A (Abstr.)

147. Ikegami M, Ueda T, Hull W, Whitsett JA, Mulligan RC, et al. 1996. Surfactant metabolism in transgenic mice after granulocyte macrophage-colony stimulating factor ablation. *Am. J. Physiol. Lung Cell Mol. Physiol.* 270:L650–L58

148. Fehrenbach H, Brasch F, Uhlig S, Weisser M, Stamme C, et al. 1998. Early alterations in intracellular and alveolar surfactant of the rat lung in response to endotoxin. *Am. J. Respir. Crit. Care Med.* 157:1630–39

149. Chi EY, Lagunoff D, Koehler JK. 1976. Abnormally large lamellar bodies in type II pneumocytes in Chediak-Higashi syndrome in beige mice. *Lab. Invest.* 34:166–73

150. Akinbi HT, Breslin JS, Ikegami M, Iwamoto HS, Clark JC, et al. 1997. Rescue of SP-B knockout mice with a truncated SP-B proprotein. Function of the C-terminal propeptide. *J. Biol. Chem.* 272:9640–47

151. Huffman Reed JA, Rice WR, Zsengeller ZK, Wert SE, Dranoff G, et al. 1997. GM-CSF enhances lung growth and causes alveolar type II epithelial cell hyperplasia in transgenic mice. *Am. J. Physiol. Lung Cell Mol. Physiol.* 273:L715–L25

152. Simonet WS, DeRose ML, Bucay N, Nguyen HQ, Wert SE, et al. 1995. Pulmonary malformation in transgenic mice expressing human keratinocyte growth factor in the lung. *Proc. Natl. Acad. Sci. USA* 92:12461–65

153. Wert SE, Yoshida M, LeVine AM,

Ikegami M, Jones T, et al. 2000. Increased metalloproteinase activity, oxidant production, and emphysema in surfactant protein D gene-inactivated mice. *Proc. Natl. Acad. Sci. USA* 97:5972–77

154. Fisher JH, Sheftelyevich V, Ho YS, Fligiel S, McCormack FX, et al. 2000. Pulmonary-specific expression of SP-D corrects pulmonary lipid accumulation in SP-D gene-targeted mice. *Am. J. Physiol. Lung Cell Mol. Physiol.* 278:L365–L73

155. Ikegami M, Whitsett JA, Chroneos ZC, Ross GF, Reed JA, et al. 2000. IL-4 increases surfactant and regulates metabolism in vivo. *Am. J. Physiol. Lung Cell Mol. Physiol.* 278:L75–L80

156. Viviano CJ, Bakewell WE, Dixon D, Dethloff LA, Hook GE. 1995. Altered regulation of surfactant phospholipid and protein A during acute pulmonary inflammation. *Biochim. Biophys. Acta* 1259:235–44

157. Lesur O, Bouhadiba T, Melloni B, Cantin A, Whitsett JA, et al. 1995. Alterations of surfactant lipid turnover in silicosis: evidence of a role for surfactant-associated protein A (SP-A). *Int. J. Exp. Pathol.* 76:287–98

158. Ikegami M, Jobe AH, Huffman Reed JA, Whitsett JA. 1997. Surfactant metabolic consequences of overexpression of GM-CSF in the epithelium of GM-CSF-deficient mice. *Am. J. Physiol. Lung Cell Mol. Physiol.* 273:L709–L14

159. Dranoff G, Crawford AD, Sadelain M, Ream B, Rashid A, et al. 1994. Involvement of granulocyte-macrophage colony-stimulating factor in pulmonary homeostasis. *Science* 264:713–16

160. Nishinakamura R, Nakayama N, Hirabayashi Y, Inoue T, Aud D, et al. 1995. Mice deficient for the IL-3/GM-CSF/IL-5 beta c receptor exhibit lung pathology and impaired immune response, while beta IL3 receptor-deficient mice are normal. *Immunity* 2:211–22

161. Nishinakamura R, Wiler R, Dirksen U, Morikawa Y, Arai K, et al. 1996. The pulmonary alveolar proteinosis in granulocyte macrophage colony-stimulating factor/interleukins 3/5 beta c receptor-deficient mice is reversed by bone marrow transplantation. *J. Exp. Med.* 183:2657–62

Annu. Rev. Physiol. 2001. 63:521–54

SURFACTANT PROTEINS A AND D AND PULMONARY HOST DEFENSE

Erika Crouch[1] and Jo Rae Wright[2]

[1]Department of Pathology and Immunology, Washington University School of Medicine, St. Louis, Missouri 63110; e-mail: crouch@path.wustl.edu
[2]Department of Cell Biology, Duke University Medical Center, Durham, North Carolina 27710; e-mail: j.wright@cellbio.duke.edu

Key Words   collectin, pulmonary surfactant, alveolar, C-type lectin

■ **Abstract**   The lung collectins, SP-A and SP-D, are important components of the innate immune response to microbial challenge and participate in other aspects of immune and inflammatory regulation within the lung. Both proteins bind to surface structures expressed by a wide variety of microorganisms and have the capacity to modulate multiple leukocyte functions, including the enhanced internalization and killing of certain microorganisms in vitro. In addition, transgenic mice with deficiencies in SP-A and SP-D show defective or altered responses to challenge with bacterial, fungal, and viral microorganisms and to bacterial lipopolysaccharides in vivo. Thus collectins could play particularly important roles in settings of inadequate or impaired specific immunity, and acquired alterations in the levels of active collectins within the airspaces and distal airways may increase susceptibility to infection.

INTRODUCTION

The epithelial lining of the alveoli and distal airways of the lung is critically positioned to participate in the neutralization and clearance of inhaled microorganisms and other toxic particles. Two surfactant proteins, SP-A and SP-D, are members of a family of innate immune molecules known as collectins, a name derived from the fact that members of this family all contain a collagen-like domain and a calcium-dependent lectin domain, also known as a carbohydrate recognition domain (CRD). The lung collectins, SP-A and SP-D, are secreted by airway epithelial cells, specifically interact with a wide range of microorganisms, show specific interactions with leukocytes, and modulate the function of phagocytic cells in vitro and in vivo (1–6) (Figure 1). Lung collectins also interact with, and modulate the cellular effects of, inhaled pollens and other complex organic antigens (7, 8). These and other findings strongly suggest that SP-A and SP-D play important roles in the innate, natural, and non-clonal defense system of the lung.

0066-4278/01/0315-0521$14.00

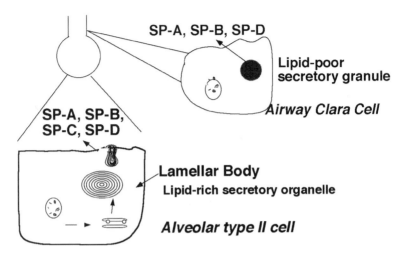

Figure 1   Cells involved in synthesis and secretion of surfactant components. Both alveolar type II cells and the airway Clara cell synthesize and secrete the lung collectins, SP-A and SP-D, as well as SP-B. Type II cells also synthesize SP-C and secrete surfactant lipids into the airspace where dipalmitoylphosphatidylcholine spreads at the air-liquid interface and reduces surface tension.

Even though the purpose of this review is to address the roles of SP-A and SP-D in host defense, it is important to note that both proteins may have multiple functions. For example, mice made deficient in SP-D by homologous recombination have enormous increases in their surfactant lipid pool sizes (9, 10). Although SP-A-null mice show normal lipid pool sizes and have only minimal perturbations in the surface tension–reducing capabilities of their surfactant and normal lung compliance (11), numerous in vitro studies have suggested potential roles of SP-A in the regulation of surfactant turnover and metabolism (reviewed in this volume by Hawgood & Poulain; 11a). Thus both proteins may contribute to the regulation of surfactant homeostasis under certain circumstances in vivo. Future studies will be required to elucidate the mechanisms by which the lung collectins contribute to such different physiological processes.

THE LUNG COLLECTINS INTERACT WITH DIVERSE CARBOHYDRATE AND LIPID LIGANDS IN VITRO

The lung collectins are members of the mannose-type subfamily of C-type (calcium-dependent) lectins. Although both proteins can bind to mannose and glucose and show little interaction with galactose, they show reproducible differences in relative saccharide selectivity (12–14). For example, human SP-A preferentially interacts with N-acetylmannosamine and L-fucose in sold-phase binding assays, whereas human SP-D preferentially interacts with inositol, maltose, and glucose. At present, the biological significance of these differences is not known. Most microbial ligands contain mannose or glucose. For example, SP-A binds to di-mannose-repeating units in certain gram-negative capsular polysaccharides (15). Likewise, SP-D shows CRD-dependent binding to the glucose-containing core oligosaccharides of gram-negative lipopolysaccharide (LPS) (1) and terminal mannosyl oligosaccharides of lipoarabinomannan from *Mycobacterium tuberculosis* (16).

The carboxy-terminal domains of SP-A and SP-D are responsible for their lectin activity, and trimeric clusters of the SP-D CRDs are required for high-affinity binding to multivalent ligands (17, 18). Thus the majority of the biologically active forms of the collectins recovered from the lung consist of multimers of trimeric subunits. Whereas SP-A accumulates predominantly as octadecamers (6 trimers), SP-D preferentially accumulates as dodecamers (4 trimers) or higher order multimers (Figure 2, see color insert). The spatial distribution of the saccharide-binding sites of a trimeric subunit allows simultaneous occupancy of two to three saccharide-binding sites by glycoconjugates displayed on the surface of a particulate ligand, and further oligomerization of these subunits permits cooperative or bridging interactions between spatially separated binding sites. Because the maximum separation of trimeric CRDs of SP-D is fivefold greater than for SP-A (approximately 100 nm versus 20 nm) and because the binding surfaces of pairs of trimeric SP-D CRDs can orient at approximately 180° with respect to one another in the intact dodecamer, SP-D has a greater capacity to mediate bridging interactions between binding sites on different particulate ligands.

Both collectins can also interact with lipids. SP-A binds to dipalmitoylphosphatidylcholine (DPPC), the major surfactant phospholipid (19, 20); the lipid A domain of gram-negative LPS (21, 22); and to several glycolipids and neutral glycosphingolipids (23–25). SP-D interacts with the inositol and lipid moieties of phosphatidylinositol (PI) (26–28) and with glucosyl-ceramide (29). The interaction of SP-D with PI is complex and involves interactions with the inositol and lipid moieties (30, 31). The interactions of collectins with lipid ligands could contribute to surfactant lipid reorganization and/or the interactions of these molecules with host cells.

LUNG COLLECTINS INTERACT WITH CONSERVED CELL WALL GLYCOCONJUGATES EXPRESSED BY THE MAJOR CLASSES OF MICROORGANISMS

Interactions of Collectins with Bacteria and Mycobacteria

Bacteria are surfaced by a complex array of polysaccharides and other glycoconjugates, including the polysaccharide constituents of capsules, gram-negative lipopolysaccharides, and the lipoteichoic acid moieties of gram-positive organisms.

Many of the polysaccharides contain covalently linked repeating units that may vary with the bacterial strain (32). However, other domains, such as the core region of LPS, are highly conserved among many species (33).

At least two surface glycoconjugates are involved in the interactions of collectins with gram-negative bacteria (Table 1). One is the core region of LPS of gram-negative bacteria, which is broadly recognized by SP-D (34). The other is the di-mannose (or di-rhamnose) repeating unit associated with some capsular polysaccharides, which interact with SP-A and the macrophage mannose receptor, another C-type lectin (15). SP-A can also interact with other cell wall constituents such as the lipid A domain of *Escherichia coli* LPS (21, 22), and the outer membrane protein of *Haemophilius influenzae*, type A (35). The interaction of lung collectins, particularly SP-D, with bacteria often results in CRD-dependent bacterial aggregation (agglutination). The lung collectins can modify the interactions of gram-positive bacteria and chlamydia, e.g. mycoplasma, with phagocytic cells. However, in most cases it remains unclear whether this involves direct or CRD-dependent interactions of the collectin with the organism.

SP-D agglutinates the virulent Erdman strain of *M. tuberculosis* through lectin-dependent interactions with cell wall glycoconjugates (16). Although some studies have shown that SP-A can enhance the phagocytosis of mycobacteria by macrophages, this appears to involve the direct activation of the phagocyte rather than CRD-dependent binding to mycobacterial glycoconjugates (36, 37).

Interactions of Collectins with Fungi and *Pneumocystis carinii*

The lung collectins show specific CRD-dependent interactions with cell wall glycoconjugates expressed by true fungi and *Pneumocystis carinii*.

TABLE 1   Interactions of lung collectins with bacterial ligands

	Bacterial ligand	Collectin	Reference
Gram-negative bacteria			
Pseudomonas aeruginosa	LPS?	SP-A	144
		SP-D	82
Klebsiella pneumoniae	LPS core (cap-phenotype)	SP-D	62, 190
	Capsule (di-mannose)	SP-A	15
Escherichia coli	LPS core	SP-D	191
	Not defined	SP-A	
H. influenzae, type A	P2 outer membrane protein	SP-A	35, 144
Gram-positive bacteria			
Group B Streptococci	Not defined	SP-A	149
Staphylococcus aureus			
Cowan I strain	Not defined	SP-A	65
Clinical isolate	Not defined	SP-A	56, 124, 192
Streptococcus pneumoniae	Not defined	SP-A	56, 144, 192

True Fungi   SP-A and SP-D show CRD-dependent agglutination of unencapsulated forms of *Cryptococcus neoformans*, but show no significant binding to encapsulated organisms (38). SP-A and SP-D also show CRD-dependent binding to the N-linked sugars of specific cell wall glycoproteins, including major glycoprotein allergens of *Aspergillus fumigatus* (39). In one study, both human proteins were found to enhance conidial agglutination (40); however, other investigators observed CRD-dependent binding and agglutination by rat SP-D and human SP-A, but not rat SP-A (41). Interestingly, the binding of human SP-A, but not SP-D, was inhibited by surfactant preparations containing both lipids and hydrophobic surfactant proteins. Recent studies have shown that SP-D, but not SP-A, interacts with wild-type *Saccharomyces cerevisiae* in a lectin-dependent fashion (42); SP-D bound efficiently to mutants with low mannosylphosphate in the cell wall, indicating that interactions do not involve N-linked phosphomannan sugars.

Pneumocystis carinii   SP-A and SP-D bind in a CRD-dependent manner to gpA (gp-140), a heavily mannosylated glycoprotein associated with the trophozoites and cysts of *Pneumocystis carinii* (43–46). In addition, β-glucans have been implicated in the interactions of SP-D with pneumocystis (47). Chelation of calcium disrupts aggregates of organisms recovered in bronchoalveolar lavage, and the isolated organisms are readily agglutinated following the addition of SP-D (48). Cysts and trophozoites are associated with SP-D in the airspaces of rats with pneumocystis pneumonia (49). Thus the collectins may contribute to the aggregation of pneumocystis cysts characteristically observed in lung biopsies of patients with pneumocystis infection.

Interactions of Lung Collectins with Respiratory Viruses

The lung collectins show specific interactions with various respiratory viruses. Although the interactions of SP-D are mediated by CRD-dependent interactions with viral envelope glycoproteins, some interactions of SP-A with viruses require binding of viral lectins to complex oligosaccharides on SP-A.

Influenza A Virus   Purified SP-D and SP-A inhibit infectivity and hemagglutination activity of influenza A virus (IAV) in vitro (50–52). However, the mechanisms and consequences of binding differ. SP-D shows CRD-dependent binding to the virus, whereas the antiviral activity of SP-A involves binding of the virus to complex oligosaccharides on SP-A (52).

SP-D binds to high mannose oligosaccharides associated with the globular HA_1 domain of the hemagglutinin (HA) molecule. Significantly, the high mannose oligosaccharide on the HA_1 domain overlies the sialic acid–binding pocket (i.e. the cell attachment site) of the HA, resulting in inhibition of hemagglutinin activity. SP-D also binds to the neuraminidase of IAV and inhibits neuraminidase enzyme activity (53).

SP-D induces massive aggregation of IAV particles (50, 52, 54, 55). Viral aggregation is calcium-dependent, is inhibited by competing sugars, and correlates with the multimerization state of SP-D. Highly multimerized preparations are significantly more potent than dodecamers, and trimeric CRDs induce minimal agglutination. Similar findings were obtained for bacteria (56) and yeast particles (38). Massive agglutination of organisms could contribute to lung host defense by promoting airway mucociliary clearance, but could also promote the internalization by phagocytic cells. As discussed below, SP-D-mediated agglutination enhances the binding and internalization of virus, increases the respiratory burst response to bound IAV, and decreases the deactivating effects of IAV binding. Whereas SP-D forms massive aggregates, SP-A forms only microscopic aggregates. Significantly, human bronchoalveolar lavage (BAL) contains sufficient concentrations of SP-D to inhibit IAV HA activity in vitro, and depletion of SP-D from BAL reduces its HA inhibitory activity (50).

Respiratory Syncytial Virus   SP-A binds to the F (fusion) glycoprotein of respiratory syncytial virus (RSV) by a calcium-dependent mechanism, with resulting loss of infectivity (57). By contrast, natural SP-D and a recombinant trimeric SP-D bind to the RSV G protein and inhibit viral infectivity by a CRD-dependent mechanism (58).

Other Viruses   Bovine SP-D inhibits the infectivity of Rotaviruses through calcium-dependent, mannose-inhibitable attachment to the major viral envelope glycoprotein (59). Although SP-A promotes the uptake of Herpes Simplex Virus by rat alveolar macrophages, this interaction involves the attachment of the virus to complex oligosaccharides on SP-A (60, 61).

SP-A AND SP-D SHOW DIFFERING MODES OF INTERACTION WITH CERTAIN MICROORGANISMS

SP-A and SP-D show obvious overlap in microbial recognition. However, as suggested above, the mechanisms of interaction of the collectin with the microbial surface are often distinct. For example, SP-A binds to di-mannose repeating units in certain gram-negative capsular polysaccharides (15) and to the lipid A domain (21, 22), whereas SP-D preferentially recognizes core oligosaccharides of LPS. In addition, SP-D inhibits IAV infectivity through attachment of the CRD to viral envelope glycoproteins, whereas SP-A activity is mediated by non-calcium-dependent attachment of IAV to SP-A (50–52). The latter differences probably depend on steric factors related to the site of carbohydrate attachment on the collectin molecule. Human SP-A has Asn-linked carbohydrate within the CRD domain (Figure 2, see color insert), which is likely accessible to the viral lectin. By contrast, SP-D is glycosylated near the amino-terminal end of the collagen domain near the hub of the SP-D dodecamer. Such differences in the mechanism of interaction of the two collectins may explain observed differences in the functional consequences of collectin binding. Differing modes of binding could favor complementary, rather than antagonistic, interactions with various multivalent ligands.

VARIATIONS IN THE MICROBIAL EXPRESSION OF CELL SURFACE GLYCOCONJUGATES CAN INFLUENCE COLLECTIN BINDING

The recognition of the surface glycoconjugates by the lung collectins depends not only on the expression of lectin-specific residues by a given strain or species, but also on the accessibility of these residues (1, 62). For example, SP-D binds inefficiently to the core region of LPS of encapsulated *Klebsiella*, but efficiently agglutinates the corresponding unencapsulated phase variants. Interactions of SP-D with the core oligosaccharides of gram-negative organisms are also influenced by the number of repeating saccharide units associated with the terminal O-antigen of the LPS (34, 63). Similarly, variations in capsular expression by *Cryptococcus neoformans* can influence the binding of SP-A and SP-D (38). Differences in the number of oligosaccharides and the sites of N-linked glycosylation can also determine the interactions of SP-D and other collectins with specific N-linked sugars on the hemagglutinin of influenza A virus (53).

ENVIRONMENTAL CONDITIONS CAN MODULATE COLLECTIN INTERACTIONS WITH MICROORGANISMS

Modulation of Microbial Surface Structures

Growth conditions can influence the expression of cell wall glycoconjugates and capsular polysaccharides and their interactions with collectins (1, 64). For example, vigorous aeration of cultures of unencapsulated variants of *Klebsiella pneumoniae*, which decreases the number of repeating units in the O-polysaccharide, markedly increases the ability of SP-D to agglutinate the bacteria (1). Although growth phase has also been shown to influence the effect of SP-A on bacterial phagocytosis by alveolar macrophages (65), the mechanism has not been elucidated.

Modulation of Collectin Activity

A number of factors can alter the activity of purified collectins in vitro and could influence collectin activity in vivo. These include the extent of subunit oligomerization (i.e. the number and distribution of trimeric subunits), interactions with competing ligands, and enzymatic or chemical modifications of collectin structure. Alterations in local calcium concentration and pH might influence collectin activity, particularly within secretory or phagocytic compartments.

Collectins synthesized in vivo and in recombinant cell systems show varying degrees of multimerization of trimeric subunits (54, 66, 67). At least in the case of SP-D, both trimers and dodecamers can be identified within the rough endoplasmic reticulum (68). At present there is no direct evidence for environmental modulation of the extent of intracellular oligomerization or of extracellular alterations in the extent of specific oligomerization of lung collectins. However, the extent of multimerization varies among species and among different individuals. SP-A and SP-D can be isolated in different multimeric forms from proteinosis lavage (66, 67). SP-D trimers and multimers isolated from this source were found to have less or greater anti-IAV activity than dodecamers, respectively (69). SP-D, isolated from human alveolar proteinosis lavage, at least the most highly multimerized fractions, can undergo further calcium-dependent self-aggregation at high concentrations in vitro. Although these interactions are CRD dependent and inhibited with maltose, the effect of this self-association on activity has not been defined.

Competing ligands could also play important modulatory roles. For example, glucose concentrations at levels encountered in diabetes can interfere with SP-D's ability to interact with specific strains of IAV in vitro, and the same strains of IAV show enhanced proliferation in the lungs of diabetic mice (70). Many microorganisms release cell wall polysaccharides or glycoconjugates, which may interfere with the binding of collectins to the same or other organisms. In this regard, SP-D recovered from rats following airway instillation of LPS shows diminished lectin activity attributable to occupancy of the CRD with LPS (71). In addition, as discussed in greater detail below, surfactant lipids can modulate some activities of the collectins in vitro, but the mechanism remains to be elucidated.

Protein modifications could also occur in the setting of lung injury and infection. For example, neutrophil elastase can degrade SP-A (72), and a protease released by *Pseudomonas aeruginosa* has been found to degrade SP-A in vitro (73). In addition, nitric oxide metabolites, particularly peroxynitrite, which are released in association with macrophage activation, can modify tyrosine residues in the CRD of SP-A (74). This is associated with defective lectin and lipid-binding activity and decreased interaction with at least one organism *Pneumocystis carinii* (75–77).

COLLECTINS CAN MODULATE IMMUNE CELL FUNCTION

A wealth of in vitro data shows that both SP-A and SP-D affect a variety of immune cell functions (reviewed in 1–3). Although the effects of the proteins have not been comprehensively evaluated, available data suggest that the proteins elicit cell-specific responses and that, in some cases, SP-A and SP-D have different effects on the same cell type.

During the response to an infection or acute lung injury, there are significant and dramatic changes in the types of cells that inhabit the alveolar airspaces. The primary immune cells in the normal, non-inflamed lung are alveolar macrophages, which are mobile, highly phagocytic cells derived from circulating monocytes. The factors that contribute to the differentiation of monocytes into macrophages are not well understood. During the course of an acute infection or inflammatory response, neutrophils emigrate into the lungs in enormous numbers (78). Other important immune effector cells transverse into the alveolar space during the response to infection of inflammation. For example, eosinophils, which contribute to the pathogenesis of asthma and other hypersensitivity disorders, and T-lymphocytes, which are critical elements of the acquired (e.g. antibody- and cell-mediated) host defense system, are both recruited to the alveolar airspaces and are affected by surfactant proteins. The responses of these different cells to collectins is discussed individually.

Macrophages and Monocytes

Although alveolar macrophages are derived from monocytes, it is clear that these two cell types have some shared and some markedly different responses to SP-A and SP-D. For example, SP-A has been shown to enhance the uptake of a variety of bacteria by both alveolar macrophages and monocytes (reviewed in 1, 2). SP-A can also act as an activation ligand to stimulate phagocytosis of bacteria (79). In this case, binding of SP-A to the cell but not the pathogen is required because the pathogen is opsonized by another ligand, for instance IgG, or may bind directly to the phagocytic cell via a cell surface receptor such as the mannose receptor. SP-A has also been reported to inhibit phagocytosis of some pathogens including *Pneumocystis carinii* (80) and *M. tuberculosis* (16). However, other studies reported that SP-A enhanced uptake of both organisms (37, 43, 81). Although SP-D binds to a variety of pathogens and induces aggregation of many (discussed in detail above), it is not a very effective opsonin and has been reported to enhance only modestly the phagocytosis of *P. aeruginosa* by alveolar macrophages (82) and to inhibit phagocytosis of *M. tuberculosis* by macrophages (16).

Both SP-A and SP-D stimulate directional actin polymerization (Figure 3, see color insert) and chemotaxis of alveolar macrophages (83). In contrast, monocyte migration was not enhanced by SP-A. SP-D also stimulates chemotaxis of alveolar macrophages and has been reported to both enhance (84) and have no effect (85) on chemotaxis of monocytes. Interestingly, the structurally homologous proteins, complement component C1q and mannose-binding lectin (MBL), only weakly stimulated the rearrangement of actin in both cell types; C1q was chemotactic for only peripheral blood monocytes and MBP did not stimulate chemotaxis of either cell type (85).

SP-A has been reported to variably affect cytokine production by alveolar macrophages, which are a primary source of these regulatory molecules that play a pivotal role in the pulmonary immune response to infection and inflammation. For example, SP-A has been reported to inhibit production of cytokines in response to the inflammatory bacterial cell wall component LPS (86) and to intact *Candida albicans* (87) and to both intact bacteria and LPS in buffy-coat cells (88). In contrast, SP-A has been shown to directly enhance the production of TNF-α by alveolar macrophages (89), as well as to increase production of TNF-α, interleukins 1 α, 1 β, and 6, and interferon-γ by human peripheral blood mononuclear cells (90), and colony-stimulating factor, by alveolar macrophages and alveolar epithelial cells (22). The reasons for these differences are not known. Recent studies with SP-A -/- mice show that levels of TNF-α and MIP-2 are greater in the SP-A-deficient mice than in wild-type mice after a challenge with either LPS (86) or pathogens such as Group B streptococcus (91), *P. aeruginosa* (92), or respiratory syncytial virus (93). A recent abstract reported that SP-D-deficient mice have an enhanced inflammatory response to respiratory syncytial virus (94) and to LPS (95). It is not yet clear if SP-D and SP-A are mediating responses to these same pathogens by similar mechanisms.

The production of reactive oxygen and nitrogen species by alveolar macrophages and monocytes can also be modulated by SP-A and SP-D. Both reactive oxygen and nitrogen are important anti-bacterial and anti-viral defenses. However, these reactive species, like the cytokines discussed above, have the potential to exacerbate an inflammatory response if their levels are not tightly regulated. Initial studies examining the effects of SP-A and SP-D in the absence of other activators, such as pathogens, reported that the collectins induce a lucigenin-dependent chemiluminescence response in alveolar macrophages, a response generally attributed to production of superoxide (96), and that SP-A adhered to a surface was a more effective activator of free radical production than was soluble SP-A (97). SP-A also was shown to enhance the production of nitric oxide by alveolar macrophages (98), although subsequent studies showed that neither SP-A nor SP-D that was treated to remove endotoxin enhanced production of nitric oxide metabolites (99). In contrast, SP-A treated to remove endotoxin has been shown to enhance the production of nitric oxide metabolites by alveolar macrophages activated with IFN-γ and challenged in vitro with *Mycoplasma pneumoniae* (100). The response to SP-A may vary with the pathogen challenge or the state of activation of the cells. For example, SP-A inhibits nitric oxide production by alveolar macrophages pre-activated with IFN-γ and exposed to *M. tuberculosis* (101). In addition, SP-A enhanced the production of nitric oxide metabolites in alveolar macrophages that were activated with IFN-γ and stimulated with LPS but inhibited production of nitric oxide metabolites by macrophages stimulated with LPS but not activated with IFN-γ (102). These studies in aggregate suggest that the state of activation of the cells as well as the presence of pathogen and the type of pathogen may affect the response to SP-A.

Neutrophils

Enormous numbers of neutrophils infiltrate the lungs during acute infection and in response to acute lung injury and perform a variety of protective functions. However, the responses of neutrophils, as those of mononuclear phagocytes, must be considered "double-edged swords." For example, neutrophils secrete factors, such as proteases and reactive species that are toxic to pathogens but, when released in excess, can be toxic to the host. Thus careful regulation of neutrophil response is essential for an effective but minimally injurious resolution of the injury or infection.

Neutrophils are also responsive to SP-A and SP-D in vitro. Both SP-A and SP-D enhance the phagocytosis of *E. coli*, *Streptococcus pneumoniae*, and *Staphylococcus aureus* by neutrophils (56). SP-A and SP-D also enhance the phagocytosis, oxidative burst, and killing of *Aspergillus fumigatus* conidia by neutrophils (40). In addition to enhancing neutrophil phagocytosis, SP-A and SP-D can enhance neutrophil migration (40, 84). The lectin domain mediates the chemotactic activity of SP-D (103).

SP-D also exhibits protective effects against influenza virus that involve neutrophils. SP-D and SP-A enhance neutrophil binding and/or uptake of IAV (50, 52, 55). However, SP-D is markedly more potent in this regard than SP-A. Viral aggregation plays an important role in the ability of SP-D to enhance neutrophil uptake of IAV, and enhanced phagocytosis strongly depends on the extent of multimerization of SP-D (52, 54, 104). Enhancement of viral binding and uptake are accompanied by attachment of large aggregates of virus to the neutrophil (55), and binding of IAV or SP-D-IAV aggregates is abrogated by pre-treatment of the phagocyte with neuraminidase (55). Thus viral internalization involves enhanced binding of the virus to sialylated glycoconjugated ligands on the neutrophil surface (55). SP-D and SP-A potentiate IAV-induced neutrophil hydrogen peroxide responses and protect neutrophils from IAV-induced inhibition of respiratory burst responses. The effects of SP-D correlate with its state of multimerization (52, 55, 104). The effects may also be phagocyte dependent. SP-A, but not SP-D, increases the uptake of IAV by rat alveolar macrophages (105).

Eosinophils

Eosinophils play a significant role in allergic inflammation and asthma. When stimulated they have the ability to secrete a variety of cytokines including IL-3, IL-4, IL-5, IL-8, IL-10, GM-CSF, TNF-α, TGF-β, and RANTES. Cheng and coworkers observed that SP-A suppresses ionomycin-induced production and release of IL-8 by eosinophils (106), suggesting that SP-A may modify the inflammatory activities of eosinophils in response to allergen challenge.

Lymphocytes

Studies from the early 1970s reported that lymphocytes isolated from lung lavage were hyporesponsive with respect to their ability to proliferate when stimulated with mitogens compared with lymphocytes isolated from peripheral blood (107, 108). Because the lung lymphocytes co-exist in the alveolar space with surfactant, these investigators postulated that surfactant was responsible for this attenuated response and showed that surfactant lipids mediated at least part of this inhibition. Subsequent studies defined a role for SP-A and SP-D in attenuating lymphocyte responses (109–111). Both SP-A, and SP-D inhibit plant lectin and anti-CD3 stimulated T-lymphocyte proliferation in highly enriched populations of peripheral blood lymphocytes (112). At least part of this inhibition is secondary to inhibition of production of IL-2, a potent mitogen for lymphocytes. Mutagenesis experiments and peptide inhibition studies suggested an integrin-dependent mechanism. Wang and co-workers observed that a recombinant peptide consisting of the neck plus CRD of SP-D could inhibit lymphocyte proliferation (113). Interestingly, the effects of the collectins were specifically inhibited with relatively high concentrations of competing sugars. These investigators found no change in the expression of HLA-DR by mononuclear cells exposed to the collectins, whereas lymphocyte integrin expression was decreased. Together, these observations suggest that the collectins can interact directly with lymphocytes by a CRD-dependent mechanism, with a resulting decrease in IL-2-dependent proliferation.

THERE ARE MULTIPLE CLASSES OF COLLECTIN RECEPTORS

The observations that the collectins mediate cell-specific functions led to the quest to identify their receptors. To date, a number of SP-A- and SP-D-binding proteins have been identified; however, none of these proteins has been characterized to the point that a detailed understanding of how collectin interactions with these receptors mediate cell responses. Although it seems logical to speculate that different cells would express different and specific receptors, this does not necessarily seem to be the case.

SP-A Receptors

Several cell surface SP-A binding proteins have been identified. However, the specific contributions of these molecules to be biological activities of SP-A remain controversial.

SPR-210 The best characterized of the SP-A receptors was first purified from the macrophage cell line U937 cells and is known as SPR-210 (surfactant protein receptor 210 kDa) (114). This receptor is also found on type II cells and alveolar macrophages. Studies with blocking antibodies suggest that this receptor is involved in SP-A-mediated inhibition of lipid secretion by isolated alveolar type II cells (114), with SP-A's ability to enhance uptake of bacillus Calmette-Guerin by alveolar macrophages (115), and with SP-A-mediated inhibition of mitogen-induced T-lymphocyte proliferation (111). The mechanism by which receptor activation affects these diverse functions is not known and important future studies will include cloning and further characterization of SPR-210.

The expression of macrophage SPR-210 on mononuclear phagocytic cells is tightly regulated and influenced by various agents and cytokines. For example, Chroneos & Shepherd (116) investigated the regulation of SPR-210 and the mannose receptor, a calcium-dependent lectin that is also expressed on macrophages and that binds and internalizes soluble and particulate ligands, such as mycobacteria, and extracellular acid hydrolases and peroxidases. Phorbol 12-myristate 13-acetate, LPS, and IFN-γ treatment of rat marrow-derived macrophages increased SP-A binding, whereas mannose receptor activity was reduced. In contrast, dexamethasone increased mannose receptor activity while decreasing SP-A-binding activity. Addition of granulocyte macrophage-colony stimulating factor (GM-CSF) to human monocytes increased mannose receptor activity. However, SP-A binding was highest in freshly isolated monocytes and decreased with differentiation in the presence of GM-CSF. These studies suggest that differential regulation of these and possibly other innate immune receptors changes during differentiation and activation of macrophages and that these changes may help orchestrate pathogen clearance during various stages of the immune response.

C1q Receptors   Because SP-A and C1q are structurally homologous, the possibility that they share a receptor has been investigated. Several C1q receptors have been identified (reviewed in 117). A C1q binding protein of 56–58 kDa was originally purified from Raj cells (118) and later shown to bind SP-A, MBL, conglutinin, and CL-43, but not SP-D (119). This receptor is highly homologous to calreticulin, a protein that is primarily, but not exclusively, an intracellular chaperone (120). A different receptor of 126 kDa was purified and recently cloned by Nepomuceno and co-workers (121, 122). This protein, which binds C1q, MBL, and SP-A, is known as C1qR$_p$; the p designation indicates that this receptor participates in the mediation of phagocytosis by C1q, MBL, and SP-A. A C1q receptor (C1qR) (123) has been shown to be involved in SP-A-mediated uptake of *Staphylococcus aureus* by monocytes (124). Several studies showed that C1q is an effective competitor for SP-A binding and that plating monocytes on C1q-coated surfaces abrogated SP-A's ability to enhance particle uptake by monocytes but not by macrophages. Thus there is indirect evidence to support the possibility that SP-A and C1q share a receptor. However, at least one of the C1q receptors does not exist in the lung (AJ Tenner, personal communication), and clarification of the role of C1q receptors in mediating SP-A function in the lung awaits further investigations. Interestingly, SP-D does not appear to interact with any of these putative receptors (reviewed in 125).

CD14   Sano et al (126) recently reported the intriguing observation that SP-A binds to CD14, a known receptor for LPS, which is a component of the outer membrane of gram-negative bacteria that is responsible for sepsis and induction of inflammation. SP-A bound to CD14 on ligand blots and in microtiter plate assays using recombinant soluble CD14. As discussed below, this interaction likely contributes to the ability of SP-A to affect LPS-mediated cell responses. SP-A has also been shown to enhance the uptake and degradation of LPS by alveolar macrophages (127). However, indirect evidence suggests that this action of SP-A is independent of CD14. Investigation of the importance of the most recently described component of the LPS receptor complex, a Toll-like receptor (128, 129), with SP-A awaits future studies.

Type II Receptors   Both SP-A and SP-D have been shown to bind to and be internalized by alveolar type II cells. The interactions of SP-A and SP-D with type II cells could be related to surfactant homeostasis (11a). However, given increasing evidence that these cells contribute to inflammatory and immune regulation within the lung, the possibility that these interactions play immunomodulatory roles requires further investigation. Several type II cell receptors for SP-A have been described. Two different SP-A binding proteins were identified using an anti-idiotypic antibody approach, including a 30 kDa protein (130) and a 55 kDa protein known as BP55 that multimerizes to 170–200 kDa (131). Another SP-A binding protein has been described by Kresch and co-workers (132). Unlike SPR-210, none of these receptors appears to be expressed on macrophages. Important future studies including cloning and characterizing the mechanism by which these receptors mediate type II cell function are needed.

SP-D Receptors

At least one binding protein for SP-D is expressed on the surface of alveolar macrophages. However, it has not been shown that these interactions can initiate signal transduction. Interactions of SP-D with cell surface glycolipids may contribute to the biological activities of SP-D.

Gp340   Gp340 is an SP-D-binding protein and a member of the scavenger receptor superfamily that was first identified in association with alveolar macrophages (133). The protein also widely co-distributes with SP-D at extrapulmonary sites (134). However, a significant proportion of gp-340 can be released by treatment of human macrophages with calcium chelators, a property that is not consistent with gp-340 being an integral membrane protein. A recent report by Mollenhauer et al (135) indicates that gp-340 is identical to some isoforms of DMBT-1 (deleted in malignant brain tumors 1), a gene product previously shown to be deleted in brain tumors. Mollenhauer and co-workers reported the identification of a putative exon with coding potential for a transmembrane domain, and they suggest that alternative splicing results in isoforms of DMBT-1 with differential utilization of scavenger receptor domains (136). The mouse and rabbit homologues of DMBT-1 are CRP-ductin and hensin, both of which have been implicated in epithelial differentiation. Thus gp-340/DMBT-1 has been proposed to play a role in both host defense and epithelial differentiation. Gp-340 was also reported to bind to SP-A and, somewhat surprisingly, found to directly affect macrophage chemotaxis (137). How these functions of gp-340 are coordinated and the role of gp-340 as a receptor and regulator of differentiation and host defense are important areas for future study. Interestingly, some, but not all, of the properties of binding of SP-D to gp-340 and to macrophages are common. For example, binding of SP-D to both macrophages and gp-340 is optimal in the presence of calcium. However, saccharides reduce binding of SP-D to macrophages but not to gp-340. One interpretation of these data is that gp-340 is not the only binding molecule on alveolar macrophages. In this regard, both SP-A and SP-D have been observed to interact with leukocytes via lectin-dependent binding to cell surface carbohydrates, as previously reviewed (1).

CD14   Sano et al (138) recently reported that SP-D, as well as SP-A (126), binds the CD14 LPS receptor. Although SP-A also interacts with CD14 (130), the mechanism of binding appears to be different. The neck domain of SP-A binds to the protein backbone of CD14, whereas the lectin domain of SP-D binds to associated sugars. The interaction of both collectins affects the binding of specific forms of LPS to CD14.

ALVEOLAR MACROPHAGES CAN INTERNALIZE AND DEGRADE LUNG COLLECTIONS

In addition to responding to the collectins, macrophages also participate in collectin (and surfactant) metabolism. Alveolar macrophages internalize and degrade SP-A (133, 139) and SP-D (140). Little is known about the regulation of these processes, although it has been shown that activation of macrophages by overnight culture enhances their capacity to degrade SP-A (141). The mechanism of this enhancement is not known, but the studies are consistent with the possibility that activation of macrophages, by in vitro culture conditions or perhaps by exposure in vivo to pathogens or allergens, may alter the contribution of macrophages to surfactant metabolism.

SURFACTANT LIPIDS CAN ALTER THE IMMUNOMODULATORY EFFECTS OF SP-A AND SP-D

Because SP-A and SP-D co-exist with surfactant, which is 90% lipid by weight, the effects of lipids on SP-A and SP-D have been evaluated. SP-A clearly binds to and affects the function and structure of surfactant lipids. SP-D binds to PI and a variety of glycolipids, which are relatively minor components of surfactant. However, some SP-D does co-isolate with surfactant lipids (142). The ability of SP-A to regulate immune cells is variably affected by the presence of lipids. For example, Phelps and co-workers reported that lipids decreased the ability of SP-A to stimulate lymphocyte proliferation (143). In contrast, SP-A enhanced the binding and uptake of LPS and bacteria by alveolar macrophages both in the presence and absence of lipids (127, 144). The binding of SP-A to *A. fumigatus* conidia was inhibited by a lipid extract of surfactant, whereas binding of SP-D was unaffected (41).

LUNG COLLECTINS MODIFY THE HOST RESPONSE TO MICROORGANISMS IN VIVO

Our understanding of the potential host defense roles of lung collectins has been greatly advanced by the development of transgenic models of SP-A and SP-D deficiency. SP-A-deficient mice (-/-), show essentially normal respiratory function and surfactant lipid metabolism (11, 145). Thus deficiencies in the response to microbial challenge that can be rescued with SP-A can be attributed to the loss of SP-A activity, either directly or indirectly. As discussed below, SP-D knockout mice show a defective response to challenge with respiratory viruses. However, this model is complicated by associated abnormalities in surfactant homeostasis and alterations in the phenotype of alveolar macrophages (9, 10). In addition, the mice spontaneously develop emphysema, which could reflect an ongoing inflammatory reaction associated with abnormal oxidant metabolism and metalloproteinase activity, possibly secondary to macrophage activation (146).

Murine Models of Bacterial, Chlamydial, and Fungal Infection

SP-A-deficient mice show increased bacterial proliferation and an increased systemic dissemination following intratracheal inoculation with the *Group B streptococci* (GBS) (147) and defective clearance of *S. aureus*, *P. aeruginosa*, and *K. pneumoniae* (92, 148). SP-A-deficient animals also show decreased phagocytosis and oxidant metabolism in response to instilled GBS (149). In general, the inflammatory response to bacteria in SP-A-deficient mice appears increased with variable increases in pro-inflammatory cytokines and/or decreases in anti-inflammatory cytokines, consistent with a net anti-inflammatory effect of SP-A. Host defense functions are normalized when organisms are instilled in the presence of purified wild-type SP-A. Interestingly, lung-targeted expression of a mutant SP-A consisting of the trimeric neck and CRD decreased the proliferation of GBS in SP-A-deficient mice, indicating that the carboxy-terminal domain, but not the multimerization of SP-A trimers, is required (150).

SP-A-deficient mice show defective killing of *M. pneumoniae*, and SP-A can augment the mycoplasmacidal activity of alveolar macrophage (151), but it is unclear whether this requires direct interactions of SP-A with mycoplasma. SP-A-deficient mice also show increased susceptibility to pneumocystis infection (152). There is still little information on the possible effects of collectin deficiency on the response to classical fungi. However, SP-A null mice showed a high rate of infection with pneumocystis following steroid immunosuppression (152).

Murine Models of IAV and RSV Infection

Murine models strongly suggest that the lung collectins play important roles in the host defense against respiratory viruses. Lung collectins probably contribute to the clearance of viruses and modify the inflammatory and immune response to viral challenge.

Influenza A Virus   There is a strong inverse correlation between the number of oligosaccharide attachments on the HA of specific IAV strains and the ability of SP-D to inhibit their infectivity in mice (53). In addition, co-administration of mannan increases replication of IAV in the lung, implicating involvement of a C-type lectin. SP-D-sensitive IAV strains replicate to higher titers in lungs of diabetic mice compared with non-diabetic controls (70); viral replication positively correlates with the level of blood glucose, and decreases with insulin treatment. Notably, the SP-D insensitive PR-8 strain of IAV replicates to the same extent in diabetic and control mice.

Respiratory Syncytial Virus and Adenovirus   SP-A-deficient mice show increased susceptibility to challenge by respiratory syncytial virus and show decreased viral clearance, increased release of proinflammatory cytokines, and decreased oxidative response following viral challenge (93). Likewise, SP-D-deficient mice show decreased viral clearance and enhanced inflammation following challenge with RSV (94). SP-A-deficient mice also show increased lung inflammation with increase in neutrophils and pro-inflammatory cytokines following intratracheal inoculation with replication-defective adenovirus (153).

COLLECTINS MODIFY THE HOST RESPONSE TO LPS

The lipid A domain of LPS (endotoxin) is responsible for many of its cellular effects. However, LPS-binding proteins are required for the uptake or detoxification of free LPS and for phagocyte activation at concentrations at or below those associated with sepsis. Serum LPS-binding protein (LBP), soluble CD14, and neutrophil bactericidal/permeability-increasing protein (BPI) preferentially bind to the lipid A domain. Thus the ability of SP-A to bind to the lipid A domain is of considerable potential significance with regard to the pulmonary responses to LPS.

Bacterial LPSs were among the first specific ligands identified for both SP-A (21, 22) and SP-D (14), and there is growing evidence that these interactions contribute to the host response to LPS. Both SP-A (86) and SP-D (95) modify the response to instilled LPS in vivo with decreased lung injury and inflammatory cell recruitment. However, the mechanism(s) have not been fully elucidated.

Human SP-A, but not SP-D, increases the uptake and deacylation of *E. coli* LPS by isolated alveolar macrophages (127), a process thought to contribute to the detoxification of LPS by immune cells. SP-A also decreases the stimulation of

TNF-α and NO production induced by exposure of macrophages to smooth LPS (106, 154). There is evidence that these effects do not involve direct interactions of SP-A with LPS but are mediated instead by interactions of SP-A with the macrophage (102). In this regard, SP-A enhances the association of recombinant soluble CD14 with rough LPS, suggesting that some cellular effects involve a direct interaction of SP-A with membrane CD14 (130).

Despite the functional importance of the lipid A domain, the biological activity of LPS can be influenced by the structure of the associated polysaccharides (63, 155, 156). Furthermore, specific antibodies and other molecules can influence the activity or availability of LPS through interactions with the core oligosaccharides (157), and competitive interactions among LPS-binding proteins have been described (158). Thus SP-D, which does not bind to the lipid A domain, but binds to the contiguous core oligosaccharide, may have the ability to modulate some cellular responses to LPS. Notably, SP-D can bind to intratracheally instilled LPS in rats, and the resulting complexes are rapidly internalized into lysosomal compartments in alveolar macrophages (71). Direct interactions of SP-D with CD14 may further modulate the cellular response to LPS (130, 142).

COLLECTINS PARTICIPATE IN THE LUNG'S RESPONSE TO INJURY

SP-A and SP-D are constitutively synthesized and secreted into the airspaces of the lung by alveolar type II and non-ciliated bronchiolar epithelial cells (Figure 1). In addition, mouse SP-D and one of the human SP-A genes, SP-A2, are expressed in larger airways, including submucosal glands (159–161). Although the lung is the major site of SP-A and SP-D production, there is increasing evidence for extrapulmonary production for both SP-A (162, 163) and SP-D (162, 164–167).

Because the airspace concentration of serum collectins (i.e. MBL) is very low in the non-inflamed or uninjured lung (168), SP-A and SP-D probably constitute the major collectin defenses in the normal lung. Significantly, the synthesis and secretion of both proteins increases with acute injury and epithelial activation (1). In particular, the production of SP-A and SP-D are quite rapidly increased following intratracheal instillation of LPS (169–171).

THE ACCUMULATION OF LUNG COLLECTINS IS ALTERED IN ASSOCIATION WITH LUNG INJURY

There are multiple reports of alterations in bronchoalveolar lavage levels of SP-A and SP-D, as well as other surfactant components, in a variety of diseases (recently reviewed by 172). Currently, it is unclear if these deficiencies are a cause or consequence of the disease. Notably, levels of cytokines are altered in disease states, and in vitro data clearly demonstrate that cytokines affect surfactant synthesis (173).

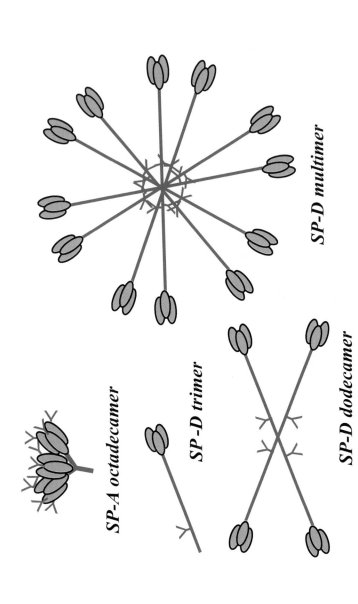

SP-A octadecamer

SP-D trimer

SP-D dodecamer

SP-D multimer

Figure 2 Molecular organization of pulmonary collectins. SP-A octadecamers and SP-D dodecamers are compared assuming maximal spatial separation of the CRDs. Differences in the localization of N-linked sugars (Y) are illustrated. The maximum molecular dimension of SP-A is approximately 20 nm, compared with 100 nm for SP-D.

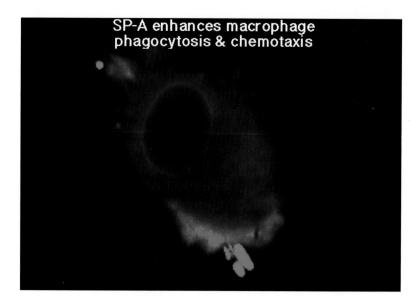

Figure 3 SP-A stimulates actin polymerization and phagocytosis in alveolar macrophages. Isolated rat alveolar macrophages were incubated with purified SP-A and fluorescent FITC-labeled bacteria. Polymerized actin was detected with rhodamine-phalloidin. Micrograph courtesy of M Tino.

For example, it has been demonstrated that lung levels of SP-A and SP-D, but not SP-B, are increased within 24 to 72 h following intratracheal instillation of LPS in rats (169, 174). At longer time points, proliferation of type II cells occurs, which undoubtedly contributes to increases in levels of all surfactant components (134). Changes in both intracellular and extracellular levels of surfactant have been reported (175). Considered together, these findings suggest that surfactant affects the inflammatory state, and conversely, the state of inflammation has an influence on surfactant homeostasis (Figure 4).

COLLECTINS MAY INFLUENCE THE DEVELOPMENT OF ACQUIRED IMMUNITY

Although lung collectins can alter the proliferation of lymphocytes, relatively little is known about the potential roles of collectins in modulating acquired humoral or cell-mediated immunity. Such roles seem likely given that the collectins interact with pulmonary antigen-presenting cells and enhance the interactions of microorganisms, microbial antigens, and other organic antigens with these cells.

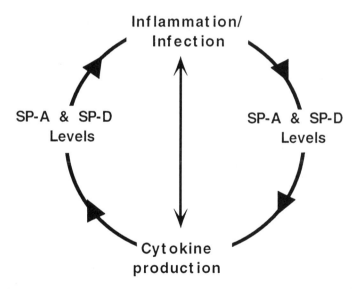

Figure 4   Relationship between surfactant pool size and inflammation. Many studies have shown that cytokines, which are produced during an inflammatory response, affect surfactant synthesis. Because SP-A and SP-D affect the host response to infection and inflammation, there is a potential feedback loop between surfactant levels and the inflammatory response. Although it is clear that alveolar levels of SP-A and SP-D are altered in many human lung diseases, it is not yet clear if the changes are a contributory factor or a consequence of the disease, or most likely, a combination of both.

For example, SP-A specifically binds to various pollens (7). In addition, SP-A and SP-D bind to oligosaccharides associated with dust-mite allergen (8) and inhibit the binding of specific IgE to these allergens (8). SP-A and SP-D have also been shown to inhibit the proliferation of sensitized lymphocytes in response to dust-mite allergen (176).

ACQUIRED DEFICIENCIES IN LUNG COLLECTINS MAY CONTRIBUTE TO PATHOGENESIS OF HUMAN DISEASE

There is mounting circumstantial evidence to suggest that alterations in the level or activity of lung collectins contribute to the pathogenesis of various diseases. The apparent host defense activities of these proteins in vitro, when combined with the results of microbial challenge experiments using SP-A and SP-D-deficient mice, strongly suggest that decreased levels or activities of one or both of the lung collectins may increase risk for lung infection under appropriate conditions in vivo (9, 86, 92, 93, 113, 149, 177). Acquired alterations in collectin activity could influence the effectiveness of microbial or particle clearance mechanisms and thereby contribute to the pathogenesis of certain infectious or immune-mediated disorders. Notably, cigarette smoking, which is associated with an increased risk of pneumonia and other lung infections, appears to be associated with a decrease in the levels of lung collectins (178).

Because host defenses are highly redundant, the effects of such deficiencies may only become evident when one or more other defense mechanisms are impaired, or under situations where individuals are exposed to an unusually large innoculum of organisms that are preferentially cleared by collectin-dependent mechanisms.

Pneumonia and septic complications are major causes of death in individuals with the adult respiratory distress syndrome, neonates with bronchopulmonary dysplasia, and children with cystic fibrosis, all situations where the levels of SP-A and/or SP-D can be reduced (179–181). Secondary infections commonly complicate pneumonias and are associated with increased morbidity and mortality. Because SP-D can decrease the influenza-induced deactivation of neutrophils, deficiencies in SP-D might be predicted to increase the risk of secondary bacterial infections following influenza A infection. Proteolytic degradation by host or microbial proteases or covalent modification of collectins within an inflammatory milieu might impair collectin-mediated defenses by damaging the carbohydrate recognition domains, disrupting biologically active multimers, or by liberating active domains that can compete with normal collectin binding. The finding that SP-D lectin activity is inhibited following intratracheal LPS instillation in rats suggests another scenario in which interactions of collectins with soluble microbial ligands of one class of microorganisms might impair other adaptive or host defense functions.

Diabetes mellitus is associated with a variety of infectious complications, including an increased risk for pneumonia. Elevated glucose concentrations associated with diabetic states can inhibit lectin-mediated defenses against specific strains of IAV in vivo, and glucose concentrations comparable to that seen in the blood of poorly controlled diabetics inhibit SP-D binding to IAV in vitro (70).

As discussed above, lung collectins have also been implicated in the clearance of complex organic particulate antigens and regulation of the immune response to complex microbial antigens. In this regard, it has been reported that patients with asthma have decreased levels of SP-A in their lung washings (182). Interestingly, patients with pollen allergy have been reported to have an increased proportion of smaller oligomeric forms of SP-A compared with controls (66). In addition, SP-A and SP-D decrease the proliferative response of dust-mite allergen and phytohemagglutinin-stimulated lymphocytes from control children and children with stable asthma; however, lymphocytes from children with unstable asthma show a decreased suppressive effect (176). The interactions with *Aspergillus furnigatus* suggest that the collectins might play a role in asthma-associated hypersensitivity disorders, such as allergic bronchopulmonary aspergillosis and other forms of fungal hypersensitivity.

The levels of SP-A and SP-D are dramatically increased in the setting of idiopathic alveolar lipoproteinosis (183, 184). Proteins isolated from proteinosis lavage show host defense activities in vitro. However, it is unclear whether the perturbations in collectin homeostasis in any way contribute to the development of infections in these patients. Given the inhibitory effects of surfactant lipids on certain collectin activities in vitro, it is possible that impairment in host defenses is secondary to the lipidosis.

The surprising finding that SP-D knockout mice develop emphysema and demonstrate abnormalities in increased metalloproteinase activity and levels of oxidants in the apparent absence of infection (146) suggests important anti-inflammatory roles of SP-D. Heightened production of pro-inflammatory cytokines and decreased levels of anti-inflammatory cytokines are also seen following certain types of microbial challenge in SP-A-deficient mice. Thus global or local deficiencies in collectins may less directly influence a variety of host defense and repair mechanisms.

Not all interactions of collectins with microorganisms or organic particulates are necessarily beneficial to the host. Under some circumstances, collectins might provide a mechanism for retaining microorganisms or other toxic particles in the lung. For example, SP-D mediates the aggregation and binding of pneumocystis to macrophages without enhanced internalization and killing. On the other hand, SP-A enhances the internalization of mycobacteria by macrophages and may thereby allow the organisms to avoid clearance by acquired immune mechanisms (16). Because SP-D does not promote uptake of mycobacteria, the local balance of SP-A and SP-D might conceivably influence the local response to this class of organisms.

There are no documented genetic deficiencies of SP-A and/or SP-D in humans; however, it is tempting to speculate that they may exist. Such is the case for the human serum MBL. Deficiencies in MBL were identified as a major contributing factor in a population of children who have increased susceptibility to infection, presumably owing to the deficiency of opsonic activity in their serum (185, 186).

Subsequent studies showed that there are mutations in MBL that interfere with its appropriate folding and/or secretion from the liver (reviewed in 187).

SUMMARY AND CONCLUSIONS

Both SP-A and SP-D specifically interact with a wide variety of respiratory pathogens, modulate the leukocyte response to these organisms, and participate in aspects of pulmonary immune and inflammatory regulation. Recent studies suggest that both SP-A (162, 163) and SP-D (162, 164–167) may also accumulate in extra-pulmonary compartments. Thus these innate immune molecules may have more widespread or generalized functional roles. Interactions between the collectin-mediated immunity and adaptive immune responses may contribute both to innate defense and to the pathogenesis of certain diseases associated with hypersensitivity to microbial or other organic antigens.

The collectins can influence the activity of phagocytes through CRD-dependent and CRD-independent interactions, and both SP-A and SP-D can function as true opsonins for certain organisms under specific assay conditions in vitro. In other cases the proteins mediate enhanced binding and/or internalization without associated microbial killing. At least some of the effects of SP-D occur as a consequence of microbial aggregation with enhanced binding of the agglutinated organism to its natural receptors. Important areas of future investigation include the elucidation of cell- and site-specific mechanisms of action in order to understand how collectins interact with their receptors to signal and regulate cellular responses.

The CRD-dependent interactions of SP-A and SP-D with specific microorganisms can be altered as a consequence of phenotypic variation in the expression of cell surface glycoconjugates, and there are many potential mechanisms whereby collectin activity may be altered in vivo. Additional studies are also needed to elucidate the functional significance of alterations in the accumulation of different multimeric forms of SP-A and SP-D. Although allelic differences have been described for the human SP-A and SP-D genes (188, 189), the impact of the associated differences in mRNA and protein structure on innate defenses remains unknown.

Because the lung collectins interact with different ligands or ligand domains and may occupy different airspace compartments, their actions are potentially complementary in vivo. The interactions of lung collectins with opportunistic pathogens may sometimes benefit the pathogen rather than the host; however, this hypothesis remains largely untested and requires further investigation.

ACKNOWLEDGMENTS

This work is supported by National Institutes of Health grants HL-29594 (EC), HL-44015 (EC), HL-51134 (JRW), and HL-30923 (JRW). We would like to acknowledge the excellent editorial assistance of Cynthia Riley in the preparation of this manuscript.

Visit the Annual Reviews home page at www.AnnualReviews.org

LITERATURE CITED

1. Crouch EC. 1998. Collectins and pulmonary host defense. *Am. J. Respir. Cell Mol. Biol.* 19:177–201

2. Wright JR. 1997. Immunomodulatory functions of surfactant. *Physiol. Rev.* 77:931–62

3. Eggleton P, Reid KBM. 1999. Lung surfactant proteins involved in innate immunity. *Curr. Opin. Immunol.* 11:28–33

4. Reid KBM. 1998. Functional roles of the lung surfactant proteins SP-A and SP-D in innate immunity. *Immunobiology* 199:200–7

5. Haagsman H. 1998. Interactions of surfactant protein A with pathogens. *Biochim. Biophys. Acta* 1480:264–77

6. Korfhagen TR, LeVine A, Whitsett JA. 1998. Surfactant protein A (SP-A) gene targeted mice. *Biochim. Biophys. Acta* 1408:296–302

7. Malhotra R, Haurum J, Thiel S, Jensenius JC, Sim RB. 1993. Pollen grains bind to lung alveolar Type-II cells (A549) via lung surfactant protein-A (SP-A). *Biosci. Rep.* 13:79–90

8. Wang JY, Kishore U, Lim BL, Strong P, Reid KB. 1996. Interaction of human lung surfactant proteins A and D with mite (*Dermatophagoides pteronyssinus*) allergens. *Clin. Exp. Immunol.* 106:367–73

9. Botas C, Poulain F, Akiyama J, Brown C, Allen L, et al. 1998. Altered surfactant homeostasis and alveolar type II cell morphology in mice lacking surfactant protein D. *Proc. Natl. Acad. Sci. USA* 95:11869–74

10. Korfhagen TR, Sheftelyevich V, Burhans MS, Bruno MD, Ross GF, et al. 1998. Surfactant protein-D regulates surfactant phospholipid homeostasis in vivo. *J. Clin. Biol. Chem.* 273:28438–43

11. Korfhagen TR, Bruno MD, Ross GF, Huelsman KM, Ikegami M, et al. 1996. Altered surfactant function and structure in

SP-A gene targeted mice. *Proc. Natl. Acad. Sci. USA* 93:9594–99

11a. Hawgood S, Poulain F. 2001. The pulmonary collectins and surfactant metabolism. *Annu. Rev. Physiol.* 63:495–519

12. Haagsman HP, Hawgood S, Sargeant T, Buckley D, White RT, et al. 1987. The major lung surfactant protein, SP 28–36, is a calcium-dependent, carbohydrate-binding protein. *J. Biol. Chem.* 262:13877–80

13. Persson A, Chang D, Crouch E. 1990. Surfactant protein D is a divalent cation-dependent carbohydrate-binding protein. *J. Biol. Chem.* 265:5755–60

14. Lim BL, Wang JY, Holmskov U, Hoppe HJ, Reid KB. 1994. Expression of the carbohydrate recognition domain of lung surfactant protein D and demonstration of its binding to lipopolysaccharides of gram-negative bacteria. *Biochem. Biophys. Res. Commun.* 202:1674–80

15. Kabha K, Schmegner J, Keisari Y, Parolis H, Schlepper-Schaefer J, Ofek I. 1997. SP-A enhances phagocytosis of *Klebsiella* by interaction with capsular polysaccharides and alveolar macrophages. *Am. J. Physiol. Lung Cell Mol. Physiol.* 16:L344–L52

16. Ferguson JS, Voelker DR, McCormack FX, Schlesinger LS. 1999. Surfactant protein D binds to *Mycobacterium tuberculosis* bacilli and lipoarabinomannan via carbohydrate-lectin interactions resulting in reduced phagocytosis of the bacteria by macrophages. *J. Immunol.* 163:312–21

17. Kishore U, Wang JY, Hoppe HJ, Reid KBM. 1996. The alpha-helical neck region of human lung surfactant protein D is essential for the binding of the carbohydrate recognition domains to

lipopolysaccharides and phospholipids. *Biochem. J.* 318:505–11

18. Hakansson K, Lim NK, Hoppe HJ, Reid KBM. 1999. Crystal structure of the trimeric alpha-helical coiled-coil and the three lectin domains of human lung surfactant protein D. *Structure* 7:255–64

19. Kuroki Y, Akino T. 1991. Pulmonary surfactant protein A (SP-A) specifically binds dipalmitoylphosphatidylcholine. *J. Biol. Chem.* 266:3068–73

20. Haagsman HP, Sargeant T, Hauschka PV, Benson BJ, Hawgood S. 1990. Binding of calcium to SP-A, a surfactant-associated protein. *Biochemistry* 29:8894–900

21. van Iwaarden JF, Pikaar JC, Storm J, Brouwer E, Verhoef J, et al. 1994. Binding of surfactant protein A to the lipid A moiety of bacterial lipopolysaccharides. *Biochem. J.* 303:407–11

22. Kalina M, Blau H, Riklis S, Kravtsov V. 1995. Interaction of surfactant protein A with bacterial lipopolysaccharide may affect some biological functions. *Am. J. Physiol. Lung Cell Mol. Physiol.* 268:L144–L51

23. Momoeda K, Hirota K, Utsuki T, Tsuchida Y, Hanaoka K, Iwamori M. 1996. Developmental changes of neutral glycosphingolipids as receptors for pulmonary surfactant protein SP-A in the alveolar epithelium of murine lung. *J. Biochem.* 119:1189–95

24. Kuroki Y, Gasa S, Ogasawara Y, Makita A, Akino T. 1992. Binding of pulmonary surfactant protein A to galactosylceramide and asialo-GM2. *Arch. Biochem. Biophys.* 299:261–67

25. Childs RA, Wright JR, Ross GF, Yuen CT, Lawson AM, et al. 1992. Specificity of lung surfactant protein SP-A for both the carbohydrate and the lipid moieties of certain neutral glycolipids. *J. Biol. Chem.* 267:9972–79

26. Persson AV, Gibbons BJ, Shoemaker JD, Moxley MA, Longmore WJ. 1992. The major glycolipid recognized by SP-D in surfactant is phosphatidylinositol. *Biochemistry* 31:12183–89

27. Ogasawara Y, Kuroki Y, Akino T. 1992. Pulmonary surfactant protein D specifically binds to phosphatidylinositol. *J. Biol. Chem.* 267:21244–49

28. Ogasawara Y, McCormack FX, Mason RJ, Voelker DR. 1994. Chimeras of surfactant proteins A and D identify the carbohydrate recognition domains as essential for phospholipid interaction. *J. Biol. Chem.* 269:29785–92

29. Kuroki Y, Gasa S, Ogasawara Y, Shiratori M, Makita A, Akino T. 1992. Binding specificity of lung surfactant protein SP-D for glucosylceramide. *Biochem. Biophys. Res. Commun.* 187:963–69

30. Saitoh M, Sano H, Chiba H, Murakami S, Iwaki D, et al. 2000. Importance of the carboxy-terminal 25 amino acid residues of lung collectins in interactions with lipids and alveolar type II cells. *Biochemistry* 39:1059–66

31. Sano H, Kuroki Y, Honma T, Ogasawara Y, Sohma H, et al. 1998. Analysis of chimeric proteins identifies the regions in the carbohydrate recognition domains of rat lung collectins that are essential for interactions with phospholipids, glycolipids, and alveolar type II cells. *J. Clin. Biol. Chem.* 273:4783–89

32. Kenne L, Lindberg B. 1983. Bacterial polysaccharides. In *The Polysaccharides*, ed. G Aspinaal, pp. 287–363. New York: Academic

33. Holst O, Brade H. 1992. Chemical structure of the core region of lipopolysaccharide. In *Bacterial Endotoxic Lipopolysaccharides*, ed. D Morrisson, J Ryan, pp. 135–70. Boca Raton, FL: CRC Press

34. Kuan SF, Rust K, Crouch E. 1992. Interactions of surfactant protein D with bacterial lipopolysaccharides. Surfactant protein D is an *Escherichia coli*-binding protein in bronchoalveolar lavage. *J. Clin. Invest.* 90:97–106

35. McNeely TB, Coonrod JD. 1994. Aggregation and opsonization of type A but not type B *Hemophilus influenzae* by surfactant protein A. *Am. J. Respir. Cell Mol. Biol.* 11:114–22

36. Downing JF, Pasula J, Wright JR, Twigg HL, Martin I. 1995. Surfactant protein A promotes attachment of *Mycobacterium tuberculosis* to alveolar macrophages during infection with human immunodeficiency virus. *Proc. Natl. Acad. Sci. USA* 92:4848–52

37. Gaynor CD, McCormack FX, Voelker DR, McGowan SE, Schlesinger LS. 1995. Pulmonary surfactant protein A mediates enhanced phagocytosis of *Mycobacterium tuberculosis* by a direct interaction with human macrophages. *J. Immunol.* 155:5343–51

38. Schelenz S, Malhotra R, Sim RB, Holmskov U, Bancroft GJ. 1995. Binding of host collectins to the pathogenic yeast *Cryptococcus neoformans*: Human surfactant protein D acts as an agglutinin for acapsular yeast cells. *Infect. Immun.* 63:3360–66

39. Madan T, Kishore U, Shah A, Eggleton P, Strong P, et al. 1997. Lung surfactant proteins A and D can inhibit specific IgE binding to the allergens of *Aspergillus fumigatus* and block allergen-induced histamine release from human basophils. *Clin. Exp. Immunol.* 110:241–49

40. Madan T, Eggleton P, Kishore U, Strong P, Aggrawal SS, et al. 1997. Binding of pulmonary surfactant proteins A and D to *Aspergillus fumigatus* conidia enhances phagocytosis and killing by human neutrophils and alveolar macrophages. *Infect. Immun.* 65:3171–79

41. Allen M, Harbeck R, Smith B, Voelker D, Mason R. 1999. Binding of rat and human surfactant proteins A and D to *Aspergillus fumigatus* conidia. *Infect. Immun.* 67:4563–69

42. Allen M, Boelker D, Mason R. 2000. Interactions of pulmonary surfactant proteins A and D with *Saccharomyces cerevisiae*. *Am. J. Respir. Crit. Care Med.* 161:A128 (Abstr.)

43. Williams MD, Wright JR, March KL, Martin WJ. 1996. Human surfactant protein A enhances attachment of *Pneumocystis carnii* to rat alveolar macrophages. *Am. J. Resp. Cell. Mol. Biol.* 14:232–38

44. Zimmerman PE, Voelker DR, McCormack FX, Paulsrud JR, Martin WJD. 1992. 120-kD surface glycoprotein of *Pneumocystis carinii* is a ligand for surfactant protein A. *J. Clin. Invest.* 89:143–49

45. O'Riordan DM, Standing JE, Kwon KY, Chang D, Crouch EC, Limper AH. 1995. Surfactant protein D interacts with *Pneumocystis carinii* and mediates organism adherence to alveolar macrophages. *J. Clin. Invest.* 95:2699–710

46. McCormack F. 1997. The carbohydrate recognition domain of surfactant protein A mediates binding to the major surface glycoprotein of *Pneumocystis carinii*. *Biochemistry* 36:8092–99

47. Vuk-Pavlovic Z, Diaz-Montes T, Standing J, Limper A. 1998. Surfactant protein-D binds to cell wall beta-lucans. *Am. J. Respir. Crit. Care Med.* 157:A236 (Abstr.)

48. Yong S-J, Vuk-Pavlovic Z, Crouch E, Limper A. 1998. Surfactant protein-D mediates aggregation of *Pseumocystis carnii*. *Am. J. Respir. Crit. Care Med.* 157:A236 (Abstr.)

49. Kwon K, Kim S, Limper A. 1998. Recognition of *Pneumocystis carinii* antigen on its surface by immunohistochemistry and immunoelectron microscopy. *J. Korean Med. Sci.* 13:131–37

50. Hartshorn KL, Crouch EC, White MR, Eggleton P, Tauber AI, et al. 1994. Evidence for a protective role of pulmonary surfactant protein D (SP-D) against influenza A viruses. *J. Clin. Invest.* 94:311–19

51. Benne CA, Kraaijeveld CA, van Strijp JA, Brouwer E, Harmsen M, et al. 1995. Interactions of surfactant protein A with

influenza A viruses: binding and neutralization. *J. Infect. Dis.* 171:335–41

52. Hartshorn K, White M, Shepherd V, Reid K, Jensenius J, Crouch E. 1997. Mechanisms of anti-influenza activity of surfactant proteins A and D: comparison with serum collectins. *Am. J. Physiol. Lung Cell Mol. Physiol.* 17:L1156–L66

53. Reading PC, Morey LS, Crouch EC, Anders EM. 1997. Collectin-mediated antiviral host defense of the lung: evidence from influenza virus infection of mice. *J. Virol.* 71:8204–12

54. Hartshorn K, Chang D, Rust K, Crouch E. 1996. Interactions of recombinant human pulmonary surfactant protein D and SP-D multimers with influenza A. *Am. J. Physiol. Lung Cell Mol. Physiol.* 271:L753–L62

55. Hartshorn KL, Reid KBM, White MR, Jensenius JC, Morris SM, et al. 1996. Neutrophil deactivation by influenza A viruses—mechanisms of protection after viral opsonization with collectins and hemaglutination-inhibiting antibodies. *Blood* 87:3450–61

56. Hartshorn KL, Crouch E, White MR, Colamussi ML, Kakkanatt A, et al. 1998. Pulmonary surfactant proteins A and D enhance neutrophil uptake of bacteria. *Am. J. Physiol. Lung Cell Mol. Physiol.* 274:L958–69

57. Ghildyal R, Hartley C, Varrasso A, Meanger J, et al. 1999. Surfactant protein A binds to the fusion glycoprotein of respiratory syncytial virus and neutralizes virion infectivity. *J. Infect. Dis.* 180:2009–13

58. Hickling TP, Bright H, Wing K, Gower D, Martin SL, et al. 1999. A recombinant trimeric surfactant protein D carbohydrate recognition domain inhibits respiratory syncytial virus infection in vitro and in vivo. *Eur. J. Immunol.* 29:3478–84

59. Reading P, Holmskov U, Anders E. 1998. Antiviral activity of bovine collectins against rotaviruses. *J. Gen. Virol.* 79:2255–63

60. van Iwaarden JF, van Strijp JAG, Ebskamp MJM, Welmers AC, Verhoeff J, van Golde LMG. 1991. Surfactant protein A is opsonin in phagocytosis of herpes simplex virus type 1 by rat alveolar macrophages. *Am. J. Physiol. Lung Cell Mol. Physiol.* 261:L204–L9

61. van Iwaarden JF, van Strijp JAG, Visser H, Haagsman HP, Verhoef J, van Golde LMG. 1992. Binding of surfactant protein A (SP-A) to herpes simplex virus type 1-infected cells is mediated by the carbohydrate moiety of SP-A. *J. Biol. Chem.* 267:25039–43

62. Ofek I, Crouch E. 1999. Interactions of microbial glycoconjugates with collectins: implications for pulmonary host defense. In *Glycomicrobiology*, ed. R Doyle, pp. 517–37. London: Plenum

63. Greene K, Voelker D. 1998. Interactions of SP-A and SP-D with LPS. *Am. J. Respir. Crit. Care Med.* 157:A562 (Abstr.)

64. Favre-Bonte S, Joly B, Forestier C. 1999. Consequences of reduction of *Klebsiella pneumoniae* capsule expression on interactions of this bacterium with epithelial cells. *Infect. Immun.* 67:554–61

65. Manz-Keinke H, Plattner H, Schlepper-Schafer J. 1992. Lung surfactant protein A (SP-A) enhances serum-independent phagocytosis of bacteria by alveolar macrophages. *Eur. J. Cell Biol.* 57:95–100

66. Hickling TP, Malhotra R, Sim RB. 1998. Human lung surfactant protein A exists in several different oligomeric states—oligomer size distribution varies between patient groups. *Mol. Med.* 4:266–75

67. Mason RJ, Nielsen LD, Kuroki Y, Matsuura E, Freed JH, Shannon JM. 1998. A 50-kDa variant form of human surfactant protein D. *Eur. Respir. J.* 12:1147–55

68. Brown-Augsburger P, Chang D, Rust K, Crouch E. 1996. Biosynthesis of surfactant protein D. Contributions of conserved NH2-terminal cysteine residues and collagen helix formation to assembly and secretion. *J. Biol. Chem.* 271:18912–19

69. Crouch E, Hartshorn K, Ofek I. 2000.

Collectins and pulmonary innate immunity. *Immunol. Rev.* 173:52–65

70. Reading P, Allison J, Crouch E, Anders E. 1999. Increased susceptibility of diabetic mice to influenza virus infection: compromise of collectin-mediated host defense of the lung by glucose? *J. Viol.* 72:6884–87

71. van Rozendaal B, van de Lest CHA, van Eijk M, van Golde LMG, Voorhout WF, et al. 1999. Aerosolized endotoxin is immediately bound by pulmonary surfactant protein D in vivo. *Biochim. Biophys. Acta* 1454:261–69

72. Ryan SF, Ghassibi Y, Liau DF. 1991. Effects of activated polymorphonuclear leukocytes upon pulmonary surfactant in vitro. *Am. J. Respir. Cell Mol. Biol.* 4:33–41

73. Mariencheck WM, Wright JR. 1999. A metalloproteinase secreted by *Pseudomonas aeruginosa* degrades pulmonary surfactant protein A (SP-A). *Am. J. Resp. Crit. Care Med.* 159:A506 (Abstr.)

74. Zhu S, Kachel DL, Martin WJ II, Matalon S. 1998. Nitrated SP-A does not enhance adherence of *Pneumocystis carinii* to alveolar macrophages. *Am. J. Physiol. Lung Cell Mol. Physiol.* 275:L1031–L39

75. Haddad IY, Zhu S, Ischiropoulos H, Matalon S. 1996. Nitration of surfactant protein A tesults in decreased ability to aggregate lipids. *Am. J. Physiol. Lung Cell Mol. Physiol.* 14:L281–L88

76. Zhu S, Kachel D, Martin WJ 2nd, Matalon S. 1998. Nitrated SP-A does not enhance adherence of *Pneumocystis carinii* to alveolar macrophages. *Am. J. Physiol. Lung Cell Mol. Physiol.* 275:L1031–L39

77. Zhu S, Haddad IY, Matalon S. 1996. Nitration of surfactant protein A (SP-A) tyrosine residues results in decreased mannose binding ability. *Arch. Biochem. Biophys.* 333:282–90

78. Xing Z, Jordana M, Kirpalani H, Driscoll KE, Schall TJ, Gauldie J. 1994. Cytokine expression by neutrophils and macrophages in vivo: Endotoxin induces tumor necrosis factor-alpha, macrophage inflammatory protein-2, interleukin-1 beta, and interleukin-6 but not RANTES or transforming growth factor-beta 1 mRNA expression in acute lung inflammation. *Am. J. Respir. Cell Mol. Biol.* 10:148–53. Erratum. *Am. J Respir. Cell Mol. Biol.* 10(3):346

79. Tenner AJ, Robinson SL, Borchelt J, Wright JR. 1989. Human pulmonary surfactant protein (SP-A), a protein structurally homologous to C1q, can enhance FcR- and CR1-mediated phagocytosis. *J. Biol. Chem.* 264:13923–28

80. Koziel H, O'Riordan D, Phelps D, Fishman JA, Armstrong MYK, et al. 1992. Surfactant protein-A inhibits binding and internalization of *Pneumocystis carinii* by alveolar macrophages. *Am. Rev. Resp. Dis.* 145:A247 (Abstr.)

81. Pasula R, Downing JF, Wright JR, Martin WJ II. 1994. Surfactant protein (SP-A) mediates attachment of *Mycobacterium tuberculosis* to murine alveolar macrophages. *Am. J. Resp. Crit. Care Med.* 149:A614 (Abstr.)

82. Restrepo C, Dong Q, Savov J, Mariencheck W, Wright JR. 1998. SP-D stimulates phagocytosis of *Pseudomonas aeruginosa* by alveolar macrophages. *Am. J. Resp. Crit. Care Med.* 157:A540 (Abstr.)

83. Tino MJ, Wright JR. 1996. Surfactant protein A stimulates actin polymerization in alveolar macrophages but not peripheral blood monocytes. *Am. J. Respir. Crit. Care Med.* 153:A663 (Abstr.)

84. Crouch EC, Persson A, Griffin GL, Chang D, Senior RM. 1995. Interactions of pulmonary surfactant protein D (SP-D) with human blood leukocytes. *Am. J. Respir. Cell Mol. Biol.* 12:410–15

85. Tino MJ, Wright JR. 1999. Surfactant proteins A and D specifically stimulate directed actin-based responses in alveolar macrophages. *Am. J. Physiol. Lung Cell Mol. Physiol.* 276:L164–L74

86. Borron P, McIntosh JC, Korfhagen TR, Whitsett JA, Taylor J, Wright JR. 2000.

Surfactant-associated protein A inhibits LPS-induced cytokine and nitric oxide production in vivo. *Am. J. Physiol. Lung Cell Mol. Physiol.* 278:L840–L47

87. Rosseau S, Hammerl P, Maus U, Gunther A, Seeger W, et al. 1999. Surfactant protein A down-regulates proinflammatory cytokine production evoked by *Candida albicans* in human alveolar macrophages and monocytes. *J. Immunol.* 163:4495–502

88. Hickling TP, Sim RB, Malhotra R. 1998. Induction of TNF-alpha release from human buffy coat cells by *Pseudomonas aeruginosa* is reduced by lung surfactant protein A. *FEBS Lett.* 437:65–69

89. Kremlev SG, Phelps DS. 1994. Surfactant protein A stimulation of inflammatory cytokine and immunoglobulin production. *Am. J. Physiol. Lung Cell Mol, Physiol.* 267:L712–L19

90. Kremlev SG, Umstead TM, Phelps DS. 1997. Surfactant protein A regulates cytokine production in the monocytic cell line THP-1. *Am. J. Physiol. Lung Cell Mol. Physiol.* 272:L996–L1004

91. LeVine AM, Reed JA, Kurak KE, Cianciolo E, Whitsett JA. 1999. GM-CSF-deficient mice are susceptible to pulmonary group B Streptococcal infection. *J. Clin. Invest.* 103:563–69

92. LeVine AM, Kurak KE, Bruno MD, Stark JM, Whitsett JA, Korfhagen TR. 1998. Surfactant protein-A-deficient mice are susceptible to *Pseudomonas aeruginosa* infection. *Am. J. Respir. Cell Mol. Biol.* 19:700–8

93. LeVine AM, Gwozdz J, Stark J, Bruno M, Whitsett J, Korfhagen T. 1999. Surfactant protein-A enhances respiratory syncytial virus clearance in vivo. *J. Clin. Invest.* 103:1015–21

94. LeVine AM, Gwozdz J, Fisher JH, Whitsett JA, Korfhagen TR. 2000. Surfactant protein-D modulates lung inflammation with respiratory syncytial virus infection in vivo. *Am. J. Respir. Crit. Care Med.* 161:A515 (Abstr.)

95. Greene K, Whitsett JA, Korfhagen TR, Fisher JH. 2000. SP-D expression regulates endotoxin mediated lung inflammation in vivo. *Am. J. Respir. Crit. Care Med.* 161:A515 (Abstr.)

96. van Iwaarden JF, Shimizu H, van Golde PHM, Voelker DR, van Golde LMG. 1992. Rat surfactant protein D enhances the production of oxygen radicals by rat alveolar macrophages. *Biochem. J.* 286:5–8

97. Weissbach S, Neuendank A, Pettersson M, Schaberg T, Pison U. 1994. Surfactant protein A modulates release of reactive oxygen species from alveolar macrophages. *Am. J. Physiol. Lung Cell Mol. Physiol.* 267:L660–L66

98. Blau H, Riklis S, Van Iwaarden JF, McCormack FX, Kalina M. 1997. Nitric oxide production by rat alveolar macrophages can be modulated in vitro by surfactant protein A. *Am. J. Physiol. Lung Cell Mol. Physiol.* 272:L1198–L204

99. Wright JR, Zlogar DF, Taylor JC, Zlogar T, Restrepo CI. 2000. Effects of endotoxin on surfactant protein A and D stimulation of nitric oxide production by alveolar macrophages. *Am. J. Physiol. Lung Cell Mol. Physiol.* 276:L650–L58

100. Hickman-Davis J, Gibbs-Erwin J, Lindsey JR, Matalon S. 1999. Surfactant protein A mediates mycoplasmacidal activity of alveolar macrophages by production of peroxynitrite. *Proc. Natl. Acad. Sci. USA* 96:4953–58

101. Pasula R, Wright JR, Kachel DL, Martin WJ. 1999. Surfactant protein A suppresses reactive nitrogen intermediates by alveolar macrophages in response to *Mycobacterium tuberculosis. J. Clin. Invest.* 103:483–90

102. Stamme C, Wright JR. 2000. Surfactant protein A enhances interferon γ-induced nitric oxide but inhibits LPS-induced nitric oxide alveolar macrophages. *Am. J. Respir. Crit. Care Med.* 161:A515 (Abstr.)

103. Cai GZ, Griffin GL, Senior RM, Long-more WJ, Moxley MA. 1999. Recombinant SP-D carbohydrate recognition domain is a chemoattractant for human neutrophils. *Am. J. Physiol. Lung Cell Mol. Physiol.* 20:L131–L36

104. Brown-Augsburger P, Hartshorn K, Chang D, Rust K, Fliszar C, et al. 1996. Site-directed mutagenesis of cys-15 and cys-20 of pulmonary surfactant protein D—expression of a trimeric protein with altered anti-viral properties. *J. Biol. Chem.* 271:13724–30

105. Benne CA, Benaissatrouw B, van Strijp JAG, Kraaijeveld CA, van Iwaarden JFF. 1997. Surfactant protein A, but not surfactant protein D, is an opsonin for influenza a virus phagocytosis by rat alveolar macrophages. *Eur. J. Immunol.* 27:886–90

106. Cheng G, Ueda T, Nakajima H, Nakajima A, Kinjyo S, et al. 1998. Suppressive effects of SP-A on ionomycin-induced Il-8 production and release by eosinophils. *Int. Arch. Allergy Immunol.* 117:59–62

107. Ansfield MJ, Kaltreider HB, Caldwell JL, Herskowitz FN. 1979. Hyporesponsiveness of canine bronchoalveolar lymphocytes to mitogens: inhibition of lymphocyte proliferation by alveolar macrophages. *J. Immunol.* 122:542–48

108. Ansfield MJ, Kaltreider HB, Benson BJ, Caldwell JL. 1979. Immunosuppressive activity of canine pulmonary surface active material. *J. Immunol.* 122:1062–66

109. Borron P, Veldhuizen RA, Lewis JF, Possmayer F, Caveney A, et al. 1996. Surfactant associated protein-A inhibits human lymphocyte proliferation and IL-2 production. *Am. J. Respir. Cell Mol. Biol.* 15:115–21

110. Borron PJ, Crouch EC, Lewis JF, Wright JR, Possmayer F, Fraher LJ. 1998. Recombinant rat surfactant-associated protein D inhibits human T lymphocyte proliferation and IL-2 production. *J. Immunol.* 161:4599–603

111. Borron P, McCormack FX, Elhalwagi BM, Chroneos ZC, Lewis JF, et al. 1998. Surfactant protein A inhibits T cell proliferation via its collagen-like tail and a 210-kDa receptor. *Am. J. Physiol. Lung Cell Mol. Physiol.* 19:L679–L86

112. Borron P, Wright JR. 2000. Pulmonary surfactant-associated proteins (SP)-A and D differentially interact with T cell subsets but have a common inhibitory effect on CD4+ cells. *FASEB J.* 14:A1203 (Abstr.)

113. Harrod KS, Trapnell BC, Otake K, Korfhagen TR, Whitsett JA. 1999. SP-A enhances viral clearance and inhibits inflammation after pulmonary adenoviral infection. *Am. J. Physiol. Lung Cell Mol. Physiol.* 277:L580–L88

114. Chroneos ZC, Abdolrasulnia R, Whitsett JA, Rice WR, Shepherd VL. 1996. Purification of a cell-surface receptor for surfactant protein A. *J. Biol. Chem.* 271:16375–83

115. Weikert LF, Edwards K, Chroneos ZC, Hager C, Hoffman L, Shepherd VL. 1997. SP-A enhances uptake of bacillus Calmette-Cuerin by macrophages through a specific SP-A receptor. *Am. J. Physiol. Lung Cell Mol. Physiol.* 272:L989–L95

116. Chroneos Z, Shepherd VL. 1995. Differential regulation of the mannose and SP-A receptors on macrophages. *Am. J. Physiol. Lung Cell Mol. Physiol.* 269:L721–L26

117. Tenner AJ. 1993. Functional aspects of the C1q receptors. *Behring Inst. Mitt.* 93:241–53

118. Ghebrehiwet B, Silvestri L, McDevitt C. 1984. Identification of the Raji cell membrane-derived C1q inhibitor as a receptor for human C1q. *J. Exp. Med.* 160:1375–89

119. Malhotra R, Thiel S, Reid KB, Sim RB. 1990. Human leukocyte C1q receptor binds other soluble proteins with collagen domains. *J. Exp. Med.* 172:955–59

120. Eggleton P, Ghebrehiwet B, Sastry KN, Coburn JP, Zaner KS, et al. 1995. Identification of a gC1q-binding protein (gC1q-R) on the surface of human neutrophils. Subcellular localization and binding properties in comparison with the cC1q-R. *J. Clin. Invest.* 95:1569–78

121. Nepomuceno RR, Henschen-Edman AH, Burgess WH, Tenner AJ. 1997. cDNA cloning and primary structure analysis of C1aRp, the human C1q/MBL/SPA receptor that mediated enhanced phagocytosis in vitro. *Immunity* 6:119–29

122. Nepomuceno RR, Ruiz S, Park M, Tenner AJ. 1999. C1qR(P) is a heavily *O*-glycosylated cell surface protein involved in the regulation of phagocytic activity. *J. Immunol.* 162:3583–89

123. Malhotra R, Haurum J, Thiel S, Sim RB. 1992. Interaction of C1q receptor with lung surfactant protein A. *Eur. J. Immunol.* 22:1437–45

124. Geertsma MF, Nibbering PH, Haagsman HP, Daha MR, van Furth R. 1994. Binding of surfactant protein A to C1q receptors mediates the phagocytosis of *Staphylococcus aureus* by monocytes. *Am. J. Physiol. Lung Cell Mol. Physiol.* 267:L578–L84

125. Malhotra R, Lu J, Holmskov U, Sim RB. 1994. Collectins, collectin receptors and the lectin pathway of complement activation. *Clin. Exp. Immunol.* 97:4–9

126. Sano H, Sohma H, Muta T, Nomura S, Voelker DR, Kuroki Y. 1999. Pulmonary surfactant protein A modulates the cellular response to smooth and rough lipopolysaccharides by interaction with CD14. *J. Immunol.* 163:387–95

127. Stamme C, Wright JR. 1999. Surfactant protein A enhances the binding and deacylation of E. coli LPS by alveolar macrophages. *Am. J. Physiol. Lung Cell Mol. Physiol.* 276:L540–L47

128. Poltorak A, He XL, Smirnova I, Liu MY, Van Huffel C, et al. 1998. Defective LPS signaling in C3H/HeJ and C57BL/10ScCr mice: mutations in Tlr4 gene. *Science* 282:2085–88

129. Ulevitch R. 1999. Toll gates for pathogen selection. *Nature* 401:755–56

130. Strayer DS, Yang S, Jerng HH. 1993. Surfactant protein-A binding proteins. *J. Biol. Chem.* 268:18679–84

131. Wissel H, Looman AC, Fritzsche I, Rustow B, Stevens PA. 1996. SP-A-binding protein Bp55 is involved in surfactant endocytosis by Type II pneumocytes. *Am. J. Physiol. Lung Cell Mol. Physiol.* 15:L432–L40

132. Kresch MJ, Christian C, Lu H. 1998. Isolation and partial characterization of a receptor to surfactant protein A expressed by rat type II pneumocytes. *Am. J. Respir. Cell Mol.* 19:216–25

133. Wright JR, Youmans DC. 1995. Degradation of surfactant lipids and surfactant protein A by alveolar macrophages in vitro. *Am. J. Physiol. Lung Cell Mol. Physiol.* 268:L772–L80

134. Sugahara K, Iyama K, Sano K, Kuroki Y, Akino T, Matsumoto M. 1996. Overexpression of surfactant protein SP-A, SP-B, and SP-C mRNA in rat lungs with lipopolysaccharide-induced injury. *Lab. Invest.* 74:209–20

135. Mollenhauer J, Herbertz S, Holmskov U, Tolnay M, Krebs I, et al. 2000. DMBT1 encodes a protein involved in the immune defense and in epithelial differentiation and is highly unstable in cancer. *Cancer Res.* 60:1704–10

136. Mollenhauer J, Holmskov U, Wiemann S, Krebs I, Herbertz S, et al. 1999. The genomic structure of the DMBT1 gene: evidence for a region with susceptibility to genomic instability. *Oncogene* 18:6233–40

137. Tino MJ, Wright JR. 1999. Glycoprotein-340 binds surfactant protein-A (SP-A) and stimulates alveolar macrophage migration in an SP-A-independent manner. *Am. J. Respir. Cell Mol. Biol.* 20:759–68

138. Sano H, Chiba H, Iwaki D, Sohma H. 2000. Surfactant proteins A and D bind

CD14 by different mechanisms. *J. Clin. Biol. Chem.* 275:22442–51

139. Bates SR, Fisher AB. 1996. Surfactant protein A is degraded by alveolar macrophages. *Am. J. Physiol. Lung Cell Mol. Physiol.* 15:L258–L66

140. Dong Q, Wright JR. 1998. Degradation of surfactant protein D by alveolar macrophages. *Am. J. Physiol. Lung Cell Mol. Physiol.* 18:L97–L105

141. Bates SR, Xu J, Dodia C, Fisher AB. 1997. Macrophages primed by overnight culture demonstrate a marked stimulation of surfactant protein A degradation. *Am. J. Physiol. Lung Cell Mol. Physiol.* 273:L831–L39

142. Kuroki Y, Shiratori M, Ogasawara Y, Tsuzuki A, Akino T. 1991. Characterization of pulmonary surfactant protein D: its copurification with lipids. *Biochim. Biophys. Acta* 1086:185–90

143. Kremlev SG, Umstead TM, Phelps DS. 1994. Effects of surfactant protein A and surfactant lipids on lymphocyte proliferation in vitro. *Am. J. Physiol. Lung Cell Mol. Physiol.* 267:L357–L64

144. Tino MJ, Wright JR. 1996. Surfactant protein A stimulates phagocytosis of specific pulmonary pathogens by alveolar macrophages. *Am. J. Physiol. Lung Cell Mol. Physiol.* 14:L677–L88

145. Ikegami M, Korfhagen TR, Bruno MD, Whitsett JA, Jobe AH. 1997. Surfactant metabolism in surfactant protein A-deficient mice. *Am. J. Physiol. Lung Cell Mol. Physiol.* 272:L479–L85

146. Wert SE, Yoshida M, LeVine AM, Ikegami M, Jones T, et al. 2000. Increased metalloproteinase activity, oxidant production, and emphysema in surfactant protein D gene-inactivated mice. *Proc. Natl. Acad. Sci. USA* 97:5972–77

147. LeVine AM, Bruno MD, Huelsman KM, Ross GF, Whitsett JA, Korfhagen TR. 1997. Surfactant protein A-deficient mice are susceptible to group B streptococcal infection. *J. Immunol.* 158:4336–40

148. Korfhagen TR, Bruno M, Silver J, Whitsett JA, LeVine AM. 2000. Enhanced *K. pneumoniae* pulmonary infection in mice lacking SP-A. *Am. J. Respir. Crit. Care Med.* 161:A514 (Abstr.)

149. LeVine AM, Kurak KE, Wright JR, Watford WT, Bruno MD, et al. 1999. Surfactant protein-A binds group B Streptococcus enhancing phagocytosis and clearance from lungs of surfactant protein-A-deficient mice. *Am. J. Respir. Cell Mol. Biol.* 20:279–86

150. McCormack F, Ikegami M, LeVine AM, Korfhagen TR, Whitsett JA, Dienger K. 2000. In vivo structure/function analyses of surfactant protein A. *Am. J. Respir. Crit. Care Med.* 161:A42 (Abstr.)

151. Hickman-Davis JM, Lindsey JR, Zhu S, Matalon S. 1998. Surfactant protein A mediates mycoplasmacidal activity of alveolar macrophages. *Am. J. Physiol. Lung Cell Mol. Physiol.* 274:L270–L77

152. Harris C, Linke M, Walzer P, Bruno M, Whitsett JA, Korfhagen TR. 1998. Increased *P. carinii* infection in lungs of SP-A deficient mice. *Am. J. Respir. Crit. Care Med.* 157:A236 (Abstr.)

153. Harrod K, LeVine A, Bruno M, Ross G, Korfhagen TR, Whitsett JA. 2000. Increased lung inflammation in surfactant protein A deficient mice following acute adenoviral infection in vivo. *Am. J. Respir. Crit. Care Med.* 159:A18 (Abstr.)

154. McIntosh JC, Mervin-Blake S, Conner E, Wright JR. 1996. Surfactant protein A protects growing cells and reduces TNF-alpha activity from LPS-stimulated macrophages. *Am. J. Physiol. Lung Cell Mol. Physiol.* 15:L310–L19

155. Capodici C, Chen S, Sidorczyk A, Elsbach P, Weiss J. 1994. Effect of lipopolysaccharide (LPS) chain length on interactions of bactericidal/permeability-increasing protein and its bioactive 23-kilodalton NH_2-terminal fragment with isolate LPS and intact *Proteus mirabilis*

and *Escherichia coli. Infect. Immun.* 62: 259–65

156. Jahr TG, Sundan A, Lichenstein HS, Espevik T. 1995. Influence of CD14, LBP and BPI in the monocyte response to LPS of different polysaccharide chain length. *Scand. J. Immunol.* 42:119–27

157. Di Padova F, Brade H, Barclay G, Poxton I, Liehl E, et al. 1993. A broadly cross-protective monoclonal antibody binding to *Escherichia coli* and *Salmonella* lipopolysaccharides. *Infect. Immun.* 61: 3863–72

158. Gazzano-Santoro H, Meszaros K, Birr C, Carroll S, Theofan G, et al. 1994. Competition between rBPI23, a recombinant fragment of bactericidal/permeability-increasing protein, and lipopolysaccharide (LPS)-binding protein for binding to LPS and gram-negative bacteria. *Infect. Immun.* 62:1185–91

159. Wong CJ, Akiyama J, Allen L, Hawgood S. 1996. Localization and developmental expression of surfactant proteins D and A in the respiratory tract of the mouse. *Pediatr. Res.* 39:930–37

160. Goss KL, Kumar AR, Snyder JM. 1998. SP-A2 gene expression in human fetal lung airways. *Am. J. Respir. Cell Mol. Biol.* 19:613–21

161. Saitoh H, Okayama H, Shimura S, Fushimi T, Masuda T, Shirato K. 1998. Surfactant protein A2 gene expression by human airway submucosal gland cells. *Am. J. Respir. Cell Mol. Biol.* 19:202–9

162. Rubio S, Lacaze-Masmonteil T, Chailley-Heu B, Kahn A, Bourbon JR, Ducroc R. 1995. Pulmonary surfactant protein A (SP-A) is expressed by epithelial cells of small and large intestine. *J. Biol. Chem.* 270:12162–69

163. Dutton JM, Goss K, Khubchandani KR, Shah CD, Smith RJH, Snyder JM. 1999. Surfactant protein A in rabbit sinus and middle ear mucosa. *Ann. Otol. Rhinol. Laryngol.* 108:915–24

164. Fisher JH, Mason R. 1995. Expression of pulmonary surfactant protein D in rat gastric mucosa. *Am. J. Respir. Cell Mol. Biol.* 12:13–18

165. Madsen J, Kliem A, Tornoe I, Skjodt K, Koch C, Holmskov U. 2000. Localization of lung surfactant protein D on mucosal surfaces in human tissue. *J. Immun.* 164:5866–70

166. Hull W, Stahlman M, Philips-Gray M, Wert SE, Whitsett JA. 2000. Immunolocalization of SP-D in human secretory tissues. *Am. J. Respir. Crit. Care Med.* 161:A42 (Abstr.)

167. Lin Z, Phelps D, deMello D, Page M, Coltun W, Floros J. 2000. Both human SP-A1 and SP-A2 genes are expressed in small and large intestine. *Am. J. Respir. Crit. Care Med.* 161:A43 (Abstr.)

168. Reading PC, Morey LS, Crouch EC, Anders EM. 1997. Collectin-mediated antiviral host defense of the lung—evidence from influenza virus infection of mice. *J. Virol.* 71:8204–12

169. McIntosh JC, Swyers AH, Fisher JH, Wright JR. 1996. Surfactant proteins A and D increase in response to intratracheal lipopolysaccharide. *Am. J. Resp. Cell Mol. Biol.* 15:509–19

170. Sugahara K, Iyama K, Sano K, Kuroki Y, Akino T. 1996. Overexpression of surfactant protein SP-A, SP-B, and SP-C mRNA in rat lungs with lipopolysaccharide-induced injury. *Lab. Invest.* 74:209–20

171. Viviano CJ, Bakewell WE, Dixon D, Dethloff LA, Hook GER. 1995. Altered regulation of surfactant phospholipid and protein A during acute pulmonary inflammation. *Biochim. Biophy. Acta* 1259:235–44

172. Hermans C, Bernard A. 1999. Lung epithelium-specific proteins. *Am. J. Respir. Crit. Care Med.* 159:646–78

173. Bry K, Lappalainen U, Hallman M. 1996. Cytokines and production of surfactant components. *Semin. Perinatol.* 20:194–205

174. Viviano CJ, Bakewell WE, Dixon D, Dethloff LA, Hook GE. 1995. Altered regulation of surfactant phospholipid and protein A during acute pulmonary inflammation. *Biochim. Biophys. Acta* 1259: 235–44

175. Fehrenbach H, Brasch F, Uhlig S, Weisser M, Stamme C, et al. 1998. Early alterations in intracellular and alveolar surfactant of the rat lung in response to endotoxin. *Am. J. Respir. Crit. Care Med.* 157:1630–39

176. Wang JY, Shieh CC, You PF, Lei HY, Reid KB. 1998. Inhibitory effect of pulmonary surfactant proteins A and D on allergen-induced lymphocyte proliferation and histamine release in children with asthma. *Am. J. Respir. Crit. Care Med.* 158:510–18

177. Korfhagen TR, Sheftelyevich V, Burhans MS, Bruno MD, Ross GF, et al. 1998. Surfactant protein D regulates surfactant phospholipid homeostasis in vivo. *J. Biol. Chem.* 273:28438–43

178. Honda Y, Takahashi H, Kuroki Y, Akino T, Abe S. 1996. Decreased contents of surfactant proteins A and D in BAL fluids of healthy smokers. *Chest* 109:1006–9

179. Coalson JJ, King RJ, Yang F, Winter V, Whitsett JA, et al. 1995. SP-A deficiency in primate model of bronchopulmonary dysplasia with infection. In situ mRNA and immunostains. *Am. J. Respir. Crit. Care Med.* 151:854–66

180. Postle AD, Mander A, Reid KBM, Wang JY, Wright SM, et al. 1999. Deficient hydrophilic lung surfactant proteins A and D with normal surfactant phospholipid molecular species in cystic fibrosis. *Am. J. Respir. Cell Mol. Biol.* 20:90–98

181. Greene KE, Wright JR, Steinberg KP, Ruzinski JT, Caldwell E, et al. 1999. Serial changes in surfactant-associated proteins in lung and serum before and after onset of ARDS. *Am. J. Respir. Crit. Care Med.* 160:1843–50

182. van de Graaf E, Jansen H, Lutter R, Alberts C, Kobesen J, et al. 1992. Surfactant protein A in bronchoalveolar lavage fluid. *J. Lab. Clin. Med.* 120:252–63

183. Honda Y, Kuroki Y, Matsuura E, Nagae H, Takahashi H, et al. 1995. Pulmonary surfactant protein D in sera and bronchoalveolar lavage fluids. *Am. J. Respir. Crit. Care Med.* 152:1860–66

184. Honda Y, Takahashi H, Shijubo N, Kuroki Y, Akino T. 1993. Surfactant protein-A concentration in bronchoalveolar lavage fluids of patients with pulmonary alveolar proteinosis. *Chest* 103:496–99

185. Turner MW, Lipscombe RJ, Levinsky RJ, Lau YL, Hill AV, et al. 1993. Mutations in the human mannose binding protein gene: their frequencies in three distinct populations and relationship to serum levels of the protein. *Immunodeficiency* 4:285–87

186. Sumiya M, Super M, Tabona P, Levinsky RJ, Arai T, et al. 1991. Molecular basis of opsonic defect in immunodeficient children. *Lancet* 337:1569–70

187. Sumiya M, Summerfield JA. 1997. The role of collectins in host defense. *Semin. Liver Dis.* 17:311–18

188. DiAngelo S, Lin Z, Wang G, Phillips S, Ramet M, et al. 1999. Novel, non-radioactive, simple and multiplex PCR-cRLFP methods for genotyping human SP-A and SP-D marker alleles. *Dis. Markers* 15:269–81

189. Floros J, DiAngelo S, Koptides M, Karinch A, Rogan P, et al. 1996. Human SP-A locus: allele frequencies and linkage disequilibrium between the two surfactant protein A genes. *Am. J. Respir. Cell Mol. Biol.* 15:489–98

190. Ofek I, Kabha K, Keisari Y, Schlepper-Schaefer J, Abraham S, et al. 1997. Recognition of *Klebsiella pneumoniae* by pulmonary C-type lectins. *Nova Acta Leopold* 75:43–54

191. Pikaar JC, Voorhout WF, van Golde

LMG, Verhoef J, van Strijp JAG, van Iwaarden JF. 1995. Opsonic activities of surfactant proteins A and D in phagocytosis of gram-negative bacteria by alveolar macrophages. *J. Infect. Dis.* 172:481–89

192. McNeely TB, Coonrod JD. 1993. Comparison of the opsonic activity of human surfactant protein A for *Staphylococcus aureus* and *Streptococcus pneumoniae* with rabbit and human macrophages. *J. Infect. Dis.* 167:91–97

Annu. Rev. Physiol. 2001. 63:555–78

FUNCTIONS OF SURFACTANT PROTEINS B AND C

Timothy E Weaver and Juliana Johnson Conkright
Division of Pulmonary Biology, Children's Hospital Medical Center,
Cincinnati, Ohio 45229-3039; e-mail: tim.weaver@chmcc.org

Key Words Type II epithelial cell, lung development, transgenic mice, respiratory distress syndrome, structure-function

■ **Abstract** SP-B is the only surfactant-associated protein absolutely required for postnatal lung function and survival. Complete deficiency of SP-B in mice and humans results in lethal, neonatal respiratory distress syndrome and is characterized by a virtual absence of lung compliance, highly disorganized lamellar bodies, and greatly diminished levels of SP-C mature peptide; in contrast, lung structure and function in SP-C null mice is normal. This review attempts to integrate recent findings in humans and transgenic mice with the results of in vitro studies to provide a better understanding of the functions of SP-B and SP-C and the structural basis for their actions.

INTRODUCTION

The maintenance of alveolar structure during cyclical changes in lung volume is critical for normal respiration. The inherent tendency of the alveolus to collapse at end expiration is due, in large part, to high surface tension generated by an aqueous layer lining the alveolar epithelium. Alveolar stability is achieved by maintenance of a phospholipid-rich film (pulmonary surfactant) at the air-liquid interface that reduces surface tension to very low levels as alveolar surface area decreases. In the absence of surfactant, the collapse of multiple alveoli rapidly progresses to severe respiratory distress, a condition marked by accumulation of characteristic intra-alveolar hyaline membranes, increased alveolo-capillary permeability and the need for ventilatory support. Human infants with surfactant insufficiency, usually the result of premature birth, respond very favorably to treatment with surfactant preparations based on the composition of native surfactant. The minimal essential elements of a therapeutic surfactant preparation include specific phospholipids, e.g. dipalmitoylphosphatidylcholine (DPPC) and phosphatidylglycerol (PG), and one of the hydrophobic surfactant peptides, surfactant protein (SP) B or SP-C. The importance of the peptide component of pulmonary surfactant is underscored by the observation that inherited deficiency of SP-B inevitably results in lethal respiratory distress syndrome (RDS) (1). This review integrates the findings of key studies, performed in vitro or in vivo, to provide a better understanding of the functions of SP-B and SP-C and the structural basis for their actions.

STRUCTURE OF SP-B AND SP-C

The goal of this section is to summarize current understanding of SP-B and SP-C structure in order to provide a basis for subsequent discussions of structure/function relationships. For a more comprehensive treatise of SP-B and SP-C structure, the reader is directed to several recent reviews of the subject (2–4).

Isolation of SP-B and SP-C

Low-speed centrifugation of bronchoalveolar lavage fluid results in isolation of surfactant with excellent surface tension–reducing properties. Surfactant isolated in this manner consists predominantly of lipid (90% by weight) with 0.5–1% each of SP-B and SP-C (2). Because of their hydrophobicity, SP-B and SP-C co-extract with lipids into the organic solvent phase following chloroform/methanol extraction of surfactant. Although this procedure results in virtually complete separation of SP-B and SP-C from the other protein components of surfactant, separation from each other and from phospholipids is more challenging. Chromatography of the acidified organic solvent extracts of surfactant on Sephadex LH-60 (5) or reverse-phase HPLC on a C18 column (6) results in elution of SP-B first, consistent with its overall more polar amino acid composition, followed by SP-C and, finally, phospholipids.

Structure of SP-B

The consensus sequence for SP-B, derived by alignment of the amino acid sequences from nine different species (Figure 1A, see color insert), indicates that the mature lipid-associated peptide is 79 residues in length and contains 52% hydrophobic amino acids (Ala, Ile, Leu, Phe, Trp, Val), and a substantial number of basic amino acids, resulting in a net charge of +5. Six of seven cysteine residues are absolutely conserved, and this feature identifies SP-B as a member of the saposin-like (SAPLIP) family of peptides (7, 8). Other SAPLIP family members include saposins A, B, C, and D, NK-lysin, and the pore-forming peptide of *Entamoeba histolytica*. SAPLIP domains have also been identified in acid sphingomyelinase, acyloxyacyl hydrolase, and plant aspartic proteinases (9); in addition, the propeptides that flank the mature peptide in the SP-B proprotein each contain a SAPLIP domain (Figure 1A). The cysteine residues of the SP-B mature peptide form intramolecular sulfhydryl bridges such that the innermost two residues (cysteines 35 and 46) form a bridge that stabilizes a hairpin loop, the outermost two cysteines (residues 8 and 77) form another bridge, and the two remaining cysteines (residues 11 and 71) form a disulfide bond between the inner and outer bridges (10, 11) (Figure 1B). This pattern of disulfide bonding has also been confirmed for

NK-lysin (12) and saposins B and C (13) and likely contributes to the remarkable thermal stability of these peptides. The three-dimensional NMR structure for NK-lysin, the only SAPLIP family member for which such data are available, suggests the presence of five amphipathic helices (14). The helical content of SP-B is similar to NK-lysin (approximately 45%), and given the constraints imposed by three disulfide bridges, it is highly likely that the three-dimensional structure of SP-B is also similar to NK-lysin (15, 16).

All SAPLIPs interact with lipids; however, unlike other SAPLIPs, which are only transiently lipid associated, the unique hydrophobic character of the 79 amino acid SP-B peptide ensures that it is always associated with surfactant phospholipids. Although the orientation of SP-B within a lipid membrane is not clear, most evidence to date supports a model in which the polar faces of the amphipathic helices interact with phospholipid headgroups, and the highly conserved positively charged amino acids interact specifically with the anionic phospholipid phosphatidylglycerol (17, 18), which constitutes approximately 10% of surfactant. This model favors location of SP-B at the surface of the membrane such that the nonpolar faces of the helices interact only with the most superficial aspect of the acyl chains.

A second unique characteristic of SP-B is the formation of oligomers, predominantly homodimers in most species. Dimerization occurs through formation of an intersubunit disulfide bridge involving cysteine 48, which is not present in other SAPLIPs (11, 19). The dimer structure may be further stabilized by formation of intersubunit hydrogen bonds/ion pairs between the strictly conserved residues Glu 51 and Arg 52 (20). It is currently unclear if both subunits are always located in the same lipid plane. The potential for SP-B units to reside in separate, adjacent membranes has important implications for packaging of phospholipids in lamellar bodies and surface film dynamics.

Addition of SP-B to liposomes leads to membrane binding, destabilization, and fusion (lipid mixing) (18, 21–26). The ability of SP-B to alter membrane structure may play a critical role in the packaging of surfactant phospholipids for storage in lamellar bodies and in the transition from storage form to the biologically active surface film. These putative in vivo functions of SP-B (discussed below) should be interpreted with caution as the in vitro properties of SP-B are strongly influenced by a number of variables including the method of SP-B isolation, the size and phospholipid composition of liposomes, the presence of SP-A and divalent cations, pH, and the manner in which SP-B is added to liposomes (3, 26, 27).

Structure of SP-C

Analysis of the SP-C consensus sequence, derived by alignment of amino acid sequences from 10 different species (Figure 2, see color insert), indicates that the mature SP-C peptide is a 35–amino acid peptide composed of 69% hydrophobic amino acids (Ala, Ile, Leu, Phe, Trp, Val). The overall hydrophobicity of the peptide is increased by palmitoylation of cysteines at positions 5 and 6 in most species (canine and mink SP-C contain a single palmitoylated cysteine at position 6). A small proportion of SP-C (less than 5%) is also palmitoylated on lysine 11 (6). Non-palmitoylated or deacylated forms of SP-C can form sulfhydryl-dependent dimers and amyloid fibrils (28–30); therefore, variable palmitoylation (non-, mono-, di- and tripalmitoylated isoforms) in combination with N-terminal truncation leads to considerable microheterogeneity of SP-C (4). The functional consequences of this heterogeneity are not known.

One of the most remarkable features of SP-C is an extremely hydrophobic domain (residues 13–28) in which valine is the predominant amino acid (69%), thus accounting for one of the original names for this peptide, surfactant proteolipid polyvaline (31). The NMR structure of porcine SP-C is consistent with a transmembrane peptide in which residues 9–34 form a rigid α helix (32). This structure can span a fluid DPPC bilayer such that the polyvaline domain is perfectly accommodated in the interior acyl chain region of the membrane (Figure 3, see color insert). The helical nature of the membrane-spanning domain is promoted by the palmitate moieties on the extramembrane N-terminal region of SP-C, which may interact with an adjacent membrane or, more likely, with the same bilayer in which the peptide resides (33). The transmembrane orientation of SP-C is further stabilized by invariant Lys-Arg residues at positions 11 and 12 that interact with phospholipid headgroups (34).

As like SP-B, SP-C has been shown to alter membrane structure in vitro. The relative mobility of the C-terminal region of SP-C may play a role in disrupting the packing of acyl chains in the bilayer leading to membrane destabilization (35, 36); however, unlike SP-B, SP-C does not appear to promote lipid mixing (fusion) (18, 25). The potential of SP-C to destabilize membranes and the putative role of this property in promoting formation of a biologically active surface film are discussed below.

SURFACTANT HOMEOSTASIS

SP-B and SP-C are associated with several different forms of surfactant (Figure 3). The major intracellular form of surfactant consists of lipid bilayers that are tightly packed into concentric layers (lamellae) within large (1–2 μm diameter) storage granules (lamellar bodies) of the Type II alveolar epithelial cell. Exocytosis results in release of the lamellar body contents (large aggregate surfactant) into the aqueous lining layer of the alveolus. Subsequent transition from storage form to functional surface film involves unraveling of the lamellae and adsorption of lipids to form an interfacial (liquid-air) film or insertion of lipids into an existing surface film. Turnover of the surface film results in the formation of vesicular forms of surfactant (small aggregate surfactant) that are internalized into catabolic pathways in Type II cells and macrophages or directed to a recycling pathway in Type II cells. The putative roles of SP-B and SP-C in promoting transition from one surfactant form to another are discussed in the succeeding sections.

INTRACELLULAR FUNCTIONS OF SP-B AND SP-C

The Role(s) of SP-B in Surfactant Biosynthesis

The mature SP-B peptide is encoded by exons 6 and 7 of a single gene (*Sftp-3*) located on chromosome 2 in the human (37, 138) and chromosome 6 in the mouse (39). Translation of the human SP-B mRNA results in synthesis of a larger precursor protein in which the mature SP-B peptide (residues 201–279) is flanked by an N-terminal prepropeptide of 200 amino acids and a C-terminal peptide of 102 amino acids (Figure 1*A*). Both flanking peptides contain saposin-like domains that are readily identified by alignment of six conserved cysteine residues (69, 72, 100, 112, 137, and 143 in the human N-terminal propeptide; 299, 302, 325, 335, 360, and 366 in the C-terminal peptide) with other members of the SAPLIP family (7, 40). Although the precise boundaries of the saposin-like domains have not been established, it is apparent that these domains differ significantly from the mature peptide in that they are much less hydrophobic, carry a net negative charge, and do not include an additional cysteine residue (comparable to Cys48 in the mature peptide) capable of mediating sulfhydryl-dependent dimerization. Possible functions for the saposin-like domains are discussed below.

Processing of the SP-B preproprotein to its mature peptide occurs during transit through the secretory pathway. Entry of SP-B into the secretory pathway is mediated by a typical N-terminal signal peptide, predicted to be 24 amino acids in length (Signalp network server, Center for Biological Sequence Analysis; Lyngby, Denmark), which is cleaved upon translation of the proprotein into the endoplasmic reticulum (41). The first 27 residues of the preproprotein have been shown to encode a functional signal peptide, but the exact cleavage site has not been experimentally determined (42). At least one point mutation in the sequence encoding the signal peptide of human SP-B has been associated with lethal RDS (Table 1).

Transit of SP-B out of the endoplasmic reticulum is dependent on the N-terminal propeptide, which likely facilitates folding and/or sequestration of the hydrophobic mature peptide (42); in contrast, the C-terminal peptide is not required for intracellular trafficking of SP-B in transfected cultured cells or in transgenic mice (43, 44). Paradoxically, mutations in the saposin-like domain of the C-terminal peptide have been associated with lethal RDS (Table 1). It is likely that these mutations lead to misfolding and trapping of the proprotein in the endoplasmic reticulum, thereby preventing processing of the proprotein to its mature peptide in the distal secretory pathway.

Trafficking of SP-B to the distal arm of the regulated secretory pathway (i.e. the lamellar body) requires both the N-terminal propeptide and the mature peptide (44). Although it is not known if the proprotein is membrane bound during transit in the secretory pathway, it is tempting to speculate that the saposin-like domain in the propeptide may play an important role in this sorting event, as has been suggested for the saposin-like domain of the plant aspartyl protease, phytepsin (45). Mutations in the saposin-like domain in the N-terminal propeptide have been associated with RDS (Table 1).

TABLE 1 Mutations in the human SP-B gene

Nucleotide[a]	Affected exon	Affected codon	Affected peptide domain	Amino acids in ORF (mature peptide?)[b]	SP-B[c] Proprotein	SP-B[c] Mature peptide	SP-C$_6$[d]	Reference
52	Exon 1	L13P	Signal peptide	381 (yes)	+	−	+	(136)
441	Exon 2	W39X	Propeptide	38 (no)	−	−	ND[e]	(136)
457 (g. 457delC)	Exon 2	45delC (frameshift)	Propeptide	51 (no)	−	−	−	(122)
469	Exon 2	C49R	Propeptide	381 (yes)	ND	ND	ND	(136)
504	Exon 2	W60X	Propeptide	59 (no)	−	−	+	(136)
523	Exon 2/intron 2 (c. 209 + 4A > G)	Splice mutation (delete exon 2 → frameshift)	Propeptide	23 (no)	+	−	+	(136)
1454	Intron 3/exon 4 (c. 282-2delA)	Splice mutation (delete exon 4)	Propeptide	339 (yes)	+	−	+	(136)
1486	Exon 4	C100G	Propeptide (sap-like)[f]	381 (yes)	++	+	+	(136)
1549	Exon 4 (g. 1549C → GAA)	121ins2 (frameshift)	Propeptide (sap-like)	214 (no)	−	−	+	(1)
1552	Exon 4 (g. 1552delC)	122delC (frameshift)	Propeptide (sap-like)	213 (no)	ND	ND	ND	(137)
1553	Exon 4 (g. 1553delT)	122delT (frameshift)	Propeptide (sap-like)	213 (no)	ND	ND	ND	(138)
2415	Exon 5	134ins2 (frameshift)	Propeptide (sap-like)	214 (no)	−	−	ND	(139)

2417	Exon 5	G135S	Propeptide (sap-like)	381 (yes)	−[g]	−[g]	+	(116)
2479	Exon 5	Splice mutation (delete 119nt of exon 5 ± exon 7)	Propeptide	210 (no)[h] 280 (no) 381 (yes)	++	++	+	L Nogee, unpublished
2913	Exon 6/intron 6 (c. 686G > A)	Splice mutation (delete exon 6)[i]	Mature peptide	351 (partial, 55aa)	ND	ND	ND	(1)
4377	Exon 7	C235R	Mature peptide	381 (yes)	++	+	+	(136)
4380	Exon 7	R236C	Mature peptide	381 (yes)	++	+	+	(136)
4418	Exon 7	C248X	Mature peptide	247 (partial, 47aa)	ND	ND	+	(136)
4428	Exon 7	R252C	Mature peptide	381 (yes)	++	+	+	(136)
4729	Exon 8 (c. 896ins18)	292-293 ins TGEWLP	C-terminal peptide	387 (yes)	−[g]	−[g]	−	L Nogee, unpublished
6109	Exon 9 (c. 1043ins3)	343-344 ins P	C-terminal peptide (sap-like)	382 (yes)	++	++	ND	(136)
6114	Exon 9	346-349 del QLLT	C-terminal peptide (sap-like)	377 (yes)	+	−	ND	(1)

[a]Nucleotide number 1 is the first base of exon 1.

[b]Indicates whether residues 201–279 (mature peptide) are included in the open reading frame (ORF).

[c]SP-B detected by immunohistochemistry or Western blot.

[d]SP-C$_6$ = incompletely processed SP-C proprotein, detected by Western blot.

[e]ND = not determined.

[f]Sap-like indicates a saposin-like domain is affected (7).

[g]Transient SP-B deficiency.

[h]Three different SP-B transcripts were detected in association with this mutation; the longest transcript (381) encodes wild type SP-B.

[i]Deletion of exon 6 has not been confirmed because RNA was not available.

Cleavage of the N-terminal propeptide and the C-terminal peptide occurs in the lumen of the multivesicular body, prior to or during fusion of the multivesicular body with the lamellar body (46). Processing of the proprotein to the mature peptide is detectable as early as day 17 in fetal mouse lung (47). The identity and number of proteases involved in proprotein processing is not known, although a cathepsin-D-like protease has been implicated in cleavage of the propeptide (48). Consistent with this hypothesis, a novel aspartyl protease, Napsin A, was recently identified and shown to be highly expressed in Type II epithelial cells (49–51); however, direct evidence for involvement of Napsin A in SP-B proprotein processing is currently lacking.

The fate of the cleaved N- and C-terminal peptides is not clear, and it is not known if they are further processed to generate smaller peptides, consisting solely of the saposin-like domain. The possibility that the released C-terminal peptide may have a function independent of the proprotein is supported by a recent study in transgenic mice (52). A human SP-B construct lacking the entire 102 amino acid C-terminal domain (SP-B$_{\Delta c}$) was able to restore lung function in SP-B $(-/-)$ mice and completely reverse the neonatal lethal phenotype; however, lamellar bodies were greatly enlarged in approximately 20% of Type II cells, and the intracellular surfactant pool size was significantly increased. One possible interpretation of this outcome is that the C-terminal peptide plays a role in the turnover of surfactant lipids, similar to the well-characterized role of the saposins in facilitating lysosomal hydrolysis of glycolipids. It should be noted, however, that enlarged lamellar bodies in Type II cells are common to a number of disorders including Chediak Higashi Syndrome (53), SP-D deficiency (54), LPS instillation (55), and certain lymphomas (56). The hypothesis that the C-terminal peptide modulates lamellar body size by promoting hydrolysis of lipids in the surfactant recycling/catabolic pathway is intriguing, but has not been directly tested.

The phenotype of SP-B-deficient human infants (57) and SP-B knockout mice (58) has provided valuable insight into the role of SP-B in the surfactant biosynthetic pathway. Type II cells in SP-B $(-/-)$ mice contain well-developed multivesicular bodies but lack lamellar bodies with typical concentric membranes. Unlike cells from wild-type and SP-B $(+/-)$ mice, Type II cells of SP-B $(-/-)$ mice are characterized by inclusions containing numerous small vesicles and electron dense masses. Multivesicular bodies fuse with the vesicular inclusions, and the contents of these organelles were detected in the airway consistent with their secretion (47). Taken together, these data suggest that the vesicular inclusions in SP-B $(-/-)$ mice are disorganized lamellar bodies in which the absence of SP-B results in failure to package surfactant phospholipids into concentric lamellae.

One of the characteristic features of the mature SP-B peptide is the formation of homodimers through cysteine 48 (10, 19). The proprotein does not form sulfhydryl-dependent oligomers, which suggests that dimer formation occurs following cleavage of the peptides flanking the mature peptide. The functional significance of SP-B homodimerization is currently not clear. Expression of an SP-B construct in which cysteine 48 (cysteine 248 in the proprotein) was mutated to serine completely

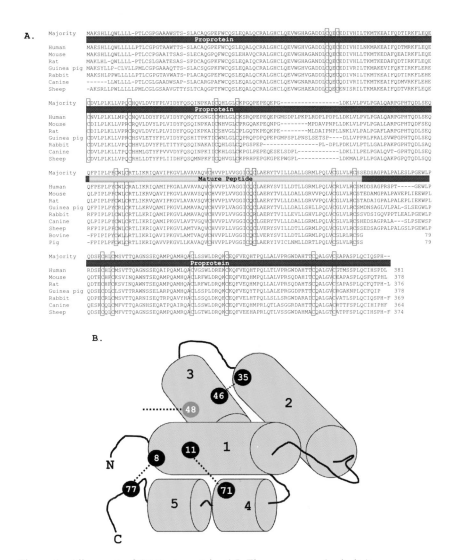

Figure 1 Alignment of SP-B proprotein. (*A*) The consensus (majority) sequence was determined by alignment of SP-B proprotein from nine species. (Only mature peptide sequence is available for bovine and porcine SP-B.) Strictly conserved cysteine residues (red boxes) identify SP-B as a member of the SAPLIP family, which contains saposin-like domains in the N-terminal propeptide (blue bar), mature peptide (yellow bar), and C-terminal peptide (blue bar). Cysteine 48 in the mature peptide allows SP-B to form homodimers (blue box). (*B*) The intramolecular sulfhydryl bridge formed between cysteines 35 and 46 stabilizes the hairpin loop formed by the antiparallel arrangement of helices 2 and 3. Additional intramolecular sulfhdryl bridges are formed between cysteines 8 and 77 and cysteines 11 and 71.

```
                    Proprotein                                    Mature Peptide
Majority  MD-GSKEVLMESPPDYSAAPRGRFGIPCCPVHLKRLLIVVVVLVVVIVGALIMGLHMSQKHTEMVLEMSIG-APEAQQRLALSEHAGTTATFSIGSTG

Human     MDVGSKEVLMESPPDYSAAPRGRFGIPCCPVHLKRLLIVVVVLIVVVIVGALIMGLHMSQKHTEMVLEMSIG-APEAQQRLALSEHLVTTATFSIGSTG
Mink      MDVGSKEVLIENPPDYSAAPQGRFGLPCEPSSLKRLLIIVVVVLVLVVVIVGALIMGLHMSQKHTEMVLEMSLG-GPEAQQRLALQERAGTTATFSIGSTG
Monkey    MDVGSKEVLMESPPDYSAAPRGRFGIPCCPVHLKRLLIIVVVVLVVVIVGALIMGLHMSQKHTEMVLEMSIG-APEAQQHLARSGHLVTTATFSFGSTG
Mouse     MDMSSKEVLMESPPDYSAGPRSQFRIPCCPVHLKRLLIIVVVVLVVVVIVGALIMGLHMSQKHTEMVLEMSIG-APETQKRLAPSERADTIATFSIGSTG
Rabbit    MDMGSKEALMESPPDYSAAPRGRFGIPCCPVHLKRLLIVVVVLVVVVIVGALIMGLHMSQKHTEMVLEMSIG-APEVQQRLALSEWAGTTATFPIGSTG
Rat       MDMGSKEVLMESPPDYSTGPRSQFRIPCCPVHLKRLLIVVVVLVVVIVGALIMGLHMSQKHTEMVLEMSIGGAPETQKRLALSEHTDTIATFSIGSTG
Sheep     -R--SKEVLMESPPDYSAVPGGRLRIPCCPVNIKRLLIVVVVLVVVVIVGALIMGLHMSQKHTEMVLEMSIA-GPEAQQRLALSERVGTTATFSIGSTG
Bovine    -------------L-IPCCPVNIKRLLIVVVVLIVVVIVGALIMGL
Canine    -------------LGIPEPSSLKRLLIIVVVIVLVVVVIVGALIMGL
Pig       -------------LRIPCCPVNLKRLLVVVVVLVVVVIVGALIMGL

                    Proprotein
Majority  IVVYDYQRLLIAYKP-APGTCCYIMKVAPESIPSLEALARK-QNF------QAKPAVPTSKLGQEEGHDAGSASSGG--DLAFLG-AVSTLCGEVPLYYI

Human     LVVYDYQQLLIAYKP-APGTCCYIMKIAPESIPSLEALNRKVHNFQMECSLQAKPAVPTSKLGQAEGRDAGSAPSGG--DPAFLGMAVNTLCGEVPLYYI
Mink      IVVYDYQRLLIAYKP-APGTCCYIMKMAPENIPSLEALTRKFQNF------QVKPAVTSKLQEEGHNAGSASPG---DLDFIGTTVSTLCGEVPLYYI
Monkey    IVVYDYQRLLIAYKP-APGTWCYIMKTAPESIPSLEALTRKVQNF------QAKPAVPTSKLDQVEGRDAGSAFSRG--DLAFLGMAVSTLCGEVPLYYI
Mouse     IVVYDYQRLLTAYKP-APGTYCYIMKMAPESIPSLEAFARKLQNF------RAKPSTPTSKLQEEGHDTGSESDSSGRDLAFLGLAVSTLCGELPLYYI
Rabbit    IVTCDYQRLLIAYKPPAPGTCCYLMKMAPKSIPSLEALARK--F------QANPAEPPTQRGQDKGPAAGPASSGG--ELAFLGAAVSTLCGEVPLIYI
Rat       IVLYDYQRLLIAYKP-APGTCCYIMKMAPESIPSLEALARKFKNF------QAKSSTPTSKLQEEGHSAGSDSSGRDLAFLGLAVSTLCGELPLYYI
Sheep     TVVYDYQRLLIAYKP-APGTCCYIMKVAPQSIPSLEALTRKLPNF------QAKPPVPSSKLQEEQGRDAGSAFSG--DLAFLGRTVSTLCGEVPLYYT
```

Figure 2 Alignment of SP-C proprotein. The consensus (majority) sequence was determined by alignment of SP-C proprotein from ten species. (Only mature peptide sequence is available for bovine, canine, and porcine SP-C.) The SP-C proprotein contains a single membrane-spanning domain (black box). The N-terminal and C-terminal peptides (blue bars) are proteolytically cleaved to generate the 35 amino acid, mature, trans-membrane peptide (yellow bar). Palmitoylation of cysteine residues (red box) occurs in all species.

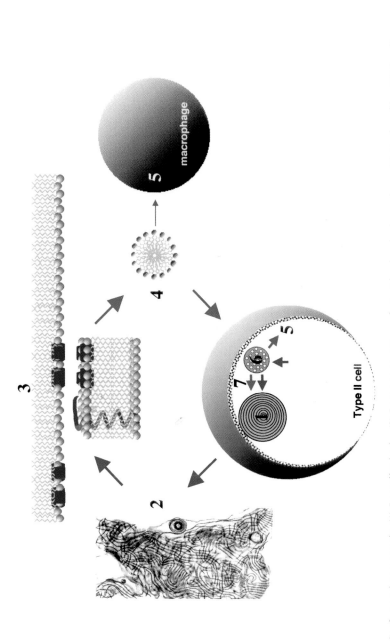

Figure 3 Surfactant homeostasis. (1) Lamellar body. (2) Large aggregate surfactant. (3) Surface film. (4) Small aggregate surfactant. (5) Surfactant catabolic pathway. (6) Multivesicular body. (7) Recycling/biosynthetic pathway. Green arrows represent anabolic pathways and blue arrows catabolic pathways. Red peptide is SP-C; blue peptide is SP-B.

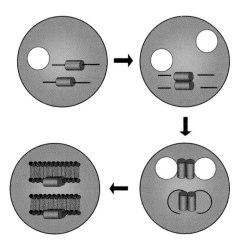

Figure 4 Processing of the SP-B proprotein. SP-B is proteolytically processed by removal of the N-terminal propeptide followed by cleavage of the C-terminal peptide (black bars) releasing the 79 amino acid mature peptide (blue cylinder). SP-B mature peptide forms homodimers, which associate with the inner vesicles of the multivesicular body leading to vesicle lysis and fusion and, ultimately, reorganization of internal membranes.

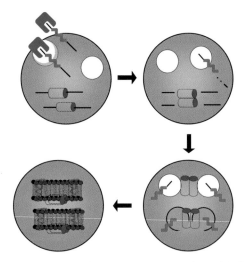

Figure 5 Processing and secretion of SP-C. SP-C proprotein (red helix flanked by black lines) interacts with unidentified cytosolic proteins (green), which selectively sort SP-C from the limiting membrane to the lumen of the multivesicular body. Inward vesiculation of the limiting membrane results in localization of SP-C proprotein on the inner vesicles. The C-terminal peptide of SP-C is accessible to proteases in the lumen of the multivesicular body and is cleaved in a step-wise fashion. Subsequent cleavage of the N-terminal propeptide of SP-C is dependent upon the lytic activity of SP-B. Fusion of the multivesicular body with the lamellar body results in secretion of SP-C.

reversed the neonatal lethality and disorganized lamellar body phenotype in SP-B
$(-/-)$ mice (19). This outcome suggests that sulfhydryl-dependent dimerization
of SP-B is not required for packaging of surfactant phospholipids in lamellar bodies or for formation and function of an interfacial film in the alveolus; however,
this study cannot exclude the possibility that SP-B oligomers form through ionic
or hydrophobic interactions (20).

A model that takes into account the SP-B $(-/-)$ phenotype and the in vitro
properties of SP-B is proposed in Figure 4 (see color insert). In this model, the
increasingly acidic milieu of the maturing multivesicular body leads to activation
of specific proteases and cleavage of the N-terminal propeptide and C-terminal
peptide of the SP-B proprotein. Processing of the proprotein in the aqueous environment of the multivesicular body lumen results in rapid dimer formation and
association of the hydrophobic mature peptide with the internal vesicles of this
organelle. SP-B mediated lysis and fusion of internal vesicles leads to the reorganization of membranes into lamellae, a process that continues following fusion of
the multivesicular body with the lamellar body. This model predicts that SP-B will
be associated with only one side of a bilayer membrane, although the functional
implications of this asymmetry are not known.

The Role(s) of SP-C in Surfactant Biosynthesis

The mature SP-C peptide is encoded by exon 2 of a single gene (*Sftp-2*) on chromosome 8 in the human (31, 59) and chromosome 14 in the mouse (39). Translation
of the human SP-C mRNA results in synthesis of a proprotein of 197 amino
acids, or 191 amino acids following alternative splicing of the primary transcript
(31, 60, 61). The organization of the proprotein is similar to SP-B in that the mature
peptide (residues 24–58) is flanked by an N-terminal propeptide and a C-terminal
peptide. However, unlike SP-B, SP-C is an integral membrane protein in which
the hydrophobic α-helix of the mature peptide serves as both signal peptide and
membrane-spanning domain. The proprotein has been identified as a Type II (62)
or Type III (63) integral membrane protein; however, since palmitoylation and
positively charged residues (K^+R^+) usually occur on the cytoplasmic side of the
membrane (64, 65), SP-C is most likely a Type II integral membrane in which
the N-terminal propeptide resides in the cytosol and the C-terminal peptide in the
lumen of the endoplasmic reticulum.

The N-terminal propeptide and/or C-terminal peptide of the proprotein likely
play an important role in trafficking of SP-C to the distal regulated secretory
pathway. Post-Golgi sorting of integral membrane proteins is generally accepted to
be dependent upon information encoded in the cytosolic tail of the protein (66, 67).
Assuming a Type II membrane orientation, the cytosolic domain of SP-C would
consist of the 23 amino acid propeptide and the first 10 residues of the mature
peptide (Figure 2). This region lacks a canonical di-leucine or tyrosine-based
motif involved in adaptor protein (AP)-associated trafficking of integral membrane
proteins to lysosomal or endosomal compartments, suggesting involvement of

a novel sorting motif. This prediction is difficult to reconcile with the results of deletion studies suggesting that the C-terminal peptide plays a critical role in intracellular trafficking of the proprotein (68, 69). The interpretation of the latter studies is significantly complicated by the use of cells lacking a typical regulated secretory pathway. It is possible that C-terminal deletions/mutations lead to misfolding and trapping of the proprotein in the endoplasmic reticulum; alternatively, but less likely, the proprotein may exist in a Type III membrane orientation such that the C-terminal peptide resides in the cytoplasm.

Trafficking of proteins through the secretory pathway involves the formation of transport vesicles in which integral membrane proteins are located in the limiting membrane of the vesicle. In the regulated secretory pathway, these vesicles ultimately fuse with larger storage granules, which are released in response to an extracellular stimulus. Exocytosis of regulated or constitutive secretory vesicles results in the fusion of the limiting membrane of the secretory vesicle with the plasma membrane, thereby leading to localization of integral membrane proteins on the cell surface. The transferrin receptor is an example of a palmitoylated transmembrane protein with a Type II membrane orientation that follows the constitutive secretory pathway to the plasma membrane. SP-C differs from the transferrin receptor in that it is secreted into the alveolus, along with the other components of surfactant, rather than retained at the cell surface; therefore, at some point along the secretory pathway, SP-C must be relocated from the limiting membrane of the vesicle to its lumen. SP-C proprotein has been detected in the limiting membrane and internal vesicles of the multivesicular body, suggesting that this compartment plays a critical role in the secretion of SP-C (63). Multivesicular bodies (endosomes) in the endocytic pathway have previously been shown to be important for segregation of membrane receptors destined for recycling to the cell surface from receptors marked for degradation. Receptors internalized into the lumen of the multivesicular body are degraded following fusion of the multivesicular body with the lysosome (70). There is growing evidence that in addition to the endocytic pathway, multivesicular bodies may also play an important role in the secretory pathway; for example, multivesicular bodies represent a developmental stage in the maturation of α-granules in platelets (71). In alveolar Type II epithelial cells, multivesicular bodies can fuse with the lamellar body, which results in the delivery of internal vesicles containing SP-C to the lumen of the lamellar body (47, 72).

The formation of internal vesicles in the multivesicular body is generally accepted to be the result of inward vesiculation of the limiting membrane (Figure 5, see color insert). The composition of the internal vesicle membranes is different from that of the limiting membrane of the multivesicular body, consistent with selective internalization of both protein and lipid components (73, 74). Apart from facilitating secretion of SP-C, this process may be important in refining the membrane environment in which SP-C is located. The lipid composition of endoplasmic reticulum and Golgi membranes through which SP-C traffics is very different from pulmonary surfactant, indicating that the membrane environment of SP-C changes during surfactant biosynthesis (75, 76).

The mechanism underlying selective internalization of membrane proteins has not been extensively studied. In yeast, fablp [a phosphatidylinositol(3)P-5-kinase] was shown to be essential for sorting of membrane proteins into the lumen of the vacuole, suggesting an important role for polyphosphoinositides in the formation of internal vesicles (77). The interaction of endosomal COP-1 and other protein partners with the cytosolic tail of specific integral membrane proteins in the limiting membrane of the multivesicular body may also be important for selective internalization of membrane proteins (78, 79). Figure 5 proposes a model in which the N-terminal propeptide encodes a signal(s) for the internalization of SP-C from the limiting membrane of the multivesicular body.

Low levels of the mature SP-C peptide are detected on day 17 of gestation in the mouse and day 27 of gestation in the rabbit (47, 80). Processing of the SP-C proprotein to its mature peptide increases dramatically on day 18 or 29 in the mouse and rabbit, respectively. As for the SP-B precursor, proteolytic processing of the SP-C proprotein likely occurs in the multivesicular body (63). Stepwise processing of the C-terminal peptide results in the generation of multiple processing intermediates (63, 81). The identity and number of proteases is not known, and it is not clear if there is any overlap in the proteases involved in processing of the SP-B and SP-C proproteins. A model of SP-C processing based on a Type II membrane orientation of the proprotein is proposed in Figure 5. Proteases located in the lumen of the multivesicular body have free access to the SP-B proprotein and the C-terminal peptide of the SP-C proprotein; the N-terminal propeptide of SP-C is not accessible to proteases because it is located in the cytosol prior to inward vesiculation and inside the internal vesicle following internalization. Processing of the SP-B proprotein leads to lysis and fusion of internal vesicle membranes by the released mature peptide. SP-B-mediated vesicle lysis exposes the N-terminal propeptide to proteases in the lumen of the multivesicular body, resulting in cleavage of the propeptide. This model accounts for the incomplete processing of SP-C proprotein in SP-B-deficient infants and SP-B $(-/-)$ mice (1, 58, 82, 83). In the absence of SP-B, levels of mature SP-C peptide are very low, and an incompletely processed form of SP-C accumulates in the airway. This form of SP-C contains the N-terminal propeptide (identified by Western blotting), and its size is very close to the predicted size of the proprotein lacking the entire C-terminal peptide (82). However, the identity of the incompletely processed SP-C proprotein has not yet been verified by amino acid sequence analysis.

The results of a previous study in transgenic mice suggested that the C-terminal peptide of the SP-B proprotein was also important for SP-C processing (52). These mice (SP-B$_{\Delta c}$ transgenic mice) expressed a truncated SP-B proprotein (lacking the entire C-terminal peptide) in the SP-B $(-/-)$ background. A small amount of incompletely processed SP-C proprotein was detected in SP-C$_{\Delta c}$ mice, suggesting a link between incomplete SP-C proprotein processing and the absence of the C-terminal peptide of SP-B. More recent studies have shown that in some transgenic lines, the SP-B transgene is expressed in most, but not all, Type II epithelial cells, leading to small amounts of incompletely processed SP-C but normal levels of mature SP-C peptide in bronchoalveolar lavage fluid. Taken together, these results support a role for the mature SP-B peptide, but not the C-terminal peptide, in processing of the SP-C proprotein.

EXTRACELLULAR FUNCTIONS OF SP-B AND SP-C

The Role(s) of SP-B and SP-C in Surface Film Formation

Numerous studies have characterized the effects of SP-B and SP-C on the formation and properties of model surface films using the Langmuir-Wilhelmy surface balance, pulsating bubble surfactometer, and most recently, the captive bubble surfactometer. The purpose of this section is not to provide a comprehensive review of these studies, but rather to re-examine some basic concepts regarding surfactant film formation and turnover in light of recent descriptions of SP-B and SP-C knockout mice.

The alveolar lining layer consists of an aqueous subphase (hypophase) and a phospholipid-rich interfacial film. Several forms of surfactant are detected in the hypophase, including the newly secreted contents of lamellar bodies, tubular myelin, and loose membrane arrays. Initial formation of the surface film during adaptation to air breathing requires rapid adsorption to and spreading of one or more of these surfactant forms at the air-liquid interface. Despite intensive investigation, our understanding of the mechanisms leading to surface film formation and the molecular composition and structure of the interfacial film is still rudimentary.

The results of extensive in vitro studies suggest that in addition to rapid adsorption and spreading, a model surfactant should require only minimal surface area compression to achieve near zero surface tension, resist collapse when compressed, and respread rapidly following film compression. It is generally agreed that in order to achieve the requisite low-surface tension during compression, the surface film must be highly enriched in DPPC. Given the heterogeneous composition of surfactant in the hypophase, it has been suggested that the interfacial film is modified by selective incorporation of DPPC during film expansion and/or exclusion (squeeze-out) of non-DPPC components during film compression (84). The processes involved in formation, refining, and maintenance of this surface film in vitro are strongly influenced by SP-B and SP-C.

SP-B and SP-C independently accelerate film formation by enhancing the adsorption and spreading of surfactant phospholipids at an air-liquid interface. In addition to facilitating formation of an initial surfactant film during the first breath, SP-B and SP-C may play an important role in maintaining a functional interfacial film by recruiting phospholipids into the expanding film, promoting respreading of a compressed film, and modulating film composition during dynamic compression and expansion (85, 86). Although SP-B and SP-C are not equivalent in each of these in vitro properties, surfactant preparations containing either SP-B or SP-C can restore lung function in surfactant-deficient animals, suggesting extensive or complete overlap in their ability to promote and maintain a functional surface film (87–90). Consistent with this hypothesis, lung function, surfactant composition, and surfactant pool sizes in SP-C $(-/-)$ mice are indistinguishable from wild-type littermates (91), indicating that SP-B alone is sufficient for surfactant function; however, rigorous testing of the functional redundancy hypothesis will require generation of transgenic animals that are deficient in SP-B and maintain normal levels of mature SP-C peptide.

The structural basis for and the mechanism(s) whereby SP-B and SP-C modulate formation and function of the surface film remain unclear. Synthetic peptides corresponding to the N and C termini of SP-B, which include helix 1 or helices 3 and 4, were shown to approximate results obtained with native SP-B in vitro and in vivo (92–95). It is not known whether the fusogenic or lytic properties of SP-B are important for the surface activities of these peptides or for native SP-B. Similar synthetic peptide studies for SP-C indicate that the membrane-spanning domain is critical for biophysical activity and that the helical structure rather than the actual amino acid sequence seems to be more important for activity (33, 96–98). SP-B synthetic peptides localize to the surface of the membrane, whereas SP-C peptides adopt a transmembrane configuration, suggesting that SP-B and SP-C work through different mechanisms to achieve similar results; alternatively, it is possible that the membranolytic activity of SP-B and SP-C are important for their interfacial activities because the peptides show overlap in this property in vitro.

The manner in which SP-B and SP-C associate with the surface film, traditionally considered to be a monolayer, is not clear. Given the transmembrane orientation of SP-C, insertion of this integral membrane protein into a monolayer would require SP-C to leave the membrane bilayer during film expansion and adopt a new orientation in the monolayer [tilted instead of parallel to the phospholipid acyl chains (99)] in order to accommodate the highly hydrophobic α-helix. Subsequent compression of the surface film would presumably require SP-C to leave the monolayer and reinsert into a lipid bilayer. A more appealing model is proposed by Schurch et al (100) who suggest that the surface film is a multi-layered structure in which membrane bilayers are associated with the interfacial film to form a surface reservoir. SP-C could remain in a bilayer membrane within the surface reservoir or, perhaps, exist in a bilayer at the interface. Electron microscopic evidence for a multi-layered surface film has been reported (100, 101), although this concept continues to be debated (102).

One further consequence of the integral membrane configuration of SP-C warrants some consideration. SP-C synthesis results in membrane asymmetry (i.e. assuming a Type II orientation, the N terminus of SP-C will always be associated with the cytosolic side of the membrane) that is likely critical for intracellular trafficking; furthermore, the model proposed in Figure 5 suggests that SP-B will always be associated with the same side of a bilayer membrane (i.e. the side opposite the N terminus of SP-C). These observations raise several questions. If SP-B and SP-C are asymmetrically distributed in surfactant bilayers, are surfactant phospholipids also asymmetrically distributed? Is membrane asymmetry maintained in the extracellular hypophase? What impact does protein and/or phospholipid asymmetry have on surface film formation and function?

The Role(s) of SP-B and SP-C in Surfactant Metabolism

Density gradient centrifugation of bronchoalveolar lavage results in isolation of a large aggregate fraction (heavy/ultra heavy subtypes) consisting primarily of lamellar bodies, tubular myelin, and loose membrane arrays, and a small aggregate fraction (light subtype) consisting of small vesicles (103–105). Large aggregate surfactant contains SP-B and SP-C, and is highly surface active in vitro and in vivo; in contrast, the small aggregate fraction lacks SP-B and SP-C and has very poor surface activity. Small aggregate surfactant is generally considered to be a catabolic form resulting from squeeze out during surface film compression. This form of surfactant is internalized more efficiently than large aggregate surfactant by lung epithelial cells in culture (106); furthermore, lipid uptake in vitro is enhanced by SP-C and, to a lesser degree, by SP-B (107). However, the interpretation of these results is not straight forward because large aggregate fraction appears to be taken up more rapidly than small aggregate in vivo (106); also, alveolar surfactant pool size was unaltered in SP-C $(-/-)$ mice. [As of this writing, it is not known if surfactant aggregate composition and clearance kinetics are altered in SP-C $(-/-)$ mice.] The potential for functional redundancy may make it difficult to determine if SP-C and/or SP-B play a critical role in modulating surfactant pool size by facilitating phospholipid clearance.

A large proportion of alveolar surfactant is taken up by the Type II epithelial cell and enters a recycling pathway (105). The idea that the protein-depleted small aggregate fraction represents the major catabolic form of surfactant lipids implies physical separation of SP-B and SP-C from surfactant lipids, a concept that is particularly difficult to accept for an integral membrane protein like SP-C; furthermore, because SP-B and SP-C can also enter the recycling pathway and are secreted with surfactant phospholipids, peptide/lipid re-association would have to occur prior to or following internalization. Given the hydrophobicity of SP-B and SP-C, a more likely explanation is that the peptides remain lipid associated and co-sedimented with large aggregate surfactant or, perhaps, constitute a catabolic form with a distinct buoyant density. Overall, the metabolic form and mechanism (i.e. receptor or non-receptor mediated) (108–110) whereby SP-B and SP-C are taken up by Type II epithelial cells is poorly understood.

Following internalization, SP-B is detected in various elements of the endocytic pathway, including multivesicular bodies (109). Multivesicular bodies are likely involved in both the surfactant recycling (111, 112) and biosynthetic (46, 63, 113) pathways. Although there is currently no direct evidence for colocalization of newly synthesized and recycled surfactant components to the same multivesicular body or population of multivesicular bodies, it is reasonable to speculate that this compartment plays a key role in surfactant homeostasis by integrating the biosynthetic, recycling, and catabolic pathways in Type II epithelial cells (Figure 3).

SP-B AND SP-C DEFICIENCY

The complete absence of SP-B results in severe, neonatal respiratory distress syndrome at term, followed by progressive respiratory failure and, inevitably, death (57, 114). Partial or transient SP-B deficiency has also been associated with chronic lung disease, and heterozygote susceptibility has been demonstrated for transgenic mice exposed to hyperoxia (115–119); however, a recent study of human patients failed to identify a clinical phenotype in individuals with a single functional SP-B allele (120). The 121ins2 mutation (insertion of 2 bases into codon 121, leading to a frame shift and early termination of translation) is present on both alleles in approximately two thirds of SP-B-deficient patients and occurs with an allele frequency of 1 per 1000–3000 individuals (121). Other mutations of the SP-B gene leading to lung disease occur in combination with the 121ins2 mutation (Table 1). Prenatal diagnosis of SP-B deficiency can be made by immunologic detection of incompletely processed SP-C and the absence of SP-B in amniotic fluid, although at least in one case, SP-C processing was not affected (82, 122).

SP-B deficiency in human infants has been associated with alveolar epithelial cell desquamation, congenital alveolar proteinosis, absence of tubular myelin, abnormal distribution of SP-A and SP-C, accumulation of incompletely processed SP-C, abnormal surfactant activity, and altered levels of phosphatidylglycerol in surfactant (123–127). Some of these features are common to SP-B $(-/-)$ mice, in particular the effects on tubular myelin formation, SP-C processing, and lung function (47, 58, 128); for technical reasons, surfactant composition has not been investigated in newborn SP-B $(-/-)$ mice. Other features of the SP-B-deficient phenotype appear to be unique to the human, most likely because of the genetic variability and/or intensive postnatal care. Treatment of affected infants with exogenous surfactant may produce a transient response, consistent with an ongoing requirement for SP-B in the airspace (129). This largely ineffective therapeutic approach may be limited by an additional intracellular requirement for the propeptide of SP-B. It is also possible that SP-B recycling may be compromised in these patients; furthermore, the accumulation of incompletely processed SP-C or other factors in the hypophase may lead to inhibition of surface film formation and function. To date, none of these hypotheses has been experimentally tested.

In contrast to the SP-B knockout mouse, SP-C $(-/-)$ mice process SP-B appropriately and lamellar body ultrastructure appears normal (91). One possible interpretation of this unexpected outcome is that SP-B compensates for loss of SP-C in SP-C $(-/-)$ mice, whereas SP-C compensation does not occur in SP-B $(-/-)$ mice because generation of the mature SP-C peptide is dependent upon SP-B expression. This hypothesis will be difficult to test in vivo because it will require a strategy to restore SP-C processing in the absence of SP-B expression. Although complete loss of SP-C protein in the knockout mouse did not result in altered lung development or function, at least two mutations in the human SP-C gene that give rise to an altered proprotein have been linked to development of interstitial lung disease (130). These mutations were identified in unrelated patients and were present on only one allele, suggesting either a dominant-negative effect or a gain of function not normally associated with SP-C. One mutation (P30L) resulted in substitution of leucine for proline at position 7 in the mature peptide (position 30 in the proprotein). This mutation may perturb the intracellular trafficking of the proprotein. The second mutation (c.460 + 1G > A) occurred in a donor splice site resulting in deletion of exon 4, which encodes 37 amino acids in the C-terminal peptide. As suggested earlier, C-terminal deletions may lead to misfolding and trapping of the proprotein in the endoplasmic reticulum. Intracellular accumulation of misfolded proteins has been causally linked to a number of diseases including α-1-antitrypsin deficiency and cystic fibrosis (131, 132). Accumulation of deacylated SP-C has also been linked to pulmonary alveolar proteinosis, although a cause-effect relationship has not been established (29, 30, 133).

SUMMARY

Although SP-C imparts important surface properties to surfactant phospholipid mixtures, the function of this peptide in vivo remains unclear. Association of altered SP-C structure with chronic lung disease may be of significant clinical importance, but a direct cause-effect relationship has not been established. SP-B is clearly essential for surfactant homeostasis, but the molecular mechanisms underlying SP-B actions are not well understood. The results of very preliminary studies suggest that SP-B may also have functions that are not directly related to surfactant homeostasis (134), including antiflammatory properties (135) and protection against oxygen-induced lung injury (117). Overall, despite considerable recent progress in characterizing the structure and functions of SP-B and SP-C, many questions remain unanswered.

Visit the Annual Reviews home page at www.AnnualReviews.org

LITERATURE CITED

1. Nogee LM, Garnier G, Dietz HC, Singer L, Murphy AM, et al. 1994. A mutation in the surfactant protein B gene responsible for fatal neonatal respiratory disease in multiple kindreds. *J. Clin. Invest.* 93: 1860–63

2. Johansson J, Curstedt T. 1997. Molecular structures and interactions of pulmonary surfactant components. *Eur. J. Biochem.* 244:675–93

3. Hawgood S, Derrick M, Poulain F. 1998. Structure and properties of surfactant protein B. *BBA Mol. Basis Dis.* 1408:150–60

4. Johansson J. 1998. Structure and properties of surfactant protein C. *BBA Mol. Basis Dis.* 1408:161–72

5. Curstedt T, Jornvall H, Robertson B, Bergman T, Berggren P. 1987. Two hydrophobic low-molecular mass protein fractions of pulmonary surfactant: characterization and biophysical activity. *Eur. J. Biochem.* 168:255–62

6. Gustafsson M, Curstedt T, Jornvall H, Johansson J. 1997. Reverse-phase HPLC of the hydrophobic pulmonary surfactant proteins: detection of a surfactant protein

C isoform containing *N*-epsilon-palmitoyl-lysine. *Biochem. J.* 326:799–806

7. Patthy L. 1991. Homology of the precursor of pulmonary surfactant-associated protein SP-B with prosaposin and sulfated glycoprotein-1. *J. Biol. Chem.* 266:6035–37

8. Munford RS, Sheppard PO, O'Hara PJ. 1995. Saposin-like proteins (SAPLIP) carry out diverse functions on a common backbone structure. *J. Lipid Res.* 36:1653–63

9. Ponting CP, Russell RB. 1995. Swaposins: circular permutations within genes encoding saposin homologues. *Trends Biochem. Sci.* 20:179–80

10. Johansson J, Curstedt T, Jornvall H. 1991. Surfactant protein-B-disulfide bridges, structural properties, and kringle similarities. *Biochemistry* 30:6917–21

11. Johansson J, Jornvall H, Curstedt T. 1992. Human surfactant polypeptide SP-B-disulfide bridges, C-terminal end, and peptide analysis of the airway form. *FEBS Lett.* 301:165–67

12. Andersson M, Gunne H, Agerberth B, Boman A, Bergman T, et al. 1995. NK-lysin, a novel effector peptide of cytotoxic T and NK cells. Structure and cDNA cloning of the porcine form, induction by interleukin 2, antibacterial and antitumour activity. *EMBO J.* 14:1615–25

13. Vaccaro AM, Salvioli R, Barca A, Tatti M, Ciaffoni F, et al. 1995. Structural analysis of saposin C and B—complete localization of disulfide bridges. *J. Biol. Chem.* 270:9953–60

14. Liepinsh E, Andersson M, Ruysschaert JM, Otting G. 1997. Saposin fold revealed by the NMR structure of NK-lysin. *Nat. Struct. Biol.* 4:793–95

15. Vandenbussche G, Clercx A, Clercx M, Curstedt T, Johansson J, et al. 1992. Secondary structure and orientation of the surfactant protein SP-B in a lipid environment: a Fourier transform infrared spectroscopy study. *Biochemistry* 31:9169–76

16. Andersson M, Curstedt T, Jornvall H, Johansson J. 1995. An amphipathic helical motif common to tumourolytic polypeptide NK-lysin and pulmonary surfactant polypeptide SP-B. *FEBS Lett.* 362:328–32

17. Baatz JE, Elledge B, Whitsett JA. 1990. Surfactant protein SP-B induces ordering at the surface of model membrane bilayers. *Biochemistry* 29:6714–20

18. Oosterlakendijksterhuis MA, Vaneijk M, van Golde LMG, Haagsman HP. 1992. Lipid mixing is mediated by the hydrophobic surfactant protein SP-B but not by SP-C. *Biochim. Biophys. Acta* 1110:45–50

19. Beck DC, Ikegami M, Na CL, Zaltash S, Johansson J, et al. 2000. The role of homodimers in surfactant protein B function in vivo. *J. Biol. Chem.* 275:3365–70

20. Zaltash S, Palmblad M, Curstedt T, Johansson J, Persson B. 2000. Pulmonary surfactant B: a structural model and a functional analogue. *Biochim. Biophys. Acta* 1466:179–86

21. Shiffer K, Hawgood S, Duzgunes N, Goerke J. 1988. Interactions of the low molecular weight group of surfactant-associated proteins (SP 5–18) with pulmonary surfactant lipids. *Biochemistry* 27:2689–95

22. Chang R, Nir S, Poulain FR. 1998. Analysis of binding and membrane destabilization of phospholipid membranes by surfactant apoprotein B. *BBA Biomembr.* 1371:254–64

23. Williams MC, Hawgood S, Hamilton RL. 1991. Changes in lipid structure produced by surfactant proteins SP-A, SP-B, and SP-C. *Am. J. Respir. Cell. Mol. Biol.* 5:41–50

24. Poulain FR, Nir S, Hawgood S. 1996. Kinetics of phospholipid membrane fusion induced by surfactant apoproteins A and B. *BBA Biomembr.* 1278:169–75

25. Poulain FR, Allen L, Williams MC, Hamilton RL, Hawgood S. 1992. Effects of surfactant apolipoproteins on liposome structure—implications for tubular myelin

formation. *Am. J. Physiol. Lung Cell Mol. Physiol.* 262:L730–L39

26. Creuwels LAJM, van Golde LMG, Haagsman HP. 1996. Surfactant protein B: effects on lipid domain formation and intermembrane lipid flow. *BBA Biomembr.* 1285:1–8

27. Cruz A, Casals C, Keough KMW, PerezGil J. 1997. Different modes of interaction of pulmonary surfactant protein SP-B in phosphatidylcholine bilayers. *Biochem. J.* 327:133–38

28. Baatz JE, Smyth KL, Whitsett JA, Baxter C, Absolom DR. 1992. Structure and functions of a dimeric form of surfactant protein C: a Fourier transform infrared and surfactometry study. *Chem. Phys. Lipids* 63:91–104

29. Li ZY, Suzuki Y, Kurozumi M, Shen KQ, Duan CX. 1998. Removal of a dimeric form of surfactant protein C from mouse lungs: its acceleration by reduction. *J. Appl. Physiol.* 84:471–78

30. Gustafsson M, Thyberg J, Naslund J, Eliasson E, Johansson J. 1999. Amyloid fibril formation by pulmonary surfactant protein C. *FEBS Lett.* 464:138–42

31. Glasser SW, Korfhagen TR, Weaver TE, Clark JC, Pilot-Matias T, et al. 1988. cDNA, deduced polypeptide structure and chromosomal assignment of human pulmonary surfactant proteolipid, SPL(pVal). *J. Biol. Chem.* 263:9–12

32. Johansson J, Szyperski T, Curstedt T, Wuthrich K. 1994. The NMR structure of the pulmonary surfactant-associated polypeptide SP-C in an apolar solvent contains a valyl-rich alpha-helix. *Biochemistry* 33:6015–23

33. Johansson J, Nilsson G, Stromberg R, Robertson B, Jornvall H, Curstedt T. 1995. Secondary structure and biophysical activity of synthetic analogues of the pulmonary surfactant polypeptide SP-C. *Biochem. J.* 307:535–41

34. Morrow MR, Taneva S, Simatos GA, Allwood LA, Keough KMW. 1993. H-2 NMR studies of the effect of pulmonary

surfactant SP-C on the 1,2-dipalmitoyl-*sn*-glycero-3-phosphocholine headgroup—a model for transbilayer peptides in surfactant and biological membranes. *Biochemistry* 32:11338–44

35. Horowitz AD, Elledge B, Whitsett JA, Baatz JE. 1992. Effects of lung surfactant proteolipid SP-C on the organization of model membrane lipids—a fluorescence study. *Biochim. Biophys. Acta* 1107:44–54

36. Johansson J, Szyperski T, Wuthrich K. 1995. Pulmonary surfactant-associated polypeptide SP-C in lipid micelles: CD studies of intact SP-C and NMR secondary structure determination of depalmitoyl-SP-C(1–17). *FEBS Lett.* 362:261–65

37. Pilot-Matias TJ, Kister SE, Fox JL, Kropp K, Glasser SW, Whitsett JA. 1989. Structure and organization of the gene encoding human pulmonary surfactant proteolipid SP-B. *DNA* 8:75–86

38. Vamvakopoulos NC, Modi WS, Floros J. 1995. Mapping the human pulmonary surfactant-associated protein B gene (SFTP3) to chromosome 2p12 → p11.2. *Cytogenet. Cell Genet.* 68:8–10

39. Moore KJ, Damore-Bruno MA, Korfhagen TR, Glasser SW, Whitsett JA, et al. 1992. Chromosomal localization of three pulmonary surfactant protein genes in the mouse. *Genomics* 12:388–93

40. Zaltash S, Johansson J. 1998. Secondary structure and limited proteolysis give experimental evidence that the precursor of pulmonary surfactant protein B contains three saposin-like domains. *FEBS Lett.* 423:1–4

41. Von Heijne G. 1986. A new method for predicting signal sequence cleavage sites. *Nucleic Acids Res.* 14:4683–90

42. Lin S, Phillips KS, Wilder MR, Weaver TE. 1996. Structural requirements for intracellular transport of pulmonary surfactant protein B (SP-B). *BBA Mol. Cell Res.* 1312:177–85

43. Liau DF, Yin NX, Huang J, Ryan SF. 1996. Effects of human polymorphonuclear

leukocyte elastase upon surfactant proteins in vitro. *BBA Lipid Lipid Metab.* 1302: 117–28

44. Lin S, Akinbi HT, Breslin JS, Weaver TE. 1996. Structural requirements for targeting of surfactant protein B (SP-B) to secretory granules in vitro and in vivo. *J. Biol. Chem.* 271:19689–95

45. Kervinen J, Tobin GJ, Costa J, Waugh DS, Wlodawer A, Zdanov A. 1999. Crystal structure of plant aspartic proteinase prophytepsin: inactivation and vacuolar targeting. *EMBO J.* 18:3947–55

46. Voorhout WF, Veenendaal T, Haagsman HP, Weaver TE, Whitsett JA, et al. 1992. Intracellular processing of pulmonary surfactant protein-B in an endosomal/lysosomal compartment. *Am. J. Physiol. Lung Cell Mol. Physiol.* 263:L479–L86

47. Stahlman MT, Gray MP, Falconieri MW, Whitsett JA, Weaver TE. 2000. Lamellar body formation in normal and surfactant protein B-deficient fetal mice. *Lab. Invest.* 80:395–403

48. Weaver TE, Lin S, Bogucki B, Dey C. 1992. Processing of surfactant protein-B proprotein by a cathepsin-D-like protease. *Am. J. Physiol. Lung Cell Mol. Physiol.* 263:L95–L103

49. Chuman Y, Bergman AC, Ueno T, Saito S, Sakaguchi K, et al. 1999. Napsin A, a member of the aspartic protease family, is abundantly expressed in normal lung and kidney tissue and is expressed in lung adenocarcinomas. *FEBS Lett.* 462:129–34

50. Tatnell PJ, Powell DJ, Hill J, Smith TS, Tew DG, Kay J. 1998. Napsins: new human aspartic proteinases. Distinction between two closely related genes. *FEBS Lett.* 441:43–48

51. Pouli AE, Kennedy HJ, Schofield JG, Rutter GA. 1998. Insulin targeting to the regulated secretory pathway after fusion with green fluorescent protein and firefly luciferase. *Biochem. J.* 331:669–75

52. Akinbi HT, Breslin JS, Ikegami M, Iwamoto HS, Clark JC, et al. 1997. Rescue of SP-B knockout mice with a truncated SP-B proprotein—function of the C-terminal propeptide. *J. Biol. Chem.* 272:9640–47

53. Chi EY, Lagunoff D, Koehler JK. 1976. Abnormally large lamellar bodies in Type II pneumocytes in Chediak-Higashi syndrome in beige mice. *Lab. Invest.* 34:166–73

54. Botas C, Poulain F, Akiyama J, Brown C, Allen L, et al. 1998. Altered surfactant homeostasis and alveolar type II cell morphology in mice lacking surfactant protein D. *Proc. Natl. Acad. Sci. USA* 95: 11869–74

55. Fehrenbach H, Brasch F, Uhlig S, Weisser M, Stamme C, et al. 1998. Early alterations in intracellular and alveolar surfactant of the rat lung in response to endotoxin. *Am. J. Respir. Crit. Care Med.* 157:1630–39

56. Perry LJ, Florio R, Dewar A, Nicholson AG. 2000. Giant lamellar bodies as a feature of pulmonary low-grade MALT lymphomas. *Histopathology* 36:240–44

57. Nogee LM. 1998. Genetics of the hydrophobic surfactant proteins. *BBA Mol. Basis Dis.* 1408:323–33

58. Clark JC, Wert SE, Bachurski CJ, Stahlman MT, Stripp BR, et al. 1995. Targeted disruption of the surfactant protein B gene disrupts surfactant homeostasis, causing respiratory failure in newborn mice. *Proc. Natl. Acad. Sci. USA* 92:7794–98

59. Fisher JH, Emrie PA, Drabkin HA, Kushnik T, Gerber M, et al. 1988. The gene encoding the hydrophobic surfactant protein SP-C is located on 8P and identifies an EcorI RFLP. *Am. J. Hum. Genet.* 43: 436–41

60. Warr RG, Hawgood S, Buckley DI, Crisp TM, Schilling J, et al. 1987. Low molecular weight human pulmonary surfactant protein (SP5): isolation, characterization and cDNA and amino acid sequences. *Proc. Natl. Acad. Sci. USA* 84:7915–19

61. Glasser SW, Korfhagen TR, Perme CM, Pilot-Matias TJ, Kister SE, Whitsett JA.

1988. Two SP-C genes encoding human pulmonary surfactant proteolipid. *J. Biol. Chem.* 263:10326–31

62. Keller A, Eistetter HR, Voss T, Schäfer KP. 1991. The pulmonary surfactant protein-C (SP-C) precursor is a Type-II transmembrane protein. *Biochem. J.* 277:493–99

63. Vorbroker DK, Voorhout WF, Weaver TE, Whitsett JA. 1995. Posttranslational processing of surfactant protein C in rat Type II cells. *Am. J. Physiol. Lung Cell Mol. Physiol.* 13:L727–L33

64. Dunphy JT, Linder ME. 1998. Signalling functions of protein palmitoylation. *Biochim. Biophys. Acta* 1436:245–61

65. Sipos L, von Heijne G. 1993. Predicting the topology of eukaryotic membrane proteins. *Eur. J. Biochem.* 213:1333–40

66. Hunziker W, Geuze HJ. 1996. Intracellular trafficking of lysosomal membrane proteins. *BioEssays* 18:379–89

67. Marks MS, Ohno H, Kirchhausen T, Bonifacino SJ. 1997. Protein sorting by tyrosine-based signals: adapting to the Ys and wherefores. *Trends Cell Biol.* 7:124–28

68. Keller A, Stienhilber W, Schäfer KP, Voss T. 1992. The C-terminal domain of the pulmonary surfactant protein C precursor contains signals for intracellular targeting. *Am. J. Respir. Cell Mol. Biol.* 6:601–8

69. Beers MF, Lomax CA, Russo SJ. 1998. Synthetic processing of surfactant protein C by alevolar epithelial cells—the COOH terminus of proSP-C is required for posttranslational targeting and proteolysis. *J. Biol. Chem.* 273:15287–93

70. Trowbridge IS, Collawn JF, Hopkins CR. 1993. Signal-dependent membrane protein trafficking in the endocytic pathway. *Annu. Rev. Cell Biol.* 9:129–61

71. Heijnen HFG, Debili N, Vainchencker W, BretonGorius J, Geuze HJ, Sixma JJ. 1998. Multivesicular bodies are an intermediate stage in the formation of platelet alphagranules. *Blood* 91:2313–25

72. Sorokin SP. 1967. A morphologic and cytochemical study on the great alveolar cell. *J. Histochem. Cytochem.* 14:884–97

73. Kobayashi T, Stang E, Fang KS, de Moerloose P, Parton RG, Gruenberg J. 1998. A lipid associated with the antiphospholipid syndrome regulates endosome structure and function. *Nature* 392:193–97

74. Griffiths G, Hoflack B, Simons K, Mellman I, Kornfeld S. 1988. The mannose 6-phosphate receptor and the biogenesis of lysosomes. *Cell* 52:329–41

75. Moreau P, Cassagne C. 1994. Phospholipid trafficking and membrane biogenesis. *Biochim. Biophys. Acta* 1197:257–90

76. Creuwels LAJM, van Golde LMG, Haagsman HP. 1997. The pulmonary surfactant system: biochemical and clinical aspects. *Lung* 175:1–39

77. Odorizzi G, Babst M, Emr SD. 1998. Fab1p PtdIns(3)P 5-kinase function essential for protein sorting in the multivesicular body. *Cell* 95:847–58

78. Gu F, Gruenberg J. 1999. Biogenesis of transport intermediates in the endocytic pathway. *FEBS Lett.* 452:61–66

79. Piguet V, Gu F, Foti M, Demaurex N, Gruenberg J, et al. 1999. Nef-induced CD4 degradation: a diacidic-based motif in Nef functions as a lysosomal targeting signal through the binding of beta-COP in endosomes. *Cell* 97:63–73

80. Ross GF, Ikegami M, Steinhilber W, Jobe AH. 1999. Surfactant protein C in fetal and ventilated preterm rabbit lungs. *Am. J. Physiol. Lung Cell Mol. Physiol.* 277:L1104–L8

81. Beers MF, Lomax C. 1995. Synthesis and processing of hydrophobic surfactant protein C by isolated rat Type II cells. *Am. J. Physiol. Lung Cell Mol. Physiol.* 13:L744–L53

82. Vorbroker DK, Profitt SA, Nogee LM, Whitsett JA. 1995. Aberrant processing of surfactant protein C (SP-C) in hereditary SP-B deficiency. *Am. J. Physiol. Lung Cell Mol. Physiol.* 268:L647–L56

83. Dadd CA, Cook RG, Allis CD. 1993. Fractionation of small tryptic phosphopeptides by alkaline PAGE followed by amino acid sequencing. *Biotechniques* 14:266–73
84. Keough KMW. 1992. Physical chemistry of pulmonary surfactant in the terminal airspaces. In *Pulmonary Surfactant: From Molecular Biology to Clinical Practice*, ed. B Robertson, LMG van Golde, JJ Batenburg, pp. 109–64. Amsterdam: Elsevier
85. Oosterlakendijksterhuis MA, Haagsman HP, van Golde LMG, Demel RA. 1991. Characterization of lipid insertion into monomolecular layers mediated by lung surfactant proteins SP-B and SP-C. *Biochemistry* 30:10965–71
86. Nag K, Munro JG, Inchley K, Schurch S, Petersen NO, Possmayer F. 1999. SP-B refining of pulmonary surfactant phospholipid films. *Am. J. Physiol. Lung Cell Mol. Physiol.* 277:L1179–L89
87. Hawgood S, Ogawa A, Yukitake K, Schlueter M, Brown C, et al. 1996. Lung function in premature rabbits treated with recombinant human surfactant protein C. *Am. J. Respir. Crit. Care Med.* 154:484–90
88. Ikegami M, Jobe AH. 1998. Surfactant protein-C in ventilated premature lamb lung. *Pediatr. Res.* 44:860–64
89. Revak SD, Merritt TA, Degryse E, Stefani L, Courtney M, et al. 1988. Use of human surfactant low molecular weight apoproteins in the reconstitution of surfactant biologic activity. *J. Clin. Invest.* 81:826–33
90. Rider ED, Ikegami M, Whitsett JA, Hull W, Absolom D, Jobe AH. 1993. Treatment responses to surfactants containing natural surfactant proteins in preterm rabbits. *Am. Rev. Respir. Dis.* 147:669–76
91. Glasser SW, Burhans MS, Korfhagen TR, Ross GF, Ikegami M, et al. 2000. Generation of an SP-C deficient mouse by targeted gene inactivation. *Proc. Natl. Acad. Sci. USA.* Submitted
92. Waring A, Taeusch W, Bruni R, Amirkhanian J, Fan B, et al. 1989. Synthetic amphipathic sequences of surfactant protein-B mimic several physicochemical and in vivo properties of native pulmonary surfactant proteins. *Pept. Res.* 2:308–13
93. Sarin VK, Gupta S, Leung TK, Taylor VE, Ohning BL, et al. 1990. Biophysical and biological activity of a synthetic 8.7-kDa hydrophobic pulmonary surfactant protein SP-B. *Proc. Natl. Acad. Sci. USA* 87:2633–37
94. Baatz JE, Sarin V, Absolom DR, Baxter C, Whitsett JA. 1991. Effects of surfactant-associated protein SP-B synthetic analogs on the structure and surface activity of model membrane bilayers. *Chem. Phys. Lipids* 60:163–78
95. Bruni R, Taeusch HW, Waring AJ. 1991. Surfactant protein-B. Lipid interactions of synthetic peptides representing the amino-terminal amphipathic domain. *Proc. Natl. Acad. Sci. USA* 88:7451–55
96. Clercx A, Vandenbussche G, Curstedt T, Johansson J, Jornvall H, Ruysschaert JF. 1995. Structural and functional importance of the C-terminal part of the pulmonary surfactant polypeptide SP-C. *Eur. J. Biochem.* 229:465–72
97. Takei T, Hashimoto Y, Ohtsubo E, Sakai K, Ohkawa H. 1996. Characterization of poly-leucine substituted analogues of the human surfactant protein SP-C. *Biol. Pharm. Bull.* 19:1550–55
98. Nilsson G, Gustafsson M, Vandenbussche G, Veldhuizen E, Griffiths WJ, et al. 1998. Synthetic peptide-containing surfactants. Evaluation of transmembrane versus amphipathic helices and surfactant protein C poly-valyl to poly-leucyl substitution. *Eur. J. Biochem.* 255:116–24
99. Gericke A, Flach CR, Mendelsohn R. 1997. Structure and orientation of lung surfactant SP-C and L-alpha-dipalmitoylphosphatidylcholine in aqueous monolayers. *Biophys. J.* 73:492–99
100. Schurch S, Green FH, Bachofen H. 1998. Formation and structure of surface films: captive bubble surfactometry. *Biochim. Biophys. Acta* 1408:180–202

101. Weibel ER, Gil J. 1968. Electron microscopic demonstration of an extracellular duplex lining layer of alveoli. *Respir. Physiol.* 4:42–57

102. Bastacky J, Lee CYC, Goerke J, Koushafar H, Yager D, et al. 1995. Alveolar lining layer is thin and continuous: low-temperature scanning electron microscopy of rat lung. *J. Appl. Physiol.* 79:1615–28

103. Magoon MW, Wright JR, Baritussio A, Williams MC, Goerke J, et al. 1983. Subfractionation of lung surfactant: implications for metabolism and surface activity. *Biochim. Biophys. Acta* 750:18–31

104. Gross NJ, Narine RK. 1989. Surfactant subtypes in mice: characterization and quantitation. *J. Appl. Physiol.* 66:342–49

105. Wright JR, Clements JA. 1987. Metabolism and turnover of lung surfactant. *Am. Rev. Respir. Dis.* 135:426–44

106. Horowitz AD, Kurak K, Moussavian B, Whitsett JA, Wert SE, et al. 1997. Preferential uptake of small-aggregate fraction of pulmonary surfactant in vitro. *Am. J. Physiol. Lung Cell Mol. Physiol.* 17:L468–L77

107. Horowitz AD, Moussavian B, Whitsett JA. 1996. Roles of SP-A, SP-B, and SP-C in modulation of lipid uptake by pulmonary epithelial cells in vitro. *Am. J. Physiol. Lung Cell Mol. Physiol.* 14:L69–L79

108. Horowitz AD, Moussavian B, Han ED, Baatz JE, Whitsett JA. 1997. Distinct effects of SP-A and SP-B on endocytosis of SP-C by pulmonary epithelial cells. *Am. J. Physiol. Lung Cell Mol. Physiol.* 17:L159–L71

109. Breslin JS, Weaver TE. 1992. Binding, uptake, and localization of surfactant protein-B in isolated rat alveolar Type-II cells. *Am. J. Physiol. Lung Cell Mol. Physiol.* 262:L699–L707

110. Bates SR, Beers MF, Fisher AB. 1992. Binding and uptake of surfactant protein-B by alveolar Type-II cells. *Am. J.* *Physiol. Lung Cell Mol. Physiol.* 263: L333–L41

111. Williams MC. 1987. Vesicles within vesicles: What role do multivesicular bodies play in alveolar Type II cells? *Am. Rev. Respir. Dis.* 135:744–46

112. Williams MC. 1984. Uptake of lectins by pulmonary alveolar Type II cells: subsequent deposition into lamellar bodies. *Proc. Natl. Acad. Sci. USA* 81:6383–87

113. Voorhout WF, Weaver TE, Haagsman HP, Geuze HJ, van Golde LMJ. 1993. Biosynthetic routing of pulmonary surfactant proteins in alveolar Type II cells. *Microsc. Res. Tech.* 26:366–73

114. Whitsett JA, Nogee LM, Weaver TE, Horowitz AD. 1995. Human surfactant protein B: structure, function, regulation, and genetic disease. *Physiol. Rev.* 75:749–57

115. Gustafsson M, Vandenbussche G, Curstedt T, Ruysschaert JM, Johansson J. 1996. The 21-residue surfactant peptide (LysLeu(4))(4)Lys(KL(4)) is a transmembrane alpha-helix with a mixed nonpolar/polar surface. *FEBS Lett.* 384:185–88

116. Klein JM, Thompson MW, Snyder JM, George TN, Whitsett JA, et al. 1998. Transient surfactant protein B deficiency in a term infant with severe respiratory failure. *J. Pediatr.* 132:244–48

117. Tokieda K, Ikegami M, Wert SE, Baatz JE, Zou Y, Whitsett JA. 1999. Surfactant protein B corrects oxygen-induced pulmonary dysfunction in heterozygous surfactant protein B-deficient mice. *Pediatr. Res.* 46:708–14

118. Tokieda K, Iwamoto HS, Bachurski C, Wert SE, Hull WM, et al. 1999. Surfactant protein-B deficient mice are susceptible to hyperoxic lung injury. *Am. J. Respir. Cell Mol. Biol.* 21:463–72

119. Clark JC, Weaver TE, Iwamoto HS, Ikegami M, Jobe AH, et al. 1997. Decreased lung compliance and air trapping

in heterozygous SP-B deficient mice. *Am. J. Respir. Cell Mol. Biol.* 16:46–52

120. Yusen RD, Cohen AH, Hamvas A. 1999. Normal lung function in subjects heterozygous for surfactant protein-B deficiency. *Am. J. Respir. Crit. Care Med.* 159:411–14

121. Cole FS, Hamvas A, Rubinstein P, King E, Trusgnich M, et al. 2000. Population-based estimates of surfactant protein B deficiency. *Pediatrics* 105:538–41

122. Tredano M, van Elburg RM, Kaspers AG, Zimmermann LJ, Houdayer C, et al. 1999. Compound SFTPB 1549C → GAA (121ins2) and 457delC heterozygosity in severe congenital lung disease and surfactant protein B (SP-B) deficiency. *Hum. Mutat.* 14:502–9

123. deMello DE, Nogee LM, Heyman S, Krous HF, Hussain M, et al. 1994. Molecular and phenotypic variability in the congenital alveolar proteinosis syndrome associated with inherited surfactant protein B deficiency. *J. Pediatr.* 125: 43–50

124. Nogee LM, DeMello DE, Dehner LP, Colten HR. 1993. Deficiency of pulmonary surfactant protein B in congenital alveolar proteinosis. *N. Engl. J. Med.* 328:406–10

125. Hamvas A, Nogee LM, Mallory GB, Spray TL, Huddleston CB, et al. 1997. Lung transplantation for treatment of infants with surfactant protein B deficiency. *J. Pediatr.* 130:231–39

126. deMello DE, Heyman S, Phelps DS, Hamvas A, Nogee L, et al. 1994. Ultrastructure of lung in surfactant protein B deficiency. *Am. J. Respir. Cell Mol. Biol.* 11:230–39

127. Beers MF, Hamvas A, Moxley MA, Gonzales LW, Guttentag SH, et al. 2000. Pulmonary surfactant metabolism in infants lacking surfactant protein B. *Am. J. Respir. Cell Mol. Biol.* 22:380–91

128. Tokieda K, Whitsett JA, Clark JC, Weaver TE, Ikeda K, et al. 1997. Pulmonary dysfunction in neonatal SP-B-deficient mice. *Am. J. Physiol. Lung Cell Mol. Physiol.* 17:L875–L82

129. Hamvas A, Cole FS, Demello DE, Moxley M, Whitsett JA, et al. 1994. Surfactant protein B deficiency: antenatal diagnosis and prospective treatment with surfactant replacement. *J. Pediatr.* 125:356–61

130. Dunbar AE, Whitsett JA, Wert SE, Askin F, Hamvas A, Nogee LM. 2000. Mutations in the surfactant protein C gene (SP-C) associated with interstitial lung disease. *N. Engl. J. Med.* Submitted

131. Riordan JR. 1999. Cystic fibrosis as a disease of misprocessing of the cystic fibrosis transmembrane conductance regulator glycoprotein. *Am. J. Hum. Genet.* 64:1499–504

132. Perlmutter DH. 1999. Misfolded proteins in the endoplasmic reticulum. *Lab. Invest.* 79:623–38

133. Shen HQ, Duan CX, Li ZY, Suzuki Y. 1997. Effects of proteinosis surfactant proteins on the viability of rat alveolar macrophages. *Am. J. Respir. Crit. Care Med.* 156:1679–87

134. Lin S, Na CL, Akinbi HT, Apsley KS, Whitsett JA, Weaver TE. 1999. Surfactant protein B (SP-B) −/− mice are rescued by restoration of SP-B expression in alveolar type II cells but not Clara cells. *J. Biol. Chem.* 274:19168–74

135. Miles PR, Bowman L, Rao KMK, Baatz JE, Huffman L. 1999. Pulmonary surfactant inhibits LPS-induced nitric oxide production by alveolar macrophages. *Am. J. Physiol. Lung Cell Mol. Physiol.* 20: L186–L96

136. Nogee LM, Wert SE, Proffit SA, Hull WM, Whitsett JA. 2000. Allelic heterogeneity in hereditary surfactant protein B (SP-B) deficiency. *Am. J. Respir. Crit. Care Med.* 161:973–81

137. Somaschini M, Wert S, Mangili G, Colombo A, Nogee L. 2000. Hereditary surfactant protein B deficiency resulting

from a novel mutation. *Intensive Care Med.* 26:97–100

138. Lin ZW, deMello DE, Wallot M, Floros J. 1998. An SP-B gene mutation responsible for SP-B deficiency in fatal congenital alveolar proteinosis: evidence for a mutation hotspot in exon 4. *Mol. Genet. Metab.* 64:25–35

139. Williams GD, Christodoulou J, Stack J, Symons P, Wert SE, et al. 1999. Surfactant protein B deficiency: clinical, histological and molecular evaluation. *J. Paediatr. Child Health* 35:214–20

140. Ballard PL, Nogee LM, Beers MF, Ballard RA, Planer BC, et al. 1995. Partial deficiency of surfactant protein B in an infant with chronic lung disease. *Pediatrics* 96:1046–52

Annu. Rev. Physiol. 2001. 63:579–605

G PROTEIN–COUPLED PROSTANOID RECEPTORS AND THE KIDNEY

Matthew D Breyer

Division of Nephrology, Department of Medicine, and Department of Molecular Physiology and Biophysics, Vanderbilt University, Nashville, Tennessee, 37232, and Department of Veterans Affairs Medical Center, Nashville, Tennessee 37212; e-mail: matthew.breyer@mcmail.vanderbilt.edu

Richard M Breyer

Division of Nephrology and Departments of Medicine and Pharmacology, Vanderbilt University, Tennessee 37232; e-mail: rich.breyer@mcmail.vanderbilt.edu

Key Words   prostaglandin E_2, prostaglandin $F_{2\alpha}$, prostaglandin I_2, thromboxane A_2, prostaglandin D_2

■ **Abstract**   Renal cyclooxygenase 1 and 2 activity produces five primary prostanoids: prostaglandin E_2, prostaglandin $F_{2\alpha}$, prostaglandin I_2, thromboxane A_2, and prostaglandin D_2. These lipid mediators interact with a family of distinct G protein–coupled prostanoid receptors designated EP, FP, IP, TP, and DP, respectively, which exert important regulatory effects on renal function. The intrarenal distribution of these prostanoid receptors has been mapped, and the consequences of their activation have been partially characterized. FP, TP, and EP_1 receptors preferentially couple to an increase in cell calcium. EP_2, EP_4, DP, and IP receptors stimulate cyclic AMP, whereas the EP_3 receptor preferentially couples to G_i, inhibiting cyclic AMP generation. EP_1 and EP_3 mRNA expression predominates in the collecting duct and thick limb, respectively, where their stimulation reduces NaCl and water absorption, promoting natriuresis and diuresis. The FP receptor is highly expressed in the distal convoluted tubule, where it may have a distinct effect on renal salt transport. Although only low levels of EP_2 receptor mRNA are detected in the kidney and its precise intrarenal localization is uncertain, mice with targeted disruption of the EP_2 receptor exhibit salt-sensitive hypertension, suggesting that this receptor may also play an important role in salt excretion. In contrast, EP_4 receptor mRNA is predominantly expressed in the glomerulus, where it may contribute to the regulation of glomerular hemodynamics and renin release. The IP receptor mRNA is highly expressed near the glomerulus, in the afferent arteriole, where it may also dilate renal arterioles and stimulate renin release. Conversely, TP receptors in the glomerulus may counteract the effects of these dilator prostanoids and increase glomerular resistance. At present there is little evidence for DP receptor expression in the kidney. These receptors act in a

0066-4278/01/0315-0579$14.00

concerted fashion as physiological buffers, protecting the kidney from excessive functional changes during periods of physiological stress. Nonsteroidal anti-inflammatory drug (NSAID)-mediated cyclooxygenase inhibition results in the loss of these combined effects, which contributes to their renal effects. Selective prostanoid receptor antagonists may provide new therapeutic approaches for specific disease states.

INTRODUCTION

Prostaglandins make up a diverse family of autacoids derived from cyclooxygenase (COX)-mediated metabolism of arachidonic acid to prostaglandin G/H$_2$ (PGG/H$_2$), generating five primary bioactive prostanoids: PGE$_2$, PGF$_{2\alpha}$, PGD$_2$, PGI$_2$, and thromboxane A$_2$ (TxA$_2$) (1, 2). These prostanoids are abundantly produced in the kidney (1, 3), where they act locally via specific heptahelical transmembrane G protein-coupled receptors designated EP (for E-prostanoid receptor), FP, DP, IP, and TP, respectively (4, 5; Figure 1). Each prostanoid receptor exhibits a unique expression pattern in the kidney and along the nephron (Figure 2). The importance of these autacoids to renal function, systemic blood pressure, and volume control is highlighted by the deleterious renal side effects of COX inhibitors (NSAIDs). In certain settings NSAIDs may induce hypertension (6), Na$^+$ retention, and edema (7, 8), suggesting an antihypertensive and natriuretic role for endogenous prostaglandins. Conversely, NSAIDs reduce blood pressure and renin levels in patients with renovascular hypertension, suggesting that in this setting endogenous prostaglandins drive hyperreninemia and blood pressure (9, 10). The complex effects of NSAIDs on blood pressure are evidence for competing hypotensive and hypertensive effects of prostanoids including PGE$_2$, PGI$_2$, and TxA$_2$ (11) and underscore the general principal that prostaglandins have the capacity to buffer physiological processes in either positive or negative directions. Finally, loss of endogenous prostaglandin synthesis may result in acute renal insufficiency and hyperkalemia (12). This review describes the intrarenal distribution and function of prostanoid receptors, highlighting new insights into their functional roles in the kidney and detailing how their activation helps maintain normal renal function.

---→

Figure 1   Synthesis and actions of the prostaglandins. Arachidonate is metabolized by COX1 or COX2 to PGG$_2$ and then PGH$_2$ in a two-step reaction. PGH$_2$ is relatively unstable and is enzymatically converted, by specific synthases (thromboxane synthase, PGE synthase, PGF synthase, PGD synthase, and PGI synthase), to one of five known primary prostanoids: PGI$_2$, PGD$_2$, PGE$_2$, PGF$_{2\alpha}$, or TxA$_2$. Each prostanoid interacts with distinct members of a subfamily of the G protein–coupled receptors. PGI$_2$ activates the IP receptor, PGD2 activates the DP receptor, PGF$_{2\alpha}$ activates the FP receptor, and TxA$_2$ activates the TP receptor. These receptors activate different functional responses and signaling pathways, as shown at the bottom of the figure. PGE$_2$ interacts with one of four distinct EP receptors, each of which also couples to distinct signaling pathways.

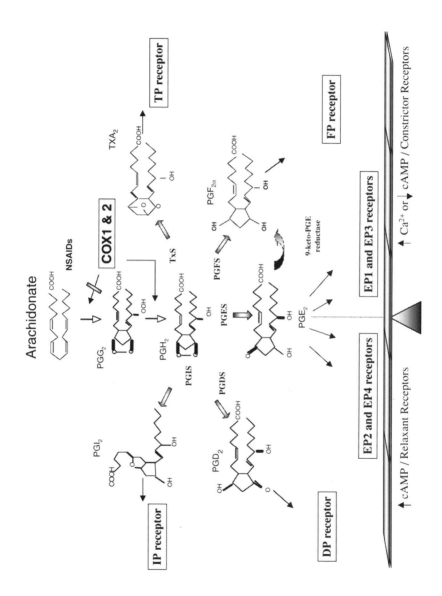

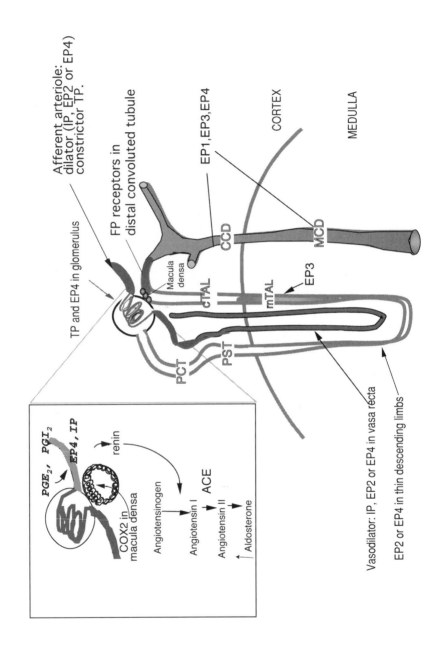

TP RECEPTORS

TxA$_2$ is produced from PGH$_2$ by thromboxane synthase (13, 14). After its formation, TxA$_2$ interacts with its receptor, designated the TP receptor. The TP receptor, which was the first eicosanoid receptor cloned (15), encodes a protein of 343 amino acids (37.4 kDa) that contains seven hydrophobic stretches of amino acids characteristic of the family of G protein–coupled receptors. Full-length murine and rat TP receptor cDNAs have also been isolated (16, 17). Two alternatively spliced variants of the human thromboxane receptor have been described (18). These variants differ in the C-terminal tail of the receptor distal to Arg-328. Similar patterns of alternative splicing have been described for both the EP$_3$ receptor and the FP receptor (see below). The original placenta-derived clone of the 343-amino-acid receptor has been designated α, and a 407-amino-acid splice variant subsequently cloned from endothelium is designated β. Although splice variants have not been described for the TP receptors in other species, the lack of homology in the variant regions of the mouse TP receptor C terminus and either of the human splice variants suggests the possible existence of further undescribed splice variants in man (5).

Competitive radioligand binding studies have demonstrated a rank order of potency toward the human platelet TP receptor of I-BOP, S145 > SQ29548 > STA2 > U-46619 (5, 19). Whereas I-BOP, STA2, and U-46619 are agonists, SQ29548 and S145 are potent TP receptor antagonists (4) (see Table 1). This is consistent with the comprehensive assessment of >25 ligands tested in binding assays using the recombinant α splice variant (20). Recent studies have also suggested that the TP receptor may mediate some of the biological effects of the non-enzymatically derived isoprostane analogs, at least at high concentrations (21). This latter finding may have significance in pathophysiological conditions associated with increased oxidative stress. Signal transduction studies have shown that the TP receptor activates phosphatidylinositol hydrolysis (PIP$_2$)-dependent Ca^{2+} influx (15, 17). Two C-terminal alternatively spliced TP receptor variants may signal differentially via G$_q$ and a novel high-molecular-weight G protein, G$_h$ (18, 22, 23). Northern analysis of mouse tissues revealed that the highest level of TP mRNA expression is in the thymus, followed by the spleen, lung, and kidney, with lower levels of expression in the heart, uterus, and brain (16).

←

Figure 2   Intrarenal localization and consequences of prostanoid receptor activation along the nephron. IP and EP receptors stimulate renin release by juxtaglomerular apparatus cells through a receptor coupled to cyclic AMP generation. Dilator and constrictor prostanoid receptors also modulate glomerular vascular tone as well as constrictor tone of the vasa recta. The FP receptor may modulate transport in the distal convoluted tubule or connecting segment. PGE$_2$ also directly inhibits NaCl absorption by the thick ascending limb (TAL) and collecting duct via effects on EP$_1$ and EP$_3$ receptors.

TABLE 1   Representative prostanoid receptor-selective ligands

Prostanoid	Receptor	Agonist	Antagonist	Signaling
Thromboxane A_2	TP	I-BOP	SQ 29548	$\uparrow Ca^{2+}/IP_3$
		U46619	S-145	
PGI_2 (prostacyclin)	IP	Cicaprost Beraprost Iloprost[a]	—	$\uparrow cAMP$
PGE	EP			
	EP_1	17-phenyl-trino PGE2[a] Iloprost[a] Sulprostone[a]	SC 53122 SC51089	$\uparrow Ca^{2+}/IP_3$
	EP_2	Butaprost	—	$\uparrow cAMP$
	EP_3	M&B 28767 Sulprostone[a] SC46275	—	$\downarrow cAMP$
	EP_4	PGE_1-OH[a]	—	$\uparrow cAMP$
$PGF_{2\alpha}$	FP	Fluprostenol latanoprost	—	$\uparrow Ca^{2+}/IP_3$
PGD	DP	BW 245C	BW A868C[b]	$\uparrow cAMP$

[a]Somewhat non-selective, binds more than one receptor with high affinity.

[b] Partial agonist.

Thromboxane is a potent modulator of platelet shape change and aggregation as well as smooth muscle contraction and proliferation. Moreover, a point mutation (Arg-60 to Leu) in the first cytoplasmic loop of the TxA_2 receptor was identified in a patient with a dominantly inherited bleeding disorder characterized by a defective platelet response to TxA_2 (24). Targeted gene disruption of the murine TP receptor also resulted in prolonged bleeding times and reduction of collagen-stimulated platelet aggregation (25).

Increased thromboxane synthesis has been linked to cardiovascular diseases including acute myocardial ischemia (26), heart failure (27), and renal diseases (28, 29). In the kidney, TP receptor mRNA has been reported in glomeruli (17, 30) and vasculature. Radioligand autoradiography using ^{125}I-BOP suggests a similar distribution of binding sites in the mouse renal cortex, but additional renal medullary binding sites have been observed (31). These medullary TxA_2 binding sites are absent following disruption of the TP receptor gene, suggesting that they also represent authentic TP receptors (25). Glomerular localization of TP receptors corresponds to the potent vasoconstrictor effects of TxA_2 on glomerular capillaries accompanied by a reduced glomerular filtration rate (GFR) (32). Mesangial TP receptors coupled to phosphatidylinositol hydrolysis, protein kinase C activation, and glomerular mesangial cell contraction has been described and may contribute to these effects (33).

An important role for TP receptors in regulating renal hemodynamics and systemic blood pressure has also been suggested. Administration of a TP receptor antagonist reduces blood pressure in spontaneously hypertensive rats (13) and in cases of angiotensin-dependent hypertension (34). Modulation of renal TP receptor mRNA expression and function by altering dietary salt intake has also been reported (35). These studies also suggested an important role for luminal TP receptors of the distal tubule in enhancing glomerular vasoconstriction indirectly via effects on the macula densa and tubuloglomerular feedback (36, 37). However, recent studies have revealed no significant difference in tubuloglomerular feedback between wild-type and TP receptor knockout mice (38).

Despite the renal effects of thromboxane mimetics, the major phenotype of TP receptor disruption in mice and human appears to be reduced platelet aggregation and prolonged bleeding time (24, 25). Thromboxane may also modulate the glomerular fibrinolytic system by increasing the production of an inhibitor of plasminogen activator (PAI-1) in mesangial cells (39). Although a specific renal phenotype in the TP receptor knockout mouse has not yet been reported, important pathogenic roles for TxA_2 and glomerular TP receptors in mediating renal dysfunction in glomerulonephritis, hypertension, diabetes mellitus, and sepsis seem likely (28, 33, 40).

FP RECEPTORS

$PGF_{2\alpha}$ is a major COX product excreted in the urine (27, 41, 42). Its synthesis may occur either from PGH_2 via a PGF synthase (43) or from PGE_2 via a 9-keto reductase (44, 45). It is interesting that the activity of the 9-keto reductase may be modulated by salt intake and AT_2 receptor activation and may play an important role in hypertension (44, 46, 47).

The cDNA encoding the $PGF_{2\alpha}$ receptor (FP receptor), which was cloned from a human kidney cDNA library (48), encodes a protein of 359 amino acid residues. The bovine and murine FP receptors, cloned from corpora lutea, similarly encode proteins of 362 and 366 amino acid residues, respectively (49, 50). Transfection of HEK293 cells with the human FP receptor cDNA conferred preferential [^{3}H]PGF$_{2\alpha}$ binding with a K_D of 4.3 $\pm$ 1.0 nM (20, 48). Selective activation of the FP receptor may be achieved using fluprostenol or latanoprost (20; Table 1). [^{3}H]PGF$_{2\alpha}$ binding was displaced by a panel of ligands with a rank order potency of $PGF_{2\alpha}$ = fluprostenol > PGD_2 > PGE_2 > U46619 > iloprost (48, 51). When the FP receptor was expressed in oocytes, either $PGF_{2\alpha}$ or fluprostenol induced a Ca^{2+}-dependent Cl^- current, consistent with the FP receptor signaling via an increase in the intracellular Ca^{2+} concentration. Recent studies also suggest the existence of protein kinase C-dependent and protein kinase C-independent *rho*-mediated signaling pathways (52). An alternatively spliced isoform with a shorter carboxy-terminal tail, which appears to signal in a manner similar to that of the originally described FP receptor (52, 53). More recent studies suggest that these two isoforms may exhibit differential desensitization (54).

Examination of the tissue distribution of FP receptor mRNA has shown that the level of expression is highest in the ovarian corpus luteum, followed by the kidney, with lower-level expression in the lung, stomach, and heart (50, 55). $PGF_{2\alpha}$ is a potent constrictor of smooth muscle in the uterus, bronchi, and blood vessels (4, 56–58). The FP receptor is also highly expressed in skin, where it may play an important role in carcinogenesis (59). The FP receptor also appears to have an important role in the eye, where it increases uveoscleral outflow and reduces ocular pressure. The FP-selective agonist latanoprost has been used clinically as an effective treatment for glaucoma (60). Finally, expression of the FP receptor in corpora lutea is critical for normal birth, and homozygous disruption of the murine FP receptor gene results in failure of partuition in females, apparently owing to the failure of the normal preterm decline in progesterone levels (55).

The role of FP receptors in regulating renal function remains poorly defined. $PGF_{2\alpha}$ increases intracellular Ca^{2+} levels in cultured glomerular mesangial cells and podocytes (61, 62), suggesting that an FP receptor may modulate glomerular contraction. In contrast to these findings, demonstration of glomerular FP receptors in vivo at the molecular level has not been forthcoming. Selective modulation of renal production of $PGF_{2\alpha}$ by sodium or potassium loading (63) and AT_2 receptor activation (44, 46, 47) suggests that FP receptor activation may regulate the salt balance. A recent study using a transgenic mouse with an FP promoter driving a β-galactosidase reporter suggests that there is significant expression of this receptor in the distal convoluted tubule (64). Because this is a critical segment for thiazide-sensitive NaCl absorption and hormone-regulated Ca^{2+} absorption (65–67), these results support the possibility that $PGF_{2\alpha}$ regulates these transport processes through the FP receptor in this segment of the nephron (42). In contrast, whereas $PGE_{2\alpha}$ increases cell Ca^{2+} levels in the cortical collecting duct, the FP-selective agonist fluprostenol has no effect (68). Because $PGF_{2\alpha}$ can also bind to EP_1 and EP_3 receptors (51, 69, 70), these data suggest that the effects of $PGF_{2\alpha}$ in the collecting duct may be mediated via an EP receptor.

EP RECEPTORS

Intrarenal PGE_2, Salt Balance, and Blood Pressure

PGE_2 is a major product of COX-initiated arachidonic acid metabolism in the kidney and is synthesized at high rates along the nephron, particularly in the collecting duct (1). A recent report describes the cloning of a glutathione-dependent microsomal enzyme that specifically converts PGH_2 to PGE_2 (71). RNA for this enzyme is expressed at a high level in reproductive tissues (71) as well as in kidney collecting ducts (72).

Renal PGE_2 synthesis is critical for the maintenance of normal renal function. PGE_2 not only dilates the glomerular microcirculation and vasa recta, supplying the renal medulla (73, 74), it also modulates salt and water transport in the distal tubule (75). The maintenance of normal renal function during physiological stress is particularly dependent on endogenous prostaglandin synthesis (76). In this setting, the vasoconstrictor effects of angiotensin II, catecholamines, and vasopressin are more effectively buffered by prostaglandins in the kidney than in other vascular beds, preserving normal renal blood flow, GFR, and salt excretion. Administration of COX-inhibiting NSAIDs in the setting of volume depletion interferes with these dilator effects and may result in a catastrophic decline in GFR, resulting in overt renal failure (8).

Other evidence points to vasoconstrictor and prohypertensive effects of endogenous PGE_2. PGE_2 stimulates the release of renin from the juxtaglomerular apparatus (JGA) (77, 78), leading to a subsequent increase in the vasoconstrictor angiotensin II. In conscious dogs, chronic intrarenal PGE_2 infusion increases renal renin secretion, resulting in hypertension (79). Treatment of salt-depleted rats with indomethacin not only decreases plasma renin activity but also reduces blood pressure, suggesting that prostaglandins support blood pressure during salt depletion perhaps via their capacity to increase renin (80, 81). Direct vasoconstrictor effects of PGE_2 on vasculature have also been observed (82, 83). It is conceivable that these latter effects might predominate in circumstances in which the kidney is exposed to excessively high perfusion pressures. Thus, depending on the setting, the primary effect of PGE_2 may be either to increase or to decrease vascular tone, effects that appear to be mediated by distinct EP receptors.

MULTIPLE EP RECEPTORS

Four EP receptor subtypes have been cloned and characterized (51, 84). Some studies suggest that additional EP receptor subtypes may exist in sperm; however, molecular correlates have not been identified (85). Although these four receptors uniformly bind PGE_2 with a higher affinity than they do other endogenous prostanoids, when examined on the basis of amino acid homology, they are not as closely related to each other as to other prostanoid receptors that use similar signaling mechanisms (5, 86). Thus, the relaxant/cyclic AMP (cAMP)-coupled EP_2 receptor is more closely related to other relaxant prostanoid receptors, such as the IP and DP receptors, whereas the constrictor/Ca^{2+}-coupled EP_1 receptor is more closely related to other Ca^{2+}-coupled prostanoid receptors, such as the TP and FP receptors (86). These receptors may also be selectively activated or antagonized by different analogues (Table 1). EP receptor subtypes also exhibit differential expression along the nephron, suggesting that there are distinct functional consequences of activating each EP receptor subtype in the kidney (50, 70, 87–90) (Figure 2).

EP_1 Receptors

The EP_1 receptor was originally described as a smooth-muscle constrictor. The cloned human EP_1 receptor cDNA encodes a 402-amino-acid polypeptide that signals via increased inositol-3-phosphate (IP_3) generation and increased cell Ca^{2+} (69, 91, 92). Studies of EP_1 receptor-related functions may utilize one of several relatively selective antagonists that block their activation, such as SC51089, SC19220, or SC53122 (93–95). EP_1 receptor mRNA predominates in the kidney, with the tissue distribution being in the order kidney ≫ gastric muscularis mucosae > adrenal tissue (91, 96–98). Interpretation of EP_1 mRNA expression by Northern blot analysis is complicated by the presence of several mRNA species of different sizes, including ~7.0, 5, 4.4, and ~3 kb. Some of these transcripts appear to derive not from EP_1 mRNA but from mRNA transcribed from the protein kinase N gene, an apparently unrelated gene that is actively transcribed from the antiparallel DNA strand and whose product possesses a sequence complementary to that of the EP_1 receptor (84, 99).

Within the kidney, EP_1 mRNA has been mapped by in situ hybridization and is expressed primarily in the collecting duct, with levels increasing from the cortex to the papillae (87, 92, 98). Activation of the EP_1 receptor increases intracellular calcium levels and inhibits Na^+ and water reabsorption in the in vitro microperfused collecting duct (68, 98, 100), suggesting that renal EP_1 receptor activation might contribute to the natriuretic and diuretic effects of PGE_2. A recent report suggests that the EP_1 receptor may also be present in glomerular mesangial cells (101), where it could play a role as a vasoconstrictor; however, this has not been confirmed by in vivo studies. Although a constrictor PGE_2 effect has been reported to occur in the afferent arteriole of the rat (82), it remains unclear whether this is mediated by an EP_1 or an EP_3 receptor. There does not appear to be very high level of expression of the EP_1 receptor mRNA in the preglomerular vasculature or other arterial resistance vessels in either mice or rabbits (83). A preliminary report suggests that EP_1 receptor knockout mice exhibit hypotension and hyperreninemia, supporting a role for this receptor in maintaining blood pressure (102).

EP_2 Receptors

The literature regarding the nomenclature for the EP_2 receptor is somewhat confusing, because prior to 1995, when the butaprost-sensitive human EP_2 receptor was cloned, the EP_4 receptor was misclassified as the EP_2 receptor (103). Authentic EP_2 receptors for the mouse, rat, rabbit, and cow have now been cloned (104–107). The human EP_2 receptor cDNA encodes a 358-amino-acid polypeptide that signals through increased cAMP (106, 108). EP_2 receptors are selectively activated by butaprost (51, 84). The EP_2 receptor may also be distinguished from the EP_4 receptor, the other major relaxant EP receptor, by its relative insensitivity to the EP_4 agonist PGE_1-OH and its insensitivity to the weak EP_4 antagonist AH23848 (106, 109).

The precise tissue distribution of the EP_2 receptor has been only partially characterized, using Northern blot analysis of mRNA distribution. This has revealed a major mRNA species of ~3.1 kb that is most abundant in the uterus, lung, and spleen, with only low levels of expression in the kidney (84, 105–107). EP_2 receptor mRNA is expressed at much lower levels than EP_4 receptor mRNA in most tissues (105). Functional studies suggest that the EP_2 receptor plays an important role in ovulation and fertilization (110–112). The EP_2 receptor may also be an important target for treating asthma by promoting bronchodilation (113). In addition, recent studies have demonstrated that targeted disruption of the EP_2 receptor interferes with fertility and may result in salt-sensitive hypertension (112). This latter finding supports an important role for the EP_2 receptor in protecting systemic blood pressure, perhaps via its vasodilator effect or effects on renal salt excretion. Possible roles for this receptor in regulating medullary blood flow and pressure natriuresis remain to be explored and are discussed below.

EP_3 Receptors

The EP_3 receptor generally acts as a constrictor of smooth muscle (4). Nuclease protection and Northern blot analyses have demonstrated high levels of EP_3 receptor expression in several tissues, including kidney, uterus, adrenal, and stomach, with Northern analysis showing major mRNA species of $\sim$2.4 and $\sim$7.0 kb (97, 114–117). This receptor is unique in that it has multiple (more than six) alternatively spliced variants defined by unique C-terminal cytoplasmic tails (114–116, 118–120). These splice variants encode proteins with predicted molecular masses of between 40 and 45 kDa (97, 114, 115). The EP_3 splice variants bind PGE_2 and the EP_3 agonists MB28767 and sulprostone (5, 121) with similar affinities, although the C-terminal tails may recruit different signaling pathways (5, 20, 118). All of the splice variants uniformly and potently inhibit cAMP generation via a pertussis toxin-sensitive G_i-coupled mechanism; however, Ca^{2+}-dependent signaling mechanisms appear to be differentially activated by different C-terminal tails (118, 122, 123). One recent study suggests that EP_3 signaling also occurs through the small G protein *rho* (122).

The physiological significance of these different C-terminal splice variants remains uncertain. Differences in agonist-independent activity have been observed for several of the splice variants, suggesting that they may play a role in constitutive regulation of cellular events (124).

In the kidney, in situ hybridization has demonstrated that EP_3 receptor mRNA is abundant in the thick ascending limb (TAL) and collecting duct (70, 87, 90). This distribution has been confirmed by reverse transcription-PCR on microdissected rat and mouse collecting ducts (88, 125). An important role for a G_i-coupled PGE receptor in regulating water and salt transport along the nephron has been recognized for many years (126, 127). PGE_2 directly inhibits salt and water absorption in both microperfused TALs and collecting ducts (68, 100, 128, 129). PGE_2 directly inhibits Cl^- absorption in the mouse or rabbit medullary TAL from either the luminal or basolateral surface (128, 130). PGE_2 also inhibits hormone-stimulated cAMP generation in TAL (131, 132). Good & George (129) demonstrated that PGE_2 modulates ion transport in the rat TAL by a pertussis toxin-sensitive mechanism. It is interesting that these effects also appear to involve protein kinase C activation (133), possibly reflecting activation of a novel EP_3 receptor signaling pathway that may correspond to alternative signaling pathways as described above (118, 123). Taken together, these data support a role for the EP_3 receptor in regulating transport in the TAL.

Blockade of endogenous PGE_2 synthesis by NSAIDs enhances urinary concentration (134). It is likely that PGE_2-mediated antagonism of vasopressin-stimulated salt absorption in the TAL and water absorption in the collecting duct contributes to its diuretic effect (135). In the in vitro microperfused collecting duct, PGE_2 inhibits both vasopressin-stimulated osmotic water absorption and vasopressin-stimulated cAMP generation (127, 136, 137). Furthermore, PGE_2 inhibition of water absorption and cAMP generation are both blocked by pertussis toxin, suggesting that the effects are mediated by the inhibitory G protein, G_i (68, 127, 136, 138). When administered in the absence of vasopressin, PGE_2 actually stimulates water absorption in the collecting duct from either the luminal or the basolateral side (68, 139). These stimulatory effects of PGE_2 on transport in the collecting duct are not mimicked by butaprost and are more likely to be related to activation of the EP_4 receptor (139). Regardless of the identity of this stimulatory receptor, in vivo studies suggest that the inhibitory effects of the EP_3 receptor on water reabsorption normally predominate.

On the basis of the preceding functional considerations, one would expect $EP_3^{-/-}$ mice to exhibit inappropriately enhanced urine concentration. Surprisingly, after administration of 1-desamino [8-D-arginine] vasopressin, $EP_3^{-/-}$ mice exhibited urinary concentration comparable to that of receptor-positive mice, and their 24-h water intakes and maximal and minimal urinary osmolalities were similar (140). The only clear difference was that in mice allowed free access to water, indomethacin increased urinary osmolality in normal mice but not the knockouts. The lack of a major renal phenotype in the $EP_3^{-/-}$ mice raises the possibility that some of the renal actions of PGE_2 that are normally mediated by the EP_3 receptor have been co-opted by other receptors (such as the EP_1 receptor). This remains to be formally tested.

Nevertheless, $EP_3^{-/-}$ mice do exhibit a clear-cut systemic phenotype (140, 141). Mice with targeted deletion of the EP_3 receptor exhibit an impaired febrile response to endotoxin, suggesting that the EP_3 receptor antagonists will be effective antipyretic agents (141). Other studies suggest that the EP_3 receptor plays an important vasopressor role in the peripheral circulation of mice (83). Studies in knockout mice also support a potential role for the EP_3 receptor as a systemic vasopressor (142).

The EP_4 Receptor

Like the EP_2 receptor, the EP_4 signals through increased cAMP (106, 108). The human EP_4 receptor cDNA encodes a 488-amino-acid polypeptide with a predicted molecular mass of $\sim$53 kDa (108). Care must be taken in reviewing the literature prior to 1995, when this receptor was generally referred to as the EP_2 receptor (103). In addition to the human receptor, EP_4 receptors for the mouse, rat, rabbit, and cow have been cloned (84, 89, 103, 108, 143, 144). EP_4 receptors may be pharmacologically distinguished from the EP_1 and EP_3 receptors by their insensitivity to sulprostone and from EP_2 receptors by their insensitivity to butaprost (51, 84) and relatively selective activation by PGE_1-OH (51, 84).

EP_4 receptor mRNA is highly expressed relative to that of the EP_2 receptor and widely distributed, with a major species of $\sim$3.8 kb detected by Northern blot analysis in the thymus, ileum, lung, spleen, adrenal gland, and kidney (89, 108, 144, 145). Important vasodilator effects of EP_4 receptor activation in venous and arterial beds have been described (4, 109). A critical role for the EP_4 receptor in regulating the perinatal closure of the pulmonary ductus arteriosus has also been suggested by recent studies of mice with targeted disruption of the EP_4 receptor gene (146, 147). On a 129-strain background, $EP_4^{-/-}$ mice had close to 100% perinatal mortality owing to persistent patent ductus arteriosus (147). It is interesting that when bred on a mixed genetic background, only 80% of $EP_4^{-/-}$ mice died whereas $\sim$21% underwent closure of the ductus and survived. Preliminary studies in these survivors support an important role for the EP_4 receptor as a systemic vasodepressor (4, 109, 148); however, their heterogeneous genetic background complicates the interpretation of these results because survival may select for modifier genes that not only allow ductus closure but also alter hemodynamics.

Other roles for the EP_4 receptor in controlling blood pressure have been suggested, including the ability to stimulate the release of aldosterone from zona glomerulosa cells (149). In the kidney, EP_4 receptor mRNA expression occurs primarily in the glomerulus, where the precise function of this receptor has not been characterized (87, 89, 90). Glomerular EP_4 receptor expression might contribute to regulation of the renal microcirculation as well as to renin release (150). This corresponds to recent studies suggesting that EP_4 receptors are expressed in cultured JGA and podocyte cells (61, 150).

Regulation of Renal Function by Prostaglandin E_2 and Corresponding EP Receptors

A myriad of effects of PGE_2 in the kidney remained to be assigned to particular EP receptors. Likely candidates for several of these effects are discussed below.

Renal Cortical Hemodynamics   The expression of the EP_4 receptor in the glomerulus suggests that it may play an important role regulating renal hemodynamics. Prostaglandins regulate the renal cortical microcirculation, and as alluded to above, both glomerular constrictor and dilator effects of prostaglandins have been observed (73, 82, 151). In the setting of volume depletion, endogenous PGE_2 helps maintain the GFR by dilating the afferent arteriole (8, 73, 152). Recent studies suggest that prostaglandins acting locally on the glomerulus may derive from COX2 present in the macula densa (153, 154). Control of the GFR by the macula densa via tubuloglomerular feedback is suggestive of both dilator and constrictor effects of prostanoids (36, 73, 151, 155). One recent study suggests that COX2-derived prostanoids are predominantly vasodilators (156). The profile of prostanoids produced by the macula densa cells remains uncharacterized. Some data suggest roles for EP and IP receptors coupled to increased cAMP generation in mediating vasodilator effects in the preglomerular circulation (151, 157, 158). Edwards (152) found that PGE_2 exerted a dilator effect on the afferent arteriole but not the efferent arteriole of rabbit glomeruli, consistent with the presence of an EP_2 or EP_4 receptor in the preglomerular microcirculation.

Renin Release   Other data suggest that the EP_4 receptor may also stimulate renin release. Soon after the introduction of NSAIDs, it was recognized that endogenous prostaglandins play an important role in stimulating renin release (151, 159). Treatment of salt-depleted rats with indomethacin not only decreases plasma renin activity but also causes blood pressure to fall, suggesting that prostaglandins support blood pressure during salt depletion via their capacity to increase renin (80, 81). Prostanoids also play a central role in the pathogenesis of renal-vascular hypertension, and administration of NSAIDs lowers blood pressure in both animals and humans with renal artery stenosis (9, 10, 160). In conscious dogs, chronic intrarenal PGE_2 infusion increases renin secretion, resulting in hypertension (79). PGE_2 induces renin release in isolated preglomerular JGA cells (78). Like the effect of β-adrenergic agents, this effect appears to be through a cAMP-coupled response, supporting a role for an EP_4 or EP_2 receptor in this process (78, 157). Although localization of EP_2 or EP_4 receptors to the JGA has not been demonstrated, EP_4 receptor mRNA has been detected in microdissected JGAs (150), supporting the possibility that renal EP_4 receptor activation contributes to enhanced renin release. Finally, regulation of plasma renin activity and intrarenal renin mRNA does not appear to be different in wild-type and EP_2 knockout mice (161), arguing against a major role for the EP_2 receptor in regulating renin release. Conversely, one report suggests that EP_3 receptor mRNA is localized to the macula densa, indicating that this cAMP-inhibiting receptor may also contribute to the control of renin release (87).

Renal Medullary Microcirculation   In the setting of systemic hypertension, the normal response of the kidney is to increase salt excretion, thereby mitigating the increase in blood pressure. This so-called pressure natriuresis plays a key role in the ability of the kidney to protect against hypertension (162, 163). Increased blood pressure is accompanied by increased renal perfusion pressure that is associated with enhanced PGE_2 excretion (164). Inhibition of prostaglandin synthesis markedly blunts (although it does not eliminate) pressure natriuresis (165). The mechanism by which PGE_2 contributes to pressure natriuresis may involve changes in resistance of the renal medullary microcirculation (165, 166). PGE_2 directly dilates descending vasa recta, and increased medullary blood flow may contribute to the increased interstitial pressure observed as renal perfusion pressure increases, leading to enhanced salt excretion (74). The identity of the dilator PGE_2 receptor controlling the contractile properties of the descending vasa recta remains uncertain, but EP_2 or EP_4 receptors seem to be likely candidates

(4). Recent studies demonstrating salt-sensitive hypertension in mice with targeted disruption of the EP_2 receptor (112) suggests that the EP_2 receptor facilitates the ability of the kidney to increase sodium excretion, thereby protecting systemic blood pressure from a high-salt diet. Given its defined role in vascular smooth muscle (112), these effects of the EP_2 receptor disruption seem more likely to relate to its effects on renal vascular tone. In particular, loss of a vasodilator effect in the renal medulla might modify pressure natriuresis and could contribute to hypertension in EP_2 knockout mice. Nonetheless, a role for either the EP_2 or EP_4 receptor in regulating renal medullary blood flow remains to be established. In conclusion, direct vasomotor effects of EP_2 and EP_4 receptors as well as effects on renin release may play critical roles in the regulation of systemic blood pressure and renal hemodynamics.

PROSTACYCLIN (IP) RECEPTORS

Prostacyclin (PGI_2) is derived by the enzymatic conversion of PGH_2 via prostacyclin synthase (14, 167). The biological effects of prostacyclin are numerous and include nociception, antithrombosis (168), and vasodilator actions that have been targeted therapeutically to treat pulmonary hypertension (169, 170). The cDNA for the IP receptor encodes a protein with seven hydrophobic (membrane-spanning) domains (171, 172). The IP receptor is selectively activated by the analogue cicaprost (51, 173). Iloprost and carbaprostacyclin potently activate the IP receptor but also activate the EP_1 receptor (51). Most evidence suggests that the PGI_2 receptor signals via stimulation of cAMP generation; however, the cloned mouse PGI_2 receptor also signal via PIP_2 (171). Stimulation of PIP_2 hydrolysis required a 10,000-fold-higher PGI_2 concentration (10 μM) than the concentrations required (10^{-10} M) to stimulate cAMP accumulation (171). It remains unclear whether PIP_2 hydrolysis plays any significant role in the physiological action of PGI_2.

IP receptor mRNA is highly expressed in the mouse thymus, heart, and spleen (171) and in the human kidney, liver, and lung (172). In situ hybridization has shown that IP receptor mRNA is predominantly expressed in neurons of the dorsal root ganglia and vascular tissue, including the aorta, pulmonary artery, and renal interlobular and glomerular afferent arterioles (174). The expression of IP receptor mRNA in the dorsal root ganglia is consistent with a role for prostacyclin in pain sensation. Mice with IP receptor gene disruption exhibit a predisposition to diminished pain perception, arterial thrombosis, and inflammatory responses (168).

PGI_2 has been demonstrated to play an important vasodilator role in the glomerular microvasculature (10, 152, 175) as well as in the regulation of renin release (77, 176). The capacities of PGI_2 and PGE_2 to stimulate cAMP generation in the glomerular microvasculature are distinct and additive (157), demonstrating that the effects of these two prostanoids are mediated via separate receptors. A preliminary report suggests that IP receptor knockout mice exhibit salt-sensitive hypertension and enhanced renin release following water deprivation (177). It is interesting that prostacyclin is a potent stimulator of renal renin release, so the mechanisms underlying these observations in $IP^{-/-}$ mice are unclear (178).

Renal epithelial effects of PGI_2 in the TAL have also been suggested (179), and IP receptors have been reported to occur in the collecting duct (180, 181), but its role in these segments are less well established. Of interest, in situ hybridization also demonstrated significant expression of prostacyclin synthase in medullary collecting ducts (167), consistent with a role for this metabolite in this region of the kidney. In summary, although IP receptors appear to play an important role in the regulation of renin release and as a vasodilator in the kidney, their role in regulating renal epithelial function remains to be firmly established.

DP RECEPTORS

PGD_2 is also derived from PGH_2 via the action of specific enzymes, designated PGD synthases (182). Once synthesized, it interacts with the DP receptor. The DP receptor has been cloned, and like the IP, EP_2, and EP_4 receptors, the DP receptor predominantly signals by increasing cAMP generation (183, 184). The human DP receptor binds PGD_2 with a high affinity of 300 pM and, at another site, with a lower affinity of 13.4 nM (20, 184). The mouse DP receptor has also been cloned, and it displays pharmacological properties similar to those of the human receptor (183). DP-selective PGD_2 analogs, including the agonist BW 245C (4, 185), are available. The DP-selective ligand BW A868C was originally described as an antagonist (186), although more recent studies have suggested that it is a partial agonist (187).

DP receptor mRNA is highly expressed in the leptomeninges, retina, and ileum but has not been detected in the kidney (183, 184, 188). PGD_2 is the major prostanoid released from mast cells following challenge with immunoglobulin E (189), and it has also been shown to affect the sleep-wake cycle (190), pain sensation (191), and body temperature (192). Peripherally, PGD_2 has been shown to mediate vasodilation as well as inhibition of platelet aggregation (186). Northern blot analysis of the human DP receptor demonstrated only low levels of mRNA expression in the small intestine (184), whereas in the mouse the DP receptor mRNA was detected in the ileum and, to a lesser extent, in the lung (183). Consistent with this latter finding, the DP receptor knockout displayed reduced inflammation in the ovalbumin model of allergic asthma (193). Wright et al (194) recently cloned the rat DP receptor and localized expression in the gut to the mucus-secreting goblet cells and columnar epithelium. Wright et al suggest that the DP receptor may therefore play a role in modulating mucus secretion. The role of PGD_2 and DP receptors in the kidney remains poorly defined (1, 3). Intrarenal infusion of PGD_2 resulted in a dose-dependent increase in renal artery flow, urine output, creatinine clearance, and sodium and potassium excretion (195). The use of DP-selective agonists should help clarify whether renal effects of PGD_2 are mediated by authentic DP receptors.

CONCLUSIONS

In summary, IP receptors are primarily expressed in vasculature, whereas TP and EP_4 receptors are expressed in the glomerulus. EP_3, FP, and EP_1 receptors are selectively expressed in specific epithelia along the nephron, including the thick limb, distal convoluted tubule, and collecting duct, respectively. FP, EP_1, and EP_3 receptors may contribute to the natriuretic and diuretic action of PGE_2 (Figure 2). In contrast, intrarenal IP, TP, EP_2, and EP_4 receptors may affect vascular and glomerular function. Finally, IP and EP_4 receptors may also play an important role in regulating renin release. Roles for the DP receptor remain speculative. Together the prostanoid receptors provide novel targets for modulating renal salt and water excretion as well as systemic blood pressure. The availability of receptor-selective antagonists should provide important physiological and therapeutic tools, thus expanding the clinical utility of prostaglandin analogs.

ACKNOWLEDGMENTS

Support for this project was provided by National Institutes of Health grant DK-37097 (to MDB) and a Veterans Administration Merit Award (MDB). Support was also provided by National Institutes of Health grants DK46205 and GM15431 (RMB).

Visit the Annual Reviews home page at www.AnnualReviews.org

LITERATURE CITED

1. Bonvalet JP, Pradelles P, Farman N. 1987. Segmental synthesis and actions of prostaglandins along the nephron. *Am. J. Physiol. Renal Physiol.* 253:F377–F87
2. Smith W. 1992. Prostanoid biosynthesis and mechanisms of action. *Am. J. Physiol. Renal Physiol.* 263:F181–F91
3. Nowak J, Wennmalm A. 1979. Human forearm and kidney conversion of arachidonic acid to prostaglandins. *Acta Physiol. Scand.* 106:307–12
4. Coleman RA, Smith WL, Narumiya S. 1994. VIII. International union of pharmacology classification of prostanoid receptors: properties, distribution, and structure of the receptors and their subtypes. *Pharmacol. Rev.* 46:205–29
5. Narumiya S, Sugimoto Y, Ushikubi F. 1999. Prostanoid receptors: structures, properties, and functions. *Physiol. Rev.* 79:1193–226

6. Gurwitz J, Avorn J, Bohn R, Glynn R, Monane M, Mogun H. 1994. Initiation of antihypertensive treatment during nonsteroidal anti-inflammatory drug therapy. *J. Am. Med Assoc.* 272:781–86
7. Murray M, Breene P, Brater D, Manatunga A, Hall S. 1992. Effect of flurbiprofen on renal function in patients with moderate renal insufficiency. *Br. J. Clin. Pharmacol.* 33:385–93
8. Schlondorff D. 1993. Renal complications of nonsteroidal anti-inflammatory drugs. *Kidney Int.* 44:643–53
9. Imanishi M, Kawamura M, Akabane S, Matsushima Y, Kuramochi M, et al. 1989. Aspirin lowers blood pressure in patients with renovascular hypertension. *Hypertension* 14:461–68
10. Jackson E. 1989. Relationship between renin release and blood pressure response

to nonsteroidal anti-inflammatory drugs in hypertension. *Hypertension* 14:469–71

11. Mistry M, Nasjletti A. 1988. Prostanoids as mediators of prohypertensive and antihypertensive mechanisms. *Am. J. Med. Sci.* 295:263–67

12. Clive DM, Stoff JS. 1984. Renal syndromes associated with nonsteroidal antiinflammatory drugs. *N. Engl. J. Med.* 310:563–72

13. Quest DW, Wilson TW. 1998. Effects of ridogrel, a thromboxane synthase inhibitor and receptor antagonist, on blood pressure in the spontaneously hypertensive rat. *Jpn. J. Pharmacol.* 78:479–86

14. Tanabe T, Miyata A, Nanayama T, Tone Y, Ihara H, et al. 1995. Human genes for prostaglandin endoperoxide synthase-2, thromboxane synthase and prostacyclin synthase. *Adv. Prostaglandin Thromboxane Leukot. Res.* 23:133–35

15. Hirata M, Hayashi Y, Ushikubi F, Yokota Y, Kageyama R, et al. 1991. Cloning and expression of cDNA for a human thromboxane A2 receptor. *Nature* 349:617–20

16. Namba T, Sugimoto Y, Hirata M, Hayashi Y, Hondo A, et al. 1992. Mouse thromboxane A2 receptor: cDNA cloning, expression and northern blot analysis. *Biochem. Biophys. Res. Commun.* 184:1197–203

17. Abe T, Takeuchi K, Takahashi N, Tsutsumi E, Taniyama Y, Abe K. 1995. Rat kidney thromaboxane A2 receptor: molecular cloning signal transduction and intrarenal expression localization. *J. Clin. Invest.* 96:657–64

18. Raychowdhury MK, Yukawa M, Collins LJ, McGrail SH, Kent KC, Ware JA. 1994. Alternative splicing produces a divergent cytoplasmic tail in the human endothelial thromboxane A2 receptor. *J. Biol. Chem.* 269:19256–61. Erratum. 1995. *J. Biol. Chem.* 270(12):7011

19. Morinelli TA, Oatis JE Jr, Okwu AK, Mais DE, Mayeux PR, et al. 1989. Characterization of an ^{125}I-labeled thromboxane A2/prostaglandin H2 receptor agonist.

J. Pharmacol. Exp. Ther. 251:557–62

20. Abramovitz M, Adam M, Boie Y, Carriere M, Denis D, et al. 2000. The utilization of recombinant prostanoid receptors to determine the affinities and selectivities of prostaglandins and related analogs. *Biochim. Biophys. Acta* 1483:285–93

21. Audoly LP, Rocca B, Fabre JE, Koller BH, Thomas D, et al. 2000. Cardiovascular responses to the isoprostanes iPF(2alpha)-III and iPE(2)-III are mediated via the thromboxane A(2) receptor in vivo. *Circulation* 101:2833–40

22. Kinsella BT, O'Mahony DJ, Fitzgerald GA. 1997. The human thromboxane A2 receptor alpha isoform (TP alpha) functionally couples to the G proteins Gq and G11 in vivo and is activated by the isoprostane 8-epi prostaglandin F2 alpha. *J. Pharmacol. Exp. Ther.* 281:957–64

23. Vezza R, Habib A, FitzGerald GA. 1999. Differential signaling by the thromboxane receptor isoforms via the novel GTP-binding protein, Gh. *J. Biol. Chem.* 274:12774–79

24. Hirata T, Kakizuka A, Ushikubi F, Fuse I, Okuma M, Narumiya S. 1994. Arg60 to Leu mutation of the human thromboxane A2 receptor in a dominantly inherited bleeding disorder. *J. Clin. Invest.* 94:1662–67

25. Thomas DW, Mannon RB, Mannon PJ, Latour A, Oliver JA, et al. 1998. Coagulation defects and altered hemodynamic responses in mice lacking receptors for thromboxane A2. *J. Clin. Invest.* 102:1994–2001

26. Oates JA, Fitzgerald GA, Branch RA, Jackson EK, Knapp HR, Roberts LJ 2d. 1988. Clinical implications of prostaglandin and thromboxane A2 formation (1). *N. Engl. J. Med.* 319:689–98

27. Castellani S, Paladini B, Paniccia R, Di Serio C, Vallotti B, et al. 1997. Increased renal formation of thromboxane A2 and prostaglandin F2 alpha in heart failure. *Am. Heart J.* 133:94–100

28. Spurney RF, Ruiz P, Pisetsky DS, Coffman TM. 1992. Chronic thromboxane receptor blockade reduces renal injury in murine lupus nephritis. *Kidney Int.* 41:973–82

29. Morinelli TA, Tempel GE, Jaffa AA, Silva RH, Naka M, et al. 1993. Thromboxane A2/prostaglandin H2 receptors in streptozotocin-induced diabetes: effects of insulin therapy in the rat. *Prostaglandins* 45:427–38

30. Båtshake B, Nilsson C, Sundelin J. 1999. Structure and expression of the murine thromboxane A2 receptor gene. *Biochem. Biophys. Res. Commun.* 256:391–97

31. Mannon RB, Coffman TM, Mannon PJ. 1996. Distribution of binding sites for thromboxane A2 in the mouse kidney. *Am. J. Physiol. Renal Physiol.* 271:F1131–F38

32. Wilkes BM, Solomon J, Maita M, Mento PF. 1989. Characterization of glomerular thromboxane receptor sites in the rat. *Am. J. Physiol. Renal Physiol.* 256:F1111–F16

33. Spurney RF, Onorato JJ, Albers FJ, Coffman TM. 1993. Thromoboxane binding and signal transduction in rat glomerular mesangial cells. *Am. J. Physiol. Renal Physiol.* 264:F292–F99

34. Nasjletti A. 1998. Arthur C. Corcoran Memorial Lecture. The role of eicosanoids in angiotensin-dependent hypertension. *Hypertension* 31:194–200

35. Welch WJ, Peng B, Takeuchi K, Abe K, Wilcox CS. 1997. Salt loading enhances rat renal TxA2/PGH2 receptor expression and TGF response to U-46,619. *Am. J. Physiol. Renal Physiol.* 273:F976–F83

36. Welch W, Wilcox C. 1988. Modulating role for thromboxane in the tubuloglomerular feedback response in the rat. *J. Clin. Invest.* 81:1843–49

37. Welch WJ, Wilcox CS. 1992. Potentiation of tubuloglomerular feedback in the rat by thromboxane mimetic: role of macula densa. *J. Clin. Invest.* 89:1857–65

38. Schnermann J, Traynor T, Pohl H, Thomas DW, Coffman TM, Briggs JP. 2000. Vasoconstrictor responses in thromboxane receptor knockout mice: tubuloglomerular feedback and ureteral obstruction. *Acta Physiol. Scand.* 168:201–7

39. Coffman TM, Spurney RF, Mannon RB, Levenson R. 1998. Thromboxane A2 modulates the fibrinolytic system in glomerular mesangial cells. *Am. J. Physiol. Renal Physiol.* 275:F262–F69

40. DeRubertis FR, Craven PA. 1994. Activation of protein kinase C in glomerular cells in diabetes: mechanisms and potential links to the pathogenesis of diabetic glomerulopathy. *Diabetes* 43:1–8

41. Naray-Fejes-Toth A, Fejes-Toth G, Fischer C, Frolich J. 1984. Effect of dexamethasone on in vivo prostanoid production in the rabbit. *J. Clin. Invest.* 74:120–23

42. Morgan LJ, Liebman M, Broughton KS. 1994. Caffeine-induced hypercalciuria and renal prostaglandins: effect of aspirin and n-3 polyunsaturated fatty acids. *Am. J. Clin. Nutr.* 60:362–68

43. Suzuki T, Fujii Y, Miyano M, Chen LY, Takahashi T, Watanabe K. 1999. cDNA cloning, expression, and mutagenesis study of liver-type prostaglandin F synthase. *J. Biol. Chem.* 274:241–48

44. Weber P, Larsson C, Scherer B. 1977. Prostaglandin E2-9-ketoreductase as a mediator of salt intake-related prostaglandin-renin interaction. *Nature* 266:65–66

45. Chaudhari A, Kirschenbaum MA. 1983. Mechanism of increased renal prostaglandin E2 in uranyl nitrate-induced acute renal failure. *Prostaglandins* 26:689–99

46. Siragy HM, Carey RM. 1997. The subtype 2 angiotensin receptor regulates renal prostaglandin F2 alpha formation in conscious rats. *Am. J. Physiol. Regulatory Integrative Comp. Physiol.* 273:R1103–R7

47. Siragy HM, Senbonmatsu T, Ichiki T, Inagami T, Carey RM. 1999. Increased renal vasodilator prostanoids prevent hypertension in mice lacking the angiotensin subtype-2 receptor. *J. Clin. Invest.* 104:181–88

48. Abramovitz M, Boie Y, Nguyen T, Rushmore TH, Bayne MA, et al. 1994. Cloning and expression of a cDNA for the human prostanoid FP receptor. *J. Biol. Chem.* 269:2632–36

49. Sakamoto K, Ezashi T, Miwa K, Okuda-Ashitaka E, Houtani T, et al. 1994. Molecular cloning and expression of a cDNA of the bovine prostglandin F2a receptor. *J. Biol. Chem.* 5:3881–86

50. Sugimoto Y, Hasumoto K, Namba T, Irie A, Katsuyama M, et al. 1994. Cloning and expression of a cDNA for mouse prostaglandin F receptor. *J. Biol. Chem.* 269:1356–60

51. Kiriyama M, Ushikubi F, Kobayashi T, Hirata M, Sugimoto Y, Narumiya S. 1997. Ligand binding specificities of the eight types and subtypes of the mouse prostanoid receptors expressed in Chinese hamster ovary cells. *Br. J. Pharmacol.* 122:217–24

52. Pierce KL, Bailey TJ, Hoyer PB, Gil DW, Woodward DF, Regan JW. 1997. Cloning of a carboxyl-terminal isoform of the prostanoid FP receptor. *J. Biol. Chem.* 272:883–87

53. Pierce KL, Fujino H, Srinivasan D, Regan JW. 1999. Activation of FP prostanoid receptor isoforms leads to Rho-mediated changes in cell morphology and in the cell cytoskeleton. *J. Biol. Chem.* 274:35944–49

54. Fujino H, Srinivasan D, Pierce KL, Regan JW. 2000. Differential regulation of prostaglandin F(2alpha) receptor isoforms by protein kinase C. *Mol. Pharmacol.* 57:353–58

55. Sugimoto Y, Yamasaki A, Segi E, Tsuboi K, Aze Y, et al. 1997. Failure of parturition in mice lacking the prostaglandin F receptor. *Science* 277:681–83

56. Griffin BW, Magnino PE, Pang IH, Sharif NA. 1998. Pharmacological characterization of an FP prostaglandin receptor on rat vascular smooth muscle cells (A7r5) coupled to phosphoinositide turnover and intracellular calcium mobilization. *J. Pharmacol. Exp. Ther.* 286:411–18

57. Muller K, Krieg P, Marks F, Furstenberger G. 2000. Expression of PGF(2alpha) receptor mRNA in normal, hyperplastic and neoplastic skin. *Carcinogenesis* 21:1063–66

58. Chen J, Woodward DF, Yuan YD, Marshall K, Senior J. 1998. Prostanoid-induced contraction of the rabbit isolated uterus is mediated by FP receptors. *Prostaglandins Other Lipid Mediat.* 55:387–94

59. Muller K, Krieg P, Marks F, Furstenberger G. 2000. Expression of PGF(2alpha) receptor mRNA in normal, hyperplastic and neoplastic skin. *Carcinogenesis* 21:1063–66

60. Linden C, Alm A. 1999. Prostaglandin analogues in the treatment of glaucoma. *Drugs Aging* 14:387–98

61. Bek M, Nusing R, Kowark P, Henger A, Mundel P, Pavenstadt H. 1999. Characterization of prostanoid receptors in podocytes. *J. Am. Soc. Nephrol.* 10:2084–93

62. Breshnahan BA, Kelefiotis D, Stratidakis I, Lianos EA. 1996. PGF2alpha-induced signaling events in glomerular mesangial cells. *Proc. Soc. Exp. Biol. Med.* 212:165–73

63. Nasjletti A, Erman A, Cagen LM, Brooks DP, Crofton JT, et al. 1985. High potassium intake selectively increases urinary PGF2 alpha excretion in the rat. *Am. J. Physiol. Renal Physiol.* 248:F382–F88

64. Hasumoto K, Sugimoto Y, Gotoh M, Segi E, Yamasaki A, et al. 1997. Characterization of the mouse prostaglandin F receptor gene: a transgenic mouse study of a regulatory region that controls its expression in the stomach and kidney but not in the ovary. *Genes Cells* 2:571–80

65. Reilly RF, Ellison DH. 2000. Mammalian distal tubule: physiology, pathophysiology, and molecular anatomy. *Physiol. Rev.* 80:277–313

66. Shimizu T, Yoshitomi K, Nakamura M,

Imai M. 1988. Site and mechanism of action of trichlormethiazide in rabbit distal nephron segments perfused in vitro. *J. Clin. Invest.* 82:721–30

67. Hoenderop JG, Willems PH, Bindels RJ. 2000. Toward a comprehensive molecular model of active calcium reabsorption. *Am. J. Physiol. Renal Physiol.* 278:F352–F60

68. Hébert RL, Jacobson HR, Fredin D, Breyer MD. 1993. Evidence that separate PGE2 receptors modulate water and sodium transport in rabbit cortical collecting duct. *Am. J. Physiol. Renal Physiol.* 265:F643–F50

69. Funk C, Furchi L, FitzGerald G, Grygorczyk R, Rochette C, et al. 1993. Cloning and expression of a cDNA for the human prostaglandin E receptor EP1 subtype. *J. Biol. Chem.* 268:26767–72

70. Breyer MD, Jacobson HR, Davis LS, Breyer RM. 1993. In situ hybridization and localization of mRNA for the rabbit prostaglandin EP3 receptor. *Kidney Int.* 43:1372–78

71. Jakobsson PJ, Thoren S, Morgenstern R, Samuelsson B. 1999. Identification of human prostaglandin E synthase: a microsomal, glutathione-dependent, inducible enzyme, constituting a potential novel drug target. *Proc. Natl. Acad. Sci. USA* 96:7220–25

72. Schneider A, Guan Y, Davis L, Breyer M. 2000. Cloning, tissue distribution, and intra-renal localization of prostaglandin E synthase in rabbit. *J. Am. Soc. Nephrol.* In press

73. Baylis C, Deen W, Myers B, Brenner B. 1976. Effects of some vasodilator drugs on transcapillary fluid exchange in renal cortex. *Am. J. Physiol.* 230:1148–58

74. Silldorf E, Yang S, Pallone T. 1995. Prostaglandin E2 abrogates endothelin-induced vasoconstriction in renal outer medullary descending vasa recta of the rat. *J. Clin. Invest.* 95:2734–40

75. Breyer M, Badr K. 1996. *Arachidonic Acid Metabolites and the Kidney,* pp. 754–88. Philadelphia, PA: Saunders

76. Yared A, Kon V, Ichikawa I. 1985. Mechanism of preservation of glomerular perfusion and filtration during acute extracellular volume depletion: importance of intrarenal vasopressin-prostaglandin interaction for protecting kidneys from constrictor action of vasopressin. *J. Clin. Invest.* 75:1477–87

77. Ito S, Carretero OA, Abe K, Beierwaltes WH, Yoshinaga K. 1989. Effect of prostanoids on renin release from rabbit afferent arterioles with and without macula densa. *Kidney Int.* 35:1138–44

78. Jensen B, Schmid C, Kurtz A. 1996. Prostaglandins stimulate renin secretion and renin mRNA in mouse renal juxtaglomerular cells. *Am. J. Physiol. Renal Physiol.* 271:F659–F69

79. Hockel G, Cowley A. 1979. Prostaglandin E2-induced hypertension in conscious dogs. *Am. J. Physiol. Heart Circ. Physiol.* 237:H449–H54

80. Francisco L, Osborn J, Dibona G. 1982. Prostaglandins in renin release during sodium deprivation. *Am. J. Physiol. Renal Physiol.* 243:F537–F42

81. Stahl R, Dienemann H, Besserer K, Kneissler U, Helmchen U. 1981. Effect of indomethacin on blood pressure in rats with renovascular hypertension: dependence on plasma renin activity. *Klin. Wochenshcr.* 59:245–46

82. Inscho E, Carmines P, Navar L. 1990. Prostaglandin influences on afferent arteriolar responses to vasoconstrictor agonists. *Am. J. Physiol. Renal Physiol.* 259:F157–F63

83. Zhang Y, Guan Y, Scheider A, Brandon S, Breyer R, Breyer M. 2000. Characterization of murine vasopressor and vasodepressor prostaglandin E2 receptors. *Hypertension* 35:1129–34

84. Boie Y, Stocco R, Sawyer N, Slipetz DM, Ungrin MD, et al. 1997. Molecular cloning and characterization of the four rat

prostaglandin E2 prostanoid receptor subtypes. *Eur. J. Pharmacol.* 340:227–41

85. Schaefer M, Hofmann T, Schultz G, Gudermann T. 1998. A new prostaglandin E receptor mediates calcium influx and acrosome reaction in human spermatozoa. *Proc. Natl. Acad. Sci. USA* 95:3008–13

86. Toh H, Ichikawa A, Narumiya S. 1995. Molecular evolution of receptors for eicosanoids. *FEBS Lett.* 361:17–21

87. Sugimoto Y, Namba T, Shigemoto R, Negishi M, Ichikawa A, Narumiya S. 1994. Distinct cellular localization of mRNAs for three subtypes of prostaglandin E receptor in kidney. *Am. J. Physiol. Renal Physiol.* 266:F823–F28

88. Taniguchi S, Watanabe T, Nakao A, Seki G, Uwatoko S, Kurokawa K. 1994. Detection and quantitation of EP3 prostaglandin E2 receptor mRNA along mouse nephron segments by RT-PCR. *Am. J. Physiol. Cell Physiol.* 266:C1453–C58

89. Breyer R, Davis L, Nian C, Redha R, Stillman B, et al. 1996. Cloning and expression of the rabbit prostaglandin EP4 receptor. *Am. J. Physiol. Renal Physiol.* 270:F485–F93

90. Breyer M, Davis L, Jacobson H, Breyer R. 1996. Differential localization of prostaglandin E receptor subtypes in human kidney. *Am. J. Physiol. Renal Physiol.* 270:F912–F18

91. Watabe A, Sugimoto Y, Irie A, Namba T, Negishi M, et al. 1993. Cloning and expression of cDNA for a mouse EP1 subtype of prostaglandin E receptor. *J. Biol. Chem.* 268:20175–78

92. Båtshake B, Nilsson C, Sundelin J. 1995. Molecular characterization of the mouse prostanoid EP1 receptor gene. *Eur. J. Biochem.* 231:809–14

93. Hallinan E, Stapelfeld A, Savage M, Reichman M. 1994. 8-chlorodibenz[B,F] [1,4]oxazepine-10(11H)-carboxylic acid, 2-[3-2-(furanylmethyl) thio]-1-oxopropyl] hydrazide(SC51322): a potent PGE2 anta-

gonist and analgesic. *Bioorg. Med. Chem. Lett.* 4:509–14

94. Hallinan E, Hagen T, Jusa R, Tsymbalov S, Rao S, et al. 1993. N-substituted dibenzoxazepines as analgesic PGE2 antagonists. *J. Med. Chem.* 36:3293–99

95. Lanthorn T, Bianchi R, Perkins W. 1995. EP1 receptor antagonist blocks the diarrheagenic, but not cytoprotective, actions of a synthetic prostaglandin. *Drug Dev. Res.* 34:35–38

96. Okuda-Ashitaka E, Sakamoto K, Ezashi T, Miwa K, Ito S, Hayaishi O. 1996. Suppression of prostaglandin E receptor signaling by the variant form of EP1 subtype. *J. Biol. Chem.* 271:31255–61

97. Abramovitz M, Adam M, Boie Y, Grygorczyk R, Rushmore T, et al. 1995. Human prostanoid receptors: cloning and characterzation. *Adv. Prostaglandin Thromboxane Leukot. Res.* 23:499–504

98. Guan Y, Zhang Y, Breyer RM, Fowler B, Davis L, et al. 1998. Prostaglandin E2 inhibits renal collecting duct Na+ absorption by activating the EP1 receptor. *J. Clin. Invest.* 102:194–201

99. Båtshake B, Sundelin J. 1996. The mouse genes for the EP1 prostanoid receptor and the PKN protein kinase overlap. *Biochem. Biophys. Res. Commun.* 227:70–76

100. Hébert RL, Jacobson HR, Breyer MD. 1991. Prostaglandin E2 inhibits sodium transport in the rabbit CCD by raising intracellular calcium. *J. Clin. Invest.* 87:1992–98

101. Ishibashi R, Tanaka I, Kotani M, Muro S, Goto M, et al. 1999. Roles of prostaglandin E receptors in mesangial cells under high-glucose conditions. *Kidney Int.* 56:589–600

102. Audoly L, Kim H, Patrick J, Stock J, McNeish J, Coffman T. 1999. Mice lacking the prostaglandin E2 EP1 receptor subtype have hypotension, hyperreninemia and altered responses to angiotensin II. *FASEB J.* 13:A1549 (Abstr.)

103. Nishigaki N, Negishi M, Honda A,

Sugimoto Y, Namba T, et al. 1995. Identification of prostaglandin E receptor EP2 cloned from mastocytoma cells as EP4 subtype. *FEBS Lett.* 364:339–41

104. Guan Y, Breyer R, Zhang Y-H, Davis L, Redha R, et al. 1996. Cloning and functional expression of the rabbit prostaglandin EP2 receptor. *J. Am. Soc. Nephrol.* 7:1646 (Abstr.)

105. Katsuyama M, Nishigaki N, Sugimoto Y, Morimoto K, Negishi M, et al. 1995. The mouse prostaglandin E receptor EP2 subtype: cloning, expression, and northern blot analysis. *FEBS Lett.* 372:151–56

106. Regan JW, Bailey TJ, Pepperl DJ, Pierce KL, Bogardus AM, et al. 1994. Cloning of a novel human prostaglandin receptor with characteristics of the pharmacologically defined EP2 subtype. *Mol. Pharmacol.* 46:213–20

107. Nemoto K, Pilbeam CC, Bilak S, Raisz L. 1997. Molecular cloning and expression of the rat prostaglandin E2 receptor of the EP2 subtype. *Prostaglandins* 54:713–25

108. Bastien L, Sawyer N, Grygorczyk R, Metters K, Adam M. 1994. Cloning, functional expression, and characterization of the human prostaglandin E2 receptor EP2 subtype. *J. Biol. Chem.* 269:11873–77

109. Coleman RA, Grix SP, Head SA, Louttit JB, Mallett A, Sheldrick RLG. 1994. A novel inhibitory prostanoid receptor in piglet saphenous vein. *Prostaglandins* 47:151–68

110. Hizaki H, Segi E, Sugimoto Y, Hirose M, Saji T, et al. 1999. Abortive expansion of the cumulus and impaired fertility in mice lacking the prostaglandin E receptor subtype EP(2). *Proc. Natl. Acad. Sci. USA* 96:10501–6

111. Lim H, Dey SK. 1997. Prostaglandin E2 receptor subtype EP2 gene expression in the mouse uterus coincides with differentiation of the luminal epithelium for implantation. *Endocrinology* 138:4599–606

112. Kennedy C, Zhang Y, Brandon S, Guan S, Coffee K, et al. 1999. Hypertension and reduced fertility in mice lacking the prostaglandin EP2 receptor. *Nat. Med.* 5:217–20

113. Sheller JR, Mitchell D, Meyrick B, Oates J, Breyer R. 2000. EP(2) receptor mediates bronchodilation by PGE(2) in mice. *J. Appl. Physiol.* 88:2214–18

114. Regan JW, Bailey TJ, Donello JE, Pierce KL, Pepperl DJ, et al. 1994. Molecular cloning and expression of human EP3 receptors: evidence for three variants with different termini. *Br. J. Pharmacol.* 112:6163–69

115. Breyer RM, Emeson RB, Breyer MD, Abromson RM, Davis LS, Ferrenbach SM. 1994. Alternative splicing generates multiple isoforms of a rabbit prostaglandin E2 receptor. *J. Biol. Chem.* 298:6163–69

116. Schmid A, Thierauch KH, Schleuning WD, Dinter H. 1995. Splice variants of the human EP3 receptor for prostaglandin E2. *Eur. J. Biochem.* 228:23–30

117. Yang J, Xia M, Goetzl E, Songzhu A. 1994. Cloning and expression of the EP3-subtype of human receptors for prostaglandin E2. *Biochem. Biophys. Res. Commun.* 198:999–1006

118. Namba T, Sugimoto Y, Negishi M, Irie A, Ushikubi F, et al. 1993. Alternative splicing of C-terminal tail of prostaglandin E receptor subtype EP3 determines G-protein specificity. *Nature* 365:166–70

119. Irie A, Sugimoto Y, Namba T, Harazono A, Honda A, et al. 1993. Third isoform of the prostaglandin-E-receptor EP3 subtype with different C-terminal tail coupling to both stimulation and inhibition of adenylate cyclase. *Eur. J. Biochem.* 217:313–18

120. An S, Yang J, So S, Zeng L, Goetzl E. 1994. Isoforms of the EP3 subtype of human prostaglandin E2 receptor transduce both intracellular calcium and cAMP signals. *Biochemistry* 33:14496–502

121. Savage M, Moummi C, Karabatsos P, Lanthorn T. 1993. SC-46275: a potent

and highly selective agonist at the EP3 receptor. *Prostaglandins Leukot. Essent Fatty Acids* 49:939–43

122. Aoki J, Katoh H, Yasui H, Yamaguchi Y, Nakamura K, et al. 1999. Signal transduction pathway regulating prostaglandin EP3 receptor-induced neurite retraction: requirement for two different tyrosine kinases. *Biochem. J.* 340:365–69

123. Audoly L, Ma L, Feoktistov I, Breyer M, Breyer R. 1999. EP3 receptor activation of cAMP response element mediated gene transcription. *J. Pharmacol. Exp. Ther.* 289:140–48

124. Hasegawa H, Negishi M, Ichikawa A. 1996. Two isoforms of the prostaglandin E receptor EP3 subtype different in agonist-independent constitutive activity. *J. Biol. Chem.* 271:1857–60

125. Takeuchi K, Abe T, Takahashi N, Abe K. 1993. Molecular cloning and intrarenal localization of rat prostaglandin E2 receptor EP3 subtype. *Biochem. Biophys. Res. Commun.* 194:885–91

126. Grantham JJ, Burg MB. 1968. Effect of prostaglandin E1 on the permeability response of the isolated collecting tubule to vasopressin, adenosine 3'5'-monophosphate, and theophylline. *J. Clin. Invest.* 47:1154–61

127. Sonnenburg WK, Zhu J, Smith WL. 1990. A prostglandin E receptor coupled to a pertussis toxin-sensitive guanine nucleotide regulatory protein in rabbit cortical collecting tubule cells. *J. Biol. Chem.* 265:8479–83

128. Stokes JB. 1979. Effect of prostaglandin E2 on chloride transport across the rabbit thick ascending limb of Henle. *J. Clin. Invest.* 64:495–502

129. Good DW, George T. 1996. Regulation of HCO_3 absorption by prostaglandin E2 and G-proteins in rat medullary thick ascending limb. *Am. J. Physiol. Renal Physiol.* 270:F711–F17

130. Culpepper RM, Andreoli TE. 1983. Interactions among prostaglandin E2, an-

tidiuretic hormone and cyclic adenosine monophosphate in modulating Cl-absorption in single mouse medullary thick ascending limbs of Henle. *J. Clin. Invest.* 71:1588–601

131. Takaichi K, Kurokawa K. 1988. Inhibitory guanosine triphosphate-binding protein-mediated regulation of vasorpessin action in isolated single medullary tubules of mouse kidney. *J. Clin. Invest.* 82:1437–44

132. Nakao A, Allen ML, Sonnenburg WK, Smith WL. 1989. Regulation of cAMP metabolism by PGE2 in cortical and medullary thick ascending limb of Henle's loop. *Am. J. Physiol. Cell Physiol.* 256:C652–C57

133. Good D. 1996. PGE2 reverses AVP inhibition of HCO_3 absorption in rat MTAL by activation of protein kinase C. *Am. J. Physiol. Renal Physiol.* 270:F978–F85

134. Anderson RJ, Berl TB, McDonald KM, Schrier RW. 1975. Evidence for an in vivo antagonism between vasopressin and prostaglandins in the mammalian kidney. *J. Clin. Invest.* 56:420–26

135. Johnston HH, Herzog JP, Lauler DP. 1967. Effect of prostaglandin E on renal hemodynamics, sodium, and water excretion. *Am. J. Physiol.* 213:939–46

136. Sonnenburg WK, Smith WL. 1988. Regulation of cyclic AMP metabolism in rabbit cortical collecting tubule cells by prostaglandins. *J. Biol. Chem.* 263:6155–60

137. Hébert R, Jacobson H, Breyer M. 1990. PGE2 inhibits AVP induced water flow in cortical collecting ducts by protein kinase C activation. *Am. J. Physiol. Renal Physiol.* 259:F318–F25

138. Breyer M, Jacobson H, Breyer R. 1996. Functional and molecular aspects of renal prostaglandin receptors. *J. Am. Soc. Nephrol.* 7:8–17

139. Sakairi Y, Jacobson HR, Noland TD, Breyer MD. 1995. Luminal prostanglandin E receptors regulate salt and water

transport in rabbit cortical collecting duct. *Am. J. Physiol. Renal Physiol.* 269:F257–F65

140. Fleming E, Athirakul K, Oliverio M, Key M, Goulet J, et al. 1998. Urinary concentrating function in mice lacking the EP3 receptors for prostaglandin E2. *Am. J. Physiol. Renal Physiol.* 275:F955–F61

141. Ushikubi F, Segi E, Sugimoto Y, Murata T, Matsuoka T, et al. 1998. Impaired febrile response in mice lacking the prostaglandin E receptor subtype EP3. *Nature* 395:281–84

142. Audoly LP, Tilley SL, Goulet J, Key M, Nguyen M, et al. 1999. Identification of specific EP receptors responsible for the hemodynamic effects of PGE2. *Am. J. Physiol. Heart Circ. Physiol.* 277:H924–H30

143. An S, Yang J, Xia M, Goetzl EJ. 1993. Cloning and expression of the EP2 subtype of human receptors for prostaglandin E2. *Biochem. Biophys. Res. Commun.* 197:263–70

144. Honda A, Sugimoto Y, Namba T, Watanbe A, Irie A, et al. 1993. Cloning and expression of a cDNA for mouse prostaglandin E receptor EP2 subtype. *J. Biol. Chem.* 268:7759–62

145. Sando T, Usui T, Tanaka I, Mori K, Sasaki Y, et al. 1994. Molecular cloning and expression of rat prostaglandin E receptor EP2 subtype. *Biochem. Biophys. Res. Commun.* 200:1329–33

146. Segi E, Sugimoto Y, Yamasaki A, Aze Y, Oida H, et al. 1998. Patent ductus arteriosus and neonatal death in prostaglandin receptor EP4-deficient mice. *Biochem. Biophys. Res. Commun.* 246:7–12

147. Nguyen M, Camenisch T, Snouwaert J, Hicks E, Coffman T, et al. 1997. The prostaglandin receptor EP4 triggers remodelling of the cardiovascular system at birth. *Nature* 390:78–81

148. Audoly L, Goulet J, Key M, Nguyen M, Koller B, Coffman T. 1998. EP4 but not EP3 receptors mediate vasodilatory ac-

tions of PGE2. *J. Am. Soc. Nephrol.* 9:333 (Abstr.)

149. Csukas S, Hanke C, Rewolinski D, Campbell W. 1998. Prostaglandin E2-induced aldosterone release is mediated by an EP2 receptor. *Hypertension* 31:575–81

150. Jensen BL, Mann B, Skott O, Kurtz A. 1999. Differential regulation of renal prostaglandin receptor mRNAs by dietary salt intake in the rat. *Kidney Int.* 56:528–37

151. Schnermann J. 1998. Juxtaglomerular cell complex in the regulation of renal salt excretion. *Am. J. Physiol. Regulatory Integrative Comp. Physiol.* 274:R263–R79

152. Edwards RM. 1985. Effects of prostaglandins on vasoconstrictor action in isolated renal arterioles. *Am. J. Physiol. Renal Physiol.* 248:F779–F84

153. Harris RC, McKanna JA, Akai Y, Jacobson HR, Dubois R, Breyer MD. 1994. Cyclooxygenase-2 is associated with the macula densa of rat kidney and increases with salt restriction. *J. Clin. Invest.* 94:2504–10

154. Guan Y, Chang M, Cho W, Zhang Y, Redha R, et al. 1997. Cloning, expression, and regulation of rabbit cyclooxygenase-2 in renal medullary interstitial cells. *Am. J. Physiol. Renal Physiol.* 273:F18–F26

155. Baer PG, McGiff JC. 1979. Comparison of effects of prostaglandins E2 and I2 on rat renal vascular resistance. *Eur. J. Pharmacol.* 54:359–63

156. Ichihara A, Imig JD, Inscho EW, Navar LG. 1998. Cyclooxygenase-2 participates in tubular flow-dependent afferent arteriolar tone: interaction with neuronal NOS. *Am. J. Physiol. Renal Physiol.* 275:F605–F12

157. Chaudhari A, Gupta S, Kirschenbaum M. 1990. Biochemical evidence for PGI2 and PGE2 receptors in the rabbit renal preglomerular microvasculature. *Biochim. Biophys. Acta* 1053:156–61

158. Schnermann J, Weber P. 1982. Reversal of indomethacin-induced inhibition of

tubuloglomerular feedback by prostaglandin infusion. *Prostaglandins* 24:351–61

159. Gerber J, Olson R, Nies A. 1981. Interrelationship between prostaglandins and renin release. *Kidney Int.* 19:816–21

160. Lin L, Mistry M, Stier C, Nasjletti A. 1991. Role of prostanoids in renin-dependent and renin-independent hypertension. *Hypertension* 17:517–25

161. Tilley SL, Audoly LP, Hicks EH, Kim HS, Flannery PJ, et al. 1999. Reproductive failure and reduced blood pressure in mice lacking the EP2 prostaglandin E2 receptor. *J. Clin. Invest.* 103:1539–45

162. Hall J, Guyton A, Coleman T, Mizelle H, Woods L. 1986. Regulation of arterial pressure: role of pressure natriuresis and diuresis. *Fed. Proc.* 45:2897–903

163. Guyton A. 1991. Blood pressure control—special role of the kidneys and body fluids. *Science* 252:1813–16

164. Carmines P, Bell P, Roman R, Work J, Navar L. 1985. Prostaglandins in the sodium excretory response to altered renal arterial pressure in dogs. *Am. J. Physiol. Renal Physiol.* 248:F8–F14

165. Roman R, Lianos E. 1990. Influence of prostaglandins on papillary blood flow and pressure—natriuretic response. *Hypertension* 15:29–35

166. Pallone T. 1994. Vasoconstriction of outer medullary vasa recta by angiotensin II is modulated by prostaglandin E2. *Am. J. Physiol. Renal Physiol.* 266:F850–F57

167. Tone Y, Inoue H, Hara S, Yokoyama C, Hatae T, et al. 1997. The regional distribution and cellular localization of mRNA encoding rat prostacyclin synthase. *Eur. J. Cell. Biol.* 72:268–77

168. Murata T, Ushikubi F, Matsuoka T, Hirata M, Yamasaki A, et al. 1997. Altered pain perception and inflammatory response in mice lacking prostacyclin receptor. *Nature* 388:678–82

169. Hoeper MM, Schwarze M, Ehlerding S, Adler-Schuermeyer A, Spiekerkoetter E, et al. 2000. Long-term treatment of primary pulmonary hypertension with aerosolized iloprost, a prostacyclin analogue. *N. Engl. J. Med.* 342:1866–70

170. Tuder RM, Cool CD, Geraci MW, Wang J, Abman SH, et al. 1999. Prostacyclin synthase expression is decreased in lungs from patients with severe pulmonary hypertension. *Am. J. Respir. Crit. Care Med.* 159:1925–32

171. Namba T, Oida H, Sugimoto Y, Kakizuka A, Negishi M, et al. 1994. cDNA cloning of a mouse prostacyclin receptor: multiple signaling pathways and expression in thymic medulla. *J. Biol. Chem.* 269:9986–92

172. Boie Y, Rushmore TH, Darmon-Goodwin A, Grygorczyk R, Slipetz DM, et al. 1994. Cloning and expression of a cDNA for the human prostanoid IP receptor. *J. Biol. Chem.* 269:12173–78

173. Coleman RA, Kennedy I, Humphrey PPA, Bunce K, Lumley P. 1990. Prostanoids and their receptors. In *Comprehensive Medicinal Chemistry,* ed. JC Emmet, pp. 643–714. Oxford, UK: Pergamon

174. Oida H, Namba T, Sugimoto Y, Ushikubi F, Ohishi H, et al. 1995. In situ hybridization studies on prostacyclin receptor mRNA expression in various mouse organs. *Br. J. Pharmacol.* 116:2828–37

175. Bolger PM, Einser GM, Ramwell PW, Slotkoff LM, Corey EJ. 1978. Renal action of prostacyclin. *Nature* 271:467–69

176. Bugge JF, Stokke ES, Vikse A, Kiil F. 1990. Stimulation of renin release by PGE2 and PGI2 infusion in the dog: enhancing effect of ureteral occlusion or administration of ethacrynic acid. *Acta Physiol. Scand.* 138:193–201

177. Yahata K, Tanaka I, Mukoyama M, Kasahara M, Ishibashi R, et al. 1998. Blood pressure, renal function, salt handling and renin release in prostacyclin receptor knockout mice. *J. Am. Soc. Nephrol.* 9:417A (Abstr.)

178. Worton A, Misono K, Hollifield J, Frolich J, Inagami T, Oates J. 1977. Prostaglandins and renin release. I. Simulation of renin release from rabbit renal cortical slices by PGI2. *Prostaglandins* 14:1095–104

179. Hebert RL, O'Connor T, Neville C, Burns KD, Laneuville O, Peterson LN. 1998. Prostanoid signaling, localization, and expression of IP receptors in rat thick ascending limb cells. *Am. J. Physiol. Renal Physiol.* 275:F904–F14

180. Komhoff M, Lesener B, Nakao K, Seyberth HW, Nusing RM. 1998. Localization of the prostacyclin receptor in human kidney. *Kidney Int.* 54:1899–908

181. Veis JH, Dillingham MA, Berl T. 1990. Effects of prostacyclin on the cAMP system in cultured rat inner medullary collecting duct cells. *Am. J. Physiol. Renal Physiol.* 258:F1218–F23

182. Urade Y, Hayaishi O. 2000. Prostaglandin D synthase: structure and function. *Vitam. Horm.* 58:89–120

183. Hirata M, Kakuzuka A, Aizawa M, Ushikubi F, Narumiya S. 1994. Molecular characterization of a mouse prostaglandin D receptor and functional expression of the cloned gene. *Proc. Nat. Acad. Sci. USA* 91:11192–96

184. Boie Y, Sawyer N, Slipetz D, Metters K, Abramovitz M. 1995. Molecular cloning and characterization of the human prostanoid DP receptor. *J. Biol. Chem.* 270:18910–16

185. Leff P, Giles H. 1992. Classification of platelet and vascular prostaglandin D2 (DP) receptors: estimation of affinities and relative efficacies for a series of novel bicyclic ligands. *Br. J. Pharmacol.* 106:996–1003

186. Giles H, Leff P, Bolofo ML, Kelly MG, Robertson AD. 1989. The classification of prostaglandin DP-receptors in platelets and vasculature using BW A868C, a novel, selective and potent competitive antagonist. *Br. J. Pharmacol.* 96:291–300

187. Liu YJ, Jackson DM, Blackham A, Leff P. 1996. Partial agonist effects of BW A868C, a selective DP receptor antagonist, on Cl-secretion in dog tracheal epithelium. *Eur. J. Pharmacol.* 304:117–22

188. Oida H, Hirata M, Sugimoto Y, Ushikubi F, Ohishi H, et al. 1997. Expression of messenger RNA for the prostaglandin D receptor in the leptomeninges of the mouse brain. *FEBS Lett.* 417:53–56

189. Lewis RA, Soter NA, Diamond PT, Austen KF, Oates JA, Roberts LJ 2d. 1982. Prostaglandin D2 generation after activation of rat and human mast cells with anti-IgE. *J. Immunol.* 129:1627–31

190. Urade Y, Hayaishi O. 1999. Prostaglandin D2 and sleep regulation. *Biochim. Biophys. Acta* 1436:606–15

191. Eguchi N, Minami T, Shirafuji N, Kanaoka Y, Tanaka T, et al. 1999. Lack of tactile pain (allodynia) in lipocalin-type prostaglandin D synthase-deficient mice. *Proc. Natl. Acad. Sci. USA* 96:726–30

192. Sri Kantha S, Matsumura H, Kubo E, Kawase K, Takahata R, et al. 1994. Effects of prostaglandin D2, lipoxins and leukotrienes on sleep and brain temperature of rats. *Prostaglandins Leukot. Essent. Fatty Acids* 51:87–93

193. Matsuoka T, Hirata M, Tanaka H, Takahashi Y, Murata T, et al. 2000. Prostaglandin D(2) as a mediator of allergic asthma. *Science* 287:2013–17

194. Wright DH, Nantel F, Metters KM, Ford-Hutchinson AW. 1999. A novel biological role for prostaglandin D2 is suggested by distribution studies of the rat DP prostanoid receptor. *Eur. J. Pharmacol.* 377:101–15

195. Rao PS, Cavanagh D, Dietz JR, Marsden K, O'Brien WF, Spaziani E. 1987. Dose-dependent effects of prostaglandin D2 on hemodynamics renal function, and blood gas analyses. *Am. J. Obstet. Gynecol.* 156:843–51

Annu. Rev. Physiol. 2001. 63:607–30

NEPHROGENIC DIABETES INSIPIDUS

Jean-Pierre Morello[1] and Daniel G Bichet[2]

[1]Department of Biochemistry, Université de Montréal, Montreal, Quebec, Canada;
e-mail: morelloj@ere.umontreal.ca; [2]Department of Medicine, Université de Montréal
and Research Centre, Hôpital du Sacré-Coeur de Montréal, Montreal, Quebec, Canada;
e-mail: D-Binette@crhsc.umontreal.ca

Key Words *AVPR2* mutations, *AQP2* mutations, countercurrent system, misfolded
V_2 receptors, pharmacological chaperones

■ **Abstract** Nephrogenic diabetes insipidus, which can be inherited or acquired, is
characterized by an inability to concentrate urine despite normal or elevated plasma
concentrations of the antidiuretic hormone arginine vasopressin. Polyuria, with hypos-
thenuria, and polydipsia are the cardinal clinical manifestations of the disease. About
90% of patients with congenital nephrogenic diabetes insipidus are males with the
X-linked recessive form of the disease (OMIM 304800) who have mutations in the arginine vasopressin receptor 2 gene (*AVPR2*), which codes for the vasopressin V_2 receptor.
The gene is located in chromosomal region Xq28. In <10% of the families studied,
congenital nephrogenic diabetes insipidus has an autosomal-recessive or autosomal-
dominant (OMIM 222000 and 125800, respectively) mode of inheritance. Mutations
have been identified in the aquaporin-2 gene (*AQP2*), which is located in chromosome
region 12q13 and codes for the vasopressin-sensitive water channel. When studied in
vitro, most *AVPR2* mutations result in receptors that are trapped intracellularly and are
unable to reach the plasma membrane. A few mutant receptors reach the cell surface
but are unable to bind arginine vasopressin or to properly trigger an intracellular cyclic
AMP signal. Similarly, aquaporin-2 mutant proteins are misrouted and cannot be expressed at the luminal membrane. Chemical or pharmacological chaperones have been
found to reverse the intracellular retention of aquaporin-2 and arginine vasopressin receptor 2 mutant proteins. Because many hereditary diseases stem from the intracellular
retention of otherwise functional proteins, this mechanism may offer a new therapeutic
approach to the treatment of those diseases that result from errors in protein kinesis.

INTRODUCTION

Resistance to the action of almost every hormone is now recognized to cause human disease (1), and nephrogenic diabetes insipidus (NDI) is an example: It is the
nephrogenic failure to concentrate urine in response to the antidiuretic hormone.
The antidiuretic hormone in humans and most mammals is 8-arginine vasopressin
(AVP). NDI may be caused by a defect in the vasopressin-induced permeability
of the distal tubules and collecting ducts to water, an insufficient buildup of the

TABLE 1   Causes of nephrogenic diabetes insipidus

Narrow definition of NDI: water permeability of the collecting duct not increased by AVP
  Congenital (idiopathic)
  Hypercalcemia
  Hypokalemia
  Drugs
    Lithium
    Demeclocycline
    Amphotericin B
    Methoxyflurane
    Diphenylhydantoin
    Nicotine
    Alcohol
Broad definition of NDI: defective medullary countercurrent function
  Renal failure, acute or chronic (especially interstitial nephritis or obstruction)
  Medullary damage
    Sickle-cell anemia and trait
    Amyloidosis
    Sjögren syndrome
    Sarcoidosis
    Hypercalcemia
    Hypokalemia
    Protein malnutrition
    Cystinosis

Modified from 3, with permission.

corticopapillary interstitial osmotic gradient, or to a combination of these two factors (2). Thus the broadest definition of the term NDI embraces any antidiuretic-hormone-resistant urinary concentration defect, including medullary disease with low interstitial osmolality, renal failure, and osmotic diuresis. In its narrower sense, NDI describes only those conditions in which AVP release fails to induce the expected increase in the permeability of the cortical and medullary collecting ducts to water (3; Table 1).

URINE CONCENTRATION AND THE COUNTERCURRENT SYSTEM

Urine is not concentrated by active transport of water from tubule fluid to blood; such a system would require a tremendous expenditure of metabolic energy. It has been estimated that >300 times the energy needed by an active salt transport and passive water equilibration system would be required because salt concentrations are ~ 0.15 mmol/liter whereas water concentrations are ~ 55 mmol/liter. Instead, urine is concentrated with relatively little expenditure of metabolic energy by a complex interaction between the loops of Henle, the medullary interstitium, the medullary blood vessels or vasa recta, and the collecting tubules. This mechanism of urine concentration is called the countercurrent mechanism because of the anatomical arrangement of the tubules and vascular elements (Figure 1; Figure 2*A*, see color insert). Tubular fluids move from the cortex toward the papillary tip of the medulla via the proximal straight tubule and the thin descending limbs. The tubules then loop back toward the cortex so that the direction of the fluid movement is reversed in the ascending limbs. Similarly, the vasa recta descend to the tip of the papilla and then loop back toward the cortex. This arrangement of tubule segments and vasa recta allows the two fundamental processes of the countercurrent mechanism—countercurrent multiplication and countercurrent exchange—to take place (2, 4).

For the following descriptions, osmolality within the medulla is considered to range from 300 mOsmol/kg at the corticomedullary tip junction to 1400 mOsmol/kg at the papillary tip (Figure 1). In keeping with tissue analysis (5), approximately half the medullary hypertonicity is assigned to NaCl and half is assigned to urea. It is also assumed that secretion of the antidiuretic hormone, AVP, occurs and that this hormone will interact with specific receptors on the collecting tubule (see below).

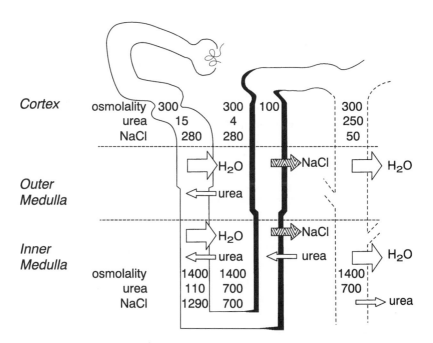

Figure 1 Schematic illustration of the model of Kokko & Rector for the renal concentrating mechanism. Heavy boundaries indicate very low permeability to water. Arrows indicate relative magnitudes of solute and water fluxes in the various segments. Note that active chloride transport in the thin ascending part of the loop of Henle is now demonstrated (14) (modified from 107 with permission).

The permeability and structural characteristics of the tubular and vascular segments responsible for the countercurrent mechanism are now described at a molecular level. The presence and abundance of the water channels of the aquaporin family seem to determine whether tubular or vascular structure is highly permeable or impermeable to water. Aquaporin-1 (AQP1), the first aquaporin to be characterized (6, 7), is present in both the apical and basolateral plasma membranes of proximal tubules, in thin descending limbs of Henle epithelia, and in descending vasa recta endothelia (8).

The facilitated urea transporter (UT2) is located in the last portion of descending thin limbs of short loops of Henle (9) (Figure 2, see color insert). Isotonic fluid entering the highly water-permeable (but urea- and Na^+-impermeable) descending thin limb is concentrated almost entirely by water abstraction, so that fluid entering the ascending limb has a higher NaCl concentration and a lower urea concentration than the medullary interstitium. These passive driving forces between the lumen and interstitium poise the system for fluid dilution (10).

Thin and thick ascending loops of Henle are highly impermeable to water because they bear no water channels. The urea transporter present in the thin ascending segment is not precisely characterized, but as fluid moves up the water-impermeable thin limb, NaCl efflux from the lumen to the interstitium exceeds passive urea influx from the interstitium to the tubular fluid, resulting in tubular fluid dilution. The recently characterized chloride channel CLC-K1 (11, 12) is critically involved in active chloride transport in the thin ascending part of the loops of Henle (13, 14; see below). This kidney-specific member of the CLC chloride channel family is found exclusively in the thin ascending limbs of loops of Henle in both the apical and basolateral membranes (12).

In the thick ascending limb, tubular fluid is diluted further by the active transport of NaCl from the tubule to the interstitium (Figure 3). The NaCl reabsorption mechanisms for the thick ascending loop of Henle and the distal convoluted tubule depend on low intracellular Na^+ activity that is maintained by active extrusion of Na^+ from the cell by the basolateral Na^+/K^+-ATPase (the Na^+ pump). K^+ entering the thick ascending loop of Henle by the Na-K-2Cl cotransporter (NKCC2) recycles back to the tubular urine through potassium channels (15) (Figure 3). This has two major consequences: It replenishes the urinary K^+ that would otherwise be lost through absorption by NKCC2, and it results in a lumen-positive transepithelial voltage that provides the driving force for paracellular transport of one half of the Na^+ reabsorbed (15). It is now recognized that loss-of-function mutations in the genes coding for the NKCC2, the apical K^+ channel, or the basolateral chloride channel are responsible for Bartter's syndrome (16–19) (Figure 3). Bartter's syndrome (OMIM 601678)[3] is a hereditary disease characterized by salt wasting, hypokalemic alkalosis, and deficits in diluting and concentrating capacity.

---

[3]Online Mendelian Inheritance in Man OMIM^{TM}. Center for medical genetics, Johns Hopkins University and National Center for Biotechnology Information, National Library of Medicine 1997. Http://www.ncbi.nlm.nih.gov/omim/.1998

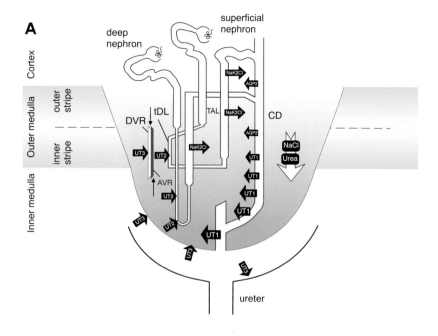

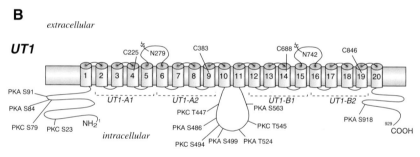

See legend next page

See figure previous page

Figure 2 (*A*) Schematic representation of urea transporters in the rat kidney. A superficial nephron with a short loop and a deep nephron with a long loop of Henle are represented. Urea transporter *UT1* is present in the apical membrane of the terminal inner medullary collecting duct and is involved in vasopressin-regulated urea reabsorption. *UT2* is located in the late part of descending thin limbs of short loops and participates in urea recycling. In the inner stripe of the outer medulla, vascular structures of ascending vasa recta (*AVR*), descending vasa recta (*DVR*), and tubule components of thin descending limb *tDL*) are arranged together to form vascular bundles. *UT3* is present in descending vasa recta and allows efficient countercurrent exchange between ascending vasa recta and descending vasa recta as well as between descending vasa recta and thin descending limbs. The vertical arrow on the right-hand side of the figure indicates the corticopapillary osmolality gradient, which is primarily formed by NaCl and urea. TAL, thick ascending limb; CD, collecting duct. [Modified from Tsukaguchi et al (9) with permission.] (*B*) Hypothetical structural model and hydropathy analysis of *UT1*, the vasopressin-regulated urea channel. *UT1* cDNA encodes a 929–amino-acid protein consisting of two similar halves, each composed of two extended hydrophobic membrane-spanning stretches (UT1A and UT1B). In addition, each half of UT1 can be further subdivided into two homologous hydrophobic domains (UT1-A1/UT1-A2 and UT1-B1/UT1-B2). UT1 has 12 potential phosphorylation sites, 7 for protein kinase A (PKA) and 5 for protein kinase C (PKC). Although there is no significant homology between water channels and urea transporters, the urea transporter repeats UT1-A1, UT1-A2, UT1-B1, and UT1-B2 contain a similar motif, Asn-Pro-Leu/Trp. This motif could conceivably form part of the urea translocation pathway. [Modified from Shayakul et al (34) with permission.]

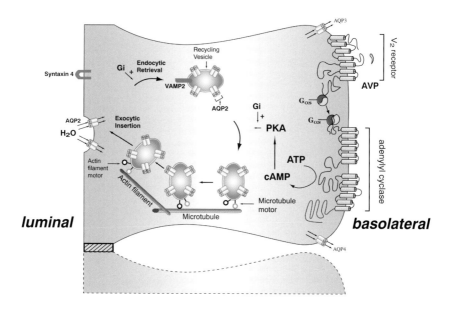

Figure 4 Schematic representation of the effect of *AVP* that increases the permeability of the principal cells of the collecting duct to water. Arginine vasopressin *(AVP)* is bound to the V_2 receptor (a G protein—linked receptor) on the basolateral membrane. The basic process of G protein—coupled receptor signaling consists of three steps: A heptahelical receptor detects a ligand (in this case, AVP) in the extracellular milieu, a G protein dissociates into α subunits bound to GTP and βγ subunits after interaction with the ligand-bound receptor, and an effector (in this case, adenylyl cyclase) interacts with dissociated G protein subunits to generate small-molecule second messengers. AVP activates adenylyl cyclase, thereby increasing the intracellular concentration of cyclic AMP *(cAMP)*. Adenylyl cyclase is characterized by two tandem repeats of six hydrophobic transmembrane domains separated by a large cytoplasmic loop, and it terminates in a large intracellular tail. Generation of cAMP follows receptor-linked activation of the heteromeric G protein (G_s) and interaction of the free $G_{\alpha s}$ chain with the adenylyl cyclase catalyst. Protein kinase A (PKA) is the target of the generated cAMP. Cytoplasmic vesicles carrying the water channel proteins (represented as homotetrameric complexes) are fused to the luminal membrane in response to AVP, thereby increasing the permeability of this membrane to water. Microtubules and actin filaments are necessary for vesicle movement toward the membrane. The mechanisms underlying docking and fusion of aquaporin-2 *(AQP2)*-bearing vesicles are not known. The detection of the small GTP-binding protein Rab3a, synaptobrevin 2, and syntaxin 4 in principal cells suggests that these proteins are involved in *AQP2* trafficking (24). When AVP is not available, water channels are retrieved by an endocytic process and water permeativity returns to its original low rate. Aquaporin-3 *(AQP3)* and aquaporin-4 *(AQP4)* water channels are expressed on the basolateral membrane.

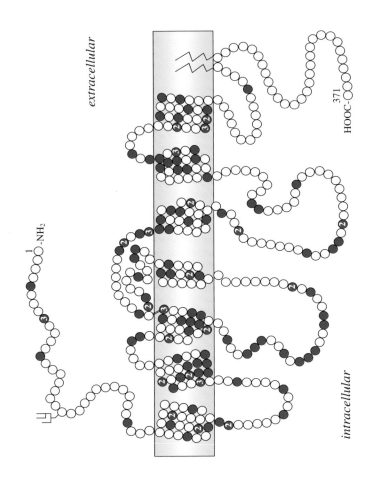

Figure 7 Schematic representation of the V$_2$ receptor and identification of 155 putative disease-causing *AVPR2* mutations. For a figure including the numbering of individual amino acids, please contact author at d-binette@crhsc.umontreal.ca. A solid circle indicates the location of (or the closest codon to) a mutation; a number indicates more than one mutation in the same codon. The names of the mutations were assigned according to recommended nomenclature (108). The extracellular (E), transmembrane (TM), and cytoplasmic (C) domains are defined according to Mouillac et al (109). The common names of the mutations are listed by type. The 78 missense mutations are as follows: L43P, L44F, L44P, L53R, N55D, N55H, L59P, L62P, H80R, L81F, L83P, L83Q, A84D, D85N, V88L, V88M, Q92R, L94Q, P95L, W99R, R106C, G107E, C112R, R113W, G122R, M123K, S126F, S127F, Y128S, A132D, L135P, R137H, [C142W: R143G], R143P, A147V, W164S, S167L, S167T, Q174L, R181C, G185C, D191G, G201D, R202C, T204N, Y205C, V206D, T207N, I209F, F214S, P217T, L219P, L219R, M272K, V277A, Y280C, A285P, P286L, P286R, P286S, L289P, L292P, A294P, L309P, S315R (AGC > AGA), S315R (AGC > AGG), N317K, C319R, N321D, N321K, N321Y, P322H, P322S, W323R, and W323S. The 17 nonsense mutations are as follows: W71X, Q119X, Y124X, W164X, S167X, Q180X, W193X (TGG > TAG), W193X (TGG > TGA), Q225X, E231X, E242X, W284X, W293X, W296X, L312X, W323X, and R337X. The 42 frameshift mutations are as follows: in E$_I$, 15delC, 27—54del, 46-47delCT, 54-55ins28, and 102delG; in TMI, 137-138delTA; in C$_I$, 185—219del, 206-207insG, and [225delC; 223C > A]; in TM$_{II}$, 247-248ins7, 268-269delCT, and 295delT; in TM$_{III}$, 331-332delCT, 335-336delGT, 340delG, and 407—446del; in C$_{II}$, 418delG, 430—442del, 442-443insG, 452delG, 457—463del, and 460delG; in E$_{III}$, 567-568insC, 572—575del, 612-613insC, and 614-615delAT; in TM$_V$, 631delC; in C$_{III}$, 682-683insC, 692delA, 717delG, 727-728delAG, 738delG, 738delA, 784delG, and 785-786insT; in TM$_{VI}$, 838-839insT, 847—851del, and 851-852ins5; and in TM$_{VII}$, 907delG, 930delC, and 969delG. The six in-frame deletions or insertions are as follows: in C$_I$, 185—193del; in TM$_{II}$, 252-253ins9; in TM$_{III}$, Y128del; in TM$_{IV}$, F176del; in E$_{III}$, R202del; and in TM$_{VI}$, V279del. The three splice site mutations are as follows: IVS2-1delG, IVS2-1G > A, and IVS2-2A > G (52, 55, 56, 58, 65—67, 110—136). Eight large deletions and one complex mutation are not shown (52, 58, 65, 126, 130).

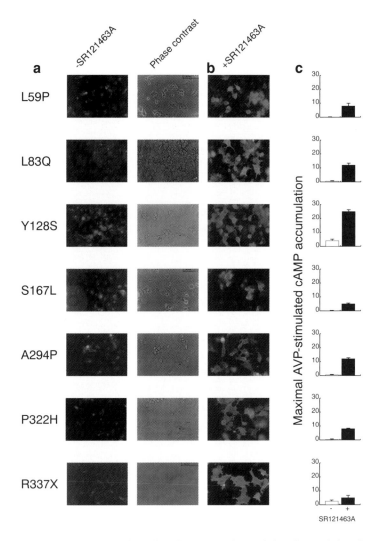

Figure 8 SR121463A increases the cell surface expression and signaling activity of several distinct nephrogenic diabetes insipidus (NDI) V$_2$ receptor mutants. (*a*) COS-1 cells transiently transfected with plasmids encoding the indicated Myc-tagged mutant V$_2$ receptors were visualized by whole-cell immunofluorescence and phase-contrast microscopy. All mutant receptors were found to be poorly expressed at the cell surface. (*b*) Treatment with 10^{-5} M SR121463A for 16 h led to appearance of these receptor mutants on the cell surface as assessed by fluorescence microscopy. Bar = 50 mm. (*c*) Effects of a 16-h pretreatment with 10^{-5} M SR121463A on vasopressin-stimulated cyclic AMP (cAMP) accumulation in COS-1 cells expressing the various mutants. The position and nature of the amino acid replacement in each NDI-causing mutation is indicated by the single-letter amino acid code. *X* indicates a stop codon. Data represent results from three separate experiments. [Reprinted from Morello et al (92) with permission].

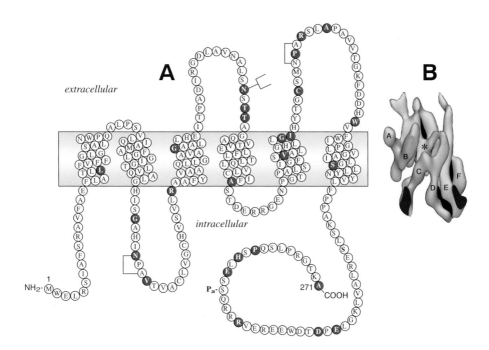

Figure 9 (*A*) Schematic representation of the aquaporin-2 (AQP2) protein and identification of 26 putative disease-causing *AQP2* mutations. A monomer with six transmembrane helices is represented. The location of the protein kinase A phosphorylation site (P_a) is indicated. This site is possibly involved in the arginine vasopressin-induced trafficking of AQP2 from intracellular vesicles to the plasma membrane and in the subsequent stimulation of endocytosis (22, 23). The extracellular (E), transmembrane (TM), and cytoplasmic (C) domains are defined according to Deen et al (98). As in Figure 7, solid circles indicate the locations of the mutations. See author at d-binette@crhsc.umontreal.ca for figure including numbering of individual amino acids. The common names of the mutations are listed by domain as follows: in TM_I, L22V; in C_{II}, G64R, N68S, V71M, and R85X; in TM_{III}, G100X; in E_{II}, 369delC, T125M, and T126M; in TM_{IV}, A147T; in TM_V, V168M, G175R, and IVS2-1G > A; in E_{III}, C181W, P185A, R187C, A190T, and W202C; in TM_{VI}, S216P; and in C_{IV}, 721delG, 727delG, 756—765del, E258K, 779-780insA, P262L, and 812—816del (98, 102, 105, 127, 132, 137—141). (*B*) Representation of the six-helix barrel of the AQP1 protein viewed parallel to the bilayer. [Modified from Cheng et al (142) with permission.]

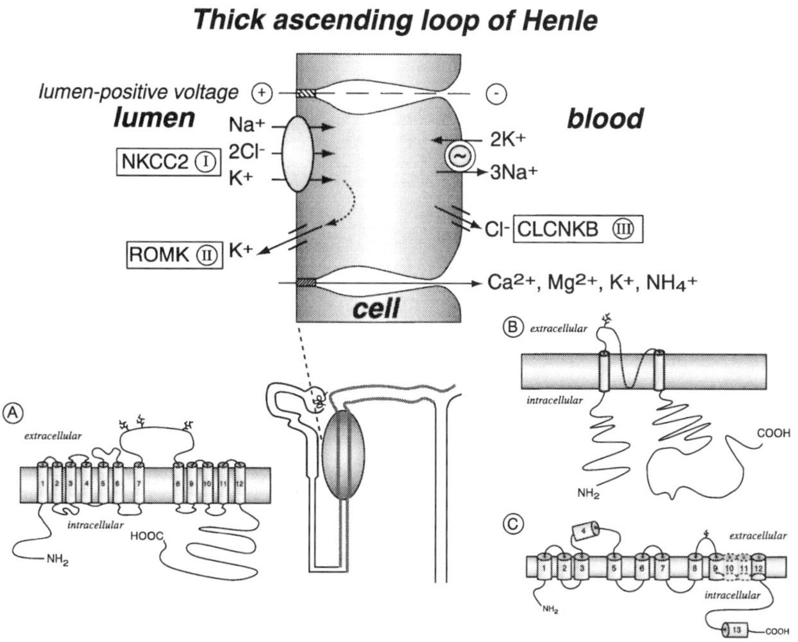

Thick ascending loop of Henle

Figure 3 Polyuric-polydipsic symptoms are frequently observed in patients with Bartter's syndrome, which is secondary to loss-of-function mutations in three genes. Mutations in the bumetamide-sensitive Na-K-2Cl gene (*NKCC2*) cause type I Bartter's syndrome (16). *NKCC2* is expressed exclusively in apical membranes of thick ascending limb cells. (*A*) NKCC2 is a large protein with a core molecular mass of ~120 kDa, and its topology includes a large hydrophobic central region with at least 12 membrane-spanning helices. Sugar residues are linked to an extracellular loop between the seventh and eighth membrane-spanning segments, making this cotransporter a glycoprotein and increasing its apparent molecular mass on Western blots to 150–165 kDa. (*B*) Mutations in the gene that encodes the inwardly rectifying renal potassium channel, *ROMK*, cause type II Bartter's syndrome (17, 18). (*C*) Mutations in the gene that encodes the renal chloride channel, *CLCNKB*, cause type III Bartter's syndrome (19).

In the collecting duct, the first step in the antidiuretic action of AVP is its binding to the vasopressin V_2 receptor (Figure 4, see color insert), located on the basolateral membrane of collecting duct cells. This step initiates a cascade of events—receptor-linked activation of the cholera toxin-sensitive G protein (G_s), activation of adenylyl cyclase, production of cyclic AMP (cAMP), and stimulation of protein kinase A (PKA)—that lead to the final step in the antidiuretic action of AVP. That is, the exocytic insertion of specific water channels, AQP2, into the luminal membrane results in increased permeability of the luminal membrane. AQP2 is the vasopressin-regulated water channel in renal collecting ducts. It is exclusively present in the principal cells of inner medullary collecting duct cells and is diffusely distributed in the cytoplasm in the euhydrated condition, whereas apical staining of AQP2 is intensified in the dehydrated condition or after administration of 1-desamino[8-D-arginine]vasopressin (dDAVP), a synthetic structural analog of AVP. The short-term regulation of AQP2 by AVP involves the movement of AQP2 from intracellular vesicles to the plasma membrane, a confirmation of the shuttle hypothesis of AVP action that was proposed two decades ago (20). In long-term regulation, which requires a sustained elevation of circulating AVP levels for 24 h or more, AVP increases the abundance of water channels, which is thought to be a consequence of increased transcription of the *AQP2* gene (21). The activation of PKA leads to phosphorylation of AQP2 on serine residue 256 in the cytoplasmic carboxyl terminus. This phosphorylation step is essential for the regulated movement of AQP2-containing vesicles to the plasma membrane upon elevation of the intracellular cAMP concentration (22, 23). A second G protein (the first being the cholera-toxin-sensitive G protein; G_s) is also essential for the AVP-induced shuttling of AQP2. This G protein is sensitive to pertussis toxin and is involved in the pathway downstream of the cAMP/cAMP-dependent protein kinase signal (24). The molecular basis for the translocation of the AQP2-containing vesicles is known, but it is thought to be analogous to neuronal exocytosis (25). This is supported by the identification of various proteins known to be involved in regulated exocytosis—for example, Rab3a and synaptobrevin II (VAMP2) or synaptobrevin II-like protein—in the vesicles (26–28). In contrast to neuronal exocytosis, which is triggered by Ca^{2+}, cAMP and PKA appear to be crucial for the translocation process (29, 30). Vesicle trafficking probably involves the interaction of AQP2-containing vesicles with the cytoskeleton (31) (Figure 4). Drugs that disrupt microtubules or actin filaments have long been known to inhibit the hormonally induced permeability response in target epithelia (32). More recently, Sabolic and coworkers (33) have shown that microtubules are required for the apical polarization of AQP2 in principal cells. AQP3 and AQP4 are the constitutive water channels in the basolateral membranes of renal medullary collecting ducts.

AVP also increases the water reabsorption capacity of the kidney by regulating the urea transporter UT1 (Figure 2), which is present in the inner medullary collecting duct, predominantly in its terminal portion (34) (Figure 5). AVP also increases the permeability of principal collecting duct cells to sodium (35).

In summary, as stated by Ward et al (35), in the absence of AVP stimulation, collecting duct epithelia exhibit very low permeabilities to sodium, urea, and water. The low permeabilities of sodium, urea, and water permit the excretion of large volumes of hypotonic urine formed during intervals of water diuresis. In contrast, AVP stimulation of the principal cells of the collecting ducts leads to selective increases in the permeability of the apical membrane to water (P_f), urea (P_{urea}), and sodium (P_{Na}).

These actions of vasopressin in the distal nephron are possibly modulated by prostaglandin E_2 and by the luminal calcium concentration. High levels of E-prostanoid (EP_3) receptors are expressed in the kidney (36). However, mice lacking EP_3 receptors for prostaglandin E_2 were found to have quasinormal regulation of urine volume and osmolality in response to various physiological stimuli (36). An apical calcium/polycation receptor protein expressed in the terminal portion of

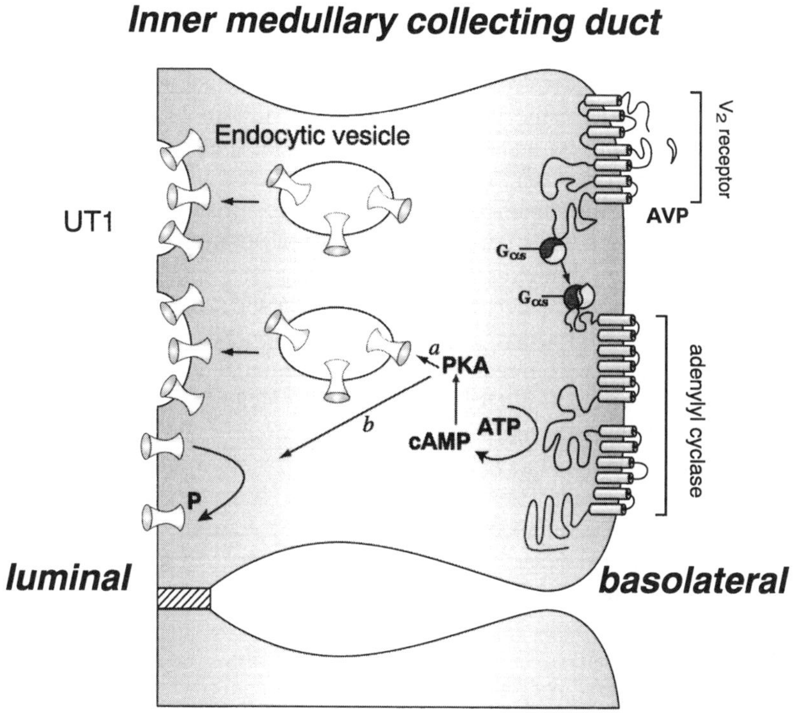

Inner medullary collecting duct

Figure 5 Potential mechanisms of urea transporter (UT1) activation by arginine vasopressin (AVP) in the inner medullary collecting duct. AVP binds to the V_2 receptor in the basolateral membrane. This results in the activation of the $G_{\alpha s}$ subunit, activation of adenylyl cyclase, production of cAMP, and stimulation of PKA. Two potential mechanisms for UT1 activation by PKA are indicated: (*a*) by increasing the insertion of vesicles containing the urea transporter and (*b*) by direct phosphorylation of urea transporter molecules. Current experimental evidence suggests that the latter mechanism is mainly involved in UT1 activation (modified from 9, with permission).

the inner medullary collecting duct of the rat has been shown to reduce AVP-elicited osmotic water permeability of the collecting duct when the luminal calcium concentration rises (37). This possible link between calcium and water metabolism may play a role in the pathogenesis of renal stone formation (37).

Knockout Mice with Urinary Concentration Defects

A useful strategy to establish the physiological function of a protein is to determine the phenotype produced by pharmacological inhibition of protein function or by gene disruption. Transgenic knockout mice individually deficient in AQP1, AQP3, and AQP4 (except AQP3 and AQP4 together) or in CLCNK1, NKCC2, or AVPR2 have been engineered (14, 38–43). To date, descriptions of knockout mice with inactivated *Aqp2* have not been published.

Aqp1 knockout mice were found to be normal in terms of survival, physical appearance, and organ morphology. However, they became severely dehydrated and lethargic after water deprivation for 36 h. Body weight decreased by 35% ± 2% (Figure 6), serum osmolality increased to ∼500 mOsmol/kg (a value not compatible with life in humans), and urinary osmolality (657 ± 59 mOsmol/kg) did not change from that before water deprivation (39) (Figure 6). In the *Aqp1* knockout mice, a decrease in the superficial glomerular filtration rate was responsible for a normal distal flow despite decreased proximal reabsorption (44). This decrease in the single-nephron glomerular filtration rate was most probably caused by activation of a tubuloglomerular feedback mechanism. That the urinary flow rate was increased despite normal distal delivery suggests that the diuresis seen in *Aqp1* knockout mice results primarily from reduced fluid absorption in the collecting duct. This defect is secondary to a low interstitium medullary tonicity as suggested more recently by Chou et al (40). Freeze-fracture electron microscopy of rat thin descending limb of Henle demonstrated an exceptionally high density of intramembranous particles that may represent tetramers of AQP1 (45). A striking decrease in the density of these intramembranous particles was observed in the thin descending limb of Henle of *Aqp1*-deficient mice (40). In isolated perfused segments of thin descending limb of Henle of wild-type mice, transepithelial osmotic permeability to water (P_f) was very high; it was reduced 8.5-fold in the *Aqp1* knockout mice. These results demonstrate that osmotic equilibration along the thin descending limb of Henle by water transport plays a key role in the renal concentrating mechanism. By contrast, inactivation of *Aqp4* (38) has little or no effect on development, survival, and growth and causes only a small defect in urinary concentration ability (46), consistent with *AQP4* expression in the medullary collecting duct. The relatively mild defect in urine concentration ability in the *Aqp4* knockout mice suggests that another water channel (e.g. AQP3) may be more critical than AQP4 for the

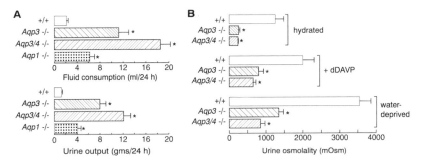

Figure 6 Urine-concentrating function in *Aqp3* single-knockout and *Aqp3 Aqp4* double-knockout mice. (*A*) Fluid consumption (*upper panel*) and urine output (*lower panel*) over 24 h in mice of indicated genotype (error bars indicate SEM; $n = 16$ mice per genotype]. (*B*) Urine osmolalities measured while mice were given free access to food and water before and after administration of 1-desamino[8-D-arginine]vasopressin (dDAVP) and after a 36-h water deprivation (error bars indicate SEM; $n = 12$ mice per genotype). $P < 0.005$ compared with wild-type mouse (modified from 41, with permission).

formation of concentrated urine. The *Aqp3*-null mice exhibited normal perinatal survival and postnatal growth but were remarkably polyuric and polydipsic (Figure 6). After dDAVP administration or water deprivation, the *Aqp3*-null mice were able to concentrate their urine partially, to ~30% of that of wild-type mice. *Aqp3 Aqp4* double-knockout mice had greater impairment of urine concentration ability than did the *Aqp3* single-knockout mice (41) (Figure 6). These findings establish the existence of a form of NDI caused by the impaired permeability of collecting duct basolateral membranes to water.

The *Aqp1* knockout mouse has no human counterpart, as demonstrated by the fact that *AQP1*-null individuals have no obvious symptoms (47). Three women bearing loss-of-function mutations of *AQP1* were identified by the presence of high titers of circulating antibodies to the Colton blood group that apparently developed during pregnancy. Linkage between the Colton blood group and *AQP1* was demonstrated (48), and subsequent sequencing of DNA samples from individuals with defined Colton phenotypes demonstrated that the Colton antigen results from a missense mutation at residue 45 of the first extracellular loop of *AQP1* (49). Members of five kindreds were found to totally lack the Colton antigen. Blood and urine specimens were obtained from three probands of three different kindreds, and DNA analysis confirmed that each was homozygous for a different *AQP1* mutation (47). Two Colton-null individuals had no detectable AQP1 in erythrocytes or renal sediment: The first was homozygous for deletion of the entire exon 1, whereas the second was homozygous for a frameshift mutation after glycine residue 104. A third Colton-null individual was homozygous for the missense mutation *P38L* at the top of the first bilayer-spanning domain. This mutation resulted in unstable AQP1 protein when expressed in oocytes and corresponded to a 99% reduction in AQP1 in erythrocytes (47). The reasons for the difference between *Aqp1* knockout mice and AQP1-null humans are unknown.

When dehydrated, *Clcnk-1* knockout ($Clcnk^{-/-}$) mice were also lethargic; they exhibited a 27% decrease in body weight, compared with the 13% decrease seen in wild-type mice (14). Serum osmolality increased 360 to 381 osmol/kg in $Clcnk^{-/-}$ mice, compared with 311–323 osmol/kg in heterozygous ($Clcnk^{+/-}$) and wild-type ($Clcnk^{+/+}$) mice, and urinary osmolality was minimally increased after dDAVP administration (636 ± 31 mOsmol/kg preadministration versus 828 ± 25 mOsmol/kg postadministration).

The absence of the gene coding for NKCC2 in the luminal membrane of the thick ascending loop of Henle in the mouse also caused polyuria that was not compensated elsewhere in the nephron and recapitulated many features of the human classical Bartter's syndrome (42). The absence of transcellular NaCl transport via NKCC2 probably abolished the positive transepithelial voltage in the lumen that enables paracellular reabsorption of Na and K across the wall of the thick ascending tubule. The combined absence of transcellular and paracellular transport of NaCl across the thick ascending limb cells prevents the establishment of the normal osmotic gradient necessary for urine concentration.

Yun et al (43) introduced the *E242X* nonsense mutation into the mouse vasopressin V_2 receptor coding sequence and generated vasopressin receptor-deficient male pups that exhibited decreased urinary osmolality, failure to thrive, and death within the first week after birth as a result of hypernatremic dehydration.

CLINICAL ASPECTS OF X-LINKED NEPHROGENIC DIABETES INSIPIDUS

X-linked NDI (OMIM 304800) is secondary to *AVPR2* mutations that result in the loss of function or a dysregulation of the V_2 receptor. The *AVPR2* gene has three exons and two small introns (50, 51). The cDNA sequence predicts a polypeptide with seven transmembrane, four extracellular, and four cytoplasmic domains that belongs to the family of G protein–coupled receptors (Figure 7, see color insert).

Rareness and Diversity of *AVPR2* Mutations

We estimated the incidence of X-linked NDI in the general population from persons born in the Canadian province of Quebec during 1988–1997 to be ~8.8 per million (standard deviation = 4.4 per million) male live births (52). Thus X-linked NDI is generally a rare disorder. On the other hand, NDI is known to be a common disorder in Nova Scotia (53). Thirty affected males, who at the time of the study resided mainly in two small villages with a combined population of 2500 (54), are descendants of members of the Hopewell pedigree studied by Bode & Crawford (53) and carry the nonsense mutation W71X (55, 56). This is the largest known pedigree with X-linked NDI and has been referred to as the Hopewell kindred, named after the Irish ship Hopewell, which arrived in Halifax in 1761 (53). Descendants of Scottish Presbyterians who migrated to Ireland's Ulster Province in the 17th century emigrated from Ireland in 1718 and settled in northern Massachusetts. A later group of immigrants were passengers on the ship Hopewell and settled in Colchester County, Nova Scotia. Members of the two groups were subsequently united in Colchester County (53). Thus it is likely that Ulster Scottish immigrants, perhaps on more than one occasion, brought the W71X mutation to North America. To date, we have identified the W71X mutation in 38 affected males, who predominantly reside in the Maritime Provinces of Nova Scotia and New Brunswick. We estimated the incidence in these two Maritime Provinces to be 6 in 104,063, or ~58 per million (standard deviation = 24 per million) male live births for the 10-year period 1988–1997.

To date, 155 putative disease-causing AVPR2 mutations have been identified in 239 NDI families (57) (additional information is available in the NDI Mutation Database at http://www.medcor.mcgill.ca/~nephros/). Of these, we identified 82 different mutations in 117 NDI families referred to our laboratory. Half of the mutations are missense mutations. Frameshift mutations caused by nucleotide deletions or insertions (27%), nonsense mutations (11%), large deletions (5%), in-frame deletions or insertions (4%), splice site mutations (2%), and one complex mutation account for the remainder of the mutations. Mutations have been identified in every domain, but on a per nucleotide basis about twice as many mutations occur in transmembrane domains as occur in the extracellular or intracellular domains. We previously identified single mutations (identified only once), recurrent mutations, and mechanisms of mutagenesis (58, 59). The 10 recurrent mutations (D85N, V88M, R113W, Y128S, R137H, S167L, R181C, R202C, A294P, and S315R) were found in 35 ancestrally independent families (52). The occurrence of the same mutation on different haplotypes was considered evidence of recurrent mutation. In addition, the most frequent mutations—D85N, V88N, R113W, R137H, S167L, R181C, and R202C—occurred at potential mutational hot spots [a C-to-T or G-to-A nucleotide substitution occurred at a CpG (2-bp sequence) dinucleotide].

Benefits of Genetic Testing

The natural history of untreated X-linked NDI includes hypernatremia, hyperthermia, mental retardation, and repeated episodes of dehydration in early infancy (60–63). Mental retardation, a consequence of repeated episodes of dehydration, was prevalent in the Crawford & Bode study (63), in which only 9 of 82 patients (11%) had normal intelligence. Early recognition and treatment of X-linked NDI, with an abundant intake of water, allows a normal life span with normal physical and mental development (64). Familial occurrence in males and mental retardation in untreated patients are two characteristics suggestive of X-linked NDI. Skewed X inactivation is the most likely explanation for clinical symptoms of NDI in female carriers (52, 65, 66).

The identification of the molecular defect underlying X-linked NDI is of immediate clinical significance because early diagnosis and treatment of affected infants can prevent the physical and mental retardation resulting from repeated episodes of dehydration. Diagnosis of X-linked NDI was accomplished by mutation testing of chorionic villus samples ($n = 4$), cultured amniotic cells ($n = 5$), or cord blood ($n = 17$). Three infants whose mutation testing was done on amniotic cells ($n = 1$) or chorionic villus samples ($n = 2$) also had their diagnoses confirmed by cord blood testing. Of the 23 offspring tested, 12 were found to be affected males, 7 were unaffected males, and 4 were noncarrier females (DG Bichet, unpublished data). The affected males were immediately treated with abundant water intake, a low-sodium diet, and hydrochlorothiazide. They have not experienced severe episodes of dehydration, and their physical and mental development remain normal; however, their urinary output is decreased by only 30%, and a normal growth curve is still difficult to attain during the first 2–3 years of life despite the above-described treatments and intensive attention. Water should be offered every 2 h day and night, and temperature, appetite, and growth should be monitored. Hospitalization for continuous gastric feeding may be necessary. The voluminous amounts of water kept in patients' stomachs will exacerbate physiological gastrointestinal reflux in infants and toddlers, and many affected boys frequently vomit and have a strong positive Tuttle test (esophageal pH test). These young patients often improve with the absorption of a H-2 (histamine-2 receptor) blocker and with metoclopramide (which may induce extrapyramidal symptoms) or with domperidone, which is better tolerated and efficacious.

DEFECTIVE INTRACELLULAR TRANSPORT AND RESCUE OF MUTANT V_2 RECEPTORS

Most Mutant V_2 Receptors Are Not Transported to the Cell Membrane and Are Retained in the Intracellular Compartments

The classification of the defects of mutant V_2 receptors is based on that of the low-density lipoprotein receptor, for which mutations have been grouped according to the function and subcellular localization of the mutant protein whose cDNA has been transiently transfected in a heterologous expression system (67, 68). In this classification system, type 1 mutant receptors reach the cell surface but display impaired ligand binding and are consequently unable to induce normal cAMP production. The presence of mutant V_2 receptors on the surface of transfected cells can be determined pharmacologically. By carrying out saturation-binding experiments using a tritiated AVP, the number and apparent binding affinity of cell surface mutant receptors can be compared with those of the wild-type receptor. In addition, the presence of cell surface receptors can be assessed directly by using immunodetection strategies to visualize epitope-tagged receptors in whole-cell immunofluorescence assays.

Type 2 mutant receptors have defective intracellular transport. This phenotype is confirmed by carrying out, in parallel, immunofluorescence experiments on cells that are intact (to demonstrate the absence of cell surface receptors) or permeabilized (to confirm the presence of intracellular receptor pools). In addition, protein expression is confirmed by Western blot analysis of membrane preparations from transfected cells. It is likely that these mutant type 2 receptors accumulate in a pre-Golgi compartment because they are initially glycosylated but fail to undergo glycosyl-trimming maturation. This is readily detected by performing pulse-chase metabolic-labeling studies and comparing the receptor maturation profiles of wild-type and mutant receptors. All complex N-linked glycosylated proteins undergo addition of a large high-mannose sugar moiety in the endoplasmic reticulum (ER) that is progressively processed by the glycosyl enzymes of the Golgi complex. This large addition and processing can be readily detected as a mobility shift of the protein in sodium dodecyl sulfate-polyacrylamide gel electrophoresis (SDS-PAGE). Asglycosylated proteins are processed past the medial Golgi complex, they are no longer sensitive to endoglycosidase H and are considered mature proteins. Metabolically labeled wild-type V_2 receptors acquire endoglycosidase H resistance, whereas mutant type 2 receptors do not, which confirms that these receptor species are being retained in a pre-Golgi compartment. The vast majority of naturally occurring mutations in the V_2 receptor that cause NDI are type 2 mutations (see below).

Type 3 mutant receptors are ineffectively transcribed. This subgroup seems to be rare because Northern blot analysis of transfected cells reveals that most V_2 receptor mutations do not affect the quantity or molecular size of the receptor mRNA.

Of the 12 mutants that we tested (N55H, L59P, L83Q, V88M, 497CC→GG, ΔR202, I209F, 700delC, 908insT, A294P, P322H, and P322S) only 3 (ΔR202, P322S, and P322H) were detected on the cell surface. Similarly, the 10 mutant receptors (Y128S, E242X, 803insG, 834delA, ΔV278, Y280C, W284X, L292P, W293X, and L312Y) tested by Schöneberg et al (69, 70) did not reach the cell membrane and were trapped in the interior of the cell. Similar results were obtained for the following mutants: L44F, L44P, W164S, S167L, and S167T (71); R143P and ΔV278 (72); and Y280C, L292P, and R333X (73).

Other genetic disorders are also characterized by protein misfolding. AQP-2 mutations responsible for autosomal-recessive NDI are characterized by misrouting of the misfolded mutant proteins and entrapment in the ER (74). The ΔF508 mutation in persons with cystic fibrosis is also characterized by misfolding and retention in the ER of the mutated cystic fibrosis transmembrane conductance regulator, which is associated with calnexin and Hsp70 (for a review see 75). The C282Y mutant HFE protein, which is responsible for 83% of hemochromatosis in the Caucasian population, is retained in the ER and middle Golgi compartment, fails to undergo late Golgi processing, and is subject to accelerated degradation (76). Other mutant renal membrane proteins, responsible for Gitelman's syndrome (77) and cystinuria (78), are also retained in the ER.

Missense mutations responsible for these various diseases are often situated in regions of the protein that are not part of the active site, the binding site, or the site of interaction with other proteins. These mutations decrease the half-life of the affected protein (79). Missense mutations and short in-frame deletions or insertions that impair the propensity of the affected polypeptide to fold into its functional conformation have led to the coining of the term conformational diseases (80). The NDI missense mutations are likely to impair folding and lead to rapid degradation of the affected polypeptide rather than to accumulation of toxic aggregates because the other important functions of the principal cells of the collecting duct (where V_2 receptors are expressed) are entirely normal. These cells express the epithelial Na channel. A decrease in function of this channel will result in a state of Na loss (81). This has not been observed in patients with *AVPR2* mutations.

In Vitro Adenovirus-Mediated Gene Transfer Experiments Have Been Successful for a Limited Number of Mutations

Schöneberg et al (69, 70) genetically rescued truncated or missense V_2 receptors by coexpression of a polypeptide consisting of the last 130 amino acids of the V_2 receptor in COS-7 cells. Four of the six truncated receptors (E242X, 804delG, 834delA, and W284X) and the missense mutant Y280C regained considerable functional activity, as demonstrated by an increase in the number of binding sites and stimulation of adenylyl cyclase activity, but the absolute number of expressed receptors at the cell surface remained low, and the precise mechanism of the rescue phenomenon (dimerization?) (82) was unclear. Most of the loss-of-function mutations secondary to *AVPR2* missense mutations are unlikely to be improved by this coexpression strategy, and delivery of the gene transfer vehicle is a major unresolved problem.

Nonpeptide Vasopressin Antagonists Act as Pharmacological Chaperones to Functionally Rescue Misfolded Mutant V_2 Receptors Responsible for X-Linked NDI

Several orally active nonpeptide AVP receptor antagonists have been reported (83, 84), and one, SR121463, is a potent and selective V_2 receptor antagonist (85). This extremely stable molecule is highly selective for V_2 receptors from several species, including humans, and exhibits powerful intravenous and oral aquaretic effects (85). SR121463 inhibits AVP-evoked cAMP formation in human kidney membranes and reverses extrarenal V_2 receptor antagonism of dDAVP-induced release of hemostatic factors in dogs (86). VPA-985 is a similar aquaretic compound (84). From a therapeutic point of view, V_2 receptor-specific antagonists able to block the action of AVP at the level of the renal collecting duct specifically promote water excretion.

As described above, a number of genetic diseases with the common property of producing intracellular, misfolded proteins that are recognized and retained by the cell's quality control system have been identified. Although the activities of the quality control system of the cell are generally advantageous to the cell, this stringent monitoring system can lead to intracellular retention and, ultimately, destruction of otherwise-salvageable proteins. Recently, members of a class of compounds called chemical chaperones were shown to reverse the intracellular retention of a number of misfolded proteins (74, 87–93). Among these, glycerol and other polyols have been reported to stabilize protein conformations (94), increase the rate of in vitro protein refolding (95), and increase the kinetics of oligomeric assembly (96). Such compounds likely facilitate the folding of mutant proteins into conformations that resemble the wild-type protein, allowing them to escape the quality control system.

Taking the concept of chemical chaperones a step farther, Loo & Clarke (91) characterized functional mutations of the multidrug resistance 1 gene that codes for the P glycoprotein transporter, which interacts with a variety of cytotoxic agents. Artificial mutations in this gene led to intracellular, misfolded proteins. Surprisingly, P glycoprotein synthesis and folding in the presence of specific substrates or modulators that bind this transporter resulted in a considerable increase in correctly folded, functionally active protein.

We recently assessed whether these selective V_2 vasopressin receptor antagonists could facilitate the folding of mutant proteins that are responsible for NDI and are retained in the ER. We monitored the biosynthesis of mutant V_2 receptors in the presence of SR121463 and VPA-985. These cell-permeant antagonists were able to convert precursor forms of mutant V_2 receptor into fully glycosylated mature receptor proteins that were now targeted to the cell surface, as determined by pulse-chase analysis and cell surface immunofluorescence microscopy. Once at their correct cellular location, these receptors were able to bind AVP and produce an intracellular cAMP response that was 15 times higher than that produced in cells not exposed to these antagonists (92) (Figure 8, see color insert). This effect could not be mediated by nor competed with V_2 receptor antagonists that are membrane impermeant, indicating that SR121463A was mediating its effects intracellularly.

On the basis of these data, we propose a model in which small nonpeptide V_2 receptor antagonists permeate into the cell and bind to incompletely folded mutant receptors. This would then stabilize a conformation of the receptor that allows its release from the ER quality control apparatus. The stabilized receptor would then be targeted to the cell surface, where upon dissociation from the antagonist it could bind vasopressin and promote signal transduction. Given that these antagonists are specific to the V_2 receptor and that they perform a chaperone-like function, we termed these compounds pharmacological chaperones (92, 97).

AQP2 GENE AND MUTANTS

The human *AQP2* gene is located in chromosome region 12q13 and has four exons and three introns (98–100). It is predicted to code for a polypeptide of 271 amino acids that is organized into two repeats, oriented at 180° to each other, and has six transmembrane, three extracellular, and four cytoplasmic domains. AQP2 is a member of the major intrinsic protein family of transmembrane channel proteins and has the characteristic NPA motifs at residues 68–70 and 184–186 (10) (Figure 9, see color insert). AQP1 and, by analogy, AQP2 are homotetramers containing four independent water channels. To date, 26 putative disease-causing *AQP2* mutations have been identified in 25 NDI families (Figure 9). By type of mutation, there are 65% missense mutations, 23% frameshift mutations caused by small nucleotide deletions or insertions, 8% nonsense mutations, and 4% splice site mutations. Additional information is available in the NDI Mutation Database at http://www.medcor.mcgill.ca/~nephros/.

Reminiscent of expression studies done with AVPR2 proteins, misrouting of AQP2 mutant proteins is the major cause underlying autosomal-recessive NDI (74, 101, 102). To determine if the severe AQP2 trafficking defect observed with the naturally occurring mutations T126M, R187C, and A147T is correctable, Chinese hamster ovary and Madin-Darby canine kidney cells were incubated with the chemical chaperone glycerol for 48 h. Using immunofluorescence microscopy, redistribution of AQP2 from the ER to the plasma membrane-endosome fractions was observed. This redistribution was correlated with improved water permeativity measurements (74, 103). It will be important to correct this defective AQP2 trafficking in vivo.

In contrast to the *AQP2* mutations seen in persons with autosomal-recessive NDI, which are located throughout the gene, the dominant mutations are predicted to affect the carboxyl terminus of AQP2 (104). One dominant mutation, *E258K*, has been analyzed in detail in vitro; AQP2-E258K had reduced water permeativity compared with wild-type AQP2 (105). In addition, AQP2-E258K was retained in the Golgi apparatus; this differs from the mutant *AQP2* seen in cases of recessive NDI, which is retained in the ER. The dominant action of *AQP2* mutations can be explained by the formation of heterotetramers of mutant and wild-type *AQP2* that are impaired in their routing after oligomerization (105, 106).

CONCLUSIONS

The deconstruction of congenital NDI allowed further characterization of key proteins involved in the countercurrent system. Clinically, greater awareness of the disease is leading to earlier diagnosis, and mutational analysis has revealed the diversity of *AVPR2* mutations. Functional studies underscore the frequent occurrence of misfolded mutant receptor proteins trapped in the ER and unable to reach the plasma membrane. The large number of different mutations, with varying functional defects, hinders the development of a specific therapy. However, pharmacological chaperones such as vasopressin receptor antagonists might constitute a general strategy to rescue a large number of different misfolded mutant V_2 receptors.

ACKNOWLEDGMENTS

JP Morello held a studentship from the Heart and Stroke Foundation of Canada and holds an MRC/PMAC Health Program Studentship. The authors' work cited in this chapter was supported by the Medical Research Council of Canada, the Canadian Kidney Foundation, and la Fondation J Rodolphe-La Haye. DG Bichet is a chercheur de carrière of le Fonds de Recherche en Santé du Québec. We thank Danielle Binette for graphical and secretarial expertise.

Visit the Annual Reviews home page at www.AnnualReviews.org

LITERATURE CITED

1. Wilson JD. 2000. Endocrinology: survival as a discipline in the 21st century? *Annu. Rev. Physiol.* 62:947–50
2. Valtin H, Schafer JA. 1995. Concentration and dilution of urine: H_2O balance. In *Renal Function*, ed. H Valtin, JA Schafer, pp. 151–82. Boston, MA: Little, Brown. 3rd ed.
3. Magner PO, Halperin ML. 1987. Polyuria—a pathophysiological approach. *Med. North Am.* 15:2987–97
4. Jamison RL, Oliver RE. 1982. Disorders of urinary concentration and dilution. *Am. J. Med.* 72:308–22
5. Valtin H. 1966. Sequestration of urea and

nonurea solutes in renal tissues of rats with hereditary hypothalamic diabetes insipidus: effect of vasopressin and dehydration on the countercurrent mechanism. *J. Clin. Invest.* 45:337

6. Agre P, Preston GM, Smith BL, Jung JS, Raina S, et al. 1993. Aquaporin CHIP: the archetypal molecular water channel. *Am. J. Physiol. Renal Physiol.* 34:F463–F76

7. Lee MD, King LS, Agre P. 1997. The aquaporin family of water channel proteins in clinical medicine. *Medicine* 76:141–56

8. Nielsen S, Smith BL, Christensen EI, Knepper MA, Agre P. 1993. CHIP28 water channels are localized in constitutively water-permeable segments of the nephron. *J. Cell Biol.* 120:371–83

9. Tsukaguchi H, Shayakul C, Berger UV, Hediger MA. 1998. Urea transporters in kidney: molecular analysis and contribution to the urinary concentrating process. *Am. J. Physiol. Renal Physiol.* 275:F319–F24

10. Reeves WB, Bichet DG, Andreoli TE. 1998. Posterior pituitary and water metabolism. In *Williams Textbook of Endocrinology*, ed. JD Wilson, DW Foster, H Kronenberg, PR Larsen, pp. 341–87. Philadelphia, PA: Saunders. 9th ed.

11. Uchida S, Sasaki S, Furukawa T, Hiraoka M, Imai T, et al. 1993. Molecular cloning of a chloride channel that is regulated by dehydration and expressed predominantly in kidney medulla. *J. Biol. Chem.* 268:3821–24. Erratum. 1994. *J. Biol. Chem.* 269(29):19192

12. Uchida S, Sasaki S, Nitta K, Uchida K, Horita S, et al. 1995. Localization and functional characterization of rat kidney-specific chloride channel, ClC-K1. *J. Clin. Invest.* 95:104–13

13. Kere J. 1999. Kidney kinetics and chloride ion pumps. *Nat. Genet.* 21:67–68

14. Matsumura Y, Uchida S, Kondo Y, Miyazaki H, Ko SB, et al. 1999. Overt nephrogenic diabetes insipidus in mice

lacking the CLC-K1 chloride channel. *Nat. Genet.* 21:95–98

15. Hebert SC. 1998. Roles of Na-K-2Cl and Na-Cl cotransporters and ROMK potassium channels in urinary concentrating mechanism. *Am. J. Physiol. Renal Physiol.* 275:F325–F27

16. Simon DB, Karet FE, Hamdan JM, DiPietro A, Sanjad SA, et al. 1996. Bartter's syndrome, hypokalaemic alkalosis with hypercalciuria, is caused by mutations in the Na-K-2Cl cotransporter NKCC2. *Nat. Genet.* 13:183–88

17. Simon DB, Karet FE, Rodriguez-Soriano J, Hamdan JH, DiPietro A, et al. 1996. Genetic heterogeneity of Bartter's syndrome revealed by mutations in the K^+ channel, ROMK. *Nat. Genet.* 14:152–56

18. Karolyil L, Konrad M, Kockerling A, Ziegler A, Zimmerman DK, et al. 1997. Mutations in the gene encoding the inwardly rectifying renal potassium channel, ROMK, cause the antenatal variant of Bartter syndrome: evidence for genetic heterogeneity. International collaborative study group for Bartter-like syndromes. *Hum. Mol. Genet.* 6:17–26. Erratum. 1997. *Hum. Mol. Genet.* 6(4):650

19. Simon DB, Bindra RS, Mansfield TA, Nelson-Williams C, Mendonca E, et al. 1997. Mutations in the chloride channel gene, CLCNKB, cause Bartter's syndrome type III. *Nat. Genet.* 17:171–78

20. Wade JB, Stetson DL, Lewis SA. 1981. ADH action: evidence for a membrane shuttle mechanism. *Ann. NY Acad. Sci.* 372:106–17

21. Knepper MA. 1997. Molecular physiology of urinary concentrating mechanism: regulation of aquaporin water channels by vasopressin. *Am. J. Physiol. Renal Physiol.* 272:F3–F12

22. Fushimi K, Sasaki S, Marumo F. 1997. Phosphorylation of serine 256 is required for cAMP-dependent regulatory exocytosis of the aquaporin-2 water channel. *J. Biol. Chem.* 272:14800–4

23. Katsura T, Gustafson C, Ausiello D, Brown D. 1997. Protein kinase A phosphorylation is involved in regulated exocytosis of aquaporin-2 in transfected LLC-PK1 cells. *Am. J. Physiol. Renal Physiol.* 272:F817–F22

24. Valenti G, Procino G, Liebenhoff U, Frigeri A, Benedetti PA, et al. 1998. A heterotrimeric G protein of the Gi family is required for cAMP-triggered trafficking of aquaporin 2 in kidney epithelial cells. *J. Biol. Chem.* 273:22627–34

25. Mandon B, Nielsen S, Kishore BK, Knepper MA. 1997. Expression of syntaxins in rat kidney. *Am. J. Physiol. Renal Physiol.* 273:F718–F30

26. Jo I, Harris HW, Amendt-Raduege AM, Majewski RR, Hammond TG. 1995. Rat kidney papilla contains abundant synaptobrevin protein that participates in the fusion of antidiuretic hormone-regulated water channel-containing endosomes in vitro. *Proc. Natl. Acad. Sci. USA* 92:1876–80

27. Liebenhoff U, Rosenthal W. 1995. Identification of Rab3-, Rab5a- and synaptobrevin II-like proteins in a preparation of rat kidney vesicles containing the vasopressin-regulated water channel. *FEBS Lett.* 365:209–13

28. Nielsen S, Marples D, Birn H, Mohtashami M, Dalby NO, et al. 1995. Expression of VAMP-2-like protein in kidney collecting duct intracellular vesicles: colocalization with aquaporin-2 water channels. *J. Clin. Invest.* 96:1834–44

29. Star RA, Nonoguchi H, Balaban R, Knepper MA. 1988. Calcium and cyclic adenosine monophosphate as second messengers for vasopressin in the rat inner medullary collecting duct. *J. Clin. Invest.* 81:1879–88

30. Snyder HM, Noland TD, Breyer MD. 1992. cAMP-dependent protein kinase mediates hydrosmotic effect of vasopressin in collecting duct. *Am. J. Physiol. Cell Physiol.* 263:C147–C53

31. Brown D, Katsura T, Gustafson CE. 1998. Cellular mechanisms of aquaporin trafficking. *Am. J. Physiol. Renal Physiol.* 275:F328–F31

32. Taylor A, Mamelak M, Reaven E, Maffly R. 1973. Vasopressin: possible role of microtubules and microfilaments in its action. *Science* 181:347–50

33. Sabolic I, Katsura T, Verbabatz JM, Brown D. 1995. The AQP2 water channel: effect of vasopressin treatment, microtubule disruption, and distribution in neonatal rats. *J. Membr. Biol.* 143:165–77

34. Shayakul C, Steel A, Hediger MA. 1996. Molecular cloning and characterization of the vasopressin-regulated urea transporter of rat kidney collecting ducts. *J. Clin. Invest.* 98:2580–87

35. Ward DT, Hammond TG, Harris HW. 1999. Modulation of vasopressin-elicited water transport by trafficking of aquaporin 2-containing vesicles. *Annu. Rev. Physiol.* 61:683–97

36. Fleming EF, Athirakul K, Oliverio MI, Key M, Goulet J, et al. 1998. Urinary concentrating function in mice lacking EP3 receptors for prostaglandin E2. *Am. J. Physiol. Renal Physiol.* 275:F955–F61

37. Sands JM, Naruse M, Baum M, Jo I, Hebert SC, et al. 1997. Apical extracellular calcium/polyvalent cation-sensing receptor regulates vasopressin-elicited water permeability in rat kidney inner medullary collecting duct. *J. Clin. Invest.* 99:1399–405

38. Ma T, Yang B, Gillespie A, Carlson EJ, Epstein CJ, et al. 1997. Generation and phenotype of a transgenic knockout mouse lacking the mercurial-insensitive water channel aquaporin-4. *J. Clin. Invest.* 100:957–62

39. Ma T, Yang B, Gillespie A, Carlson EJ, Epstein CJ, et al. 1998. Severely impaired urinary concentrating ability in transgenic mice lacking aquaporin-1 water channels. *J. Biol. Chem.* 273:4296–99

40. Chou C-L, Knepper MA, van Hoek AN, Brown D, Yang B, et al. 1999. Reduced water permeability and altered ultrastructure in thin descending limb of Henle

in aquaporin-1 null mice. *J. Clin. Invest.* 103:491–96

41. Ma T, Song Y, Yang B, Gillespie A, Carlson EJ, et al. 2000. Nephrogenic diabetes insipidus in mice lacking aquaporin-3 water channels. *Proc. Natl. Acad. Sci. USA* 97:4386–91

42. Takahashi N, Chernavvsky DR, Gomez RA, Igarashi P, Gitelman HJ, et al. 2000. Uncompensated polyuria in a mouse model of Bartter's syndrome. *Proc. Natl. Acad. Sci. USA* 97:5434–39

43. Yun J, Erlenbach I, Kostenis E, Schmidt C, Zhu X, et al. 2000. V2 vasopressin receptor function studied in mice and yeast. *Proc. Nephrogenic Diabetes Insipidus Conf., La Jolla,* p. 25. Eastsound, WA: NDI Found.

44. Schnermann J, Chou CL, Ma T, Traynor T, Knepper MA, et al. 1998. Defective proximal tubular fluid reabsorption in transgenic aquaporin-1 null mice. *Proc. Natl. Acad. Sci. USA* 95:9660–64

45. Verbavatz JM, Brown D, Sabolic I, Valenti G, Ausiello DA, et al. 1993. Tetrameric assembly of CHIP28 water channels in liposomes and cell membranes: a freeze-fracture study. *J. Cell Biol.* 123:605–18

46. Chou CL, Ma T, Yang B, Knepper MA, Verkman AS. 1998. Fourfold reduction of water permeability in inner medullary collecting duct of aquaporin-4 knockout mice. *Am. J. Physiol. Cell Physiol.* 274:C549–C54

47. Preston GM, Smith BL, Zeidel ML, Moulds JJ, Agre P. 1994. Mutations in aquaporin-1 in phenotypically normal humans without functional CHIP water channels. *Science* 265:1585–87

48. Zelinski T, Kaita H, Gilson T, Coghlan G, Philipps S, et al. 1990. Linkage between the Colton blood group locus and ASSP11 on chromosome 7. *Genomics* 6:623–25

49. Smith BL, Preston GM, Spring FA, Anstee DJ, Agre P. 1994. Human red cell aquaporin CHIP. I. Molecular characterization of ABH and Colton blood group antigens. *J. Clin. Invest.* 94:1043–49

50. Birnbaumer M, Seibold A, Gilbert S, Ishido M, Barberis C, et al. 1992. Molecular cloning of the receptor for human antidiuretic hormone. *Nature* 357:333–35

51. Seibold A, Brabet P, Rosenthal W, Birnbaumer M. 1992. Structure and chromosomal localization of the human antidiuretic hormone receptor gene. *Am. J. Hum. Genet.* 51:1078–83

52. Arthus M-F, Lonergan M, Crumley MJ, Naumova AK, Morin D, et al. 2000. Report of 33 novel *AVPR2* mutations and analysis of 117 families with X-linked nephrogenic diabetes insipidus. *J. Am. Soc. Nephrol.* 11:1044–54

53. Bode HH, Crawford JD. 1969. Nephrogenic diabetes insipidus in North America: the Hopewell hypothesis. *N. Engl. J. Med.* 280:750–54

54. Bichet DG, Hendy GN, Lonergan M, Arthus M-F, Ligier S, et al. 1992. X-linked nephrogenic diabetes insipidus: from the ship Hopewell to restriction fragment length polymorphism studies. *Am. J. Hum. Genet.* 51:1089–102

55. Bichet DG, Arthus M-F, Lonergan M, Hendy GN, Paradis AJ, et al. 1993. X-linked nephrogenic diabetes insipidus mutations in North America and the Hopewell hypothesis. *J. Clin. Invest.* 92:1262–68

56. Holtzman EJ, Kolakowski LF, O'Brien D, Crawford JD, Ausiello DA. 1993. A null mutation in the vasopressin V2 receptor gene (AVPR2) associated with nephrogenic diabetes insipidus in the Hopewell kindred. *Hum. Mol. Genet.* 2:1201–4

57. Bichet DG, Fujiwara TM. 2000. Nephrogenic diabetes insipidus. In *The Metabolic and Molecular Bases of Inherited Disease,* ed. CR Scriver, AL Beaudet, WS Sly, D Vallee, B Childs, B Vogelstein. New York: McGraw-Hill. 8th ed. In press

58. Bichet DG, Birnbaumer M, Lonergan M, Arthus M-F, Rosenthal W, et al. 1994. Nature and recurrence of AVPR2 mutations in X-linked nephrogenic diabetes insipidus. *Am. J. Hum. Genet.* 55:278–86

59. Fujiwara TM, Morgan K, Bichet DG. 1996. Molecular analysis of X-linked nephrogenic diabetes insipidus. *Eur. J. Endocrinol.* 134:675–77

60. Forssman H. 1942. On the mode of hereditary transmission in diabetes insipidus. *Nord. Med.* 16:3211–13

61. Waring AG, Kajdi L, Tappan V. 1945. Congenital defect of water metabolism. *Am. J. Dis. Child.* 69:323–25

62. Williams RM, Henry C. 1947. Nephrogenic diabetes insipidus transmitted by females and appearing during infancy in males. *Ann. Intern. Med.* 27:84–95

63. Crawford JD, Bode HH. 1975. Disorders of the posterior pituitary in children. In *Endocrine and Genetic Diseases of Childhood and Adolescence*, ed. LI Gardner, pp. 126–58. Philadelphia, PA: Saunders. 2nd ed.

64. Niaudet P, Dechaux M, Trivin C, Loirat C, Broyer M. 1984. Nephrogenic diabetes insipidus: clinical and pathophysiological aspects. *Adv. Nephrol. Necker Hosp.* 13:247–60

65. van Lieburg AF, Verdijk MAJ, Schoute F, Ligtenberg MJL, van Oost BA, et al. 1995. Clinical phenotype of nephrogenic diabetes insipidus in females heterozygous for a vasopressin type 2 receptor mutation. *Hum. Genet.* 96:70–78

66. Nomura Y, Onigata K, Nagashima T, Yutani S, Mochizuki H, et al. 1997. Detection of skewed X-inactivation in two female carriers of vasopressin type 2 receptor gene mutation. *J. Clin. Endocrinol. Metab.* 82:3434–37

67. Ala Y, Morin D, Mouillac B, Sabatier N, Vargas R, et al. 1998. Functional studies of twelve mutant V2 vasopressin receptors related to nephrogenic diabetes insipidus: molecular basis of a mild clinical phenotype. *J. Am. Soc. Nephrol.* 9:1861–72

68. Hobbs HH, Russell DW, Brown MS, Goldstein JL. 1990. The LDL receptor locus in familial hypercholesterolemia: mutational analysis of a membrane protein. *Annu. Rev. Genet.* 24:133–70

69. Schöneberg T, Yun J, Wenkert D, Wess J. 1996. Functional rescue of mutant V2 vasopressin receptors causing nephrogenic diabetes insipidus by a coexpressed receptor polypeptide. *EMBO J.* 15:1283–91

70. Schöneberg T, Sandig V, Wess J, Gudermann T, Schultz G. 1997. Reconstitution of mutant V2 vasopressin receptors by adenovirus-mediated gene transfer. *J. Clin. Invest.* 100:1547–56

71. Oksche A, Schulein R, Rutz C, Liebenhoff U, Dickson J, et al. 1996. Vasopressin V2 receptor mutants that cause X-linked nephrogenic diabetes insipidus: analysis of expression, processing, and function. *Mol. Pharmacol.* 50:820–28

72. Tsukaguchi H, Matsubara H, Taketani S, Mori Y, Seido T, et al. 1995. Binding, intracellular transport, and biosynthesis-defective mutants of vasopressin type 2 receptor in patients with X-linked nephrogenic diabetes insipidus. *J. Clin. Invest.* 96:2043–50

73. Wenkert D, Schoneberg T, Merendino JJ Jr, Rodriguez Pena MS, Vinitsky R, et al. 1996. Functional characterization of five V2 vasopressin receptor gene mutations. *Mol. Cell. Endocrinol.* 124:43–50

74. Tamarappoo BK, Verkman AS. 1998. Defective aquaporin-2 trafficking in nephrogenic diabetes insipidus and correction by chemical chaperones. *J. Clin. Invest.* 101:2257–67

75. Kuznetsov G, Nigam SK. 1998. Folding of secretory and membrane proteins. *N. Engl. J. Med.* 339:1688–95

76. Waheed A, Parkkila S, Zhou XY, Tomatsu S, Tsuchihashi Z, et al. 1997. Hereditary hemochromatosis: effects of C282Y and H63D mutations on association with beta2-microglobulin, intracellular processing, and cell surface expression of the HFE protein in COS-7 cells. *Proc. Natl. Acad. Sci. USA* 94:12384–89

77. Kunchaparty S, Palcso M, Berkman J, Velazquez H, Desir GV, et al. 1999. Defective processing and expression of thiazide-sensitive Na-Cl cotransporter as a cause of Gitelman's syndrome. *Am. J. Physiol. Renal Physiol.* 277:F643–F49

78. Chillaron J, Estevez R, Samarzija I, Waldegger S, Testar X, et al. 1997. An intracellular trafficking defect in type I cystinuria rBAT mutants M467T and M467K. *J. Biol. Chem.* 272:9543–49

79. Bross P, Corydon TJ, Andresen BS, Jorgensen MM, Bolund L, et al. 1999. Protein misfolding and degradation in genetic diseases. *Hum. Mutat.* 14:186–98

80. Carrell RW, Lomas DA. 1997. Conformational disease. *Lancet* 350:134–38

81. Bonnardeaux A, Bichet DG. 2000. Inherited disorders of the renal tubule. In *The Kidney*, ed. BM Brenner, pp. 1656–98. Philadelphia, PA: Saunders. 6th ed.

82. Schulz A, Grosse R, Schultz G, Gudermann T, Schöneberg T. 2000. Structural implication for receptor oligomerization from functional reconstitution studies of mutant V2 vasopressin receptors. *J. Biol. Chem.* 275:2381–89

83. Serradeil-Le Gal C. 1998. Nonpeptide antagonists for vasopressin receptors: pharmacology of SR 121463A, a new potent and highly selective V2 receptor antagonist. *Adv. Exp. Med. Biol.* 449:427–38

84. Chan PS, Coupet J, Park HC, Lai F, Hartupee D, et al. 1998. VPA-985 a nonpeptide orally active and selective vasopressin V2 receptor antagonist. *Adv. Exp. Med. Biol.* 449:439–43

85. Serradeil-Le Gal C, Lacour C, Valette G, Garcia G, Foulon L, et al. 1996. Characterization of SR 121463A, a highly potent and selective, orally active vasopressin V2 receptor antagonist. *J. Clin. Invest.* 98:2729–38

86. Bernat A, Hoffmann P, Dumas A, Serradeil-le Gal C, Raufaste D, et al. 1997. V2 receptor antagonism of DDAVP-induced release of hemostasis factors in conscious dogs. *J. Pharmacol. Exp. Ther.* 282:597–602

87. Brown CR, Hong-Brown LQ, Biwersi J, Verkman AS, Welch WJ. 1996. Chemical chaperones correct the mutant phenotype of the delta F508 cystic fibrosis transmembrane conductance regulator protein. *Cell Stress Chaperones* 1:117–25

88. Sato S, Ward CL, Krouse ME, Wine JJ, Kopito RR. 1996. Glycerol reverses the misfolding phenotype of the most common cystic fibrosis mutation. *J. Biol. Chem.* 271:635–38

89. Rubenstein RC, Egan ME, Zeitlin PL. 1997. In vitro pharmacologic restoration of CFTR-mediated chloride transport with sodium 4-phenylbutyrate in cystic fibrosis epithelial cells containing delta F508-CFTR. *J. Clin. Invest.* 100:2457–65

90. Burrows JA, Willis LK, Perlmutter DH. 2000. Chemical chaperones mediate increased secretion of mutant alpha 1-antitrypsin (alpha 1-AT) Z: a potential pharmacological strategy for prevention of liver injury and emphysema in alpha 1-AT deficiency. *Proc. Natl. Acad. Sci. USA* 97:1796–801

91. Loo TW, Clarke DM. 1997. Correction of defective protein kinesis of human P-glycoprotein mutants by substrates and modulators. *J. Biol. Chem.* 272:709–12

92. Morello JP, Salahpour A, Laperriäre A, Bernier V, Arthus M-F, et al. 2000. Pharmacological chaperones rescue cell-surface expression and function of misfolded V2 vasopressin receptor mutants. *J. Clin. Invest.* 105:887–95

93. Fan JQ, Ishii S, Asano N, Suzuki Y. 1999. Accelerated transport and maturation of lysosomal alpha-galactosidase A in Fabry lymphoblasts by an enzyme inhibitor. *Nat. Med.* 5:112–15

94. Gekko K, Timasheff SN. 1981. Thermodynamic and kinetic examination of protein stabilization by glycerol. *Biochemistry* 20:4677–86

95. Sawano H, Koumoto Y, Ohta K, Sasaki Y, Segawa S, et al. 1992. Efficient in vitro folding of the three disulfide derivatives of hen lysozyme in the presence of glycerol. *FEBS Lett.* 303:11–14

96. Shelanski ML, Gaskin F, Cantor CR. 1973. Microtubule assembly in the absence of added nucleotides. *Proc. Natl. Acad. Sci. USA* 70:765–68

97. Welch WJ, Howard M. 2000. Commentary: antagonists to the rescue. *J. Clin. Invest.* 105:853–54

98. Deen PMT, Verdijk MAJ, Knoers NVAM, Wieringa B, Monnens LAH, et al. 1994. Requirement of human renal water channel aquaporin-2 for vasopressin-dependent concentration of urine. *Science* 264:92–95

99. Deen PMT, Weghuis DO, Sinke RJ, Geurts van Kessel A, Wieringa B, et al. 1994. Assignment of the human gene for the water channel of renal collecting duct aquaporin 2 (AQP2) to chromosome 12 region q12→q13. *Cytogenet. Cell Genet.* 66:260–62

100. Sasaki S, Fushimi K, Saito H, Saito F, Uchida S, et al. 1994. Cloning, characterization, and chromosomal mapping of human aquaporin of collecting duct. *J. Clin. Invest.* 93:1250–56

101. Deen PMT, Croes H, van Aubel RAMH, Ginsel LA, van Os CH. 1995. Water channels encoded by mutant aquaporin-2 genes in nephrogenic diabetes insipidus are impaired in their cellular routing. *J. Clin. Invest.* 95:2291–96

102. Mulders SB, Knoers NVAM, van Lieburg AF, Monnens LAH, Leumann E, et al. 1997. New mutations in the AQP2 gene in nephrogenic diabetes insipidus resulting in functional but misrouted water channels. *J. Am. Soc. Nephrol.* 8:242–48

103. Tamarappoo BK, Yang B, Verkman AS. 1999. Misfolding of mutant aquaporin-2 water channels in nephrogenic diabetes insipidus. *J. Biol. Chem.* 274:34825–31

104. van Os CH, Deen PM. 1998. Aquaporin-2 water channel mutations causing nephrogenic diabetes insipidus. *Proc. Assoc. Am. Physicians* 110:395–400

105. Mulders SM, Bichet DG, Rijss JPL, Kamsteeg E-J, Arthus M-F, et al. 1998. An aquaporin-2 water channel mutant which causes autosomal dominant nephrogenic diabetes insipidus is retained in the Golgi complex. *J. Clin. Invest.* 102:57–66

106. Kamsteeg EJ, Wormhoudt TA, Rijss JP, van Os CH, Deen PM. 1999. An impaired routing of wild- type aquaporin-2 after tetramerization with an aquaporin-2 mutant explains dominant nephrogenic diabetes insipidus. *EMBO J.* 18:2394–400

107. Reeves WB, Andreoli TE. 1995. Nephrogenic diabetes insipidus. In *The Metabolic and Molecular Bases of Inherited Disease*, ed. CR Scriver, AL Beaudet, WS Sly, D Valle, pp. 3045–71. New York: McGraw-Hill. 7th ed.

108. Antonarakis S, Nomenclature Working Group. 1998. Recommendations for a nomenclature system for human gene mutations. *Hum. Mutat.* 11:1–3

109. Mouillac B, Chini B, Balestre MN, Elands J, Trumpp-Kallmeyer S, et al. 1995. The binding site of neuropeptide vasopressin V1a receptor: evidence for a major localization within transmembrane regions. *J. Biol. Chem.* 270:25771–77

110. Pan Y, Metzenberg A, Das S, Jing B, Gitschier J. 1992. Mutations in the V2 vasopressin receptor gene are associated with X-linked nephrogenic diabetes insipidus. *Nat. Genet.* 2:103–6

111. Rosenthal W, Seibold A, Antaramian A, Lonergan M, Arthus M-F, et al. 1992. Molecular identification of the gene responsible for congenital nephrogenic diabetes insipidus. *Nature* 359:233–35

112. van den Ouweland AM, Dreesen JC, Verdijk M, Knoers NV, Monnens LA, et al. 1992. Mutations in the vasopressin type 2 receptor gene (AVPR2) associated with nephrogenic diabetes insipidus. *Nat. Genet.* 2:99–102

113. Holtzman EJ, Harris HWJ, Kolakowski LFJ, Guay-Woodford LM, Botelho B, et al. 1993. Brief report: a molecular defect in the vasopressin V2-receptor gene causing nephrogenic diabetes insipidus. *N. Engl. J. Med.* 328:1534–37

114. Merendino JJJ, Speigel AM, Crawford JD, O'Carroll AM, Brownstein MJ, et al. 1993. Brief report: a mutation in the vasopressin V2-receptor gene in a kindred with X-linked nephrogenic diabetes insipidus. *N. Engl. J. Med.* 328:1538–41

115. Tsukaguchi H, Matsubara H, Aritaki S, Kimura T, Abe S, et al. 1993. Two novel mutations in the vasopressin V2 receptor gene in unrelated Japanese kindreds with nephrogenic diabetes insipidus. *Biochem. Biophys. Res. Commun.* 197:1000–10

116. Faa V, Ventruto ML, Loche S, Bozzola M, Podda R, et al. 1994. Mutations in the vasopressin V2- receptor gene in three families of Italian descent with nephrogenic diabetes insipidus. *Hum. Mol. Genet.* 3:1685–86

117. Friedman E, Bale AE, Carson E, Boson WL, Nordenskjold M, et al. 1994. Nephrogenic diabetes insipidus: an X chromosome-linked dominant inheritance pattern with a vasopressin type 2 receptor gene that is structurally normal. *Proc. Natl. Acad. Sci. USA* 91:8457–61

118. Holtzman EJ, Kolakowski LFJ, Geifman-Holtzman O, O'Brien DG, Rasoulpour M, et al. 1994. Mutations in the vasopressin V2 receptor gene in two families with nephrogenic diabetes insipidus. *J. Am. Soc. Nephrol.* 5:169–76

119. Knoers NV, van den Ouweland AM, Verdijk M, Monnens LA, van Oost BA. 1994. Inheritance of mutations in the V2 receptor gene in thirteen families with nephrogenic diabetes insipidus. *Kidney Int.* 46:170–76

120. Oksche A, Dickson J, Schülein R, Seyberth HW, Müller M, et al. 1994. Two novel mutations in the vasopressin V2 receptor gene in patients with congenital nephrogenic diabetes insipidus. *Biochem. Biophys. Res. Commun.* 205:552–57

121. Pan Y, Wilson P, Gitschier J. 1994. The effect of eight V2 vasopressin receptor mutations on stimulation of adenylyl cyclase and binding to vasopressin. *J. Biol. Chem.* 269:31933–37

122. Wenkert D, Merendino JJJ, Shenker A, Thambi N, Robertson GL, et al. 1994. Novel mutations in the V2 vasopressin receptor gene of patients with X-linked nephrogenic diabetes insipidus. *Hum. Mol. Genet.* 3:1429–30

123. Wildin RS, Antush MJ, Bennett RL, Schoof JM, Scott CR. 1994. Heterogeneous AVPR2 gene mutations in congenital nephrogenic diabetes insipidus. *Am. J. Hum. Genet.* 55:266–77

124. Yuasa H, Ito M, Oiso Y, Kurokawa M, Watanabe T, et al. 1994. Novel mutations in the V2 vasopressin receptor gene in two pedigrees with congenital nephrogenic diabetes insipidus. *J. Clin. Endocrinol. Metab.* 79:361–65

125. Tsukaguchi H, Matsubara H, Inada M. 1995. Expression studies of two vasopressin V2 receptor gene mutations, R202C and 804insG, in nephrogenic diabetes insipidus. *Kidney Int.* 48:554–62

126. Jinnouchi H, Araki E, Miyamura N, Kishikawa H, Yoshimura R, et al. 1996. Analysis of vasopressin receptor type II (V2R) gene in three Japanese pedigrees with congenital nephrogenic diabetes insipidus: identification of a family with complete deletion of the V2R gene. *Eur. J. Endocrinol.* 134:689–98

127. Oksche A, Moller A, Dickson J, Rosendahl W, Rascher W, et al. 1996. Two novel mutations in the aquaporin-2 and the vasopressin V2 receptor genes in patients with congenital nephrogenic diabetes insipidus. *Hum. Genet.* 98:587–89

128. Tajima T, Nakae J, Takekoshi Y, Takahashi Y, Yuri K, et al. 1996. Three novel

AVPR2 mutations in three Japanese families with X-linked nephrogenic diabetes insipidus. *Pediatr. Res.* 39:522–26

129. Yokoyama K, Yamauchi A, Izumi M, Itoh T, Ando A, et al. 1996. A low-affinity vasopressin V2-receptor gene in a kindred with X-linked nephrogenic diabetes insipidus. *J. Am. Soc. Nephrol.* 7:410–14

130. Cheong HI, Park HW, Ha IS, Moon HN, Choi Y, et al. 1997. Six novel mutations in the vasopressin V2 receptor gene causing nephrogenic diabetes insipidus. *Nephron* 75:431–37

131. Sadeghi H, Robertson GL, Bichet DG, Innamorati G, Birnbaumer M. 1997. Biochemical basis of partial NDI phenotypes. *Mol. Endocrinol.* 11:1806–13

132. Vargas-Poussou R, Forestier L, Dautzenberg MD, Niaudet P, Déchaud M, et al. 1997. Mutations in the vasopressin V2 receptor and aquaporin-2 genes in 12 families with congenital nephrogenic diabetes insipidus. *J. Am. Soc. Nephrol.* 8:1855–62

133. Csaba S, Erika M, Peter S, Czinner A. 1998. Nephrogen diabetes insipidusos betegek molekularis biologia vizsgalata. *Orv. Hetil.* 139:883–87

134. Schöneberg T, Schulz A, Biebermann H, Grüters A, Grimm T, et al. 1998. V2 vasopressin receptor dysfunction in nephrogenic diabetes insipidus caused by different molecular mechanisms. *Hum. Mutat.* 12:196–205

135. Shoji Y, Takahashi T, Suzuki Y, Suzuki T, Komatsu K, et al. 1998. Mutational analyses of AVPR2 gene in three Japanese families with X-linked nephrogenic diabetes insipidus: two recurrent mutations, R137H and delta V278, caused by the hy-

permutability at CpG dinucleotides. *Hum. Mutat. Suppl.* 1:S278–83

136. Wildin RS, Cogdell DE, Valadez V. 1998. AVPR2 variants and V2 vasopressin receptor function in nephrogenic diabetes insipidus. *Kidney Int.* 54:1909–22

137. van Lieburg AF, Verdijk MAJ, Knoers NVAM, van Essen AJ, Proesmans W, et al. 1994. Patients with autosomal nephrogenic diabetes insipidus homozygous for mutations in the aquaporin 2 water-channel gene. *Am. J. Hum. Genet.* 55:648–52

138. Canfield MC, Tamarappoo BK, Moses AM, Verkman AS, Holtzman EJ. 1997. Identification and characterization of aquaporin-2 water channel mutations causing nephrogenic diabetes insipidus with partial vasopressin response. *Hum. Mol. Genet.* 6:1865–71

139. Hochberg Z, van Lieburg A, Even L, Brenner B, Lanir N, et al. 1997. Autosomal recessive nephrogenic diabetes insipidus caused by an aquaporin-2 mutation. *J. Clin. Endocrinol. Metab.* 82:686–89

140. Goji K, Kuwahara M, Gu Y, Matsuo M, Marumo F, et al. 1998. Novel mutations in aquaporin-2 gene in female siblings with nephrogenic diabetes insipidus: evidence of disrupted water channel function. *J. Clin. Endocrinol. Metab.* 83:3205–9

141. Kuwahara M. 1998. Aquaporin-2, a vasopressin-sensitive water channel, and nephrogenic diabetes insipidus. *Int. Med.* 37:215–17

142. Cheng A, van Hoek AN, Yeager M, Verkman AS, Mitra AK. 1997. Three-dimensional organization of a human water channel. *Nature* 387:627–30

Annu. Rev. Physiol. 2001. 63:631–45

CHLORIDE CHANNELS IN THE LOOP OF HENLE[1]

W Brian Reeves[2], Christopher J Winters[2], and Thomas E Andreoli[3]

[2]Division of Nephrology, [3]Department of Internal Medicine, University of Arkansas College of Medicine and the John L McClellan Veterans Hospital, Little Rock, Arkansas, 72205; e-mail: WReeves@psu.edu; WintersChristopherJ@exchange.uams.edu; AndreoliThomasE@exchange.uams.edu

Key Words kidney, ClC-K1, ClC-K2, chloride transport, Bartter's syndrome

■ **Abstract** Cl^- transport in the loop of Henle is responsible for reclamation of 25–40% of the filtered NaCl load and for the formation of dilute urine. Our understanding of the physiologic and molecular mechanisms responsible for Cl^- reabsorption in both the thin ascending limb and thick ascending limb of Henle's loop has increased greatly over the last decade. Plasma membrane Cl^- channels are known to play an integral role in transcellular Cl^- transport in both the thin and thick ascending limbs. This review focuses on the functional characteristics and molecular identities of these Cl^- channels, as well as the role of these channels in the pathophysiology of disease.

INTRODUCTION

The loop of Henle is responsible for absorbing 25 to 40% of the filtered sodium load (1–3). Moreover, the dissociation of salt and water absorption by the loop of Henle is ultimately responsible for the capacity of the kidney either to concentrate or to dilute the urine. Urinary dilution begins in the thin ascending loop of Henle and occurs through passive efflux of NaCl. The subsequent active absorption of NaCl in the water-impermeable medullary thick ascending limb of Henle (MTAL) serves both to dilute the urine and supply the energy for the single effect of counter-current multiplication. The movement of NaCl in both the thin and thick ascending limbs of Henle proceeds primarily via transcellular pathways. Current evidence indicates that plasma membrane Cl^- channels play a critical role in transcellular Cl^- transport in these segments and are a site of physiologic regulation of net NaCl transport. This review focuses on the functional and molecular characteristics of Cl^- channels, which subserve Cl^- transport in the loop of Henle.

---

[1]The US Government has the right to retain a nonexclusive, royalty-free license in and to any copyright covering this paper.

TABLE 1 Permeability properties of thin ascending limb of Henle

	P_f $(10^{-3}$ cm/s)	P_{Na} $(10^{-5}$ cm/s)	P_{Cl}	P_{Na}/P_{Cl}	P_{urea} $(10^{-5}$ cm/s)
Rabbit	0	25.5	117	0.29	6.7
Rat	2.5	67.9	183.7	0.43	23.0
Hamster	3	87.6	196	0.47	18.5

P_f, osmotic water permeability; P_{Na}, P_{Cl} determined from isotope flux measurements. P_{Na}/P_{Cl} determined from salt dilution voltages (modified from 77).

Cl⁻ TRANSPORT BY THE THIN ASCENDING SEGMENT

General Features of Cl⁻ Transport

According to the passive models for urinary concentration (4, 5), the thin ascending limb (tAL) should be rather impermeable to water, highly permeable to sodium chloride, and only modestly permeable to urea. As indicated in Table 1, in vitro microperfusion studies of tAL segments have demonstrated that these requirements are, in fact, satisfied.

The formation of dilute urine begins in the tAL of Henle. Fluid from the tAL is more dilute than fluid obtained from the descending limb at the same level (6, 7). The decrease in osmolality is primarily from a fall in the NaCl content of the luminal fluid. The mechanism for NaCl transport across the tAL epithelium is not completely understood.

Electrophysiology of Thin Ascending Limb Cl⁻ Conductance

Measurements of salt dilution potentials in microperfused tAL segments reveal them to be chloride selective with P_{Cl}/P_{Na} ratios of 2.2 to 3.5 in rats and hamsters (8). Segments perfused and bathed with symmetric solutions do not generate a spontaneous transepithelial voltage (8–11) and do not show net transport of solute (9). These observations, together with the very low activity of $(Na^+ + K^+)$-ATPase in this segment (12), have been interpreted to indicate that salt transport in vivo results from passive electrodiffusion rather than active transport. Although driven by passive electrochemical gradients, Cl⁻ movement across the tAL proceeds through a transcellular and regulated pathway. $^{36}Cl^-$ flux ratios and salt dilution voltages indicate that the Cl⁻ pathway discriminates among anions and is saturable (8, 10). Reduction of the Cl⁻ concentration of the basolateral solution causes a spike-like depolarization of the basolateral cell membrane (13). Likewise, reductions of the luminal perfusate Cl⁻ concentration cause a depolarization of the apical membrane. These results are consistent with the presence of conductive pathways for Cl⁻ in both the apical and basolateral membranes of tAL cells (13). The basolateral Cl⁻ conductance is inhibited at low pH (13) by low intracellular Ca^{2+} concentrations (14) and by compounds known to block Cl⁻ channels in other tissues (15).

Molecular Identity of Thin Ascending Limb Cl⁻ Channels

A chloride channel cloned from the renal medulla, ClC-K1, represents the major Cl⁻ channel in the tAL (16). This channel, which belongs to the ClC family of Cl channels, is expressed exclusively within the kidney and has been localized by immunohistochemistry to both the apical and basolateral membranes of the tAL of Henle (17). The expression of ClC-K1 is increased by dehydration (16, 18). The initial reports of the functional characteristics of ClC-K1 showed some similarities with the Cl⁻ conductance observed in isolated tAL segments, suggesting that this channel forms the primary Cl⁻ conductance in this segment (16). Namely, Uchida et al (16) reported that, when expressed in *Xenopus* oocytes, rat ClC-K1 induced Cl⁻ selective currents with outward rectification that were inhibited at low pH. Although initial attempts to confirm the functional expression of ClC-K1 were unsuccessful (19), it now appears that ClC-K1 does, in fact, function as an anion channel and exhibits certain characteristics of the tAL Cl⁻ conductance (20).

The importance of ClC-K1 to the urinary concentrating mechanism and tAL Cl⁻ transport was elegantly demonstrated by Matsumura et al (21). Mice lacking a functional ClC-K1 gene were produced by homologous recombination. Immuno-histochemical analysis of kidneys from these mice confirmed that ClC-K1 protein was not expressed in the tAL. Although the mice appeared to maintain normal salt and water balance on an unrestricted diet, they were unable to concentrate their urine during water restriction and developed hypernatremic dehydration. Failure of the mice to respond to exogenous vasopressin confirmed that loss of the ClC-K1 gene resulted in nephrogenic diabetes insipidus. Finally, dissected tALs were perfused in vitro and shown to have a dramatically lower Cl⁻ permeability when compared with segments obtained from normal mice. Taken together, these results indicate that (*a*) ClC-K1 is expressed in the thin ascending limb, (*b*) ClC-K1 is necessary for the high Cl⁻ permeability of that segment, and (*c*) the Cl⁻ permeability of the tAL is important for urinary concentrating ability, as predicted by passive countercurrent multiplication models (4).

NaCl ABSORPTION IN THE THICK ASCENDING LIMB

General Features of Cl⁻ Transport

In vitro microperfusion studies established the salient characteristics of salt absorption in rabbit medullary (22) and cortical thick ascending limb (CTAL) segments (23). First, net salt absorption resulted in a lumen-positive transepithelial voltage (V_e, mV) that could be abolished by furosemide and in dilution of the luminal fluid. Second, the transport of Cl⁻ under these circumstances occurred against both electrical and chemical gradients and hence involved an active transport process. Third, both net chloride absorption and the transepithelial voltage depended on $(Na^+ + K^+)$-ATPase activity, present in large amounts along the basolateral membrane of this segment (12). A final curious feature of tAL segments is that these

TABLE 2   Basal electrophysiological parameters of thick ascending limb segments

	V_e (mV)	G_e	G_c	G_s	V_a	V_{bl}	R_a/R_b	Reference
		(mS/cm^2)			(mV)			
Rabbit CTAL	4–8	33	12	21	76	−69	2.0	(30)
Mouse MTAL	3–7	70–100	45–50	40–60	55.4	−50.7	1.2	(35, 71, 78)
Mouse CTAL	7–14	88	39	49				(79)
Hamster MTAL	4.0	934				−72		(37)

Abbreviations: V_e, transepithelial voltage; G_e, transepithelial conductance; G_c, transcellular conductance; G_s, paracellular conductance; V_a, apical membrane voltage; V_{bl}, basolateral membrane voltage; R_a/R_b, apical to basolateral membrane resistance.

segments are, as noted previously (24), hybrid epithelia possessing a very low permeability to water, yet a high ionic conductance. This high electrical conductance is unusual among epithelia with low water permeabilities.

Studies of the electrophysiologic (Table 2) and biochemical properties of intact isolated perfused medullary thick limb segments and of apical and basolateral membranes of medullary thick limb cells have provided insights into the specific transport mechanisms involved in salt absorption and the origin of the lumen-positive transepithelial voltage in this nephron segment (24–34). A model for salt absorption by the MTAL, which integrates the results of these studies, is shown in Figure 1. NaCl absorption by CTAL segments is not as well characterized but appears to depend in part on $(CO_2 + HCO_3^-)$.

According to the model shown in Figure 1, net Cl^- absorption by the MTAL is a secondary active transport process. Luminal Cl^- entry into the cell is mediated by an electroneutral $Na^+/K^+/2Cl^-$ cotransport process driven by the favorable electrochemical gradient for sodium entry.

In contrast to the electroneutral entry of Cl^- across the apical membrane, the majority of Cl^- efflux across the basolateral membrane proceeds through conductive pathways (34–36). The notion that basolateral Cl^- transport is electrogenic first derived from the observations that, in the mouse medullary TAL (24) and rabbit CTAL, net Cl^- absorption accounts for about 90% of the equivalent short-circuit current. Measurements of the basolateral membrane voltage by Greger & Schlatter (31) confirmed that reductions in bath chloride concentration depolarized the basolateral membrane, whereas reductions in intracellular chloride concentration produced by blocking Cl^- entry with furosemide, hyperpolarized the basolateral membrane. Both sets of observations are consistent with the presence of a Cl^- conductance in the basolateral membrane. Yoshitomi et al (37) also identified a large chloride conductance in the basolateral membrane of hamster MTAL cells.

A favorable electrochemical gradient for Cl^- efflux through dissipative pathways has been demonstrated by Greger et al (28) in the rabbit CTAL. In this study, an intracellular Cl^- activity of 22 mM, measured using single-barrel

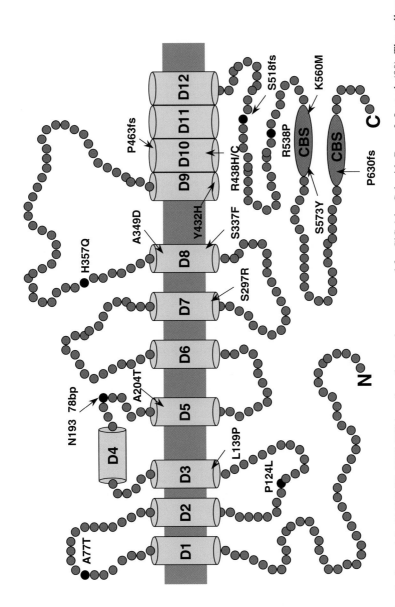

Figure 3 Topologic model of hClC-Kb (ClC-K2) based on the topology proposed for ClC-1 by Schmidt-Rose & Jentsch (80). The yellow barrels represent predicted α-helices, the small circles represent amino acids. Mutations found in patients with Bartter's syndrome are indicated by black circles and arrows (62, 69). CBS, cystathionine-β synthase motifs; fs, frame shift.

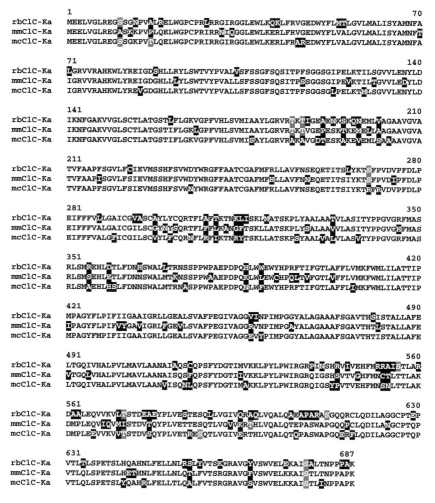

Figure 4 Alignment of the deduced amino acid sequences of rbClC-Ka, mmClC-Ka, and mcClC-Ka. The amino acids colored black represent differences in the amino acid sequences. The amino acids colored red represent potential PKA phosphorylation sites (from Reference 76).

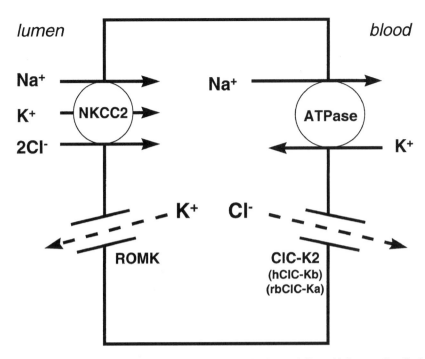

Figure 1 A model of transepithelial NaCl transport in the medullary thick ascending limb of Henle. Cl⁻ entry across the apical membrane is mediated by NKCC2, the electroneutral, furosemide-sensitive Na⁺/K⁺/2Cl⁻ cotransporter. K⁺ recycles out of the cell via the ROMK K⁺ channel to provide additional K⁺ for further Na⁺ and Cl⁻ entry. Cl⁻ exits the cells across the basolateral membrane via ClC-K2 (hClC-Kb or rbClC-Ka) Cl⁻ channels.

Cl⁻-selective microelectrodes, was substantially above the equilibrium value (5 mM) predicted from the intracellular voltage. Intracellular Cl⁻ is maintained at concentrations above electrochemical equilibrium by the continued entry of Cl⁻ via the apical Na⁺/K⁺/2Cl⁻ cotransporter. Blocking Cl⁻ entry through this pathway with furosemide, or substitution of extracellular Cl⁻ by gluconate, caused the intracellular Cl⁻ activity to fall to a value close to its equilibrium (28). Measurements of intracellular Cl⁻ activity in *Amphiuma* diluting segments using double-barrel microelectrodes have also documented a favorable electrochemical gradient for basolateral Cl⁻ efflux under transporting conditions (38).

Consistent with the view that basolateral Cl⁻ transport is via chloride channels, a variety of compounds known to block Cl⁻ channels also inhibit salt absorption in tAL segments. Wangemann et al (39) have cataloged the electrophysiologic effects, relative potencies, and structure-function relations of over 200 such compounds. The major effects of these agents, when present in the peritubular bathing solutions are inhibition of transepithelial voltage, inhibition of the equivalent short-circuit current, and hyperpolarization of the basolateral membrane.

Electrophysiology of TAL Cl⁻ Channels

Application of the patch-clamp technique to the TAL has established that Cl⁻ channels are present in the basolateral membrane of tAL cells. Paulais & Teulon (40) have detected a 40 pS anion-selective channel ($P_{Cl}/P_{Na} = 20$) in the basolateral membrane of collagenase-treated mouse cortical TAL segments. The I-V relations of the channel were linear in both the cell-attached and excised configurations. The open probability of the channel in the cell attached state was voltage dependent, increasing as the membrane was depolarized. In the excised patch configuration, the open probability was no longer voltage dependent. Greger et al (41) have described a Cl⁻ channel in the basolateral membrane of rat CTAL segments. This channel also has a conductance of about 40 pS, but rather than having a linear I-V relation, this channel exhibits outward rectification. The open probability increases with depolarization in both the cell-attached and excised patch configuration.

Reeves et al have performed patch-clamp studies on cultured mouse medullary TAL cells (42). These cells, derived from a single medullary TAL segment dissected from the kidney of a mouse bearing a transgene for the SV40 T antigen, exhibit furosemide-sensitive Na⁺ uptake and respond to vasopressin as do native TAL cells. The predominant Cl⁻ channel observed in excised patches shows outward rectification with a single-channel conductance of $\sim$20 pS for inward current and $\sim$40 pS for outward current (42). The open probability of the channel is also voltage dependent, increasing with membrane depolarization.

A key feature of these channels, and one also observed in Cl⁻ channels reconstituted from medullary membrane vesicles into lipid bilayers (see below), is the dependence of channel gating on the concentration of Cl⁻ in the solutions. Specifically, reducing the Cl⁻ concentration of the solution facing the intracellular surface of the channel from 150 mM to 2 mM caused an immediate and reversible suppression of channel open probability, P_o (Figure 2). The effect of Cl⁻ on P_o was most pronounced over the range of 2–25 mM Cl⁻ (42), which corresponds to physiologic intracellular Cl⁻ concentrations in TAL cells (28). A low-conductance Cl⁻ channel (8–10 pS) having linear I-V relations has also been detected in the basolateral membrane of MTAL cells (43, 44). The activity of this channel is increased following incubation with cAMP-dependent protein kinase and ATP (44).

Evidence for MTAL Cl⁻ channels also comes from studies of Cl⁻ flux in renal medullary membrane vesicles. Because MTALs make up approximately 70% of the volume in the inner stripe of outer medulla, vesicles prepared from this region should be predominantly derived from this segment. ^{36}Cl⁻ flux into vesicles from porcine (45) and rabbit outer medulla (46) is electrogenic, cation independent, inhibitable by chloride channel blockers, and has a low activation energy ($E_a = 6.4$ kcal/mol), characteristic of transport through a channel. Moreover, when vesicles from rabbit outer medulla were incorporated into planar lipid bilayers, chloride channel activity was demonstrated (47). These channels

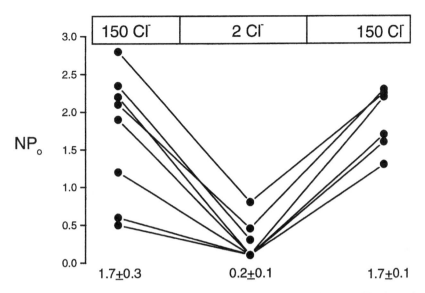

Figure 2 Effect of cytoplasmic face Cl⁻ concentrations on gating of MTAL Cl⁻ channels. Excised patches of tAL cells containing Cl⁻ channels were exposed to solutions containing 150 mM Cl⁻ or 2 mM Cl⁻. Reduction of the Cl⁻ concentration produced a reversible suppression of channel activity (from Reference 42).

were anion selective ($P_{Cl}/P_K = 10$) and had a single-channel conductance of 80–90 pS in 320 mM KCl solution. The I-V relations in symmetric solution were linear, and in asymmetric solutions the I-V relations conformed to the Goldman-Hodgkin-Katz equation. The open probability of this channel was voltage dependent, increasing activity with depolarizing voltages. These channels are also seen in vesicles made from highly purified suspensions of mouse MTAL (48) and from cultured mouse MTAL cells (42) confirming their origin as the MTAL.

A unique feature of these medullary chloride channels is the asymmetric dependence of channel activity on the chloride activity of the solutions bathing the lipid bilayer (42, 49). Increases in the Cl⁻ concentration of the *cis*, or extracellular, solution over the range of 50 to 300 mM produced almost linear increases in channel open probability. In contrast, the Cl⁻ concentration dependence of the *trans*, or intracellular surface of the channel, was most pronounced in the range of 0 to 50 mM Cl⁻ and was almost saturated at 50 mM Cl⁻. Similar Cl⁻ dependence was observed in channels studied in excised patches of cultured MTAL cells indicating that the effect is not an artifact of the lipid bilayer reconstitution technique (42). Dependence of channel activity on extracellular Cl⁻ has also been shown for certain members of the ClC family of Cl⁻ channels (50). As is discussed below, it is believed that the basolateral Cl⁻ channel of the MTAL is a member of the ClC family of chloride channels.

Molecular Identity of TAL Cl⁻ Channels

A chloride channel, termed ClC-0, was cloned from the electric organ of the *Torpedo* ray by Jentsch et al (51) using an expression cloning strategy. This work led to the identification of a large number of related choride channels that form the ClC family of channels (52). Based on homology to the ClC-0 channel, Uchida et al (16), Adachi et al (53), and Kieferle et al (19) reported the cloning of two chloride channels, ClC-K1 and ClC-K2, expressed exclusively within the rat kidney. In the human, the two corresponding channels are denoted hClC-Ka and hClC-Kb and are located contiguously on chromosome 1 (54). In human, rat, and mouse, these two genes are separated by only a few kilobases and have similar intron-exon boundaries, suggesting that they arose by gene duplication.

Due to the high degree of sequence similarity between hClC-Ka and hClC-Kb, it is not certain which of the human channels correspond to ClC-K1 or ClC-K2, although the distribution of ClC-K2 along the nephron most closely matches that of hClC-Kb (55). As noted above, ClC-K1 is expressed predominantly in the thin ascending limb of Henle (17) and mediates passive Cl⁻ reabsorption in that segment (21). Zimniak et al (56) have cloned a cDNA from rabbit renal outer medulla, called rbClC-Ka, which shares 80% homology to the rat CLC-K1 and CLC-K2. The distribution of rbClC-Ka along the nephron resembles that of CLC-K2 rather than ClC-K1 (56, 57).

Several lines of evidence support the view that CLC-K2 (or the human homolog hCLC-Kb and rabbit homolog rbClC-Ka) is the channel that mediates chloride efflux across the basolateral membrane of the MTAL. First, using polymerase chain reaction amplification of single-tubule segments, the ClC-K2 and rbClC-Ka channels were shown to be expressed primarily in the thick ascending limb and the collecting duct (53, 56). Second, immunohistochemical studies using an antibody against the rbClC-Ka channel revealed predominantly basolateral staining in the medullary and cortical thick ascending limb (58). Similar results were obtained by Vandewalle using an antibody that recognizes both ClC-K1 and ClC-K2 (18). However, these immunohistochemical findings are clouded by the high degree of homology between the ClC-K1 and ClC-K2 channels and the uncertain specificity of the antibodies used. Fortunately, the untranslated regions of ClC-K1 and ClC-K2 differ sufficiently that specific oligonucleotide probes can distinguish between the two genes. Using such probes, Yoshikawa et al (59) examined the distribution of ClC-K2 mRNA in rat kidney by in situ hybridization. They found expression of ClC-K2 primarily in medullary, rather than cortical TAL, as well as in the distal convoluted tubule, connecting tubules and cortical collecting ducts.

Taken together, these data indicate that the ClC-K2 (rbClC-Ka) channel is located in the MTAL. However, these results do not establish which, if any, of the Cl⁻ channels identified in electrophysiologic studies is the ClC-K2 channel nor what is the physiologic role of the ClC-K2 channel. An obstacle in addressing these issues has been the inability to obtain functional expression of ClC-K2 (or rbClC-Ka) channels (19, 20, 56). The reason for this lack of functional expression in heterologous systems is not clear but may indicate the need for a tissue-specific cofactor for Cl⁻ channel activity. The inability to achieve functional expression of ClC-K2 is particularly curious because ClC-K1, which shares over 90% identity with ClC-K2, can be expressed in *Xenopus* oocytes (16, 20). Waldegger & Jentsch (20) have exploited this discrepancy to explore the structural requirements for functional ClC-K expression. They created a series of chimeric molecules containing parts of both ClC-K1 and ClC-K2 and tested their ability to induce a Cl⁻ conductance in oocytes. When the C terminus of ClC-K2 (or actually hClC-Kb) was replaced with the C terminus of ClC-K1, a Cl⁻ conductance was induced that had permeability characteristics quite distinct from those of ClC-K1. Further experiments determined that replacement of the hydrophobic region in ClC-K2, which lies between the D9 domain and the first CBS domain (Figure 3, see color insert), with the corresponding region of ClC-K1 was sufficient to allow functional expression of ClC-K2 (20). The reason that this region from ClC-K1 supports channel function, while the same region from ClC-K2 does not, remains unknown.

Given the lack of functional expression of ClC-K2, Andreoli and colleagues have taken an alternative approach to provide evidence that the ClC-K2 (rbClC-Ka) gene encodes the Cl⁻-sensitive Cl⁻ channel characterized in renal medullary vesicles (47–49, 60, 61) and in excised patches of cultured MTAL cells (42). In this regard, treatment of cultured medullary thick ascending limb cells with an antisense oligonucleotide to rbClC-Ka (but not a random oligonucleotide) reduced the number of chloride channels in membrane vesicles derived from those cells (57). Moreover, they produced an antibody against the C terminus of rbClC-Ka and found that it inhibited the activity of these Cl⁻-sensitive chloride channels in lipid bilayers (57). This antibody also reduced chloride efflux in intact thick ascending limb segments (58). This series of results provides strong support for the view that the ClC-K2 (rbClC-Ka) channel is the Cl⁻-sensitive channel of tAL cells and that this channel mediates basolateral Cl⁻ efflux.

Finally, and most compelling, is the identification of mutations in the human homolog of CLC-K2/rbClC-Ka (hCLC-Kb) in patients with Bartter's syndrome (62). Bartter's syndrome is an autosomal-recessive disorder characterized by hypokalemia, metabolic alkalosis, renal salt-wasting, and hyperrenninemic hyperaldosteronism. The physiologic defect accounting for these features is a failure to reabsorb NaCl in the TAL (63). Indeed, this view has been confirmed by genetic analyses of Bartter families, which have identified mutations in three different proteins involved in TAL NaCl transport (Figure 1). Specifically, Bartter's syndrome can be caused by mutations in (*a*) the apical membrane furosemide-sensitive Na⁺/K⁺/2Cl⁻ cotransporter, NKCC2 (64–66), (*b*) the apical membrane K⁺ channel, ROMK (67, 68), and (*c*) the Cl⁻ channel, hClC-Kb (62, 69). Thus identification of causal mutations in the hClC-Kb gene in some patients with Bartter's syndrome, a disorder of TAL NaCl transport, clearly establishes that the human ClC-Kb (rat ClC-K2/rbClC-Ka) channel plays an important role in MTAL Cl⁻ transport.

Many of the hClC-Kb mutations in Bartter patients produce large deletions, even of the entire hClC-Kb gene, or premature truncations that likely cause a loss of hClC-Kb function. In addition, a number of point mutations have been reported (Figure 3) but, given the lack of heterologous expression systems for hClC-Kb, it has not been possible to determine the effect of these mutations on hClC-Kb function. However, the recent expression of chimeric hClC-Kb/ratClC-K1 channels has allowed an examination of this issue. When the point mutations found in Bartter families (P124L, A204T, A349D, Y432H, and R438C) were introduced into the hClC-Kb/ratClC-K1 chimera, the resulting currents were strongly reduced or abolished (20). These results confirm that the mutations found in patients with Bartter syndrome do indeed alter Cl$^-$ channel function.

Heterogeneity Among Medullary and Cortical TAL Cl$^-$ Channels

Microperfused mouse medullary (MTAL) and cortical (CTAL) thick ascending limb segments differ functionally (24, 32, 70). In MTAL segments, ADH, operating via the adenylate cylcase cascade, augments both apical membrane Na$^+$/K$^+$/2Cl$^-$ activity (35, 71, 72) and apical K$^+$ channel activity (71, 35, 73), thus increasing net rates of NaCl absorption. Pari passu, there is a secondary increase in the basolateral membrane Cl$^-$ conductance (71). None of these ADH-dependent events occurs in microperfused CTAL segments (24, 70).

Individual basolateral Cl$^-$ channels from the MTAL and from the CTAL also differ functionally. When MTAL Cl$^-$ channels are fused into bilayers using basolateral membrane vesicles prepared either from rabbit outer medulla (48, 49, 60, 74) or from cultured mouse MTAL cells (42, 58), or studied by excised inside-out patch clamping of mouse MTAL cells (42), (ATP + PKA) increase P$_o$, the open time probability, when cytosolic face Cl$^-$ concentrations are 2 mM, but have no effect on P$_o$ when cytosolic face Cl$^-$ concentrations are 25 mM. Without (ATP + PKA), increasing cytosolic face Cl$^-$ concentrations, as such, augments P$_o$ with a K$_{1/2}$ of 10 mM Cl$^-$ (42, 49, 60). In contrast, basolateral Cl$^-$ channels from cultured mouse CTAL cells, studied either by fusing channels from basolateral vesicles into bilayers or by excised inside-out patch clamping, are not affected by these maneuvers (75). That is, in basolateral CTAL Cl$^-$ channels, neither (ATP + PKA), at low cytosolic face Cl$^-$ concentrations, nor increased cytosolic face Cl$^-$ concentrations without (ATP + PKA), has any effect on P$_o$. In short, basolateral Cl$^-$ channels from the MTAL and CTAL exhibit significant functional heterogeneity.

Recent work points to a molecular basis for this functional heterogeneity. Winters et al (76) obtained two independent, but highly homologous, cDNA clones from mouse kidney medulla and cortex. These clones, termed mmClC-Ka and mcClC-Ka, respectively, shared ∼85% homology with rbClC-Ka (Figure 4, see color insert). The functional significance of these two clones was examined using cultured mouse CTAL and MTAL cells. Treatment of MTAL cells with an antisense oligonucleotide specific for mmClC-Ka reduced mmClC-Ka protein levels and reduced the rate of Cl$^-$ efflux in these cells. Likewise, treatment of CTAL cells with an mcClC-Ka antisense oligonucleotide reduced mcClC-Ka protein levels and

Cl⁻ efflux rates (76). Conversely, treatment of MTAL cells with mcClC-Ka antisense oligonucleotides, or treatment of CTAL cells with mmClC-Ka antisense oligonucleotides had no effects on protein levels or Cl⁻ transport rates. These results are consistent with the view that mmClC-Ka is the chief basolateral Cl⁻ channel in the MTAL, whereas mcClC-Ka predominates in the CTAL. It was also noted that the mmClC-Ka and rbClC-Ka contain several putative PKA phosphorylation sites that are not present in mcClC-Ka (Figure 4). Given that PKA increases P_o in MTAL channels (42, 49, 60, 75) but not CTAL channels (75), it is possible that these phosphorylation sites account for the differences in the response to PKA by these two regions. Functional expression of these channels will aid greatly in evaluating these issues further.

Visit the Annual Reviews home page at www.AnnualReviews.org

LITERATURE CITED

1. Bennett CM, Brenner BM, Berliner RW. 1968. Micropuncture study of nephron function in the Rhesus monkey. *J. Clin. Invest.* 47:203–16
2. Giebisch G, Klose RM, Windhager EE. 1964. Micropuncture study of hypertonic sodium chloride loading in the rat. *Am. J. Physiol.* 206:687–93
3. Landwehr DM, Klose RM, Giebisch G. 1967. Renal tubular sodium and water reabsorption in the isotonic sodium chloride loaded rat. *Am. J. Physiol.* 212:1327–33
4. Kokko JP, Rector FC Jr. 1972. Countercurrent multiplication system without active transport in inner medulla. *Kidney Int.* 2:214–23
5. Stephenson JL. 1972. Concentration of urine in a central core model of the renal counterflow system. *Kidney Int.* 2:85–94
6. Jamison RL. 1968. Micropuncture study of segments of thin loop of Henle in the rat. *Am. J. Physiol.* 215:236–42
7. Jamison RL, Bennett CM, Berliner RW. 1967. Countercurrent multiplication by the thin loops of Henle. *Am. J. Physiol.* 212:357–66
8. Imai M. 1977. Function of the thin ascending limb of Henle of rats and hamsters perfused in vitro. *Am. J. Physiol. Renal Physiol.* 232:F201–F9
9. Imai M, Kokko JP. 1974. Sodium chloride, urea and water transport in the thin ascending limb of Henle. Generation of osmotic gradients by passive diffusion of solutes. *J. Clin. Invest.* 53:393
10. Imai M, Kokko JP. 1976. Mechanism of sodium and chloride transport in the thin ascending limb of Henle. *J. Clin. Invest.* 58:1054–60
11. Imai M, Kusano E. 1982. Effect of arginine vasopressin on the thin ascending limb of Henle of hamsters. *Am. J. Physiol. Renal Physiol.* 243:F167–F72
12. Katz AI, Doucet A, Morel F. 1979. Na-K-ATPase activity along the rabbit, rat, and mouse nephron. *Am. J. Physiol. Renal Physiol.* 237:F114–F20
13. Yoshitomi K, Kondo Y, Imai M. 1988. Evidence for conductive Cl⁻ pathways across the cell membranes of the thin ascending limb of Henle's loop. *J. Clin. Invest.* 82:866–71
14. Kondo Y, Yoshitomi K, Imai M. 1988. Effect of Ca²⁺ on Cl⁻ transport in thin ascending limb of Henle's loop. *Am. J. Physiol. Renal Physiol.* 254:F232–F39
15. Kondo Y, Yoshitomi K, Imai M. 1987. Effect of anion transport inhibitors and ion substitution on Cl transport in the thin ascending limb of Henle's loop. *Am. J.*

Physiol. Renal Physiol. 253:F1206–F15

16. Uchida S, Sasaki S, Furukawa T, Hiraoka M, Imai T, et al. 1993. Molecular cloning of a chloride channel that is regulated by dehydration and expressed predominantly in kidney medulla. *J. Biol. Chem.* 268:3821–24

17. Uchida S, Sasaki S, Nitta K, Uchida K, Horita S, et al. 1995. Localization and functional characterization of rat kidney-specific chloride channel, ClC-K1. *J. Clin. Invest.* 95:104–13

18. Vandewalle A, Cluzeaud F, Bens M, Kieferle S, Steinmeyer K, et al. 1997. Localization and induction by dehydration of ClC-K chloride channels in the rat kidney. *Am. J. Physiol. Renal Physiol.* 272:F678–F88

19. Kieferle S, Fong P, Bens M, Vandewalle A, Jentsch TJ. 1994. Two highly homologous members of the ClC chloride channel family in both rat and human kidney. *Proc. Natl. Acad. Sci. USA* 91:6943–47

20. Waldegger S, Jentsch TJ. 2000. Functional and structural analysis of ClC-K chloride channels involved in renal disease. *J. Biol. Chem.* 275:24527–33

21. Matsumura Y, Uchida S, Kondo Y, Miyazaki H, Ko SBH, et al. 1999. Overt nephrogenic diabetes insipidus in mice lacking the CLC-K1 chloride channel. *Nat. Genet.* 21:95–98

22. Rocha AS, Kokko JP. 1973. Sodium chloride and water transport in the medullary thick ascending limb of Henle. *J. Clin. Invest.* 52:612–23

23. Burg MB, Green N. 1973. Function of the thick ascending limb of Henle's loop. *Am. J. Physiol.* 224:659–68

24. Hebert SC, Culpepper RM, Andreoli TE. 1981. NaCl transport in mouse thick ascending limbs. I. Functional nephron heterogeneity and ADH-stimulated NaCl cotransport. *Am. J. Physiol. Renal Physiol.* 241:F412–F31

25. Greger R. 1988. Chloride transport in thick ascending limb, distal convolution and collecting duct. *Annu. Rev. Physiol.* 50:111–22

26. Greger R. 1981. Chloride reabsorption in the rabbit cortical thick ascending limb of the loop of Henle. A sodium dependent process. *Pflügers Arch.* 390:38–43

27. Greger R. 1981. Coupled transport of Na^+ and Cl^- in the thick ascending limb of Henle's loop of rabbit nephron. *Scand. Audiol. Suppl.* 14:1–14

28. Greger R, Oberleithner H, Schlatter E, Cassola AC, Weidtke C. 1983. Chloride activity in cells of isolated perfused cortical thick ascending limbs of rabbit kidney. *Pflügers Arch.* 399:29–34

29. Greger R, Schlatter E. 1981. Presence of luminal K^+, a prerequisite for active NaCl transport in the cortical thick ascending limb of Henle's loop of rabbit kidney. *Pflügers Arch.* 392:92–94

30. Greger R, Schlatter E. 1983. Properties of the lumen membrane of the cortical thick ascending limb of Henle's loop of rabbit kidney. *Pflügers Arch.* 396:315–24

31. Greger R, Schlatter E. 1983. Properties of the basolateral membrane of the cortical thick ascending limb of Henle's loop of rabbit kidney. A model of secondary active chloride transport. *Pflügers Arch.* 396:325–34

32. Hebert SC, Culpepper RM, Andreoli TE. 1981. NaCl transport in mouse thick ascending limbs. II. ADH enhancement of transcellular NaCl cotransport; origin of transepithelial voltage. *Am. J. Physiol. Renal Physiol.* 241:F432–F42

33. Hebert SC, Culpepper RM, Andreoli TE. 1981. NaCl transport in mouse thick ascending limbs. III. Modulation of the ADH effect by peritubular osmolality. *Am. J. Physiol. Renal Physiol.* 241:F443–F51

34. Hebert SC, Friedman PA, Andreoli TE. 1984. Effects of antidiuretic hormone on cellular conductive pathways in mouse medullary thick ascending limbs of Henle. I. ADH increases transcellular conductance pathways. *J. Membr. Biol.* 80:201–29

35. Hebert SC, Andreoli TE. 1984. Effects of antidiuretic hormone on cellular conductance pathways in mouse medullary thick ascending limbs of Henle. II. Determinants of the ADH-mediated increases in transepithelial voltage and in net Cl⁻ absorption. *J. Membr. Biol.* 80:221–33

36. Schlatter E, Greger R. 1985. cAMP increases the basolateral Cl⁻-conductance in the isolated perfused medullary thick ascending limb of Henle's loop of the mouse. *Pflügers Arch.* 405:367–76

37. Yoshitomi K, Koseki C, Taniguchi J, Imai M. 1987. Functional heterogeneity in the hamster medullary thick ascending limb of Henle's loop. *Pflügers Arch.* 408:600–8

38. Oberleithner H, Guggino W, Giebisch G. 1982. Mechanism of distal tubular chloride transport in *Amphiuma* kidney. *Am. J. Physiol. Renal Physiol.* 242:F331–F39

39. Wangemann P, Wittner M, DiStefano A, Englert HC, Lang HJ, et al. 1986. Cl⁻ channel blockers in the thick ascending limb of the loop of Henle. Structure activity relationship. *Pflügers Arch.* 407:S128–41

40. Paulais M, Teulon J. 1990. cAMP-activated chloride channel in the basolateral membrane of the thick ascending limb of the mouse kidney. *J. Membr. Biol.* 113:253–60

41. Greger R, Bleich M, Schlatter E. 1990. Ion channels in the thick ascending limb of Henle's loop. *Renal Physiol. Biochem.* 13:37–50

42. Reeves WB, Winters CJ, Filipovic DM, Andreoli TE. 1995. Cl− channels in basolateral renal medullary vesicles. IX. Channels from mouse MTAL cell patches and medullary vesicles. *Am. J. Physiol. Renal Physiol.* 269:F621–F27

43. Guinamard R, Paulais M, Teulon J. 1996. Inhibition of a small-conductance cAMP-dependent Cl− channel in the mouse thick ascending limb at low internal pH. *J. Physiol.* 490:759–65

44. Guinamard R, Chraibi A, Teulon J. 1995. A small-conductance Cl⁻ channel in the mouse thick ascending limb that is activated by ATP and protein kinase A. *J. Physiol.* 485:97–112

45. Breuer W. 1989. Characterization of chloride channels in membrane vesicles from the kidney outer medulla. *J. Membr. Biol.* 107:35–42

46. Bayliss JM, Reeves WB, Andreoli TE. 1990. Cl⁻ transport in basolateral renal medullary vesicles. I. Cl⁻ transport in intact vesicles. *J. Membr. Biol.* 113:49–56

47. Reeves WB, Andreoli TE. 1990. Cl⁻ transport in basolateral renal medullary vesicles. II. Cl− channels in planar lipid bilayers. *J. Membr. Biol.* 113:57–65

48. Winters CJ, Reeves WB, Andreoli TE. 1992. Cl⁻ channels in basolateral renal medullary vesicles. V. Comparison of basolateral mTALH Cl⁻ channels with apical Cl⁻ channels from jejunum and trachea. *J. Membr. Biol.* 128:27–39

49. Winters CJ, Reeves WB, Andreoli TE. 1991. Cl⁻ channels in basolateral renal medullary membranes. III. Determinants of single channel activity. *J. Membr. Biol.* 118:269–78

50. Pusch M, Ludewig U, Rehfeldt A, Jentsch TJ. 1995. Gating of the voltage-dependent chloride channel ClC-0 by the permeant anion. *Nature* 373:527–31

51. Jentsch TJ, Steinmeyer K, Schwarz G. 1990. Primary structure of *Torpedo marmorata* chloride channel isolated by expression cloning in *Xenopus* oocytes. *Nature* 348:510–14

52. Jentsch TJ. 1996. Chloride channels: a molecular perspective. *Curr. Opin. Neurobiol.* 6:303–10

53. Adachi S, Uchida S, Ito H, Hata M, Hiroe M, et al. 1994. Two isoforms of a chloride channel predominantly expressed in thick ascending limb of Henle's loop and collecting ducts of rat kidney. *J. Biol. Chem.* 269:17677–83

54. Saito-Ohara F, Uchida S, Takeuchi Y, Sasaki S, Hayashi A, et al. 1996. Assignment of the genes encoding the human

chloride channels, CLCNKA and CLC-NKB, to 1p36 and of CLCN3 to 4q32–q33 by in situ hybridization. *Genomics* 36:372–74

55. Takeuchi Y, Uchida S, Marumo F, Sasaki S. 1995. Cloning, tissue distribution, and intrarenal localization of ClC chloride channels in human kidney. *Kidney Int.* 48:1497–503

56. Zimniak L, Winters CJ, Reeves WB, Andreoli TE. 1995. Cl⁻ channels in basolateral renal medullary vesicles. X. Cloning of a Cl⁻ channel from rabbit outer medulla. *Kidney Int.* 48:1828–36

57. Zimniak L, Winters CJ, Reeves WB, Andreoli TE. 1996. Cl⁻ channels in basolateral renal medullary vesicles XI. *rbClC-Ka* cDNA encodes basolateral MTAL Cl⁻ channels. *Am. J. Physiol. Renal Physiol.* 270:F1066–F72

58. Winters CJ, Zimniak L, Reeves WB, Andreoli TE. 1997. Cl⁻ channels in basolateral renal medullary membranes. XII. Anti-rbClC-Ka antibody blocks MTAL Cl⁻ channels. *Am. J. Physiol. Renal Physiol.* 273:F1030–F38

59. Yoshikawa M, Uchida S, Yamauchi A, Miyai A, Tanaka Y, et al. 1999. Localization of rat CLC-K2 chloride channel mRNA in the kidney. *Am. J. Physiol. Renal Physiol.* 276:F552–F58

60. Winters CJ, Reeves WB, Andreoli TE. 1993. Cl⁻ channels in basolateral renal medullary membranes. VII. Characteristics of the intracellular anion binding sites. *J. Membr. Biol.* 135:145–52

61. Winters CJ, Reeves WB, Andreoli TE. 1994. Cl⁻ channels in basolateral renal medullary vesicles. VIII. Partial purification and functional reconstitution of basolateral mTAL Cl⁻ channels. *Kidney Int.* 45:803–10

62. Simon DB, Bindra RS, Mansfield TA, Nelson-Williams C, Mendonca E, et al. 1997. Mutations in the chloride channel gene, CLCNKB, cause Bartter's syndrome type III. *Nat. Genet.* 17:171–78

63. Gill JR, Bartter FC. 1978. Evidence for a prostaglandin-independent defect in chloride reabsorption in the loop of Henle as a proximal cause of Bartter's syndrome. *Am. J. Med.* 65:766–72

64. Simon DB, Karet FE, Hamdan JM, DiPietro A, Sanjad SA, et al. 1996. Bartter's syndrome, hypokalaemic alkalosis with hypercalciuria, is caused by mutations in the Na-K-2Cl cotransporter NKCC2. *Nat. Genet.* 13:183–88

65. Vargas-Poussou R, Feldmann D, Vollmer M, Konrad M, Kelly L, et al. 1998. Novel molecular variants of the Na-K-2Cl cotransporter gene are responsible for antenatal Bartter syndrome. *Am. J. Hum. Genet.* 62:1332–40

66. Kurtz CL, Karolyi L, Seyberth HW, Koch MC, Vargas R, et al. 1997. A common NKCC2 mutation in Costa Rican Bartter's syndrome patients: evidence for a founder effect. *J. Am. Soc. Nephrol.* 8:1706–11

67. Simon DB, Karet FE, Rodriguez-Sorianon J, Hamdan JH, DiPietro A, et al. 1996. Genetic heterogeneity of Bartter's syndrome revealed by mutations in the K⁺ channel, ROMK. *Nat. Genet.* 14:152–56

68. Vollmer M, Koehrer M, Topaloglu R, Strahm B, Omran H, et al. 1998. Two novel mutations of the gene for Kir 1.1 (ROMK) in neonatal Bartter syndrome. *Pediatr. Nephrol.* 12:69–71

69. Konrad M, Vollmer M, Lemmink HH, Van Den Heuvel LPWJ, Jeck N, et al. 2000. Mutations in the chloride channel gene *CLCNKB* as a cause of classic Bartter syndrome. *J. Am. Soc. Nephrol.* 11:1449–59

70. Friedman PA, Andreoli TE. 1982. CO_2-stimulated NaCl absorption in the mouse renal cortical thick ascending limb of Henle. *J. Gen. Physiol.* 80:683–711

71. Molony DA, Reeves WB, Hebert SC, Andreoli TE. 1987. ADH increases apical Na⁺:K⁺:2Cl⁻ entry in mouse medullary thick ascending limbs of Henle. *Am. J. Physiol. Renal Physiol.* 252:F177–F87

72. Sun A, Grossman EB, Lombardi MJ, Hebert SC. 1991. Vasopressin alters the mechanism of apical Cl^- entry from $Na^+:Cl^-$ to $Na^+:K^+:2Cl^-$ cotransport in mouse medullary thick ascending limb. *J. Membr. Biol.* 120:83–94

73. Reeves WB, McDonald GA, Mehta P, Andreoli TE. 1989. Activation of K^+ channels in renal medullary vesicles by cAMP-dependent protein kinase. *J. Membr. Biol.* 109:65–72

74. Winters CJ, Reeves WB, Andreoli TE. 1991. Cl^- channels in basolateral renal medullary membrane vesicles. IV. Analogous channel activation by Cl^- or cAMP-dependent protein kinase. *J. Membr. Biol.* 122:89–95

75. Winters CJ, Reeves WB, Andreoli TE. 1998. Cl^- channels in basolateral TAL membranes. XIII. Heterogeneity between basolateral MTAL and CTAL Cl^- channels. *Kidney Int.* 55:593–601

76. Winters CJ, Zimniak L, Mikhailova MV, Reeves WB, Andreoli TE. 2000. Cl^- channels in basolateral TAL membranes. XV. Molecular heterogeneity between cortical and medullary channels. *J. Membr. Biol.* 177:221–30

77. Reeves WB, Andreoli TE. 1992. Sodium chloride transport in the loop of Henle. In *The Kidney: Physiology and Pathophysiology*, ed. DW Seldin, G Giebisch, pp. 1975–2001. New York: Raven. 2nd ed.

78. Molony DA, Andreoli TE. 1988. Diluting power of thick limbs of Henle. I. Peritubular hypertonicity blocks basolateral Cl^- channels. *Am. J. Physiol. Renal Physiol.* 255:F1128–F37

79. Friedman PA, Andreoli TE. 1986. Effects of $(CO_2 + HCO_3^-)$ on electrical conductance in cortical thick ascending limbs. *Kidney Int.* 30:325–31

80. Schmidt-Rose T, Jentsch TJ. 1997. Transmembrane topology of a CLC chloride channel. *Proc. Natl. Acad. Sci. USA* 94:7633–38

Annu. Rev. Physiol. 2001. 63:647–76

MOLECULAR ANALYSIS OF MAMMALIAN CIRCADIAN RHYTHMS

Steven M Reppert and David R Weaver

*Laboratory of Developmental Chronobiology, Mass General Hospital for Children,
and Harvard Medical School, Boston, Massachusetts 02114;
e-mail: reppert@helix.mgh.harvard.edu; weaver@helix.mgh.harvard.edu*

Key Words   suprachiasmatic nucleus, biological clock, clock genes, molecular biology

■ **Abstract**   In mammals, a master circadian "clock" resides in the suprachiasmatic nuclei (SCN) of the anterior hypothalamus. The SCN clock is composed of multiple, single-cell circadian oscillators, which, when synchronized, generate coordinated circadian outputs that regulate overt rhythms. Eight clock genes have been cloned that are involved in interacting transcriptional-/translational-feedback loops that compose the molecular clockwork. The daily light-dark cycle ultimately impinges on the control of two clock genes that reset the core clock mechanism in the SCN. Clock-controlled genes are also generated by the central clock mechanism, but their protein products transduce downstream effects. Peripheral oscillators are controlled by the SCN and provide local control of overt rhythm expression. Greater understanding of the cellular and molecular mechanisms of the SCN clockwork provides opportunities for pharmacological manipulation of circadian timing.

INTRODUCTION

Researchers who are analyzing the circadian clock have been working day and night to uncover the mechanisms that make our biological clock tick. Their collective discoveries are remarkable. Over the past four years, eight genes have been cloned that are intimately involved in the mammalian clockwork. We now have a firm molecular framework upon which the functions of clock genes and their protein products can be placed—the main focus of this review.

So what are circadian rhythms? They are the external expression of an internal timing mechanism that measures daily time. Circadian clocks are normally set or entrained by periodic environmental cues, with the daily light-dark cycle being the most pervasive and potent entraining stimulus in mammals. An entrained circadian clock ensures that expressed rhythms in physiology and behavior are coordinated to the 24-h day.

The suprachiasmatic nuclei (SCN) make up the site of a master circadian clock in mammalian brain that generates circadian rhythms (1). The SCN are small paired structures in the anterior hypothalamus, just above the optic chiasm. Each nucleus contains about 10,000 neurons. The nuclei are strategically positioned for receiving visual input for light-dark entrainment through both direct and indirect retina-to-SCN pathways.

The most complete understanding of the molecular control of a circadian clock mechanism in metazoans has been accomplished in the fruit fly, *Drosophila melanogaster*; molecular analysis of the *Drosophila* clock is reviewed extensively by Williams & Sehgal in this volume (2). There are great similarities between the core clock mechanisms of *Drosophila* and mice, with both clocks having interlocking positive and negative transcriptional-/translational-feedback loops. There are differences, however, in the molecular details of how the loops operate between the two species. These differences are highlighted as the mammalian system is described below.

Using mutational analysis, protein interaction screens, and homology-based approaches, homologs of most genes involved in the fly clockwork have now been cloned in mammals (Table 1). However, over the course of evolution, there has been a substantial reassignment of specific functions between several structurally homologous components of the fly and mouse circadian clocks. Gene

TABLE 1   List of clock-relevant genes

Drosophila	**Mouse**
period[a]	*mPeriod1*[a]
	mPeriod2[a]
	mPeriod3[a]
timeless[a]	—[b]
timeout	*mTimeless*[c]
cryptochrome[a]	*mCryptochrome1*[a]
	mCryptochrome2[a]
clock[a]	*Clock*[a]
	MOP4[d]
cycle[a]	*Bmal1 (MOP3)*
	Bmal2 (MOP9)[d]
doubletime[a]	casein kinase I epsilon[a]
	casein kinase I delta[d]

[a]Mutation causes altered circadian phenotype.

[b]No mammalian ortholog yet identified.

[c]Null mutation is an embryonic lethal.

[d]Clock function possible, but not yet shown.

duplication has also led to more complexity among mammalian clock genes, with most *Drosophila* clock genes represented by two or more mammalian homologs.

THE SUPRACHIASMATIC NUCLEAR CLOCKWORK IS CELL AUTONOMOUS

The oscillatory machinery is contained within single SCN neurons, and it is possible that all 20,000 cells that compose the SCN are clock cells. The cell-autonomous nature of the SCN clock was discovered by Welsh et al (3), using a system for culturing dispersed SCN cells on microelectrode arrays in which spontaneous action potentials could be recorded from individual neurons for weeks. Studies with this culture system in *tau* mutant hamsters (4) and *Clock* mutant mice (5) have shown that genetic alterations in the circadian period (cycle length) are expressed in single clock cells. Recent studies have also shown that the daily variation in responsiveness of the SCN to phase-shifting agents is manifested by individual clock neurons (6). Thus two signature features of circadian clocks, period length and rhythmic sensitivity to resetting stimuli, are properties of single clock cells. The cell-autonomous nature of the SCN clockwork focuses attention on the intracellular loops and the molecular components that compose them.

OVERVIEW OF THE MOLECULAR CLOCKWORK

A brief overview of the molecular clockwork in the mouse is presented first, followed by an analysis of the details. As already mentioned, the intracellular molecular clockwork of the SCN consists of interacting positive and negative transcriptional-/translational-feedback loops (Figure 1, see color insert). The negative-feedback loop involves the dynamic regulation of three *Period* genes (in the mouse, designated *mPer1–3*) and two *Cryptochrome* genes (*mCry1* and *mCry2* in the mouse). The rhythmic transcription of the *mPer* and *mCry* genes is driven by the basic helix-loop-helix (bHLH)–PER-ARNT-SIM (PAS) protein-containing transcription factors CLOCK and BMAL1 [PAS is an acronym for the first three proteins found to share this functionally important protein dimerization domain: *Drosophila* PER, the human aryl hydrocarbon receptor nuclear translocator (ARNT), and the *Drosophila* single-minded protein (SIM)]. PAS domain-containing proteins represent a diverse family (7), and PAS domains are also a common feature of clock-relevant proteins among diverse organisms (plants, fungi, insects, and mammals) (8, 9).

As the mPER and mCRY proteins are translated, they form multimeric complexes that are translocated to the nucleus. In the nucleus, the mCRY proteins act as negative regulators by directly interacting with CLOCK and/or BMAL1 to inhibit transcription. At the same time, mPER2 contributes to the rhythmic transcription of *Bmal1*, which expresses a phase opposite that of *mPer/mCry*, forming a positive-feedback loop. Increased availability of BMAL1 presumably promotes CLOCK:BMAL1 heterodimerization needed to restart the *mPer/mCry* transcriptional cycles. The positive-feedback loop thereby augments regulation of the negative-feedback loop, perpetuating the clock cycle.

A working model of the SCN clockwork based on interacting positive- and negative-feedback loops proposes that, at the start of the circadian day (CT 0), *mPer* and *mCry* transcription is driven by accumulating CLOCK:BMAL1 heterodimers (Figure 2, see color insert). The circadian oscillations of *mPer* and *mCry* RNA levels in the SCN exhibit similar yet distinct temporal profiles, with the *mPer1* RNA rhythm peaking from CT 4 through 6, *mPer3* from CT 4 through 8, *mPer2* at CT 8, and *mCry1* at CT 10. By midcircadian day (CT 12), the mPER and mCRY proteins are synchronously expressed in the nucleus where the mCRY proteins shut off CLOCK:BMAL1-mediated transcription. At the same time, mPER2 either shuttles a transcriptional activator into the nucleus or coactivates a transcriptional complex to enhance *Bmal1* transcription, leading to peak *Bmal1* RNA levels from CT 15 through 18 (Figure 2). We presume that the *Bmal1* RNA rhythm drives a BMAL1 protein rhythm after a 4- to 6-h delay. The renewal of BMAL1 levels at the end of the night presumably increases CLOCK:BMAL1 heterodimers at the appropriate circadian time to drive *mPer/mCry* transcription, thereby restarting the cycle (Figure 2). It appears that BMAL1 availability is rate limiting for heterodimer formation and is critical for restarting the loops at the start of a new circadian day (CT 0).

TRANSCRIPTIONAL CONTROL BY CLOCK:BMAL1

Clock was the first clock gene cloned in mammals (10). The *Clock* mutation, isolated in a chemical mutagenesis screen, is a semidominant, autosomal mutation that causes abnormally long circadian periods in behavior, with homozygous mutant mice eventually becoming arrhythmic in constant darkness (DD) (11). Positional cloning and functional rescue showed that *Clock* encodes a bHLH-PAS transcription factor (10, 12). CLOCK heterodimerizes with BMAL1 to enhance transcription through E box elements (13–15). The dominant-negative phenotype of the *Clock* mutation is explained by the 51 amino acids that are deleted from the putative transcriptional-activation domain of the mutant protein (10). The mutant CLOCK protein can still form heterodimers with BMAL1 that bind to DNA, but the heterodimers are deficient in transcriptional activity (13). CLOCK is thus critical for transactivation activity of the CLOCK:BMAL1:E-box complex.

The nature of the *Clock* mutation predicts that the rhythmic expression of components of the negative-feedback loop should be down-regulated in *Clock/Clock* mutant mice. In fact, the peak of the RNA rhythms of *mPer1–3* and *mCry1* are all significantly reduced in the SCN of homozygous *Clock* mutant mice (13, 16, 17). In addition, *mCry2* RNA levels, which express a weak circadian rhythm (18), are significantly depressed in *Clock/Clock* mice (17).

In each case of down-regulated RNA levels, it is unclear, however, whether CLOCK-mediated transcriptional enhancement is direct (through interaction with DNA elements of each gene) or indirect (the result of a direct action on other genes). In vitro studies indicate that CLOCK:BMAL1 heterodimers are highly selective in their preference for E boxes with the nucleotide sequence CACGTG (14, 19). The importance of flanking sequences for transcriptional activation has not been rigorously studied. CACGTG E boxes have been found in the 5′ flanking regions of *mPer1* and *mCry1* and in intronic regions of *mPer2* and *mPer3* (13, 16, 17). The importance of these E boxes for transcriptional regulation in vivo has yet to be examined.

The best in vivo evidence to date that the CACGTG motif is indeed necessary for circadian enhancement of transcription comes from reporter transgene studies using the *mPer1* promoter. A green fluorescent protein reporter transgene driven by 2.1 kb of 5′ flanking region of the *mPer1* gene (which contains three CACGTG E boxes) directs expression to the SCN in mice that is rhythmically regulated like the endogenous gene (20). Similar transgene approaches with and without mutated elements need to be applied to *mPer1* and other putative clock genes for in vivo mapping of regulatory regions, in combination with identifying DNase I-hypersensitive sites.

For some oscillating genes down-regulated in *Clock/Clock* mutant mice, it is possible that CLOCK heterodimerizes with other partners and/or activates transcription through more promiscuous E box enhancers (CANNTG) or as-yet unidentified DNA-binding elements. Indeed, a second *Bmal* gene was identified recently in zebrafish (21) and in mice (*MOP9*) (22) that may add to the complexity of CLOCK-mediate transcriptional enhancement. The delayed phase of the *mPer2* and *mCry1* RNA rhythms relative to the phase of the *mPer1* and *mPer3* rhythms may support the existence of a different transcriptional-activation cascade. On the other hand, these slight phase differences may merely reflect differences in the kinetics of gene transcription and RNA turnover among these genes, even though transcription of each may be driven by CLOCK:BMAL1 heterodimers acting through CACGTG E box enhancers. Several other bHLH-PAS-containing transcription factors are expressed in the mouse SCN (23), and their functions remain to be examined. MOP4 is a bHLH-PAS-containing transcription factor closely related to CLOCK that can also heterodimerize with BMAL1 and activate transcription from CACGTG E boxes in vitro (14, 17), but it is not expressed at detectable levels in the SCN of normal mice or *Clock/Clock* mutant mice (17, 23).

CRYPTOCHROMES ARE NEGATIVE REGULATORS

Both in vivo and in vitro studies indicate that the mCRY proteins are the preeminent regulators of the negative limb of the feedback loop in the SCN clockwork. This function was a complete surprise because in plants and in *Drosophila* cryptochromes act as blue-light photoreceptors for the circadian system (24). Cryptochromes are pterin/flavin-containing proteins that are structural homologs of the DNA repair enzyme DNA photolyase, but they lack DNA repair activity (24). Mammalian cryptochromes were cloned by their homology with *Drosophila* (6-4) photolyase and plant cryptochromes (25, 26).

The mouse *Cryptochrome* genes are expressed in the SCN (17, 27). The first hard evidence that the mCRYs might be involved in the core clock mechanism was the finding that targeted deletion of *mCry2* lengthens the circadian period (28, 29). Targeted deletion of *mCry1*, on the other hand, shortens the circadian period (29, 30). But the astonishing finding came when circadian behavior was assessed in mice bearing targeted deletions of both *mCry1* and *mCry2*. These *mCry*-deficient animals exhibit a complete loss of circadian rhythmicity in wheel-running behavior immediately upon placement in contant darkness (DD) (29, 30).

In *mCry*-deficient mice, *mPer1* and *mPer2* RNA levels are arrhythmic and expressed at mid to high values in the SCN (18, 30). This is consistent with in vitro studies showing that the mCRY proteins are potent inhibitors of CLOCK:BMAL1-mediated transcription (17). Further in vitro analysis has shown that mCRY inhibition of CLOCK:BMAL1-mediated transcription is through direct protein-protein interactions, independently of the mPER and mTIM proteins (31) and independently of the effects of light (32). Moreover, mCRY1 and mCRY2 exhibit synchronous oscillations of nuclear localization in the SCN at the appropriate circadian time for negatively regulating their own transcription and the transcription of the *mPer* genes (17). The peak in the mCRY1 oscillation follows the peak in the *mCry1* RNA rhythm by 2–3 h (Figure 2). For mCRY2, the prominent protein oscillation is not accompanied by a similarly striking circadian oscillation in RNA levels. It thus appears that post-transcriptional mechanisms are primarily driving the mCRY2 rhythm.

It is still unclear how the mCRY proteins negatively regulate CLOCK:BMAL1-mediated transcription. Each mCRY protein could either directly pull the CLOCK:BMAL1 heterodimer off the E box while leaving the heterodimer intact (as appears to occur for PER and TIM inhibition of CLOCK:CYC-mediated transcription in the fly) (33) or the mCRYs could disrupt the heterodimer. Because the mCRY proteins have a binding site for the electron-transferring flavin, it is possible that their interaction with transcription factors initiates a reduction oxidation reaction. In fact, redox changes regulate the DNA-binding activity of another bHLH-PAS transcription factor, the aryl hydrocarbon receptor (34).

It is also possible that other proteins are involved in the inhibitory mechanism. mCRY2 has been shown to heterodimerize through the tetratricopeptide motifs of serine-threonine protein phosphatase and tetratricopeptide repeat protein 1 (35). Serine-threonine protein phosphatase also binds heat-shock protein 90, the latter of which can interact with bHLH-PAS-containing transcription factors (including BMAL1) to potentially regulate transcription (7). Thus tetratricopeptide-containing proteins could be important for mediating and/or modulating the effects of the mCRY proteins on CLOCK:BMAL1 activity, as well as modifying the activities of other mCRY dimerization partners, for example, the mPER proteins (36). Further work is needed to identify clock-relevant protein-protein interactions.

mCRY1 and mCRY2 are mutually redundant but collectively essential components of the negative limb of the clock feedback loop. The redundant function of these proteins is indicated by the maintenance of circadian rhythmicity when either gene is deleted. Their necessity is demonstrated by the arrhythmic phenotype of double-knockout mice (29, 30). The different direction of period change in $mCry1^{-/-}$ versus $mCry2^{-/-}$ mice may result from differing affinities of these proteins for other clock components and/or different levels of protein expression that alter the overall kinetics of the feedback loops.

PERturbations

If CLOCK and BMAL1 are the positive elements and the cryptochromes are the negative elements of the negative-feedback loop, then what are the functions of the mPER proteins? The three mammalian *Period* genes were identified by their homology with *Drosophila per* (37–43). Similar to their insect counterpart, each of the mPER proteins possesses a protein dimerization PAS domain, suggesting that protein-protein interactions are important for their clock actions. A variety of mPER-mPER interactions have been demonstrated in vitro and in vivo (17, 44–46); these interactions appear to be PAS mediated (44, 46). In vitro studies in mammalian cell lines have also shown that each of the mPER proteins can modestly inhibit CLOCK:BMAL1-mediated transcription (16, 47). Recent gene-targeting studies have shown, however, that the mPER proteins have distinct functions. Moreover, the mPER proteins have surprisingly little effect on negative regulation of the clock feedback loop, unlike the autoinhibitory function of *Drosophila* PER (2).

The behavioral and molecular phenotypes of *mPer2* mutant animals support a role of mPER2 in positive, rather than negative, transcriptional regulation (48). The mutant *mPer2* allele (designated $mPer2^{Brdm1}$) is a deletion mutation encoding a protein that is missing 87 residues in the carboxyl portion of the PAS dimerization domain (48). Homozygous $mPer2^{Brdm1}$ mutant mice show shorter circadian periods followed by loss of circadian rhythmicity in DD. At the molecular level, *mPer1, mPer2,* and *mCry1* RNA levels are still rhythmic in the SCN of homozygous mutants on initial placement in DD, but the rhythms are severely reduced in peak level (31, 48). The molecular phenotype of the mutant mice is surprising because reduction in RNA levels is not consistent with a potent role of mPER2 in its own negative regulation or the negative regulation of the *mPer1* or *mCry1* RNA oscillations. Instead, the molecular phenotype of the $mPer2^{Brdm1}$ mutation is consistent with a strong positive regulatory function of mPER2 in the core clock mechanism (48). It is not yet clear whether the $mPer2^{Brdm1}$ mutation is a partial or complete loss-of-function defect.

An interdigitating positive-feedback loop that has at its core the rhythmic regulation of *Bmal1* nicely explains the phenotypes of the *mPer2^{Brdm1}* mutant animals (31). In rats and mice, *Bmal1* RNA levels are rhythmic in the SCN with a phase opposite of that described for the *mPer1, mPer2*, and *mPer3* rhythms (49, 50), whereas *Clock* RNA levels do not oscillate (23, 31, 38). Because mPER1, mPER2, mCRY1, and mCRY2 exhibit synchronous oscillations of nuclear localization in the SCN (17, 45) (Figure 2), some of these proteins (the mCRY proteins) could be negatively regulating their own transcription, while others (e.g. mPER2) simultaneously increase the transcription of *Bmal1*.

Clock/Clock mutant mice and mice homozygous for the *mPer2^{Brdm1}* mutation both have reduced *mPer2* RNA levels and show blunted *Bmal1* RNA rhythms, consistent with a role of mPER2 in the positive regulation of the *Bmal1* loop (16, 31, 48). Moreover, mPER2 levels are severely reduced in *mCry*-deficient animals even though *mPer2* RNA levels in the SCN are expressed at constant levels in the mid to high range (31). Taken together, the data are consistent with mCRY being important for stabilization of mPER2 and with mPER2 being a positive regulator of *mBmal1* transcription.

Because mPER-mCRY interactions that mediate nuclear transport of the mPER proteins occur outside the PAS region (as opposed to PAS-dependent PER-TIM interactions in *Drosophila*), the PAS domain of a mPER2-mCRY heterodimer would be free to bind to a transcription factor and shuttle it into the nucleus to activate *Bmal1* transcription (31). Alternatively, once in the nucleus, mPER2-mCRY heterodimers or mPER2 monomers could coactivate *Bmal1* transcription through a PAS-mediated interaction with a transcription factor. Direct mPER2-mediated transcription seems unlikely because the protein does not appear to possess DNA-binding motifs (40). The race is on to find the missing mPER2 interactor. Analysis of the *Bmal1* promoter will also be informative.

The role of mPER2 is distinct among the *mPer* genes. Preliminary studies by Zheng et al (cited in 31) show that the diurnal oscillation in *mPer2* RNA is not altered in the SCN of *mPer1*-deficient mice and that circadian rhythms in behavior are sustained in these animals. No studies have yet been published on the phase-shifting capabilities of *mPer1*- or *mPer2*-deficient mice. These will be important studies because mPER1 may be the protein necessary for transducing light-induced phase-shifting responses to the molecular loops (see below).

Mice with targeted disruption of *mPer3* have a subtle circadian phenotype, with shortening of their circadian period but persistent rhythmicity in DD (51). The only molecular phenotype detected is a reduction in the peak levels of mutant *mPer3* transcripts in the SCN and skeletal muscle. No major up- or down-regulation of other molecular oscillations (*mPer1, mPer2, mCry1*, and *Bmal1* RNA levels) occurs, suggesting that the lack of a robust behavioral phenotype is not caused by up-regulation of related genes with overlapping function. These results indicate that mPER3 is not essential for a functioning circadian clock. Likewise, mPER3-mPER1 interactions that influence subcellular distribution of these proteins in cell culture (17, 46) are not critical for circadian function. mPER3 may actually be involved in clock output function as discussed below.

MAMMALIAN *Timeless*

Where does mammalian *Timeless* fit into the clock gene story? *tim* is essential for circadian function in *Drosophila* (2). TIM is necessary for translocating itself and PER into the nucleus and is the point within the feedback loops at which photic stimuli reset the fly circadian clock (2). A putative mammalian homolog of *Drosophila tim* has been identified by expressed-sequence-tag database searches, but placing its function within the molecular mechanism of the mammalian clock has been difficult (44, 47, 52–54). Although mouse *Timeless (mTim)* is expressed at low levels in the SCN, its RNA levels do not consistently oscillate there under constant conditions. Moreover, mTIM is a nuclear protein, and its levels in the SCN are not rhythmic and are not altered by light pulses that cause phase shifts in circadian behavior (45, 55).

Mammalian TIM does not interact with the three mPER proteins in yeast nor in vivo in the SCN (44, 45), but it has been reported to interact with mPER1 in COS-7 cells (53) and with *Drosophila* PER in vitro (47). Immunofluorescence studies of overexpressed proteins in cell culture fail to show any alteration in the cellular location of the mPER proteins when coexpressed with mTIM (17, 56, 56a). This contrasts with the potent ability of either mCRY1 or mCRY2 to translocate each of the three mPER proteins into the nucleus (17). Coimmunoprecipitation experiments with overexpressed proteins in vitro and native proteins in vivo show that mTIM interacts with mCRY1 and mCRY2 (17, 45). The biological relevance of mTIM-mCRY interactions is unknown.

Studies in mammalian cell lines indicate that mTIM can inhibit CLOCK: BMAL1-mediated transcription (16, 47). In an insect cell line, however, mTIM cannot directly inhibit transcription, indicating that its inhibitory effect is dependent on interactions with other mammalian proteins (57). This is in contrast to the direct inhibitory effect of *Drosophila* TIM (33). Database searches of the completed *Drosophila* genome further show that mTIM is not the true ortholog of *Drosophila* TIM, but it is the likely ortholog of a newly described fly gene, *timeout* (57, 57a). Targeted disruption of *mTim* shows that embryos homozygous for the targeted allele die before midgestation. Mice carrying only one copy of the *mTim* gene have normal circadian function (57). Thus *mTim* is a developmental gene without substantiated circadian function. Only time will tell whether a true clock-relevant ortholog of fly *tim* exists in mammals. At present, it appears that many of the core clock functions of TIM in the fly have been supplanted by the mCRY proteins in the mouse.

THE 24-H TIME CONSTANT

Phosphorylation and proteolysis of clock proteins are likely to be important for imparting a 24-h time constant to the SCN clockwork. These processes may affect stability and nuclear transport of clock proteins, as occurs in *Drosophila* (2).

The synchronous oscillations of nuclear localization of mPER1, mPER2, mCRY1, and mCRY2 in the SCN suggest that mCRY-mPER interactions are important for nuclear translocation of the mPER proteins (Figure 2). In cell culture, the mCRY proteins are potent translocators of the mPER proteins from cytoplasm to nucleus, but the mPER proteins appear to have little effect on mCRY location, which is mainly nuclear in cell culture (17, 31). The mCRY proteins are not always necessary for nuclear translocation of the mPER proteins, however. In *mCry*-deficient mice, mPER1 can gain access to the nuclei of SCN neurons (31, 46). In addition, areas outside the SCN that constitutively express PER in the nucleus in wild-type animals (e.g. piriform cortex) still show nuclear mPER1 and mPER2 staining in *mCry*-deficient animals (31). Finally, the mPER proteins can enter the nucleus of *mCry*-deficient cells in vitro (46).

Recent studies suggest that, in addition to mPER1-mCRY interactions, the phosphorylation state of mPER1 influences cellular location. Phosphorylation of mPER1 by casein kinase I epsilon (CKIε, a mammalian ortholog of *Drosophila* DOUBLETIME) alters its cellular location in vitro (56, 56a). Thus the nuclear location of both mPER1 and mPER2 in vivo may depend on several factors, including interactions with mCRY, other mPERs, other proteins, and their state of phosphorylation. This emphasizes the importance of cellular context for in vitro studies in which interactions are examined. A nuclear location for mPER3 has not yet been confirmed in vivo. Taken as a whole, the data are still consistent with the mCRYs being important for the circadian regulation of mPER nuclear entry in the SCN.

A major discovery concerning the importance of phosphorylation for the SCN clockwork was the recent cloning of the *tau* mutation in the Syrian hamster. *tau* is a spontaneous, semidominant mutation causing a short-period phenotype (58). The *tau* mutant hamster has played an important role in defining the physiological basis of circadian timing in mammals over the past decade (see 59, 60).

Using a positional syntenic cloning strategy, Takahashi and colleagues (61) showed that the *tau* locus encodes CKIε and that the mutation causes substitution of a cysteine for a conserved arginine at residue 178. Functional analysis shows that the mutant enzyme has reduced maximal velocity and reduced autophosphorylation. Mutant CKIε can bind mPER1 and mPER2, perhaps with increased affinity, but it has decreased ability to phosphorylate the mPER proteins. It is possible that the binding of mutant enzyme to the mPER proteins has dominant-negative effects, rendering the bound protein unable to interact with functional enzyme(s). Casein kinase I delta (CKIδ) is highly homologous to CKIε (76% identical at the amino acid level) and efficiently binds and phosphorylates mPER1 in vitro (56). This proposed dominant-negative scenario is consistent with the semidominant circadian phenotype of the *tau* mutation.

The precise way in which phosphorylation by CKIε (or CKIδ) influences circadian timing remains to be defined. In *Drosophila*, DOUBLETIME phosphorylation destabilizes PER so that its levels accumulate only when TIM levels are rising, thereby controlling the timing of nuclear entry and subsequent negative feedback

(62). Phosphorylation by CKIε also makes mPER1 less stable in cell culture (56, 63). Thus one way in which phosphorylation may contribute to circadian timing in mammals is to destabilize mPERs so that their levels accumulate only when mCRY levels are rising. However, several questions remain. Which mPER proteins are normally phosphorylated by CKIε and/or CKIδ? Are other clock components phosphorylated by these enzymes (e.g. the mCRY proteins)? What is the fate of phosphorylated proteins? It is also not yet known whether proteosomal proteolysis plays an important role in the SCN clockwork, as it does in *Drosophila* (1, 64).

LIGHT TO SUPRACHIASMATIC NUCLEI

As a molecular clock mechanism has emerged in mammals, understanding how the feedback loops are reset by light has been the focus of considerable attention (Figure 3, see color insert). The mammalian SCN detect light via the retina. In both rodents and humans, the eyes are necessary for entrainment of behavioral rhythms to light-dark cycles (65, 66).

Remarkably, the identity of the circadian photoreceptive molecules in the mammalian eye remains unclear (see 67, 68). The absorption spectrum of the circadian visual pigment suggests a photoreceptive molecule consisting of an opsin and an 11-*cis* retinal-based pigment (68, 69). Studies of mutant mice reveal that the retinal photoreceptor cells, the rods and cones, are not necessary for circadian light perception (70, 71). SCN responses to light are also preserved in mCRY-deficient mice (18, 30), suggesting that cryptochromes are not necessary for circadian photoreception in mice. A novel opsin, melanopsin, is expressed in the inner retina (72), compatible with the expected distribution of a putative non-rod-, non-cone-photoreceptive molecule. Examination of the effects of targeted disruption of the melanopsin gene on circadian responses in mice is awaited.

RETINA TO SUPRACHIASMATIC NUCLEAR PATHWAYS

Lighting information is conveyed to the SCN by several convergent pathways (73). The major light input pathway to the SCN is the retinohypothalamic tract (RHT), which arises from a widely distributed population of retinal ganglion cells (74).

The major neurotransmitter of the RHT is glutamate (75). Two peptides present in the RHT, substance P and pituitary adenylate cyclase-activating peptide, modulate the entrainment process (76, 77).

Two indirect pathways provide retinal input to the SCN. The first is from the intergeniculate leaflet of the lateral geniculate nucleus, which receives input from the same retinal cells whose axons compose the RHT (78). A geniculohypothalamic tract, rich in γ-aminobutyric acid (GABA), neuropeptide Y, and enkephalin converges on the retinorecipient region of the SCN (73). The second indirect pathway from the retina to the retinorecipient SCN is routed via the serotonergic raphe nuclei. Transmitters in both the intergeniculate leaflet and raphe pathways appear to play a role in mediating nonphotic phase shifts, for example those caused by behavioral arousal (79, 80).

Finally, neurohumoral signals reach the SCN. The pineal hormone, melatonin, can subtly influence circadian rhythms in adult mammals, but it has a dramatic impact during development (81, 82). Mel1a melatonin receptor activation inhibits firing of SCN neurons, whereas both Mel1a and Mel1b receptors appear capable of mediating phase shifts (83). The inhibitory effect of melatonin may augment other mechanisms, leading to the day-night difference in levels of SCN electrical activity (see below).

LIGHT-INDUCED SIGNAL TRANSDUCTION CASCADES IN THE SUPRACHIASMATIC NUCLEI

An extensive series of studies has examined signal transduction events occurring in SCN neurons after neurochemical stimulation (84). These studies reveal that the signal transduction pathways activated by glutamate receptor activation depend on the circadian time at which the stimulus is applied. Early in the subjective night, light exposure causes a phase delay, via glutamate acting at N-methyl-D-aspartate receptors (85). The effects of glutamate appear mediated by release of intracellular calcium via ryanodine receptors (86). The downstream actions of calcium likely include activation of calcium/calmodulin, MAP kinase, and other kinases; phosphorylation of cAMP response element-binding protein (CREB); and induction of gene expression via calcium/cAMP response elements (Ca/CREs) (84, 87).

Later in the night, light exposure in vivo (or glutamate receptor activation in vitro) causes phase advances. At this phase, glutamate appears to activate nitric oxide production, activate soluble guanylyl cyclase, increase cGMP, activate cGMP-dependent protein kinase, and phosphorylate CREB (86, 88).

CREB phosphorylation is regulated by the circadian clock; the ability of light (in vivo) or glutamate receptor activation (in vitro) to induce P-CREB is limited to a nocturnal zone of sensitivity (88, 89). Thus one output of the circadian clock is the ability to regulate its responsiveness to inputs at specific times of the circadian cycle (see 84).

In the 1990s, there was great interest in the hypothesis that the induction of c-*fos* is a critical step in the photic transduction pathway. The phase-response and fluence-response curves for c-*fos* induction parallel those for light-induced phase shifts (90). Additional studies have revealed that, although c-*fos* induction frequently occurs in parallel with a phase-shift after various stimuli, c-*fos* induction in the SCN is not necessary or sufficient for phase-shifting responses to light (91–93).

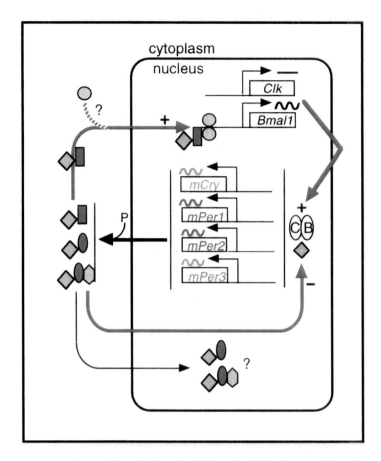

Figure 1 Model of circadian clockwork within an individual suprachiasmatic nucleus neuron. The clockwork is composed of interacting positive- (green lines) and negative- (red lines) feedback loops. The protein products are color-coded shapes (mCRYs, gold diamond; mPER1, blue oval; mPER2, red rectangle; mPER3, green hexagon; hypothetical activator-coactivator of *Bmal1* transcription, small gray circle). CLOCK (oval with C) and BMAL1 (oval with B) heterodimers activate (+) rhythmic transcription of *mCry* and *mPer* genes. The mCRY and mPER proteins form complexes important for nuclear translocation of the mPER proteins. The phosphorylation (P) state of the mPER proteins may also regulate their cellular location and stability. mPER2 positively regulates *Bmal1* transcription by translocating an activator into the nucleus and/or acting as a coactivator (?). The nuclear-localized mCRY proteins directly interact with CLOCK and BMAL1 to negatively regulate (-) CLOCK:BMAL1-mediated transcription. The functions of nuclear mPER1 and mPER3 have not yet been clearly defined (?).

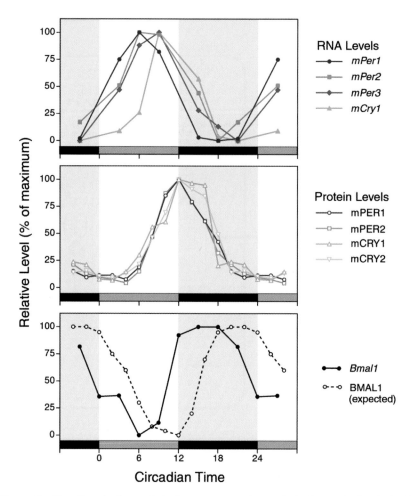

Figure 2 Circadian rhythms of clock gene expression and clock protein levels in the mouse suprachiasmatic nuclei. Rhythmic abundance of *mPer1*, *mPer2*, *mPer3*, and *mCry1* RNAs (*top*); mPER1, mPER2, mCRY1, and mCRY2 proteins (*middle*); and *Bmal1* RNA (solid line, *bottom*) and hypothetical data (dashed line, *bottom*) represent the expected rhythmic variations in BMAL1 protein. Rhythmic expression of *mPer1-3* and *mCry1* RNAs is driven by E-box-mediated transcriptional activation. As the proteins accumulate (*middle*), transcription of these RNAs is inhibited, while *Bmal1* transcription is stimulated. The antiphase rhythm in *Bmal1* RNA presumably leads to production of BMAL1 protein necessary to restart the next circadian cycle. Data modified from 17, 31, 41, 45, and 55. RNA levels were assessed by in situ hybridization on sections of the SCN. Values were converted from film optical density values by subtracting the minimum value for each probe from all values, then expressing other values as a percent of the highest net value. Protein levels were assessed by immunocytochemistry and are expressed as a percent of the maximum number of immunoreactive nuclei per SCN. Gray bar, subjective day; black bar, subjective night.

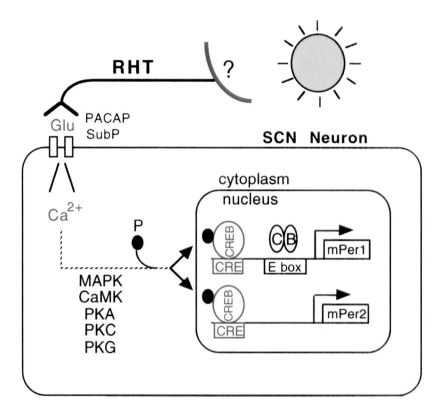

Figure 3 Schematic of light input pathway to the SCN clockwork. Highlighted in red are the elements known to be important for light activation of behaviorally relevant pathways. Photons are captured by an unidentified photoreceptor (?) in the retina (green arc). Light causes glutamate (Glu) release from terminals of the retinohypothalamic tract (RHT), which innervates the retinorecipient SCN. Glutamate, through both N-methyl-D-aspartate and non-N-methyl-D-aspartate receptors, differentially activates Ca^{2+}-dependent signaling pathways in a time-of-day-dependent manner; substance P (SubP) and pituitary adenylate cyclase-activating peptide (PACAP) released from the RHT modulate glutamate action. Activated kinases phosphorylate cAMP response element-binding protein (CREB). Phosphorylated CREB presumably activates *mPer1* and *mPer2* transcription by direct interaction with a calcium/cAMP response element (CRE, blue) in the promoter region of each gene. Light activation occurs when CLOCK (C) and BMAL1 (B) heterodimers are inactive. CaMK, calcium/calmodulin-dependent kinases; MAPK, MAP kinase; PKA, protein kinase A, PKC, protein kinase C; PKG, protein kinase G.

PER REGULATION BY LIGHT

With the cloning of mammalian *Per* homologs came interest in their regulation by light. Both *mPer1* and *mPer2* are regulated by light at night, whereas *mPer3* gene expression is unresponsive (39–43, 94). The temporal profile of *mPer* gene induction in the SCN after light is very rapid, with increases in *mPer1* occurring by 10 min (94). *mPer* induction lags slightly behind c-*fos* induction, but it is sufficiently rapid to show that FOS is not regulating *mPer1*. Instead, it seems most likely that *mPer1* is directly regulated by P-CREB acting via a CRE element in the 5′-flanking region of the *mPer1* gene. In transgenic mice expressing reporter genes under control of an *mPer1* promoter fragment containing a consensus CRE element, reporter expression is induced by light (20, 95). Studies in fibroblasts and ovine pars tuberalis cells indicate that the induction of *mPer* gene expression does not require protein synthesis (96, 97), further supporting an immediate-early-like character to *mPer* gene regulation. *mPer2* gene expression is also acutely induced by light, but this occurs most prominently during early subjective night, with little response to light pulses during late subjective night (40, 41). The 5′-flanking region of the *mPer2* gene also contains a consensus CRE element. Mutational analysis of the CRE elements in *mPer1* and *mPer2* is needed to show their functional importance in vivo.

For alterations in gene expression to be functionally meaningful, they must be translated to alterations in protein levels. Hastings and colleagues (45) recently characterized levels of clock gene expression and protein levels in mice after exposure to light at night. The results are consistent with a model in which the photic induction of *mPer1* is the primary stimulus for resetting the circadian clock. Of the proteins studied, only mPER1 levels were altered by exposure to light at night. Remarkably, the alterations in mPER1 levels were small and were detected only 4–9 h after a light pulse. One reason for this small, delayed response may be the measure used; counts of mPER1-immunoreactive nuclei are relatively insensitive to the level of protein within each cell. Induction of new mPER in a cell already mPER positive would not be detected until the new mPER1 outlasted the half-life of the older mPER1 molecules already in the cell. There were no alterations in the abundance of TIM or CRY proteins after brief light exposure (45), revealing that mammalian resetting mechanisms are different from those in flies (2).

The importance of mPER1 in resetting the circadian clock is also suggested by studies using antisense oligonucleotides to *Per1*; antisense pretreatment blunts resetting responses in vivo and in vitro (98). Furthermore, nonphotic phase shifts during subjective day lead to a reduction in *Per* RNA levels in the hamster SCN, suggesting that regulation of PER levels may be a common mechanism for resetting (99, 99a). It will be interesting to determine whether mice deficient in *mPer1* can phase shift in response to light and other stimuli. Mice with a mutation of *mPer2* leading to deletion of a portion of the PAS domain entrain and phase shift in response to light, although their ability to maintain rhythms in constant conditions is impaired (48).

Important questions remain about how mPER1 induction can affect the core clock loop, especially in view of recent evidence that the mCRYs, rather than the mPERs, are preeminent for negative regulation in the core clock loop. These data suggest that mPER1 stabilizes mCRY1, extending the duration of negative feedback on the clock (45). Although this explanation makes sense for the phase delay in response to light pulses early in subjective night, it is less consistent with the observation that the only alteration in clock proteins detected in the SCN after exposure to a phase-advancing light pulse late in the subjective night was an increase in mPER1. Perhaps the small amplitude of light-induced phase advances in mice reflects a subtle change in clock proteins. If this is the case, examination of species with a more prominent phase-advance portion in the phase-response curve should be informative. Another possibility is that elevations of mPER1 late at night can positively influence the clock loop. Finally, to date it has not been possible to examine regulation of BMAL1 protein in the SCN; photic regulation of BMAL1 needs to be examined.

LINKING CLOCK GENES TO RHYTHMS OF ELECTRICAL ACTIVITY IN THE SUPRACHIASMATIC NUCLEI

A goal of research in circadian biology is defining the ways in which the core clockwork regulates the temporal variations in diverse biological processes. Ultimately, the oscillations of gene expression in the clockwork must be translated into a form that can impart rhythmicity on other neural substrates. With elucidation of a firm molecular framework for the SCN clock mechanism, more effort is being directed at how clock genes ultimately regulate behavior.

Sodium-dependent action potentials provide the most important mechanism by which the SCN communicate with their surroundings. Rats receiving chronic infusions of tetrodotoxin or anesthetic agents to block SCN neuronal firing exhibit arrhythmic behavior (100, 101). Once treatment is discontinued, however, rhythmicity is restored at the phase predicted by extrapolating from the previous phase of rhythmicity. Similar results have been observed following tetrodotoxin treatment of individual SCN clock cells in vitro, emphasizing the role of intracellular processes in generating the circadian rhythms in electrical activity (3). The finding that the clock continues to keep time even though its electrical output is silenced clearly demonstrates that the rhythmic electrical activity of the SCN neurons is an output, not a necessary component of the clock.

Rhythmic alterations in membrane potential and/or channel activity probably underlie the rhythmic electrical activity of SCN neurons (102, 103). Although it is possible that there is direct transcriptional regulation of channel abundance or regulatory factors affecting channel activity by CLOCK:BMAL1, it seems more likely that this circadian enhancement is indirect. The most probable way for the clockwork to regulate downstream events is to use proteins from clock-controlled genes (CCGs) that are regulated (directly or indirectly) by the core feedback loops. CCGs are rhythmically regulated by the circadian clock, but differ from clock genes in that their protein products are not essential for function of the clockwork.

Some CCGs are directly regulated by CLOCK:BMAL1 heterodimers acting through CACGTG E box enhancers in SCN neurons (Figure 4). Vasopressin prepropressophysin (AVP) gene expression is the first example of a directly regulated CCG (16). Albumin D-element-binding protein (DBP) is also a directly regulated CCG (104). Both AVP and DBP RNAs are highly rhythmic in the SCN. The peaks in the rhythms of transcript levels are severely reduced in the SCN of *Clock/Clock* mutant mice. In vitro studies of the AVP promoter indicate that gene expression is positively enhanced through CLOCK:BMAL1 action on a CACGTG E box (16) and that CLOCK:BMAL1-mediated transcription is negatively regulated by the same molecules that act as negative elements in the core clockwork (17). Similarly, in vivo and in vitro analyses reveal intronic E boxes that contribute to the circadian cycling of DBP gene expression (104, 105). DBP may also have functions within the clockwork itself because DBP-deficient mice have significantly shortened circadian periods in wheel-running behavior (106). In fact, in vitro experiments suggest that the *mPer1* promoter may be cooperatively activated by DBP, a leucine zipper transcription factor, and CLOCK:BMAL1 heterodimers (105). A role for DBP in the circadian enhancement of *mPer1* gene expression needs to be verified in DBP-deficient mice, however.

The putative clock genes *mPer1* and *mPer3* may also represent CCGs involved in output. Each of the three *mPer* genes is rhythmic and is depressed in the SCN of *Clock/Clock* mice (16), and the evidence for E-box-mediated transcriptional enhancement is quite strong in the case of *mPer1* (see above) (13, 20, 95). Results from mice with targeted disruption of each of these genes suggest that the genes are not necessary for circadian clock function, but that gene targeting slightly alters circadian function (31, 51).

How could rhythmic expression of CCGs within SCN neurons influence their electrical activity? AVP appears to augment the magnitude of the electrical activity rhythm in the SCN through a receptor-mediated excitation of SCN neurons (107, 108). AVP may act in both autocrine and paracrine manners to augment SCN excitability. Importantly, Brattleboro rats, which lack vasopressin peptide due to a mutation in the AVP gene, still express circadian rhythms (of reduced amplitude), indicating that vasopressin is not essential for circadian clock function (108–110). The transcription factor DBP may regulate the abundance of a channel important for regulating membrane potential. In this way, gene products directly regulated by the core loops may serve a second role as regulators of events more removed from the central clock mechanism. Identification of the mechanisms by which clock genes and/or CCGs regulate excitability will require characterization of the membrane properties of SCN neurons at known circadian phases, an undertaking that will be facilitated by in vitro identification of individual, oscillating SCN neurons using reporter gene technology (20, 111).

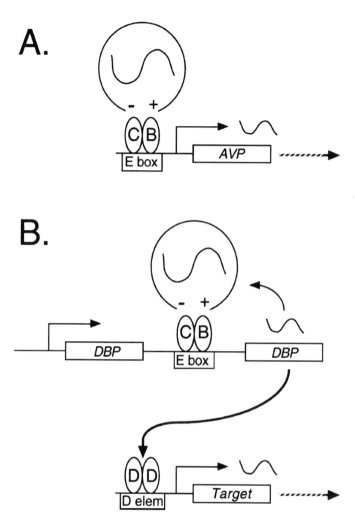

Figure 4   Direct regulation of output genes by the SCN clockwork. (*A*) Rhythmic regulation of the vasopressin prepropressophysin (*AVP*) gene. Circadian enhancement of transcription occurs through an E box element in the promoter region. Rhythmic transcription is controlled by the same positive and negative elements that control the core clock loops (large oval), ultimately generating rhythmic alterations in the functional activity of CLOCK (C):BMAL1 (B) heterodimers. The neuropeptide regulates downstream activities through its receptors. (*B*) Rhythmic regulation of the D-element-binding protein (*DBP*) gene. Circadian enhancement occurs through E-box elements in intronic regions. DBP is a transcription factor that can control rhythmic transcription of genes that are not involved in the core circadian clock. DBP homodimers (D-D) can bind to D-element enhancers in the promoter region of responsive genes. DBP also feeds back to modulate the core clock mechanism.

SYNCHRONIZATION AMONG CLOCK CELLS

For the SCN to operate as a functional unit, the individual clock cells must become synchronized to generate a coordinated output signal. Possible mechanisms for synchronization include gap junctional communication, neurotransmitter-based interactions, and ephaptic interactions (112).

On the basis of electron microscopy, gap junctions appear to be rare between neurons in the adult SCN (113). However, recent studies indicate the presence and dynamic regulation of functional gap junctions in the SCN (114). Shinohara and colleagues reported transfer of Lucifer Yellow between adult rat SCN neurons and inhibition of this transfer by the GABA(A) receptor agonist muscimol (114). Gap-junctional communication is not necessary for the maintenance of circadian function in SCN clock cells, however, because intracellular injection of neurobiotin failed to reveal dye coupling between SCN neurons in a dissociated culture system, whereas extensive gap-junctional connections were found between astrocytes (115). Collectively, these results indicate that gap junctions, although not necessary for the intracellular machinery of the core clock loop, may contribute to coordinating subsets of SCN neurons and amplifying their collective output.

GABA is the principal transmitter of the SCN (73, 113, 116). Although GABA activity is usually inhibitory, Wagner et al reported that GABA excited SCN neurons during daytime, whereas at night GABA inhibited SCN electrical activity (117). This dual action of GABA could serve to translate a rhythm in ionic concentrations (e.g. intracellular chloride) into a rhythm in excitability in individual clock neurons, or it could provide a mechanism to augment the amplitude of rhythmicity in a population of SCN neurons. While this hypothesis is attractive, the data have been difficult to replicate; using three independent methods, Gribkoff et al (118) reported only inhibitory responses to GABA in the SCN during subjective day.

Work with electrical activity rhythms of SCN clock cells in culture shows that GABA is an important transmitter for synchronizing SCN neurons (6). Application of GABA leads to phase shifts and entrainment of clock cells in culture. Notably, all acute responses to GABA were inhibitory in the clock cell culture system, but neuronal inhibition alone was insufficient to cause a phase shift (6). Although the clock cell data support an important role of GABA in synchronizing the collective SCN in vivo, other diffusible substances, such as neuropeptides (e.g. AVP; see above), could also be involved.

The very high neuronal density of the SCN and the extensive membrane appositions among SCN neurons suggest that changes in the microenvironment serve as a mechanism for coordination (112, 119). A form of neuronal cell adhesion molecule (NCAM) that is high in polysialic acid (PSA-NCAM) has been implicated in the regulation of plasticity of neuronal interactions in other systems (120) and appears to play a role in circadian rhythmicity (121). Mice deficient for PSA-NCAM show shortened circadian periods, becoming arrhythmic after several weeks in constant conditions, and enzymatic removal of PSA moieties from endogenous NCAM similarly shortens the circadian period (121). The phenotype of the PSA-NCAM-deficient mice, with gradual loss of rhythmicity in constant conditions, suggests that the role of PSA-NCAM is to promote interactions among SCN neurons that are necessary for a coherent circadian clock. Glia, through insulating and/or biochemical means, may also contribute to SCN coupling (112, 115).

Comparison of the period of the electrical activity rhythms in individual clock cells with the period of locomotor activity rhythms in *tau* mutant hamsters, *Clock* mutant mice, and normal rats show that the circadian period in the whole animal is determined by averaging widely dispersed periods of individual clock cells (3–5, 122). The clock cell periods detected by multielectrode plate recordings reflect the potential variability within the population of clock cells, but it appears likely that the cells interact to produce a common compromise period in vivo through the mechanisms described above.

A formal model of the SCN as an oscillator network has been proposed (4), which predicts that, as coupling strength increases, an increasing number of clock cells will become synchronized to the mean frequency. Thus a completely synchronized network will oscillate at a frequency close to the mean of the frequencies of the population. This oscillator network model will likely need refinement as molecular evidence for functionally distinct populations of clock cells emerges (123).

A biological advantage of a coupled multi-oscillatory system is the flexibility it provides for entrainment of the circadian clock (4). Thus when a portion of the oscillators in the network are phase shifted, the whole network will resynchronize to a new phase. In this way, only a subpopulation of clock cells needs to respond to a specific entraining stimulus to generate a phase shift in the whole network. Indeed, light first induces *mPer1* gene expression in the ventrolateral SCN, with induction then proceeding throughout the nucleus at later times (94).

The stable phase of the SCN clock maintained in light-dark conditions is probably a balance between internal synchronization (e.g. via GABA) and phase-shifting responses to light (e.g. via glutamate). Proper SCN function thus requires precise coordination between the intercellular synchronizing processes and the intracellular molecular loops (6).

OUTPUT PATHWAYS

The mechanisms and efferent pathways by which the synchronized SCN regulate overt rhythmicity in target tissues are not fully characterized for any output rhythm. AVP and GABA originating in the SCN are implicated in some output pathways. AVP of SCN origin may be involved in driving rhythmic hypothalamo-pituitary-adrenal axis activity in rats, ultimately regulating corticosterone release from the adrenal gland (124, 125). Similarly, AVP may play a role in activation of the hypothalamo-pituitary-gonadal axis (126). Thus a link between the molecular oscillations in pacemaker cells, the clock-controlled production of AVP, and overt rhythms can be proposed.

GABA release from SCN terminals in the paraventricular nuclei region appears to regulate melatonin synthesis from the pineal gland by turning off a stimulatory signal emanating from the paraventricular nuclei (127). Although the link between the circadian clockwork and the mechanisms regulating GABA release from the SCN is unclear, it seems likely that increased SCN electrical activity leads to increased GABA release.

In addition to neuronal output pathways, the SCN may convey information within the brain by humoral routes. Silver and coworkers (128) have shown that a diffusible substance from transplanted fetal SCN tissue can restore weak circadian rhythmicity in locomotor activity in SCN-lesioned hamsters. Although vasopressin is rhythmically secreted into the cerebrospinal fluid from the SCN (129), the unidentified diffusible substance does not appear to be vasopressin (130).

PHASE SWAPPING

The metabolic and electrical activity rhythms of the SCN are higher during daytime in both day-active and night-active species (1, 131). Similarly, AVP levels in cerebrospinal fluid are higher during the day than at night, regardless of whether species are day active or night active (129). Melatonin is produced at night in all species. Other rhythms, including rhythms in activity, body temperature, and hypothalamic-pituitary-adrenal activity, are more labile. This indicates that the sign of the output signals from the SCN can be reversed downstream. How this is accomplished is not known.

Yamazaki et al have proposed that phase differences between rhythms in peripheral tissues are because of differential response of the peripheral tissues to a common output signal (95). This seems a reasonable explanation for the differences between tissues, but it is not likely to explain the difference between nocturnal and diurnal species. More likely, the sign of the signal has already been changed by the time peripheral oscillators receive an SCN-based signal. This focuses attention on identifying sites along the output pathways where the sign of rhythmicity is reversed.

PERIPHERAL OSCILLATORS

Prior to the cloning of clock genes, the retina was considered to be the only other structure containing a bona fide circadian clock in mammals. Hamster retinae express circadian rhythms of melatonin production in vitro that can be directly entrained by light (132). Moreover, studies with *tau* mutant hamsters show that the period alterations in SCN-driven behavioral rhythms are also present in rhythms monitored from the retina in vitro (132). With the cloning of the mammalian *Per* genes, it was found that the three *mPer* genes show circadian expression patterns in mouse eye. Curiously, the eye rhythms are delayed by 3–6 h relative to the SCN oscillations (40, 41). Because the retina oscillators are considered self-sustaining and can function independently of the SCN, the biological significance of the phase difference in clock gene expression between retina and SCN is unclear. It will be important to determine how the molecular machinery that runs the retinal clock compares with that described for the SCN. It will be especially interesting to define which clock genes and/or proteins are light responsive in retina, given the skewed relationship of the retinal *mPer1* and *mPer2* RNA rhythms to the light-dark cycle compared with corresponding rhythms in the SCN.

Once a family of *Per* genes was cloned in mammals, it also became clear that these genes are widely expressed. Indeed, the *mPer* genes are expressed throughout brain and in many peripheral tissues. In several peripheral tissues (e.g. liver and skeletal muscle) circadian rhythms in RNA abundance are apparent for each of the *mPer* genes (41). In these tissues, the phase of the RNA oscillation of each *mPer* gene is delayed by 3–9 h relative to the oscillation in the SCN, suggesting that the peripheral oscillations are either driven or synchronized by the SCN.

Studies with SCN-lesioned rats suggest that these peripheral RNA oscillations are in fact controlled by the SCN. Day-night *Per2* oscillations are abolished in peripheral tissues after complete SCN lesions (133). A problem with this study is that only two time points were examined. Furthermore, one cannot distinguish between loss of rhythmicity in peripheral oscillators and continuing rhythmicity within an asynchronous population of single-cell oscillators. The studies do suggest, however, that the SCN are at least involved in maintaining the phase of the peripheral oscillations.

Studies with mammalian cells in tissue culture show that peripheral tissues actually contain circadian oscillators. Serum shock (50% serum) of the Rat-1 fibroblast cell line induces RNA rhythms of several transcription factors normally expressed in peripheral tissues, as well as *Per1* and *Per2* (96). The rhythms are circadian in period length and apparent for three cycles in culture. But do these oscillations represent true clocks? Recent studies using transgenic rats in which luciferase is expressed under the control of the *mPer1* promoter show that liver, lung, and skeletal muscle express circadian rhythms in vitro that dampen after 2–7 cycles (95), like the Rat-1 fibroblast cell line. The ability to induce additional cycles of gene expression by a serum shock reveals that loss of tissue viability is not responsible for the loss of rhythmicity. What is not yet known, however, is whether these oscillators are truly damped and unable to sustain prolonged rhythmicity or whether damping is due to asynchrony of a population of self-sustaining clock cells. Reporter gene assays of single cells from these peripheral tissues or from cell lines should soon resolve this issue. Current data suggest that peripheral tissues contain damped oscillators that require intermittent input to sustain oscillation and that the SCN are involved in the process in vivo.

One of the great promises of finding oscillating transcripts in cell culture was that it would expedite biochemical and molecular analyses of general clock mechanisms in mammals (134). This seemed to be particularly appealing for analysis of signal transduction cascades mediating entrainment because serum shock elicits rapid induction of *Per1* and *Per2* gene expression in cultured cells, similar to the effects of light on *Per1* and *Per2* expression in the SCN. Taking this approach, Akashi & Nishida (135) showed that the MAP kinase cascade is involved in inducing circadian gene expression in cultured cells. This seems analogous to the situation in the SCN in which stimulation of MAP kinase leads to phosphorylation of CREB (87). It is not known, however, whether serum-induced gene expression in cell culture is analogous to light-induced *mPer1* and *mPer2* expression in the SCN. In cell culture, it appears that gene induction starts the circadian oscillation, whereas in the SCN, gene induction by light resets an already running circadian clock.

This also brings up the critical question: Is the core clock mechanism the same between the SCN and peripheral oscillators? The data suggest that there are substantial differences. In addition to delayed phases of *mPer* RNA rhythms in peripheral tissues, relative to those in the SCN, the *Bmal1* RNA rhythm shows strikingly different responses in the SCN and peripheral tissues of *Clock/Clock* mutant mice (136). *Bmal1* RNA levels are elevated to the upper range of the normal oscillation in peripheral tissues of *Clock/Clock* mutant mice, while in the same animals the RNA rhythm is severely blunted in the SCN (136). The elevated *Bmal1* levels in peripheral tissues of *Clock* mutant mice suggest that CLOCK:BMAL1 heterodimers are normally repressing the transcription of the *Bmal1* gene in periphery, analogous to what has been proposed for CLOCK:CYC repression of *clock* transcription in the *Drosophila* clockwork (137). This does not occur in the SCN (31, 136). It therefore appears that there are substantial differences in clock gene regulation in peripheral tissues, compared with the SCN. Further study may provide a molecular explanation for the difference between true clocks and damped oscillators. Meanwhile, use of peripheral tissue rhythms to understand circadian mechanisms in the SCN is an expeditious but potentially dangerous endeavor.

How are peripheral oscillators in mammals maintained by daily time cues? Unlike *Drosophila*, in which peripheral clocks are directly reset by light (138), the data in SCN-lesioned and transgenic rats suggest that light-dark signals are transduced by the SCN into output signals that provide the time cue (95, 133). The nature of the SCN-dependent signal to peripheral tissues is not yet known. It is unlikely to involve melatonin because strains of mice incapable of making melatonin (C57BL/6) still have circadian oscillations in *mPer* gene expression in peripheral tissues (41). It is probable that the time giver is a complex mix of SCN-driven neural and humoral signals (139, 140, 140a), similar to what has been proposed for signals generated from the maternal SCN that entrain the fetal circadian clock (141).

So what is the function of peripheral oscillators? One idea is that centrally generated signals ultimately impinge on peripheral oscillators, entraining them and coordinating expression of locally controlled CCGs that in turn regulate biological processes. DBP is a clear example of a CCG in peripheral tissues because it is expressed rhythmically in many peripheral organs. Moreover, DPB regulates rhythmic transcription of key enzymes in hepatocytes directly involved in the metabolism of cholesterol, amino acids, xenobiotics, and androgens (142). Thus DBP could play a dual role; it appears to be involved in regulating circadian output through its expression both in the SCN and in liver. Locally controlled CCGs in peripheral organs would provide the flexibility needed to control the vast array of circadian rhythms.

Each of the eight genes involved in the SCN clockwork is widely expressed throughout the body. This has made analysis of the function of specific genes difficult in cell culture because of the contaminating effects of endogenous expression in mammalian cell lines. In addition to clock gene participation in damped circadian oscillators in periphery, there may be functions of these genes in higher-frequency oscillations. As an example, the frequency of the male courtship rhythm in *Drosophila* is affected by PER mutations in a manner that parallels the effect on circadian clock frequency (143).

A non-rhythmic function of several clock genes has recently emerged. In *Drosophila*, some clock genes are required for cocaine sensitization, whereas others are not (144). Flies carrying mutations of *per, clock, cyc,* and *doubletime* do not sensitize; many of these mutations (e.g. null *per* mutations) result in nonfunctional circadian clocks. Intriguingly, flies lacking a functional *tim* gene sensitize normally, even though they also have disrupted circadian rhythms. Therefore, the clock gene effect on cocaine sensitization is distinct from the effects on circadian behavior. This study begs for similar analysis of clock gene function in mammals because cocaine sensitization is seen in mammals, including humans, and is associated with increased drug craving (144).

There may well be other nonrhythmic biological processes in mammals regulated or modulated by genes essential for the core clockwork. It will therefore be important that mice with genetic manipulation of clock genes be fully examined for a wide range of phenotypes. As demonstrated by the role of orexins (urocortins) in the regulation of sleep (145), targeted gene disruption can produce profound yet easily overlooked phenotypes.

BENCH TO BEDSIDE

Circadian rhythms are an important aspect of human biology (146). Temporal variations in hormone levels, pharmacokinetics, and aspects of disease reveal the pervasive influence of the circadian clock on human physiology and pathophysiology. Disorders of the human circadian system include jet lag and more chronic conditions such as circadian-based sleep disorders and shift work.

Understanding how clock genes and their protein products interact to form the molecular clock provides an unprecedented opportunity for pharmacological manipulation of the SCN clockwork. The great promise of this approach is developing pharmacological interventions that can quickly reset the biological clock to new times. This approach could revolutionize treatment of jet lag, sleep disorders, and some neuropsychiatric illnesses.

Visit the Annual Reviews home page at www.AnnualReviews.org

LITERATURE CITED

1. Klein DC, Moore RY, Reppert SM, eds. 1991. *Suprachiasmatic Nucleus: The Mind's Clock.* New York: Oxford Univ. Press. 467 pp.
2. Williams JA, Sehgal A. 2000. Circadian rhythms in flies. *Annu. Rev. Physiol.* 63: 729–55
3. Welsh DK, Logothetis DE, Meister M, Reppert SM. 1995. Individual neurons dissociated from rat suprachiasmatic nucleus express independently phased circadian firing rhythms. *Neuron* 14:697–706
4. Liu C, Weaver DR, Strogatz SH, Reppert SM. 1997. Cellular construction of a circadian clock: period determination in the suprachiasmatic nuclei. *Cell* 91:855–60
5. Herzog ED, Takahashi JS, Block GD. 1998. *Clock* controls circadian period in isolated suprachiasmatic nucleus neurons. *Nat. Neurosci.* 1:708–13
6. Liu C, Reppert SM. 2000. GABA synchronizes clock cells within the suprachiasmatic circadian clock. *Neuron* 25:123–28
7. Hogenesch JB, Chan WK, Jackiw VH, Brown RC, Gu YZ, et al. 1997. Characterization of a subset of the basic-helix-loop-helix-PAS superfamily that interacts with components of the dioxin signaling pathway. *J. Biol. Chem.* 272:8581–93
8. Dunlap JC. 1999. Molecular bases for circadian clocks. *Cell* 96:271–90
9. Somers DE, Schultz TF, Milnamow M, Kay SA. 2000. ZEITLUPE encodes a novel clock-associated PAS protein from *Arabidopsis. Cell* 101:319–29
10. King DP, Zhao Y, Sangoram AM, Wilsbacher LD, Tanaka M, et al. 1997. Positional cloning of the mouse circadian *Clock* gene. *Cell* 89:641–53
11. Vitaterna MH, King DP, Chang AM, Kornhauser JM, Lowrey PL, et al. 1994. Mutagenesis and mapping of a mouse gene,

Clock, essential for circadian behavior. *Science* 264:719–25
12. Antoch MP, Song EJ, Chang AM, Vitaterna MH, Zhao Y, et al. 1997. Functional identification of the mouse circadian *Clock* gene by transgenic BAC rescue. *Cell* 89:655–67
13. Gekakis N, Staknis D, Nguyen HB, Davis FC, Wilsbacher LD, et al. 1998. Role of the CLOCK protein in the mammalian circadian mechanism. *Science* 280:1564–69
14. Hogenesch JB, Gu YZ, Jain S, Bradfield CA. 1998. The basic-helix-loop-helix-PAS orphan MOP3 forms transcriptionally active complexes with circadian and hypoxia factors. *Proc. Natl. Acad. Sci. USA* 95:5474–79
15. Takahata S, Sogawa K, Kobayashi A, Ema M, Mimura J, et al. 1998. Transcriptionally active heterodimer formation of an Arnt-like PAS protein, Arnt3, with HIF-1α, HLF, and Clock. *Biochem. Biophys. Res. Commun.* 248:789–94
16. Jin X, Shearman LP, Weaver DR, Zylka MJ, De Vries GJ, et al. 1999. A molecular mechanism regulating rhythmic output from the suprachiasmatic circadian clock. *Cell* 96:57–68
17. Kume K, Zylka MJ, Sriram S, Shearman LP, Weaver DR, et al. 1999. mCRY1 and mCRY2 are essential components of the negative limb of the circadian clock feedback loop. *Cell* 98:193–205
18. Okamura H, Miyake S, Sumi Y, Yamaguchi S, Yasui A, et al. 1999. Photic induction of *mPer1* and *mPer2* in *Cry*-deficient mice lacking a biological clock. *Science* 286:2531–34
19. Darlington TK, Wagner-Smith K, Ceriani MF, Staknis D, Gekakis N, et al. 1998. Closing the circadian loop: CLOCK-induced transcription of its own inhibitors *per* and *tim. Science* 280:1599–603
20. Kuhlman SJ, Quintero JE, McMahon

DG. 2000. GFP fluorescence reports *Period1* circadian gene regulation in the mammalian biological clock. *NeuroReport* 11:1479–82

21. Cermakian N, Whitmore D, Foulkes NS, Sassone-Corsi P. 2000. Asynchronous oscillations of two zebrafish CLOCK partners reveal different clock control and function. *Proc. Natl. Acad. Sci. USA* 97:4339–44

22. Hogenesch JB, Gu YZ, Moran SM, Shimomura K, Radcliffe LA, et al. 2000. The basic helix-loop-helix-PAS protein MOP9 is a brain-specific heterodimeric partner of circadian and hypoxia factors. *J. Neurosci.* 20:RC83

23. Shearman LP, Zylka MJ, Reppert SM, Weaver DR. 1999. Expression of basic helix-loop-helix/PAS genes in the mouse suprachiasmatic nucleus. *Neuroscience* 89:387–97

24. Cashmore AR, Jarillo JA, Wu YJ, Liu D. 1999. Cryptochromes: blue light receptors for plants and animals. *Science* 284:760–65

25. Hsu DS, Zhao X, Zhao S, Kazantsev A, Wang RP, et al. 1996. Putative human blue-light photoreceptors hCRY1 and hCRY2 are flavoproteins. *Biochemistry* 35:13871–77

26. Todo T, Tyo H, Yamamoto K, Toh H, Inui T, et al. 1996. Similarity among the *Drosophila* (6-4) photolyase, a human photolyase homolog, and the DNA photolyase-blue-light photoreceptor family. *Science* 272:419–21

27. Miyamoto Y, Sancar Y. 1998. Vitamin B2-based blue-light photoreceptors in the retinohypothalamic tract as the photoactive pigments for setting the circadian clock in mammals. *Proc. Natl. Acad. Sci. USA* 95:6097–102

28. Thresher RJ, Vitaterna MH, Miyamoto Y, Kazantsev A, Hsu DS, et al. 1998. Role of mouse cryptochrome blue-light photoreceptor in circadian photoresponses. *Science* 282:1490–94

29. van der Horst GTJ, Muijtjens M, Kobayashi K, Takano R, Kanno SI, et al. 1999. Mammalian Cry1 and Cry2 are essential for maintenance of circadian rhythms. *Nature* 398:627–30

30. Vitaterna MH, Selby CP, Todo T, Niwa H, Thompson C, et al. 1999. Differential regulation of mammalian period genes and circadian rhythmicity by cryptochromes 1 and 2. *Proc. Natl. Acad. Sci. USA* 96:12114–19

31. Shearman LP, Sriram S, Weaver DR, Maywood ES, Chaves I, et al. 2000. Interacting molecular loops in the mammalian circadian clock. *Science* 288:917–24

32. Griffin EA, Staknis D, Weitz CJ. 1999. Light-independent role of CRY1 and CRY2 in the mammalian circadian clock. *Science* 286:768–71

33. Lee C, Bae K, Edery I. 1999. PER and TIM inhibit the DNA binding activity of *Drosophila* CLOCK-CYC/dBMAL1 heterodimer without disrupting formation of the heterodimer: a basis for circadian transcription. *Mol. Cell. Biol.* 19:5316–25

34. Xu C, Siu CS, Pasco DS. 1998. DNA binding activity of the aryl hydrocarbon receptor is sensitive to redox changes in intact cells. *Arch. Biochem. Biophys.* 358:149–56

35. Zhao S, Sancar A. 1997. Human blue-light photoreceptor hCRY2 specifically interacts with protein serine/threonine phosphatase 5 and modulates its activity. *Photochem. Photobiol.* 66:727–31

36. Zylka MJ. 1999. *Characterization of a mammalian circadian feedback loop.* PhD thesis. Harvard Univ., Cambridge, MA

37. Sun ZS, Albrecht U, Zhuchenko O, Bailey J, Eichele G, et al. 1997. RIGUI, a putative mammalian ortholog of the *Drosophila period* gene. *Cell* 90:1003–11

38. Tei H, Okamura H, Shigeyoshi Y, Fukuhara C, Ozawa R, et al. 1997. Circadian oscillation of a mammalian homolog of the *Drosophila period* gene. *Nature* 389:512–16

39. Albrecht U, Sun ZS, Eichele G, Lee CC. 1997. A differential response of two

putative mammalian circadian regulators, *mper1* and *mper2*, to light. *Cell* 91:1055–64

40. Shearman LP, Zylka MJ, Weaver DR, Kolakowski LF Jr, Reppert SM. 1997. Two *period* homologs: circadian expression and photic regulation in the suprachiasmatic nuclei. *Neuron* 19:1261–69

41. Zylka MJ, Shearman LP, Weaver DR, Reppert SM. 1998. Three *period* homologs in mammals: differential light responses in the suprachiasmatic circadian clock and oscillating transcripts outside of brain. *Neuron* 20:1103–10

42. Takumi T, Matsubara C, Shigeyoshi Y, Taguchi K, Yagita K, et al. 1998. A new mammalian *period* gene predominantly expressed in the suprachiasmatic nucleus. *Genes Cells* 3:167–76

43. Takumi T, Taguchi K, Miyake S, Sakakida Y, Takashima N, et al. 1998. A light-independent oscillatory gene *mPer3* in mouse SCN and OVLT. *EMBO J.* 17:4753–59

44. Zylka MJ, Shearman LP, Levine JD, Jin X, Weaver DR, et al. 1998. Molecular analysis of mammalian *Timeless*. *Neuron* 21:1115–22

45. Field MD, Maywood ES, O'Brien JA, Weaver DR, Reppert SM, et al. 2000. Analysis of clock proteins in mouse SCN demonstrates phylogenetic divergence of the circadian clockwork and resetting mechanisms. *Neuron* 25:437–47

46. Yagita K, Yamaguchi S, Tamanini F, van der Horst GJT, Hoeijmakers JHJ, et al. 2000. Dimerization and nuclear entry of mPER proteins in mammalian cells. *Genes Dev.* 14:1353–63

47. Sangoram AM, Saez L, Antoch MP, Gekakis N, Staknis D, et al. 1998. Mammalian circadian autoregulatory loop: a *Timeless* ortholog and *mPer1* interact and negatively regulate CLOCK-BMAL1-induced transcription. *Neuron* 21:1101–13

48. Zheng B, Larkin DW, Albrecht U, Sun ZS, Sage M, et al. 1999. The *mPer2* gene encodes a functional component of the mammalian clock. *Nature* 400:167–73

49. Honma S, Ikeda M, Abe H, Tanahashi Y, Namihira M, et al. 1998. Circadian oscillation of BMAL1, a partner of a mammalian clock gene *Clock*, in rat suprachiasmatic nucleus. *Biochem. Biophys. Res. Commun.* 250:83–87

50. Oishi K, Sakamoto K, Okada T, Nagase T, Ishida N. 1998. Antiphase circadian expression between BMAL1 and *period* homologue mRNA in the suprachiasmatic nucleus and peripheral tissues of rats. *Biochem. Biophys. Res. Commun.* 253:199–203

51. Shearman LP, Jin X, Lee C, Reppert SM, Weaver DR. 2000. Targeted disruption of the *mPer3* gene: subtle effects on circadian clock function. *Mol. Cell. Biol.* 20:6269–75

52. Koike N, Hida A, Numano R, Hirose M, Sakaki Y, et al. 1998. Identification of the mammalian homologue of the Drosophila *timeless* gene, *Timeless1*. *FEBS Lett.* 441:427–31

53. Takumi T, Nagamine Y, Miyake S, Matsubara C, Taguchi K, et al. 1999. A mammalian ortholog of Drosophila *timeless*, highly expressed in SCN and retina, forms a complex with mPER1. *Genes Cells* 4:67–75

54. Tischkau SA, Barnes JA, Lin FJ, Myers EM, Soucy JW, et al. 1999. Oscillation and light induction of *timeless* mRNA in the mammalian circadian clock. *J. Neurosci.* 19:RC15

55. Hastings MH, Field MD, Maywood ES, Weaver DR, Reppert SM. 1999. Differential regulation of mPER1 and mTIM proteins in the mouse suprachiasmatic nuclei: new insights into a core clock mechanism. *J. Neurosci.* 19:RC11

56. Vielhaber E, Eide E, Rivers A, Gao ZH, Virshup DM. 2000. Nuclear entry of the circadian regulator mPER1 is controlled by mammalian casein kinase Iε. *Mol. Cell Biol.* 20:4888–99

56a. Takano A, Shimizu K, Kani S, Buijs RM, Okada M, Nagai K. 2000. Cloning and characterization of rat casein kinase 1 epsilon. *FEBS Lett.* 477:106–12

57. Gotter AL, Manganaro T, Weaver DR, Kolakowski LF Jr, Possidente B, et al. 2000. A timeless function for mouse *Timeless. Nat. Neurosci.* 3:755–56

57a. Benna C, Scannapieco P, Piccin A, Sandrelli F, Zordan M, et al. 2000. A second *timeless* gene in *Drosophila* shares greater sequence similarity with mammalian *tim. Curr. Biol.* 10:R512–12

58. Ralph MR, Menaker M. 1988. A mutation of the circadian system in golden hamsters. *Science* 241:1225–27

59. Reppert SM, Weaver DR. 1997. Forward genetic approach strikes gold: cloning of a mammalian *Clock* gene. *Cell* 89:487–90

60. Young MW. 2000. Circadian rhythms: marking time for a kingdom. *Science* 288:451–53

61. Lowrey PL, Shimomura K, Antoch MP, Yamazaki S, Zemenides PD, et al. 2000. Positional syntenic cloning and functional characterization of the mammalian circadian mutation *tau. Science* 288:483–91

62. Price JL, Blau J, Rothenfluh A, Adodeely M, Kloss B, et al. 1998. *Double-time* is a new *Drosophila* clock gene that regulates PERIOD protein accumulation. *Cell* 94:83–95

63. Keesler GA, Camacho F, Guo Y, Virshup D, Mondadori C, et al. 2000. Phosphorylation and destabilization of human *period1* clock protein by human casein kinase Iε *NeuroReport* 11:951–55

64. Naidoo H, Song W, Hunter-Ensor M, Sehgal A. 1999. A role for the proteosome in the light response of the *timeless* clock protein. *Science* 285:1737–41

65. Yamizaki S, Goto M, Menaker M. 1999. No evidence for extraocular photoreceptors in the circadian system of the Syrian hamster. *J. Biol. Rhythms* 14:197–201

66. Weaver DR. 2000. Is there more to light than meets the eye? *NeuroReport* 11(4):F1–F2

67. Lucas RJ, Foster RG. 1999. Photoentrainment in mammals: a role for cryptochrome? *J. Biol. Rhythms* 14:4–10

68. Foster RG. 1998. Shedding light on the biological clock. *Neuron* 20:829–32

69. Nelson DE, Takahashi JS. 1991. Sensitivity and integration in a visual pathway for circadian rhythm entrainment in the hamster (*Mesocricetus auratus*) *J. Physiol.* 439:115–45

70. Freedman MS, Lucas RJ, Soni B, von Schantz M, Munoz M, et al. 1999. Regulation of mammalian circadian behavior by non-rod, non-cone, ocular photoreceptors. *Science* 284:502–4

71. Lucas RJ, Freedman MS, Munoz M, Garcia-Fernandez J, Foster RG. 1999. Regulation of the mammalian pineal gland by non-rod, non-cone, ocular photoreceptors. *Science* 284:505–7

72. Provencio I, Rodriguez IR, Jiang G, Hayes WP, Moreira EF, et al. 2000. A novel human opsin in the inner retina. *J. Neurosci.* 20:600–5

73. Morin LP. 1994. The circadian visual system. *Brain Res. Rev.* 19:102–27

74. Moore RY, Speh JC, Card JP. 1995. The retinohypothalamic tract originates from a distinct subdivision of retinal ganglion cells. *J. Comp. Neurol.* 352:351–66

75. Ebling FJP. 1996. The role of glutamate in the photic regulation of the suprachiasmatic nucleus. *Prog. Neurobiol.* 50:109–32

76. Hamada T, Yamanouchi S, Watanabe A, Shibata S, Watanabe S. 1999. Involvement of glutamate release in substance P-induced phase delays of suprachiasmatic neuron activity rhythms in vitro. *Brain Res.* 836:190–93

77. Chen D, Buchanan GF, Ding JM, Hannibal J, Gillette MU. 1999. Pituitary adenylyl cyclase-activating peptide: a pivotal modulator of glutamatergic regulation of the suprachiasmatic circadian clock. *Proc. Natl. Acad. Sci. USA* 96:13468–73

78. Pickard GE. 1985. Bifurcating axons of retinal ganglion cells terminate in the hypothalamic suprachiasmatic nucleus and the intergeniculate leaflet of the thalamus. *Neurosci. Lett.* 55:211–17

79. Mistlberger RE, Antle MC, Glass JD, Miller JD. 2000. Behavioral and serotonergic regulation of circadian rhythms. *Biol. Rhythms Res.* 31:240–83

80. Byku M, Gannon RL. 2000. SNC 80, a delta-opioid agonist, elicits phase advances in hamster circadian activity rhythms. *NeuroReport* 11:1449–52

81. Viswanathan N, Davis FC. 1997. Single prenatal injections of melatonin or the D1-dopamine receptor agonist SKF 38393 to pregnant hamsters sets the offsprings' circadian rhythms to phases 180 degrees apart. *J. Comp. Physiol. A* 180:339–46

82. Weaver DR. 1999. Melatonin and circadian rhythmicity in vertebrates: physiological roles and pharmacological effects *In* FW Turek, P Zee, ed., *Neurobiology of Sleep and Circadian Rhythms.* New York: Dekker, pp. 197–262

83. Liu C, Weaver DR, Jin X, Shearman LP, Pieschl RL, et al. 1997. Molecular dissection of two distinct actions of melatonin on the suprachiasmatic circadian clock. *Neuron* 19:91–102

84. Gillette MU, Tischkau SA. 1999. Suprachiasmatic nucleus: the brain's clock. *Rec. Prog. Hormone Res.* 54:33–59

85. Colwell CS, Menaker M. 1992. NMDA as well as non-NMDA receptor antagonists can prevent the phase-shifting effects of light on the circadian system of the golden hamster. *J. Biol. Rhythms* 7:125–36

86. Ding JM, Buchanan GF, Tischkau SA, Chen D, Kuriashkina L, et al. 1998. A neuronal ryanodine receptor mediates light-induced phase delays of the circadian clock. *Nature* 394:381–84

87. Obrietan K, Impey S, Storm DR. 1998. Light and circadian rhythmicity regulate MAP kinase activation in the suprachiasmatic nuclei. *Nat. Neurosci.* 8:693–700

88. Ding JM, Faiman LE, Hurst WJ, Kuriashkina LR, Gillette MU. 1997. Resetting the biological clock: mediation of nocturnal CREB phosphorylation via light, glutamate, and nitric oxide. *J. Neurosci.* 17:667–75

89. Ginty DD, Kornhauser JM, Thompson MA, Bading H, Mayo KE, et al. 1993. Regulation of CREB phosphorylation in the suprachiasmatic nucleus by light and a circadian clock. *Science* 260:238–41

90. Kornhauser JM, Nelson DE, Mayo KE, Takahashi JS. 1990. Photic and circadian regulation of c-fos gene expression in the hamster suprachiasmatic nucleus. *Neuron* 5:127–34

91. Colwell CS, Kaufman CM, Menaker M. 1993. Phase-shifting mechanisms in the mammalian circadian system: new light on the carbachiol paradox. *J. Neurosci.* 13:1454–59

92. Weber ET, Gannon RL, Michel AM, Gillette MU, Rea MA. 1995. Nitric oxide synthase inhibition blocks light-induced phase shifts of the circadian activity rhythm, but not c-*fos* expression in the suprachiasmatic nucleus of the Syrian hamster. *Brain Res.* 692:137–42

93. Honrado GI, Johnson RS, Golombek DA, Spiegelman BM, Papaioannou VE, et al. 1996. The circadian system of c-*fos* deficient mice. *J. Comp. Physiol. A* 178:563–70

94. Shigeyoshi Y, Taguchi K, Yamamoto S, Takekida S, Yan L, et al. 1997. Light-induced resetting of a mammalian circadian clock is associated with rapid induction of the *mPer1* transcript. *Cell* 91:1043–53

95. Yamazaki S, Numano R, Abe M, Hida A, Takahashi R, et al. 2000. Resetting central and peripheral circadian oscillators in transgenic rats. *Science* 288:682–85

96. Balsalobre A, Damiola F, Schibler U. 1998. A serum shock induces circadian gene expression in mammalian tissue culture cells. *Cell* 93:929–37

97. Morgan PJ, Ross AW, Graham ES, Adam C, Messager S, et al. 1998. *oPer1* is an early response gene under photoperiodic regulation in the ovine pars tuberalis. *J. Neuroendocrinol.* 10:319–23

98. Akiyama M, Kouzu Y, Takahashi S, Wakamatsu H, Moriya T, et al. 1999. Inhibition of light- or glutamate-induced *mPer1* expression represses the phase shifts into the mouse circadian locomotor and suprachiasmatic firing rhythms. *J. Neurosci.* 19:1115–21

99. Maywood ES, Mrosovsky N, Field MD, Hastings MH. 1999. Rapid downreguation of mammalian *Period* genes during behavioral resetting of the circadian clock. *Proc. Natl. Acad. Sci. USA* 96:15211–16

99a. Horikawa K, Yokota S, Fuji K, Akiyama M, Moriya T, et al. 2000. Nonphotic entrainment by 5-HT1A/7 receptor agonists accompanied by reduced *Per1* and *Per2* mRNA levels in suprachiasmatic nuclei. *J. Neurosci.* 20:5867–73

100. Schwartz WJ, Groos RA, Morton M. 1987. The suprachiasmatic nuclei contain a tetrodotoxin-resistant circadian pacemaker. *Proc. Natl. Acad. Sci. USA* 84:1694–98

101. Schwartz WJ. 1991. Further evaluation of the tetrodotoxin-resistant circadian pacemaker in the suprachiasmatic nuclei. *J. Biol. Rhythms* 6:149–58

102. de Jeu M, Hermers M, Pennartz C. 1999. Circadian modulation of membrane properties in slices of rat suprachiasmatic nucleus. *NeuroReport* 9:3725–29

103. Schaap J, Bos NP, de Jeu MT, Geurtsen AM, Meiher JH, Pennartz CM. 1999. Neurons of the rat suprachiasmatic nucleus show a circadian rhythm in membrane potential that is lost during prolonged whole-cell recording. *Brain Res.* 815:154–66

104. Ripperger JA, Shearman LP, Reppert SM, Schibler U. 2000. CLOCK, an essential pacemaker component, controls expression of the circadian transcription factor DBP. *Genes Dev.* 14:679–89

105. Yamaguchi S, Mitsui S, Yan L, Yagita K, Miyake S, et al. 2000. Role of DBP in the circadian oscillatory mechanism. *Mol. Cell. Biol.* 20:4773–81

106. Lopez-Molina L, Conquet F, Dubois-Dauphin M, Schibler U. 1997. The DBP gene is expressed according to a circadian rhythm in the suprachiasmatic nucleus and influences circadian behavior. *EMBO J.* 16:6762–71

107. Mihai R, Coculescu M, Wakerley JB, Ingram CD. 1994. The effects of [Arg^8] vasopressin and [Arg^8] vasotocin on the firing rate of suprachiasmatic neurons in vitro. *Neuroscience* 62:783–92

108. Ingram CD, Snowball RK, Mihai R. 1996. Circadian rhythm of neuronal activity in suprachiasmatic nucleus slices from the vasopressin-deficient Brattleboro rat. *Neuroscience* 75:635–41

109. Groblewski TA, Nunez AA, Gold RM. 1981. Circadian rhythms in vasopressin-deficient rats. *Brain Res. Bull.* 6:125–30

110. Brown MH, Nunez AA. 1989. Vasopressin-deficient rats show a reduced amplitude of the circadian sleep rhythm. *Physiol. Behav.* 46:759–62

111. Weaver DR. 2000. A clockwork green: timely reporting on circadian clock function. *NeuroReport* 11(7):F9–10

112. van den Pol AN, Dudek FE. 1993. Cellular communication in the circadian clock, the suprachiasmatic nucleus. *Neuroscience* 56:793–811

113. van den Pol AN. 1980. The hypothalamic suprachiasmatic nucleus of the rat: intrinsic anatomy. *J. Comp. Neurol.* 191:661–702

114. Shinohara K, Hiruma H, Funabashi T, Kimura F. 2000. GABAergic modulation of gap junction communication in slice cultures of the rat suprachiasmatic nucleus. *Neuroscience* 96:591–96

115. Welsh DK, Reppert SM. 1996. Gap junctions couple astrocytes but not neurons

in dissociated cultures of rat suprachias-matic nucleus. *Brain Res.* 706:30–36

116. Moore RY, Speh JC. 1993. GABA is the principal neurotransmitter of the circadian system. *Neurosci. Lett.* 150:112–16

117. Wagner S, Castel M, Gainer H, Yarom Y. 1997. GABA in the mammalian suprachiasmatic nucleus and its role in diurnal rhythmicity. *Nature* 387:598–603

118. Gribkoff VK, Pieschl RL, Wisialowski TA, Park WK, Strecker GJ, et al. 1999. A reexamination of the role of GABA in the mammalian suprachiasmatic nucleus. *J. Biol. Rhythms* 14:126–30

119. Elliott AS, Nunez AA. 1994. An ultra-structural study of somal appositions in the suprachiasmatic nucleus and anterior hypothalamus of the rat. *Brain Res.* 662:278–82

120. Theodosis DT, Bonhomme R, Vitiello S, Rougon G, Poulain DA. 1999. Cell surface expression of polysialic acid on NCAM is a prerequisite for activity-dependent morphological neural and glial plasticity. *J. Neurosci.* 19:10228–36

121. Shen H, Watanabe M, Tomasiewicz H, Rutishauser U, Magnuson T, et al. 1997. Role of neural cell adhesion molecule and polysialic acid in mouse circadian clock function. *J. Neurosci.* 17:5221–29

122. Honma S, Shirakawa T, Katsuno Y, Namihira M, Honma K. 1999. Circadian periods of single suprachiasmatic neurons in rats. *Neurosci. Lett.* 250:157–60

123. Jagota A, de la Iglesia HO, Schwartz WJ. 2000. Morning and evening circadian oscillations in the suprachiasmatic nucleus in vitro. *Nat. Neurosci.* 3:372–76

124. Kalsbeek A, van Heerikhuize JJ, Wortel J, Buijs RM. 1996. A diurnal rhythm of stimulatory input to the hypothalamo-pituitary-adrenal system as revealed by timed intrahypothalamic administration of the vasopressin V1 antagonist. *J. Neurosci.* 16:5555–65

125. Buijs RM, Wortel J, van Heerikhuize JJ,

Feenstra MG, Ter Horst GJ, et al. 1999. Anatomical and functional demonstration of a multisynaptic suprachiasmatic nucleus adrenal (cortex) pathway. *Eur. J. Neurosci.* 11(5):1535–44

126. Palm IF, van der Beek EM, Wiegant VM, Buijs RM, Kalsbeek A. 1999. Vasopressin induces a luteinizing hormone surge in ovariectomized, estradiol-treated rats with lesions of the suprachiasmatic nucleus. *Neuroscience* 93:659–66

127. Kalsbeek A, Cutrera RA, Van Heerikhuize JJ, van der Vliet J, Buijs RM. 1999. GABA release from suprachiasmatic nucleus terminals is necessary for the light-induced inhibition of nocturnal melatonin release in the rat. *Neuroscience* 91:453–61

128. Silver R, LeSauter J, Tresco PA, Lehman MN. 1996. A diffusible coupling signal from the transplanted suprachiasmatic nucleus controlling circadian locomotor rhythms. *Nature* 382:810–13

129. Reppert SM, Schwartz WJ, Uhl GR. 1987. Arginine vasopressin: a novel peptide rhythm in cerebrospinal fluid. *Trends Neurosci.* 10:76–80

130. Boer GJ, van Esseveldt KE, van der Geest BA, Duindam H, Reitveld WJ. 1999. Vasopressin-deficient suprachiasmatic nucleus grafts reinstate circadian rhythmicity in suprachiasmatic nucleus-lesioned arrhythmic rats. *Neuroscience* 89:375–85

131. Schwartz WJ, Reppert SM, Eagan SM, Moore-Ede MC. 1983. In vivo metabolic activity of the suprachiasmatic nuclei: a comparative study. *Brain Res.* 274:184–87

132. Tosini G, Menaker M. 1996. Circadian rhythms in cultured mammalian retina. *Science* 272::419–21

133. Sakamoto K, Nagase T, Fukui H, Horikawa K, Okada T, et al. 1998. Multitissue circadian expression of rat period homolog (*rPer2*) mRNA is governed by the mammalian circadian clock,

the suprachiasmatic nucleus in the brain. *J. Biol. Chem.* 273:27039–42

134. Rosbash M. 1998. Why the Rat-1 fibroblast should replace the SCN as the in vitro model of choice. *Cell* 93:917–19

135. Akashi M, Nishida E. 2000. Involvement of the MAP kinase cascade in resetting of the mammalian circadian clock. *Genes Dev.* 14:645–49

136. Oishi K, Fukui H, Ishida N. 2000. Rhythmic expression of BMAL1 mRNA is altered in *Clock* mutant mice: differential regulation in the suprachiasmatic nucleus and peripheral tissues. *Biochem. Biophys. Res. Commun.* 268:164–71

137. Glossop NR, Lyons LC, Hardin PE. 1999. Interlocked feedback loops within the *Drosophila* circadian oscillator. *Science* 286:766–68

138. Plautz JD, Kaneko M, Hall JC, Kay SA. 1997. Independent photoreceptive circadian clocks throughout *Drosophila*. *Science* 278:1632–35

139. Ueyama T, Krout KE, Nguyen XV, Karpitskiy V, Kollert A, et al. 1999. Suprachiasmatic nucleus: a central autonomic clock. *Nat. Neurosci.* 2:1051–53

140. Oishi K, Sakamoto K, Okada T, Nagase T, Ishida N. 1998. Humoral signals mediate the circadian expression of rat *period* homologue (*rPer2*) mRNA in peripheral tissues. *Neurosci. Lett.* 256:117–19

140a. Balsalobre A, Brown SA, Maracci L, Tronche F, Kellendonk C, et al. 2000. Resetting of circadian time in peripheral tissues by glucocorticoid signaling. *Science* 289:2344–47

141. Reppert SM. 1995. Interaction between the circadian clocks of mother and fetus. *Ciba Found. Symp.* 183:198–207

142. Lavery DJ, Lopez-Molina L, Margueron R, Fleury-Olela F, Conquet F, et al. 1999. Circadian expression of the steroid 15 alpha-hydroxylase (Cyp2a4) and coumarin 7-hydroxylase (Cyp2a5) genes in mouse liver is regulated by the PAR leucine zipper transcription factor DBP. *Mol. Cell. Biol.* 19:6488–99

143. Hall JC. 1996. Are cycling gene products as internal Zeitgebers no longer the Zeitgeist of chronobiology? *Neuron* 17:799–802

144. Andretic R, Chaney S, Hirsh J. 1999. Requirement of circadian genes for cocaine sensitization in *Drosophila*. *Science* 285:1066–68

145. Chemelli RM, Willie JT, Sinton CM, Elmquist JK, Scammell T, et al. 1999. Narcolepsy in orexin knockout mice: molecular genetics of sleep regulation. *Cell* 98:437–51

146. Moore RY. 1997. Circadian rhythms: basic neurobiology and clinical applications. *Annu. Rev. Med.* 48:253–66

Annu. Rev. Physiol. 2001. 63:677–94

CIRCADIAN PHOTOPERCEPTION

Paul F Devlin[1] and Steve A Kay[2]

[1]*Division of Life Sciences, Kings College London, London SE1 8WA, UK;
e-mail: paul.devlin@kcl.ac.uk*
[2]*Department of Cell Biology, The Scripps Research Institute, La Jolla, California 92037;
e-mail: stevek@scripps.edu*

Key Words   clock, rhythm, photoreceptors, light, genetics

■ **Abstract**   The circadian clock is intrinsically linked to the daily cycle of day and night. A capacity for entrainment to light-dark cycles has proven to be a universal feature of the clock in all organisms examined. Here we review a wealth of recent advances that reveal more about the light input mechanisms by which the circadian clock is set to the correct time in a range of different systems. Now that we are identifying more of the molecular components of both the light input pathway and the clock mechanism itself, we are becoming increasingly less able to distinguish between the two.

INTRODUCTION

Throughout biology, a broad range of biochemical and physiological processes oscillate with approximately 24-h periodicity as an adaptation to the cycle of day and night generated by the rotation of the earth. These rhythms persist even if the organism is maintained in constant environmental conditions, indicating that they are under the control of an endogenous oscillator, the circadian clock. The circadian clock controls processes as diverse as the rhythms of conidiation in fungi, leaf movement in plants, eclosion in flies, and the sleep/wake cycle in humans (1). It allows an organism to anticipate and prepare for the dramatic changes in the natural environment that occur at sunrise and sunset. Furthermore, the circadian clock provides a timing mechanism for the measurement of day length, allowing an organism to follow the changing of the seasons as Earth orbits the Sun. In this way, the clock is also involved in the regulation of processes such as timing of flowering in plants and timing of the reproductive cycle in many mammals (2–4).

To be of use to an organism, the clock must first be synchronized with the day and night cycle. The changes in light and temperature that accompany dawn and dusk form the robust stimuli that are used by organisms in the setting of the clock. The mechanisms of temperature entrainment remain elusive, but in the last two years we have begun to unravel the mechanisms of circadian photoperception.

The ability to respond to light is a universal feature of clocks in all systems (5, 6). The appearance of light at dawn and the disappearance of light at dusk cause adjustments to the phase of the clock on a daily basis to keep it perfectly synchronized. Light pulses in the early morning advance the circadian oscillator whereas identical light pulses in the evening delay the oscillator. This requires that the clock impart a time-of-day-specific interpretation to the light signal. In fact, both the direction and magnitude of the response of the clock to light change over the course of the day, resulting in a phase response curve (PRC) like that shown in Figure 1. The observation of a PRC is universal for entrainment in all organisms, but the shape of the PRC varies greatly from one organism to another (7). Organisms often display an asymmetric PRC in which phase advances in the morning are more extreme than phase delays in the afternoon or vice versa. Additionally, many organisms show a "dead zone" of insensitivity to light during

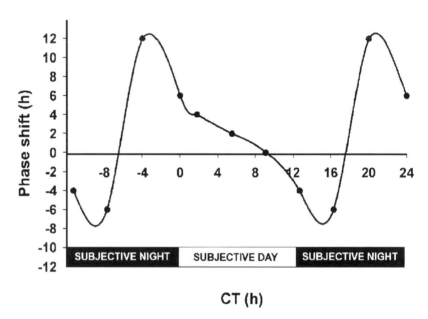

Figure 1   Phase response curve for *Arabidopsis thaliana*. Seedlings expressing a firefly luciferase bioluminescent reporter linked to the circadian-clock-controlled *CAB2* promoter construct were germinated and grown in 12-12 white-light–dark cycles for 6 days and then transferred to constant low fluence rate red light (3 μmol m^{-2} s^{-1}) for 5 days, during which the rhythm of bioluminescence was followed as described previously (43). At 4-h intervals after transfer to constant red light, successive batches of seedlings were given a phase-shifting light pulse. Phase shifts were induced using 3 h of bright red light (300 μmol m^{-2} s^{-1}). The magnitudes of the resulting phase shifts were calculated as the difference between the mean phase of the rhythm in each batch of seedlings after the light pulse and the mean phase of the rhythm exhibited by control seedlings. Phase shifts are plotted against the circadian time (CT) of the pulse (the time relative to one complete cycle of the free-running rhythm, which is designated as 24 CT h). Advances are plotted as positive values, and phase delays are plotted as negative values.

the course of the day, with phase shifts restricted to the mornings and evenings when information about the time of day is most important (7).

In general, a prolonged pulse of irradiation is required to reset the clock to prevent small fluctuations in light level from causing large changes in phase. Organisms display tremendous reciprocity in response to phase-shifting light pulses whereby the total amount of light given determines the extent of the response, regardless of whether this light is given as a very bright pulse for a short period of time or as a prolonged pulse of dim light. Reciprocity has been demonstrated to extend to light pulses of ≤45 min, far exceeding any reciprocity demonstrated for visual responses (8).

This entrainment by pulses of light is known as nonparametric entrainment (9). However, in the field environment, the conditions encountered by an organism are quite different from those used in generating a phase response curve. Over the course of a day, a diurnal organism is subjected not to pulses of light but to a prolonged period of irradiation. The resulting effect on the circadian clock is the net effect of phase advances in the morning and phase delays in the late afternoon and evening, constituting a continuous or parametric entrainment (9, 10).

In general, when diurnal organisms are maintained in constant light, the period length of the clock shortens as light intensity increases, whereas, in nocturnal organisms, the period length of the clock lengthens as light intensity increases (3, 11). An organism's response to continuous irradiation can be predicted from the shape of the PRC, in that this determines whether the phase advances outweigh the phase delays over the course of a day (10). A predominance of advances over delays results in a shortening of the period, whereas a predominance of delays over advances results in a lengthening of the period. In general, advances predominate in diurnal organisms such as *Arabidopsis thaliana*, but delays predominate in nocturnal organisms such as mice. Furthermore, the magnitude of a phase shift correlates with the intensity of the phase-resetting light pulse. As a result, period length continues to shorten in diurnal organisms as light intensity increases and to lengthen in nocturnal organisms as light intensity increases. This phenomenon is known as Aschoff's rule (3).

Recent advances in the field of circadian biology have begun to reveal the components of the clock in a range of different systems (1). Clocks in microorganisms, plants, insects, and mammals all share a common feature; they are made up of a transcriptional-feedback loop that generates a circadian oscillation in the level of one or more critical clock components. The phase of the circadian clock at any point is defined by the level of this critical clock component. One requirement for the action of light on the clock is that the phase-resetting light pulse must act to change the concentration of such a critical clock component. This change in concentration would then phase shift the clock to a new point in the cycle with the extent of change in concentration determining the magnitude of the phase shift (2).

Although the concept of a transcriptional-feedback loop is conserved, clocks in microorganisms, plants, insects, and mammals have quite different components, suggesting that clocks have arisen multiple times with different components being recruited in each of the biological kingdoms. Despite this, the presence of PER-ARNT-SIM (PAS) protein domains, implicated in protein interactions, has proven to be a common feature of critical clock components in all organisms (see other reviews in this section). Similarly, the mechanism of light resetting, when elucidated, has been shown to differ dramatically among microorganisms, plants, and animals (12–15). Significantly though, one feature common to all circadian systems is that they are intimately associated with their photoreceptors (6). In many systems, this association occurs to such an extent that it becomes difficult to distinguish between light input components and the components of the pacemaker itself, clearly indicating the central importance of light signaling in the functioning of the circadian clock.

GREEN ALGAE

Much of the earliest work within the field of circadian photoperception was carried out in the green alga *Gonyaulax polyedra* (16–18). Two distinct light input pathways appear to maintain the entrainment of the central oscillator. Under continuous light, the relationship between light intensity and free-running period length is dependent on the wavelength of incident light. Increased fluence rates of blue light lead to a shortening of period length, whereas increased fluence rates of red light lead to a lengthening of period length [11, 19; Figure 2 (see color insert)]. A study of the phase response curve in *G. polyedra* revealed that a specifically blue-sensitive light input pathway acts to cause phase advances during the subjective night. A red- and blue-light-sensitive system causes delays during the subjective day (19). Significantly, flavoprotein inhibitors were found to block the blue-light input to the clock that might occur during the subjective night, suggesting that in some way a flavoprotein affects the blue-light input pathway (20). Furthermore, evidence for the involvement of photosynthesis has come from the use of the photosynthetic electron transport inhibitor 3-(3,4-dichlorophenyl)-1,1-dimethylurea, possibly accounting for the red- and blue-light-sensitive input pathway (21, 22) (Figure 2). However, little is known about the nature of the photoreceptors or the mechanism of the clock itself in *G. polyedra*.

FUNGI

In the fungus *Neurospora crassa*, although the nature of the circadian photoreceptors also remains elusive, a considerable amount of information is known about some of the critical clock components themselves (1). The *white-collar* genes *wc-1* and *wc-2* are required for all known photoresponses in *N. crassa* (23–27). WC-1 and WC-2 form both homo- and heterodimers in vitro and occur within a WC complex within the cell (28). WC-1 and WC-2 are members of the GATA family of transcription factors (recognizing the core consensus 5′-GATA with the promoters of the genes they regulate), and each contains a PAS domain common to a number of higher plant photoreceptors and to components of the circadian clock itself in insects and mammals (29, 30). It is uncertain whether the WCs act as photoreceptors themselves, but it has been proposed that the PAS domain may bind flavin, as is the case with the plant photoreceptor phototropin (31). Mutants lacking WC-1 or WC-2 fail to show rhythmic, clock-controlled conidiation after a light-to-dark transfer (26). WC-1 is required for induction of transcription of the *frequency* (*frq*) gene in response to pulses of light, which reset the clock (12). The *frq* gene is a rhythmically expressed critical clock component essential for light-mediated entrainment of the circadian clock in *N. crassa* (32). *frq* forms part of an autoregulatory-feedback loop in *N. crassa* in that the FRQ protein negatively feeds back on its own transcription (33). The induction of transcription of the *frq* gene is a key factor in light-mediated resetting because it results in a phase shift in the clock to a phase corresponding to the new level of *frq* message (34). Both WC-1 and WC-2 appear to be positively acting factors that maintain robust *frq* cycling, but the requirement for WC-1 for light induction of *frq* transcription particularly indicates the importance of WC-1 in the light input pathway (12) (Figure 3, see color insert). However, the arrhythmicity observed in *wc-1* and *wc-2* mutants is not purely a result of a lack of light-mediated synchronization within the culture because the products of the *wc-1* and *wc-2* genes are also necessary for temperature entrainment of the circadian clock in *N. crassa* (12). Unlike the *frq*-null mutant that can be entrained to temperature cycles (32), the *wc-1* and *wc-2* mutants can be entrained by neither light nor temperature (12). Strictly, WC-1 and WC-2 can therefore be classed as critical clock components exemplifying the close association between light input and the circadian clock that has proven to be a characteristic of the clock in all organisms examined.

HIGHER PLANTS

The first evidence identifying a photoreceptor responsible for mediating light input to the clock came from higher plants (13). The requirement for light in the photosynthesis reaction means that the acquisition of information about the light environment is essential to the plant. Light is a crucial developmental regulator throughout the life history of a plant, from the regulation of seed germination through seedling establishment to timing of flowering (35). Plants have consequently evolved an array of photoreceptors capable of detecting light over a large range of fluence rates and wavelengths (36). Plant photoreceptors fall into three main classes: the phytochromes, which absorb in the red and far-red region of the spectrum, and the cryptochromes and the phototropins [or nonphototropic hypocotyls (nphs)], both of which absorb in the blue, UV-A region of the spectrum. The majority of recent work on plant photoperception has been carried out in *A. thaliana* (37), which contains five phytochromes, phyA to phyE, the products of a divergent gene family (38, 39). The phytochromes make up a protein moiety of ~124 kDa, with a covalently attached linear tetrapyrrole chromophore (40). Phytochromes exist in two photointerconvertible forms, a red-absorbing (Pr) form and a far-red-absorbing (Pfr) form. Phytochromes are synthesized in the inactive Pr form and, upon absorption of a photon of light, are converted to the active Pfr form (40). PhyA is light labile; the Pfr form is unstable and undergoes rapid proteolysis. PhyA predominates in dark-grown or etiolated seedlings and is rapidly degraded in the light. PhyB through E are more light stable, with phyB predominating in light-grown seedlings (35). Significantly, the protein moiety of all phytochromes contains a C-terminal PAS domain. PAS domains are generally involved in protein-protein interaction and ligand binding and have been found in many clock-associated proteins in other systems, in which they play a central role in the function of the components of the clock (see below; 41).

Two cryptochromes are present in *A. thaliana*, cry1 and cry2 (42). The N terminus of the plant cryptochromes shares strong homology with the chromophore-binding domain of type-II photolyases. Cryptochromes absorb strongly in blue and UV-A wavelengths of light; they bind two chromophores, a light-absorbing pterin chromophore and a catalytic flavine adenine dinucleotide. cry1 is light stable, whereas cry2 is light labile, being degraded at higher fluence rates of light (42).

The phototropin family of photoreceptors in *A. thaliana* has two members, nph1 and nph1-like. Mutants deficient in nph1 fail to show bending and growth toward unidirectional light. The nph photoreceptors bind two flavin chromophores, each non-covalently bound by a PAS domain in the protein moiety (31).

In an elegant assay that measured the rhythm in bioluminescence from the firefly luciferase (*LUC*) reporter gene linked to the *CAB2* promoter, both the phytochromes and the cryptochromes were demonstrated to be involved in light input to the clock in plants (43). The *CAB2* gene encodes a component of the photosynthetic machinery of *A. thaliana* and shows a strong rhythm of transcription, peaking during the early part of the day (44). Increasing light intensity results in a shortening of period length of the rhythm of *CAB2::LUC* bioluminescence in *A. thaliana*, resulting in a classical fluence rate response curve (13). In darkness, the circadian clock runs with a period length of 30–36 h. Both red and blue light have been demonstrated to be effective in shortening period length, suggesting the possible involvement of all of the plant photoreceptors (13, 43) (Figure 4). Analysis of the fluence rate response curves of mutants deficient in one or more of these photoreceptors has revealed a plasticity in the recruitment of different photoreceptors under varying conditions. Mutants lacking in light-labile phyA are deficient in the response to both red and blue light of low fluence rates, suggesting the involvement of phyA as a circadian photoreceptor specifically acting under low fluence rates of light (13). Consistent with this, phyA has previously been shown to play an important role in regulating development under canopy shade or as seedlings are emerging through soil, displaying a tremendous sensitivity to light (45). Although the phytochromes are primarily red-light photoreceptors,

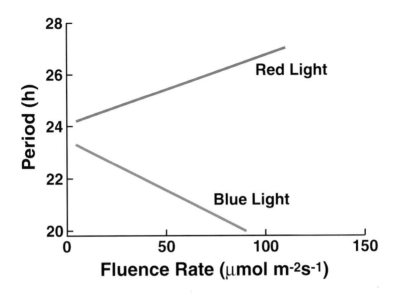

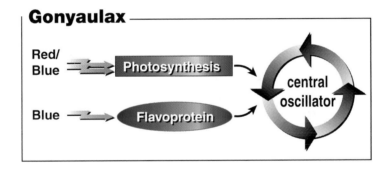

Figure 2 Light input to the clock in *Gonyaulax polyedra*. *Upper panel*, Fluence rate response curve for period length of the free-running rhythm of vertical migration in constant red or blue light. Increasing red-light intensity causes a lengthening of the period, whereas increasing blue light causes a shortening of the period, which suggests the action of two distinct light input pathways (reproduced from Reference 6). *Lower panel*, Schematic diagram of light input pathways to the clock in *G. polyedra*. A combined red- and blue-light-sensitive pathway shows a requirement for photosynthesis, whereas a second blue-light-sensitive pathway shows a requirement for flavoprotein.

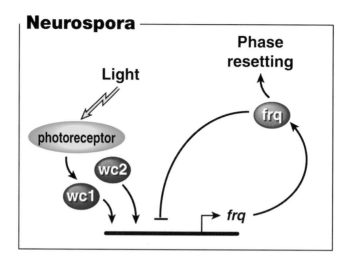

Figure 3 Light input to the clock in *Neurospora crassa*. The *FREQUENCY* (*FRQ*) gene forms a negative, autoregulatory transcriptional-feedback loop that is essential for light entrainment of the *N. crassa* circadian clock. The white-collar proteins WC1 and WC2 (wc1 and wc2 in the figure) act as positive regulators of *FRQ* transcription, with WC1 essential for light induction of *FRQ* leading to phase resetting.

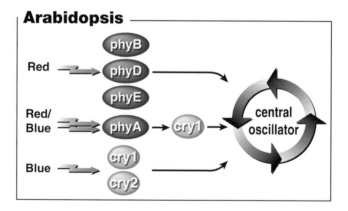

Figure 5 Light input to the clock in *Arabidopsis thaliana*. Both the red-light-activated phytochromes (phy) and the blue-light-activated cryptochromes (cry) act as photoreceptors that mediate light input to the clock in higher plants. Phytochromes B, D, and E mediate light input at high-fluence rate red. Cryptochromes 1 and 2 act as photoreceptors for high fluence rates of blue light. Phytochrome A acts as a photoreceptor for low fluence rates of both red and blue light but shows a functional dependence on the presence of cryptochrome 1. Even in red wavelengths at which cryptochrome is not activated, cry1 is still essential for phyA signaling, which suggests that cry1 acts as a signal transduction component downstream of phyA in light input to the clock.

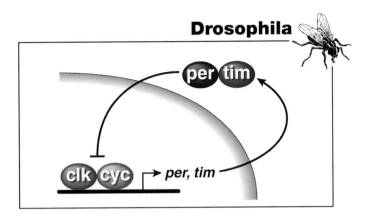

Figure 6 The mechanism of the circadian clock in *Drosophila melanogaster*. Transcription from the *PERIOD* (*per*) and *TIMELESS* (*tim*) genes leads to accumulation of PER and TIM (per and tim in figure) protein during the late afternoon and early evening. PER and TIM then feedback to inhibit their own transcription by repressing the activity of a positively acting transcriptional-activation complex made up of CLOCK (clk) and CYCLE (cyc). Levels of PER and TIM subsequently fall, releasing the inhibition of transcription, and then the cycle repeats. In a second, interlocked feedback loop (not shown) CLK and CYC act as repressors of their own transcription, whereas PER and TIM act as derepressors.

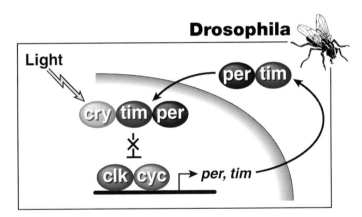

Figure 7 Light input to the circadian clock in *Drosophila melanogaster*. The blue-light photoreceptor cryptochrome (cry) binds to the timeless protein (tim) in a light-dependent manner. This resets the phase of the clock by removing the PER-TIM-mediated repression of the CLK-CYC transcriptional-activation complex (see Figure 6).

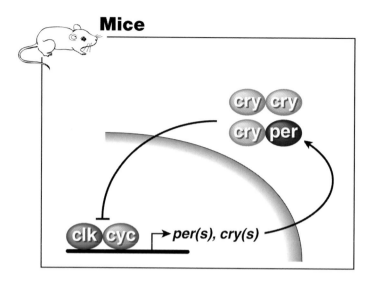

Figure 8 The mechanism of the circadian clock in mice. The *PER* and *CRY* genes in mice form a transcriptional-feedback loop that negatively feeds back on their own transcription. Mice possess three *PER* genes and two *CRY* genes (per and cry in figure). CRY-PER and CRY-CRY homo and heterodimers reenter the nucleus and repress the activity of a CLK-CYC (clk and cyc in figure) transcriptional-activation complex. In a second, interlocking loop, PER2 acts as a positive activator of CYC transcription, whereas CRY stablizes PER2.

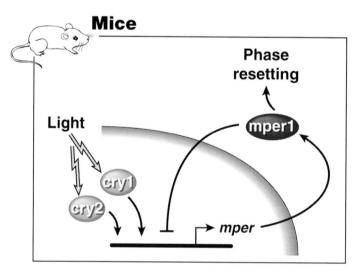

Figure 9 In the mouse, mCRY1 and mCRY2 are involved in light induction of mPER1 (mper1 in the figure) transcription, which can induce phase resetting.

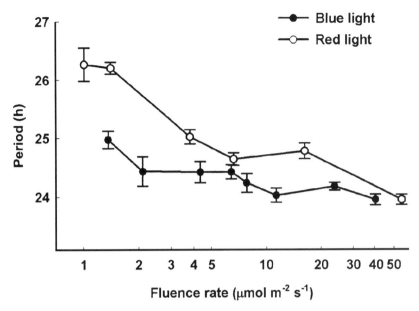

Figure 4 Fluence rate response curve for period length of the free-running rhythm of *CAB2::LUC* bioluminescence (see Figure 1) in constant red or blue light in seedlings of *A. thaliana*. Seedlings were germinated and grown in 12-12 white-light–dark cycles for 6 days and then transferred to constant red or blue light at the intensities indicated. The rhythm of bioluminescence was monitored using sensitive video-imaging cameras, and the period length was calculated as described previously (43, 96). Increasing intensities of either red or blue light caused a shortening of period length of the free-running rhythm, indicating that both red light and blue light are capable of mediating light input to the clock in *A. thaliana*.

they show a small peak of absorption in the blue region of the spectrum, and such is the sensitivity of the phyA-signaling pathway that it is capable of mediating responses to both blue and red wavelengths (46). Conversely, phyB has been demonstrated to be a major player in regulating plant development specifically under higher intensities of light such as those found in an open environment (47). Mutants lacking phyB show a deficiency in responses to high fluence rates of red light for shortening of period length (13), whereas the *phyA phyB* double mutant shows additivity in the effects of these two mutations, displaying a long period at all fluence rates of red light (PF Devlin, unpublished observations). Plants, therefore, can maintain a circadian period length under a whole range of light conditions. They do so by using highly sensitive photoreceptors, which are degraded under higher intensities of light, coupled with more stable but less sensitive photoreceptors, which act at higher light intensities without overstimulating the circadian phototransduction pathway.

Analysis of mutants deficient in one or both of the cryptochrome photoreceptors reveals a redundancy in the action of *cry1* and *cry2* in blue light. At intermediate fluence rates of blue light, *cry1* and *cry2* redundantly act to maintain circadian period length, whereas at higher fluence rates of blue light, in which *cry2* would be degraded, *cry1* acts alone in circadian photoperception (13; PF Devlin, unpublished observations). Thus the *cry2* mutant shows a wild-type phenotype at intermediate and high fluence rates of blue light. The *cry1* mutant shows a wild-type phenotype at intermediate fluence rates of blue light but has a deficiency in the perception of high fluence rates of blue. Only in the *cry1,cry2* double mutant is the action of the cryptochromes seen at intermediate fluence rates of blue light.

Significantly, the *cry1* monogenic mutant is also deficient in responses to low fluence rates of blue light in the range in which phyA is known to act (13). Despite the fact that both phyA and cry1 act in this range, they fail to compensate for loss of each other, suggesting that they are both required to mediate low fluence rate blue-light input to the clock. When the *cry1* mutant was examined in red light, it also showed a deficiency in response to low fluence rates of red light (PF Devlin, unpublished observations) even though the cryptochromes show only minimal absorption in the red region of the spectrum (48). Hence, both phyA and cry1 are also required for low fluence rate red-light input to the clock. Because only phyA, of these two, is capable of acting as a photoreceptor in red light, this implicates cry1 as a signal transduction component downstream of phyA in light input to the clock (Figure 5, see color insert).

Thus phyA appears to be the major photoreceptor for low fluence rate light input to the clock for all wavelengths, with cry1 acting in the phyA signal transduction pathway. This conclusion is supported by the finding that the *phyA* mutation is epistatic to the *cry1* mutation at low fluence rates of white light (PF Devlin, unpublished observations). Under white light, both *phyA* and *cry1* are capable of absorbing light, yet no additivity is observed between the *phyA* and *cry1* mutations. Furthermore, there is evidence for a direct interaction between phyA and cry1, with phyA mediating a light-dependent phosphorylation of cry1 (49). The role of cry1 as a signal transduction component downstream of phyA in light input to the clock provides the first real physiological relevance to this molecular interaction.

Although the phytochromes play a role in light input to the clock, their own expression is circadianly regulated, thus also placing them in the output pathway from the clock. The significance of this oscillation in phytochrome gene expression is not clear, but this provides another example of the close association between components of the input pathway and the clock itself.

Mutants deficient in nph1 show no observable defect in light signaling to the clock, and so far the sole role of nph1 appears to be in the regulation of phototropism (DE Somers, unpublished observations).

One further component of the input pathway was recently discovered in *A. thaliana*. The *zeitlupe* (*ztl*) mutant was isolated in a screen for seedlings displaying aberrant period length of *cab2::luc* bioluminescence (50). The *ztl* mutant shows a long period for several clock-controlled processes including rhythmic transcription of circadian-regulated genes and the rhythmic movement of the seedling cotyledons (51). The phenotype of the *ztl* mutant shows a strong dependence on fluence rate in that the period-lengthening effect of the mutation is more extreme at low fluence rates of light (51). This suggests that ZTL is involved in the light input pathway to the clock. Significantly, ZTL contains a PAS domain similar to that found in the blue-light receptor nph1 or in the WC-1 circadian clock-associated protein of *N. crassa* (51) and also an F-box, which may be involved in the targeting of proteins for ubiquitination and a kelch domain typically involved in protein-protein interaction. ZTL forms part of a small gene family comprising two other members, FKF1 and LKP2, which show a similar proposed structure. FKF1 also affects circadian clock-regulated gene expression, and, like the *ztl1* mutant, the *fkf1* mutant is late flowering (51, 52).

INSECTS

Subsequent to their discovery in plants, cryptochromes were also found to exist in the animal kingdom (14, 53–56). The animal cryptochromes appear to be derived from 6-4 photolyases, but, like the plant cryptochromes, they show no photolyase activity (57, 58). A single cryptochrome, dCRY, in *Drosophila melanogaster*, has also been demonstrated to be involved in light input to the clock (14, 55). The core clock components in which a transcriptional-feedback loop involving four key molecules generates sustained oscillation at the molecular level with a relatively tight circadian period have been well characterized in *D. melanogaster* (59–61). Transcription of the genes *PERIOD* (*PER*) and *TIMELESS* (*TIM*) leads to a rise in PER and TIM protein levels in the afternoon and early evening. PER-TIM dimers then enter the nucleus and repress their own transcription by inhibiting the activity of a positively acting transcriptional activation complex consisting of the proteins CLOCK (CLK) and CYCLE (CYC). Consequently, levels of PER and TIM protein fall again as these proteins are degraded until they reach a level at which they no longer inhibit their own transcription, and the cycle begins again (59–61) (Figure 6, see color insert).

A second, interlocked negative-feedback loop causes CLK to cycle in antiphase with PER and TIM. Here, CLK feeds back as a repressor of its own transcription, whereas PER and TIM act as derepressors (62).

The interactions of these factors provide further examples of the involvement of PAS proteins in the circadian clock. PER and TIM dimerize via a PAS domain in the PER protein, and this dimerization allows their nuclear entry (63, 64). Likewise, CLK and CYC both contain PAS domains thought to be involved in the dimerization, which allows them to bind to DNA (59, 65).

Additional proteins such as DOUBLETIME act on this feedback loop to delay the speed with which a cycle occurs, resulting in an approximately circadian period length (66). In addition, another protein, VRILLE (VRI), was recently demonstrated to be involved in the fly clock. Cycles of *vri* expression are essential for function of the clock, but its precise role remains unclear (67).

In the *Drosophila* mutant *cry^baby^* (*cry^b^*), which lacks cryptochrome, rhythms of PER and TIM expression in the body of the fly fail to entrain to light-dark cycles (14). However, the rhythm of PER and TIM expression within lateral neuron cells remains entrainable by light, as do behavioral rhythms, suggesting that photoreceptors other than dCRY are able to entrain these rhythms. Significantly, *norpA^p41^ cry^b^* double-mutant flies fail to show normal entrainment of behavioral rhythms (14). The *norpA^p41^* mutation causes the compound eyes and ocelli to be completely unresponsive to light, although monogenic *norpA^p41^* mutant flies show normal entrainment. This suggests that behavioral entrainment in *D. melanogaster* is mediated by a combination of signals from cryptochromes and from the visual-photoperception pathway.

Monogenic *cry^b^* mutant flies also show a reduced response to pulses of light that will induce a phase shift in behavioral rhythms in wild-type flies (14). Responses of overexpressors of *dCRY* vary. Emery et al observed an enhanced response to light pulses for phase-shifting in *dCRY* overexpressors (56), whereas Ishikawa et al observed a decreased response (67a). Furthermore, in wild-type flies, as in other arthropods, period length in constant light increases with increasing fluence rate, to the extent that, at very high intensities of light, wild-type flies become arrhythmic (3, 68). Mutant *cry^b^* flies, however, continue to display strong rhythmicity even in intense constant illumination, indicating that circadian photoperception is impaired to the extent that *cry^b^* flies cannot perceive constant light (69). This phenotype is rescued by expression of wild-type dCRY in lateral neuron cells, confirming dCRY as the key circadian photoreceptor (69). It would appear from these latter experiments that the visual photoperception pathway does not, in fact, impinge directly on the clock. One possibility, therefore, to explain the behavioral entrainment of *cry^b^* flies by light is that visual stimuli may act to drive a rhythm of physical activity that, in turn, entrains the circadian clock.

Recent experiments have gone some way toward elucidating the mode of action of dCRY in resetting the clock at the molecular level. For the clock to be reset, a light signal must be able to change the concentration of one of the core clock molecules. Illumination results in a rapid degradation of TIM in *D. melanogaster*, which results in resetting the clock to the point in the cycle at which TIM would normally be low (70, 70a). Significantly, dCRY has been shown to interact directly with TIM in a light-dependent manner and to inhibit the PER-TIM dimer from feeding back on *PER* and *TIM* transcription, consistent with its role as the circadian photoreceptor (71) (Figure 7, see color insert).

MAMMALS

In mammals the central circadian oscillator was recently shown to have two interlocking feedback loops consisting of the same core clock components as were demonstrated in *D. melanogaster*. Mice contain three *PER* genes (*mPER1–3*) and two *CRY* genes (*mCRY1–2*) as well as *TIM*, *CLK*, and *CYC* (also called *BMAL*)

(55, 72–76). However, it appears that the molecular interaction between these components to generate the feedback loops is quite different from that in *D. melanogaster*. In cultured mammalian cells, mPER1, mPER2, mPER3, and mTIM can inhibit the CLK-CYC transcriptional complex (77). Furthermore, mCRY1 or mCRY2 alone is also able to independently inhibit CLK-CYC-mediated transcription (77) by directly binding to the CLK-CYC complex (78).

In a further divergence from the mechanism of the fly circadian clock, although mTIM and mPER have been shown to dimerize in vitro (79), attempts to coimmunoprecipitate mTIM and mPER from microdissected mouse suprachiasmatic nucleus (SCN) tissue showed no evidence of dimerization between mTIM and any of the mPER gene products (80). However, the mammalian CRYs are able to dimerize with the mPER and mTIM proteins in vivo and, for the PER proteins, this dimerization facilitates their entry into the nucleus (77). Homo- and heterodimers were also shown to form between the various mPER proteins to facilitate their entry to the nucleus (77) and between the two mCRYs (80). Although the significance of these mCRY dimers remains elusive (Figure 8, see color insert), it appears that inhibition of the CLC-CK transcriptional complex is effected largely by the CRY proteins (see Reppert & Weaver, this volume; 80a)

The second feedback loop in the mammalian clock is a positive one in which mPER2 acts as a promoter of *CYC* transcription. In this loop, CRY also plays a role acting to stabilize mPER2 (78).

Thus in mammals, mCRY1 and mCRY2 act as components of the clock mechanism itself. Consistent with this, mutant mice lacking both mCRY1 and mCRY2 are arrhythmic in constant conditions (81). It is interesting that mutant mice lacking mCRY1 show a shorter free-running period than wild-type mice and that mutant mice lacking mCRY2 show a longer free-running period than wild-type mice, which suggests that the two CRYs somehow act antagonistically within the clock mechanism (81, 82). Significantly, transcription of *mCRY1* shows circadian regulation (55) and contains a sequence within the upstream regulatory region known to be the target of the CLK-CYC complex (77), which suggests that mCRY1 itself may form an autoregulatory feedback loop.

It is not certain whether the mammalian CRYs play any role as photoreceptors for the clock. One of the early events associated with phase resetting in response to a light pulse during the night is a rapid induction of mPER1 transcript. Mutants lacking mCRY1 or mCRY2 show reduced mPER1 induction in response to a light pulse during the night, whereas mutants lacking both mCRY1 and mCRY2 fail to show any acute induction of mPER1 in response to a light pulse (72, 82). The disruption of light-induced mPER1 induction in the mCRY mutants suggests that the mCRYs may, in fact, be photoreceptors in addition to clock components (Figure 9, see color insert). However, if mCry1$^{-/-}$ mCry2$^{-/-}$ double-mutant mice are maintained in darkness for 52 h prior to a light pulse, an acute light induction of mPER1 can be observed, suggesting the action of another photoreceptor in addition to mCRY1 and mCRY2 (83). This may be a light-labile photoreceptor that requires a long period of darkness to allow its re-accumulation, hence its action is observed only in mice maintained in such prolonged darkness. It is curious that, although the mCRYs are implicated in the perception of phase-shifting light pulses, *mCRY2* mice show an increased phase shift in behavioral activity rhythm in response to a light pulse (82). Again this may reflect some antagonism in action between the two cryptochromes.

The eyes are essential for light detection in entrainment of the circadian clock in mammals (84). However, mutant mice lacking both rod and cone visual photoreceptors show normal phase shifting in response to a light pulse, which suggests that other retinal photoreceptors are acting in these mice to reset the clock in response to light signals (85). In an elegant experiment, viral-tract tracing was used to trace the endings of axons of the retinohypothalamic tract running from the eyes to the SCN (the site of the central clock in the mammalian brain). These axons have extensive dendritic arbors, diffusely branched over a relatively large area of the retinal surface (86). The cryptochromes are highly expressed in retinal ganglion cells spread evenly across the inner nuclear layer of the retina (55), which makes these cryptochromes strong candidates for the photoreceptors stimulating the SCN. This further supports the idea that cryptochromes may act as circadian photoreceptors in mammals. It is notable that this arrangement would give very poor spatial resolution but would be ideal for light input to the clock, where information about only the intensity of light is important.

The full story as to the mechanism of circadian photoperception in mammals is far from clear. Although there is strong evidence for the involvement of the cryptochromes, several pieces of evidence suggest that, if cryptochromes are involved, they are not the only circadian photoreceptors. The critical clock component, mPER2, is induced in response to a light pulse in both wild-type and $Cry1^{-/-}$ $Cry2^{-/-}$ mice, indicating the involvement of photoreceptors other than cryptochromes (72). However, it is not clear whether induction of mPER2 alone can result in clock resetting. A further conundrum is that the spectral maximum for clock resetting in mammals is at $\sim$500 nm, corresponding better to an opsin such as rhodopsin or possibly a novel opsin (87, 88) rather than cryptochrome (which absorbs maximally at 370–440 nm) (89). It is possible that in mammals, as in flies, both cryptochrome and the visual photoperception pathway redundantly act to entrain the clock. Alternatively, an as-yet-unidentified nonvisual photoreceptor may be involved. Candidates include melanopsin and vertebrate ancient opsin recently found in *Xenopus laevis* and salmon, respectively (89a, 89b). Generation of $Cry1^{-/-}$ $Cry2^{-/-}$ flies also lacking rods and cones will be necessary to answer these questions.

CONCLUSION

An interesting feature to emerge from the study of circadian photoperception is that there is an increase in complexity in the mechanism by which the overt rhythms throughout an organism are synchronized to entraining light-dark cycles.

In plants, which have no central nervous system, the clock appears to be able to run independently in each organ if not within each cell, with no evidence of coupling between the various organs making up the plant. These rhythms in different organs can be independently entrained by light, and, consistent with this, the photoreceptors involved in light input to the clock are expressed throughout the plant (90). In flies, which have a relatively simple central nervous system, the behavioral-activity rhythm is centrally controlled by oscillation in the level of clock components within the lateral neurons (14). The lateral neurons are synchronized by light input from cryptochromes but also at least indirectly by light input from the visual photoreceptors (14). In peripheral tissues, however, entrainment of the oscillation in the level of clock components is largely dependent on light input via cryptochromes (14). Furthermore, when peripheral organs are removed from the fly, the clock within these isolated organs can be entrained to light-dark cycles independently of any signal from the central nervous system (91). In mammals, which have a complex central nervous system, entrainment is entirely dependent on light input via the eyes to the SCN. Enucleated mammals fail to show any behavioral entrainment to light-dark cycles (84). Furthermore, in mammals in which the SCN has been lesioned, peripheral rhythms of PER transcription become completely desynchronized even in light-dark cycles, which suggests that these rhythms cannot be directly entrained by light on the periphery (92). Thus with increasing complexity of the central nervous system, the dependence of peripheral circadian rhythms on a central coupling mechanism also increases (93). Now that the mechanisms of circadian photoperception are becoming clearer, an important avenue for future research will be to determine the mechanism by which the circadian clock is coupled throughout the mammalian body.

Finally, many problems in sleep patterns are related to an inability to properly entrain the circadian clock to the day-night cycle. Furthermore, disruptions of the sleep pattern due to jet lag or shift work are also related to the entrainment of the circadian clock (94, 95). The elucidation of the mechanism whereby light sets the phase of the circadian clock will, therefore, be of great benefit in addressing these problems.

Visit the Annual Reviews home page at www.AnnualReviews.org

LITERATURE CITED

1. Dunlap JC. 1999. Molecular bases for circadian clocks. *Cell* 96:271–90
2. Pittendrigh CS. 1993. Temporal organization: reflections of a Darwinian clock-watcher. *Annu. Rev. Physiol.* 55:17–54
3. Aschoff J. 1979. Circadian rhythms: influences of internal and external factors on the period measured in constant conditions. *Z. Tierpsychol.* 49:225–49
4. Hastings MH, Maywood ES, Ebling FJP. 1995. The role of the circadian system in photoperiodic time measurement in mammals. *NATO ASI A* 277:95–106
5. Edmunds LN. 1988. *Cellular and Molecular*

Bases of Biological Clocks. New York: Springer-Verlag

6. Roenneberg T, Foster RG. 1997. Twilight times: light and the circadian system. *Photochem. Photobiol.* 66:549–61

7. Johnson CH. 1990. *PRC Atlas.* http://johnsonlab.biology.vanderbilt.edu/prcatlas/prcatlas.html

8. Nelson DE, Takahashi JS. 1991. Sensitivity and integration in a visual pathway for circadian entrainment in the hamster (Mesocricetus auratus). *J. Physiol.* 439:115–45

9. Pittendrigh CS. 1960. Circadian rhythms and the circadian organization of living systems. *Cold Spring Harbor Symp. Quant. Biol.* 25:159–84

10. Daan S, Pittendrigh CS. 1976. A functional analysis of circadian pacemakers in nocturnal rodents. III. Heavy water and constant light: homeostasis of frequency? *J. Comp. Physiol.* 106:267–90

11. Roenneberg T, Hastings JW. 1988. Two photoreceptors control the circadian clock of a unicellar alga. *Naturwissenshaften* 75:206–7

12. Crosthwaite SK, Dunlap JC, Loros JJ. 1997. *Neurospora wc-1* and *wc-2*: transcription, photoresponses, and the origins of circadian rhythmicity. *Science* 276:763–69

13. Somers DE, Devlin PF, Kay SA. 1998. Phytochromes and cryptochromes in the entrainment of the *Arabidopsis* circadian clock. *Science* 282:1488–90

14. Stanewsky R, Kaneko M, Emery P, Beretta B, Wager-Smith K, et al. 1998. The *cry[b]* mutation identifies cryptochrome as a circadian photoreceptor in *Drosophila. Cell* 95:681–92

15. Lucas RJ, Foster RG. 1999. Circadian rhythms: something to cry about? *Curr. Biol.* 9:R214–17

16. Roenneberg T. 1996. The complex circadian system of *Gonyaulax polyedra. Physiol. Plant.* 96:733–37

17. Roenneberg T, Mittag M. 1996. The circadian program of algae. *Semin. Cell Dev. Biol.* 7:753–63

18. Hastings JW, Sweeney BM. 1960. The action spectrum for shifting the phase of the rhythm of luminescence in *Gonyaulax polyedra. J. Gen. Physiol.* 43:697–706

19. Roenneberg T, Deng TS. 1997. Photobiology of the *Gonyaulax* circadian system. 1. Different phase response curves for red and blue light. *Planta* 202:494–501

20. Deng TS, Roenneberg T. 1997. Photobiology of the *Gonyaulax* circadian system. 2. Allopurinol inhibits blue-light effects. *Planta* 202:502–9

21. Johnson CH, Hastings JW. 1989. Circadian phototransduction: phase resetting and frequency of the circadian clock of *Gonyaulux* cells in red light. *J. Biol. Rhythms* 4:417–37

22. Roenneberg T, Taylor W. 1994. Light-induced phase responses in *Gonyaulax* are drastically altered by creatine. *J. Biol. Rhythms* 9:1–12

23. Arpaia G, Loros JJ, Dunlap JC, Morelli G, Macino G. 1993. The interplay of light and the circadian clock. *Plant Physiol.* 102:1299–305

24. Lauter FR, Russo VE. 1991. Blue light induction of conidiation-specific genes in *Neurospora crassa. Nucleic Acids Res.* 19:6883–86

25. Sommer T, Chambers JA, Eberle J, Lauter FR, Russo VE. 1989. Fast light-regulated genes of *Neurospora crassa. Nucleic Acids Res.* 17:5713–23

26. Russo VE. 1988. Blue light induces circadian rhythms in the *bd* mutant of *Neurospora*: Double mutants *bd,wc-1* and *bd,wc-2* are blind. *J. Photochem. Photobiol.* 2:59–65

27. Harding RW, Melles S. 1983. Genetic analysis of phototropism of *Neurospora crassa* perithecial beaks using white collar and albino mutants. *Plant Physiol.* 72:996–1000

28. Talora C, Franchi L, Linden H, Ballario P, Macino G. 1999. Role of a white collar-1-white collar-2 complex in blue-light signal transduction. *EMBO J.* 18:4961–68

29. Linden H, Macino G. 1997. White collar 2, a partner in blue-light signal transduction, controlling expression of light-regulated genes in *Neurospora crassa*. *EMBO J.* 16:98–109

30. Ballario P, Vittorioso P, Magrelli A, Talora C, Cabibbo A, Macino G. 1996. White collar-1, a central regulator of blue light responses in *Neurospora*, is a zinc finger protein. *EMBO J.* 15:1650–57

31. Christie JM, Salomon M, Nozue K, Wada M, Briggs WR. 1999. LOV (light, oxygen, or voltage) domains of the blue-light photoreceptor phototropin (nph1): binding sites for the chromophore flavin mononucleotide. *Proc. Natl. Acad. Sci. USA* 96:8779–83

32. Merrow M, Brunner M, Roenneberg T. 1999. Assignment of circadian function for the *Neurospora* clock gene frequency. *Nature* 399:584–86

33. Aronson BD, Johnson KA, Loros JJ, Dunlap JC. 1994. Negative feedback defining a circadian clock: autoregulation of the clock gene frequency. *Science* 263:1578–84

34. Crosthwaite SK, Loros JJ, Dunlap JC. 1995. Light-induced resetting of a circadian clock is mediated by a rapid increase in frequency transcript. *Cell* 81:1001–12

35. Kendrick RE, Kronenberg GHM, eds. 1994. *Photomorphogenesis in Plants*. Dordrecht, The Netherlands: Kluwer

36. Plant Cell Environment. 1997. Special issue: Photomorphogenesis, 1997. *Plant Cell Environ.* 20(6):657–844

37. Whitelam GC, Devlin PF. 1998. Light signalling in *Arabidopsis*. *Plant Physiol. Biochem.* 36:125–33

38. Sharrock RA, Quail PH. 1989. Novel phytochrome sequences in *Arabidopsis thaliana*: structure, evolution, and differential expression of a plant regulatory photoreceptor family. *Genes Dev.* 3:1745–57

39. Clack T, Mathews S, Sharrock RA. 1994. The phytochrome apoprotein family in *Arabidopsis* is encoded by five genes: the sequences and expression of *PHYD* and *PHYE*. *Plant Mol. Biol.* 25:413–27

40. Quail PH. 1991. Phytochrome: a light-activated molecular switch that regulates plant gene expression. *Annu. Rev. Genet.* 25:389–409

41. Millar AJ. 1997. Circadian rhythms: PASsing time. *Curr. Biol.* 7:R474–76

42. Devlin PF, Kay SA. 1999. Cryptochromes—bringing the blues to circadian rhythms. *Trends Cell Biol.* 9:295–98

43. Millar AJ, Straume M, Chory J, Chua N-H, Kay SA. 1995. The regulation of circadian period by phototransduction pathways in *Arabidopsis*. *Science* 267:1163–66

44. Millar AJ, Kay SA. 1991. Circadian control of *cab* gene transcription and mRNA accumulation in *Arabidopsis*. *Plant Cell* 3:541–50

45. Yanovsky MJ, Casal JJ, Whitelam GC. 1995. Phytochrome A, phytochrome B and HY4 are involved in hypocotyl growth responses to natural radiation in *Arabidopsis*: weak de-etiolation of the *phyA* mutant under dense canopies. *Plant Cell Environ.* 18:788–94

46. Whitelam GC, Johnson E, Peng J, Carol P, Anderson ML, et al. 1993. Phytochrome A null mutants of *Arabidopsis* display a wild-type phenotype in white light. *Plant Cell* 5:757–68

47. Whitelam GC, Patel S, Devlin PF. 1998. Phytochromes and photomorphogenesis in *Arabidopsis*. *Philos. Trans. R. Soc. London Ser. B* 353:1445–53

48. Lin C, Robertson DE, Ahmad M, Raibekas AA, Jorns MS, et al. 1995. Association of flavin adenine dinucleotide with the *Arabidopsis* blue light receptor CRY1. *Science* 269:968–70

49. Ahmad M, Jarillo JA, Smirnova O, Cashmore AR. 1998. The CRY1 blue light photoreceptor of *Arabidopsis* interacts with phytochrome A in vitro. *Mol. Cell* 1:939–48

50. Millar AJ, Carré IA, Strayer CA, Chua N-H, Kay SA. 1995. Circadian clock mutants

in *Arabidopsis* identified by luciferase imaging. *Science* 267:1161–63

51. Somers DE, Schultz TF, Milnamow M, Kay SA. 2000. *ZEITLUPE*, a novel clock associated PAS protein from *Arabidopsis*. *Cell* 101:319–29

52. Nelson DC, Lasswell J, Rogg LE, Cohen MA, Bartel B. 2000. *FKF1*, a clock-controlled gene that regulates the transition to flowering in *Arabidopsis*. *Cell* 101:331–40

53. Todo T, Ryo H, Yamamoto K, Toh H, Inui T, et al. 1996. Similarity among the *Drosophila* (6-4) photolyase, a human photolyase homolog, and the DNA photolyase-blue-light receptor family. *Science* 272:109–12

54. Van Der Spek PJ, Kobayashi K, Bootsma D, Takao M, Eker APM, Yasui A. 1996. Cloning, tissue expression and mapping of a human photolyase homolog with similarity to plant blue light receptors. *Genomics* 37:177–82

55. Miyamoto Y, Sancar A. 1998. Vitamin B_2-based blue-light photoreceptors in the retinohypothalamic tract as the photoactive pigments for setting the circadian clock in mammals. *Proc. Natl. Acad. Sci. USA* 95:6097–102

56. Emery PT, So WV, Kaneko M, Hall JC, Rosbash M. 1998. CRY, a *Drosophila* clock and light-regulated cryptochrome, is a major contributor to circadian rhythm resetting and photosensitivity. *Cell* 95:669–79

57. Hsu DS, Zhao XD, Zhao SY, Kazantsev A, Wang RP, et al. 1996. Putative human blue light photoreceptors hCRY1 and hCRY2 are flavoproteins. *Biochemistry* 35:13871–77

58. Okano S, Kanno S, Takao M, Eker AP, Isono K, et al. 1999. A putative blue-light receptor from *Drosophila melanogaster*. *Photochem. Photobiol.* 69:108–13

59. Darlington TK, Wager-Smith K, Ceriani MF, Staknis D, Gekakis N, et al. 1998. Closing the circadian loop: CLOCK-induced transcription of its own inhibitors

per and *tim*. *Science* 280:1599–603

60. Allada R, White NE, So WV, Hall JC, Rosbash M. 1998. A mutant *Drosophila* homolog of mammalian *Clock* disrupts circadian rhythms and transcription of *period* and *timeless*. *Cell* 93:791–804

61. Rutila JE, Suri V, Le M, So WV, Rosbash M, Hall JC. 1998. CYCLE is a second bHLH-PAS clock protein essential for circadian rhythmicity and transcription of *Drosophila period* and *timeless*. *Cell* 93:805–14

62. Glossop NR, Lyons LC, Hardin PE. 1999. Interlocked feedback loops within the *Drosophila* circadian oscillator. *Science* 286:766–68

63. Saez L, Young MW. 1996. Regulation of nuclear entry of the *Drosophila* clock proteins period and timeless. *Neuron* 17:911–20

64. Huang ZJ, Edery I, Rosbash M. 1993. PAS is a dimerization domain common to *Drosophila period* and several transcription factors. *Nature* 364:259–62

65. Lee C, Bae K, Edery I. 1999. PER and TIM inhibit the DNA binding activity of a *Drosophila* CLOCK-CYC/dBMAL1 heterodimer without disrupting formation of the heterodimer: a basis for circadian transcription. *Mol. Cell. Biol.* 19:5316–25

66. Kloss B, Price JL, Saez L, Blau J, Rothenfluh A, et al. 1998. The *Drosophila* clock gene *double-time* encodes a protein closely related to human casein kinase Iε. *Cell* 94:97–107

67. Blau J, Young MW. 1999. Cycling vrille expression is required for a functional *Drosophila* clock. *Cell* 99:661–71

67a. Ishikawa T, Matsomoto A, Kato T Jr, Togashi S, Ryo H, et al. 1999. dCRY is a *Drosophila* photoreceptor protein implicated in light entrainment of circadian rhythm. *Genes Cells* 4:57–65

68. Konopka RJ, Pittendrigh CS, Orr D. 1989. Reciprocal behavior associated with altered homeostasis and photosensitivity of

Drosophila clock mutants. *J. Neurogenet.* 6:1–10

69. Emery P, Stanewsky R, Hall JC, Rosbash MA. 2000. A unique circadian rhythm photoreceptor. *Nature* 404:456–57

70. Suri VP, Qian ZW, Hall JC, Rosbash M. 1998. Evidence that the TIM light response is relevant to light-induced phase shifts in *Drosophila melanogaster*. *Neuron* 21:225–34

70a. Yang Z, Emerson M, Su HS, Sehgal A. 1998. Response of the Timeless protein to light correlates with behavioral entrainment and suggests a nonvisual pathway for circadian photoreception. *Neuron* 21:215–23

71. Ceriani MF, Darlington TK, Staknis D, Mas P, Petti AA, et al. 1999. Light-dependent sequestration of TIMELESS by CRYPTOCHROME. *Science* 285:553–56

72. Vitaterna MH, Selby CP, Todo T, Niwa H, Thompson C, et al. 1999. Differential regulation of mammalian period genes and circadian rhythmicity by cryptochromes 1 and 2. *Proc. Natl. Acad. Sci. USA* 96:12114–19

73. Shearman LP, Zylka MJ, Weaver DR, Kolakowski LF Jr, Reppert SM. 1997. Two *period* homologs: circadian expression and photic regulation in the suprachiasmatic nuclei. *Neuron* 19:1261–69

74. Zylka MJ, Shearman LP, Weaver DR, Reppert SM. 1998. Three *period* homologs in mammals: differential light responses in the suprachiasmatic circadian clock and oscillating transcripts outside of brain. *Neuron* 20:1103–10

75. Zylka MJ, Shearman LP, Levine JD, Jin X, Weaver DR, Reppert SM. 1998. Molecular analysis of mammalian timeless. *Neuron* 21:1115–22

76. Hogenesch JB, Chan WK, Jackiw VH, Brown RC, Gu YZ, et al. 1997. Characterization of a subset of the basic-helix-loop-helix-PAS superfamily that interacts with components of the dioxin signaling pathway. *J. Biol. Chem.* 272:8581–93

77. Kume K, Zylka MJ, Sriram S, Shearman LP, Weaver DR, et al. 1999. mCRY1 and mCRY2 are essential components of the negative limb of the circadian clock feedback loop. *Cell* 98:193–205

78. Shearman LP, Sriram S, Weaver DR, Maywood ES, Chaves I, et al. 2000. Interacting molecular loops in the mammalian circadian clock. *Science* 288:1013–19

79. Sangoram AM, Saez L, Antoch MP, Gekakis N, Staknis D, et al. 1998. Mammalian circadian autoregulatory loop: a timeless ortholog and mPer1 interact and negatively regulate CLOCK-BMAL1-induced transcription. *Neuron* 21:1101–13

80. Field MD, Maywood ES, O'Brien JA, Weaver DR, Reppert SM, Hastings MH. 2000. Analysis of clock proteins in mouse SCN demonstrates phylogenetic divergence of the circadian clockwork and resetting mechanisms. *Neuron* 25:437–47

80a. Reppert SM, Weaver DR. 2001. Molecular analysis of mammalian circadian rhythms. *Annu. Rev. Physiol.* 63:647–76

81. van der Horst GTJ, Muijtjens M, Kobayashi K, Takano R, Kanno S, et al. 1999. Mammalian Cry1 and Cry2 are essential for maintenance of circadian rhythms. *Nature* 398:627–30

82. Thresher RJ, Vitaterna MH, Miyamoto Y, Kazantsev A, Hsu DS, et al. 1998. Role of mouse cryptochrome blue-light photoreceptor in circadian photoresponses. *Science* 282:1490–94

83. Okamura H, Miyake S, Sumi Y, Yamaguchi S, Yasui A, et al. 1999. Photic induction of mPer1 and mPer2 in cry-deficient mice lacking a biological clock. *Science* 286:2531–34

84. Foster RG. 1998. Shedding light on the biological clock. *Neuron* 20:829–32

85. Freedman MS, Lucas RJ, Soni B, von Schantz M, Munoz M, et al. 1999. Regulation of mammalian circadian behaviour

by non-rod, non-cone ocular photoreceptors. *Science* 284:502–4

86. Provencio I, Cooper HM, Foster RG. 1998. Retinal projections in mice with inherited retinal degeneration: implications for circadian photoentrainment. *J. Comp. Neurol.* 395:417–39

87. Provencio I, Foster RG. 1995. Circadian rhythms in mice can be regulated by photoreceptors with cone-like characteristics. *Brain Res.* 694:183–90

88. Yoshimura T, Ebihara S. 1996. Spectral sensitivity of photoreceptors mediating phase-shifts of circadian rhythms in retinally degenerate CBA/J (rd/rd) and normal CBA/N (+/+) mice. *J. Comp. Physiol. A.* 178:797–802

89. Sancar A. 2000. Cryptochrome: the second photoactive pigment in the eye and its role in circadian photoreception. *Annu. Rev. Biochem.* 69:31–67

89a. Provencio I, Jiang G, DeGrip WJ, Hayes WP, Rollag MD. 1998. Melanopsin: an opsin in melanophores, brain, and eye. *Proc. Natl. Acad. Sci. USA* 95:430

89b. Soni BG, Philip A, Knox BE, Foster RG. 1998. Novel retinal photoreceptors. *Nature* 394:27

90. Thain SC, Hall A, Millar AJ. 2000. Functional independence of circadian clocks that regulate plant gene expression. *Curr. Biol.* 10:951–56

91. Plautz JD, Kaneko M, Hall JC, Kay SA. 1997. Independent photoreceptive circadian clocks throughout *Drosophila*. *Science* 278:1632–35

92. Sakamoto K, Nagase T, Fukui H, Horikawa K, Okada T, et al. 1998. Multitissue circadian expression of rat period homolog (rPer2) mRNA is governed by the mammalian circadian clock, the suprachiasmatic nucleus in the brain. *J. Biol. Chem.* 273:27039–42

93. Yamazaki S, Numano R, Abe M, Hida A, Takahashi R, et al. 2000. Resetting central and peripheral circadian oscillators in transgenic rats. *Science* 288:682–85

94. Redfern PH, Lemmer B. 1997. *Physiology and Pharmacology of Biological Rhythms*. Berlin: Springer-Verlag

95. Smith L, Folkard S, Poole CJ. 1994. Increased injuries on night shift. *Lancet* 344:1137–39

96. Plautz JD, Straume M, Stanewsky R, Jamison CF, Brandes C, et al. 1997. Quantitative analysis of *Drosophila* period gene transcription in living animals. *J. Biol. Rhythms* 12:204–17

Annu. Rev. Physiol. 2001. 63:695–728

ENDOGENOUS TIMEKEEPERS IN PHOTOSYNTHETIC ORGANISMS

Carl Hirschie Johnson

Department of Biological Sciences, Vanderbilt University, Nashville, Tennessee 37235; e-mail: carl.h.johnson@vanderbilt.edu

Key Words circadian, photoperiodism, clock, fitness, *kai*, *TOC*, *LHY*, *CCA1*, ultraviolet, calcium

■ **Abstract** Circadian and photoperiodic timing mechanisms were first described in photosynthetic organisms. These organisms depend upon sunlight for their energy, so adaptation to daily and seasonal fluctuations in light must have generated a strong selective pressure. Studies of the endogenous timekeepers of photosynthetic organisms provide evidence for both a fitness advantage and for selective pressures involved in early evolution of circadian clocks. Photoperiodic timing mechanisms in plants appear to use their circadian timers as the ruler by which the day/night length is measured. As in animals, the overall clock system in plants appears to be complex; the system includes multiple oscillators, several input pathways, and a myriad of outputs. Genes have now been isolated from plants that are likely to encode components of the central clockwork or at least that act very close to the central mechanism. Genetic and biochemical analyses of the central clockwork of a photosynthetic organism are most highly advanced in cyanobacteria, where a cluster of clock genes and interacting factors have been characterized.

KEEPERS OF THE TIME IN PHOTOSYNTHETIC ORGANISMS

This review is about the endogenous biochemical programs that allow photosynthetic organisms to keep track of daily and seasonal time. These timekeepers are the circadian (daily) and photoperiodic (seasonal) timing mechanisms. As discussed below, there appears to be an intrinsic linkage between the two timing mechanisms in that a circadian mechanism appears to be the timer by which the day and night length is measured at different times of the year to allow the appropriate timing of seasonal responses. This review covers the entire gamut of photosynthetic organisms for which these timing mechanisms have been documented, from prokaryotic algae to eukaryotic algae and plants. The literature is vast, and no single review can do justice to all the relevant research. I therefore apologize to my colleagues whose work does not appear herein; I could not include many excellent and

0066-4278/01/0315-0695$14.00

important studies. For information concerning the photobiology of circadian and photoperiodic timekeepers, see the review by Devlin & Kay, this volume (1).

Plants were the first organisms to provide evidence for endogenous circadian and photoperiodic timekeepers. No doubt prehistoric humans had noted that the plants and animals around them organized their activities on a daily cycle, but probably they concluded that these biological rhythms were a direct response to the day/night cycle. The first report that these oscillations might be the result of an endogenous timing mechanism dates from 1729 and a Frenchman named de Mairan, who noticed that "sensitive plants" (probably *Mimosa pudica*) maintained their 24-h rhythms of leaf movement when maintained in constant darkness where there were no light/dark cues as to the time of day (2). Subsequent studies extended de Mairan's observations. In particular, the circadian pioneer, Erwin Bünning, made careful measurements of the leaf movement rhythm of the common bean *Phaseolus*. He found that the leaf movements of beans oscillated in constant darkness with a period of 25.4 h (reviewed in 3), thereby establishing a salient property of circadian clocks: They "free-run" in constant conditions with a period close to, but never exactly, 24 h. This free-running behavior in constant conditions is a diagnostic characteristic of circadian rhythms (namely, persistence). The other two characteristics are temperature compensation and entrainment (4, 5).

What Processes Are Controlled by These Temporal Programs?

Photosynthetic organisms depend upon sunlight. The availability of this energy is a 24-h phenomenon, and therefore it is not surprising that photosynthetic organisms rhythmically mobilize many processes so as to optimally collect every possible drop of the sun's energy. Consequently, there are many circadian-controlled processes in photosynthetic organisms. Examples among physiological functions include circadian rhythms of leaf movements, hypocotyl elongation, stomatal conductance, photosynthetic capacity, phototaxis, cell division, flower movements, fragrance emissions, chloroplast movements, nitrogen fixation, ion fluxes, and many others (3). There are also many genes whose expression is known to be regulated by the circadian clock (6–8); in fact, it was in photosynthetic organisms that the first rhythms of abundance of specific proteins and mRNAs were described (9, 10).

How pervasive is the circadian control over gene expression? In cyanobacteria, a sensitive and comprehensive method was used to address this question: the random insertion of a promoter-less bacterial luciferase (*luxAB*) gene set throughout the genome (11). Whenever the *lux* gene set inserted into a genomic locus that was sufficiently close to a promoter, the expression of the *lux* genes was turned on, and the colonies became luminescent. Those luminescent patterns were analyzed, and the astounding result was that, irrespective of the site of *lux* insertion, all the luminescent colonies displayed circadian rhythms. The luminescence rhythms exemplified different phases, waveforms, and amplitudes, but all were circadian.

Apparently the cyanobacterial clock globally controls gene expression—in this case, the activity of promoters (11). [In a different species of cyanobacteria, Huang et al (12) also found evidence for global control of gene expression based on rhythms of protein abundance.]

In the plant *Arabidopsis*, a global screen for gene expression was performed using fluorescent differential display (13). This technique allows high-throughput measurements of mRNA abundances. That study found at least 17 different cycling transcripts—a number that is significantly smaller than that found in cyanobacteria. The study of global gene expression in cyanobacteria measured promoter activity rather than mRNA abundance, and this difference in methodology may also be pertinent to the fact that a higher percentage of genes appears to be under circadian control in cyanobacteria. For example, data obtained from *Arabidopsis* indicate that the mRNA abundance of the *Lhcb1* gene is regulated by posttranscriptional mechanisms that confer an overall constitutive expression pattern, despite a circadian rhythm of promoter activity (14). Consequently, there still may be circadian control of a gene's promoter activity even when its mRNA abundance is constant. Therefore, the differential display results in *Arabidopsis* may be an underestimate of the total number of promoters that are puppets of the circadian clock in plants. In tomato, there are 19 different *Lhc* genes that are controlled by the circadian clock (6). Taken together, these data suggest that there are numerous clock-regulated genes in photosynthetic organisms.

Photoperiodic timekeepers control physiological processes that are mainly reproductive and developmental, as befits the need for predominantly sessile photosynthetic organisms to respond to seasonal changes in temperature and light intensity by overwintering as seeds and/or in a dormant stage. Therefore, changes in the photoperiod (day length) can elicit floral development, bud dormancy, tuber/bud formation, etc (15). Undoubtedly, myriad changes in gene expression will be found to accompany these reproductive and developmental transitions.

Are the Central Timekeepers Dependent Upon Energy from the Sun?

In most animals, circadian rhythms are expressed in both constant darkness (DD) and in constant light (at least, in dim constant light). In contrast, many observable rhythms in photosynthetic organisms dampen rapidly in DD. This leads to a key question: Is the clockwork in photosynthetic organisms still ticking in DD, or is it stopped? A number of lines of evidence support the conclusion that the central circadian clocks of photosynthetic organisms are still running in DD even though the observable rhythms are not. For example, normally photoautotrophic cyanobacteria that can be adapted to heterotrophic growth on exogenous carbon sources express sustained rhythms in DD when the carbon source is supplied (16, 17). Essentially the same results have been obtained with the green alga *Chlamydomonas*: In photoautotrophic cultures, rhythms of gene expression damp within one cycle in DD (18), but in cultures growing with the carbon source acetate, these algae now express sustained rhythms of gene expression in DD (19, 20). In the angiosperms *Lemna* (21), *Chenopodium* (22), and *Samanea* (23), exogenous sugars maintain rhythmic expression in DD for a significantly longer time than in the absence of a carbon source.

While the above data could be interpreted to mean that light sustains circadian rhythms merely by supplying the metabolic energy necessary to power the clockwork, other data indicate that the central clock runs even when energy levels are low. For example, in cyanobacteria, *Chlamydomonas*, and tobacco growing in photoautotrophic conditions, light and/or dark pulse protocols indicate that an underlying circadian clock continues to operate in DD, even when the overt rhythms are dampened (24–27). Moreover, in many plants, daily exposure to brief red light pulses of intensities and duration far below that necessary for photosynthesis will maintain a rhythm of robust amplitude (28). A mutant (*supernova*) of *Arabidopsis* expresses a rhythm of gene expression in DD for at least 4 days, even though the same rhythm damps in a wild-type background under DD (29). Finally, circadian oscillations of cytosolic-free calcium persist in tobacco seedlings in DD for at least 3 days in the absence of any carbon source (30).

These data show that the rapid damping of circadian expression by photosynthetic organisms in DD comes probably from the uncoupling of output rhythms from a clockwork that is still ticking. It is likely that photosynthetic organisms use light as an indirect sensor of energy status. In DD, the organisms shut down many otherwise rhythmically expressed processes, probably to conserve energy. This shutdown can be circumvented by providing exogenous carbon sources to those organisms that can utilize them, or by "tricking" the organism into believing that abundant light energy is available, as by giving them brief red light pulses or by mutations in which the light sensor is locked in the on position. The clockwork itself, however, appears to have a preferred status and is maintained in low-energy conditions for a longer time than its outputs.

WHY DO PHOTOSYNTHETIC ORGANISMS HAVE ENDOGENOUS TEMPORAL PROGRAMS?

Circadian and photoperiodic timers are found in photosynthetic and non-photosynthetic organisms but, as mentioned above, the light/dark cycle is central to photosynthetic organisms because light is their source of energy and life. It is probably not a coincidence that the prokaryotes in which circadian rhythms were first discovered were photosynthetic cyanobacteria. Other prokaryotes may have circadian clocks, but they have not yet been documented.

Presumably, the advantage of having a daily biological clockwork is that it organizes a temporal program that cues processes to occur at specific phase relationships to the daily environmental cycle. This programming can enable the organism to anticipate changes in the environment that are important and enable it to respond appropriately. For example, a circadian alarm clock that heralds dawn can allow an organism to ready its photosynthetic apparatus so as to utilize the first photons of dawn. Temporal programming also permits the phasing of incompatible processes to occur at different times, as in the case of photosynthesis and nitrogen fixation in unicellular cyanobacteria (31). The nitrogen-fixing enzyme nitrogenase is inactive in the presence of oxygen, which creates a dilemma for organisms whose photosynthesis releases oxygen. As one of several tactics to allow these mutually incompatible tasks, some cyanobacteria have separated photosynthesis and nitrogen fixation temporally: photosynthesis in the daytime, nitrogen fixation at night. Other examples of temporal separation of processes include (*a*) the separation of motility taxes in the alga *Chlamydomonas*, phototaxis in the daytime and *chemotaxis* (to ammonium) in the night-time (32), and (*b*) day versus night expression of different forms of catalase in *Arabidopsis* (33).

Evolution of Daily Timers: Escape from Light?

The question of why organisms have endogenous temporal programs is closely linked with identifying the selective forces that encouraged the original evolution of these timers. The presence of circadian oscillators in cyanobacteria, whose ancestors appear in the fossil record at least 3.5 billion years ago, implies that circadian clocks might have been an ancient invention of evolution (although it remains possible that circadian timers may have been absent in ancient cyanobacteria and evolved relatively recently). It is possible that a selective pressure for elaborating an internal timekeeper could have been the advantage of anticipation and/or temporal separation of metabolic activities suggested above.

Perhaps a strong initial driving force for the early evolution of circadian clocks could have been the advantage inherent in phasing cellular events that are sensitive to deleterious wavelengths of sunlight so that they occur in the night. This idea has been called the escape from light hypothesis (34). That speculation seems plausible when one considers the numerous examples of microorganisms with 24-h cell division cycles in which DNA replication and cell division occur during the night (35). Perhaps some of the events of the cell division cycle in these microorganisms are sensitive to sunlight. This kind of selective pressure would be even more potent for photosynthetic than for non-photosynthetic organisms because their dependence on light energy means that they cannot hide from the damaging side effects of the sunlight; they have to take the good with the bad.

If this hypothesis about the early evolution of circadian programs is correct, then we would predict that present-day organisms might still exhibit temporal regulation of light-sensitive processes to the night. Because the most generally deleterious wavelengths of sunlight are in the ultraviolet range, a test of the daily sensitivity to ultraviolet light could be illuminating. Such a study has recently been completed in the alga *Chlamydomonas* (36). As shown in Figure 1, these algae are more sensitive to ultraviolet light near sunset and into the early night. The rhythmic sensitivity persists in constant conditions, albeit with a reduced amplitude (36). Even though there is some sensitivity in the late daytime, ultraviolet light is

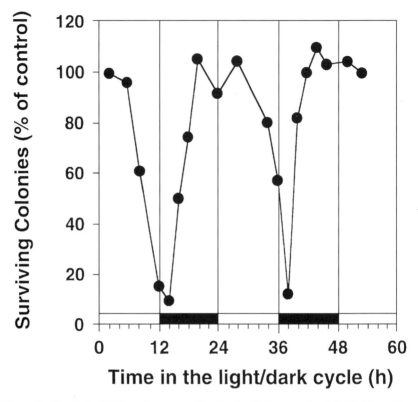

Figure 1   Survival of *Chlamydomonas* cells after irradiation by ultraviolet light as a function of the time in a light/dark cycle. *Chlamydomonas* cultures were plated onto agar medium and treated with equal amounts of ultraviolet light at different phases of a 12-h light:12-h dark cycle. Survival was measured as the colony-forming ability of cells following treatment compared with that of cells that were not irradiated with ultraviolet light (modified from 36).

strongly scattered at twilight and is therefore nearly absent from sunlight around the time of sunset, so the ultraviolet sensitivity of *Chlamydomonas* near dusk would not be expected to pose a significant problem in the natural environment. In *Chlamydomonas*, the circadian clock regulates the timing of the cell division cycle (25), and these ultraviolet light-sensitive phases correspond with the times in which S/G2 would be expected to occur.

These data are consistent with the hypothesis that the daily cycle of ultraviolet radiation may have created a selective pressure favoring the evolution of circadian clocks. This hypothesis dovetails with the recent discovery of a role for cryptochromes in circadian systems. Cryptochromes, pigmented photoreceptors, are involved in blue light–mediated photomorphogenesis, circadian entrainment, and photoperiodism in plants (1). Cryptochromes share sequence homology with

DNA photolyase, another blue-light-activated protein from which they probably evolved. DNA photolyase uses blue-light energy to repair ultraviolet-induced damage of DNA. Possibly, an ancestral photolyase that repaired DNA damaged by the daily cycle of ultraviolet light may have been enlisted for duties in biological timing mechanisms and evolved into cryptochromes (36).

Do Daily Timekeepers Really Enhance the Fitness of Organisms?

Several paragraphs above, I said "presumably, the advantage of having a daily biological clockwork is that it organizes a temporal program that cues processes to occur at specific phase relationships to the daily environmental cycle." However, let us not presume. Is there direct evidence that circadian clocks enhance fitness in photosynthetic organisms? For many circadian rhythms, the adaptive significance is unclear and certainly has not been rigorously tested. A prime example is that of the first circadian rhythm to be documented—the leaf movement rhythm observed by de Mairan to persist in DD. We still do not understand the function of the leaf movement rhythm even though several hypotheses have been advanced (37).

In the 1950s, several studies addressed the key question of the adaptive significance of having a circadian oscillator. For example, tomatoes were found to grow optimally when maintained on a light/dark cycle that was similar to that encountered in nature; in other words, tomatoes on a 12-h light:12-h dark cycle outgrew those in 6-h light:6-h dark or 24-h light:24-h dark cycles (38–40). Remarkably, tomato plants on a 12:12 cycle grew even faster than those in continuous light, even though the plants in constant light were receiving twice as much photonic energy (40). In addition, there was an interdependence between the temperature and the optimal light cycle; at colder temperatures (when the clock might be expected to run slower), the optimal light/dark cycle was longer than at higher temperatures (41). The Q10 for the effect was about 1.2, which is approximately what would be expected for the temperature dependence of a circadian oscillator's period. Those data indicated that tomato plants were optimally adapted to growth in light/dark cycles that were similar to those found in nature and implied that it was a circadian timekeeper that was responsible for that adaptation.

However, there were two problems with those conclusions. First, many plant species other than tomato (e.g. *Arabidopsis*) do not exhibit reduced growth in constant light. Second, while growth may be indirectly related to fitness, there is not a necessary correspondence between growth and fitness, for example, if a slowly growing plant produces more successful seeds than a rapidly growing plant, the slow-grower may be more fit. A direct test of the effect of a circadian clock on fitness is needed. The adaptive significance of circadian programs was first rigorously tested in competition experiments using asexual cyanobacteria (42). The cyanobacteria that were used are not known to conjugate under laboratory conditions and several mutant strains exhibit different free-running periods. For asexual microbes, differential growth of one strain under competition with other strains is a good measure of reproductive fitness. The circadian phenotypes of the strains used had free-running periods of about 22, 25, (wild-type), and 30 h. In pure culture, the strains grew at about the same rate in constant light and in light/dark cycles, so there did not appear to be a significant advantage or disadvantage to having different circadian periods when the strains were grown individually. As depicted in Figure 2A, the fitness test was to mix different strains together and grow them in competition to determine if the composition of the population changes as a function of time. The cultures were diluted at intervals to allow growth to continue.

The results of this competition test were remarkable (42). When each of the strains was mixed with another strain and grown together in competition, a pattern emerged that depended upon the frequency of the light/dark cycle and the circadian period (Figure 2B). When grown on a 22-h cycle (11 h light, 11 h dark), the 22 h-period mutant became the dominant cell type in the mixed cultures. On a 30-h cycle (15 h light, 15 h dark), the 30-h-period mutant could defeat either wild-type strain or the 22-h-period mutant. On a normal 24-h cycle (12 h light, 12 h dark), the wild-type strain could overgrow either mutant. Clearly, the strain whose period most closely matched that of the light/dark cycle eliminated the competitor. Under a nonselective condition (in this case, constant light), each strain was able to maintain itself in the mixed cultures (Figure 2B). Because the mutant strains could defeat the wild-type strain in light/dark cycles in which the periods are similar to their endogenous periods, the observed differential effects are likely to result from the differences in the circadian clock. A genetic test was also performed to demonstrate that only the clock gene mutation was responsible for the differential effects in the competition experiment (42).

This is the first rigorous demonstration in any organism of a fitness advantage conferred by a circadian system. But what is the basis of the competitive advantage? In the original publication, two possibilities were introduced: (*a*) Clocks allow optimal utilization of limiting resources such as light, nutrients, carbon dioxide, or (*b*) cyanobacteria rhythmically secrete diffusible factors that inhibit the growth of other cyanobacterial strains. No physiological data are currently

---

Figure 2   Competition of circadian strains in different light/dark cycles. *A*. Different strains of cyanobacteria were mixed together in batch cultures and grown in competition under different light/dark cycles. Every 8 days, the cultures were diluted with fresh medium. At various times during the competition, aliquots were plated as single colonies, and the luminescence rhythms of individual colonies were monitored to determine the frequency distribution of the different circadian phenotypes. *B*. The strain whose endogenous free-running period most closely matched that of the environmental light/dark cycle was able to out-compete strains with a non-optimal period. In constant light (non-selective conditions), all the strains were able to maintain their initial fraction in the population. *C*. Phase of a luminescence rhythm for wild-type (= wt) and the mutant exhibiting a 30-h period (= C28a) on a light/dark cycle of 12 h light/12 h dark (*left*) versus 15 h light/15 h dark (*right*) (modified from 42).

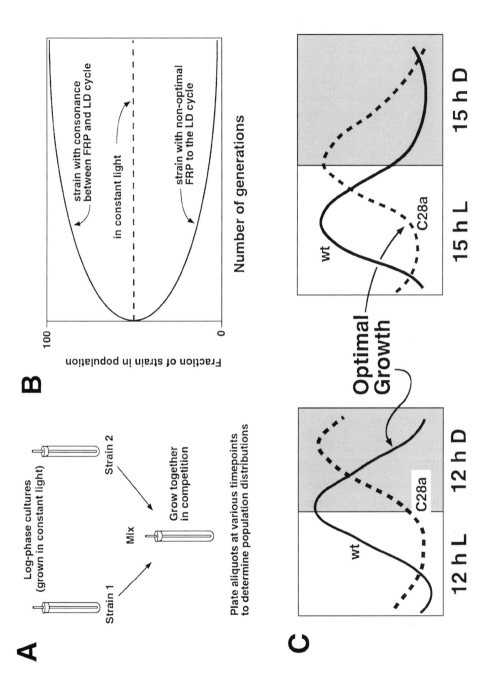

available that distinguish between these hypotheses, but a modeling study favored the rhythmic inhibitor alternative (43).

We know that the various cyanobacterial strains entrain to the different light/dark cycles, so the periods of the cyanobacteria in the light cycles are always the same as that of the light cycle. If so, why should the strains having an endogenous period similar to that of the light/dark cycle out-compete other strains? We know from circadian entrainment theory that the phase of circadian events under entrainment will change if the frequency of either the free-running period or the light cycle is altered (44). Consistent with this expectation, a clear correlation from the cyanobacterial competition data is that the phasing of gene expression rhythms is altered as a function of the frequency of the light/dark cycle and free-running period; as shown in Figure 2C, the luminescence rhythm that reports the rhythm of a photosynthetic gene's promoter activity peaks near dusk for wild-type cells on 12:12 cycles and for long-period mutant (C28a) cells on 15:15 cycles. These are the free-running period:light/dark cycle combinations that correlate with optimal fitness in the competition experiment. In non-optimal combinations, the phasing of the rhythms is different. Therefore, a likely explanation for the differences in selective advantage is that the phase relationships between biological rhythms and environmental cycles are predictably altered in different combinations of free-running period versus the period of the light/dark cycle (42). This conclusion is consistent with the postulate that the circadian system regulates temporal programming of metabolic processes and that fitness is maximized when the phasing of those processes relative to the environmental cycles is optimized.

How do the competition data from cyanobacteria relate to fitness in plants? The data from the 1950s examined growth rates, but that parameter is not directly related to fitness. For plants, a better gauge of fitness than growth would be fecundity, i.e. the number and quality of seeds produced by wild-type and mutant plant varieties under light/dark cycles of different periods. These tests should be performed.

Photoperiodic Time Measurement: A Clock to Time Day Length

One clock-involved process for which the adaptive significance is clear is that of photoperiodic time measurement (PTM). PTM is the ability of plants and animals to sense the season of the year by measuring the duration of the day and/or night in the natural environment and then to respond appropriately to annual changes. Without this ability, many photosynthetic organisms could not survive the winter. The first demonstration that organisms sense the changing season by measuring the duration of the day or night was in plants, where their seasonal flowering was shown to be controlled by photoperiod in 1920 (45).

The transition from vegetative growth to reproductive growth is arguably the most dramatic and important event in plant development. In most flowering plants, this developmental transition is controlled by the environmental cues of photoperiod and temperature. The annual modulation of photoperiod is the most reliable cue for plants to anticipate annual changes. In photoperiodically responding species, the developmental transition to reproductive growth is regulated by the duration of light versus darkness in the 24-h light:dark cycle. Garner & Allard found that some species/strains flowered in response to short days, while other species/strains flowered in response to long days (45). Other species/strains flowered independently of photoperiod. These different types of responses to photoperiod have come to be known as short-day plants (SDP), long-day plants (LDP), or day-neutral plants (DNP) (15, 45). Figure 3A illustrates the different responses of a SDP and a LDP to various photoperiods.

Before venturing further, we must clearly distinguish between a simple response to photoperiod and a true PTM response. Because photosynthetic organisms depend upon light, there may be trivial stimulatory responses on longer photoperiods because they receive more light than on short photoperiods (at equal intensity). Or, there may be a stress response to short photoperiods if there is not enough light to sustain robustness [this might be the case for the reputed photoperiodic response in the alga, *Gonyaulax* (46), which is stressed by short photoperiods at low temperature]. A true PTM response is one that absolutely depends on the duration and/or timing of the photoperiod. To distinguish between a simple response to photoperiod and a PTM response, experimenters can either use night-break or resonance experiments or compare long photoperiods of low-light intensity with short photoperiods of higher-light intensity to equalize photonic exposure. In the latter

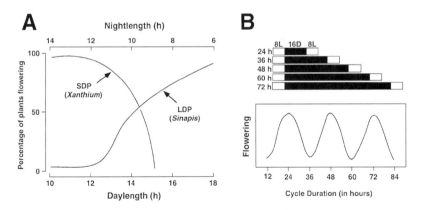

Figure 3 Photoperiodic time measurement. *A.* Flowering profiles of a short-day plant (SDP; *Xanthium*) and a long-day plant (LDP; *Sinapis*) on light-dark cycles of different day and night lengths (total cycle time was always 24 h) (adapted from 15, figure 1.4). *B.* Resonance experiment showing the involvement of a circadian timer in PTM. *Upper panel* depicts the experimental protocol: cycles of light and dark where the light interval is always 8 h, separated by various durations of darkness to achieve different cycle times (the light and dark exposures repeat for many days). *Lower panel*, flowering responses of a SDP (soybeans) to these cycles. The 24-, 48-, and 72-h cycles are inductive, whereas 12-, 36-, 60-, and 84-h cycles are not (adapted from 47).

case, if the flowering response of a plant is similar on a short photoperiod of high-fluence rate to that on a long photoperiod of low-fluence rate, then it would appear that the number of photons received is more important than the duration of day.

Another kind of test is the night-break experiment. Plants that have a true PTM system often interpret a brief interruption (e.g. 15 min of dim light) in the middle of the night of a short day (e.g. LD 8:16) as a long day. Apparently, the plants perceive the night-break light pulse as a dawn or dusk signal. Night-break experiments were first interpreted to mean that PTM involves the measurement of the duration of the night, and not of the day (47). Early models for the night-measuring timer were based on evidence that some members of the phytochrome photoreceptor family were part of the photoreceptive apparatus involved in PTM (48, 49). Borthwick & Hendricks even proposed that phytochrome was an integral part of an "hourglass" timing mechanism, where the spontaneous reversion of the Pfr form of phytochrome to the Pr form in darkness could function as a time-measuring system (50). This model was subsequently discredited by a variety of measurements (15, 51), but it exemplified a mechanistic model based on a simple biochemical timer.

The model for PTM that has become generally accepted is that a circadian oscillator is the timer that somehow measures the length of the day and night and triggers the developmental events. This model was proposed by Bünning in 1936 (52), and has since become known as Bünning's Hypothesis. When it was first proposed, this model seemed too fantastic to be realistic, but later studies using light and dark cycles with a range of durations supported his idea (15, 47). In particular, one such experiment is illustrated in Figure 3B in which a SDP is exposed to light/dark cycles composed of an 8-h light pulse that recurs over a range of periodicities. Only light/dark cycles with a modulo-circadian periodicity induced photoperiodic responses (SDPs usually show clearer results than LDPs in this protocol). This kind of experiment is called a resonance experiment because the induction is envisioned to be a resonance between the circadian PTM timer and the light/dark cycle. By virtue of its cyclic nature, a circadian oscillator (but not a simple hourglass timer) can interpret these unnatural light/dark cycles as short and long days (53). Therefore, we believe at the present time that a circadian clock is the timer by which the day and/or night length is gauged in PTM, but how it does this is unknown.

The resonance experiment depicted in Figure 3B is one type of physiological evidence that the PTM timer is a circadian oscillator, but there is also genetic evidence that there are shared molecular components between the PTM timer and circadian oscillators controlling daily rhythms of leaf movement, gene expression, and so on. The genetic evidence comes primarily from the facultative LDP, *Arabidopsis thaliana*. *Arabidopsis* is currently the predominant flag-bearer for genetic dissection of biological questions in plants, including that of photoperiodic flowering (54, 55). Unfortunately, it is not an optimal plant for studying PTM because it is not an obligate SDP or LDP, and because it usually requires multiple cycles of stimulatory photoperiods before flowering is induced. Nevertheless, considerable headway in the genetics of PTM and circadian timers has been accomplished with this model system. The evidence for common molecular components between the PTM and other circadian rhythms comes from observations that *Arabidopsis* mutants isolated on the basis of aberrant timing of flowering sometimes have altered properties of other circadian rhythms and vice versa (56). Here are a few examples of genes affecting these processes:

1. *ELF3*: The *elf3* mutant flowers early under a variety of growth conditions and is photoperiod insensitive with respect to floral intiation. The *elf3* mutation disrupts circadian rhythms of leaf movement or *Lhcb* promoter activity (essentially arhythmic) in constant light but does not have a major impact on the *Lhcb* promoter activity rhythm in constant darkness (29).

2. *GI*: Some mutant alleles of the *GI* gene are insensitive to photoperiod. The circadian periods of leaf movement and *Lhcb* promoter activity rhythms are altered in two of these alleles, *gi-1* and *gi-2* (57). The period of *Lhcb* promoter activity rhythm in *gi-1* mutant plants also has an altered fluence response to red light.

3. *LHY*: The *lhy* mutant exhibits a late-flowering, photoperiod-insensitive phenotype. Three other circadian rhythms are disrupted in *lhy*: leaf movement, *Lhcb* promoter activity, and *CCR2* mRNA abundance (58).

4. *CCA1*: Overexpression of the *CCA1* gene delays flowering and disrupts the circadian expression of several genes (59). This gene is likely to be involved in phytochrome phototransduction pathways in *Arabidopsis* (60).

5. *FLC*: A quantitative trait locus (QTL) analysis has linked observations of natural allelic variation in circadian period to the *FLC* locus for which photoperiodic mutant alleles had already been discovered (61).

6. *FKF1*: The *fkf1* mutant causes a late-flowering phenotype that is rescued by vernalization or gibberellin treatment. The abundance of the *FKF1* mRNA exhibits a circadian rhythm, and the *fkf1* mutation may slightly disrupt the phasing of two circadianly expressed genes, *CCA1* and *CAT2* (62).

The action of several of the above genes/alleles varies as a function of light fluence and/or spectrum (e.g. *ELF3*, *GI*, *CCA1*), implying that they are involved in phototransduction. Mutation of other genes encoding phototransduction components can also modulate photoperiodic flowering (63). It could be that the common ground at the genetic/molecular level between the photoperiodic and other circadian systems is shared phototransduction pathways.

HOW DO THESE TEMPORAL PROGRAMS WORK?

The evidence summarized above clearly indicates that these biological oscillators confer an adaptive advantage. What makes these clocks tick? This question has two major facets: What is the organization/mechanism of the circadian systems at the organismal level and at the cellular/molecular level? Until recently, circadian clock systems have generally been diagrammed as a simple pathway, from light to photoreceptor to clockwork to outputs, with coupling steps between photoreceptor and clockwork and between clockwork and outputs [see Williams & Sehgal, this volume (63a)]. The pathway was unidirectional; while it was supposed that there were feedback loops within the clockwork itself, feedback of outputs to the clockwork or clockwork to photoreceptive pathway was not part of previous dogma about circadian organization.

We now know that the overall organization of circadian systems is more complex (Figure 4). For example, in photosynthetic organisms, there is more than one photoreceptor (1). As described below, there are multiple clockworks as well. We also know of many observable output rhythms. Finally, we now know of cases where feedback of the clockwork onto the photoreceptive pathway is strongly suspected (64, 65) (an arrow indicating such feedback is included in Figure 4). The web of interactions whereby these different components are coupled is unknown, but several possibilities are shown in Figure 4 and are discussed below.

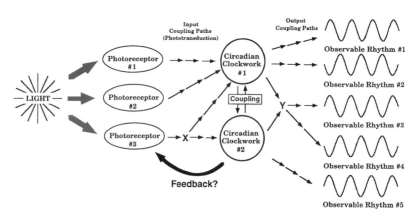

Figure 4   A hypothetical model for the organization of the major components of circadian systems. Light information is perceived by photoreceptors that pass the information along to central clockworks by input coupling pathways. The clockworks are circadian oscillators that are phased by input pathways and control via output coupling paths various observable rhythms (outputs). The multiple inputs, clockworks, and outputs may be coupled in a variety of ways, including components that might be common to more than one input (e.g. X) or output (e.g. Y) pathway. Note the following definitions: a rhythm is an observable biological activity that oscillates and can be used to monitor and infer the action of an underlying clock (rhythm = output). Clock and oscillator are used interchangeably to refer to a central endogenous timekeeper that controls myriad overt rhythms. The term clockwork refers to the biochemical mechanism of a clock.

Links in the Web: Coupling Pathways

Figure 4 depicts the four major components that make up circadian systems: photoreceptors, clockworks, outputs, and the coupling factors that link these components together. Clock photoreceptors are reviewed elsewhere in this volume (1); the multiplicity of clock outputs was briefly considered above. Coupling pathways (*a*) are the links between input pathways and clockworks, (*b*) are the means by which a clockwork manages its outputs, and (*c*) function to couple multiple oscillators together. Our understanding of the nature of these couplers is currently incomplete, but we will need to characterize these pathways before we can understand how the clock controls various physiological and/or biochemical events.

Coupling by Transcriptional Regulation   In the context of the coupling of rhythmically expressed genes to central oscillators, a common mechanism by which clocked genes are controlled is transcriptional control. The first report of circadian rhythms of specific mRNA abundance in plants was that of Kloppstech (10). Since that time, the mRNA abundance of many different genes has been shown to oscillate over the circadian cycle in photosynthetic organisms, and in most cases these abundance rhythms have been found to be at least partially from transcriptional control (6–8).

A curious observation of the studies of mRNA abundance rhythms is that in some cases, they do not promote equivalently robust rhythms of the levels of their corresponding proteins (66, 67). What is the function of the mRNA rhythms if there is no rhythm of the corresponding protein? It has been shown in higher plants (68) and in *Chlamydomonas* (69) that there are rhythms of light-harvesting complex (LHC) protein synthetic rate even though the overall LHC protein abundance is essentially constant. Apparently the proteins turn over much more slowly than their mRNA counterparts. In such a case, one wonders about the adaptive significance of the mRNA abundance rhythms. One speculation is that there is tissue and/or developmental specificity such that at some developmental phases or in some tissues, there are rhythms of protein abundance that follow the mRNA abundance rhythms (66). Another likely possibility is that the significance of the mRNA rhythm has to do with rhythmic turnover of the proteins, even though the total amount of protein is constant (6, 67, 69). For example, degradative rates of LHC proteins are likely to be higher during the day owing to damage from sunlight; therefore, to maintain a constant level of intact LHCs, new synthesis of LHC protein is necessary every day (6, 69). We suggested a similar explanation for the significance of the *psbAI* mRNA rhythm in cyanobacteria (70).

A recent discovery relating to coupling pathways was the tracking of an output rhythm—the rhythm of *Lhcb* gene expression—upstream to the *CCA1* gene (59). CCA1, a Myb-related transcription factor, was identified by its ability to bind to promoter regions of clock-controlled *Lhcb* genes. *CCA1* mRNA and *CCA1* protein are expressed rhythmically, and these rhythms may account for the rhythmic regulation of *Lhcb* expression (59). As is summarized below, several experimental results suggest that CCA1 is either a component of a central clockwork or at least a crucial component of the output coupling path that acts close to the clockwork, e.g. at a position like that of Y in Figure 4. That an output-tracking strategy discovered a key component of the clock or coupling pathway is satisfying to those of us who have struggled in other systems to follow output rhythms back to their source.

Coupling by Translational Regulation   In contrast to many studies implicating transcriptional control in controlling circadian gene expression, there are only a few examples of translational control of a circadian rhythm. The best characterized have been those in the dinoflagellate alga *Gonyaulax*, which exhibits a precise circadian rhythm of spontaneous light emission that is one of the best characterized circadian outputs at the molecular level (71). The biochemical components of the bioluminescent reaction have been identified, so it has been possible to assess the mechanisms by which the circadian clock modulates each individual component and thus determines how the bioluminescence capacity is controlled rhythmically. The intracellular concentration of each of the three major components, the enzyme (luciferase), substrate luciferin, and luciferin-binding protein (LBP), oscillate during the circadian cycle (9, 71). In fact, an entire organelle, the scintillon, undergoes circadian synthesis and degradation (72).

The molecular control of the LBP has been extensively studied, due to the fact that it is more abundant than the luciferase enzyme. When *lbp* mRNA was assayed, the results were unexpected. Even though the abundance of LBP and the rate of LBP synthesis undergo a large circadian change, the abundance of the mRNA that encodes LBP is constant over the daily cycle (71). The circadian clock controls when the translation of this mRNA is initiated. In subsequent studies of this apparent translational control, a protein that specifically binds to the 3′ untranslated region of the *lbp* mRNA was discovered (73). The abundance of this RNA-binding protein undergoes a circadian oscillation, with its lowest levels coinciding with the phases at which the *lbp* mRNA is translated. This result implicates the specific mRNA-binding protein as a translational repressor of LBP synthesis (73). When *lbp* mRNA was tested with extracts from the green alga *Chlamydomonas*, a homologous circadian-binding activity was discovered, implying a conservation of translational regulatory mechanisms in diverse algae (74).

Coupling by Signal Transduction Mechanisms   A number of studies implicate regulatory networks that are usually considered to be second messenger signal transduction mechanisms in the output and/or input pathways of circadian clock systems. These signal transduction pathways, including cyclic nucleotides, intracellular free calcium, and protein phosphorylation, are especially attractive candidates for clock-to-hand couplers because they can globally affect many cellular processes. For example, at least two lines of evidence implicate cyclic nucleotides in the input/output transduction pathways in photosynthetic organisms. One example of involvement in an output pathway was given by Carré & Edmunds (75) who concluded that rhythmic changes in cyclic AMP were the mechanism by which the clockwork triggered circadian cell division in *Euglena*. In the case of cyclic GMP, Millar et al (76) have concluded on the basis of numerous lines of evidence that phytochrome phototransduction includes an initial G protein step that then activates both cyclic GMP and cytosolic free calcium $[Ca^{2+}]_c$ pathways. Therefore, it is possible that phytochrome-mediated phase resetting of central oscillators is transduced via changes in cyclic GMP levels.

If G proteins mediate phytochrome transduction, then it is also possible that phytochrome mediation of phase shifting involves changes of $[Ca^{2+}]_c$ levels. Alternatively (or additionally), there might be circadian oscillations of $[Ca^{2+}]_c$ levels that could confer rhythmicity on many cellular output processes. There are several studies suggesting that changes in $[Ca^{2+}]_c$ levels are key components of circadian input and/or output (or even in the clockwork mechanism) (e.g. 77, 78). To test these alternatives, we monitored the free calcium levels of tobacco and *Arabidopsis* seedlings (30). Our transgenic seedlings expressed the calcium photoprotein aequorin, which provides a gauge of $[Ca^{2+}]_c$ levels by $[Ca^{2+}]$-specific luminescence. As shown in Figure 5, when aequorin was targeted to the cytosol, we discovered circadian oscillations of $[Ca^{2+}]_c$ levels in constant light that could be entrained by light/dark signals. We also observed oscillations of $[Ca^{2+}]_c$ levels (albeit of lower amplitude) when the seedlings were in constant darkness. When aequorin was targeted to the chloroplast, damped chloroplast $[Ca^{2+}]$ rhythms were likewise observed in DD, but not in constant light. These data indicate that there is compartment-specific circadian control of intracellular free calcium (30).

It is possible that changes of $[Ca^{2+}]_c$ levels could mediate light-induced phase shifting (76, 78). Circadian oscillations in $[Ca^{2+}]_c$ levels can be expected to control many Ca^{2+}-dependent enzymes (e.g. kinases and phosphatases) that could account for circadian outputs. Based on other studies suggesting that the promoter activity of the *Lhcb* gene is regulated by $[Ca^{2+}]_c$ levels (79), we tested whether the rhythm of $[Ca^{2+}]_c$ levels might be a coupling factor that drives the *Lhcb* promoter rhythm. We found that in the same conditions, the rhythm of $[Ca^{2+}]_c$ levels free-ran with a different period than that of *Lhcb* promoter activity (Figure 5). This result established that the $[Ca^{2+}]_c$ rhythm was not controlling the rhythm of *Lhcb* promoter activity (80). The role of the $[Ca^{2+}]_c$ oscillation is not currently known, but by virtue of the potent effect of $[Ca^{2+}]_c$ on fluxes of other ions, it might regulate circadian outputs that involve rhythmic fluxes of potassium and other ions, for example, the leaf movement rhythm (81, 82) or rhythms of stomatal conductance (83).

Changes of cyclic nucleotide and $[Ca^{2+}]_c$ levels would ultimately be expected to affect the phosphorylation status of key regulatory enzymes. We, therefore, anticipate that phosphorylation and/or dephosphorylation events will dispatch the circadian couriers that directly regulate outputs. The field of circadian regulation by phosphorylation and dephosphorylation in photosynthetic organisms is almost

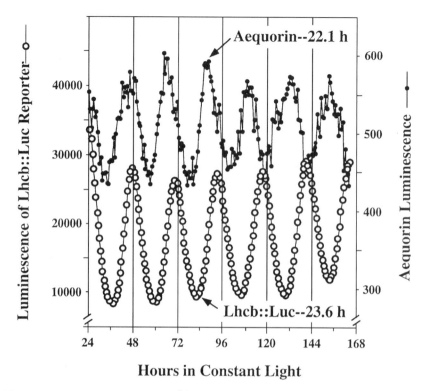

Figure 5 Desynchronization of $[Ca^{2+}]_c$ and *Lhcb* activity rhythms in tobacco seedlings under constant red illumination. A double reporter strain was constructed in which luminescence from aequorin reports $[Ca^{2+}]_c$ levels (closed circles) and luminescence from luciferase reports the promoter activity for the *Lhcb* gene (= *Lhcb::Luc*, open circles). The two luminescence rhythms were measured under the same conditions; the average values for the two rhythms are shown (modified from 80).

totally untilled. One exception is the circadian regulation of the enzyme phosphoenolpyruvate carboxylase (PEPc) in the CAM plant *Kalanchoë* (84). The activity of this enzyme is modulated by rhythmically phosphorylating and dephosphorylating PEPc, apparently via the rhythmic activation of a PEPc-specific protein kinase (84).

In addition to a role for phosphorylation in controlling output pathways, Comolli & Hastings (85) have suggested that protein phosphorylation plays a role in the central clock mechanism or in the input pathway in *Gonyaulax*. They found that continuous exposure to protein kinase inhibitors can lengthen the period of the bioluminescence rhythm in this alga. Pulses of the inhibitors cause phase delays of the rhythm. Moreover, they can disrupt light-induced phase shifting. It is likely that protein phosphorylation events will be important factors in circadian rhythmicity of photosynthetic organisms.

Multiple Oscillators?

Although we know of multiple output rhythms in single organisms, it is quite possible that more than one rhythm could be controlled by a single clockwork, as in Figure 4 where clockwork #1 controls two rhythms (#1 and #2) independently. Even if the rhythms peak at different phases, a single oscillator could control those rhythms. However, if different rhythms have different, stable periods under the same free-running conditions or can be phase-shifted independently from each other, then it is possible that those rhythms are driven by different underlying oscillators.

When rhythms with different free-running periods are found simultaneously in the same organism (suggesting different underlying oscillators), the phenomenon is called internal desynchronization. If internal desynchronization occurs in a multicellular, multitissue organism, there are several possibilities of how it may be obtained (86). The most obvious is that there are different clockworks driving the different rhythms. On the other hand, if one rhythm is expressed in a distinct tissue (e.g. leaf movement in pulvinar tissue) from another rhythm (e.g. stomatal conductance in guard cells), then it is possible that the same clockwork drives both rhythms, but that differences in the intracellular environment between the two tissues (e.g. pulvinar cells versus guard cells) modify the properties of the clockwork such that it oscillates with a slightly different period in the two tissues. Therefore, when different free-running periods are found for different rhythms, an important unanswered question is whether the underlying difference is the same mechanism operating in different biochemical environments or distinct clockwork mechanisms.

On the other hand, when internal desynchronization occurs in a single-celled organism, the likelihood of different clockworks is high, but there are two caveats. The first is that for single-celled organisms monitored in a population, the cells in the population may be segregating into two subgroups that express different rhythms (there is not yet a good example of internal desynchronization in a single isolated cell). Second, even within a single cell, it is possible that the same molecular components are oscillating in more than one compartment (e.g. cytosol versus mitochondria versus chloroplast); differences in intracompartmental milieu could result in different rhythms driven from different compartments.

Given that it is difficult to know definitively how many clockworks are involved, is there evidence for internal desynchronization at either the tissue or cellular level in photosynthetic organisms? The answer is clearly yes. One of the best studies is that of Hennessey & Field (87), who showed a 3-h difference in the free-running periods of the leaf movement and stomatal conductance rhythms measured simultaneously in the same leaflets of *Phaseolus*. In another study, the leaf movement rhythm of wild-type *Arabidopsis* free-runs with a period that is about 0.5 h longer than that of the rhythm of *Lhcb* promoter activity, whereas in the *toc1* mutant of *Arabidopsis*, the periods of these rhythms are separated by about 2.5 h (88). These differences might be partly due to the fact that the two rhythms were not measured under identical conditions. However, the result suggests that internal desynchronization is facilitated by the *toc1* mutation. In another case where the rhythm of *Lhcb* promoter expression was compared under identical conditions with the rhythm of cytosolic free calcium ($[Ca^{2+}]_c$) in tobacco seedlings, there was at least a 1.5-h difference in the free-running periods, as shown in Figure 5 (80). As mentioned above, this result is important because it established that the $[Ca^{2+}]_c$ rhythm is not a coupling factor that drives the rhythm of *Lhcb* promoter activity; additionally, it demonstrated clear internal desynchronization of circadian oscillators regulating these two rhythms.

The cases mentioned above could be occurring at either the intercellular or intracellular level—the answer is not yet known. However, there is also evidence for internal desynchronization that is likely to be at the intracellular level. In populations of the unicellular alga *Gonyaulax*, two different rhythms (bioluminescence and motility/aggregation) free-run with different periods in constant red light (89). Moreover, the *Gonyaulax* data provide evidence for coupling between the oscillators controlling these rhythms; while the two rhythms free-run with clearly distinguishable periods, there appears to be relative coordination between the two rhythms when their peak phases coincide. There is also evidence for internal desynchronization within single plant cells; in young *Arabidopsis* seedlings, a study that monitored the promoter activity rhythms of the *Lhcb* versus chalcone synthase genes within mesophyll cells discovered that the two rhythms free-run with periods that are approximately 1.5 h apart (SC Thain, G Murtas, JR Lynn, RB McGrath & AJ Millar, unpublished observations). The latter study did not assay isolated cells, and it is difficult to be absolutely sure at this time that the same mesophyll cells were expressing both rhythms with distinct periods, but the currently available data support the conclusion of multiple oscillators driving these rhythms.

If multiple oscillators occur in photosynthetic organisms, are they coupled together (as are clockworks #1 and #2 in Figure 4), or do they operate completely independently? Again, this question can be asked at both the cellular and tissue levels of organization. At the cellular level, little is known about the coupling of independent oscillators except for two observations in the case of *Gonyaulax*: Internal desynchronization is facilitated under only some conditions (e.g. constant red light), which suggests that environmental conditions modulate coupling strength; and the relative coordination between the two rhythms implies coupling that is dependent upon the phase-relationship between the rhythms (89). At the tissue level in plants, a new study (90) has entrained different sections of leaves to different light/dark cycles, then allowed them to free-run in constant conditions. If there were coupling of oscillators among the cells in different parts of the leaves (e.g. by hormonal signals), then we should expect the phases of the rhythms in the two areas of a leaf to rapidly (for strong coupling) or gradually (for weak coupling) attain a coincident phase. This is not what was observed; for the rhythm of *phyB* promoter activity, the differently entrained leaf sections maintained approximately their original phase for at least four days in constant light, implying that at the tissue level, these spatially separated regions are either autonomous or weakly coupled (90).

A particularly important issue that relates to multiple oscillators in plants is whether the circadian clockwork that controls PTM is the same as that (or those) controlling the many observable daily rhythms, such as leaf movement. A number of studies, primarily in SDPs, have found that the entrainment/phase-setting of the leaf movement rhythm and the clock underlying PTM is different; that is, various night-break and other entrainment protocols have different fluence/duration/frequency responses for setting the phase of the two rhythms (15, 91–94). These results imply that the clockwork underlying the leaf movement rhythm is different from that underlying PTM, although they do not eliminate the possibility of a single master oscillator with two different slave oscillators whose phasing can be altered under different entrainment protocols (15).

If there are different clockworks for PTM versus those regulating other circadian rhythms, how can these data be reconciled with the genetic data summarized above that support the conclusion of common molecular components in these clock systems? One possibility is that the genetic lesions that disrupt PTM and other circadian rhythms in parallel might be in components of the input or output pathways shared by the two systems, as in components X or Y illustrated in Figure 4 (*ELF3*, *GI*, etc could be like X in the figure). Mutations that thereby modulate the input or output of two clockworks having different biochemistries could alter the expression of each clockwork. Another possibility is that mutations disrupting both processes could act by affecting the parameters of two distinct clockworks without being the specific "state variables" of those pacemakers. For example, if protein turnover is intrinsic to both clockworks, then a mutation that affects general proteolytic rates could have a major impact on two oscillators whose specific protein components are different. Another example would be a mutation that affects the regulation of the general intracellular milieu, e.g. the basal level of cytosolic free calcium. Alterations of such basic characteristics could affect multiple clockworks. In conclusion, the current evidence strongly supports the existence of multiple oscillator systems in plants and eukaryotic algae, but we do not yet know whether there are distinct biochemical mechanisms or whether the same clockwork is modulated in different intracellular milieu.

What Makes these Clocks Tick?

In eukaryotic fungi and animals, a web of evidence supports a model that proposes autoregulatory feedback loops of central clock gene expression (95, 96). The evidence supporting the autoregulatory feedback loop model is most highly developed in *Drosophila* and *Neurospora* (63a, 97, 98). In *Drosophila*, there are at least five major molecular components known to participate in the feedback loop: PERIOD (PER), TIMELESS (TIM), dCLOCK (dCLK), CYCLE (CYC), and DOUBLE-TIME (DBT). The protein and mRNA levels of at least three of these genes, *per, tim*, and *dclk*, are rhythmic. In the evening, PER and TIM accumulate and associate in the cytoplasm, move to the nucleus, and repress the transcription of their own genes in a negative feedback loop. CYC and dCLK associate as positive regulatory elements to stimulate transcription at E-box sequences of the *per* and *tim* promoters (63a, 97). The *Drosophila* central oscillator may be composed of two interlocked negative feedback loops: a PER/TIM loop that is activated by dCLK/CYC and repressed by PER/TIM, and a dCLK loop that is repressed by dCLK/CYC and derepressed by PER/TIM (99). In the mouse, the emerging clockwork story is similar to that found in *Drosophila* in that some homologous components appear to be involved in roughly equivalent ways: mPER and mCRY as negative elements, and mCLK and mBMAL (the homolog of CYC) as positive elements (100). The well-characterized feedback loop of *Neurospora* (98) includes positive elements (WHITE COLLAR 1 and 2) and a negative element [FREQUENCY (FRQ)]. The FRQ protein is rhythmically abundant and represses its own transcription. Even though the clock molecules in the *Neurospora* versus *Drosophila*/mammalian systems are different, they share some sequence similarities, especially of PAS domain-containing proteins (98), and functionally the oscillator networks appear to be similar.

In prokaryotic cyanobacteria (discussed in more detail below), there are also negative (KaiC) and positive elements (KaiA). Therefore, a common theme of circadian clock components in both eukaryotes and prokaryotes is the interplay between positive and negative elements to form feedback loops (96). This organization was predicted by earlier modeling of circadian oscillators, (Figure 6A), which is based on analogous high-frequency neural and metabolic oscillators (101). In Figure 6A, positive excitatory input stimulates the production of the state variables that negatively feed back upon themselves. A delay function must

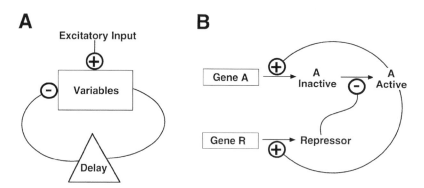

Figure 6 Feedback models of oscillators that incorporate positive and negative elements. *A*. Excitatory input (which might or might not be rhythmic) stimulates production of state variables that are regulated by a negative feedback loop with a delay factor (adapted from 101). *B*. A hysteresis-based oscillation mechanism in which a positive element (A) increases its own expression as well as that of a negative element (R). Strong binding of R to A inhibits the activity of A and thereby represses the expression of both elements (adapted from 102).

be introduced to get stable oscillations, and this delay could result from thresholds, hysteresis, etc (101). A recent, more specific, model based on transcriptional repression and hysteresis expands upon these predictions to propose two genes (or sets of genes), a positive activator A and a negative repressor R (102). As shown in Figure 6*B*, A stimulates its own expression along with that of R. R binds to A, preventing its activation and thereby represses the expression of both elements. The authors argue that the positive/negative element organization with delay based on hysteresis allows stable oscillations even in the face of internal fluctuations (noise) in metabolic or transcriptional rates (102). Consequently, this model suggests a theoretical basis for the positive/negative element structure that is emerging in circadian clockworks.

Genetic Insights into the Circadian Clockwork

Without a doubt, the most successful strategy for unveiling circadian components has been screening for mutants with altered phenotypes, cloning the genes that have been mutated, and characterizing the expression patterns and products of those genes. Because it takes at least several days of continuous monitoring to establish a circadian phenotype, successful screens of circadian mutations necessitate some kind of high-throughput screening; manual assays of small numbers of samples cannot yield a sufficient variety of relevant mutants. High-throughput screening is now fashionable for genomics and proteomics, but pioneering methods for high-throughput screens of circadian mutations were established years ago. In the case of photosynthetic organisms, efficient high-throughput screens of circadian phenotypes have been based on in vivo luminescence assays of rhythmic promoter activities in transgenic cyanobacteria (70, 103) and plants (104). These luminescence assays allow high throughput, high precision, and non-invasive screening that tremendously facilitates the identification of circadian mutants (88, 105). By virtue of the interlocked PTM and circadian mechanisms, it has also been possible to use the time-to-flowering in *Arabidopsis* as a "low-tech" but nevertheless high-throughput screening method to identify mutants of both flowering pathways and circadian rhythms; in fact, the genes *LHY, GI, FLC, FKF1*, and *ELF3* were all first identified in flowering-time screens.

The investments in these mutant screens are now paying dividends. Although genetic analyses of circadian mechanisms in photosynthetic organisms have lagged those in *Drosophila* and *Neurospora*, that situation is changing rapidly. With respect to testing of specific hypotheses, the molecular analysis of the circadian system in cyanobacteria has nearly caught up with those in *Drosophila* and *Neurospora* (see below). We are on the verge of an explosion of information about the circadian systems of plants. For example, the luminescence-based screening for clock mutants in *Arabidopsis* discovered several clock mutants that were temporarily named *toc1, toc2*, etc (88). Two *TOC* genes can now be "ticked" off. The *TOC7* gene has been identified as a PAS-domain–containing protein that is similar to the *Arabidopsis* blue-light receptor *NPH1* and the *Neurospora* positive clock element *WC-1* (106). This *TOC* gene has been renamed *ZEITLUPE (ZTL)*— German for slow motion—because the mutation at this locus (*toc7*) slows the period of the luminescence rhythm that reports *Lhcb* promoter activity by 3 h or more. The *FKF1* gene that was first identified as a late-flowering mutant is also a member of this PAS-containing gene family (62).

Most recently, the *TOC1/APRR1* gene has been identified (106a,b,c). *TOC1/APRR1* encodes a nuclear-transporting protein that has a partial response-regulator receiver domain. Its C-terminal domain has a basic motif that is similar to the *CONSTANS* family of transcription factors. *TOC1/APRR1* is regulated by a circadian clock and the *toc1* mutation of *TOC1/APRR1* affects the period of circadian rhythms and the photoperiodic responsivity of *Arabidopsis* (106a,b,c).

As mentioned above, several genes appear to be involved in both PTM and circadian timing systems. *ELF3, GI*, and *FKF1* were all initially identified in flowering-time screens and some evidence suggests that each plays a role in circadian/PTM phototransduction. *CCA1* and *LHY* also affect flowering time and circadian phenotype and deserve special attention here because the analysis of their genetics and biochemistry is the most advanced of the plant clock-associated genes. *LHY* was isolated from a transposon-mutagenesis screen for late-flowering phenotypes (58), and *CCA1* is one of the very few clock-associated genes that was not initially identified by either a mutant screen or by homology to a gene isolated in a mutant screen; as mentioned above, *CCA1* was identified by tracking an output rhythm upstream toward the clockwork (59). Both CCA1 and LHY are closely related Myb-like transcription factors. The levels of CCA1 and LHY proteins oscillate over the circadian cycle, and overexpression of these proteins represses their own gene's transcription (58, 59). Constitutive overexpression of *CCA1* disrupted the rhythms of *Lhcb, CAT3*, and *CCR2* mRNA abundance, and the *lhy* mutation disrupts the rhythms of leaf movement, *Lhcb* promoter activity, and *CCR2* mRNA abundance. A casein kinase (CK2) interacts with CCA1, thus phosphorylation may regulate the action of CCA1 (107).

These data indicate that CCA1 and LHY are important for clock functions in *Arabidopsis*. But are they components of the central clockwork? A strain that is null for *CCA1* still exhibits robust mRNA rhythms, but the period of these rhythms is shorter than in wild type (60). It is difficult to interpret that result. On the one hand, clearly CCA1 is not necessary for the clock to run, but the shorter period in its null strain implies that it plays a role in the clock's feedback loop. It is possible that CCA1 and LHY are partially redundant components of the central clock that can substitute for each other's absence, but when strongly overexpressed, they cause major disruptions (60). Alternatively, their effects on different output rhythms might be from their action as a parameter that could be crucial to more than one oscillator (e.g. a general purpose protease or kinase, or cytosolic free calcium levels). Or, perhaps they are a crucial component of the output coupling path that acts close to the clockwork, e.g. at a position like that of Y in Figure 4 (and in the case of CCA1, has some feedback to the clockwork).

It is too early to accurately assess the role(s) of CCA1 and LHY. Double nulls of *CCA1* and *LHY* need to be tested. However, it is likely that even more Myb-like factors are involved in the *Arabidopsis* clock (C Andersson, personal communication), and so even a *CCA1/LHY* double null may remain rhythmic; Myb-factor redundancy is rife. If a useful inducible promoter becomes available for plants, pulsed expression of CCA1 and/or LHY by the same strategy pursued for PER in *Drosophila*, FRQ in *Neurospora*, and KaiC in cyanobacteria (24, 96) can help to tell us whether the clock's phase is set by the rhythms of CCA1 and LHY expression.

There is yet another strategy to identify circadian clock genes: quantitative trait loci (QTL) analyses. Swarup et al (61) pursued a QTL analysis of rhythms in *Arabidopsis* by crossing different ecotypes and monitoring the leaf movement rhythms of the hybrids. QTL analyses take advantage of naturally occurring genetic variation. In the case of *Arabidopsis*, the QTL analysis clearly shows that the circadian free-running period is determined polygenetically and that in populations under natural selection, the effects of different alleles counterbalance each other so that a (presumably) optimal value for the period is established. In different ecotypes the allelic composition differs, thus the interaction among these genes to achieve the current counterbalancing is dependent upon the different evolutionary histories of the ecotypes. In addition to yielding that fascinating result, the authors also mapped the positions of four period QTLs, one of which was identified to be a locus (*FLC*) that has a mutant allele which alters flowering time (61).

Clock Genes in Cyanobacteria

Among photosynthetic organisms, our knowledge of clockwork components and interactions is most highly advanced in the cyanobacteria, particularly in the genetically malleable *Synechococcus elongatus* strain PCC 7942. Using a bacterial luciferase reporter strain in a saturational mutagenesis screen, more than 100 mutants exhibiting various circadian phenotypes, including arhythmia, altered waveforms, and atypical periods (ranging between 14 and 60 h) were isolated (105). Most of these mutants grow apparently as well as wild-type and exhibit no obvious phenotype other than circadian anomalies. Over 30 of these mutants have been rescued by the introduction of libraries of wild-type *Synechococcus* DNA. DNA fragments from several rescued mutants complemented other mutant phenotypes, including short-period, long-period, and arhythmic phenotypes.

These rescue experiments allowed us to pinpoint a cluster of three adjacent genes, *kaiA, kaiB,* and *kaiC* (108). The locus was named thus because *kai* means rotation or cycle in Japanese. All of the mutants so far complemented can be rescued by a plasmid carrying the entire *kaiABC* cluster, and 19 mutations were mapped by DNA sequencing to the 3 *kai* genes. All are missense mutants resulting from single-nucleotide exchanges. Most of the mutations are recessive (rescue by wild-type DNA is complete), but a few are semidominant, such as the

60-h period mutant *C60a*. Each of the three genes has at least two clock mutations mapped to it, and the largest gene, *kaiC*, has multiple mutations that include many clock phenotypes: short period, long period, low amplitude, and arhythmia. The *kaiABC* cluster appears to be a clock-specific region of the chromosome in cyanobacteria because deletion of the entire cluster or of any one of the *kai* genes separately does not affect viability (in single-strain cultures), but does cause arhythmicity. None of the Kai proteins has an obvious DNA-binding motif. The *kaiC* gene appears to be an internally duplicated gene; it has two parts that are very similar to each other (109). In each half of the *kaiC* gene, there is a Walker A or P-loop motif. This motif, [G or A]XXXXGK[T or S], is an ATP/GTP nucleotide-binding region, and mutation of the motif results in arhythmicity (110; T Mori & CH Johnson, unpublished observation). The evolutionary relationships of the *kai* genes to genes in other organisms are discussed below.

The expression patterns of the *kai* genes are reminiscent of *Drosophila* and *Neurospora* clock genes. Promoter activities were found in the upstream regions of both the *kaiA* and *kaiB* genes. The *kaiA* promoter gives rise to a monocistronic *kaiA* mRNA, whereas the *kaiB* promoter produces a dicistronic *kaiBC* mRNA (108). Both *kaiA* and *kaiBC* transcripts are rhythmically abundant (108, 111). Continuous overexpression of *kaiC* repressed the *kaiBC* promoter (negative feedback), whereas *kaiA* overexpression enhanced it (positive feedback). The abundance of the KaiB and KaiC proteins undergoes circadian oscillations in constant light, whereas the pattern of the KaiA protein exhibits little, if any, circadian variation (24). The circadian rhythms of KaiC levels persist when the metabolic rate is inhibited by partial blockage of translation or by constant darkness (24). Pulsatile expression of the *kaiC* gene from an inducible promoter to physiological levels resets the phase of the rhythms in a dose-dependent fashion (24). Consequently, the level of KaiC expression (or some forms of KaiC) is directly linked to the phase of the oscillation.

Another feature of the *kai* genes that reminds us of clock genes in animals is that the Kai proteins appear to interact. Two-hybrid, in vitro binding, and resonance energy transfer assays indicate that the KaiA, KaiB, and KaiC proteins interact both homotypically and heterotypically (109, 112). One long-period mutant exhibits an altered heterotypic interaction between KaiA and KaiB, suggesting that inter-Kai contact is important to the clock mechanism (109). These results suggest that there is negative feedback control of *kaiC* expression by the KaiC protein to generate a circadian oscillation in cyanobacteria involving protein-protein interactions and that KaiA sustains the oscillation by enhancing *kaiC* expression. Superficially, KaiA could be akin to the positive factor and KaiC to the negative factor in the model of Barkai & Leibler (102).

However, the analysis of this clockwork has only just begun. Yet another similarity between the cyanobacterial clock system and that of *Drosophila* and *Neurospora* is that phosphorylation events appear to play a role. KaiC appears to be able to autophosphorylate (110), and KaiC may exist in different phosphorylation states at different phases of the circadian cycle (T Nishiwaki, H Iwasaki &

T Kondo, unpublished observations). Furthermore, in a two-hybrid screen for KaiC-interacting proteins, a histidine protein kinase, SasA, was discovered (111). The N-terminal sequence of SasA is significantly similar to the sequence of KaiB. Disruption of *sasA* lowers *kaiBC* expression and results in arhythmicity of most genes in moderate-to-high light intensities. Clearly, SasA is necessary for robust expression of the cyanobacterial clock (111). Interestingly, low-amplitude rhythms were observed in dim constant light, implying that the role of SasA has something to do with light perception or light intensity compensation.

Prompted by considerations relating to the endosymbiotic theory of the origin of eukaryotic organelles, we considered whether an ancestral clock that originated in cyanobacteria might have been passed to eukaryotes. Therefore, databases were searched for possible *kai* homologs in eukaryotes. At the present time, no encouraging candidates have appeared. In particular, there are no apparent homologs in the chloroplast genomes of tobacco or other higher plants, nor is there any significant hybridization between *kai* DNA and the chloroplast genome of the eukaryotic alga *Chlamydomonas*. Furthermore, there is not yet any significant homology between *kai* gene sequences and those of any nuclear genes in the *Arabidopsis* genome database. Therefore, no data yet encourage the view that the clockwork that evolved in cyanobacteria was directly transferred to eukaryotes (especially plants) by endosymbiosis or by another mechanism of transfer.

On the other hand, when the *kai* sequences are used to search the genomic databases of other prokaryotes, strong candidates for homologs were found. Most obviously, in other cyanobacterial species (*Synechocystis, Anabaena*, and others) there are clear *kai* cluster homologs (113). In the archaea *Methanobacterium thermoautotrophicum, Methanococcus jannaschii, Pyrococcus horikoshii, Archaeoglobus fulgidus*, and *Halobacterium salinarium*, there are *kaiC*-similar sequences (114). In some cases (*Methanobacterium, Pyrococcus*, and *Archaeoglobus*), the *kaiC*-similar sequences indicate a protein of similar size and duplicated structure as in *Synechococcus*, but in *Methanococcus* and *Halobacterium*, the sequences that are similar to *kaiC* are half size, with a single Walker A motif. It is possible that these smaller *kaiC*-like sequences are more similar to an ancestral form that preceded an internal duplication event. If these half-size KaiCs perform a similar clock function in the archaea to that performed in cyanobacteria, it is conceivable that they form dimers; the duplication in cyanobacterial and archaeal KaiC may have been a fusion of a gene that already acted in dimeric structures.

Finally, a recent genomic survey claims that KaiC is a member of the bacterial RecA/DnaB family (115). RecA is an ATP-dependent DNA recombinase, and DnaB is the replication fork helicase in bacteria. The authors of this study hypothesized that the ancestral KaiC was a single-domain, RecA-like protein that originated in the eubacteria and was laterally transferred to archaea, where a gene duplication and fusion event occurred. Later, the double-domain gene underwent a second lateral transfer from the archaea to the cyanobacteria after the main eubacterial lineages had been established (115). Whether this model is correct or not, the similarity of KaiC to two enzymes that act on DNA (i.e. RecA and DnaB) implies that KaiC might also somehow act directly on DNA (even though it does not have an obvious DNA-binding motif). It is tempting to consider that KaiC might mediate both its own negative feedback regulation (108) and global regulation of the cyanobacterial genome (11) by orchestrating transcription rates throughout the entire cyanobacterial chromosome.

CONCLUDING REMARKS

Photosynthetic organisms were the first to give evidence for endogenous circadian and photoperiodic timekeepers. They have also provided tantalizing clues as to how circadian clocks might have evolved and what fitness advantage they confer. Although genetic analyses of these green clocks have lagged those in animals and fungi, progress in this area has ignited. Sophisticated analyses of cyanobacterial clockwork components have already begun, and comparable analyses in plants will undoubtedly soon follow. It is a matter of time.

ACKNOWLEDGMENTS

I thank colleagues who provided information on their work prior to publication and to my collaborators on research about clocks in photosynthetic organisms: Drs. Takao Kondo, Susan Golden, Anthony Trewavas, and Marc Knight. Research in my laboratory has been supported by the National Institute of Mental Health (R01 MH43836 and K02 MH01179), the National Science Foundation (MCB 9874371), and the Human Frontier Science Program (#RG-385/96).

Visit the Annual Reviews home page at www.AnnualReviews.org

LITERATURE CITED

1. Devlin P, Kay SA. 2001. Circadian photoperception. *Annu. Rev. Physiol.* 63:677–94
2. de Mairan JJ. 1729. Observation botanique. *Hist. Acad. R. Sci. (Paris)*, p. 35. Engl. Transl. 1979, *Sleep* 2:155–60
3. Sweeney BM. 1987. *Rhythmic Phenomena in Plants*. San Diego: Academic. 2nd. ed.
4. Pittendrigh CS. 1960. Circadian rhythms and the circadian organization of living systems. *Cold Spring Harbor Symp. Quant. Biol.* 25:159–84
5. Johnson CH, Knight M, Trewavas A, Kondo T. 1998. A clockwork green: circadian pro-

grams in photosynthetic organisms. See Ref. 116, pp. 1–34
6. Piechulla B. 1993. 'Circadian clock' directs the expression of plant genes. *Plant Mol. Biol.* 22:533–42
7. Fejes E, Nagy F. 1998. Molecular analysis of circadian clock-regulated gene expression in plants: features of the "output" pathways. See Ref. 116, pp. 99–118
8. McClung CR. 2000. Circadian rhythms in plants: a millennial view. *Physiol. Plant.* 109:359–71
9. Johnson CH, Roeber J, Hastings JW. 1984. Circadian changes in enzyme concentration

account for rhythm of enzyme activity in *Gonyaulax. Science* 223:1428–30

10. Kloppstech K. 1985. Diurnal and circadian rhythmicity in the expression of light-induced plant nuclear messenger RNAs. *Planta* 165:502–6

11. Liu Y, Tsinoremas NF, Johnson CH, Lebedeva NV, Golden SS, et al. 1995. Circadian orchestration of gene expression in cyanobacteria. *Genes Dev.* 9:1469–78

12. Huang T-C, Chen H-M, Pen S-Y, Chen T-H. 1994. Biological clock in the prokaryote *Synechococcus* RF-1. *Planta* 193:131–36

13. Kreps JA, Muramatsu T, Furuya M, Kay SA. 2000. Fluorescent differential display identifies circadian clock regulated genes in *Arabidopsis thaliana. J. Biol. Rhythms* 15:208–17

14. Millar AJ, Kay SA. 1991. Circadian control of *cab* gene transcription and mRNA accumulation in *Arabidopsis. Plant Cell* 3:541–50

15. Thomas B, Vince-Prue D. 1997. *Photoperiodism in Plants.* San Diego: Academic. 2nd. ed.

16. Aoki S, Kondo T, Wada H, Ishiura M. 1997. Circadian rhythm of the cyanobacterium *Synechocystis* sp. PCC 6803 in the dark. *J. Bacteriol.* 179:5751–55

17. Schneegurt MA, Sherman DM, Sherman LA. 1997. Growth, physiology, and ultrastructure of a diazotrophic cyanobacterium, *Cyanothece* sp. strain ATCC 51142, in mixotrophic and chemoheterotrophic cultures. *J. Phycol.* 33:632–42

18. Jacobshagen S, Johnson CH. 1994. Circadian rhythms of gene expression in *Chlamydomonas reinhardtii*: circadian cycling of mRNA abundances of *cabII*, and possibly of β-tubulin and cytochrome *c. Eur. J. Cell Biol.* 64:142–52

19. Hwang S, Herrin D. 1994. Control of *lhc* gene transcription by the circadian clock in *Chlamydomonas reinhardtii. Plant Mol. Biol.* 26:557–69

20. Nikaido SS, Locke CR, Weeks DP. 1994. Automated sampling and RNA isolation at room temperature for measurements of circadian rhythms in *Chlamydomonas reinhardtii. Plant Mol. Biol.* 26:275–84

21. Kondo T. 1982. Persistence of the potassium uptake rhythm in the presence of exogenous sucrose in *Lemna gibba* G3. *Plant Cell Physiol.* 23:467–72

22. Cumming BG. 1967. Circadian rhythmic flowering responses in *Chenopodium rubrum*: effects of glucose and sucrose. *Can. J. Bot.* 45:2173–93

23. Simon E, Satter RL, Galston AW. 1976. Circadian rhythmicity in excised *Samanea pulvini*. I. Sucrose-white light interactions. *Plant Physiol.* 58:417–20

24. Xu Y, Mori T, Johnson CH. 2000. Circadian clock-protein expression in cyanobacteria: rhythms and phase-setting. *EMBO J.* 19:3349–57

25. Goto K, Johnson CH. 1995. Is the cell division cycle gated by a circadian clock? The case of *Chlamydomonas reinhardtii. J. Cell Biol.* 129:1061–69

26. Kondo T, Johnson CH, Hastings JW. 1991. Action spectrum for resetting the circadian phototaxis rhythm in the CW15 strain of *Chlamydomonas*. I. Cells in darkness. *Plant Physiol.* 95:197–205

27. Nagy F, Fejes E, Wehmeyer B, Dallman G, Schafer E. 1993. The circadian oscillator is regulated by a very low fluence response of phytochrome in wheat. *Proc. Natl. Acad. Sci. USA* 90:6290–94

28. Kay SA, Millar AJ. 1992. Circadian regulated *Cab* gene transcription in higher plants. In *Molecular Genetics of Biological Rhythms*, ed. MW Young, pp. 73–89. New York: Marcel Dekker

29. Hicks KA, Millar AJ, Carré IA, Somers DE, Straume M, et al. 1996. Conditional circadian dysfunction of the *Arabidopsis early-flowering 3* mutant. *Science* 274:790–92

30. Johnson CH, Knight MR, Kondo T, Masson P, Sedbrook J, et al. 1995. Circadian oscillations of cytosolic and chloroplastidic

free calcium in plants. *Science* 269:1863–65

31. Mitsui A, Kumazawa S, Takahashi A, Ikemoto H, Arai T. 1986. Strategy by which nitrogen-fixing unicellular cyanobacteria grow photoautotrophically. *Nature* 323:720–22

32. Byrne TE, Wells MR, Johnson CH. 1992. Circadian rhythms of chemotaxis to ammonium and of methylammonium uptake in *Chlamydomonas*. *Plant Physiol.* 98:879–86

33. Zhong HH, McClung CR. 1996. The circadian clock gates expression of two *Arabidopsis* catalase genes to distinct and opposite circadian phases. *Mol. Gen. Genet.* 251:196–203

34. Pittendrigh CS. 1993. Temporal organization: reflections of a Darwinian clockwatcher. *Annu. Rev. Physiol.* 55:17–54

35. Edmunds LN. 1984. Circadian oscillators and cell cycle controls in algae. In *The Microbial Cell Cycle*, ed. P Nurse, E Streiblová, pp. 209–230. Boca Raton, FL: CRC Press

36. Nikaido SS, Johnson CH. 2000. Daily and circadian variation in survival from ultraviolet radiation in *Chlamydomonas reinhardtii*. *Photochem. Photobiol.* 71:758–65

37. Enright JT. 1982. Sleep movements of leaves: in defense of Darwin's interpretation. *Oecologia* 54:253–59

38. Withrow AP, Withrow RB. 1949. Photoperiodic chlorosis in tomato. *Plant Physiol.* 24:657–63

39. Highkin HR, Hanson JB. 1954. Possible interaction between light-dark cycles and endogenous daily rhythms on the growth of tomato plants. *Plant Physiol.* 29:301–2

40. Hillman WS. 1956. Injury of tomato plants by continuous light and unfavorable photoperiodic cycles. *Am. J. Bot.* 43:89–96

41. Went FW. 1960. Photo- and thermoperiodic effects in plant growth. *Cold Spring Harbor Symp. Quant. Biol.* 25:221–30

42. Ouyang Y, Andersson CR, Kondo T, Golden SS, Johnson CH. 1998. Resonating circadian clocks enhance fitness in cyanobacteria. *Proc. Natl. Acad. Sci. USA* 95:8660–64

43. Roussel MR, Gonze D, Goldbeter A. 2000. Modeling the differential fitness of cyanobacterial strains whose circadian oscillators have different free-running periods: comparing the mutual inhibition and substrate depletion hypotheses. *J. Theor. Biol.* 205:321–40

44. Aschoff J. 1965. The phase-angle difference in circadian periodicity. In *Circadian Clocks*, ed. J Aschoff, pp. 262–76. Amsterdam: North-Holland .

45. Garner WW, Allard HA. 1920. Effect of the relative length of day and night and other factors of the environment of growth and reproduction in plants. *J. Agric. Res.* 18:553–606

46. Balzer I, Hardeland R. 1991. Photoperiodism and effects of indoleamines in a unicellular alga, *Gonyaulax polyedra*. *Science* 253:795–97

47. Hamner KC, Takimoto A. 1964. Circadian rhythms and plant photoperiodism. *Am. Nat.* 98:295–322.

48. Lumsden PJ. 1991. Circadian rhythms and phytochrome. *Annu. Rev. Plant Physiol. Plant Mol. Biol.* 42:351–71

49. Jackson SD, Heyer A, Dietze J, Prat S. 1996. Phytochrome B mediates the photoperiodic control of tuber formation in potato. *Plant J.* 9:159–66

50. Borthwick HA, Hendricks SB. 1960. Photoperiodism in plants. *Science* 132:1223–28

51. King RW, Vince-Prue D, Quail PH. 1978. Light requirement, phytochrome, and photoperiodic induction of flowering of *Pharbitis nil* Chois. III. A comparison of spectrophotometric and physiological assay of phytochrome of phototransformation during induction. *Planta* 141:15–22

52. Bünning E. 1936. Die endogene Tagesrhythmik als Grundlage der photoperiodischen Reaktion. *Ber. Dtsch. Bot. Ges.* 54:590–607

53. Elliott JA, Goldman BD. 1981. Seasonal reproduction: photoperiodism and biological clocks. In *Neuroendocrinology of Reproduction, Physiology and Behavior*, ed. NT Adler, pp. 377–423. New York: Plenum

54. Koornneef M, Alonso-Blanco C, Petters AJM, Soppe W. 1998. Genetic control of flowering time in *Arabidopsis*. *Annu. Rev. Plant Physiol. Plant Mol. Biol.* 49:345–70

55. Coupland G. 1998. Photoperiodic regulation of flowering time in *Arabidopsis*. See Ref. 116, pp. 243–55

56. Carré IA. 1998. Genetic dissection of the photoperiod-sensing mechanism in the long-day plant *Arabidopsis thaliana*. See Ref. 116, pp. 257–69

57. Park DH, Somers DE, Kim YS, Choy YH, Lim HK, et al. 1999. Control of circadian rhythms and photoperiodic flowering by the *Arabidopsis GIGANTEA* gene. *Science* 285:1579–82

58. Schaffer R, Ramsay N, Samach A, Corden S, Putterill J, et al. 1998. The *late elongated hypocotyl* mutation of Arabidopsis disrupts circadian rhythms and the photoperiodic control of flowering. *Cell* 93:1219–29

59. Wang Z-Y, Tobin EM. 1998. Constitutive expression of the *CIRCADIAN CLOCK ASSOCIATED 1 (CCA1)* gene disrupts circadian rhythms and suppresses its own expression. *Cell* 93:1207–17

60. Green RM, Tobin EM. 1999. Loss of the circadian clock-associated protein 1 in *Arabidopsis* results in altered clock-regulated gene expression. *Proc. Natl. Acad. Sci. USA* 96:4176–79

61. Swarup K, Alonso-Blanco C, Lynn JR, Michaels SD, Amasino RM, et al. 1999. Natural allelic variation identifies new genes in the *Arabidopsis* circadian system. *Plant J.* 20:67–77

62. Nelson DC, Lasswell J, Rogg LE, Cohen MA, Bartel B. 2000. *FKF1*, a clock-controlled gene that regulates the transition to flowering in Arabidopsis. *Cell* 101:331–40

63. Guo H, Yang H, Mockler TC, Lin C. 1998. Regulation of flowering time by *Arabidopsis* photoreceptors. *Science* 279:1360–63

63a. Williams JA, Sehgal A. 2001. Molecular components of the circadian system in *Drosophila*. *Annu. Rev. Physiol.* 63:729–55

64. Merrow M, Brunner M, Roenneberg T. 1999. Assignment of circadian function for the *Neurospora* clock gene *frequency*. *Nature* 399:584–86

65. Lakin-Thomas PL, Johnson CH. 1999. Commentary: molecular and cellular models of circadian systems. *J. Biol. Rhythms* 14:486–89

66. Beator J, Kloppstech K. 1994. Circadian rhythmicity in the expression of genes in higher plants. *Mol. Biol.* 13:203–19

67. Heintzen C, Melzer S, Fischer R, Kappeler S, Apel K, et al. 1994. A light- and temperature-entrained circadian clock controls expression of transcripts encoding nuclear proteins with homology to RNA-binding proteins in meristematic tissue. *Plant J.* 5:799–813

68. Riesselmann S, Piechulla B. 1992. Diurnal and circadian light-harvesting complex and quinone B-binding protein synthesis in leaves of tomato (*Lycopersicon esculentum*). *Plant Physiol.* 100:1840–45

69. Shan L. 1995. *Circadian clock control of CAB protein synthesis in* Chlamydomonas reinhardtii. Masters thesis. Vanderbilt Univ. Nashville, TN. 55 pp.

70. Liu Y, Golden SS, Kondo T, Ishiura M, Johnson CH. 1995. Bacterial luciferase as a reporter of circadian gene expression in cyanobacteria. *J. Bacteriol.* 177:2080–86

71. Morse D, Fritz L, Hastings JW. 1990. What is the clock? Translational regulation of circadian bioluminescence. *Trends Biochem. Sci.* 15:262–65

72. Fritz L, Morse D, Hastings JW. 1990. The circadian bioluminescence rhythm of *Gonyaulax* is related to daily variations in

the number of light-emitting organelles. *J. Cell Sci.* 95:321–28

73. Mittag M, Lee D-H, Hastings JW. 1994. Circadian expression of the luciferin-binding protein correlates with the binding of a protein to the 3′ untranslated region of its mRNA. *Proc. Natl. Acad. Sci. USA* 91:5257–61

74. Mittag M. 1998. Molecular mechanisms of clock-controlled proteins in phytoflagellates. *Protist* 149:101–7

75. Carré IA, Edmunds LN. 1993. Oscillator control of cell division in *Euglena*: cyclic AMP oscillations mediate the phasing of the cell division cycle by the circadian clock. *J. Cell Sci.* 104:1163–73

76. Millar AJ, McGrath RB, Chua N-H. 1994. Phytochrome phototransduction pathways. *Annu. Rev. Genet.* 28:325–49

77. Goto K. 1984. Causal relationships among metabolic circadian rhythms in *Lemna*. *Z. Naturforsch.* 39:73–84

78. Gómez LA, Simón E. 1995. Circadian rhythm of *Robinia pseudoacacia* leaflet movements: role of calcium and phytochrome. *Photochem. Photobiol.* 61:210–15

79. Bowler C, Neuhaus G, Yamagata H, Chua N-H. 1994. Cyclic GMP and calcium mediate phytochrome phototransduction. *Cell* 77:73–81

80. Sai J, Johnson CH. 1999. Different circadian oscillators control Ca^{2+} fluxes and *Lhcb* gene expression. *Proc. Natl. Acad. Sci. USA* 96:11659–63

81. Kim HY, Coté GG, Crain RC. 1993. Potassium channels in *Samanea saman* protoplasts controlled by phytochrome and the biological clock. *Science* 260:960–62

82. Moran N, Yueh YG, Crain RC. 1996. Signal transduction and cell volume regulation in plant leaflet movements. *News Physiol. Sci.* 11:108–14

83. Webb AAR. 1998. Stomatal rhythms. See Ref. 116, pp. 69–79

84. Wilkins MB. 1992. Circadian rhythms: their origin and control. *New Phytol.* 121:347–75

85. Comolli JC, Hastings JW. 1999. Novel effects on the *Gonyaulax* circadian system produced by the protein kinase inhibitor staurosporine. *J. Biol. Rhythms* 14:11–19

86. Millar AJ. 1998. The cellular organisation of circadian rhythms in plants: not one but many clocks. See Ref. 116, pp. 51–68

87. Hennessey TL, Field CB. 1992. Evidence of multiple circadian oscillators in bean plants. *J. Biol. Rhythms* 7:105–13

88. Millar AJ, Carré IA, Strayer CA, Chua NH, Kay SA. 1995. Circadian clock mutants in *Arabidopsis* identified by luciferase imaging. *Science* 267:1161–63

89. Roenneberg T, Morse D. 1993. Two circadian oscillators in one cell. *Nature* 362:362–64

90. Thain SC, Hall A, Millar AJ. 2000. Functional independence of multiple circadian clocks that regulate plant gene expression. *Curr. Biol.* 10:951–56

91. Salisbury FB, Denney A. 1971. Separate clocks for leaf movements and photoperiodic flowering in *Xanthium strumarium* L. In *Biochronometry*, ed. M Menaker, pp. 292–311. Washington, DC: Natl. Acad. Sci. Press

92. King RW. 1975. Multiple circadian rhythms regulate photoperiodic flowering responses in *Chenopodium rubrum*. *Can. J. Bot.* 53:2631–38

93. Bollig I. 1977. Different circadian rhythms regulate photoperiodic flowering response and leaf movement in *Pharbitis nil* (L.) Choisy. *Planta* 135:137–42

94. Salisbury FB. 1985. *Xanthium strumarium*. In *Handbook of Flowering*, ed. A Halevy, 4:473–522. Boca Raton, FL: CRC Press

95. Hardin PE, Hall JC, Rosbash M. 1990. Feedback of the *Drosophila period* gene product on circadian cycling of its messenger RNA levels. *Nature* 343:536–40

96. Dunlap JC. 1999. Molecular bases for circadian clocks. *Cell* 96:271–90

97. Deleted in proof

98. Loros JJ, Dunlap JC. 2001. Genetic and molecular analysis of circadian rhythms in *Neurospora*. *Annu. Rev. Physiol.* 63:757–94

99. Glossop NRJ, Lyons LC, Hardin PE. 1999. Interlocked feedback loops within the *Drosophila* circadian oscillator. *Science* 286:763–65

100. Reppert SM, Weaver DR. 2001. Molecular analysis of mammalian circadian rhythms. *Annu. Rev. Physiol.* 63:647–76

101. Friesen WO, Block GD. 1984. What is a biological oscillator? *Am. J. Physiol. Regulatory Integrative Comp. Physiol.* 246:R847–R51

102. Barkai N, Leibler S. 2000. Circadian clocks limited by noise. *Nature* 403:267–68

103. Kondo T, Strayer CA, Kulkarni RD, Taylor W, Ishiura M, et al. 1993. Circadian rhythms in prokaryotes: luciferase as a reporter of circadian gene expression in cyanobacteria. *Proc. Natl. Acad. Sci. USA* 90:5672–76

104. Millar AJ, Short SR, Chua N-H, Kay SA. 1992. A novel circadian phenotype based on firefly luciferase expression in transgenic plants. *Plant Cell* 4:1075–87

105. Kondo T, Tsinoremas NF, Golden SS, Johnson CH, Kutsuna S, et al. 1994. Circadian clock mutants of cyanobacteria. *Science* 266:1233–36

106. Somers DE, Schultz TF, Milnamow M, Kay SA. 2000. *ZEITLUPE* encodes a novel clock-associated PAS protein from Arabidopsis. *Cell* 101:319–29

106a. Makino S, Kiba T, Imamura A, Hanaki N, Nakamura A, et al. 2000. Genes encoding pseudo-response regulators: insight into His-to-Asp phosphorelay and circadian rhythms in *Arabidopsis thaliana*. *Plant Cell Physiol.* 41:791–803

106b. Strayer C, Oyama T, Schultz TR, Roman R, Somers DE, et al. 2000. Cloning of the *Arabidopsis* clock gene TOC1, an autoregulatory response regulator homolog. *Science* 289:768–71

106c. Matsushika A, Makino S, Kojima M, Mizuno T. 2000. Circadian waves of expression of the APRR1/TOC1 family of pseudo-response regulators of *Arabidopsis thaliana*: insight into the plant circadian clock. *Plant Cell Physiol.* 41:1002–12

107. Sugano S, Andronis C, Green RM, Wang Z-Y, Tobin EM. 1998. Protein kinase CK2 interacts with and phosphorylates the *Arabidopsis* circadian clock-associated 1 protein. *Proc. Natl. Acad. Sci. USA* 95:11020–25

108. Ishiura M, Kutsuna S, Aoki S, Iwasaki H, Andersson CR, et al. 1998. Expression of a gene cluster *kaiABC* as a circadian feedback process in cyanobacteria. *Science* 281:1519–23

109. Iwasaki H, Taniguchi Y, Kondo T, Ishiura M. 1999. Physical interactions among circadian clock proteins, KaiA, KaiB and KaiC, in cyanobacteria. *EMBO J.* 18:1137–45

110. Nishiwaki T, Iwasaki H, Ishiura M, Kondo T. 2000. Nucleotide binding and autophosphorylation of the clock protein KaiC as a circadian timing process of cyanobacteria. *Proc. Natl. Acad. Sci. USA* 97:495–99

111. Iwasaki H, Williams SB, Kitayama Y, Ishiura M, Golden SS, et al. 2000. A KaiC-interacting sensory histidine kinase, SasA, necessary to sustain robust circadian oscillation in cyanobacteria. *Cell* 101:223–33

112. Xu Y, Piston D, Johnson CH. 1999. A bioluminescence resonance energy transfer (BRET) system-application to interacting circadian clock proteins. *Proc. Acad. Natl. Acad. Sci. USA* 96:151–56

113. Lorne J, Scheffer J, Lee A, Painter M, Miao VPW. 2000. Genes controlling

circadian rhythm are widely distributed in cyanobacteria. *FEMS Microbiol. Lett.* 189:129–33

114. Johnson CH, Golden SS. 1999. Circadian programs in cyanobacteria: adaptiveness and mechanism. *Annu. Rev. Microbiol.* 53:389–409

115. Leipe DD, Aravind L, Grishin NV, Koonin EV. 2000. The bacterial replicative helicase DnaB evolved from a RecA duplication. *Genome Res.* 10:5–16

116. Lumdsen PJ, Millar AJ, eds. 1998. *Biological Rhythms and Photoperiodism in Plants*. Oxford, UK: BIOS

Annu. Rev. Physiol. 2001. 63:729–55

MOLECULAR COMPONENTS OF THE CIRCADIAN SYSTEM IN DROSOPHILA

Julie A Williams and Amita Sehgal

Howard Hughes Medical Institute, Department of Neuroscience, University of Pennsylvania Medical School, Philadelphia, Pennsylvania 19104;
e-mail: jwillia3@mail.med.upenn.edu; amita@mail.med.upenn.edu

Key Words   period, timeless, Clock, PDF, locomotor activity

■ **Abstract**   Much of our current understanding of how circadian rhythms are generated is based on work done with *Drosophila melanogaster*. Molecular mechanisms used to assemble an endogenous clock in this organism are now known to underlie circadian rhythms in many other species, including mammals. The genetic amenability of Drosophila has led to the identification of some genes that encode components of the clock (so-called clock genes) and others that either link the clock to the environment or act downstream of it. The clock provides time-of-day cues by regulating levels of specific gene products such that they oscillate with a circadian rhythm. The mechanisms that synchronize these oscillations to light are understood to some extent. However, there are still large gaps in our knowledge, in particular with respect to the mechanisms used by the clock to control overt rhythms. It has, however, become clear that in addition to the brain clock, autonomous or semi-autonomous clocks occur in peripheral tissues where they confer circadian regulation on specific functions.

INTRODUCTION

The widespread manifestation of circadian ($\sim$24 h) rhythms across the phylogenetic tree attests to their physiological importance. Organisms that display such rhythms range from unicellular cyanobacteria to mammals, including humans. Thus temporal organization of physiology/metabolism, even when it is confined to a single cell, is obviously advantageous to an organism. Given that we live in a cyclic environment, it is not difficult to envision how adaptation would be facilitated through the cyclic control of biological functions. As to how this cyclic control is generated at a molecular level is an area of research in which major breakthroughs have recently been made. This review and others in this section describe our current understanding of the molecular basis of circadian rhythms in organisms that are phylogenetically distant from one another.

As one might expect, functions that occur with a circadian rhythm vary greatly from one organism to another and also within an organism. However, whether

0066-4278/01/0315-0729$14.00   **729**

it is the circadian production of asexual spores in the bread mold *Neurospora crassa*, or rest:activity cycles in the fruit fly *Drosophila melanogaster*, circadian rhythms share some basic properties: (*a*) They all can be synchronized or entrained by environmental stimuli (zeitgebers). The dominant entraining cue is light with virtually all rhythms being synchronized to the day:night cycle. (*b*) They persist or free-run in constant conditions, i.e. in the absence of cycling zeitgebers. Under these conditions, the length of a complete cycle (the period) is usually a little different from the 24-h rhythm of the environmental cycle—therefore the term circa (about). The free-running period varies from one species to another and also somewhat between individuals. (*c*) The periodicity of a circadian rhythm is temperature compensated in that the period does not change over a wide temperature range. Note that compensation of the period in response to temperature does not preclude temperature as a zeitgeber. Temperature changes do change the phase of the rhythm, although not the period, and temperature also affects rhythms in other ways that are discussed below.

The conserved general nature of these rhythms has encouraged researchers to dissect underlying mechanisms in simple organisms, with the expectation that mechanisms will also be conserved. Indeed, as described elsewhere in this volume, there are striking similarities in the molecular mechanisms used to generate circadian rhythms in very diverse species. Whether in cyanobacteria, Drosophila, or mammals, a molecular feedback loop in which cycling proteins regulate the synthesis of their own messenger RNAs constitutes the endogenous clock (1, 2). Although the precise molecules that make up these loops may differ, the manner in which they are regulated is remarkably conserved, perhaps providing examples of convergent evolution. As expected of the endogenous clock, these feedback loops are self-sustaining but can be reset by environmental cues.

The clock clearly does not work in isolation, and chronobiologists prefer to think in terms of a circadian system that, in addition to the central clock, contains an input pathway that transmits environmental signals to the clock and one or more output pathways that carry temporal signals away from the clock to other physiological pathways of the organism. The overt rhythm reflects the activity of this entire circadian system (Figure 1). Although input and output are depicted here as discrete, linear pathways, this is probably an oversimplification of the system. More likely, all these pathways affect one another and, as is evident from the molecular analysis, it is frequently difficult to classify a component into one unique category (e.g. input alone) because it can affect more than one function. In addition, as discussed in the accompanying reviews on circadian rhythms, some of the feedback mechanisms that are characteristic of the clock are sometimes also found in the input and output pathways, further complicating the distinction. Nevertheless, a specific set of criteria has been proposed that would facilitate the identification of clock components, i.e. those molecules that play a role in the timekeeping mechanism (3). Clock components that actually provide time cues, usually through oscillations of their abundance or activity, are called state variables (Figure 1).

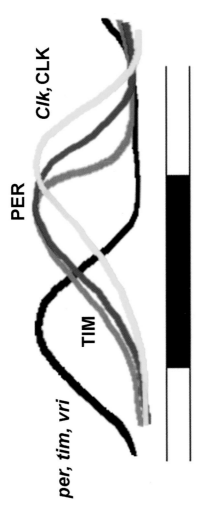

Figure 3 Schematic representation of the oscillations of putative clock genes. The phase of RNA cycling is shown for *per*, *tim*, *Clk*, and *vri* and protein cycling for *per*, *tim* and *Clk* (data are not available for *vri*). The bars at the bottom denote the light:dark cycle. Open bar denotes lights-on or day time, black bar denotes the 12-h dark period. The figure is not representative of the relative levels of the different components and the amplitude of their oscillations. These details are still not completely understood, particularly in lateral neurons. *per*, *tim*, and *vri* mRNA (in black) peak at approximately ZT 14 (2 h into the dark period). PER (in blue) and TIM (in red) proteins peak 6 h later, toward the end of the night. CLK mRNA and protein oscillate in phase with each other and are therefore depicted by a single line (in yellow). Other components of the clock that do not oscillate, such as DBT or CYC, are omitted from the figure for clarity. Also, cycling components that are not known to be part of the clock (e.g. *cry*) are not included.

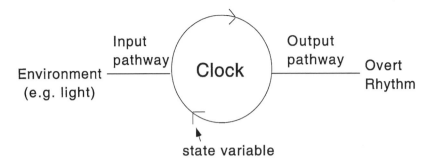

Figure 1   A simple circadian system (based upon 132). The circadian system, in its simplest form, consists of a central clock, an input pathway, and an output pathway. The clock consists of a feedback loop generated through oscillations and feedback activity of at least one state variable. Most known systems are much more complicated than this, involving more than one feedback loop, and multiple inputs and outputs.

OVERT RHYTHMS IN *DROSOPHILA MELANOGASTER*

Analysis of circadian rhythms in Drosophila has clearly paved the way for similar analyses in other systems, particularly mammals. Although Drosophila is always an obvious choice for genetic studies, its use for circadian purposes preceded the application of any genetic technology. Years of research documented not only the presence of well-defined, easily quantified rhythms in Drosophila, but also the properties of these rhythms (4). Most of these studies were done in *Drosophila pseudoobscura* (5), which unfortunately lacks the genetic advantages of *D. melanogaster*. Thus the focus shifted toward *D. melanogaster*, while continuing to use some of the assays that had been developed for *D. pseudoobscura*. Genetic screens in *D. melanogaster* have largely relied on two major rhythmic behavioral outputs—eclosion and locomotor activity. Eclosion refers to the hatching of adult flies from their pupal cases, and it is regulated by the circadian clock such that it occurs predominantly at dawn. Since there are no data indicating circadian control of development, the restricted timing of eclosion indicates that it is a gated process. Thus fully developed flies may be held in their pupal cases for several hours to await the next dawn (6). The other robust overt rhythm displayed by flies is the rest:activity cycle. In the presence of light:dark cycles, flies usually show a bimodal distribution of activity confined largely to daylight hours (7). Under free-running conditions (constant darkness), the bimodality usually disappears and activity is observed throughout the subjective day.

In recent years, other processes that occur with a circadian rhythm have been documented, although they have not yet been exploited for genetic purposes. For instance, olfactory responses are regulated in a circadian fashion and are highest at night (8). Visual pigment and sensitivity, as measured through microspectrophotometry (MSP) and electroretinogram (ERG) assays, respectively, cycle with a circadian rhythm in the compound eye (9). In addition egg-laying is controlled by a circadian clock (10, 11). In general, all these rhythms appear to be controlled by the same clock genes, the only possible exception being the visual sensitivity rhythm, which is apparently not affected by mutations in the *period* (*per*) gene (9). However, considerable data have since shown that clock genes are expressed in the compound eye, yet this tissue is not required for persistence or entrainment of rest:activity rhythms, indicating that clock proteins in the eye serve to control an eye-specific function (12–15). Thus it may be worth reexamining visual sensitivity cycles in known clock mutants. It is clear, however, that there will be molecular differences in the output pathways that control different rhythms, and some of these differences are already emerging. Below we discuss known molecular components in the Drosophila circadian system and evaluate the relative contribution of each one to the circadian system (summarized in Table 1). In addition, the presence of multiple oscillators in Drosophila, together with their implications for physiology, are discussed.

CLOCK AND CLOCK-CONTROLLED MOLECULES IN DROSOPHILA

The *period* and *timeless* Genes

The isolation of the *period* (*per*) mutants by Konopka in 1971 is perhaps the most important landmark in the molecular analysis of circadian rhythms (16). The demonstration that mutations in a single gene could affect circadian behavior in a variety of ways was an important discovery, not only for the field of circadian rhythms, but for behavioral studies in general. Until the isolation of the *timeless* (*tim*) mutation in 1994 (17), *per* remained the only known bona fide clock gene. In the interim, a second X-chromosome linked mutation, *Andante*, was shown to lengthen free-running period of both eclosion and locomotor activity rhythms (18). However, although *Andante* was mapped to the *miniature-dusky* locus, which is thought to encode a transmebrane receptor (FlyBase), no further data are available on this gene (19). A genetic screen for autosomal mutants led to the identification of three circadian mutants, but these had weak phenotypes and were, therefore, difficult to analyze genetically (20). *tim*, on the other hand, had a strong behavioral phenotype and, moreover, had an effect on PER expression, immediately making it a candidate for a clock gene (17, 21). We now know that both *per* and *tim* can be mutated to give diverse behavioral phenotypes (22–26, 26a).

Regulation of per/tim—The Feedback Loop   Unfortunately, sequence analysis of *per* and *tim* did not provide clues to their biochemical function (previous predictions that PER was a proteoglycan have not held up with subsequent studies). The TIM sequence is entirely unique (27), and the only protein motif found in PER is a PAS domain, named for the proteins it was first found in—per, single-minded and aryl hydrocarbon receptor nuclear translocator (28). PAS domains have since been found in other clock molecules, photoreceptors, developmental proteins, and proteins involved in hypoxia and may confer on many of these proteins the ability to sense environmental signals (29). However, such a function has not yet been described for PER.

The cyclic regulation of per and tim and the manner in which they generate a molecular clock have been described in numerous reviews and, therefore, are only briefly summarized here (also see Figure 2). Transcription of both genes is initiated in the early part of the day, and peak levels of both mRNAs are expressed from the end of the day through the beginning of night (30–32). The two proteins accumulate during the night and form a heterodimer that enters the nucleus and binds to transcription factors CLOCK (CLK) and CYCLE (CYC) (Figure 2). This interaction prevents CLK/CYC from binding to E-box sequences in the per and tim promoters and results in a cessation of transcriptional activity (discussed under Clock and cycle). Turnover of the proteins—TIM in the late night and PER in the morning—allows RNA levels of the two genes to rise once again. Cyclic phosphorylation of both proteins likely plays an important role in their degradation (33, 34). Phosporylation of PER by the double-time (DBT) kinase also renders it unstable in the absence of TIM (35, 36). An additional level of regulation is conferred by the presence in both proteins of cytoplasmic localization domains (CLD), which retain them in the cytoplasm until they bind each other (37).

The feedback loop described above is fine-tuned in many ways. Each of the two genes contains an E-box in the first intron in addition to the one in the promoter (G Wang & A Sehgal, unpublished data). Although the in vivo role of these E-boxes has not been determined it appears that sequences within transcribed regions of the two genes contribute to RNA cycling (38; G Wang & A Sehgal, unpublished data). In case of per RNA, the additional control is most likely posttranscriptional, perhaps through the cyclic regulation of its stability (30, 39). In fact, TIM protein appears to increase levels of per RNA through a posttranscriptional mechanism (40, 41). It may be the case that the daily appearance of TIM facilitates the accumulation of PER by stabilizing per RNA as well as PER protein. This type of positive feedback may be required to maintain a resonating oscillation.

Mutations in per and tim affect the feedback loop in ways that are consistent with their effects on overt rhythms. For instance, the per^{long} (per^l) mutation decreases the affinity of the PER-TIM interaction, thereby delaying nuclear entry of the heterodimer and extending the cycle (42, 43). Presumably this accounts for the longer behavioral rhythms observed in these flies. The per^{short} (per^s) mutation accelerates the daily disappearance of PER, mostly likely by decreasing its stability, thereby truncating the phase of feedback inhibition and shortening the cycle (44).

Although all these data support the notion that the feedback loop is the underlying basis of overt rhythms, the regulation of this feedback loop is not as simple as indicated thus far. Based upon the studies already discussed, it would seem that

TABLE 1 Components that affect circadian rhythms in Drosophila[a]

Component	Biochemical features	Cyclic expression?	Role in the circadian system
period (per)	None (contains a PAS domain, but no DNA-binding domain)	RNA and protein cycle	Part of the clock, together with tim generates a circadian feedback loop
timeless (tim)	None	RNA and protein cycle	Part of the clock, together with per generates a circadian feedback loop
Clock (Clk)	bHLH-PAS-containing transcription factor	RNA and protein cycle	Part of the clock, activates transcription of per, tim and other (e.g. virille) genes. Also negatively regulates itself generating a second feedback loop
cycle (cyc)	bHLH-PAS-containing transcription factor	None	Part of the clock, activates transcription of per, tim and other (e.g. vrille) genes
doubletime (dbt)	Casein kinase I	None	Part of the clock, phosphorylates PER and renders it unstable in the absence of TIM
vrille (vri)	bZIP transcription factor	RNA cycles, protein ND	May be a component of clock and output pathways, negatively regulates per and tim expression, negatively regulates expression of PDF protein

Cryptochrome (CRY)	Photoreceptor	RNA shows circadian regulation. Protein cycles only in light:dark cycles	Photic entrainment, binds TIM in a light-dependent manner
Pigment dispersing factor	Secreted peptide	Accumulates at axon terminals in a cyclic fashion that may be indicative of regulated release	Output from lateral neurons
lark	RNA-binding protein	Protein cycles, but not RNA	Output molecule specific for eclosion
ebony	Postulated β alanyl dopamine synthetase	ND	Output, mutants affect locomotor activity, but not eclosion rhythms
Andante (*miniature dusky*)	*dusky* encodes a transmembrane receptor that may correspond to *Andante*	ND	Lengthens period of eclosion and locomotor activity rhythms, role in the circadian system not known
cAMP pathway *dunce* (*dnc*)	cAMP phosphodiesterase	ND for *dnc* (cAMP levels cycle)	Mutants affect entrainment and shorten circadian period, mechanisms unknown
Protein kinase A	cAMP-dependent kinase	None found	Output, mutants (*DCO*) affect locomotor activity, but not eclosion rhythms
CREB	Transcription factor	Activity cycles	Mutants (*S162*) shorten circadian period and affect cycling of PER

[a]The table is based on a vast body of work from multiple laboratories (primary references can be found in the text) and lists components that are known to affect eclosion or locomotor activity rhythms. In the text as well as here components that were first identified through molecular genetic approaches are indicated in italics to denote the gene. Proteins that were known before the identification of their corresponding genes are not italicized. Unless otherwise indicated (e.g. see CRY protein), cyclic regulation indicates persistence of cycling in constant darkness and requires the known clock genes.

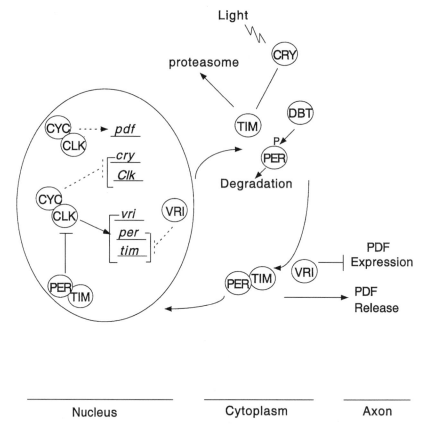

Figure 2   The clock mechanism in lateral neurons. The different subcellular compartments and molecules known to act in these are shown. Dotted arrows indicate signals that have not been characterized and may not be direct. For instance, *vrille* affects expression of *per* and *tim* RNA, but the mechanisms are not known and could be indirect (e.g. through PDF). Likewise, the regulation of *Clk* RNA is not understood. It is speculated that the positive effect of PER and TIM on *Clk* RNA is through a block in negative feedback by CLK. Mechanisms that mediate autoregulation of *Clk* are not known. CRY is known to interact with TIM in a light-dependent fashion (see text), therefore the solid arrow. The role of CRY in TIM degradation is inferred, based on effects of light on TIM and the role of both CRY and TIM in circadian entrainment (see text).

cycling of RNA drives cycling of protein. The caveat is that the role of *per* RNA cycling has been challenged by several studies. Constitutive promoters, which are not subject to feedback, produce cycling PER protein that in some cases restores behavioral rhythms in *per*[01] flies (45–47). As long as this was true only for *per*, one could argue that the loop was driven by feedback upon the *tim* promoter, which rhythmically expresses *tim* RNA and protein. It is easy to see how cyclic stabilization by TIM could drive oscillations of PER independently of the cycling of its RNA (35, 48). However, it turns out that constitutive expression of *tim* also rescues behavioral rhythms in tim^{01} flies (Z Yang & A Sehgal, unpublished observations), indicating that cycling of TIM is also controlled independently of the cycling of its RNA. Independent control of protein cycling may account for the different phases of the RNA and protein oscillations (Figure 3, see color insert). More specifically, there is a 6-h delay in the expression of the two proteins compared with their mRNAs (13, 14, 31–34). This delay contributes to the maintenance of molecular cycles because it helps to separate the phase of RNA synthesis from its inhibition by the two proteins. Translational mechanisms do not account for the delay of either *per* or *tim*, indicating that, as for PER, turnover of TIM is temporally regulated (39, Y Chen & A Sehgal, unpublished data). However, factors that stabilize or destabilize TIM are not known.

Thus it is reasonable to assume that two of the state variables in this system are the PER and TIM proteins. Oscillations of these molecules provide time cues that drive behavioral rhythms, presumably by temporally regulating expression of downstream genes. Consistent with its classification as a state variable, alterations in levels of *per* alter circadian period (49, 50). While similar studies have not been reported for TIM, it is clear that a reduction in TIM levels correlates with resetting of the clock in response to light (see below).

Spatial Expression of per and tim   Both *per* and *tim* are expressed in lateral neurons in the central brain, in glial cells in the optic lobes, and in photoreceptor cells of the compound eye (13, 14, 51, 52). In addition, *per* is expressed in many regions of the body including the prothoracic gland, the antenna, the proboscis, the Malphigian tubules, ovaries, testis, and the gut (51–54). TIM is also known to be expressed in the body (53). However, it is clear from the following lines of evidence that rest:activity rhythms are controlled by PER-TIM in the lateral neurons: (*a*) Restricted expression of *per* in these cells (through transgenic rescue experiments) drives behavioral rhythms (45). Prior to the cell-specific rescue by transgenes, mosaic analysis indicated that expression of PER in these cells is necessary for robust circadian rhythmicity (55). In the mosaic study, PER expression only in glial cells was also associated with some rhythmicity, but the rhythms were much weaker (55). The role of glial cells in rest:activity rhythms is unclear. (*b*) *disconnected* (*disco*) flies, which lack lateral neurons, are arrhythmic (56, 57). Interestingly, analysis of *disco* flies with varying penetrance of the mutant phenotype suggests that the clock runs with a slightly different period in individual lateral neurons, and the overall period of the activity rhythm is the average of these different periodicities (56). (*c*) Ablation of lateral neurons with cell death genes results in significant loss of rhythmicity (58). (*d*) Loss of a neuropeptide, pigment dispersing factor (PDF), which is expressed specifically in ventral lateral neurons, produces behavioral arrhythmia (58).

Thus lateral neurons are necessary for rest:activity rhythms and may even be sufficient to drive this rhythm although other cells may play a modulatory role.

Consistent with their unique role as clock cells, the intracellular milieu of lateral neurons appears to be particularly conducive to cyclic expression of clock proteins (45, 59). In fact, clock proteins cycle in these neurons in larvae, although activity rhythms are not manifested until the adult stage (60, 61). In earlier stages these neurons may serve to retain the memory of entraining stimuli (62, 63). Expression of PER and TIM in other tissues in the fly generates autonomous or semi-autonomous oscillators that control local tissue-specific functions (further discussed below).

Resetting of the Clock by Environmental Signals   Light resets the Drosophila clock by reducing levels of the TIM protein (13, 14, 34, 64). Pulses of light in the early part of the night that delay the phase of the rhythms, as well as those in the second half of the night that advance the rhythm, reduce TIM levels. Dose-response studies, analyses of spectral sensitivity, and phenotypes of specific mutants demonstrate that the strength of the TIM response to light correlates with the behavioral response to light (15, 65). It is not yet clear why the same effect on TIM produces a delay at one time of night and an advance at another. Levels of *tim* RNA (high in the early part of the night and low in the latter half) or the phosphorylation state of TIM (low in the early night and high later) may determine the direction of the shift (14, 66).

The mechanisms that degrade TIM in response to light are now known. TIM is phosphorylated on tyrosine residues and ubiquitinated and degraded by the proteasome (67). This response appears to use the dedicated circadian photoreceptor, cryptochrome (CRY) (68–71), which binds TIM in a light-dependent fashion (72). The visual system is not required for circadian entrainment in Drosophila, although it may participate when present. Thus some mutations of the visual system affect the TIM response as well as the behavioral response to light, although neither is completely eliminated by any visual mutation (15). In addition, *cry*[b] flies, which are deficient in CRY function, can still entrain to light:dark cycles, although the response to pulses of light is severely affected (68). Presumably the visual system contributes to the entrainment of the clock in these mutants, which is supported by the fact that *cry*[b]; *NorpA* double mutants show deficits in their ability to synchronize to LD cycles (68). *NorpA* encodes a phospholipase C that is required for signal transduction in the visual system (73). Whether the visual system acts directly on the clock or indirectly [by driving an overt rhythm that in turn entrains the clock (70)] remains to be determined. In this context, adult flies that lack PER or TIM or even lateral neurons can be driven to display rhythmic behavior in the presence of light:dark cycles (17, 57, 74). These rhythms represent a startle response that obviously bypasses the clock. They are apparently driven by either the visual system or other photoreception mechanisms, supported by the observation that *per*[01]; *NorpA* flies, which are defective in clock function as well as visual transduction, are driven by light:dark cycles (74).

The effects of temperature on the clock are less clear. In part this is due to the complexity of the temperature response, which consists not only of resetting the phase of the rhythm, but also an adjustment of some clock variables in order to keep the period constant (temperature compensation). In addition, temperature defines the limits of rhythmicity such that there is a specific temperature range over which overt rhythms are observed (75). These different effects are obviously mediated by distinct molecular mechanisms, most of which are not known. During the second half of the night, a pulse of high temperature degrades both PER and TIM, but fails to reset the behavioral rhythm because degradation of the two proteins is followed by an acceleration of the molecular cycle (76). This indicates that the clock may be able to alter its speed to offset the effects of some stimuli. However, temperature cycles can clearly drive and entrain circadian rhythms, and pulses at other times can also reset rhythms (68). Moreover, the phase of activity in a light:dark cycle is also dependent upon the ambient temperature. At lower temperatures the activity tends to be concentrated in daytime hours, whereas at higher temperatures there is a shift toward morning and evening hours. This effect appears to be mediated by a specific splicing event in the *per* gene (77).

The mechanisms underlying temperature compensation are a matter of debate. Although a number of mutations that affect temperature compensation have been described, there is no consensus on a specific mechanism or even a specific region of PER or TIM that controls this property (22, 23, 26a, 42, 66, 78–80). It may be that most mutations or structural changes that alter protein conformation/stability affect temperature compensation. One of the regions implicated is a glycine-threonine repeat domain in PER, the length of which affects temperature compensation and is apparently distributed as a latitudinal cline with higher numbers of the repeat in northern climates (80). This repeat and the region that coevolved with it may be important for maintaining the integrity of PER protein (81).

Independent Functions of PER and TIM   Everything discussed thus far would indicate that PER and TIM are codependent proteins that exert all their effects on downstream pathways as heterodimers. Indeed, phylogenetic analysis of the two proteins across insect species shows conservation of TIM-interaction domains on PER and vice versa (82–86). However, we now know that there are TIM-independent effects of PER and likewise for TIM. Thus PER can effect negative feedback in the absence of TIM, which may account for the continued repression of RNA levels after TIM levels have declined in a daily cycle (87). In addition, the two genes have differential effects on other, apparently noncircadian, processes. PER affects the fly's sensitivity to cocaine, but TIM does not (88). This phenotype of *per* mutants is thought to be related to the previously reported effects of PER on the enzyme tyrosine decarboxylase (89). TIM, but not PER, affects the rebound response to rest deprivation, suggesting that it is relevant to the homeostatic as well as the circadian control of rest (90). Finally, *per* is critical for the ultradian rhythm of the Drosophila courtship song (91). A role for *tim* in this process has not been reported.

It is not clear where or how these proteins act independently of each other. Given that PER is unstable in the cytoplasm without TIM, it is likely that all of its effects are exerted in the nucleus—some as a heterodimer with TIM and some after dissociation from TIM. This is supported by the recently reported effects of PER on transcription (87). TIM, on the other hand, is stable in the cytoplasm without PER and also appears to be present in excess (34). Thus a fraction of it constantly remains in the cytoplasm where it may mediate PER-independent effects. In support of independent effects of *per* and *tim*, it was recently shown that the two genes are not co-expressed in all cells (91a).

Cryptochrome

The role of cryptochrome as a photoreceptor is covered elsewhere in this volume and therefore is not discussed here. However, in light of the data implicating CRY in central clock mechanisms in mammals (see 91b), it is worth considering such a role for it in Drosophila. In support of a clock-related role, *cry* RNA cycles and highest levels are found in the early part of the day (69). This cycling persists in constant darkness and is dependent on PER, TIM, CLK, and CYC. In *per* and *tim* null mutants, *cry* RNA levels are constantly low and in *Clk* and *cyc* mutants the levels are constantly high, indicating positive regulation by the former and negative regulation by the latter two components. However, CRY protein cycles only in the presence of light:dark cycles. Apparently this cycling is driven by light-sensitivity of the protein because DD (constant dark) conditions lead to constant accumulation of CRY (69).

In the lateral neuron clock, CRY appears to function only in the photoreceptive pathway. PER and TIM continue to cycle in these cells in *cry*^{b} mutants and behavior is rhythmic (68). However, in photoreceptor cells, which constitute a peripheral oscillator, PER and TIM cycling is abolished in *cry*^{b} mutants (68). One possible explanation is that the lack of a circadian photoreceptor prevents synchronization of molecular oscillations between flies and also between individual cells, leading to a noncyclic profile when flies are assayed at different time points (note that oscillations in lateral neurons in these flies are driven by visual input. The photoreceptor clock may not be linked to the visual system). However, the interpretation of immuno-cytochemistry experiments did not support this explanation (68), thus suggesting that CRY is a clock component in peripheral oscillators in Drosophila. In addition, as the *cry*^{b} mutant is not a null, it is still formally possible that CRY is also part of the lateral neuron clock. Future experiments will undoubtedly address this issue.

Clock and *cycle*

The Drosophila *Clock* (*dClk*) and *cycle* (*cyc*) genes were identified through a genetic screen for mutations that affect rest:activity rhythms in flies (92, 93). *Clock* was also isolated independently, on the basis of its homology to the mouse *Clock* gene (94, 95). Mutations in either gene reduce levels of *per* and *tim* RNA as well as protein and render flies arrhythmic for rest:activity and eclosion (92, 93). As discussed above, *Clk* and *cyc* encode transcription factors that directly activate *per* and *tim* expression by binding to sequences that contain E-boxes (94, 96). Like all other proteins that bind E-boxes, both CLK and CYC contain a basic region and a helix-loop-helix domain (bHLH). In addition, each has a PAS domain, which, as mentioned above, is turning out to be a conserved motif in circadian rhythm proteins. CLK binds to PER as well as TIM in vivo and in vitro (96, 97). In vitro studies demonstrate that the binding of PER or TIM, or even the heterodimer, to CLK does not disrupt the interaction between CLK and CYC but prevents the CLK-CYC heterodimer from binding to DNA (96).

cyc RNA and protein do not cycle and are not regulated by any of the other known clock genes (93, 98). In addition, the only phenotype associated with CYC thus far is arrhythmia; period-altering mutations have not been described. Based upon these observations, CYC can be categorized as a parameter, a molecule that plays a regulatory rather than a timekeeping role in the clock. Clearly, it is required for appropriate regulation of clock genes and ultimately for behavioral rhythms, but it itself does not appear to provide timekeeping cues. *Clk*, on the contrary, is emerging as another state variable of the Drosophila clock. mRNA and protein levels of *Clk* cycle with a circadian rhythm, are positively regulated by PER and TIM, and are negatively autoregulated by CLK. (Figure 2). This generates a feedback loop similar to the one seen for *per* and *tim* (94, 95, 97, 99). One difference from the *per/tim* feedback loop is the lack of a lag separating the phases of *Clk* mRNA and protein (97) (Figure 3, see color insert). This suggests that CLK cycling depends upon the cycling of its mRNA and not upon additional levels of control, as do PER and TIM. Finally, CLK appears to be the least abundant of the clock proteins and thus could be the limiting component in the Drosophila central clock (98). However, it should be noted that CLK regulation is not well understood and some aspects of it are difficult to reconcile with proposed models. For instance, high levels of CLK do not correlate with times of maximal transcriptional activation of *per* and *tim*. In fact, peak transcription of *per* and *tim* occurs during the trough of the CLK expression profile (30, 97). This would indicate that in a daily cycle lowest levels of CLK drive maximal expression of *per* and *tim*.

The role of CLK-CYC extends beyond the transcriptional activation of *per* and *tim*. The *vrille* gene, a clock-controlled gene required for behavioral rhythms, contains upstream E-boxes that are likely regulated by CLK-CYC (100). In addition, both CLK and CYC are required for the expression of pigment-dispersing factor (PDF), a peptide hormone that is expressed specifically in clock cells and sustains free-running behavioral rhythms (discussed below).

double-time (*dbt*)

Genetic screens identified two alleles of the same gene that affected periodicity of locomotor activity. *doubletime*[short] or *dbt*[S] mutants exhibit free-running periods as short as 18 h, whereas *dbt*[L] lengthens the period up to 27 h (36). Similar effects of each allele were observed for eclosion behavior. PER and TIM cycling were affected in a similar manner indicating that *doubletime* was likely an essential component of the endogenous pacemaker. Subsequent cloning showed that *dbt* encodes a casein kinase that is closely related to the human casein kinase Iε (101). Levels of *dbt* mRNA do not oscillate. Although the lack of cyclic mRNA expression might predict a similar pattern of the protein, the possibility remains that DBT activity is regulated in a circadian manner.

In addition to its effects on circadian rhythms, DBT is essential for both cell proliferation and growth arrest of imaginal discs during development (102). Based on this finding, it is not surprising that a null mutation of the *dbt* gene is lethal during pupal, or in some cases, larval development (36, 102). In order to determine the effects of a more severe allele on the circadian pacemaker, *per* and *tim* expression was studied in third instar larvae carrying a null, P-insertion mutation in the *dbt* gene (*dbt*^{P}) (36, 102). Although levels of *per* mRNA were normal, PER protein was expressed at higher than normal levels throughout the day in *dbt*^{P} mutants, indicating that the effects on the protein were posttranscriptional. Consistent with this interpretation, phosphorylated forms of PER, which normally appear after PER reaches peak levels and begins to decline, were absent. In addition, high levels of protein were observed under conditions that degrade TIM (constant light and the light phase of the light:dark cycle), indicating that PER is stable in the absence of TIM in these flies. Cyclic expression of TIM was also disrupted in DD, and the protein was not detectable after two days in constant darkness. Based on these observations, Price et al (36) concluded that DBT plays a role in PER turnover by regulating phosphorylation of the protein and rendering it unstable when it is not bound to TIM. The effects of *dbt*^{P} on TIM are likely secondary to those on PER, as well as consistent with the predicted consequences of high levels of PER expression (this is expected to result in low levels of *tim* RNA owing to constant negative feedback). Thus DBT confers TIM-dependence on PER, thereby generating the lag that separates the synthesis of *per* RNA from the expression of PER protein (note that we still do not know how the lag is generated for TIM). It also promotes cycling of PER by controlling its turnover at the end of each cycle; this is supported by the *dbt*^{s} and *dbt*^{l} mutants, which change both the daily accumulation and the decline of PER levels by accelerating or delaying them, respectively (36).

Whether phosphorylation of PER by DBT is important for aspects of PER function/regulation other than its stability has not been directly addressed, but appears unlikely based upon available data. A recent study showed that deleting a serine-threonine rich region in the *per* gene (*per*-ΔC2) results in poor temperature compensation as well as in altered phase-resetting responses (66). Underlying these behavioral defects are poor protein turnover of PER and an effect on feedback. The additional effect of the C2 mutation indicates either that PER is also regulated by another kinase or that the defect in feedback is attributable to some other regulatory sequence within the deletion.

vrille

Differential screens for clock-controlled transcripts identified another circadian component also important for development (100). *vrille* (*vri*) was first described as a bZIP transcription factor essential for signaling in the *decapentaplegic* pathway during embryogenesis (103). Although homologous to the PAR domain family of proteins, *vrille* itself lacks the PAR protein-interaction domain, and it is not known if other proteins are required for its signaling. However, analysis of the promoter sequence revealed that *vrille* contains an E-box, the recognition site for the CLK-CYC heterodimer. Expression of *vrille* in S2 cells is indeed driven by CLK, as measured by luciferase reporter activity. Additionally, *vrille* RNA expression is substantially lower in the Clk^{jrk} and cyc^0 flies, indicating that *vrille* is under transcriptional control by CLK and CYC in vivo (100).

Although isolated as a gene whose expression cycles under control of the clock, the following observations suggest that *vrille* may be a component of the central clock. First, the *vrille* gene co-localizes with TIM in the retina and in lateral neurons, as well as other areas of the central brain. Consistent with the observation that *vrille* expression is under transcriptional control by CLK and CYC, the mRNA cycles in phase with that of *per* and *tim*, and the peak expression occurs during the first half of the night, with lowest levels occurring during the first half of the day (100) (Figure 3). Second, *vrille* expression affects circadian behavior. Heterozygosity for a null mutation in *vrille* shortens the free-running period of the locomotor activity rhythm by 0.4 to 0.8 h. Overexpression of *vrille* in clock cells using the GAL4-UAS system not only results in a longer period or arrhythmia, but also has a severe effect on expression of PER and TIM. Both *per* and *tim* RNA are low or undetectable; this is also true for their respective proteins, which are confined to the cytoplasm. Taken together, these data indicate that the protein encoded by *vrille* might be important for nuclear turnover of clock proteins and/or repressing transcription. Although the mechanism by which this occurs has yet to be elucidated, and the null phenotype for *vrille* is not yet known, the VRI protein appears to be required for normal molecular clockwork.

In addition to affecting *per* and *tim*, the VRI protein affects output through PDF (discussed below). Overexpression of VRI results in reduced levels of PDF protein, but no changes in RNA levels (100). Thus VRI affects a posttranscriptional modification of PDF that likely reduces its stability. The interaction between VRI, PDF, and the rest of the clock has yet to be described and should provide new insights into how a functioning molecular clock confers circadian behavior.

Pigment-Dispersing Factor (PDF)

PDF was named for its ability to disperse pigment granules in the visual system of crabs, where it was first identified (104). In Drosophila its expression pattern, which is restricted largely to the lateral neurons, made it a candidate for a secreted clock output (58, 105). Mutants lacking PDF were recently described and, as one would expect of an output molecule, show deficits in free-running behavioral rhythms (58). Thus a large proportion of flies that lack PDF are arrhythmic in constant darkness. However, rhythms are displayed by some *pdf*-null flies, particularly during the first three days of free-run, suggesting the existence of additional output mechanisms (58).

Levels of *pdf* RNA do not cycle (106). Expression of the protein is also non-cyclic in the cell bodies of lateral neurons, but cycles at their axon terminals, which may be indicative of cyclic release (107). Accumulation of PDF is highest in the early part of the day and lowest at night. Overexpression of PDF in lateral neurons does not eliminate its cycling or behavioral rhythms, suggesting that the mechanisms that mediate its cyclic release are not easily saturated (108). The cycling is clock dependent in that it is maintained in constant darkness and is affected by all the clock mutants (107). It is abolished in per^0 and tim^0 mutants, and a constant high expression is maintained at the terminals (100, 107). Assuming that high accumulation at terminals represents a block in PDF release, PER and TIM may normally stimulate its release through unknown mechanisms. In *Clk* and *cyc* mutants, PDF expression is diminished in the small ventral lateral neurons, the ones likely most critical for rest:activity rhythms, and projections from the large ventral neurons are altered in some flies. Thus CLK and CYC may be required for the expression of an axon-guidance factor in lateral neurons. Their effects on PDF expression may not be direct because they are not mediated by an E-box in the *pdf* promoter (107).

PDF is clearly going to be a critical tool for the elucidation of output mechanisms in the circadian system. An elegant series of studies used antibodies to PDF to trace projections of the lateral neurons and thereby identify putative neural substrates of behavioral rhythms (105). Interestingly, ectopic expression of PDF in the vicinity of the normal targets of lateral neurons generates behavioral arrhythmia, but in remote locations it does not do so (108). This indicates that it is a local-acting signal rather than one that is released into the general circulation. However, it is also possible that processing of PDF is inefficient in cells that do not normally produce it, and the amounts released are too small to diffuse over large distances. Thus, it could still be directly responsible for the rescue of behavioral rhythms in per^0 flies by an abdominally transplanted per^s brain (109). Alternatively, the transplanted brain may release a factor that is controlled by PDF.

ARE THE LATERAL NEURONS THE MASTER CLOCK IN DROSOPHILA?

All the components discussed above are expressed in lateral neurons and, as expected, are relevant to rest:activity rhythms. However, clock genes are also expressed in peripheral tissues where they, at least in part, generate oscillators that control tissue-specific functions. Several fly tissues, including the Malphigian tubules, the wings, the antennae, and the bristles maintain oscillations of clock gene products and can be entrained by light after they are severed from the head (53, 110). Thus not only are these self-sufficient oscillators, they even contain their own photoreceptors, most likely cryptochrome. Although all the output rhythms controlled by peripheral oscillators are not known, data are available for some of them. For instance, the oscillator in the antennae generates a circadian rhythm in the olfactory response measured as EOG waves in response to olfactory stimuli (8). Visual sensitivity cycles with a circadian rhythm in the Drosophila eye, although as mentioned above it does not appear to be affected by the *per* mutants (9). Additional functions that may be regulated by the clock are easily envisioned, e.g. excretion in the Malphigian tubules, perhaps through control of osmoregulation and/or sensitivity of an ion channel.

The extent to which these peripheral oscillators are completely autonomous is a subject of great debate. The olfactory rhythm requires clock gene expression in the antennae because PER expression in lateral neurons alone can not drive this rhythm in a *per⁰* background (8). However, this does not preclude a regulatory role for the lateral neurons. In mammals, available data indicate that the suprachiasmatic nuclei (SCN) constitute the master oscillator that drives oscillations in peripheral tissues (111, 112). Oscillations in the periphery are lost in SCN-lesioned animals, and molecular oscillations are sustained in the isolated, cultured SCN for a much longer period of time than they are in cultures of peripheral tissues (111, 112). Experiments of the latter kind are difficult to do in flies, although the presence of photoreceptors in these peripheral tissues already distinguishes them from their mammalian counterparts. In addition, transplantation of Malphigian tubules from one fly to another apparently does not change the phase of the endogenous oscillator in this tissue (113). Within the transplanted tissue, PER and TIM continue to cycle with the phase of the donor animal, which is the reverse of that of the host animal.

While the contribution of lateral neurons to other peripheral rhythms is debatable, they do seem to be important for the eclosion rhythm. Eclosion is regulated by cells within the ring gland, which express PER themselves (51, 52, 54), but may also be subject to control by the lateral neurons. *disco* flies, which lack lateral neurons, not only lack rest:activity rhythms but also eclosion rhythms (57). Moreover, flies that ectopically express PDF show deficits in eclosion rhythms (108). Based on the variation in the behavior of different peripheral oscillators, it is likely that the circadian organization of the fly consists of a collection of autonomous and semi-autonomous oscillators. In mammals, the autonomy is lost, which is consistent with the general centralization of function through evolution.

OTHER OUTPUT GENES

PDF is obviously a prime candidate for an output molecule that is secreted by the lateral neurons and regulates activity rhythms and possibly even other outputs. In general, however, given the diverse outputs alluded to above, it is likely that a large proportion of output genes are specific for a single overt rhythm. They may also be restricted in their expression to specific central or peripheral tissues that contain oscillators. Thus identification of these genes will require molecular or genetic screens that focus on these tissues. To date, molecular screens to identify genes regulated in a circadian fashion (putative output genes) have used entire heads (100, 114–116). Differential screening approaches led to the identification of *vrille*, which is required for rest:activity rhythms; *takeout*, which is required for survival of the fly in response to starvation; and several others about which much less is known (100, 114–117). Other putative output molecules relevant to eclosion or locomotor activity rhythms have come out of genetic approaches, either from a random mutagenesis screen or from assays of candidate mutants. For instance, *ebony* mutants, which have altered levels of dopamine and show some behavioral phenotypes, display aberrant locomotor activity rhythms but normal eclosion rhythms (118). Their specificity for one type of overt rhythm suggests that they act in the output pathway. Output components that have been characterized to some degree are discussed below. For the most part, the relationship of these molecules to the clock or to the overt rhythm is not understood.

lark

lark was identified in a mutagenesis screen for genes affecting the circadian gating of eclosion (119). These mutants do not have a significant effect on locomotor activity rhythms, indicating the specificity of *lark* for eclosion. *lark* mutants were named for their early eclosion behavior, where most heterozygous adults emerge approximately 2 h earlier in the day than their wild-type siblings. Homozygous expression of the *lark* mutation results in lethality during embryonic development, indicating a crucial, noncircadian function of the *lark* gene product (120).

Lark encodes a ~40 kDa protein containing an RNA recognition motif (RRM) and a retroviral-type zinc finger, which indicates that the product plays a role in translational regulation (120). Based on the observation that the gene dosage of *lark* affects eclosion gating, i.e. three copies of the gene result in a later eclosion gate (in contrast to the earlier gate in the *lark/+* flies), Newby & Jackson hypothesize that LARK is associated with repressor activity (121). In support of this notion, analysis of protein abundance throughout the day showed that LARK protein cycles with peak levels during the midday in an LD cycle and 10-fold lower levels at night (122). Thus a critical low threshold of LARK may trigger a chain of events that leads to adult eclosion by early morning. In the case of *lark/+* flies, eclosion occurs earlier because of the lower levels of protein that reach the critical threshold earlier in the cycle. Consistent with a role in eclosion, LARK co-localizes with CCAP (crustacean cardioactive peptide), a neuropeptide required for ecdysis (122).

As one might predict, oscillation of LARK protein is abolished in *per^0* flies (122). Interestingly, the protein is expressed at intermediate levels in the *per^0* background. Because eclosion events persist in *per^0* flies, perhaps the intermediate protein level, or random decreases in LARK protein levels are sufficient for de-repression of the eclosion process. *lark* mRNA does not exhibit circadian oscillation, which suggests that protein cycling is likely the result of a clock-controlled posttranscriptional modification.

Clearly, at least two distinct signaling pathways that act downstream of the core oscillator are each responsible for regulating different circadian-controlled behaviors, eclosion and locomotor activity. To date, *lark* is the only characterized *Drosophila* gene that is required specifically in the output for eclosion. While other components in the eclosion process are known to be clock-controlled in moths (123), the mechanism by which this occurs is unknown.

Components of cAMP Pathways

cAMP-dependent protein kinase (PKA) is implicated in the control of locomotor activity rhythms by the clock. Flies carrying mutations in the PKA gene, *DC0*, show arrhythmicity in DD (124, 125). The stronger the effect of *DC0* alleles on PKA activity, the greater the proportion of flies that are arrhythmic for locomotor activity. There is no effect on eclosion gating, nor on the cycling of PER protein and mRNA (125). Such observations are consistent with a role of PKA in a circadian output pathway that is specific for locomotor activity.

Other lines of evidence suggest that components of cAMP signaling are important for clock input. Levine et al (124) described a circadian phenotype associated with the *dunce* (*dnc*) mutation that results in decreased activity of phosphodiesterase, the enzyme mediating metabolism of cAMP (124). Both loss-of-function (*dnc¹*) and null (*dnc^ML*) mutants exhibit shortened free-running periods, and the null background results in up to 50% arrhythmicity. Additionally, these flies exhibit altered phase-resetting responses such that the delay part of the phase-response curve is significantly increased compared with that of wild-type flies. These observations suggest an effect on an input mechanism. While the authors confirmed that cAMP activity is markedly increased in *dnc* and also exhibits increased amplitude in circadian oscillation (124), the mechanism by which cAMP acts on the endogenous pacemaker remains to be determined.

A more recent study by Belvin et al (126) described a circadian phenotype in a mutant lacking the dCREB2 gene, *S162* (126, 127). These flies exhibited a short free-running period, as well as diminished oscillation of the PER protein and RNA, shown by Western blot analysis of head extracts and by measuring activity of a luciferase reporter gene, respectively (126, 127). With the exception of a shorter period length of cycling, the *S162* mutation did not affect the expression of TIM. Additionally, these authors determined the effects of the clock on CREB activity by designing a reporter construct in which luciferase expression was controlled by multiple cAMP-response element (CRE) sites. Flies carrying the CRE-luc transgene exhibited daily oscillations of luciferase reporter activity in both LD and DD. As one might predict, these oscillations were absent when studied in a *per⁰* background, and overall activity was dramatically reduced in *S162* mutants. Taken together, these data indicate that the CRE-luc reporter reflects CREB activity and that the circadian clock regulates CREB. Thus a feedback loop likely exists between CREB and PER. Based on the phenotype associated with *S162*, one potential function of this loop may be to fine-tune protein oscillation for determining period length. In addition, CREB-PER may act in the same pathway as *dnc* to affect entrainment of the clock.

The studies described above provide evidence that cAMP signaling is involved in events that are both upstream and downstream from the endogenous pacemaker. Although these observations appear contradictory, several possibilities may account for these effects. For instance, the effects of *dnc* on input may involve PKA-independent targets of cAMP such as cyclic nucleotide–gated ion channels (128) and receptors. A recent study showed that rap1, a small ras-like GTPase, is activated by cAMP independently of PKA (129). In Drosophila, *roughened*, which is involved in eye development and cell differentiation (130), is a homologue of rap1. Another example of a signaling pathway that is possibly affected by *dunce*, but not by *DC0* may be through adenosine, which is a metabolic product of cAMP. Adenosine receptors have not been identified in Drosophila, but their existence is supported through pharmacological experiments demonstrating the effects of adenosine agents on rest behavior (90, 131). Although none of these targets has been implicated in circadian behavior, the possibility remains that any one of these or perhaps a yet-to-be identified cAMP-dependent signaling mechanism is required for normal clock function.

UNANSWERED QUESTIONS

It is clear that output represents the least understood aspect of circadian rhythms. For activity rhythms, we know that PDF is an important, although perhaps not the only output signal from lateral neurons. However, the manner in which the clock genes regulate expression and release of PDF and the effector mechanisms mediated by a PDF receptor are completely unknown. The identity and functional importance of the target tissues are also unknown, although a clue to their location is provided by studies in which PDF-containing projections of lateral neurons were traced. Note that at the present we can not exclude the possibility that PDF is also released into the hemolymph and acts on tissues that are not directly innervated by lateral neurons. In addition, practically nothing is known about how peripheral oscillators control overt rhythms. In many cases the nature of the rhythm determined by these oscillators has not been identified. Clearly, analysis of output alone can keep Drosophila researchers busy for many years to come.

Although we know much more about the clock and input pathways, these areas are by no means completely understood. How TIM cycling is maintained in the absence of light, what kinase phosphorylates TIM in response to light, how CLK feedback regulates its own expression, how *vrille* affects the whole process, and how exactly the CLK and PER/TIM loops interlock with each other are some of the clock-related outstanding questions. Regarding the input pathway, we still do not know how CRY transmits photic signals to the clock or what accounts for the typical phase response curve (PRC) that depicts the fly response to light at different times in a circadian cycle. In a typical PRC for a wild-type fly there are not only delays in the early part of the night and advances in the latter half, but also a crossover point that corresponds to a time in the middle of the night when light pulses have no effect on the behavioral rhythm. Although models have been proposed to explain these different effects, they have never been directly tested. In addition, although perhaps not directly clock-relevant, it would be intriguing to know how light drives rhythmic behavior in the absence of a clock. Finally, the complicated effects of temperature and other possible nonphotic inputs are a long way from being elucidated.

Visit the Annual Reviews home page at www.AnnualReviews.org

LITERATURE CITED

1. Dunlap JC. 1999. Molecular bases for circadian biological clocks. *Cell* 96:271–90
2. Scully AL, Kay SA. 2000. Time flies for *Drosophila*. *Cell* 100:297–300
3. Zatz M. 1992. Perturbing the pacemaker in the chick pineal. *Disc. Neurosci.* 8:67–73
4. Pittendrigh CS. 1960. Circadian rhythms and the circadian organization of living things. *Cold Spring Harbor Symp. Quant. Biol.* 25:159–84
5. Pittendrigh CS. 1967. Circadian systems I. The driving oscillation and its assay in *Drosophila pseudoobscura. Proc. Natl. Acad. Sci. USA* 58:1762–67
6. Qiu J, Hardin PE. 1996. Developmental state and the circadian clock interact to influence the timing of eclosion in *Drosophila melanogaster. J. Biol. Rhythms* 11:75–86
7. Hamblen-Coyle MJ, Wheeler DA, Rutila JE, Rosbash M, Hall JC. 1992. Behavior of period-altered circadian rhythm mutants of *Drosophila* in light:dark cycles (Diptera:Drosophilidae). *J. Insect Behav.* 5:417–45
8. Krishnan B, Dryer SE, Hardin PE. 1999. Circadian rhythms in olfactory responses of *Drosophila melanogaster. Nature* 400:375–78
9. Chen DM, Christianson JS, Sapp RJ, Stark WS. 1992. Visual receptor cycle in normal and *period* mutant Drosophila: microspectrophotometry, electrophysiology, and ultrastructural morphometry. *Visual Neurosci.* 9:125–35
10. Allemand R, David JR. 1984. Genetic analysis of the circadian oviposition rhythm in *Drosophila melanogaster*: effects of drift in laboratory strains. *Behav. Genet.* 14:31–43
11. McCabe C, Birley A. 1998. Oviposition in the *period* genotypes of *Drosophila melanogaster. Chronobiol. Int.* 15:119–133
12. Siwicki KK, Eastman C, Petersen G, Rosbash M, Hall JC. 1988. Antibodies to the *period* gene product of *Drosophila* reveal diverse tissue distribution and rhythmic changes in the visual system. *Neuron* 1:141–50
13. Hunter-Ensor M, Ousley A, Sehgal A. 1996. Regulation of the *Drosophila* protein timeless suggests a mechanism for resetting the circadian clock by light. *Cell* 84:677–86
14. Myers MP, Wager-Smith K, Rothenflugh A, Young MW. 1996. Light-induced degradation of TIMELESS and entrainment of the *Drosophila* circadian clock. *Science* 271:1736–40
15. Yang Z, Emerson M, Su HS, Sehgal A. 1998. Response of the timeless protein to light correlates with behavioral entrainment and suggests a non-visual pathway for circadian photoreception. *Neuron* 21:215–23
16. Konopka RJ, Benzer S. 1971. Clock mutants of *Drosophila melanogaster. Proc. Natl. Acad. Sci. USA* 68:2112–16
17. Sehgal A, Price JL, Man B, Young MW. 1994. Loss of circadian behavioral rhythms and *per* RNA oscillations in the *Drosophila* mutant *timeless. Science* 263:1603–6
18. Konopka RJ, Smith RF, Orr D. 1991. Characterization of *Andante*, a new *Drosophila* clock mutant, and its interactions with other clock mutants. *J. Neurogenet.* 7:103–14
19. Newby LM, White L, Bartolomeis SM, Walker BJ, Dowse HB, et al. 1991. Mutational analysis of the *Drosophila miniature-dusky (m-dy)* locus: effects on cell size and circadian rhythms. *Genetics* 128:571–82
20. Jackson FR. 1983. The isolation of biological rhythm mutations in the autosomes

of *Drosophila melanogaster. J. Neurogenet.* 1:3–10

21. Vosshall LB, Price JL, Sehgal A, Saez L, Young MW. 1994. Block in nuclear localization of period protein by a second clock mutation, *timeless. Science* 263:1606–9

22. Matsumoto A, Tomioka K, Chiba Y, Tanimura T. 1999. *tim^{rit}* Lengthens circadian period in a temperature-dependent manner through suppression of PERIOD protein cycling and nuclear localization. *Mol. Cell. Biol.* 19:4343–54

23. Hamblen MJ, White NE, Emery PTJ, Kaiser K, Hall JC. 1998. Molecular and behavioral analysis of four *period* mutants in *Drosophila melanogaster* encompassing extreme short, novel long, and unorthodox arrhythmic types. *Genetics* 149:165–78

24. Konopka RJ, Hamblen-Coyle MJ, Jamison CF, Hall JC. 1994. An ultrashort clock mutation at the *period* locus of *Drosophila melanogaster* that reveals some new features of the fly's circadian system. *J. Biol. Rhythms* 9:189–216

25. Rutila JE, Zeng H, Le M, Curtin KD, Hall JC, Rosbash M. 1996. The *tim^{SL}* mutant of the *Drosophila* rhythm gene *timeless* manifests allele-specific interactions with *period* gene mutants. *Neuron* 17:921–29

26. Rothenflugh A, Young MW, Saez L. 2000. A TIMELESS-independent function for PERIOD proteins in the *Drosophila* clock. *Neuron* 26:505–14

26a. Rothenflugh A, Abodeely M, Price JL, Young MW. 2000. Isolation and analysis of six *timeless* alleles that cause short or long period circadian rhythms in *Drosophila. Genetics* 156:665–75

27. Myers MP, Wager SK, Wesley CS, Young MW, Sehgal A. 1995. Positional cloning and sequence analysis of the *Drosophila* clock gene, *timeless. Science* 270:805–8

28. Crews ST, Thomas JB, Goodman CS. 1988. The *Drosophila single-minded* gene encodes a nuclear protein with sequence similarity to the *per* gene product. *Cell* 52:143–52

29. Crews ST, Fan CM. 1999. Remembrance of things PAS: regulation of development by bHLH-PAS proteins. *Curr. Opin. Genet. Dev.* 9:580–87

30. So WV, Rosbash M. 1997. Post-transcriptional regulation contributes to *Drosophila* clock gene mRNA cycling. *EMBO J.* 16:7146–55

31. Hardin PE, Hall JC, Rosbash M. 1990. Feedback of the *Drosophila period* gene on circadian cycling of its messenger RNA levels. *Nature* 343:536–40

32. Sehgal A, Rothenflugh-Hilfiker A, Hunter-Ensor M, Chen Y, et al. 1995. Rhythmic expression of *timeless*: a basis for promoting circadian cycles in *period* gene autoregulation. *Science* 270:808–10

33. Edery I, Zwiebel LJ, Dembinska ME, Rosbash M. 1994. Temporal phosphorylation of the *Drosophila period* protein. *Proc. Natl. Acad. Sci. USA* 91:2260–64

34. Zeng H, Qian Z, Myers MP, Rosbash M. 1996. A light entrainment mechanism for the *Drosophila* circadian clock. *Nature* 380:129–35

35. Price JL, Dembinska ME, Young MW, Rosbash M. 1995. Suppression of PERIOD protein abundance and circadian cycling by the *Drosophila* clock mutation *timeless. EMBO J.* 14:4044–49

36. Price JL, Blau J, Rothenflugh A, Abodeely M, Kloss B, Young MW. 1998. *double-time* is a novel *Drosophila* clock gene that regulates PERIOD protein accumulation. *Cell* 94:83–95

37. Saez L, Young MW. 1996. Regulation of nuclear entry of the *Drosophila* clock proteins Period and Timeless. *Neuron* 17:911–20

38. Stanewsky R, Jamison CF, Plautz JD, Kay SA, Hall JC. 1997. Multiple circadian-regulated elements contribute to cycling *period* gene expression in *Drosophila. EMBO J.* 16:5006–18

39. Chen Y, Hunter-Ensor M, Schotland P,

Sehgal A. 1998. Alterations of *per* RNA in noncoding regions affect periodicity of circadian behavioral rhythms. *J. Biol. Rhythms* 13:364–79

40. Suri V, Lanjuin A, Rosbash M. 1999. TIMELESS-dependent positive and negative autoregulation in the *Drosophila* circadian clock. *EMBO J.* 18:675–86

41. Deleted in proof

42. Gekakis N, Saez L, Delahaye BA, Myers MP, Sehgal A, et al. 1995. Isolation of *timeless* by PER protein interaction: defective interaction between *timeless* protein and long-period mutant PERL. *Science* 270:811–15

43. Curtin KD, Huang ZJ, Rosbash M. 1995. Temporally regulated nuclear entry of the *Drosophila* period protein contributes to the circadian clock. *Neuron* 14:365–72

44. Marrus SB, Zeng H, Rosbash M. 1996. Effect of constant light and circadian entrainment of *perS* flies: evidence for light-mediated delay of the negative feedback loop in *Drosophila*. *EMBO J.* 15:6877–86

45. Frisch B, Hardin PE, Hamblen CM, Rosbash M, Hall JC. 1994. A promoterless *period* gene mediates behavioral rhythmicity and cyclical *per* expression in a restricted subset of the *Drosophila* nervous system. *Neuron* 12:555–70

46. Vosshall LB, Young MW. 1995. Circadian rhythms in *Drosophila* can be driven by *period* expression in a restricted group of central brain cells. *Neuron* 15:345–60

47. Cheng Y, Hardin PE. 1998. *Drosophila* photoreceptors contain an autonomous circadian oscillator that can function without *period* mRNA cycling. *J. Neurosci.* 18:741–50

48. Dembinska ME, Stanewsky R, Hall JC, Rosbash M. 1997. Circadian cycling of a *period-lacZ* fusion protein in *Drosophila*: evidence for cyclic degradation. *J. Biol. Rhythms* 12:157–72

49. Smith R, Konopka R. 1982. Effects of dosage alterations at the *per* locus on the period of the circadian clock of

Drosophila. Mol. Gen. Genet. 185:30–36

50. Baylies MK, Bargiello TA, Jackson FR, Young MW. 1987. Changes in abundance or structure of the *per* gene product can alter periodicity of the *Drosophila* clock. *Nature* 326:390–92

51. Liu X, Lorenz L, Yu Q, Hall JC, Rosbash M. 1988. Spatial and temporal expression of the *period* gene in *Drosophila melanogaster. Genes Dev.* 2:228–38

52. Saez L, Youg MW. 1988. In situ localization of the per clock protein during development of *Drosophila melanogaster. Mol. Cell. Biol.* 8:5378–85

53. Giebultowicz JM, Hege DM. 1997. Circadian clock in Malphigian tubules. *Nature* 386:664

54. Emery IF, Noveral JM, Jamison CF, Siwicki KK. 1997. Rhythms of *Drosophila period* gene expression in culture. *Proc. Natl. Acad. Sci. USA* 94:4092–96

55. Ewer J, Frisch B, Hamblen CM, Rosbash M, Hall JC. 1992. Expression of the *period* clock gene within different cell types in the brain of *Drosophila* adults and mosaic analysis of these cells' influence on circadian behavioral rhythms. *J. Neurosci.* 12:3321–49

56. Helfrich-Forster C. 1998. Robust circadian rhythmicity of *Drosophila melanogaster* requires the presence of lateral neurons: a brain-behavioral study of *disconnected* mutants. *Comp. Physiol. A* 182:435–53

57. Dushay MS, Rosbash M, Hall JC. 1989. The *disconnected* visual system mutations in *Drosophila melanogaster* drastically disrupt circadian rhythms. *J. Biol. Rhythms* 4:1–27

58. Renn SCP, Park JH, Rosbash M, Hall JC, Taghert PH. 1999. A pdf neuropeptide gene mutation and ablation of PDF neurons each cause severe abnormalities of behavioral circadian rhythms in *Drosophila. Cell* 99:791–802

59. Stanewsky R, Frisch B, Brandes C, Hamblen-Coyle M, Rosbash M, Hall JC. 1997. Temporal and spatial expression

patterns of transgenes containing increasing amounts of the *Drosophila* clock gene *period* and a *lacZ* reporter: mapping elements of the PER protein involved in circadian cycling. *J. Neurosci.* 17:676–96

60. Kaneko M, Helfrich-Forster C, Hall JC. 1997. Spatial and temporal expression of the *period* and *timeless* genes in the developing nervous system of *Drosophila*: newly identified pacemaker candidates and novel features of clock gene product cycling. *J. Neurosci.* 17:6745–60

61. Sawin EP, Dowse HB, Hamblen-Coyle MJ, Hall JC, Sokolowski MB. 1994. A lack of locomoter activity rhythms in *Drosophila melanogaster* larvae. *Insect Behav.* 7:249–62

62. Sehgal A, Price J, Young MW. 1992. Ontogeny of a biological clock in *Drosophila melanogaster*. *Proc. Natl. Acad. Sci. USA* 89:1423–27

63. Kaneko M, Hamblen MJ, Hall JC. 2000. Involvement of the *period* gene in developmental time-memory: effect of the *per^short* mutation on phase shifts induced by light pulses delivered to *Drosophila* larvae. *J. Biol. Rhythms* 15:13–30

64. Lee C, Parikh V, Itsukaichi T, Bae K, Edery I. 1996. Resetting the *Drosophila* clock by photic regulation of PER and a PER-TIM complex. *Science* 271:1740–44

65. Suri V, Zuwei Q, Hall JC, Rosbash M. 1998. Evidence that the TIM light response is relevant to light-induced phase shifts in *Drosophila melanogaster*. *Neuron* 21:225–34

66. Schotland P, Hunter-Ensor M, Lawrence T, Sehgal A. 2000. Altered entrainment and feedback loop function effected by a mutant period protein. *J. Neurosci.* 20:958–68

67. Naidoo N, Song W, Hunter-Ensor M, Sehgal A. 1999. A role for the proteasome in the light response of the timeless clock protein. *Science* 285:1737–41

68. Stanewsky R, Kaneko M, Emery P, Beretta B, Wager-Smith K, et al. 1998. The *cry^b*

mutation identifies cryptochrome as a circadian photoreceptor in *Drosophila*. *Cell* 95:681–92

69. Emery P, Venus W, Kaneko M, Hall JC, Rosbach M. 1998. CRY, a *Drosophila* clock and light-regulated cryptochrome, is a major contributor to circadian rhythm resetting and photosensitivity. *Cell* 95:669–679

70. Emery P, Frisch B, Hamblen-Coyle MJ, Rosbash M, Hall JC. 2000. dCRY is a unique *Drosophila* circadian photoreceptor. *Nature* 404:45–57

71. Emery P, Stanewsky R, Helfrich-Forster C, Emery-Le M, Hall JC, Rosbach M. 2000. *Drosophila* CRY is a deep brain ciracadian photoreceptor. *Neuron* 26:493–504

72. Ceriani MF, Darlington TK, Staknis D, Mas P, Petti AA, Weitz CJ, Kay SA. 1999. Light-dependent sequestration of timeless by cryptochrome. *Science* 285:553–56

73. Zuker CS. 1996. The biology of vision in *Drosophila*. *Proc. Natl. Acad. Sci. USA* 93:571–76

74. Wheeler DA, Hamblen-Coyle MJ, Dushay MS, Hall JC. 1993. Behavior in light:dark cycles of *Drosophila* mutants that are arrhythmic, blind or both. *J. Biol. Rhythms* 8:67–94

75. Liu Y, Garceau N, Loros J, Dunlap J. 1997. Thermally regulated translational control of FRQ mediates aspects of temperature responses in the *Neurospora* circadian clock. *Cell* 89:477–86

76. Sidote D, Majercak J, Parikh V, Edery I. 1998. Differential effects of light and heat on the *Drosophila* circadian clock proteins PER and TIM. *Mol. Cell. Biol.* 18:2004–13

77. Majercak J, Sidote D, Hardin PE, Edery I. 1999. How a circadian clock adapts to seasonal decreases in temperature and day length. *Neuron* 24:219–30

78. Konopka RJ, Pittendrigh C, Orr D. 1989. Reciprocal behavior associated with altered homeostasis and photosensitivity of *Drosophila* clock mutants. *J. Neurogenet.* 6:1–10

79. Huang ZJ, Curtin KD, Rosbash M. 1995. PER protein interactions and temperature compensation of a circadian clock in Drosophila. *Science* 267:1169–72

80. Sawyer LA, Hennessy JM, Peixoto AA, Rosato E, Parkinson H, et al. 1997. Natural variation in a *Drosophila* clock gene and temperature compensation. *Science* 278:2117–20

81. Peixoto A, Hennessy JM, Townson I, Hasan G, Rosbash M, et al. 1998. Molecular coevolution within a *Drosophila* clock gene. *Proc. Natl. Acad. Sci. USA* 95:4475–80

82. Ousley A, Zafarullah K, Chen Y, Emerson M, Hickman L, Sehgal A. 1998. Conserved regions of the *timeless* (*tim*) clock gene in *Drosophila* analyzed through phylogenetic and functional studies. *Genetics* 148:815–25

83. Myers MP, Rothenflugh A, Chang M, Young MW. 1997. Comparison of chromosomal DNA composing timeless in *Drosophila melanogaster* and *D. virilis* suggests a new conserved structure for the TIMELESS protein. *Nucleic Acids Res.* 25:4710–14

84. Colot HV, Hall JC, Rosbash M. 1988. Interspecific comparison of the *period* gene of *Drosophila* reveals large blocks on nonconserved coding DNA. *EMBO J* 7:3929–37

85. Reppert SM, Tsai T, Roca AL, Sauman I. 1994. Cloning of a structural and functional homolog of the circadian clock gene *period* from the giant silkmoth *Antheraea pernyi*. *Neuron* 13:1167–76

86. Piccin A, Couchman M, Clayton JD, Chalmers D, Costa R, Kyriacou CP. 2000. The clock gene *period* of the housefly, *Musca domestica*, rescues behavioral rhythmicity in *Drosophila melanogaster*: evidence for intermolecular coevolution. *Genetics* 154:747–58

87. Rothenflugh A, Young MW, Saez L. 2000. A TIMELESS-independent function for PERIOD proteins in the *Drosophila* clock. *Neuron* 26:505–14

88. Andretic R, Chaney S, Hirsh J. 1999. Requirement of circadian genes for cocaine sensitization in *Drosophila*. *Science* 285:1066–68

89. Livingstone MS, Tempel BL. 1983. Genetic dissection of monoamine neurotransmitter synthesis in *Drosophila*. *Nature* 305:67–70

90. Hendricks JC, Finn SM, Panchkeri KA, Chawkin J, Williams JA, et al. 2000. Rest in Drosophila is a sleep-like state. *Neuron* 25:129–38

91. Kyriacou CP, Hall JC. 1980. Circadian rhythm mutations in *Drosophila melanogaster* affect short-term fluctuations in the male's courtship song. *Proc. Natl. Acad. Sci. USA* 11:6729–33

91a. Kaneko M, Hall JC. 2000. Neuroanatomy of cells expressing clock genes in *Drosophila*: Transgenic manipulation of the *period* and *timeless* genes to mark the perikarya of circadian pacemaker neurons and their projections. *J. Comp. Neurol.* 422:66–94

91b. Reppert SM, Weaver DR. 2001. Molecular analysis of mammalian circadian rhythms. *Annu. Rev. Physiol.* 63:In press

92. Allada R, White NE, So WV, Hall JC, Rosbash M. 1998. A mutant Drosophila homolog of mammalian *Clock* disrupts circadian rhythms and transcription of *period* and *timeless*. *Cell* 93:791–804

93. Rutila JE, Suri V, Le M, Venus So W, Rosbash M, Hall JC. 1998. CYCLE is a second bHLH-PAS clock protein essential for circadian rhythmicity and transcription of *Drosophila period* and *timeless*. *Cell* 93:805–14

94. Darlington TK, Wagner-Smith K, Ceriani MF, Staknis D, Gekakis N, et al. 1998. Closing the circadian loop: clock-induced transcription of its own inhibitors *per* and *tim*. *Science* 280:1599–603

95. Bae K, Lee C, Sidote D, Chuang KY, Edery I. 1998. Circadian regulation of a

Drosophila homolog of the mammalian *Clock* gene: PER and TIM function as positive regulators. *Mol. Cell. Biol.* 18:6142–51

96. Lee C, Bae K, Edery I. 1999. PER and TIM inhibit the DNA binding activity of a *Drosophila* CLOCK-CYC/dBMAL1. Heterodimer without disrupting formation of the heterodimer: a basis for circadian transcription. *Mol. Cell. Biol.* 19:5316–25

97. Lee C, Bae K, Edery I. 1998. The *Drosophila* CLOCK protein undergoes daily rhythms in abundance, phosphorylation and interactions with the PER-TIM complex. *Neuron* 21:857–67

98. Bae K, Lee C, Hardin PE, Edery I. 2000. dCLOCK is present in limiting amounts and likely mediates daily interactions between the dCLOCK-CYC transcription factor and the PER-TIM complex. *J. Neurosci.* 20:1746–53

99. Glossop NRJ, Lyons LC, Hardin PE. 1999. Interlocked feedback loops within the *Drosophila* circadian oscillator. *Science* 286:766–68

100. Blau J, Young MW. 1999. Cycling *vrille* expression is required for a functional *Drosophila* clock. *Cell* 99:661–71

101. Kloss B, Price JP, Saez L, Blau J, Rothenflugh A, et al. 1998. The *Drosophila* clock gene *double-time* encodes a protein closely related to human casein kinase I. *Cell* 94:97–107

102. Zilian O, Frei E, Burke R, Brentrup D, Gutjhar T, et al. 1999. *double-time* is identical to *discs overgrown*, which is required for cell survival, proliferation and growth arrest in *Drosophila* imaginal discs. *Development* 126:5409–20

103. George H, Terracol R. 1997. The *vrille* gene of *Drosophila* is a maternal enhancer of *decapentaplegic* and encodes a new member of the bZIP family of transcription factors. *Genetics* 146:1345–63

104. Rao KR, Riehm JP. 1993. Pigment-

dispersing hormones. *Ann. NY Acad. Sci.* 680:78–88

105. Helfrich-Forster C. 1995. The *period* clock gene is expressed in central nervous system neurons which also produce a neuropeptide that reveals the projections of circadian pacemaker cells within the brain of *Drosophila melanogaster. Proc. Natl. Acad. Sci. USA* 92:612–16

106. Park JH, Hall JC. 1998. Isolation and chronobiological analysis of a neuropeptide pigment-dispersing factor gene in *Drosophila melanogaster. J. Biol. Rhythms* 13:219–28

107. Park JH, Helfrich-Forster C, Lee G, Liu L, Rosbash M, Hall JC. 2000. Differential regulation of circadian pacemaker output by separate clock genes in *Drosophila. Proc. Natl. Acad. Sci. USA* 97:3608–13

108. Helfrich-Forster C, Tauber M, Park JH, Muhlig-Versen M, Schneuwly S, Hofbauer A. 2000. Ectopic expression of the neuropeptide pigment-dispersing factor alters behavioral rhythms in *Drosophila melanogaster. J. Neurosci.* 20:3339–53

109. Handler A, Konopka R. 1979. Transplantation of a circadian pacemaker in *Drosophila. Nature* 279:236–38

110. Plautz JD, Kaneko M, Hall JC, Kay SA. 1997. Independent photoreceptive circadian clocks throughout *Drosophila. Science* 278:1632–35

111. Sakamoto K, Nagase T, Fukui H, Horikawa K, Okada T, et al. 1998. Multitissue circadian expression of Rat period homolog (*rPer2*) mRNA is governed by the mammalian circadian clock, the suprachiasmatic nucleus in the brain. *J. Biol. Rhythms* 273:27039–42

112. Yamazaki S, Numano R, Abe M, Hida A, Takahashi R, et al. 2000. Resetting central and peripheral circadian oscillators in transgenic rats. *Science* 288:682–85

113. Giebultowicz JM, Stanewsky R, Hall JC, Hege DM. 2000. Transplanted *Drosophila* excretory tubules maintain

circadian clock cycling out of phase with the host. *Curr. Biol.* 10:107–10

114. Van Gelder RN, Bae H, Palazzolo MJ, Krasnow MA. 1995. Extent and character of circadian gene expression in *Drosophila melanogaster*: identification of twenty oscillating mRNAs in the fly head. *Curr. Biol.* 5:1424–36

115. Van Gelder RN, Krasnow MA. 1996. A novel circadianly expressed *Drosophila melanogaster* gene dependent on the *period* gene for its rhythmic expression. *EMBO J.* 15:1625–31

116. Rouyer F, Rachidi M, Pikielny C, Rosbash M. 1997. A new gene encoding a putative transcription factor regulated by the *Drosophila* circadian clock. *EMBO J.* 16:3944–54

117. Sarov-Blat L, So WV, Liu L, Rosbash M. 2000. The *Drosophila* takeout gene is a novel molecular link between circadian rhythms and feeding behavior. *Cell* 101:647–56

118. Newby LM, Jackson FR. 1991. *Drosophila* ebony mutants have altered circadian activity rhythms but normal eclosion rhythm. *J. Neurogenet.* 7:85–101

119. Newby LM, Jackson FR. 1993. A new biological rhythm mutant of *Drosophila melanogaster* that identifies a gene with an essential embryonic function. *Genetics* 135:1077–90

120. McNeil GP, Zhang X, Roberts M, Jackson FR. 1999. Maternal function of a retroviral-type zinc-finger protein is essential for *Drosophila* development. *Dev. Genet.* 25:387–96

121. Newby LM, Jackson FR. 1996. Regulation of a specific circadian clock output pathway by lark, a putative RNA-binding protein with repressor activity. *J. Neurobiol.* 31:117–28

122. McNeil GP, Zhang X, Genova G, Jackson FR. 1998. A molecular rhythm mediating circadian clock output in *Drosophila*. *Neuron* 20:297–303

123. Tublitz NJ, Copenhauer PF, Taghert PH, Truman JW. 1986. Peptidergic regulation of behavior: an identified neuron approach. *Trends Neurosci.* 9:359–63

124. Levine JD, Casey CI, Kalderon DD, Jackson FR. 1994. Altered circadian pacemaker functions and cyclic AMP rhythms in the *Drosophila* learning mutant *dunce*. *Neuron* 13:1167–76

125. Majercak J, Kalderon D, Edery I. 1997. *Drosophila melanogaster* deficient in protein kinase A manifests behavior-specific arrhythmia but normal clock function. *Mol. Cell. Biol.* 17:5915–22

126. Belvin MP, Zhou H, Yin JC. 1999. The *Drosophila* dCREB2 gene affects the circadian clock. *Neuron* 22:777–87

127. Eberl DF, Perkins LA, Engelstein M, Hilliker AJ, Perrimon N. 1992. Genetic and developmental analysis of polytene section 17 of the X chromosome of *Drosophila melanogaster*. *Genetics* 130:569–83

128. Finn JT, Krautwurst D, Schroeder JE, Chen TY, Reed RR, Yau KW. 1998. Functional co-assembly among subunits of cyclic-nucleotide-activated, nonselective cation channels, and across species from nematode to human. *Biophys. J.* 74:1333–45

129. de Rooij J, Zwartkruis FJT, Verheijen MHG, Cool RH, Nijman SMB, et al. 1998. Epac is a Rap1 guanine-nucleotide-exchange factor directly activated by cyclic AMP. *Nature* 396:474–77

130. Hariharan IK, Carthew RW, Rubin GM. 1991. The *Drosophila* roughened mutation: activation of a Rap homolog disrupts eye development and interferes with cell determination. *Cell* 67:717–22

131. Shaw PJ, Cirelli C, Greenspan RJ, Tononi G. 2000. Correlates of sleep and waking in *Drosophila melanogaster*. *Science* 287:1834–37

132. Eskin A. 1979. Identification and physiology of circadian pacemakers. *Fed. Proc.* 38:2570–72

Annu. Rev. Physiol. 2001. 63:757–94

GENETIC AND MOLECULAR ANALYSIS OF CIRCADIAN RHYTHMS IN *NEUROSPORA*

Jennifer J Loros[1] and Jay C Dunlap[2]

*Departments of [1]Biochemistry and [2]Genetics, Dartmouth Medical School, Hanover,
New Hampshire 03755; e-mail: jennifer.loros@dartmouth.edu;
jay.c.dunlap@dartmouth.edu*

Key Words *frq, wc-1, wc-2*, clock genes

■ **Abstract** Over the course of the past 40 years *Neurospora* has become a well-known and uniquely tractable model system for the analysis of the molecular basis of eukaryotic circadian oscillatory systems. Molecular bases for the period length and sustainability of the rhythm, light, and temperature resetting of the circadian system and for gating of light input and light effects are becoming understood, and *Neurospora* promises to be a suitable system for examining the role of coupled feedback loops in the clock. Many of these insights have shown or foreshadow direct parallels in mammalian systems, including the mechanism of light entrainment, the involvement of PAS:PAS heterodimers as transcriptional activators in essential clock-associated feedback loops, and dual role of FRQ in the loop as an activator and a repressor; similarities extend to the primary sequence level in at least one case, that of WC-1 and BMAL1. Work on circadian output in *Neurospora* has identified more than a dozen regulated genes and has been at the forefront of studies aimed at understanding clock control of gene expression.

DEFINITION

"A circadian rhythm is an oscillation in a biochemical, physiological, or behavioral function which under conditions in nature has a period of exactly 24 hours, in phase with the environmental light and darkness, but which continues to oscillate with a period of approximately but usually not exactly 24 hours." (1, 1a)

INTRODUCTION

Circadian rhythms and the ensembles of cellular oscillators that underlie them have been appreciated as an adaptive aspect of living things for several centuries. They were first described by observing the leaf movements of higher plants (2), but the extension of the basic observation to similarly timed physiological and behavioral events in humans was almost immediate, as seen in the oft-quoted reference to

0066-4278/01/0315-0757$14.00

De Mairan's work (3). Circadian rhythms represent a common aspect of cellular and organismal organization, a way for organisms with life spans that are long compared with the length of a day, or with inescapable rhythmic environments, to cope with the robustly rhythmic nature of life on earth. These organisms are not unusual and are found all major assemblages of organisms except the Archaebacteria (4). Circadian rhythms represent the preponderance of rhythmic phenomena studied from nature; however, there are other ways to cope with a rhythmic environment: responding directly to environmental changes, use of hourglass-type timers that are tripped by environmental transitions, or use of noncompensated developmental timers, and not all biological cycles are truly circadian in nature.

In no organism do we understand enough about the general assembly of a circadian system to be able to seriously contemplate an in vitro or even an in vivo, e.g. in yeast, reconstruction of a circadian clock. However, work to date does allow some generalizations. First, the clock entails molecular feedback loops that involve nonessential genes whose functions are devoted solely to circadian timekeeping; clocks are adaptive and not essential to life (5, 6). Second (7–9), the circadian system probably involves the interaction of multiple feedback loops; at present we can describe only a few. Third, although the capacity for circadian timekeeping probably arose more than once in evolution, there is much to suggest that it arose only a few times and that the clocks in those organisms among the crown eukaryotes that share a most recent common ancestor, the higher plants, fungi, and animals, share elements and similar components in the assembly and operation of their clocks. In the pre-molecular era, the similarities in the overt characteristics of these rhythms—a period length of about a day (or more generally ~15–35 h in mutants) that is compensated so that it remains about the same in different temperatures or nutritional states, with a phase that is set by pertinent environmental cues—prompted speculation that the underlying biochemical basis of the rhythms might be the same in all organisms. This has been confirmed, at least among the eukaryotes, with a stream of functional and sequence-based similarities that have emerged as the molecular bases of circadian oscillatory systems are coming to be understood. Initially, insights about eukaryotic clocks arose chiefly in *Neurospora* and *Drosophila*, but more recent work with mice and higher plants has reinforced the similarities in the components, assembly, operation, and internal regulation of eukaryotic circadian timekeepers. A synopsis of these similarities is shown in Figure 1 and can serve as a reference point for understanding the overall organization of feedback loops that form a part of all known eukaryotic clocks.

This review focuses on *Neurospora*. We introduce this experimental system and provide some historical context for why *Neurospora* was a great choice as a malleable system for discovering how clocks are assembled. After a brief overview of the means by which rhythms are analyzed, we concentrate on what is known about how the *Neurospora* clock works, including a focus on recent data. We also discuss what is known about output and the regulation of overt rhythms in this organism, with a short digression beforehand on non-circadian rhythms in fungi.

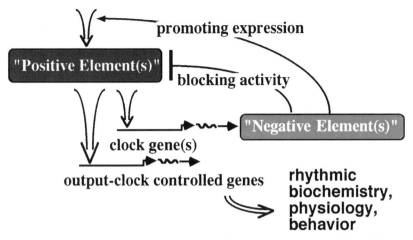

Positive elements in eukaryotic circadian loops:

WC-1 and WC-2 in *Neurospora*
CLK and CYC in *Drosophila*
CLOCK and BMAL1 in mammals

Negative elements in eukaryotic circadian loops:

FRQ in *Neurospora*
PER and TIM in *Drosophila*
CRY1 and CRY2 and perhaps mPERs
in mammals

Figure 1   Some common elements in the clock-associated transcription/translation feedback loops of eukaryotic circadian oscillators. See text for details (adapted from 4).

THE *NEUROSPORA* CIRCADIAN SYSTEM

Neurospora has been one of the systems of choice for genetic and molecular dissection of complex biological regulatory phenomena for well over 50 years (10). Studies with some of the first auxotrophs by Beadle & Tatum gave rise to the one-gene-one-enzyme hypothesis (and a Nobel Prize for them), and *Neurospora* was used to study the first conditional mutants, translational suppression, channeling of pathway-specific enzymes, coordinate regulation of unlinked genes, and a host of more genetic observations (10, and references therein).

In Tatum's laboratory and later in Ryan's, there developed a need to accurately determine growth rates of different strains; thus was the race tube born. Race tubes are glass tubes one half to three-quarters of an inch in diameter and from one to three feet long that are bent up at a 45° angle at both ends. With these ends held up, the tube will hold an agar medium for growth. Apparently, thousands of strains were screened and rhythmic growth patterns with varying periodicity on some media or in some strains were often seen (A Chovnick, personal communication). With no reason to keep these strains or the data concerning rhythmicity, this observation was dismissed, but the race tube stayed.

In the larger context of filamentous fungal biology, such rhythmic growth patterns are well known and have been observed in the growth of a wide variety of fungi on petri dishes (2). Suffice it to say (discussed in detail below) that most rhythmic growth patterns of fungi are not circadian, including some in *Neurospora*. For instance, *Aspergillus* sp. (often the black-spored *Aspergillus niger*) is endemic to most air handling systems in university laboratories, and it is not uncommon to find a petri dish left open long enough to become contaminated and grow a culture that forms concentric rings around the point of contamination (= inoculation). However, these growth rhythms are generally not circadian in that they fail most or all of the circadian criteria: They are often not light-entrainable, rarely have period lengths in the circadian range (often over 60 h and in many cases more than 100 h), and they are almost never compensated against changes in temperature or nutrition. Although studied years ago in a variety of fungi (e.g. 11–13), this train of research lost momentum as the distinctions between these rhythms and more classical circadian rhythms mounted. However, there was general awareness of rhythms in fungi, and the technology to analyze them was available in the 1950s. The first report of a rhythm in *Neurospora* (14) used a gene called *patch* that arose in a *pro*-1 (proline auxotrophic) background; this observation remained unexamined until one of several connections made Pittendrigh aware of the potential of the system. As a student with Dobzhansky at Columbia, Pittendrigh was well acquainted with Ryan who would have made him aware of race tubes, and he almost certainly saw his friend Perkins using race tubes in 1947. Perkins became a distinguished *Neurospora* geneticist and remained Pittendrigh's friend. Later, when Pittendrigh was at Princeton, he would also have known a student of John Bonner's, D Stadler, whose note on the genetics of *patch* followed immediately after his report, in the same 1959 issue of *Nature*, on the *Neurospora* rhythm. Pittendrigh described the true circadian nature of this rhythm (15), and noted, "The *Neurospora* system appears potentially valuable for an attack on the basic problem of the nature of oscillations that constitute the circadian clock."

Although described and correctly identified as a circadian rhythm, genetic crosses and detailed analyses of strains was not Pittendrigh's metier, so taming of the system was left to others and was chiefly carried out by Sargent and colleagues who identified the mutant strain containing *band* (*bd*) (16), a mutant allele that clarifies the rhythm and that is still included in virtually all analyses of rhythms in *Neurospora*. Sargent and several colleagues systematically determined the growth media and conditions that promoted the best expression of the circadian rhythm (17), provided the first light- and temperature-phase response curves (18, 19), provided biochemical clues as to the identity of the photoreceptor (20, 21), and began to study the biochemistry of rhythmic clock output (22, 23). During this period there was the first sorting out of circadian versus non-circadian rhythms in *Neurospora*. Initially there was some confusion, with strains or genes that promoted the expression of non-circadian rhythms being given names like *clock* (24), but within a few years, nearly all members of the community were aware of the distinction. Both circadian and non-circadian rhythms were described in the same strains (25), and the phenotype generally tamed. Credit for the initial development of *Neurospora* clock genetics goes to Feldman who, in the late 1960s (while a contemporary of Konopka's at CalTech), began looking for circadian clock mutants in *Neurospora* (26) and eventually identified *frequency* (*frq*) (27) and a number of other clock-affecting genes (see below). The phenotype he used was based on the race tube assay, but there are now several ways of assessing circadian function.

Assays of Circadian Clock Function in *Neurospora*

Clock assays are typically carried out in hollow glass tubes that are partially filled with a solid medium, although petri dishes or capped, horizontal 150-mm test tubes can also been used. The developmental switch for the production of macroconidiophores or conidia is activated in the late subjective night of the circadian cycle, eventually resulting in the production of conidial spores for a defined proportion of the day (16) (See Asexual Development below.) Once the asexual pathway is initiated, this developmental process proceeds with kinetics dependent on non-clock factors such as culture and strain type (28). The signal for development is switched off some time later in the middle of the subjective circadian day, and undifferentiated filamentous mycelia again predominate. At the cellular level, the clock is responsible for a major cellular remodeling, the activation of the large number of genes and gene products necessary for the assembly of the components of the aerial hyphae and conidia instead of surface hyphae. This results in a conidial banding pattern seen in wild-type *Neurospora*. Elevated levels of CO_2 in race tubes suppress conidiation and therefore mask this banding pattern. For this reason, all commonly used laboratory stocks carry a mutation in the *band* gene (*bd*) (16) to alleviate the CO_2 masking effect. In some laboratories as well as the classroom, researchers and instructors prefer to limit the wind-borne dispersal of fungal spores as students attempt sterile transfers (for a brief discussion of *Neurospora* in the classroom, see Reference 29), thereby reducing this potential source of contamination. For this, genetically mutant strains bearing the *csp-1*, *csp-2* (conidial separation), or *eas* (easily wettable) mutations are used in conjunction with the *bd* mutation.

The central assumption in the use of the race tube assay to estimate circadian period length and phase is that the linear growth rate is close to constant. This is because the position of the growth front is marked once per day, and calculations assume a linear relationship between distance along the tube and time elapsed. Although all cultures tend to grow more slowly during the period of time when conidiation is occurring, the assumption is, as a first approximation (within 10% or so), true for growth of most strains including circadian rhythm mutants (16). However, in some slow-growing strains such as *chol*-1, changes in growth can vary over 200% from day to day depending on the developmental state of the culture during that period of time (see below).

While observation of the periodicity of asexual development is the historical assay used to monitor the clock in *Neurospora*, in recent years molecular assays for clock function have been developed that include the monitoring of the molecular cycling of mRNAs and proteins that are either under control of the oscillator or part of the clock mechanism itself (30–32). These assays arose from the development of liquid culture methods, resulting in the production of rhythmic mycelial cultures that could then be harvested for biochemical analysis (33, 34). Generally, mycelia are grown in a high-concentration glucose medium in standing cultures, disks are cut from the resulting hyphal mat, and then transferred to a low-growth medium. Disks can be held in starvation conditions, or under supplement limitation if an auxotrophic strain is used, for several days with uniformly low respiratory output but a normally functioning clock. Individual disks cut with a cork borer are placed in the medium in the dark and progressively harvested at times throughout the following circadian cycles (33, 34). This method was adapted for the isolation of time-specific mRNAs that were used for subtractive hybridizations (30) and was later modified so that all cultures at harvest would be approximately synchronous for developmental age while at the same time varied for circadian time (35), thereby avoiding complications of introducing the variable of growth stage to experimental protocols. A virtue of this method of following the rhythm for morphological or slow-growth mutants is that it obviates the need to use the race tube assay.

Using these assays, a number of rhythm-affecting alleles have been identified. Table 1 is an update of that provided in 1993 (8) and provides a list of mutant alleles in *Neurospora* that have arisen from untargeted screens or from targeted knockouts. (Not included are a number of alleles of *frq* and the *wc* genes produced in vitro for specific needs.) It should be noted that, although Feldman's original screen for rhythm mutants required an altered but still functional clock, more recent screens (J Loros & J Dunlap, unpublished; H Nakashima, personal communication) are based on unbiased screens for arrhythmic mutants that require only the ability to sustain reasonably healthy and steady linear growth on the race tube. These screens have turned up additional alleles of many of the same genes found previously by other means, including *frq* and *wc-1*. Although the repeated identification of the same genes in different screens and laboratories suggests that we could be approaching saturation, this seems unlikely; it is clear that there are additional genes left to be identified. Beyond this, first it is obvious that several genes have turned up more than once and appear to be either hot spots for mutation and/or central for clock function. Second, although it is clearly possible to affect only period length, several genes including *frq* and *wc-2* have alleles affecting both period length and temperature compensation, and one recently identified gene (*vvd*) (36) has a primary affect on light resetting and phase with only a small lengthening affect on period. Third, some genes have only very small affects on the clock and may be acting pleiotropically, and alleles of other genes such as *chol-1* allow the visualization of growth rhythms reminiscent of those mentioned above that lack most circadian characteristics. Conditional clock mutants exist: Ongoing screens for temperature-conditional clock mutations in the laboratories of Nakashima and Feldman identified an allele of *frq* (*frq11*) (37), *prd-6* (38), and several genes of unknown function (39). Although additional rhythm assays now exist based on the cycling of molecular markers, the ease of the race tube assay, combined with the continuing likelihood of finding something of interest in a routine screen, have conspired to keep investigators from branching out to other screens. Still, the reliance on the race tube and plate assays that require growth has created problems, some of which are based on the observation cited above that non-circadian rhythms in growth can also be observed during growth on surfaces.

For instance, a nutritional condition (like addition of sorbose) (25) or a secondary mutation that affected growth rate could phenocopy a circadian rhythm mutation, although the expression of this circadian-like rhythm phenotype would depend on use of the race tube assay. Because the biochemistry of the clock is based on feedbacks that happen within the cell, genuine circadian rhythm mutations should show their affects equally well whether assayed on race tubes or in liquid culture, and this might be a useful secondary test to determine whether putative rhythm mutations or rhythm-affecting mutations are really affecting the circadian clock rather than a non-circadian oscillatory phenomenon.

The General Layout of Molecular Elements Within the *Neurospora* Circadian System

Although the molecular identities of many of the genes in Table 1 are not known, and the molecular identities of others have not been informative yet as to the molecular mechanism of the clock, present information has allowed the development of an internally consistent view of parts of the circadian system that are conserved among the other eukaryotic systems studied to date.

It is traditional for heuristic reasons to view the system as the sum of component parts governing input, the oscillator(s), and output, although this view is retained only as a convenient "straw man." It has been surmised for some time (e.g. 40) that "at the molecular level, the circadian clock will be found to be the result of coupling multiple, presumably intracellular oscillators so that their collective output is robust and has a period length of about a day" (7). Beyond this it is clear that as the circadian system actually operates there are multiple regulatory connections linking the central oscillator(s) with both input and output, linking output with input, and internal oscillators among themselves. To the extent that each of these interconnections imparts something to the operation of the whole, the elimination of any connection must have an effect on the operation of the whole. This elimination, through pharmacology or by genetic lesion, should manifest itself as a change in some clock characteristic such as period length, entrainability, phase, and, perhaps, also as a partial loss of temperature compensation. In this context there are a plethora of genes potentially identifiable as clock genes in that they will affect the observable operation of the clock. Given the relative strength of our insights into clock mechanism now, as distinct from 20 years ago, the usefulness of a strict application of the term clock gene needs to be re-evaluated. Two decades ago, we were all trying to penetrate the molecular machinery required to run a circadian clock. Now that we have gotten within the circadian system and can discern qualitative differences in the importance of some genes and proteins, it may be that the phrase has outlived its usefulness in terms of apportioning significance to novel genes. We are now in a position to analyze, at the molecular level, how novel gene products affect the operation of existing feedback loops that are known to be required for normal clock function. As we do this, some clock genes (i.e. genes whose mutation affects the clock) will be found to be acting pleiotropically, or in an organism-specific manner, and will not to be very informative as to how

TABLE 1 Nuclear genes affecting expression of *Neurospora* rhythms

Name of gene	Abbreviation; allele name	Period length (h) (25°C)	Comments; other clock properties affected	Reference
Arginine-13	*arg-13*	19[a,b]		97
Chain elongation	*cel*	Variable[a,c]	Temperature compensation	101
Choline-1	*chol-1*	Conditional-NC[a,d]		106
Chlorpromazine Resistance-1	*cpz-1*		Period shortened by chlorpromazine addition	141
Chlorpromazine Resistance-2	*cpz-2*		Period shortened by chlorpromazine addition	141
Chrono	*chr*	23.5	Temperature compensation	142, 143, 144
Cytochrome a-5	*cya-5*	19[b]	Cytochrome aa3-deficient	145
Cytochrome b-2	*cyb-2*	18[b]	Cytochrome b-deficient	145
Cytochrome b-3	*cyb-3*	20[b]	Cytochrome b-deficient	146
Cysteine-4	*cys-4*	19[a,b]		144, 147
Cysteine-9	*cys-9*	Short, variable[a,d]		99
Cysteine-12	*cys-12*	19[a,b]		144, 147
Cytochrome-4	*cyt-4*	20[b]	Cytochromes aa3- and b-deficient	146
Female fertility-1 (allelic to glycerol phosphate-3)	*ff-1 (glp-3)*	19[b]		145

Frequency[e]	*frq1*	16		27
	frq2 (same as *frq4* and *frq6*)[f]	19		27, 148
	frq3	24	Temperature compensation	27, 148, 155
	frq7 (same as *frq8* and *cla-1*)[g]	29	Temperature compensation	27, 148, 155
	frq9	Conditional-NC, variable	Frame shift mutant; temperature compensation, nutritional compensation, entrainment	44, 90
	frq10	Conditional-NC, variable	*frq*-null created by targeted gene replacement with *hph* via DNA transformation; temperature compensation, nutritional compensation,	42
	frq11	Conditional-NC	Rhythmic only at temperatures below ~27°C	37, 31, 87
Maternally inherited	*mi* (*mi-2, mi-3, mi-5*)	18–19[b]	Mitochondrial cytochrome oxidase subunit 1-deficient	145
Oligomycin resistant	*oli*	18–19[b]	Mitochondrial ATPase, subunit 9	149

(*Continued*)

TABLE 1 (*Continued*)

Name of gene	Abbreviation; allele name	Period length (h)	Comments; other clock properties affected	Reference
Phenylalanine-1	*phe-1*	19[a,b]	Ergosterol synthesis-deficient	146
Period-1	*prd-1*	26	Temperature compensation	144, 150
Period-2	*prd-2*	25.5		142, 144, 148
Period-3	*prd-3*	25	Temperature compensation	142, 144, 148
Period-4	*prd-4*	18	Temperature compensation	142, 144, 148
Period-6	*prd-6*	Short	Temperature sensitive; epistatic to *prd-2*	38
Polymerase-1	*pol-1*	Long		151
Rhythm-1	*rhy-1*	Conditional		152
Spermidine-3	*spe-3*		Spermidine synthase; mutation suppresses *cpz* (see above)	153
Unknown-10	*un-10*	Long		90
Unknown-16	*un-16*	Long, conditional	Temperature-sensitive mutation	39
Unknown-18	*un-18*	Long, conditional	Temperature-sensitive mutation, RNA polymerase I subunit	39

Vivid	*vvd*	23	Phase mutant—output delayed 4 h; insertion, translocation, targeted replacement alleles	36
White collar-1	*wc-1^null*	Conditional-NC		43
	wc-1^ERS3	Conditional-NC		
White collar-2	*wc-2^null*	Conditional-NC		45
	wc-2^ER24	Long (28 h at 25°C)	Temperature compensation	

aThis strain was originally isolated as an auxotroph. Period length is gradually altered by increasing the degree of starvation for the required supplement.

bWhile the period lengths in these strains are measurably shorter than wild type under the same experimental conditions, the small magnitude of the differences, combined with the degree of variation obtainable in wild-type strains just from manipulation of growth conditions, raises questions about the biological significance of these period differences.

cMutation of this locus renders the period length of the clock manipulable by changes in the fatty acid composition of the medium.

dConditional-NC refers to strains that are under some conditions arrhythmic and that display noncircadian (very long period length, not entrainable by light to 24 h, etc) rhythms under other conditions.

eMany different alleles of *frq* have been derived from targeted manipulation of the gene followed by reinsertion into the genome. With the exception of *frq^10*, these are not listed here and the list is confined to alleles that have turned up in screens for rhythm-affecting mutations. See text for more detail.

fAlthough isolated independently, these alleles are genotypically identical (i.e. have the same DNA sequence) and therefore are completely redundant (42).

gcla-1 was originally identified in a strain bearing a chromosomal translocation and was thought to be associated with a spontaneous chromosomal translocation (154). However, more recent genetic and molecular analysis of this strain has shown the clock-affecting mutation to be genetically separable for the translocation, and to be due to the identical base change seen in *frq^7* (155).

While a desire for completeness compels the listing of all mutations that have been described as having period length effects, it is highly likely that some of these have little to do with the assembly or operation of the clock, their clock affects being due to subtle changes in the metabolic state.

eukaryotic circadian rhythms actually work. Others will be generally informative, and this appears to be the case.

A number of genes giving rise to products of known biochemical function can now be fit into an internally consistent model for a feedback loop whose function is essential for normal operation of the *Neurospora* circadian clock under constant conditions in the dark. Some, e.g. *wc-1* and *wc-2*, are also required for light entrainability, a finding that should not distract from the fact that they are required for rhythmicity under constant conditions in the dark. The general pattern describing how these gene products and genes act together in the circadian system is similar in all eukaryotes studied to date, and some of the components show significant similarities at the level of amino acid sequence (41) (see below). Furthermore, the action of some of the proteins has allowed accurate descriptions and predictions for explaining general circadian properties, such as the mechanism of light resetting and maintenance of clock amplitude. There is a lot about the circadian system that we do not understand, not the least of which is how the multiple feedback loops in it interact to give rise to the circadian properties of the system. However, we want to concentrate on outlining the feedback loops we do understand and what they tell us about the operation of the clock under free-running conditions with no influence of entraining conditions of cyclic light or temperature: Genes that are essential for the maintenance of circadian rhythmicity at constant temperatures in the dark may be understood as essential for the circadian system, whatever their additional roles may be under light/dark cycles.

Feedback Between FRQ and the White Collar Complex in the **Neurospora** ***Clock***
The *Neurospora* circadian oscillator contains an auto-regulatory negative feedback cycle where the White Collar-1 (WC-1) and White Collar-2 (WC-2) proteins and both *frq* mRNA and FRQ protein serve as central components (4, 32, 42, 43) (Figure 2, see color insert). Although all components are subject to several aspects of regulation that provide the long 22-h time constant of the period and ensure robustness and sustainability to the rhythm, in brief form this feedback loop can be understood in this way: WCC, a heterodimer of WC-1 and WC-2 (the standard PAS:PAS heterodimer of eukaryotic circadian clock loops) (9), activates expression of the *frq* gene. *frq* mRNA then encodes FRQ proteins (31) that feed back to block this activation. In support of this, it is known that loss-of-function mutations in *frq, wc-1,* or *wc-2* result in loss of normal circadian rhythmicity, although non-circadian oscillations [and therefore oscillator(s)] remain in the background of at least the *frq*-nulls (42, 44) (see below). Mutations in *frq* or *wc-2* (45) that preserve sufficient function to sustain circadian rhythmicity can result in substantial period length defects (yielding periods from 16 to 29 h) and partial loss of temperature and nutritional compensation of the clock. Both *frq* mRNA and FRQ protein are rhythmically expressed daily, and FRQ protein acts to repress the abundance of its own transcript (31, 32, 46). Importantly, the rhythmic expression of *frq* appears essential for the negative feedback loop, as shown by the facts that constitutively elevated expression of *frq* results in the loss of the overt rhythm, and step changes

in *frq* expression reset the phase of the clock (32). Light and temperature, two of the most important environmental signals, reset the *Neurospora* clock by changing the levels of *frq* mRNA and FRQ protein (47, 48), as further outlined below.

Figure 2 shows the progress of the *Neurospora* clock cycle. Starting from late at night, most of the FRQ protein in the cell has been degraded and *frq* RNA levels are low but are beginning to rise, a process that will take about 10 h to reach peak. Two other players in the loop are the proteins White Collar-1 (WC-1) and White Collar-2 (WC-2); these are transcription factors containing DNA binding regions, *trans*-activation domains, and PAS domains, that form a complex (the White Collar Complex, WCC) (49, 50–53). WC-1 and WC-2 are both required for normal sustained circadian rhythmicity under constant conditions (43). The WCC binds to the promoter of the *frq* gene at two sites; binding is necessary to drive the circadian rhythm in transcription of the *frq* gene (A Froehlich, J Loros & J Dunlap, in preparation). Under the activation of the WCC, *frq* transcript is produced, and these primary transcripts are spliced in a complex manner (H Colot, J Loros & J Dunlap, in preparation) that has major effects on the proteins that can be produced. Gradually by the early morning, FRQ proteins appear (31) and soon enter the nucleus (31, 54) where specific interactions occur between FRQ and the WCC (55) (see below) that block the activity of the WCC. By midday WCC activity is declining to its lowest level just as FRQ levels rise, thereby turning down the expression of the *frq* gene. We know from reconstruction experiments where *frq* expression is driven from the inducible *qa-2* promoter that induction of high levels of *frq* expression results in a decrease in *frq* transcript levels (32), and the interaction of FRQ protein with the WCC provides a clear molecular correlate for this action. At this point, now close to midday, FRQ levels are high and continue to rise, and FRQ has entered the nucleus to bind to the WCC. We infer that this action blocks the activation of the *frq* promoter because *frq* transcript levels begin to decline even though ongoing translation causes FRQ protein levels to continue to rise; thus *frq* mRNA levels peak in the mid-morning (32, 47), about 4–6 h before the peak of total FRQ in the afternoon (31). Midday finds FRQ levels rising and WC-1 levels low. But at about this time the second role of FRQ in the cycle is manifest: FRQ promotes the synthesis of WC-1 from existing *wc-1* message (41) so that levels of WC-1 begin to rise even as phosphorylation-promoted turnover of FRQ (56) begins. Thus at close to the same time, FRQ is blocking activation of the *frq* promoter by the WCC while promoting WC-1 synthesis to increase the level of the WCC. Because WC-2 is available at constitutively high levels (55), this creates a bolus of WCC held inactive by FRQ. Finally, the processive phosphorylation of FRQ ultimately triggers its precipitous turnover (31, 56), FRQ-promoted synthesis of WC-1 is balanced by WC-1 degradation, and WC-1 levels peak in the night near to when FRQ levels drop to their low point (41). The wave of WC-1 created by the juxtaposition of FRQ-promoted WC-1 synthesis and the blockage of WCC activation creates a sharp transition, with high WCC activity to initiate the next cycle and to maintain a robust amplitude in the feedback loop. Steps in this loop that have been studied in depth within the past year are considered in greater detail below.

Phosphorylation of FRQ Contributes to the Period of the Clock   Coincident in
time with its interaction with the WCC FRQ is phosphorylated (31, 56), an event
that appears to govern the time-of-day regulation of FRQ stability and is of central
importance to the kinetics of the circadian cycle. For instance, a general kinase inhibitor, 6-dimethylaminopurine, retards the phosphorylation of FRQ in vivo, slows
its turnover, and lengthens the period of the clock in a dose-dependent manner (56).
There are multiple phosphorylation events and it appears that the phosphorylation
may be processive in that one event elicits the next (31, 56). It is also quite possible
that multiple kinases are involved in this action because there are several kinases
that can phosphorylate FRQ in vitro, including *Neurospora* casein kinase 1, an
attractive candidate given its involvement in the phosphorylation of PER and in
the *Drosophila* and mammalian clocks (57, 58). However, given the promiscuous nature of most kinases with large in vitro-prepared substrates, no significance
can be attributed to in vitro phosphorylation data such as these, and the identity
of the actual kinase(s) is not known. A first step toward the identification of the
true kinases, however, is the identification of the actual phosphorylated residues.
Liu et al (56) used a biochemical approach and localized a prominent cluster of
sites in the middle of the FRQ protein, in particular demonstrating that specific
phosphorylation at Serine 513 is critical for clock function. A single substitution
of SER513 with a non-phosphorylatable isoleucine residue greatly stabilizes FRQ
and lengthens the period of the clock from 22 to 35 h (56). Substitution of an
acidic glutamate residue for the serine, a substitution that in other proteins mimics
the phosphorylation and in FRQ might have resulted in an unstable FRQ and a
fast clock, instead yielded a FRQ of moderate stability and overt arrhythmicity.
These data strongly suggest that the issue of the FRQ kinases and FRQ phosphorylation is complicated. In any case, whereas the inhibition part of the loop
was fast, reconstruction experiments using the regulatable *qa-2* promoter to drive
FRQ expression showed that nearly 14 h are required for FRQ to become phosphorylated and to turn over, leading to the conclusion that regulation affecting
the turnover of FRQ is important in setting the period length of the clock. This
is very similar to the conclusion reached in several theoretical and experimental
studies that examined heat- and cycloheximide-induced resetting with modeling
of the *Neurospora* system (59–62). Recent data on the nuclear versus cytoplasmic
distribution of FRQ (D Denault, A Froehlich, J Loros & J Dunlap, unpublished)
have suggested that, subsequent to reaching their peak, intranuclear levels of FRQ
much more closely mimic cytoplasmic levels than had been previously thought
(e.g. 54). Thus for most of the day, *frq* transcript levels are low, and FRQ levels
both within the nucleus and in the cytoplasm are higher.

WC-1 and WC-2, Positive Elements in the Clock-Associated Feedback Loop
Thus far little has been said about the regulation of the positive elements in the
loop, WC-1 and WC-2, that interact via their PAS domains to form the WCC.
Exclusive of their role in the dark in circadian timekeeping, both are interesting
in their own right in that as the WCC complex they mediate the light-induction of

most of the known light-induced genes in *Neurospora*. Both genes were cloned by Macino and colleagues (49, 51) and shown to contain functional Zn-finger DNA-binding domains, transcriptional activation domains, and PAS domains, one in WC-2 and three in WC-1 (41, 50, 53), that mediate interactions between the proteins. Although their essential role in light-influenced processes ranging from carotenogenesis to sexual reproduction to phase resetting of the clock had been appreciated for decades, the essential role they play in the dark in the operation of the circadian clock was not shown until 1997 (43). That report provided the first precedent for the role of PAS:PAS heterodimers as activators in a circadian feedback loop, although it was followed just two weeks later by the cloning and description of the mammalian CLOCK gene (63) in which similar conclusions were independently reached. In general, the cellular circadian systems of eukaryotes all include a transcriptional/translational feedback loop in which negative elements (FRQ in *Neurospora*, PER/TIM in *Drosophila*, and CRY1, and CRY2 and perhaps the mPERs in mammals; see 63a) act to block activation by heterodimeric PAS domain-containing positive elements (WC-1/WC-2 in *Neurospora*, dCLK/CYC in *Drosophila*, and CLOCK/BMAL1 in mammals). Although all genes conferring negative elements are rhythmically expressed and diverse regulation has been reported for the positive elements, in general one of the two positive elements is rhythmically expressed and one is constitutive. This is seen in the regulation of (rhythmic) WC-1 and (constitutive) WC-2 in *Neurospora*, and determining the roles of each protein in the overall regulation of the cycle will be instructive for understanding eukaryotic clocks in general.

White Collar-1, a Sequence and Functional Homolog of Mammalian BMAL1

WC-1, a large (117-kDa) protein, is regulated posttranscriptionally at the level of synthesis (41) and also through both phosphorylation (41, 64) and protein:protein interactions (53, 55). Although the *wc-1* gene can be induced by light (49), in the dark under the constant conditions used for assay of free-running circadian rhythmicity, its expression does not vary substantially over time. Surprisingly, however, there is a clear rhythm in WC-1 protein content, suggesting that rhythmicity of WC-1 is conferred by a posttranscriptional mechanism. The rhythm in WC-1 protein content is out of phase with that seen in FRQ; WC-1 peaks in the night (41), whereas FRQ peaks late in the day (31). Mutations in *frq* influence the period of the WC-1 oscillation and the level of its expression. WC-1 levels are very low in *frq*-null strains, and when FRQ is driven from the regulatable *qa-2* promoter, it not only negatively regulates its own endogenous expression as previously shown (32), but also positively regulates WC-1 synthesis. Starting from a level of FRQ below detection prior to the addition of inducer, FRQ levels increase to a peak between 4 and 8 h after addition of inducer, and (with constant levels of *wc-1* mRNA) WC-1 levels begin to increase with a phase lag of about 4 h to a peak at 16 h. This 8-h phase delay between the FRQ and WC-1 peaks is similar to that seen in the wild-type clock (41). FRQ thus plays dual roles in this cycle and with WC-1 forms a second feedback loop in the *Neurospora* circadian system (Figure 2).

Similar interlocked loops exist in flies and mammals. The PER/TIM and CLK/CYC complexes also serve dual roles with activators repressing and repressors activating at different times of day (65, 66). Thus it is now understood that elements in the existing feedback loops thought to have an exclusively negative role also act in a positive manner to up-regulate the synthesis of one of the positive elements. These data emphasize a similar functional organization underlying the structure of circadian oscillators in fungi, flies, and mammals that promote robustness and stability of the overt rhythms. The data also suggest an answer to a central question that has always existed in efforts to model the transcription/translation-based feedback loops as a part of the circadian system: How do oscillators incorporating such loops keep from winding down?

White Collar-2, Mediator of Interactions   In contrast to WC-1, *wc-2* is constitutively expressed, giving rise to a protein with a single activation domain, two PAS domains, and a Zn-finger that is always in the nucleus. WC-2 is abundantly expressed compared with WC-1 and FRQ (55), and neither its levels nor the protein itself appears to be highly regulated (55, 67). WC-2, however, is a key element in the WCC because it mediates interactions between the regulated components: GST-pull-down assays, sucrose gradient sedimentation, and immunoprecipitations using a novel WC-2 specific antisera show that WC-2 forms complexes with WC-1 and with FRQ, consistent with the model in which FRQ acts to depress the level of its own transcript by physically interfering with the activation of the *frq* gene by the WCC (55). Significantly, WC-1 and FRQ do not interact in the absence of WC-2, nor is DNA required for the interactions. By carefully calibrating the immunoprecipitations and Western blots, it is possible to count the relative numbers of WC-2, FRQ, and WC-1 proteins in cell extracts and thereby predict the number and type of complexes forming at different times in the circadian cycle. These data show that WC-2 is both the most abundant component in this feedback loop and, in addition, is required for WC-1:FRQ interaction. That WC-2, FRQ, and WC-1 physically interact in solution confirms a central prediction of the current model for the *Neurospora* circadian clock (Figure 2) in which FRQ acts to depress the level of its own transcript, at least in part by interfering with the formation of the WCC, thereby blocking activation of the *frq* gene by the WCC. Constitutive and abundant WC-2 apparently provides a scaffold allowing for the interaction of two limiting proteins, FRQ and WC-1, a relationship responsible for regulation of rhythmic expression of *frq*. Similar interactions are central to the *Drosophila* clock (68). Given the cyclical but out-of-phase nature of FRQ and WC-1 expression, and approximating the abundance profiles of these proteins in time, these data suggest that the ability to form an active WCC not blocked by FRQ may be the limiting variable responsible for regulation of *frq* transcription in this clock-associated negative feedback loop. Because in flies and mammals, as well as fungi, PAS:PAS heterodimers are important for the operation of the clock, and in each of these systems one member of the partner appears to be constitutive [WC-2 in *Neurospora*, CYC in flies (69), CLOCK in mammals (70)] and one rhythmic (WC-1 in *Neurospora*, CLK in flies (71, 72), and BMAL1 in mammals (66, 73))], these data are consistent with a model in which the PAS-protein activating heterodimers in eukaryotic clock loops may be regulated by protein:protein interactions occurring in solution rather than on clock gene promoters (55, 68).

Conserved Aspects of Circadian Feedback Loops   Given these overall similarities in the appearance of the insect, mammalian, and *Neurospora* circadian feedback loops and the roles and regulation of the PAS proteins within the loops, it is perhaps not surprising that the WC-1 sequence shows extended similarity to mammalian BMAL1, a similarity that is not limited to only the 3 PAS domains of WC-1 but extends to the full extent of all mammalian BMAL1 sequences—48% of residues are identical or similar, and the smallest sum probability values from basic local search and alignment tool (BLAST2) are about 10^{-6} (41). No other vertebrate proteins show comparable similarities, nor the functional connection to circadian rhythmicity seen between WC-1 and BMAL, which play similar roles in circadian feedback loops. The similarities in time of expression, sequence, and activation function, and participation in interconnected cycles within the eukaryotic circadian feedback loops suggest a remarkable degree of conservation. Since functions of proteins can converge but primary sequences do not, the extended similarity in sequence and abundant similarities in function among these feedback loop-associated proteins strongly suggest a common ancestral origin for eukaryotic circadian systems.

Environmental Entrainment of the *Neurospora* Circadian System

Light Input Pathways   The goal of entrainment by light is to move the day phase of the clock (subjective day) to coincide with the day phase of the external world. Therefore, the molecular basis of entrainment by light is that the same photic cue should have opposite effects on the timing mechanism depending on whether light is seen late at night (when advances to the next day are needed) or early in the evening (when delays to the previous day are needed). In many circadian systems, the clock is not a passive player in this regulation either, but instead exerts its own regulation of the light response system so that light input to the clock is gated; this is known from classic work in scorpions (reviewed in 74), in plants (75), and in mammals even at the molecular level (76–79). A molecular basis for both phenomena is known in *Neurospora*.

In terms of resetting the clock, with clock components that peak in the daytime (*Neurospora* and mammals), photic induction of the components will reset the clock appropriately (Figure 3, see color insert). In *Neurospora*, light acts rapidly through WC-1 and WC-2, which bind at two sites within the *frq* promoter (80; A Froelich, JJ Loros & JC Dunlap, in preparation), to induce *frq* (43, 47). Because *frq* mRNA and FRQ levels cycle with a defined phase (i.e. the peak in *frq* mRNA means late morning), any abrupt change in *frq* levels yields an abrupt change in time. Thus in the late night when *frq* mRNA levels are rising, induction of *frq* by light rapidly advances the clock to a point corresponding to midday, whereas through the subjective evening and early night when *frq* is falling, induction rapidly sends the clock back in time to peak levels (corresponding to midday) yielding a phase delay (47). Similar results are seen in the induction of the mammalian putative clock genes *per1* and *per2* (76–79, 81, 82).

An analysis of *wc-2* alleles has revealed significant differences in the molecular mechanism of light-inducible *frq* expression versus other genes (such as *al-3* or *ccg-2*) driven by WC-2. First, *frq* expression shows the standard transient response to light but is also able to sustain induction well over dark levels in constant illumination, an unusual feature for a light-inducible gene, but critical for clock response to a full or long-day photoperiod. A definitive knockout of *wc-2* indicates that WC-2 is required for light induction of both *frq* and other light-inducible genes but, surprisingly, several alleles with mutations in the Zn-finger region of the WC-2 protein that are generally photo-blind retain *frq* photo-inducibility (45).

In terms of gating, one would anticipate a molecular output for the clock that would feed back to regulate input to the clock, i.e. an additional clock-associated feedback loop. The vivid (*vvd*) gene and VVD protein provide this. VVD, a novel member of the PAS protein superfamily, was recently cloned and studied (36); it identifies an autoregulatory negative feedback loop that closes outside of the core oscillator but impacts all aspects of circadian timing. Expression of *vvd* is rapidly induced by light and independently controlled by the clock, and VVD in turn feeds back to regulate the expression of a number of input and output genes including itself. VVD is a small protein with a PAS domain as its only distinct functional motif. A model thus posits VVD, via its PAS domain, interacting with and transiently down-regulating the transcriptional activator WCC (Figure 2). Because WCC is required both for light-induced transcription of most *Neurospora* genes and also for the activation of *frq* and expression of circadian rhythms in the dark, VVD affects both input and output. It is not required for circadian rhythmicity, however, as *vvd*-null strains still have robust circadian rhythmicity. Nonetheless, loss of the VVD protein has far-reaching effects on the perception of light and on the entire circadian system, from input, as seen in the phase response curve, to oscillator function, as measured by period length, to output, as manifested in the phasing and expression levels of clock-controlled genes. Clock regulation of the immediate and transient repressor VVD could contribute to circadian entrainment by making dark to light transitions more discrete; it supplies a molecular explanation for circadian gating of the light response at the level of the cell and oscillator and provides a generally applicable precedent that may be extrapolated to illuminate light adaptation and gating of input in other circadian systems.

Temperature Effects on the Clock   The other major zeitgeber (time-giver) for most clocks is temperature; ambient temperature influences the circadian system in several ways. First, temperature steps reset the clock in a manner similar to light pulses. Second, there are physiological temperature limits for the clock, but within these limits the period length is more or less the same (temperature compensation). Compensation is approached in different organisms through both theoretical (e.g. 60) and molecular routes (83), the latter of which in *Drosophila* demonstrate the influence of natural selection on the sequence of the clock gene *per*. Temperature resetting responses, a classic property of rhythms, have been described in model organisms including *Neurospora* (19, 48, 84) and *Drosophila* (85, 86). In *Neurospora*, unlike the case with light where transcriptional regulation is key, temperature effects are likely mediated through posttranscriptional control so far as they are understood (48). *frq* transcripts give rise to both a long and short form of FRQ as a result of alternative initiation of translation (31), and although either form alone is sufficient for a functional clock at some temperatures, both forms are necessary for robust overt rhythmicity (87). A regulated translational control process may also occur with TIM in insects (88). Temperature regulates both the total amount of FRQ and the ratio of the two FRQ forms by favoring different initiation codons at different temperatures; when either initiation codon is eliminated, the temperature range permissive for rhythmicity is reduced. This novel adaptive mechanism extends the physiological temperature range over which the clock functions (31, 87).

Resetting of the clock by temperature steps also reflects posttranscriptional regulation in *Neurospora* (87): *frq* transcript oscillations at different temperatures are close to superimposable, but FRQ amounts oscillate around higher levels at higher temperatures. The lowest point in the curve (late night) at 28°C is higher than the highest point in the curve (late day) at 21°C, such that the time associated with a given number of molecules of FRQ is different at different temperatures (Figure 4). Thus a shift in temperature corresponds to a shift in the state of the clock (literally a step to a different time), although initially no synthesis or turnover of components occurs. After the step, relative levels of *frq* and FRQ are assessed in terms of the new temperature, and they respond rapidly and proportionally according to the dynamics of the feedback loop; i.e. if there is too little FRQ present to shut down the WCC at a new higher temperature, more is made. In this way, unlike light, temperature changes reset the circadian cycle instantaneously and from within the loop (48). In *Drosophila*, a 12-h exposure to an elevated but physiological temperature (a 20 to 28°C step) yields strong resetting (85), and heat shock (a short duration step to 37°C) results in the turnover of PER and TIM but yields only small phase delays in the early evening with no effect seen in the late night (89). Non-extreme temperature changes in *Neurospora* can have a stronger influence on circadian timing than light (48), contrary to our expectations, but in all cases light and temperature cues reinforce each other to keep clocks synchronous in the real world.

FRQ-Less Oscillators (FLOs) and Other Rhythms in *Neurospora*

The discussion of clock mechanism thus far has focused on what we know about the FRQ/WCC feedback loop for the simple reason that it is the only circadian-associated feedback loop with known molecular components. However, there is

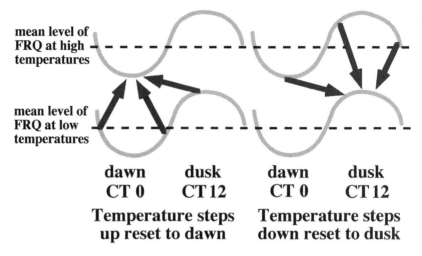

mean level of
FRQ at high
temperatures

mean level of
FRQ at low
temperatures

dawn   **dusk**   **dawn**   **dusk**
CT 0   **CT 12**   **CT 0**   **CT 12**
Temperature steps   **Temperature steps**
up reset to dawn   **down reset to dusk**

Figure 4 Resetting the *Neurospora* clock with temperature shifts. Shown is the daily rhythm in FRQ protein levels, which cycle around a higher mean point at higher temperatures within the physiological range (48); one cycle is shown from dawn to dusk. On the left, arrows depict the effect of a step up in temperature; no matter what time of day this occurs, the amount of FRQ in the cell will be low compared with the amount needed in the cycle even at the lowest point in the cycle at the higher temperature, so the clock is reset to the low point in the curve, near to dawn. On the right is shown the effects of a step down; no matter what time of day this occurs, the clock is reset to late in the day (48) (adapted from 4).

little reason to believe that even a complete understanding of this feedback loop alone would explain the molecular working of the entire oscillatory system; i.e. it is clear that the FRQ/WCC feedback loop is required for circadian rhythmicity, but it is probably not sufficient for circadian rhythmicity. What we know about the FRQ/WCC loop is the result of molecular studies initiated by the cloning of *frq* in the mid-1980s; just as what we know about the molecular bases of insect clocks has derived from the cloning and analysis of *per* in *Drosophila*. In these systems, it is clear that mutations at these loci affect circadian clocks and thus analysis of these loci and others connected to them via regulatory relationships will provide information about components within the circadian system. In addition, unfocused screens for arrhythmic mutations in several laboratories (see above) have turned up other alleles of both *frq* and the *wc* genes. However, the initial report of the *frq9* allele (44, 90) revealed that such strains retained the ability to express a rhythm (albeit one lacking most circadian characteristics). This elusive rhythmicity was again identified, studied, characterized, and confirmed to be the *frq*-null phenotype (42). The rhythm appears in only a fraction of all race tube cultures, displays a highly variable period length ranging from 12 to 35 h, cannot be entrained by light cycles, and lacks the temperature and nutritional compensation that characterizes the circadian system. More recently, Roenneberg and colleagues studied the rhythm again, using full (not skeleton) temperature cycles to drive it, and showed that this occasionally expressed furtive rhythmicity in *frq*-null strains could be reproducibly generated from an oscillator coupled to the FRQ/WCC feedback loop (91). This valuable contribution may obviate problems with the *frq9* rhythm's irreproducibility and lack of phase control, both of which factors have interfered with its study in the 15 years since this residual rhythm in *frq*-null strains was first described.

This oscillator(s), known as the FRQ-less oscillator or FLO (92, 93), is coupled to the FRQ/WCC loop and likely contributes to the operation of the *Neurospora* circadian system, although this will not be known for certain until the FLO can be genetically or possibly pharmacologically manipulated. It should be noted that we cannot discern whether the FLO is a single oscillator or a system of tightly coupled oscillators. Recent studies (91), as well as the original report (44), place the intrinsic period length of the FLO at $\sim$12–13 h, arguably close to within the circadian range, but otherwise the rhythm bears few circadian characteristics (lacking temperature or nutritional compensation, entrainability by light, sustainability, or consistency of period length), all of which are seen only with the FRQ/WCC loop in the system. Thus it seems unlikely that the FLO can produce circadian rhythms. However, in part because the FLO can be entrained to a circadian period length (with appropriate duration and amplitude temperature cycles) and does exist in the absence of the FRQ/WCC loop, Roenneberg and colleagues have advanced the idea that it is "the circadian oscillator" (94). If so and if modeling studies (95, 96) are correct and the FRQ/WCC loop can also oscillate, then there are two circadian oscillators in *Neurospora*, perhaps neither of which on its own can generate a circadian rhythm. Whether the FLO constitutes the circadian oscillator seems more a matter of semantics than of substance, revolving as it must about the definition of circadian oscillator. Many, including ourselves, view the circadian oscillator as the minimal set of feedback loops capable of generating a circadian rhythm; if so, a circadian oscillator should be able to generate a circadian rhythm, and by this definition FLO is important but somewhat lacking in completeness. Others (94) who place the emphasis on the oscillator believe that if the FLO by itself can generate an oscillation, then it is sufficient to be called a circadian oscillator even if other parts of the system are needed to make the oscillation circadian. In the context of each definition, each interpretation is correct. Semantics aside, all would agree that the goal is to understand how the circadian system operates and that any parts needed to make it work correctly are of interest. We and others have initiated genetic screens to identify components of the FLO, and as soon as a discrete element can be assigned it can be included in the next generation of Figure 2, but until a gene or protein is identified, this model is just a cartoon.

What might some of the components of the FLO be? As is clear from Table 1, many other loci have been identified that, when mutant, affect circadian timing or, in some cases, other aspects of timing. The molecular identities of the products of some of these are known but many are not. Some will probably play roles in the FLO, and some in the FRQ/WCC loop (where the kinase is an obvious missing part). More generally, some will be informative as to the mechanism of the clock and some will exert their effects pleiotropically. A good candidate for this latter class would be *arg-13*, which was reported to have a slightly short-period length on arginine-limited medium (97). When cloned, *arg-13* was shown to encode an amino acid carrier in the mitochondrial membrane whose loss had a slight effect on the arginine metabolism, aspects of which occur in both the cytoplasm and mitochondrion (98). Because *arg-13*-null mutations are still fully rhythmic and the period effects are small, it seems likely that the lesion results in a minor distortion in the cellular, presumably mitochondrial, milieu that in some way results in a slightly fast-running clock. Does this mean that the small period effects resulting from mutation in other mitochondrially localized or associated gene products (*oli, cya-5, cyb-2, cyb-3, cyt-4, mi, spe-3*) similarly result from pleiotropic actions? This remains a possibility.

Another group of mutations affecting the clock are those associated with metabolic defects. Genetic screens for novel conditional clock mutants ought to have the potential to identify important components that are also essential for the life of the cell; only Nakashima has reported such screens to date (37). A class of mutants that might arise from such a screen are those having metabolic defects remedied by supplementation. For instance, five mutations affecting cysteine metabolism (99) have characteristics similar to *arg-13*, i.e. the effect is a minor methionine-starvation-dependent shortening of period length; however, *cys-9*, which encodes thioredoxin reductase, results in a 5-h shortening initially, which after three days grades into an unstable rhythm that varies between 11 and 31 h. The logical inference (37) is that reduced thioredoxin is important for the operation of a protein within the clock mechanism. Another example of nutritionally manipulable rhythms is that reported by Brody and colleagues in the *cel* strain in which the mutation renders the period length and temperature-compensation properties of the clock manipulable through the addition of exogenous fatty acids to the medium (100–102). For instance, addition of short-chain fatty acids (8–13 carbons long) to *cel* lengthened period in a dose-dependent manner up to 33 h. However, in these studies, direct incorporation of the short-chain (period lengthening) fatty acids into mycelial total lipids appeared not responsible for the period lengthening because, instead of incorporation, extensive metabolic conversion resulting in liberation of CO_2 was observed (102).

A related example, also possibly associated with lipid metabolism, is that of the choline-repairable morphological mutant *chol-1*. Strains bearing *chol-1* display swollen hyphal tips and abnormal colony morphology on unsupplemented minimal medium, and growth can be somewhat episodic (grows slightly then stops) (103). Growth of this leaky choline-requiring strain on a solid surface under choline-starvation conditions (e.g. 104) can sometimes after a transition period of arrhythmicity elicit a long-period rhythm (period length to over 100 h depending on conditions). This rhythm, although lacking most characteristics of a circadian rhythm, is robust, unlike that seen with the unentrained FLO, and represents an interesting aspect of the biology of this organism. But is it circadian? A caveat is

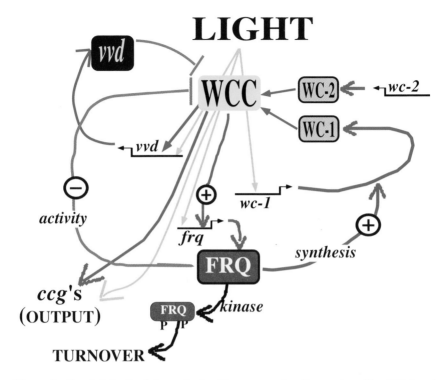

Figure 2 Coupled feedback loops in the *Neurospora* circadian system. The WC-1 and WC-2 proteins form a white collar complex (WCC) that activates (green) *frq* gene expression and also clock-controlled gene (*ccg*, output) expression in the dark. The WCC also mediates light-induced transcription from *frq, ccgs*, and *wc-1* (yellow arrows). *frq* mRNA is translated to make FRQ proteins, which have two roles: (*a*) FRQ feeds back into the nucleus (blue) to rapidly block the positive effect of the WCC in driving *frq* transcription; (*b*) FRQ acts to promote (green) the synthesis of new WC-1. Phosphorylation of FRQ triggers its turnover (black) and is a major determinant of period length in the clock. Coupled to these loops in the circadian system is a FRQ-less oscillator (FLO); it is not shown because neither components of the FLO nor its point of coupling to the FRQ/WCC loop are known. See text for details (adapted from 41).

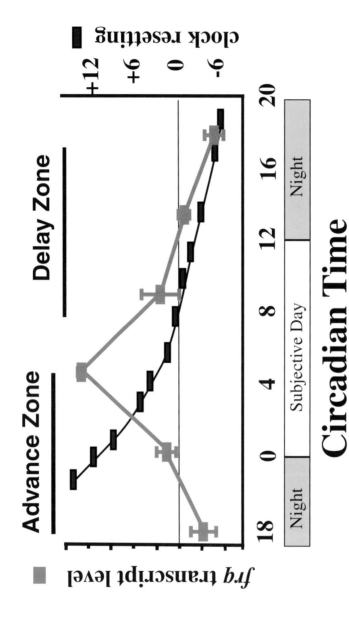

Figure 3 Resetting the *Neurospora* clock with light. Shown in dark blue is the response of the clock to short duration light treatments that serve to advance the clock when received in the late night and early morning and to delay the clock when received in the early evening. In orange is the daily cycle in *frq* transcript levels. Light acts through the WCC to acutely transcriptionally induce *frq* transcript, resetting the FRQ/WCC feedback loop and thereby resetting the clock. See text for details (adapted from 4).

the use of growth on a solid medium (a morphological assay) to assay rhythms of morphological mutants that, by virtue of the mutation, display a pronounced cycle in linear growth rate (along with a loss of both compensation and the ability to be entrained to a 24-h cycle).

Non-circadian developmental rhythms are well known in fungi. Bünning noted, "Several developmental cycles in fungi also belong to those processes that become rhythmic in nature because they themselves have 'wheels' of a clock, without being coupled to a master clock which runs independently of these overt morphological events. This may be true, for example, for growth rings in several species of fungi...." These periods under certain conditions may deviate very much from circadian (from less than 20 to more than 100 h) indicating that we are not dealing here with a control by a cellular mechanism of the type that is responsible for most of the more typical circadian rhythms. Other indications are the strong dependence on the chemical composition of the growth medium, a strong influence of temperature on the periods and the fact that (in *Neurospora* and *Ascobolus*) it is even possible to set the phase by transfer to fresh medium. Influences such as these are not known for the "classical; examples of circadian rhythms" (2 and references therein). These rhythms are known not only in *Neurospora*, but in a number of other fungi, where different conditions of nitrogen and carbon allow strains to switch to and from circadian (temperature-compensated, light entrainable) to non-circadian rhythms (temperature- and nutrition-dependent period length, light-dependent or non-light dependent) (reviewed in 12). The *clock* strain of *Neurospora*, for instance, exhibits a non-circadian rhythm in growth (24, 105) that can be phenocopied in normal circadian strains by the addition of sorbose, which slows growth (25). Although this literature is extensive and was well known to most chronobiologists 30 years ago, few studying circadian rhythms today are grounded in it. Suffice it to say that although *Neurospora* can display a rhythm in development that is by all criteria circadian, it should not follow that every developmental rhythm exhibited by *Neurospora* is regulated in the same way or by the same circadian oscillatory system.

The rhythms seen in the *chol-1* strain share some but not all of the characteristics of these non-circadian rhythms. They have been measured on solid medium on race tubes and petri plates (106, 107); the rhythm has not been measured in liquid culture so it is not possible to dissociate the morphological rhythm from the linear growth defects of this strain. In general, as the level of supplement is reduced during growth on solid medium, the period does not begin to lengthen until the growth rate has declined by about 30%; then the slower the growth the longer the period. Circadian rhythmicity is seen at high levels of supplements (choline, monomethylethanolamine, and dimethylethanolamine) that bypass the partial block in phosphatidylcholine synthesis. At moderate levels of supplementation with choline, but not monomethylethanolamine, strains are often seen to be arrhythmic. With monomethylethanolamine supplementation, but not choline, between a third and a half of cultures are reported to display 15–20-h rhythms for the first few days before settling into an ultra-long period length (107), suggesting the possibility of a transition between two forms of rhythmic control. Long-period cultures exhibit random phases due to period variability within each culture. In all *Neurospora* strains there is a low-amplitude rhythm in rate of growth (see above) (16); this rhythm is accentuated as growth slows in *chol-1* strains so that at the slowest growth (longest period length), cultures are spreading up to eight-fold faster in interband regions compared with growth rates during band formation (106; P Lakin-Thomas, personal communication). Whereas the sorbose-induced hyphal branching rhythm retains phase control but is not temperature compensated, suppressed by light, nor light entrained, the *chol-1* rhythm lacks temperature compensation and phase control but is photo-suppressed and can be light entrained to long photoperiods (such as LD 24:24) (104, 106). Choline starvation can induce rhythms in *frq* and *wc* mutant strains, and these rhythms are then no longer affected by light (108). Given this, if starvation-induced rhythm is considered circadian, then it follows that the PAS protein-associated transcription/translation feedback loop of *Neurospora*, and by extension to other species studied including *Drosophila* and mice, is not an essential part of the circadian oscillatory system (108a). This would be significant, but the caveat of relying on a variable growth rate to measure morphological rhythm in a mutant, together with the history of non-circadian growth rhythms in fungi, suggests that it may not be simple to understand what the starvation-induced rhythms can tell us about normal temperature and nutritionally compensated, 24-h light-entrainable, circadian rhythms. In all cases with nutritionally supplemented rhythms, normal rhythmicity can be restored by chronic addition of a substance (rhythmic addition is never required), but only in the presence of FRQ and WC proteins.

From the subjective look of overt rhythms on the race tubes it seems unlikely that the oscillator manifested as the FLO is the same as the one elicited by choline-starvation; the choline-induced rhythm is much more robust and the bands appear different from those seen with the FLO, perhaps reflecting the rhythm in linear growth rate. We believe it remains likely, as we proposed a decade ago, that the *Neurospora* circadian clock "will be found to be the result of coupling multiple, presumably intracellular oscillators so that their collective output is robust and has a period length of about a day." (7).

Output from the Clock—Control
of Overt Rhythms in *Neurospora*

Biologically, the most interesting property of the clock is its use as a major endogenous regulatory network for most living eukaryotes, as well as for some photosynthetic prokaryotes. The diversity of biological processes regulated by the clock is enormous: Clocks time many important functions of life. A major question in clock research has centered on determining how the clock transfers information out into a cell or organism. A common clock function is to program cellular and organismal metabolism and behavior such that appropriate activities take place at particular times of the day, controlling diverse aspects of a cell or organism's life that range from basic energy metabolism to cognitive behavior. A few of these rhythmic processes, many occurring across phyla, include phototaxis, enzymatic activities, photosynthetic capacity, insect eclosion, locomotion, sleep and many other (including conscious) behaviors, electrical potential, respiratory function, cellular morphology, intracellular ionic concentrations, hormonal signaling, and the circadian gating of the cell division cycle (109). An additional use of the clock is in avian and insect navigation. An important third use of the daily clock is as a timer for circannual activities such as photoperiodism, the ability of plants and animals to time their reproduction.

Asexual Development   The issue of clock regulation of biological processes such as metabolism, reproduction, or behavior reflects the biology of the particular system being studied. In 1953, a periodic zonation in the pattern of growth in a *Neurospora* strain was reported (14) and later determined to have a genetic basis (110) and be the formation of asexual coniospores (16). In 1959, Pittendrigh and others (15) demonstrated that this zonation in growth was present in constant conditions of temperature and darkness and the periodicity of about 22 h was maintained across a physiological temperature range, concluding that *Neurospora* had a biological clock. In this work they recognized the difference between the clock and clock-controlled output; that the zonation itself and the processes leading to it were not a reflection of the clock itself but were a distinct process that was coupled and uncoupled from the clock. Since that time *Neurospora*'s three cell–type asexual developmental cycle has been well studied (e.g. 28). After germination of a conidiophore, branching vegetative mycelium grow rapidly as a syncytium with incomplete cell walls allowing the nuclei and cytoplasm to flow freely. Development can be initiated by numerous signals from the environment, including blue light, dessication, and carbon deprivation. An endogenously generated signal capable of throwing the developmental switch is under control of the circadian clock, initiating the formation of a second cell-type called aerial hyphae that then elaborate the formation of complete cross walls between mature vegetative spores, the conidiophores, each containing one to several nuclei. The conidia eventually break away from the parent organism, are dispersed by air or water, and when appropriate will germinate and establish a new vegetative clone of the original parent organism. In constant conditions, clock regulation of this developmental cycle is initiated in the late subjective night every circadian cycle, producing conidia for a defined proportion of the day. Once initiated, this developmental process is determined and proceeds with clock-independent kinetics. Sometime later in the early to middle of the subjective circadian day the signal is switched back and a region of undifferentiated hyphae is laid down, resulting in the well-known banding pattern of asexual development.

In addition to understanding the mechanism of transferring temporal information within a cell or organism, it is also desirable to know what and how much of the biology in a given system is under clock control. It is unknown in any organism just how broadly clock regulation is applied. In *Neurospora* it is clear that at the cellular level, at some times of the subjective day, the clock is responsible for organizing the assembly of the components of the aerial hyphae and conidia instead of the surface hyphae. This major cellular remodeling involves a many genes and gene products, all generally organized by the clock, and it is expected that most, if not all, of these genes or their protein products will be expressed in a time-of-day manner. Although the production of asexual spores is the best characterized rhythm in *Neurospora*, other persisting rhythms at the physiological level have been described, which include the production of CO_2, lipid metabolism (107, 108, 111), a number of enzymatic activities (e.g. 22), and heat shock proteins (e.g. 112). It is apparent that the rhythmic production of aerial hyphae and spores entails major cellular remodeling with attendant gross changes in protein, carbohydrate, and lipid content, and enzyme activities, etc. Many experiments describing these rhythms have employed harvesting of rhythmically developing cultures; in these cases it can be difficult to know which of these rhythms is independent of conidial production and therefore whether clock regulation of those rhythms only reflects circadian control of development.

Rhythmic Changes in Transcript Abundance Is a Common Means of Regulation   The first step in answering the questions of how the cell reads time-of-day from the clock and what extent of cell metabolism is clock regulated has been the identification and examination of clock control of gene activity via the isolation of genes whose abundance is clock regulated over the course of a day, that is, the clock-controlled genes that we called *ccgs* (30). They have been found in several systems (e.g. 30, 113–117) and in some cases, the nature of the regulation has been shown to be at the level of transcription (e.g. 35, 114, 118). Systematic screens for clock-regulated genes have been carried out in *Neurospora* using morning versus evening mRNA subtractive hybridizations (30) and differential screens involving time-of-day-specific cDNA libraries (119). The search for clock-controlled genes is currently being extended using bulk sequencing of morning and evening cDNA libraries in a collaborative effort (*Neurospora crassa* cDNA Sequencing Project, http://www.genome.ou.edu/fungal.html). Currently, there are many *ccgs* from *Neurospora* (Table 2); the best characterized are late-night to morning specific and most are additionally regulated by light and developmental cues.

The next step in understanding clock regulation has been the dissection of *ccg* promoters to identify "clock-boxes" or clock control regulatory elements (CCREs), then proceeding to isolate the *trans*-acting factors that bind and control these CCREs. At some point, as you move backward up this cascade, the isolated factors must interface with the components of the clock mechanism. One prediction is that clock output pathways will, in part, be organism specific based on individual requirements, but the mechanisms used by the clock to confer temporal rhythmicity may be conserved, thus yielding information not just for *Neurospora* and possibly other fungal systems but for all systems. Deletion and *cis*-analysis of the transcriptionally controlled *eas* (*ccg-2*) promoter has separated sequence-specific regions that confer development and light regulation from each other and from the clock.

TABLE 2 *Neurospora* clock-controlled genes

Gene name	mRNA[a] Peak	Identity[b]	Light regulation	Developmental[c] regulation	Reference
ccg-1	CT3	Unknown glucose repressible heat shock inducible	+	+	30, 133
eas (ccg-2)	CT22	Hydrophobin	+	+	30, 126, 127, 156
ccg-4	CT5	Unknown	+	+	119
ccg-6	CT19	Unknown	+	+	119
ccg-7	CT21	GAPDH	−	−	119, 135
ccg-8	CT20	Unknown	−	−	119
ccg-9	CT19	Trehalose synthase	+	+	119, 130
cmt (ccg-12)	CT18	CuMT	−	−	119, 157
al-3	CT3	GGPPS	+	+	36, 125
con-6	ZT20	Unknown	+	+	121
con-10	ZT20	Unknown	+	+	121
vvd	CT3	Light repressor	+	ND	36
bli-3	CT3	Unknown	+	ND	36, 158
frq	CT3	Clock component; transcriptional corepressor	+	ND	32, 47

[a]The peak in message accumulation, determined from Northern blots, can vary in different culture conditions and between experiments (119). Only the longer *al-3*c transcript has been demonstrated to be rhythmic (125). The *con-6* and *con-10* transcripts were shown to peak about 20 hours after a light pulse representing zeitgeber time (ZT) 20 (121).

[b]Abbreviations are as follows: GAPDH, glyceraldehyde 3-phosphate dehydrogenase; CuMT, copper metallothionein; GGPPS, geranylgeranyl pyrophosphate synthase.

[c]ND, not done.

A 68-base pair sequence located close to the start of transcription binds protein factor(s) and is sufficient to confer clock regulation on this and other promoters (120; D Bell-Pedersen, J Dunlap & J Loros, in preparation). The development and light-regulated genes *con-6* and *con-10* are also under circadian control (121, 122) and a pair of papers outlining extensive promoter resection of the *con-10* gene separates and defines several regions within the promoter involved in activation and repression in response to environmental regulation (123, 124) although no region has yet been earmarked for circadian control. One of the carotenoid biosynthetic enzymes in *Neurospora*, geranylgeranyl pyrophosphate synthase, the product of the *albino-3 (al-3)* locus, encodes two overlapping mRNAs, one predominately expressed in the mycelium after light induction and the other detectable in conidiating cultures both as a light-induced RNA and also in the dark (125). In the dark, the conidiation-specific transcript is rhythmically expressed with a dawn peak in mRNA abundance.

The formal definition of a *ccg* has been a gene whose rhythmic expression persists under constant conditions, with a period length that reflects the strain genotype and, importantly, whose loss-of-function phenotype is not clock related, a definition that classified all clock-controlled genes as strictly output. This has been a convenient means of defining clock-regulated activities but as we discover more gene products involved with the circadian system as a whole and know more molecular details of their regulation, these definitions have become blurred. We know that expression from the *frq* gene is also under clock control by an autoregulatory mechanism and is directly controlled by light. Recent dissection of the *frq* promoter has identified two sequence regions of less than 100 bps each that define the light regulatory elements (LRE) and clock *cis*-regulatory domains. These domains, both shown by deletion to be necessary for appropriate light regulation while only one is necessary for clock regulation, have also been placed in front of a heterologous promoter construct. Either the distal or the proximal region alone is sufficient to drive light-regulated expression of a reporter, and wild-type levels are achieved when both elements are placed in combination. Additionally, both of these DNA sequences have been shown by electrophoretic mobility shift assay to specifically bind the protein products of the *wc-1* and *wc-2* loci (A Froehlich, J Loros & J Dunlap, in preparation). Neither of the *wc* genes is rhythmically regulated at the level of expression (41, 55), although the WC-1 protein is rhythmically expressed by a posttranscriptional mechanism directly controlled by the FRQ protein (41). Finally, the light-regulated *vvd* gene, whose protein product is a small PAS protein involved in light repression and adaptation (see above), is also clock regulated, with a peak of expression near dawn similar to the majority of *Neurospora ccgs* (36). In addition, VVD acts broadly to influence both phase and abundance of many of the other clock-controlled genes and even of the *frq* gene. Therefore, although *vvd* is an output gene from the clock, in that its expression is directly under clock control and it also modulates output from the clock to other genes, it is also clear that *vvd* has a major role in regulating the light input pathway to the clock. Its knockout phenotype shows a marked change in the photoentrainment properties of the clock (36). Hence, the *Neurospora* clock is capable of driving synthesis of macromolecules in the cell by both transcriptional and posttranscriptional mechanisms, and rhythmic output activities can feed back onto clock components like *frq*, or onto input stimuli such that input into the clock can be circadianly gated.

Development Is Only One Aspect of Clock Regulation   Through the isolation and the identification of function for many of these output genes it is becoming clear that diverse aspects of the biology of the organism are under clock regulation. There are identified functions for many of the *ccgs*, and, as predicted, some are involved in development. The *eas* (*ccg-2*) gene encodes the *Neurospora* hydrophobin (126, 127), small highly expressed and exported hydrophobic proteins found coating conidia and aerial hyphae that are the fungal kingdom's specialized method of allowing structures to emerge from a wet substrate into the air (128, 129). Other *ccgs* (*ccg-7, -8,* and *-12*), two of unknown function, were found to be neither developmentally nor light induced, supporting a role for the *Neurospora* clock in controlling output pathways other than conidiation (119). The *ccg-9* gene encodes a novel form of trehalose synthase responsible for catalyzing the synthesis of the disaccharide trehalose, which plays an important role in protecting cells from environmental stresses. Additionally, inactivation of *ccg-9* results in altered conidiophore morphology and abolishes circadian control of conidiation, although the underlying clock continues to operate normally (130). Both *ccg-9* and *ccg-12* (identical to the previously cloned *Neurospora cmt* gene) encode copper metallothionein (119). The functions of *cmt* and *ccg-1* (*grg-1*), which are induced by heat shock and repressed by glucose (131–133), suggest that the clock controls stress responses. Induction of heat shock and general stress responses has been associated with asexual development (134) and possibly with clock resetting (62) in *Neurospora*. Other genes have been found to be involved in central metabolic functions of the cell not previously known to be clock regulated. The *ccg-7* gene encodes the glycolytic enzyme, glyceraldehyde-3-phosphate dehydrogenase (previously shown to have a rhythm in enzymatic activity in developing cultures 22), and the enzyme activity as well as the transcript abundance cycle in the non-conidiating liquid culture system (135). Interestingly, the activity of the plastid-targeted isoform of GAPDH has been found to cycle, although not at the level of transcript, in the marine dinoflagellate *Gonyaulax* (136), suggesting that there may be some specific role for the clock in controlling discrete points in general metabolism from phylogenetically disparate organisms.

In order to gain a much broader perspective on clock control in *Neurospora*, a collaborative effort was developed with the Human Genome Center at the University of Oklahoma. Starting from two separate time-of-day-specific cDNA libraries generated from RNAs present in the subjective morning and evening (119), this work has so far yielded sequence of over 6000 cDNAs from the evening *Neurospora crassa* cDNA library and over 7000 cDNAs from the morning cDNA library (*Neurospora crassa* cDNA Sequencing Project, http://www.genome.ou.edu/fungal.html) (136a). Assembly of these identified approximately 1400 unique transcripts, all of which have been BLASTed (137) in searches against GenBank to identify functional or sequence homologs. There were two goals to this effort, one to identify novel genes in this system, and the other to identify genes that are regulated in a time-of-day-specific manner. Of the unigene set, around 40% have occurred at least eight times in each library, and of these 248 showed clear matches (smallest sum probability scores from BLAST2 $> 10^{-5}$); over 220 appear to encode novel proteins. Based on the differential appearance of these 448 contigs from the morning or evening libraries, a rough conservative estimate suggests 10% might be differentially expressed, although verification by Northern analysis is currently being carried out. The high percentage of sequences showing no extended homology to other genes is not entirely unexpected since homology searches of

Neurospora-expressed sequences in the other large-scale *Neurospora* EST project at the University of New Mexico also turned up high proportions of novel or orphan sequences (138, 139). Regardless of the outcomes from these studies, the collections of unigene sets from these *Neurospora* sequencing projects will allow definitive answers from microarray type experiments (140) using time-of-day-specific probes.

CONCLUSIONS

We have just passed the fortieth anniversary of the original determination that *Neurospora* possessed a circadian clock, and next year will be the fifteenth anniversary of the cloning of *frq* that helped push *Neurospora* rhythms research into the molecular era. Based on work in this system we can now formulate plausible, albeit not complete, molecular explanations for the period length and sustainability of the rhythm, light, and temperature resetting of the circadian system and for gating of light input and light effects. In terms of output, work on *Neurospora* has been at the forefront of searches for clock control of gene expression. With the selection of *Neurospora* as a reference filamentous fungus for genomics development and the archival quality genomic sequence anticipated within a year, the development of genomic and microarray resources, and a growing research community, this system promises to remain both useful and tractable.

ACKNOWLEDGMENTS

We thank the members of our laboratories for valuable comments and critical reading of the manuscript, and H Nakashima, V Gooch, D Bell-Pedersen, P Lakin-Thomas for fact-checking parts of the manuscript or for unpublished information. We apologize for having to delete some references due to space limitations. This work was supported by grants from the National Institutes of Health (R37-GM 34985 to JCD, MH44651 to JCD and JJL), the National Science Foundation (MCB-9307299 to JJL), and the Norris Cotton Cancer Center core grant at Dartmouth Medical School.

Visit the Annual Reviews home page at www.AnnualReviews.org

LITERATURE CITED

1. Hastings JW, Schweiger HG, eds. *The Molecular Basis of Circadian Rhythms.* Berlin: Dahlem Konferenzen

1a. Sweeney BM. 1976. Circadian rhythms, definition and general characterization. See Ref. 1, pp. 77–83

2. Bünning E. 1973. *The Physiological Clock.* New York: Springer-Verlag

3. De Mairan JJ. 1729. Observation botanique. *Hist. Acad. R. Sci.* 47–48

4. Dunlap JC. 1999. Molecular bases for circadian clocks. *Cell* 96:271–90

5. DeCoursey PJ, Krulas JR. 1998. Behavior of SCN-lesioned chipmunks in a natural habitat: a pilot study. *J. Biol. Rhythms* 13:229–44

6. Ouyang Y, Andersson CR, Kondo T, Golden SS, Johnson CH. 1998. Resonating circadian clocks enhance fitness in cyanobacteria. *Proc. Natl. Acad. Sci. USA* 95:8660–64

7. Dunlap JC. 1992. Genetic and molecular dissection of the *Neurospora* circadian system. In *Biological Clocks and Ethology*, ed. T Hiroshige, K Honma, pp. 3–18. Sapporo: Hokkaido Univ. Press

8. Dunlap JC. 1993. Genetic analysis of circadian clocks. *Annu. Rev. Physiol.* 55:683–728

9. Dunlap JC. 1998. An end in the beginning. *Science* 280:1548–49

10. Perkins DD. 1992. *Neurospora*: the organism behind the molecular revolution. *Genetics* 130:687–701

11. Jerebzoff S, Jerebzoff-Quintin S, Lambert E. 1974. *Aspergillus niger*: characteristics of endogenous and low frequency rhythms. *Int. J. Chronobiol.* 2:131–44

12. Jerebzoff S. 1976. Metabolic steps involved in periodicity. See Ref. 1, pp. 193–213

13. Lysek G, Esser K. 1970. Rhythmic mycelial growth in *Podospora anserina*. *Arch. Mikrobiol.* 73:224–30

14. Brandt WH. 1953. Zonation in a prolineless strain of *Neurospora*. *Mycologia* 45:194–208

15. Pittendrigh CS, Bruce VG, Rosenzweig NS, Rubin ML. 1959. A biological clock in *Neurospora*. *Nature* 184:169–70

16. Sargent ML, Briggs WR, Woodward DO. 1966. The circadian nature of a rhythm expressed by an invertaseless strain of *Neurospora crassa*. *Plant Physiol.* 41:1343–49

17. Sargent ML, Kaltenborn SH. 1972. Effects of medium composition and carbon dioxide on circadian conidiation in *Neurospora*. *Plant Physiol.* 50:171–75

18. Sargent ML, Briggs WR. 1967. The effect of light on a circadian rhythm of conidiation in *Neurospora*. *Plant Physiol.* 42:1504–10

19. Francis C, Sargent ML. 1979. Effects of temperature perturbations on circadian conidiation in *Neurospora*. *Plant Physiol.* 64:1000–9

20. Paietta J, Sargent M. 1981. Photoreception in *Neurospora crassa*: correlation of reduced light sensitivity with flavin deficiency. *Proc. Natl. Acad. Sci. USA* 78:5573–77

21. Paietta J, Sargent ML. 1983. Isolation and characterization of light-insensitive mutants of *Neurospora crassa*. *Genetics* 104:11–20

22. Hochberg ML, Sargent ML. 1974. Rhythms of enzyme activity associated with circadian conidiation in *Neurospora crassa*. *J. Bacteriol.* 120:1164–75

23. Martens CL, Sargent ML. 1974. Conidiation rhythms of nucleic acid metabolism in *Neurospora crassa*. *J. Bacteriol.* 117:1210–5

24. Sussman AS, Lowrey RJ, Durkee T. 1964. Morphology and genetics of a periodic colonial mutant of *Neurospora crassa*. *Am. J. Bot.* 51:243–52

25. Feldman J, Hoyle MN. 1974. A direct comparison between circadian and noncircadian rhythms in *Neurospora crassa*. *Plant Physiol.* 53:928–30

26. Feldman JF, Waser N. 1971. New mutations affecting circadian rhythmicity in *Neurospora*. In *Biochronometry*, ed. M Menaker, pp. 652–56. Washington, DC: Natl. Acad. Sci.

27. Feldman JF, Hoyle M. 1973. Isolation of circadian clock mutants of *Neurospora crassa*. *Genetics* 75:605–13

28. Springer ML. 1993. Genetic control of fungal differentiation: the three sporulation pathways of *Neurospora crassa*. *BioEssays* 15:365–74

29. Sargent M. 1985. *Neurospora* in the classroom. *Neurospora Newsl.* 2:12–13

30. Loros JJ, Denome SA, Dunlap JC. 1989. Molecular cloning of genes under the control of the circadian clock in *Neurospora*. *Science* 243:385–88

31. Garceau N, Liu Y, Loros JJ, Dunlap JC. 1997. Alternative initiation of translation and time-specific phosphorylation yield multiple forms of the essential clock protein FREQUENCY. *Cell* 89:469–76
32. Aronson B, Johnson K, Loros JJ, Dunlap JC. 1994. Negative feedback defining a circadian clock: autoregulation in the clock gene frequency. *Science* 263:1578–84
33. Perlman J, Nakashima H, Feldman J. 1981. Assay and characteristics of circadian rhythmicity in liquid cultures of *Neurospora crassa*. *Plant Physiol.* 67:404–7
34. Nakashima H. 1981. A liquid culture system for the biochemical analysis of the circadian clock of *Neurospora*. *Plant Cell Physiol.* 22:231–38
35. Loros J, Dunlap JC. 1991. *Neurospora crassa* clock-controlled genes are regulated at the level of transcription. *Mol. Cell. Biol.* 11:558–63
36. Heintzen C, Loros JJ, Dunlap JC. 2000. VIVID, light adaptation and the circadian clock: the PAS protein VVD defines a feedback loop that represses light input pathways and regulates clock resetting. *Cell* Submitted
37. Nakashima H, Onai K. 1996. The circadian conidiation rhythm in *Neurospora crassa*. *Semin. Cell Dev. Biol.* 7:765–74
38. Morgan L, Feldman J. 1997. Isolation and characterization of a temperature-sensitive circadian clock mutant in *Neurospora crassa*. *Genetics* 146:525–30
39. Goto R, Kaue R, Morishita M, Nakashima H. 1994. Effects of temperature on the circadian conidiation rhythm of temperature-sensitive mutants of *Neurospora crassa*. *Plant Cell Physiol.* 25:613–18
40. Pavlidis T. 1969. Populations of interacting oscillators and circadian rhythms. *J. Theor. Biol.* 22:418–36
41. Lee K, Loros JJ, Dunlap JC. 2000. Interconnected feedback loops in the *Neurospora* circadian system. *Science* 289:107–10
42. Aronson BD, Johnson KA, Dunlap JC. 1994. The circadian clock locus frequency: a single ORF defines period length and temperature compensation. *Proc. Natl. Acad. Sci. USA* 91:7683–87
43. Crosthwaite SC, Dunlap JC, Loros JJ. 1997. *Neurospora wc-1* and *wc-2*: transcription, photoresponses, and the origins of circadian rhythmicity. *Science* 276:763–69
44. Loros JJ, Feldman JF. 1986. Loss of temperature compensation of circadian period length in the *frq-9* mutant of *Neurospora crassa*. *J. Biol. Rhythms* 1:187–98
45. Collett M, Dunlap JC, Loros JJ. 2000. Altered circadian period length and temperature compensation in a partial loss of function mutant of *white collar-2*. *Mol. Cell. Biol.* In press
46. Merrow M, Garceau N, Dunlap JC. 1997. Dissection of a circadian oscillation into discrete domains. *Proc. Natl. Acad. Sci. USA* 94:3877–82
47. Crosthwaite SC, Loros JJ, Dunlap JC. 1995. Light-induced resetting of a circadian clock is mediated by a rapid increase in frequency transcript. *Cell* 81:1003–12
48. Liu Y, Merrow M, Loros JJ, Dunlap JC. 1998. How temperature changes reset a circadian oscillator. *Science* 281:825–29
49. Ballario P, Vittorioso P, Magrelli A, Talora C, Cabibbo A, Macino G. 1996. *White collar-1*, a central regulator of blue-light responses in *Neurospora crassa*, is a zinc-finger protein. *EMBO J.* 15:1650–57
50. Ballario P, Talora C, Galli D, Linden H, Macino G. 1998. Roles in dimerization and blue light photoresponse of the PAS and LOV domains of *Neurospora crassa* WHITE COLLAR proteins. *Mol. Microbiol.* 29:719–29
51. Linden H, Macino G. 1997. White collar-2, a partner in blue-light signal transduction, controlling expression of light-regulated genes in *Neurospora crassa*. *EMBO J.* 16:98–109

52. Linden H, Ballario P, Macino G. 1997. Blue light regulation in *Neurospora crassa*. *Fungal Genet. Biol.* 22:141–50

53. Talora C, Franchi L, Linden H, Ballario P, Macino G. 1999. Role of a *white collar-1-white collar-2* complex in blue-light signal transduction. *EMBO J.* 18:4961–68

54. Luo C, Loros JJ, Dunlap JC. 1998. Nuclear localization is required for function of the essential clock protein FREQUENCY. *EMBO J.* 17:1228–35

55. Denault DL, Loros JJ, Dunlap JC. 2000. Interacting positive and negative clock components within the circadian autoregulatory feedback loop of *Neurospora crassa*. *EMBO J.* In press

56. Liu Y, Loros J, Dunlap JC. 2000. Phosphorylation of the *Neurospora* clock protein FREQUENCY determines its degradation rate and strongly influences the period length of the circadian clock. *Proc. Natl. Acad. Sci. USA* 97:234–39

57. Lowrey PL, Shimomura K, Antoch MP, Yamazaki S, Zemenides PD, et al. 2000. Positional syntenic cloning and functional characterization of the mammalian circadian mutation tau. *Science* 288:483–92

58. Price JL, Blau J, Rothenfluh A, Adodeely M, Kloss B, Young MW. 1998. *double-time* is a new Drosophila clock gene that regulates PERIOD protein accumulation. *Cell* 94:83–95

59. Ruoff P, Mohsenzadeh S, Rensing L. 1996. Circadian rhythms and protein turnover: the influence of temperature on the period length of clock mutants simulated by the Goodwin oscillator. *Naturwissenschaften* 83:514–17

60. Ruoff P, Rensing L, Kommedal R, Mohsenzadeh S. 1997. Modeling temperature compensation in chemical and biological oscillators. *Chronobiol. Int.* 14:499–510

61. Ruoff P, Vinsjevik M, Mohsenzadeh S, Rensing L. 1999. The Goodwin model: simulating the effect of cycloheximide and heat shock on the sporulation rhythm of *Neurospora crassa*. *J. Theor. Biol.* 196:483–94

62. Ruoff P, Vinsjevik M, Mohsenzadeh S, Rensing L. 1999. The Goodwin oscillator: on the importance of degradation reaction in the circadian clock. *J. Biol. Rhythms* 14:469–79

63. King D, Zhao Y, Sangoram A, Wilsbacher L, Tanaka M, et al. 1997. Positional cloning of the mouse circadian CLOCK gene. *Cell* 89:641–53

63a. Reppert SM, Weaver DR. 2001. Molecular analysis of mammalian circadian rhythms. *Annu. Rev. Physiol.* 63:647–76

64. Arpaia G, Cerri F, Baima S, Macino G. 1999. Involvement of protein kinase C in the response of *Neurospora crassa* to blue light. *Mol. Gen. Genet.* 262:314–22

65. Glossup NJR, Lyons LC, Hardin PE. 1999. Interlocked feedback loops within the *Drosophila* circadian oscillator. *Science* 286:766–69

66. Shearman L, Sriram S, Weaver D, Maywood E, Chaves I, et al. 2000. Interacting molecular loops in the mammalian circadian clock. *Science* 288:1013–19

67. Schwerdtfeger C, Linden H. 2000. Localization and light-dependent phosphorylation of White Collar-1 and 2, the two central components of blue light signaling in *Neurospora crassa*. *Eur. J. Biochem.* 267:414–22

68. Bae K, Lee C, Hardin PE, Edery I. 2000. dCLOCK is present in limiting amounts and likely mediates daily interactions between the dCLOCK-CYC transcription factor and the PER-TIM complex. *J. Neurosci.* 20:1746–53

69. Rutila JE, Suri V, Le M, So WV, Rosbash M, Hall JC. 1998. CYCLE is a second bHLH-PAS clock protein essential for circadian rhythmicity and transcription of Drosophila *period* and *timeless*. *Cell* 93:805–13

70. Hogenesch JB, Gu Y-Z, Jain S,

Bradfield CA. 1998. The basic-helix-loop-helix-PAS orphan MOP3 forms transcriptionally active complexes with circadian and hypoxia factors. *Proc. Natl. Acad. Sci. USA* 95:5474–79

71. Lee C, Bae K, Edery I. 1998. The *Drosophila* CLOCK protein undergoes daily rhythms in abundance, phosphorylation, and interactions with the PER-TIM complex. *Neuron* 21:857–67

72. Bae K, Lee C, Sidote D, Chuang K-Y, Edery I. 1998. Circadian regulation of a *Drosophila* homolog of the mammalian *Clock* gene: PER and TIM function as positive regulators. *Mol. Cell. Biol.* 18:6142–51

73. Honma S, Ikeda M, Abe H, Tanahashi Y, Narmihira M, et al. 1998. Circadian oscillation of BMAL1, a partner of a mammalian clock gene *Clock*, in rat suprachiasmatic nucleus. *Biochem. Biophy. Res. Commun.* 250:83–87

74. Fleissner G, Fleissner G. 1992. Feedback loops in the circadian system. *Disc. Neurosci.* 8:79–84

75. Millar AJ, Kay SA. 1996. Integration of circadian and phototransduction pathways in the network controlling CAB gene transcription in *Arabidopsis. Proc. Natl. Acad. Sci. USA* 93:15491–96

76. Shigeyoshi Y, Taguchi K, Yamamoto S, Takeida S, Yan L, et al. 1997. Light-induced resetting of a mammalian circadian clock is associated with rapid induction of the *mPer1* transcript. *Cell* 91:1043–53

77. Shearman L, Zylka M, Weaver D, Kolakowski L, Reppert S. 1997. Two period homologs: circadian expression and photic regulation in the suprachiasmatic nuclei. *Neuron* 19:1261–69

78. Takumi T, Matsubara C, Shigeyoshi Y, Taguchi K, Yagita K, et al. 1998. A new mammalian period gene predominantly expressed in the suprachiasmatic nucleus. *Genes Cells* 3:167–76

79. Albrecht U, Sun Z, Eichele G, Lee C. 1997. A differential response of two putative mammalian circadian regulators, *mper1* and *mper2*, to light. *Cell* 91:1055–64

80. Deleted in proof

81. Sun S, Alsbrecht U, Zhuchenko O, Bailey J, Eichele G, Lee C. 1997. RIGUI, a putative mammalian ortholog of the Drosophila *period* gene. *Cell* 90:1003–11

82. Tei H, Okamura H, Shigeyoshi Y, Fukuhara C, Ozawa R, et al. 1997. Circadian oscillation of a mammalian homologue of the Drosophila *period* gene. *Nature* 389:512–16

83. Sawyer LA, Hennessy JM, Peixoto AA, Rosato E, Parkinson H, et al. 1997. Natural variation in a Drosophila clock gene and temperature compensation. *Science* 278:2117–20

84. Gooch VD, Wehseler RA, Gross CG. 1994. Temperature effects on the resetting of the phase of the *Neurospora* circadian rhythm. *J. Biol. Rhythms* 9:83–94

85. Winfree A. 1972. Acute temperature sensitivity of the circadian rhythm in *Drosophila. J. Insect Physiol.* 18:181–85

86. Zimmerman WF, Pittendrigh CS, Pavlidis T. 1968. Temperature compensation of the circadian oscillator in *Drosophila pseudoobscura* and its entrainment by temperature cycles. *J. Insect Physiol.* 14:669–84

87. Liu Y, Garceau N, Loros JJ, Dunlap JC. 1997. Thermally regulated translational control mediates an aspect of temperature compensation in the *Neurospora* circadian clock. *Cell* 89:477–86

88. Rosato E, Trevisan A, Sandrelli F, Zordan M, Kyriacou C, Costa R. 1997. Conceptual translation of *timeless* reveals alternative initiating methionines. *Nucleic Acids Res.* 25:455–57

89. Sidote D, Majercak J, Parikh V, Edery I. 1998. Differential effects of light and heat on the Drosophila circadian clock proteins PER and TIM. *Mol. Cell. Biol.* 18:2004–13

90. Loros JJ, Richman A, Feldman JF. 1986.

A recessive circadian clock mutant at the *frq* locus in *Neurospora crassa. Genetics* 114:1095–110

91. Merrow M, Bruner M, Roenneberg T. 1999. Assignment of circadian function for the *Neurospora* clock gene *frequency. Nature* 399:584–86

92. Iwasaki H, Dunlap JC. 2000. Microbial circadian oscillatory systems in *Neurospora* and *Synechococcus*: models for *Cellular* clocks. *Curr. Opin. Microbiol.* 3:189–96

93. McWatters H, Dunlap JC, Millar A. 1999. Clocks for the real world. *Curr. Biol.* 9:633–35

94. Roenneberg T, Merrow M. 1999. Circadian systems and metabolism. *J. Biol. Rhythms* 14:449–59

95. Leloup JC, Gonze D, Goldbeter A. 1999. Limit cycle models for circadian rhythms based on transcriptional regulation in *Drosophila* and *Neurospora. J. Biol. Rhythms* 14:433–38

96. Gonze D, Leloup JC, Goldbeter A. 2000. Theoretical models for circadian rhythms in *Neurospora* and *Drosophila. CR Acad. Sci.* 323:57–67

97. Taylor WR, Feldman JF. 1982. Nutritional manipulation of circadian period length of auxotrophic mutants. *Neurospora Newsl.* 29:12

98. Liu Q, Dunlap JC. 1996. Isolation and analysis of the *arg-13* gene of *Neurospora crassa. Genetics* 142:1163–74

99. Onai K, Nakashima H. 1997. Mutation of the *cys-9* gene, which encodes thioredoxin reductase, affects the circadian conidiation rhythm in *Neurospora crassa. Genetics* 146:101–10

100. Mattern DL. 1985. Unsaturated fatty acid isomers: effects on the circadian rhythm of a fatty-acid-deficient *Neurospora crassa* mutant. *Arch. Biochem. Biophys.* 237:402–10

101. Mattern DL, Forman LR, Brody S. 1982. Circadian rhythms in *Neurospora crassa*: a mutation affecting temperature compensation. *Proc. Natl. Acad. Sci. USA* 79:825–29

102. Mattern D, Brody S. 1979. Circadian rhythms in *Neurospora crassa*: effects of unsaturated fatty acids. *J. Bacteriol.* 139:977–88

103. Perkins DD, Radford A, Newmeyer D, Bjorkman M. 1982. Chromosomal loci of *Neurospora crassa. Microbiol. Rev.* 46:426–570

104. Lakin-Thomas P. 1998. Choline depletion, *frq* mutations, and temperature compensation of the circadian rhythm in *Neurospora crassa. J. Biol. Rhythms* 13:268–77

105. Sussman AS, Durkee T, Lowrey RJ. 1965. A model for rhythmic and temperature-independent growth in the "clock" mutants of *Neurospora. Mycopathol. Mycol. Appl.* 25:381–96

106. Lakin-Thomas P. 1996. Effects of choline depletion on the circadian rhythm in *Neurospora crassa. Biol. Rhythm Res.* 27:12–30

107. Ramsdale M, Lakin-Thomas PL. 2000. sn-1,2-diacylglycerol levels in the fungus *Neurospora crassa* display circadian rhythmicity. *J. Biol. Chem.* 275:27541–50

108. Lakin-Thomas PL, Brody S. 2000. Circadian rhythms in *Neurospora crassa. Proc. Natl. Acad. Sci. USA* 97:256–61

108a. Lakin-Thomas P. 2000. Circadian rhythms—new functions for old clock genes? *Trends Genet.* 16:135–42

109. Edmunds LN Jr. 1988. *Cellular and Molecular Bases of Biological Clocks.* New York: Springer-Verlag. 497 pp.

110. Stadler DR. 1959. Genetic control of a cyclic growth pattern in *Neurospora. Nature* 184:170–71

111. Roeder PE, Sargent ML, Brody S. 1982. Circadian rhythms in *Neurospora crassa*: oscillations in fatty acids. *Biochemistry* 21:4909–16

112. Rensing L, Bos A, Kroeger J, Cornelius G. 1987. Possible link between circadian

rhythm and heat shock response in *Neurospora crassa*. *Chronobiol. Int.* 4:543–49

113. Kloppstech K. 1985. Diurnal and circadian rhythmicity in the expression of light-induced plant nuclear messenger RNAs. *Planta* 165:502–6

114. Nagy F, Kay SA, Chua N-H. 1988. A circadian clock regulates transcription of the wheat *Cab-1* gene. *Genes Dev.* 2:376–82

115. Bernard M, Klein DC, Zatz M. 1997. Chick pineal clock regulates serotonin *N*-acetyltransferase mRNA rhythm in culture. *Proc. Natl. Acad. Sci. USA* 94:304–9

116. Coon SL, Roseboom PH, Baler R, Weller JL, Namboodiri A, et al. 1995. Pineal serotonin *N*-acetyltransferase: expression cloning and molecular analysis. *Science* 270:1681–83

117. Sarov-Blat L, So WV, Liu L, Rosbash M. 2000. The Drosophila *takeout* gene is a novel molecular link between circadian rhythms and feeding behavior. *Cell* 101:647–56

118. Green CB, Besharse JC. 1996. Identification of a novel vertebrate circadian clock-regulated gene encoding the protein nocturnin. *Proc. Natl. Acad. Sci. USA* 93:14884–88

119. Bell-Pedersen D, Shinohara M, Loros J, Dunlap JC. 1996. Circadian clock-controlled genes isolated from *Neurospora crassa* are late night to early morning specific. *Proc. Natl. Acad. Sci. USA* 93:13096–101

120. Bell-Pedersen D, Dunlap JC, Loros JJ. 1996. Distinct *cis*-acting elements mediate clock, light, and developmental regulation of the *Neurospora crassa eas* (*ccg-2*) gene. *Mol. Cell. Biol.* 16:513–21

121. Lauter F-R, Yanofsky C. 1993. Day/night and circadian rhythm control of *con* gene expression in *Neurospora*. *Proc. Natl. Acad. Sci. USA* 90:8249–53

122. Berlin V, Yanofsky C. 1985. Isolation of conidiation-specific genes in *Neurospora*. *Mol. Cell. Biol.* 5:849–55

123. Lee K, Ebbole DJ. 1998. Tissue-specific repression of starvation and stress responses of the *Neurospora crassa con-10* gene is mediated by RCO1. *Fungal Genet. Biol.* 23:268–78

124. Lee K, Ebbole DJ. 1998. Analysis of two transcriptional activation elements in the promoter of the developmentally regulated *con-10* gene of *Neurospora crassa*. *Fungal Genet. Biol.* 23:259–68

125. Arpaia G, Carattoli A, Macino G. 1995. Light and development regulate the expression of the *albino-3* gene in *Neurospora crassa*. *Dev. Biol.* 170:626–35

126. Bell-Pedersen D, Dunlap JC, Loros JJ. 1992. The *Neurospora* circadian clock-controlled gene, *ccg-2*, is allelic to *eas* and encodes a fungal hydrophobin required for formation of the conidial rodlet layer. *Genes Dev.* 6:2382–94

127. Lauter F, Russo V, Yanofsky C. 1992. Developmental and light regulation of *eas*, the structural gene for the rodlet protein of *Neurospora*. *Genes Dev.* 6:2373–81

128. Wessels JG. 1999. Fungi in their own right. *Fungal Genet. Biol.* 27:134–45

129. Talbot N. 1999. Fungal biology. Coming up for air and sporulation. *Nature* 398:295–96

130. Shinohara ML, Correa A, Bell-Pedersen D, Loros JJ, Dunlap JC. 2001. The *Neurospora crassa-controlled gene-9* (*ccg-9*) encodes a novel form of trehalose synthase required for circadian-regulated conidiation. *Mol. Cell. Biol.* Submitted

131. Garceau N. 1996. *Molecular and genetic studies on the frq and ccg-1 loci of Neurospora*. PhD thesis. Dartmouth Coll.: Hanover, NH. 212 pp.

132. Lindgren KM. 1994. *Characterization of ccg-1, a clock-controlled gene of Neurospora crassa*. PhD thesis. Dartmouth Coll.: Hanover, NH. 222 pp.

133. McNally M, Free S. 1988. Isolation and characterization of a *Neurospora* glucose repressible gene. *Curr. Genet.* 14:545–51

134. Hafker T, Techel D, Steier G, Rensing L. 1998. Differential expression of glucose-regulated (grp78) and heat-shock-inducible (hsp70) genes during asexual development of *Neurospora crassa*. *Microbiology* 144:37–43

135. Shinohara M, Loros JJ, Dunlap JC. 1998. Glyceraldehyde-3-phosphate dehydrogenase is regulated on a daily basis by the circadian clock. *J. Biol. Chem.* 273:446–52

136. Fagan T, Morse D, Hastings JW. 1999. Circadian synthesis of a nuclear-encoded chloroplast glyceraldehyde-3-phosphate dehydrogenase in the dinoflagellate *Gonyaulax polyedra* is translationally controlled. *Biochemistry* 38:7689–95

136a. Zhu H, Nowrousian M, Kupfer D, Colot HV, Berrocal-Tito G, et al. 2000. Analysis of ESTs from two starvation, time of day-specific libraries of *Neurospora crassa* reveals novel clock-controlled genes. *Genetics*. Submitted

137. Altschul SF, Madden TL, Schaffer AA, Zhang J, Zhang Z, et al. 1997. Gapped BLAST and PSI-BLAST: a new generation of protein database search programs. *Nucleic Acids Res.* 25:3389–402

138. Braun EL, Halpern AL, Nelson MA, Natvig DO. 2000. Large-scale comparison of fungal sequence information: mechanisms of innovation in *Neurospora crassa* and gene loss in *Saccharomyces cerevisiae*. *Genome Res.* 10:416–30

139. Nelson MA, Kang S, Braun E, Crawford M, Dolan P, et al. 1997. Expressed sequences form conidial, mycelial, and sexual stages of *Neurospora*. *Fungal Genet. Biol.* 21:348–63

140. Eisen MB, Spellman PT, Brown PO, Botstein D. 1998. Cluster analysis and display of genome-wide expression patterns. *Proc. Natl. Acad. Sci. USA* 95:14863–68

141. Susuki S, Katagiri S, Nakashima H. 1996. Mutants with altered sensitivity to a calmodulin antagonist affect the circadian clock in *Neurospora*. *Genetics* 143:1175–80

142. Feldman JF. 1982. Genetic approaches to circadian clocks. *Annu. Rev. Plant Physiol.* 33:583–608

143. Gardner GF, Feldman JF. 1981. Temperature compensation of circadian periodicity in clock mutants of *Neurospora crassa*. *Plant Physiol.* 68:1244–48

144. Feldman JF, Gardner GF, Dennison RA. 1979. Genetic analysis of the circadian clock of *Neurospora*. In *Biological Rhythms and their Central Mechanism*, ed. M Suda, pp. 57–66. Amsterdam: Elsevier

145. Brody S, MacKensie L, Chuman L. 1987. Circadian rhythms in *Neurospora crassa*: the effects of mitochondrial mutations and inhibitors. *Genetics* 116:S30

146. Lakin-Thomas P, Cot Ç G, Brody S. 1990. Circadian rhythms in *Neurospora*. *CRC Crit. Rev. Microbiol.* 17:365–416

147. Feldman JF, Widelitz R. 1977. Manipulation of circadian periodicity in cysteine auxotrophs of *Neurospora crassa*. *Ann. Meet. Am. Soc. Microbiol. Abstr.* 158

148. Gardner GF, Feldman JF. 1980. The *frq* locus in *Neurospora crassa*: a key element in circadian clock organization. *Genetics* 96:877–86

149. Dieckmann C, Brody S. 1980. Circadian rhythms in *Neurospora crassa*: oligomycin-resistant mutations affect periodicity. *Science* 207:896–98

150. Feldman JF, Atkinson CA. 1978. Genetic and physiological characterization of a slow growing circadian clock mutant of *Neurospora crassa*. *Genetics* 88:255–65

151. Onai K, Katagiri S, Akiyama M, Nakashima H. 1998. Mutation of the gene for the second largest subunit of the RNA polymerase I prolongs the period length of the circadian conidiation rhythm in *Neurospora crassa*. *Mol. Gen. Genet.* 259:264–71

152. Chang B, Nakashima H. 1998. Isolation of temperature sensitive rhythm mutant in *Neurospora crassa*. *Genes Genet. Syst.* 73:71–3

153. Katagiri S, Onai K, Nakashima H. 1998. Spermidine determines the sensitivity to the calmodulin antagonist, chlorpromazine, for the circadian conidiation rhythm but not for the mycelial growth in *Neurospora crassa*. *J. Biol. Rhythms* 13:452–60

154. Brody S, Willert K, Chuman L. 1988. Circadian rhythms in *Neurospora crassa*: the effects of mutations at the *ufa* and *cla-1* loci. *Genome* 30(Suppl.):299

155. Collett M, Dunlap JC, Loros JJ. 2001. Rhythms defects in the clock-affecting strain *cla-1* are due to a re-isolation of the *frq*[7] allele. *Fungal Genet. Newsl.* Submitted

156. Kaldenhoff R, Russo VE. 1993. Promoter analysis of the *bli-7/eas* gene. *Curr. Genet.* 24:394–99

157. Munger K, Germann UA, Lerch K. 1987. The *Neurospora crassa* metallothionein gene. Regulation of expression and chromosomal location. *J. Biol. Chem.* 262:7363–67

158. Eberle J, Russo VE. 1994. *Neurospora crassa* blue light-inducible gene *bli-3*. *Biochem. Mol. Biol. Int.* 34:737–44

Annu. Rev. Physiol. 2001. 63:795–813

DYNAMIC SIGNALING BETWEEN ASTROCYTES AND NEURONS

Alfonso Araque[1], Giorgio Carmignoto[2], and Philip G Haydon[3]

[1]Instituto Cajal, CSIC, Doctor Arce 37, Madrid 28002, Spain;
e-mail: araque@cajal.csic.es;
[2]Department of Experimental Biomedical Sciences, and CNR Center for the Study of
Biomembranes, University of Padova, 35121 Padova, Italy;
e-mail: gcarmi@civ.bio.unipd.it;
[3]Department of Zoology and Genetics, Roy J. Carver Laboratory for Ultrahigh Resolution
Biological Microscopy, Iowa State University, Ames, Iowa 50011;
e-mail: pghaydon@iastate.edu

Key Words glia, glutamate, synapse, plasticity, modulation

■ **Abstract** Astrocytes, a sub-type of glia in the central nervous system, are dynamic signaling elements that integrate neuronal inputs, exhibit calcium excitability, and can modulate neighboring neurons. Neuronal activity can lead to neurotransmitter-evoked activation of astrocytic receptors, which mobilizes their internal calcium. Elevations in astrocytic calcium in turn trigger the release of chemical transmitters from astrocytes, which can cause sustained modulatory actions on neighboring neurons. Astrocytes, and perisynaptic Schwann cells, by virtue of their intimate association with synapses, are strategically positioned to regulate synaptic transmission. This capability, that has now been demonstrated in several studies, raises the untested possibility that astrocytes are an integral element of the circuitry for synaptic plasticity. Because the highest ratio of glia-to-neurons is found at the top of the phylogenetic tree in the human brain, these recent demonstrations of dynamic bi-directional signaling between astrocytes and neurons leave us with the question as to whether astrocytes are key regulatory elements of higher cortical functions.

BACKGROUND

Since the original discovery and description of glia, these non-neuronal cells were largely ignored or believed to play roles in the nervous system that were subservient to those of neurons. The lack of understanding of their functional roles probably resulted from the inability of the available techniques to reveal dynamic properties of these cells. However, even during the early period of glial investigations, Cajal recognized that they were likely to have roles beyond passive functions.

The prejudice that the relation between neuroglial fibers and neuronal cells is similar to the relation between connective tissue and muscle or gland cells, that is, a passive weft for merely filling and support (and in the best case, a gangue for taking nutritive juices), constitutes the main obstacle that the researcher needs to remove to get a rational concept about the activity of the neuroglia.

—S Ramón y Cajal (1)

During this initial period of documentation of the structural features of the nervous system, significant focus turned to neurons as a result of the recognition that their electrical excitability permitted them to convey relevant information in the nervous system. In contrast, as anyone who has recorded from glial cells knows, the membrane potential of glia is relatively stable, and although they can express voltage-gated channels (2–6), they exhibit little or no fluctuation in membrane potential. Indeed, early electrophysiological studies demonstrated that glial cells were electrically inexcitable and responded only passively to neuronal activity by sensing extracellular potassium levels (7). Only during the past 10 to 15 years, with the advent of molecular biology, the patch-clamp technique, and ion imaging methods have the potentially diverse dynamic roles of glial cells begun to be appreciated. Our objective in this review article is to focus attention on one of the most recently identified roles of glial cells—as integrators and modulators of neuronal activity and synaptic transmission.[4]

Glial cells of the central nervous system can be divided into two groups, micro- and macroglia. Microglia are macrophage-like cells that serve a phagocytic function. Macroglia are composed of two types of cell; oligodendrocytes, which are the central equivalent of the myelinating Schwann cell, and astrocytes, the glial cells, which are the focus of much of our discussion. Additionally we will include an examination of the properties of perisynaptic Schwann cells because they intimately interact with the nerve muscle junction in a manner akin to the astrocyte and the central synapse.

PROXIMITY OF ASTROCYTES TO NEURONS

Astrocytes are positioned to act as a conduit for the routing of signals between different cell types in the nervous system (Figure 1, see color insert). Because the same astrocyte can make contact with a neuron and a capillary, it has the potential to shuffle nutrients and metabolites between the blood supply and the active neuron. Indeed, this structural association led to the initial ideas about astrocytes playing metabolic roles in the nervous system. Furthermore, because a single astrocyte can make contacts with multiple neurons, these non-neuronal cells are

---

[4]Color images and digital movies that supplement this review are available on the World Wide Web in the supplemental section of the main Annual Reviews site (http://www. AnnualReviews.org).

also positioned to provide information transfer between neighboring neurons, an intriguing potential role that has only been recently appreciated. Examination of the nervous system at the ultrastructural level has shown that astrocytes can be intimately associated with the synapse, literally enwrapping many pre- and postsynaptic terminals. In the hippocampus, 57% of the axon-spine interfaces are associated with astrocytes (8). In the cerebellum there are eight Bergmann glia for each Purkinje cell, and each Bergmann cell ensheaths between 2142 and 6358 synapses (9). It is likely that this close physical relationship provides an opportunity for many functional interactions between astrocytes and neurons. We discuss the potential role of astrocytes in integrating synaptic signals and providing feedback responses, in the form of the release of the transmitter glutamate, which regulates neuronal excitability and synaptic function (10). However, our focus on this area is not meant to diminish the importance of other roles of astrocytes, for example, in the clearance of elevated extracellular K^+ from the extracellular space (11), as well as in the uptake of neurotransmitters from the synapse (12, 13). However, since these functional roles, as well as other metabolic and structural functions, have been the topic of many review articles, our discussion of these issues is limited.

Astrocytes Possess a Form of Excitability Based on Variations of Intracellular Calcium

The development of optical probes and methods to study intracellular ions in living cells provided the technological capability to make breakthroughs in our understanding of astrocyte functions. In the late 1980s and early 1990s numerous studies demonstrated that astrocytes exhibit calcium excitability. Calcium-imaging studies changed our view of astrocytes. These investigations demonstrated that astrocytes, once thought to be relatively passive cells, express functional receptors for many different neurotransmitters that lead to changes in intracellular calcium levels and even to oscillations in internal calcium (14–23).

In many examples, neurotransmitters elevate astrocytic calcium levels as a result of the release of calcium from internal stores. For example, ATP, acting through $P2Y_1$ receptors, and presumably the GTP-binding protein G_q, activate phospholipase C, leading to the formation of inositol triphosphate (IP_3) (24). Subsequently IP_3 activates the IP_3 receptors of endoplasmic reticulum calcium stores, leading to the release of calcium into the cytosol. This IP_3-mediated release of calcium from internal stores is a mechanism that is shared by many neurotransmitters including glutamate, ATP, and acetylcholine (ACh) (14, 23).

Many of the initial studies demonstrating calcium excitability of astrocytes were performed in cell culture, which raised concerns about whether this property was representative of the physiological state of these cells in the intact nervous system (14). Studies using acutely isolated brain slices have supported the calcium excitability property of astrocytes and have demonstrated that transmitters including glutamate, γ-aminobutyric acid (GABA), norepinephrine, histamine, ATP, and ACh do regulate the internal calcium levels of astrocytes (14, 16, 23, 25–33).

Waves of Calcium Elevation Within and Between Astrocytes

Calcium elevations in astrocytes can propagate along the processes of the cell so that a localized elevation of internal calcium can eventually initiate calcium signals throughout the processes of that cell (Figure 2, see color insert). This wave of intracellular calcium elevation may be important because, like the neuronal action potential, it might relay information to other regions of the cell about inputs located on distant processes.

In cell culture, intracellular calcium waves have frequently been shown to propagate between astrocytes and cause a wave of calcium elevation that can continue for hundreds of micrometers (20, 34–37). The mechanism of generation of the intercellularly propagating calcium wave has been the focus of significant debate. Several studies have suggested a role for gap junctions in mediating intercellular signaling in such calcium waves, whereas more recently, a role for an extracellular signal has become appreciated. Because addition of gap junction blockers can block calcium waves, it was initially hypothesized that gap junctions permit the intercellular spread of IP_3 between neighboring cells. In support of this hypothesis, it has been demonstrated that glia cell lines, which do not form gap junctions and do not exhibit calcium waves, can be made to do so by the expression of connexins, which permits the formation of gap junctions (38). While these data support a role of gap junctions in calcium wave propagation, increasing evidence supports the presence of an extracellular signal. For example, calcium waves were shown to cross cell-free gaps between cells (39), the direction of a wave could be affected by local perfusion of the extracellular saline (39), and waves were still present in cultured astrocytes of connexin 43 knockout mice (40, 41). Furthermore, purine receptor antagonists or extracellularly applied Apyrase (an ATPase) decreased the propagation of the calcium wave (36, 42). Additionally, studies using luciferin and luciferase demonstrated that ATP can be released from astrocytes during a calcium wave, suggesting that ATP is the extracellular signal involved in the calcium wave propagation (36, 42).

Thus evidence supports the possibility of an important role for gap junctions, as well as extracellular ATP, in mediating calcium waves. Although these data seem contradictory, the expression of connexins increases the release of ATP from astrocytes (42, 43). How the connexins couple to ATP release is unknown, but its expression helps put together a rational explanation for data that had seemed contradictory. Despite this convergence of data, intercellular diffusion of messengers may also, under certain conditions, mediate some forms of calcium wave.

Recently, the role for ATP in mediating calcium waves has been further supported by the use of ATP imaging techniques (44). In these studies photon-counting imaging was used to detect the presence of ATP in the saline solution around astrocytes. Astrocytes were bathed in a saline solution containing luciferin and luciferase. Stimulation of a calcium wave was shown to be correlated with a wave of extracellular ATP. By chopping between chemiluminescence measurements of extracellular ATP and fluorescence detection of calcium levels, this study showed the appropriate correlated timing of the calcium and ATP waves. Additionally, the application of the ATP antagonist, suramin, blocked the ATP and calcium waves. Taken together, these studies indicate that ATP causes an elevation of astrocytic internal calcium and an additional release of ATP. Presumably this ATP-induced ATP release is critical for the spread of the calcium waves in cell cultures. In addition to ATP acting as an extracellular signal critical for calcium wave propagation, a recent study has demonstrated that nitric oxide might also regulate calcium waves (45).

Although waves of elevated internal calcium have been repeatedly observed in cell cultures, their presence in the CNS is less clear. An intracellular calcium wave can propagate throughout the processes of a given astrocyte (Figure 2) (46); however, intercellular waves have not been seen in acutely isolated preparations of hippocampus (25, 46). In the retina, however, concentrically propagating waves of elevated calcium can be initiated in astrocytes and Müller cells, the two principal glial cells of the retina (47). In contrast to the lack of calcium waves in hippocampal slices, organotypic cultures of the hippocampus do exhibit long-range calcium signals (15, 18, 48). Perhaps the presence of the calcium wave in slice cultures represents a change in property that is associated with injury and the transformation to reactive astrocytes. This is an intriguing possibility because it might indicate that reactive astrocytes are hyperexcitable with a lower threshold for calcium oscillations. The functional impact of such enhanced excitability is not yet clear.

ASTROCYTES INTEGRATE NEURONAL INPUTS

Astrocytes express many neurotransmitter receptors and transporters that have the potential to be activated by synaptically released neurotransmitters (49–51). In addition, as discussed above, astrocytes possess a number of neurotransmitter receptors coupled to intracellular calcium mobilization. Therefore, a potential functional consequence of the ability of neurotransmitters to mobilize astrocytic calcium is that neuronal activity could regulate astrocytic calcium levels. Indeed, several laboratories have demonstrated that astrocytes and perisynaptic Schwann cells do respond to synaptic activity through the activation of glial receptors.

The perisynaptic Schwann cells that loosely wrap the nerve terminal at the neuromuscular junctions play different functions and express different molecules than myelinating Schwann cells. Measurements of intracellular calcium in these perisynaptic Schwann cells have shown that, just as with astrocytes, they can respond to neurotransmitters with elevations of their internal calcium level (52, 53). Stimulation of the presynaptic axons can, in addition to causing the end plate potential, evoke a substantial elevation of perisynaptic Schwann cell calcium (52). It has been difficult to unequivocally determine which neurotransmitter evokes these calcium changes. Two candidates are ATP and ACh, which are co-released from the nerve terminal. Experimental data are consistent with roles for activity-dependent ATP release contributing to the induced calcium elevation in the perisynaptic Schwann cell (29). ACh might also be involved in such responses although this possibility has been difficult to test because of the lack of availability of good muscarinic antagonists for this system (28).

Studies with hippocampal slices have demonstrated that neuronal activity causes glutamate-dependent astrocytic calcium elevations. Organotypic cultures of hippocampal slices were initially utilized to test the hypothesis that neuronal activity could regulate astrocyte calcium levels. Indeed following stimulation of mossy fibers, calcium levels were elevated in cells, located in area CA3 of the hippocampus, that were later shown to be glial fibrillary acidic protein (GFAP) positive (18). Studies using acutely isolated slices have also demonstrated the presence of this neuron-to-astrocyte pathway. In the hippocampus, as well as in the visual cortex, high (but not low) frequency stimulation of neuronal afferents triggers repetitive intracellular calcium elevations in astrocytes (25, 46). In the presence of either tetrodotoxin (TTX) or the metabotropic glutamate receptor (mGluR) antagonist α-methyl-4-carboxyphenylglycine (MCPG), the astrocyte response is abolished, thus providing evidence that glutamate released from active synaptic terminals can activate astrocytic mGluRs and trigger intracellular calcium oscillations. The additional observation that an increase in neuronal firing results in an increase in the frequency of intracellular calcium oscillations in astrocytes suggests, on the one hand, that the frequency of these intracellular calcium oscillations is under dynamic control by neuronal activity and, on the other hand, that astrocytes possess the remarkable capacity to discriminate between different levels and patterns of synaptic activity. The frequency of intracellular calcium oscillations may ultimately represent the code of neuron-astrocyte signaling (46).

Glutamate is not the only neuronally released transmitter that controls astrocytic calcium. Stimulation of GABAergic interneurons in hippocampal slices can elevate the calcium level of nearby astrocytes, an action that is blocked by the GABA$_B$ receptor antagonist CGP55845A and mimicked by baclofen (31). Application of norepinephrine (16, 33, 54), histamine, or acetylcholine (32) mobilizes astrocytic calcium in hippocampal slices, and stimulation of either the molecular or granule cell layer of the cerebellum causes an α_1 adrenoreceptor-dependent elevation of Bergmann glial calcium (54). Because electron micrographs have shown putative noradrenergic terminals making synaptic-like contacts with astrocytes (55, 56), these data suggest that extrinsic axon pathways can act on target astrocytes to regulate astrocytic calcium.

The elaborate ramified structure of astrocytes, which individually make contact with numerous neurons and synapses, raises questions about the relative autonomy of distinct regions of a given astrocyte. Put another way, does an individual site of neurotransmitter action on an astrocyte lead to a global change in the astrocytic calcium, or can individual sites act as functionally isolated regions? Stimulation of parallel fibers causes a calcium elevation in Bergmann glia of the cerebellum (57). These neuronally evoked calcium elevations can be highly localized to distinct domains in a glial cell, suggesting that glia can be functionally compartmentalized (57). Imaging studies also clearly show that in hippocampal astrocytes a calcium elevation can either propagate along the astrocytic process to promote coherent activity of the processes of that cell or remain restricted to that process (Figure 2) (46). Because one astrocyte makes many intimate contacts with numerous synapses, an understanding of the conditions that lead to the switch between local and global calcium signals in an astrocyte is likely to guide our understanding of the roles of these calcium signals in astrocyte function.

NEURONAL ACTIVITY CAN INDUCE ASTROCYTIC PLASTICITY

In the adult nervous system, we now know that the synaptic connections between neurons are subject to reorganization, a process that underlies learning and memory. Indeed, it was recently established that individual dendritic spines extend during the induction of long-term potentiation (LTP) (58, 59). Whether astrocytes exhibit similar structural plasticity and whether such a process would be important for synaptic plasticity are not clear. However, testosterone treatment causes a rapid stellation of astrocytes in the arcuate nucleus (60–62), and in cell culture the application of glutamate causes the extension of filopodia from astrocytes (63). While we do not know whether neural activity triggers structural change in astrocytes, it is clear that these non-neuronal cells can integrate neural information and respond with long-term changes in certain properties. For example, multiple applications of glutamate, or the delivery of multiple afferent stimuli, lead to prolonged changes in the frequency of oscillations of astrocytic calcium levels (46, 64). Axonal activity can regulate GFAP expression in perisynaptic Schwann cells (65). Finally, the activity-dependent nonsynaptic release of ATP from sensory neurons regulates Schwann cell internal calcium levels in culture and the expression of the immediate early genes c-*fos* and *krox-24* (66). Because astrocytes have been shown to be important regulators of synaptogenesis (67, 68), the relation between astrocytes, astrocytic structural dynamics, and the formation of new synapses during plasticity is an exciting area for future study.

BI-DIRECTIONAL GLUTAMATE-MEDIATED SIGNALING BETWEEN ASTROCYTES AND NEURONS

Astrocytes not only integrate neurotransmitter inputs but also can release their own transmitters that act on neighboring neurons (10). Thus there is a bi-directional signaling pathway between astrocytes and neurons, which opens the possibility for a rich information exchange in the nervous system. Our initial insights into the presence of an astrocyte-to-neuron signaling pathway that is mediated by the release of chemical transmitters were obtained from cell culture studies and later confirmed and extended using more intact preparations (Figure 3, see color insert).

Starting in 1994 there was a sequence of four reports demonstrating that elevations of astrocytic calcium lead to delayed elevations in neuronal calcium

(17, 35, 69, 70). One problem in this type of study, however, is in providing selective stimuli that would lead to the activation of only the astrocyte. To overcome this obstacle, either mechanical or focal electrical stimulation was provided. Such stimuli raised calcium in an astrocyte that then spread as a radially propagating wave of elevated calcium among the astrocytic network. As the calcium wave passed underneath co-cultured neurons, a delayed neuronal calcium elevation was detected (17, 35, 69, 70). Initially, the mechanism underlying this astrocyte-to-neuron signal was not clear, and electrotonic coupling between astrocytes and neurons was suggested to mediate the pathway (69). However, with no initial evidence supporting gap junctions connecting astrocytes and neurons, this hypothesis fell into disfavor, and the presence of a chemical signal that was released from the astrocyte became more popular.

The addition of neuroligands that elevate astrocytic internal calcium was shown to cause the calcium-dependent release of glutamate. When neurons were co-cultured with astrocytes, either mechanical stimulation of an astrocyte to raise its calcium level (17, 35), or application of the neuroligand, bradykinin (17), which elevates astrocyte calcium, caused a delayed neuronal calcium elevation that was sensitive to glutamate receptor antagonists. Further support for glutamate-mediated signaling from astrocytes to neurons was obtained by electrophysiological studies demonstrating that calcium elevations in astrocytes induce a glutamate-dependent slow inward current, or a depolarization, in neurons (35, 71, 72).

These cell culture studies paved the way for many subsequent exciting studies about the bi-directional signaling between astrocytes and neurons. However, because they were performed in culture, it was essential that similar experiments were performed in more intact preparations in order to determine whether this phenomenon represents a physiological signaling pathway or merely a curiosity of cell culture. Confocal imaging studies performed using hippocampal and visual cortex slices provided the first demonstration of the presence of bi-directional signaling between astrocytes and neurons (46). When mGluR agonists were applied to slices, astrocytic calcium was elevated, which was followed by a delayed neuronal calcium spike that was sensitive to the ionotropic glutamate receptor antagonists 2,3-dihydroxy-6-nitro-7-sulphamoylbenzo(f)-quinoxalinedione (NBQX) and D-2-amino-5-phosphonopentanoic acid (D-AP5) (46). Taken together with the results from enzymatic glutamate assays (37, 73), these data provided the first compelling demonstration of the presence of not only neurotransmitter-mediated neuron-to-astrocyte signaling but also of chemical transmitter-mediated astrocyte-to-neuron modulation.

Although several lines of evidence support the notion that glutamate is a chemical transmitter that mediates astrocyte-neuron signaling, other transmitters might also underlie signaling in this pathway. Recent work has reported that D-serine is an endogenous ligand of the glycine site of N-methyl-D-aspartate (NMDA) receptors responsible for modulating NMDA receptor-mediated synaptic transmission in cultured hippocampal neurons (74). Because the serine racemase responsible for the biosynthesis of D-serine from L-serine is highly expressed by glial cells, and

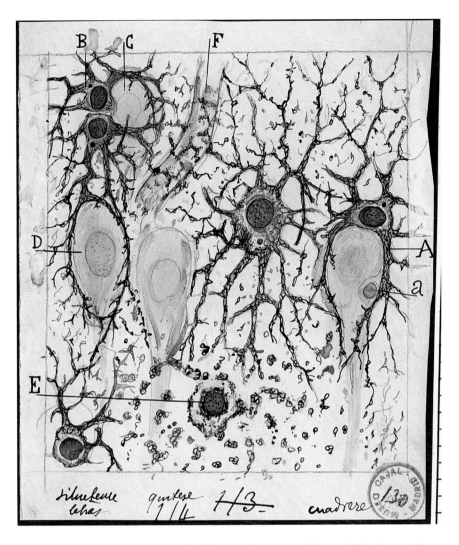

Figure 1 "Neuroglia of the pyramidal layer and stratum radiatum of the Ammon horn. Adult man autopsied three hours after death. Chloride of gold. (*A*) big astrocyte embracing a pyramidal neuron. (*B*) twin astrocytes forming a nest around a cell (*C*), while one of them sends two branches forming another nest (*D*). (*E*) cell with signs of autolysis" (1). Figure reproduced from original drawing with permission of Legado Cajal.

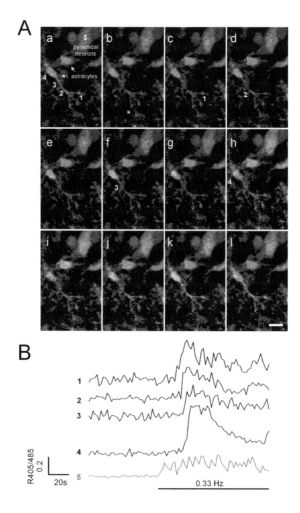

Figure 2 Propagation of internal calcium changes along astrocytic processes. (*A*) Time series of pseudocolor images illustrating the spreading of an internal calcium elevation along the process of an astrocyte that is located in area CA1 of the hippocampus. The calcium response in the astrocyte was triggered by stimulation of Schaffer collaterals at 0.33 Hz, i.e. train of pulses delivered at 30 Hz for 100 ms that were applied every 3s. Slices were obtained from a nine-day old rat and loaded with the calcium indicator Indo-1. Labels 1—4 indicate discrete portions of the astrocyte processes; label 5 indicates a pyramidal neuron. The time interval between images a—h is 2 s; between h-l is 12 s. Scale bar 10 µm. (*B*) Kinetics of the internal calcium changes as measured at the level of different portions of the astrocytic process and soma shown in *A* upon neuronal stimulation. The kinetics of the calcium change in neuron 5 is also reported. It is noteworthy that in image *A*b, the process indicated by the asterisk displayed a transient and localized calcium elevation that remained restricted to the process.

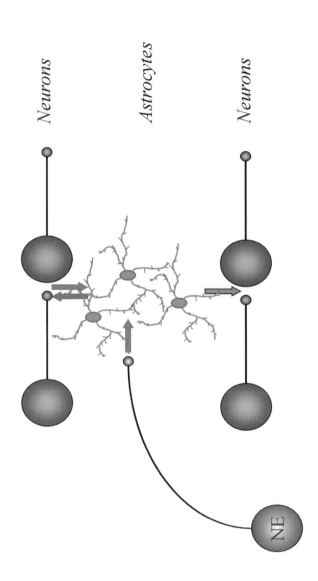

Figure 3 Bi-directional signaling between astrocytes and neurons. Activity at synaptic connections (*top*) can lead to neurotransmitter signaling from neurons to astrocytes (red arrow), which mobilizes calcium in the adjacent astrocytes (blue). Calcium elevations in astrocytes can then initiate feedback signals (green arrows) in the form of the release of chemical transmitters, which modulate either the initiatally active synapse, or more distant synapses (green arrow, *bottom*). In addition to intrinsic synapses leading to the activation of astrocytes, extrinsic axonal inputs, which can form apparent release sites directly with astrocytes, can also mobilize astrocytic calcium and potentially lead to the calcium-dependent release of chemical transmitters from astrocytes onto neighboring neurons and synapses. In this example, NE represents the neurotransmitter norepinephrine.

astrocytes possess high levels of D-serine (75) that can be released from astrocytes upon stimulation with glutamate (76), D-serine might represent a newly identified messenger for astrocyte-neuron signaling. Thus it would appear that D-serine (76), ATP (44), secretogranin II (77), and glutamate (17) are chemical transmitters that can be released from astrocytes in a regulated manner. It will be intriguing to determine the numbers of different chemical transmitters that different astrocytes release and to ask whether astrocytes release as large a variety of transmitters as neurons.

MECHANISM OF GLUTAMATE RELEASE FROM ASTROCYTES

In order to unravel the functional consequences of glutamate-mediated astrocyte-to-neuron signaling, it is essential that a mechanistic understanding of the release pathway is gained. Three prominent mechanisms have been suggested as potential pathways to underlie the release of glutamate from astrocytes (78): reverse operation of glutamate transporters, swelling-induced release, and calcium-dependent exocytosis. Glial cells are known to express high levels of glutamate transporters that normally function to clear glutamate from the extracellular space, especially in the vicinity of the synapse. Under conditions of depolarization or when the Na^+/K^+ electrochemical gradient used by these transporters has been reversed, glutamate can be released through these transporters (79). This does not underlie calcium-dependent glutamate release because ligands that cause glutamate release do not depolarize astrocytes, and transport inhibitors do not attenuate the magnitude of ligand-induced glutamate release (17, 72, 73, 80). Although swelling can lead to significant liberation of glutamate from astrocytes (81), imaging studies designed to monitor cell volume have demonstrated an absence of volumetric change during or after addition of ligands that cause calcium-dependent glutamate release (73, 82).

The calcium-dependent release of neurotransmitters is caused, in neurons, by the exocytosis of quanta of neurotransmitter-filled vesicles from the nerve terminal. While this property was initially thought to be a unique property of neuronal and exocrine tissues, there are several examples of quantal transmitter release from atypical preparations. For example, during patch recordings from myocytes, ACh quanta are detected when the cell is dialyzed with this transmitter (83). Similarly patch recordings from fibroblasts have demonstrated the presence of calcium-dependent quantal transmitter release (83, 84). To test the possibility that the release of glutamate from astrocytes is mediated by a vesicular mechanism, a variety of studies have been performed. First, the potent secretagogue, α-latrotoxin, which induces the exocytosis of vesicles at nerve terminals, also stimulates glutamate release from astrocytes (82). Second, the SNARE proteins, syntaxin, synaptobrevin II (VAMP) (85), and SNAP-23 (a homolog of SNAP-25) (86), which are known to be essential for vesicle fusion, are present in astrocytes. A member of the ras family of GTPases, rab3, which is associated with synaptic vesicles and is likely involved in mediating docking and fusion events in neurons, is also expressed in astrocytes (87, 88). Third, treatment of astrocytes with clostridial toxins, which are highly selective proteases that cleave SNARE proteins (89–92), causes a blockade of calcium-dependent glutamate release from these cells (73, 80, 93). Fourth, glutamate release from astrocytes is attenuated after treatment with bafilomycin A1 (80). This toxin inhibits the V-ATPase of vesicles, which pumps protons into the vesicle lumen. Because the filling of vesicles with glutamate requires this proton gradient, an attenuation of glutamate release by bafilomycin is consistent with glutamate being stored in and then released from a vesicular compartment.

The final piece of evidence supporting vesicle-mediated glutamate release from astrocytes derives from results obtained through a novel experimental approach that used HEK cells transfected with the cDNA for the green fluorescent protein (GFP) and the NMDA receptor 1 and 2A subunits (94). After transfection, HEK cells were plated onto cultured astrocytes and used as sensors for glutamate release. Activation in astrocytes of AMPA receptors and mGluRs caused calcium signaling and glutamate release, thus leading in HEK cells to repetitive NMDA-mediated inward currents. These currents were similar in kinetics to those activated by quantal release of glutamate from synaptic terminals. Cleavage of astrocytic synaptobrevin by tetanus toxin or inhibition of the V-ATPase of astrocytic vesicles by bafilomycin greatly reduced glutamate release from astrocytes.

While all these results provide strong support for the existence in astrocytes of an exocytotic mechanism for transmitter release similar to that in neurons, ultrastructural evidence for the presence of transmitter-containing, small clear vesicles in astrocytes has not been found. However, immunoelectron microscopic analysis revealed that synaptobrevin II and synaptophysin are associated with the membrane of vesicular organelles in cultured astrocytes (88). Dense-core and clear vesicles have also been detected in a subpopulation of hippocampal astrocytes in culture, and a calcium-dependent regulated release of secretogranin II-containing vesicles has been demonstrated (77). Although further experiments need to be performed, a vesicle-mediated release process is the most plausible, perhaps the only, mechanism that could account for calcium-dependent glutamate release from astrocytes.

GLUTAMATE RELEASED FROM ASTROCYTES MODULATES SYNAPTIC TRANSMISSION AND NEURONAL EXCITABILITY

Astrocytes are intimately associated with neurons, especially at synaptic sites. Consequently, after demonstrating calcium-dependent glutamate release from astrocytes a highly logical question concerns the functional consequences of this transmitter release pathway upon synaptic transmission. To address such a question is highly challenging because it is necessary to have independent experimental control over the calcium levels in astrocytes, as well as voltage control of the pre- and postsynaptic neurons. Thus an interplay of experiments have been performed in cell culture, where the system offers exquisite experimental control, and in slice preparations, which are less controlled but offer insights into the physiological relevance of the identified signaling pathways.

Cell culture studies of synaptic transmission between rat hippocampal neurons have shown that the elevation of astrocytic calcium causes a modulation of synaptic transmission mediated by released glutamate. Initiation of a calcium wave between astrocytes causes a transient depression of evoked synaptic transmission at hippocampal synapses that is sensitive to mGluR antagonists (71). Furthermore, in some cases, astrocytic calcium elevations lead to glutamate-dependent NMDA receptor-mediated increase in the frequency of miniature postsynaptic currents (mPSCs) (95). A modulation of synaptic transmission has also been demonstrated by recording from pyramidal neurons in hippocampal slices (31). Depolarization of astrocytes, or activation of GABAergic interneurons, elevates calcium in these glial cells and causes an AP5 and 6-cyano-7-nitroquinoxaline-2,3-dione (CNQX) -sensitive modulation of the frequency of mPSCs in pyramidal neurons. Of particular interest is the observation that this increase in miniature synaptic current frequency is of sustained duration, lasting in excess of 15 min, suggesting that glutamate released from astrocytes can contribute to synaptic plasticity.

Further support for a role for synaptically associated glia in regulating synaptic transmission has been provided by studies performed at frog neuromuscular junction. As discussed earlier, perisynaptic Schwann cells are intimately associated with the nerve muscle junction, and activity in the presynaptic axon can cause calcium elevations in these cells (52). To test the potential role of these synaptically associated non-neuronal cells in modulating synaptic transmission, guanine nucleotide analogs were directly injected into the perisynaptic Schwann cell. Activation of GTP-binding proteins by injection of GTPγS caused a dramatic reduction in the magnitude of the nerve-evoked end-plate potential, supporting the concept that the synaptically associated glial cell can modulate synaptic transmission (96). To determine whether this glial cell might be recruited into a modulatory role by neuronal activity, glial GTP-binding proteins were inactivated through the microinjection of GTPγS. In an unperturbed preparation, high-frequency activity in the axon causes a gradual decrease in the amplitude of the end-plate potential. GTPγS microinjection into the glial cell caused a surprising result. Although GTP-binding protein inactivation did not affect the magnitude of spike-to-spike transmission, it largely blocked the frequency-dependent depression of the end-plate potential (96). Prior to this experiment it was thought that this activity-dependent reduction in the magnitude of transmitter release resulted from an intrinsic property of the nerve terminal. On the contrary, these results clearly demonstrate a role for glia in integrating inputs from neurons, and then, in providing feedback modulation to the synapse.

In addition to modulating synaptic transmission, glia can also regulate neuronal excitability. As discussed above, calcium elevations in astrocytes in cell culture can induce glutamate-dependent slow inward currents in neurons that depolarize the membrane potential, thus regulating membrane excitability (35, 71, 72). Astrocytic regulation of neuronal activity has also been demonstrated in an in situ preparation. Initiation of a calcium wave in Müller cells and astrocytes in the retina can modulate the output of retinal ganglion cells that is initiated by light activation of the photoreceptors (97). When the glial calcium wave approaches the region of the retina containing the recorded ganglion cell, either an excitation or inhibition of ganglion cell activity is detected. The glial-evoked inhibition was studied pharmacologically. Addition of either the glutamate receptor antagonists, NBQX (AMPA receptors) and D-2-amino-7-phosphonoheptanoic acid (D-AP7) (NMDA receptors), or the $GABA_A$ and glycine antagonists, bicuculine and strychnine, blocked the glial-evoked inhibition of activity. It is not known whether calcium elevations in these glia lead to transmitter release. However, given that several studies have demonstrated a calcium-dependent release of glutamate from astrocytes (10), one potential interpretation of the retinal studies is that glutamate released from retinal glia, acting indirectly through GABAergic interneurons, causes the modulation of the ganglion cell electrical activity. Indeed, Newman & Zahs (97) suggest that glutamate is released from the glia onto amacrine cells, which in turn release GABA and glycine to inhibit retinal ganglion cell activity. Despite the uncertainty about mechanism, studies at the frog neuromuscular junction (96) and in the retina (97) clearly demonstrate that glial modulation of synaptic transmission and neuronal excitability are properties of glia in intact systems, not just properties of astrocytes in cell culture.

Work in several preparations now indicates that astrocytes and perisynaptic Schwann cells can produce a variety of forms of neuronal modulation. As discussed above, astrocytes can cause a mGluR-dependent inhibition of hippocampal synaptic transmission (10, 71), and activation of perisynaptic Schwann cells suppresses transmission at the neuromuscular junction (96). In contrast, however, in the hippocampal slice preparation, activation of GABAergic interneurons elevates astrocytic calcium, which causes an ionotropic glutamate receptor-mediated increase in frequency of mIPSCs detected in pyramidal neurons (31). It is likely that glutamate release from astrocytes can indeed cause facilitatory or inhibitory effects on the same synapse. Although elevation of astrocytic calcium causes an mGluR-mediated suppression of synaptic transmission between hippocampal pyramidal neurons in culture (71), removal of Mg^{2+} from the saline selects for an NMDA receptor-dependent elevation of miniature synaptic current frequency following the elevation of astrocytic calcium (95). It is not yet clear which physiological conditions select for astrocyte-mediated facilitation or depression of the synapse, but it is tempting to speculate that co-activation of the synapse and the astrocyte would lead to a facilitation of the synaptic interaction.

Where is the Target of Action of Transmitter that is Released from Astrocytes?

Until the sites of transmitter release from astrocytes are identified it will be difficult to determine the target(s) of glutamate action, although physiological studies do provide at least a clue to these locations. Because glutamate that is released from astrocytes can modulate synapses, it is likely that a target of action is in the vicinity of the synapse. However, it is unlikely that this glutamate can access the receptors located in the synapse because even low concentrations of glutamate would desensitize these receptors, an action that we do not detect (95). Additionally, studies using MK-801 have demonstrated that glutamate released from astrocytes acts on extrasynaptic NMDA receptors to enhance the frequency of mPSCs (95). In this work, hippocampal cultures were incubated in the presence of MK-801, which causes an open channel block of NMDA receptors in order to block synaptically activated NMDA receptors. Despite demonstrating a blockade of synaptic NMDA receptors, subsequent elevation of astrocytic calcium levels was still able to cause an AP5-sensitive increase in mPSC frequency. The location of these extrasynaptic NMDA receptors is unknown. However, an interesting possibility is that they are located extrasynaptically on the presynaptic terminal. Certainly, NMDA receptors have been demonstrated in this location in some preparations (98, 99). Consistent with an extrasynaptic target for glutamate action is ultrastructural data that have demonstrated the presence of mGluRs at extrasynaptic sites in presynaptic terminals (100). Perhaps these receptors mediate the mGluR-mediated depression of the synaptic transmission, which can be induced by glutamate that is released from astrocytes.

PHYSIOLOGICAL ROLES OF GLUTAMATE-MEDIATED ASTROCYTE-TO-NEURON SIGNALING

With the variety of information that is now available about astrocyte-induced neuromodulation we are approaching a period in which we can begin to speculate about the physiological roles for this signaling pathway. It should first be stated that neurons are obviously critical for nervous system function. Without the neuron we would be forced to rely on a calcium signaling pathway that propagates at rates of only 20 μm/s instead of the action potential, which can propagate at rates in excess of 20 m/s. Phylogeny provides a clue about the potential role of glia. In *Caenorhabditis elegans* there are 302 neurons and only 56 glial and associated support cells (101). As one rises through phylogeny, the ratio of glia to neurons increases. The human brain contains the greatest numbers of glia and the highest ratio of glia to neurons (at least 10:1). Consequently, one is tempted to suggest that glial cells, and particularly astrocytes, play roles in higher cognitive functions that are normally associated with higher species.

One area related to these higher functions that could potentially be investigated is the role of astrocytes in learning and memory. There is little information about this relationship. However, the elevation of astrocytic calcium can cause a sustained increase in the frequency of mPSCs recorded in hippocampal pyramidal neurons (31). GFAP-deficient mice exhibit an enhancement of LTP (102), and impaired LTD (103). However, until a mechanistic understanding of these changes is identified, it is not clear how they should be interpreted. Nonetheless, our knowledge of the thresholds for activation of calcium signaling in astrocytes indicates that they might play a role in activity-dependent synaptic plasticity because astrocytes are typically activated by elevated stimulation frequencies (15, 18, 25, 46, 52, 53) that are frequently used to induce synaptic plasticity. While this possibility has not yet been systematically evaluated, perturbation of astrocytic calcium signaling in transgenic mice can affect synaptic plasticity. Mice in which the astrocyte-specific calcium-binding protein S-100 has been over-expressed show altered synaptic plasticity and impaired spatial learning (104). Thus data support the possible role of astrocytes in contributing to synaptic plasticity; however, carefully designed experiments are required to thoroughly test this hypothesis.

We have entered into a new era of physiological studies in the neurosciences in which it is now appreciated that astrocytes are dynamic signaling elements that integrate neuronal inputs, exhibit calcium excitability, and can modulate neighboring neurons through the calcium-dependent release of the chemical transmitter glutamate. Astrocytes, and perisynaptic Schwann cells, by virtue of their intimate association with synapses, are strategically positioned to regulate synaptic transmission. This capability, which has been demonstrated in several studies, raises the possibility that astrocytes are an integral element of the circuitry for synaptic plasticity. Because the highest ratio of glia to neurons is found at the top of the phylogentic tree in the human brain, these recent demonstrations of dynamic bidirectional signaling between astrocytes and neurons leave us with the question as to whether astrocytes are key regulatory elements of higher cortical functions.

Visit the Annual Reviews home page at www.AnnualReviews.org

LITERATURE CITED

1. Ramón y Cajal S. 1899. *Contribución al conocimiento de la neuroglia del cerebro humano. Trabajos del Laboratorio de Investigaciones Biológicas de la Universidad de Madrid Tomo XI*
2. Sontheimer H, Waxman SG. 1992. Ion channels in spinal cord astrocytes in vitro. II. Biophysical and pharmacological analysis of two Na+ current types. *J. Neurophysiol.* 68:1001–11
3. Barres BA. 1991. Glial ion channels. *Curr. Opin. Neurobiol.* 1:354–59
4. Barres BA. 1991. Five electrophysiological properties of glial cells. *Ann. NY Acad. Sci.* 633:248–54
5. Barres BA. 1991. New roles for glia. *J. Neurosci.* 11:3685–94
6. Sontheimer H, Black JA, Waxman SG. 1996.

Voltage-gated Na+ channels in glia: properties and possible functions. *Trends Neurosci.* 19:325–31
7. Orkand RK, Nicholls JG, Kuffler SW. 1966. Effect of nerve impulses on the membrane potential of glial cells in the central nervous system of amphibia. *J. Neurophysiol.* 29:788–806
8. Ventura R, Harris KM. 1999. Three-dimensional relationships between hippocampal synapses and astrocytes. *J. Neurosci.* 19:6897–906
9. Reichenbach A, Siegel A, Rickmann M, Wolf JR, Noone D, Robinson SR. 1995. Distribution of Bergmann glial somata and processes: implications for function. *J. Hirnforsch.* 36:509–17
10. Araque A, Parpura V, Sanzgiri RP,

Haydon PG. 1999. Tripartite synapses: glia, the unacknowledged partner. *Trends Neurosci.* 22:208–15

11. Newman E, Reichenbach A. 1996. The Muller cell: a functional element of the retina. *Trends Neurosci.* 19:307–12

12. Bergles DE, Jahr CE. 1998. Glial contribution to glutamate uptake at Schaffer collateral-commissural synapses in the hippocampus. *J. Neurosci.* 18:7709–16

13. Bergles DE, Jahr CE. 1997. Synaptic activation of glutamate transporters in hippocampal astrocytes. *Neuron* 19:1297–308

14. Verkhratsky A, Kettenmann H. 1996. Calcium signalling in glial cells. *Trends Neurosci.* 19:346–52

15. Dani JW, Smith SJ. 1995. The triggering of astrocytic calcium waves by NMDA-induced neuronal activation. *Ciba. Found. Symp.* 188:195–205

16. Duffy S, MacVicar BA. 1995. Adrenergic calcium signaling in astrocyte networks within the hippocampal slice. *J. Neurosci.* 15:5535–50

17. Parpura V, Basarasky TA, Liu F, Jeftinija K, Haydon PG. 1994. Glutamate-mediated astrocyte-neuron signalling. *Nature* 369:744–47

18. Dani JW, Chernjavsky A, Smith SJ. 1992. Neuronal activity triggers calcium waves in hippocampal astrocyte networks. *Neuron* 8:429–40

19. Cornell Bell AH, Finkbeiner SM. 1991. Ca^{2+} waves in astrocytes. *Cell Calcium* 12:185–204

20. Cornell Bell AH, Finkbeiner SM, Cooper MS, Smith SJ. 1990. Glutamate induces calcium waves in cultured astrocytes: long-range glial signaling. *Science* 247:470–73

21. Smith SJ. 1994. Neural signalling. Neuromodulatory astrocytes. *Curr. Biol.* 4:807–10

22. Smith SJ. 1992. Do astrocytes process neural information? *Prog. Brain Res.* 94:119–36

23. Verkhratsky A, Orkand RK, Kettenmann H. 1998. Glial calcium: homeostasis and signaling function. *Physiol. Rev.* 78:99–141

24. Fam SR, Gallagher CJ, Salter MW. 2000. P2Y(1) purinoceptor-mediated $Ca(2+)$ signaling and $Ca(2+)$ wave propagation in dorsal spinal cord astrocytes. *J. Neurosci.* 20:2800–8

25. Porter JT, McCarthy KD. 1996. Hippocampal astrocytes in situ respond to glutamate released from synaptic terminals. *J. Neurosci.* 16:5073–81

26. Shao Y, Porter JT, McCarthy KD. 1994. Neuroligand receptor heterogeneity among astroglia. *Perspect. Dev. Neurobiol.* 2:205–15

27. Porter JT, McCarthy KD. 1997. Astrocytic neurotransmitter receptors in situ and in vivo. *Prog. Neurobiol.* 51:439–55

28. Robitaille R, Jahromi BS, Charlton MP. 1997. Muscarinic Ca^{2+} responses resistant to muscarinic antagonists at perisynaptic Schwann cells of the frog neuromuscular junction. *J. Physiol.* 504:337–47

29. Robitaille R. 1995. Purinergic receptors and their activation by endogenous purines at perisynaptic glial cells of the frog neuromuscular junction. *J. Neurosci.* 15:7121–31

30. Shelton MK, McCarthy KD. 1999. Mature hippocampal astrocytes exhibit functional metabotropic and ionotropic glutamate receptors in situ. *Glia* 26:1–11

31. Kang J, Jiang L, Goldman SA, Nedergaard M. 1998. Astrocyte-mediated potentiation of inhibitory synaptic transmission. *Nat. Neurosci.* 1:683–92

32. Shelton MK, McCarthy KD. 2000. Hippocampal astrocytes exhibit Ca^{2+}-elevating muscarinic cholinergic and histaminergic receptors in situ. *J. Neurochem.* 74:555–63

33. Shao Y, McCarthy KD. 1997. Responses of Bergmann glia and granule neurons in situ to N-methyl-D-aspartate,

norepinephrine, and high potassium. *J. Neurochem.* 68:2405–11

34. Charles AC, Merrill JE, Dirksen ER, Sanderson MJ. 1991. Intercellular signaling in glial cells: calcium waves and oscillations in response to mechanical stimulation and glutamate. *Neuron* 6:983–92

35. Hassinger TD, Atkinson PB, Strecker GJ, Whalen LR, Dudek FE, et al. 1995. Evidence for glutamate-mediated activation of hippocampal neurons by glial calcium waves. *J. Neurobiol.* 28:159–70

36. Guthrie PB, Knappenberger J, Segal M, Bennett MV, Charles AC, Kater SB. 1999. ATP released from astrocytes mediates glial calcium waves. *J. Neurosci.* 19:520–28

37. Innocenti B, Parpura V, Haydon PG. 2000. Imaging extracellular waves of glutamate during calcium signaling in cultured astrocytes. *J. Neurosci.* 20:1800–8

38. Charles AC, Naus CC, Zhu D, Kidder GM, Dirksen ER, Sanderson MJ. 1992. Intercellular calcium signaling via gap junctions in glioma cells. *J. Cell Biol.* 118:195–201

39. Hassinger TD, Guthrie PB, Atkinson PB, Bennett MV, Kater SB. 1996. An extracellular signaling component in propagation of astrocytic calcium waves. *Proc. Natl. Acad. Sci. USA* 93:13268–73

40. Scemes E, Suadicani SO, Spray DC. 2000. Intercellular communication in spinal cord astrocytes: fine tuning between gap junctions and P2 nucleotide receptors in calcium wave propagation. *J. Neurosci.* 20:1435–45

41. Scemes E, Dermietzel R, Spray DC. 1998. Calcium waves between astrocytes from Cx43 knockout mice. *Glia* 24:65–73

42. Cotrina ML, Lin JH, Alves-Rodrigues A, Liu S, Li J, et al. 1998. Connexins regulate calcium signaling by controlling ATP release. *Proc. Natl. Acad. Sci. USA* 95:15735–40

43. Cotrina ML, Lin JH, Lopez-Garcia JC, Naus CC, Nedergaard M. 2000. ATP-mediated glia signaling. *J. Neurosci.* 20:2835–44

44. Wang Z, Haydon PG, Yeung ES. 2000. Direct observation of calcium-dependent ATP signaling in astrocytes. *Anal. Chem.* 72:2001–7

45. Willmott NJ, Wong K, Strong AJ. 2000. A fundamental role for the nitric oxide-G-kinase signaling pathway in mediating intercellular Ca(2+) waves in glia. *J. Neurosci.* 20:1767–79

46. Pasti L, Volterra A, Pozzan T, Carmignoto G. 1997. Intracellular calcium oscillations in astrocytes: a highly plastic, bidirectional form of communication between neurons and astrocytes in situ. *J. Neurosci.* 17:7817–30

47. Newman EA, Zahs KR. 1997. Calcium waves in retinal glial cells. *Science* 275:844–47

48. Harris-White ME, Zanotti SA, Frautschy SA, Charles AC. 1998. Spiral intercellular calcium waves in hippocampal slice cultures. *J. Neurophysiol.* 79:1045–52

49. Mennerick S, Benz A, Zorumski CF. 1996. Components of glial responses to exogenous and synaptic glutamate in rat hippocampal microcultures. *J. Neurosci.* 16:55–64

50. Mudrick-Donnon LA, Williams PJ, Pittman QJ, MacVicar BA. 1993. Postsynaptic potentials mediated by GABA and dopamine evoked in stellate glial cells of the pituitary pars intermedia. *J. Neurosci.* 13:4660–68

51. Clark BA, Barbour B. 1997. Currents evoked in Bergmann glial cells by parallel fibre stimulation in rat cerebellar slices. *J. Physiol.* 502:335–50

52. Jahromi BS, Robitaille R, Charlton MP. 1992. Transmitter release increases intracellular calcium in perisynaptic Schwann cells in situ. *Neuron* 8:1069–77

53. Reist NE, Smith SJ. 1992. Neurally evoked calcium transients in terminal Schwann cells at the neuromuscular junction. *Proc. Natl. Acad. Sci. USA* 89:7625–29

54. Kulik A, Haentzsch A, Luckermann M, Reichelt W, Ballanyi K. 1999. Neuron-glia signaling via alpha(1) adrenoceptor-mediated Ca(2+) release in Bergmann glial cells in situ. *J. Neurosci.* 19:8401–8

55. Milner TA, Kurucz OS, Veznedaroglu E, Pierce JP. 1995. Septohippocampal neurons in the rat septal complex have substantial glial coverage and receive direct contacts from noradrenaline terminals. *Brain Res.* 670:121–36

56. Paspalas CD, Papadopoulos GC. 1996. Ultrastructural relationships between noradrenergic nerve fibers and non-neuronal elements in the rat cerebral cortex. *Glia* 17:133–46

57. Grosche J, Matyash V, Moller T, Verkhratsky A, Reichenbach A, Kettenmann H. 1999. Microdomains for neuron-glia interaction: parallel fiber signaling to Bergmann glial cells. *Nat. Neurosci.* 2:139–43

58. Engert F, Bonhoeffer T. 1999. Dendritic spine changes associated with hippocampal long-term synaptic plasticity. *Nature* 399:66–70

59. Wong WT, Wong RO. 2000. Rapid dendritic movements during synapse formation and rearrangement. *Curr. Opin. Neurobiol.* 10:118–24

60. Mong JA, McCarthy MM. 1999. Steroid-induced developmental plasticity in hypothalamic astrocytes: implications for synaptic patterning. *J. Neurobiol.* 40:602–19

61. Mong JA, Glaser E, McCarthy MM. 1999. Gonadal steroids promote glial differentiation and alter neuronal morphology in the developing hypothalamus in a regionally specific manner. *J. Neurosci.* 19:1464–72

62. Garcia-Segura LM, Naftolin F, Hutchison JB, Azcoitia I, Chowen JA. 1999. Role of astroglia in estrogen regulation of synaptic plasticity and brain repair. *J. Neurobiol.* 40:574–84

63. Cornell-Bell AH, Thomas PG, Smith SJ. 1990. The excitatory neurotransmitter glutamate causes filopodia formation in cultured hippocampal astrocytes. *Glia* 3:322–34

64. Pasti L, Pozzan T, Carmignoto G. 1995. Long-lasting changes of calcium oscillations in astrocytes. A new form of glutamate-mediated plasticity. *J. Biol. Chem.* 270:15203–10

65. Georgiou J, Robitaille R, Trimble WS, Charlton MP. 1994. Synaptic regulation of glial protein expression in vivo. *Neuron* 12:443–55

66. Stevens B, Fields RD. 2000. Response of Schwann cells to action potentials in development. *Science* 287:2267–71

67. Pfrieger FW, Barres BA. 1996. New views on synapse-glia interactions. *Curr. Opin. Neurobiol.* 6:615–21

68. Pfrieger FW, Barres BA. 1997. Synaptic efficacy enhanced by glial cells in vitro. *Science* 277:1684–87

69. Nedergaard M. 1994. Direct signaling from astrocytes to neurons in cultures of mammalian brain cells. *Science* 263:1768–71

70. Charles AC. 1994. Glia-neuron intercellular calcium signaling. *Dev. Neurosci.* 16:196–206

71. Araque A, Parpura V, Sanzgiri RP, Haydon PG. 1998. Glutamate-dependent astrocyte modulation of synaptic transmission between cultured hippocampal neurons. *Eur. J. Neurosci.* 10:2129–42

72. Araque A, Sanzgiri RP, Parpura V, Haydon PG. 1999. Astrocyte-induced modulation of synaptic transmission. *Can. J. Physiol. Pharmacol.* 77:699–706

73. Bezzi P, Carmignoto G, Pasti L, Vesce S, Rossi D, et al. 1998. Prostaglandins stimulate calcium-dependent glutamate release in astrocytes. *Nature* 391:281–85

74. Mothet JP, Parent AT, Wolosker H, Brady RO Jr, Linden D, et al. 2000. D-Serine is an endogenous ligand for the glycine site of the *N*-methyl-D-aspartate receptor. *Proc. Natl. Acad. Sci. USA* 97:4926–31

75. Wolosker H, Sheth KN, Takahashi M, Mothet JP, Brady RO Jr, et al. 1999. Purification of serine racemase: biosynthesis of

the neuromodulator D-serine. *Proc. Natl. Acad. Sci. USA* 96:721–25

76. Schell MJ, Molliver ME, Snyder SH. 1995. D-serine, an endogenous synaptic modulator: localization to astrocytes and glutamate-stimulated release. *Proc. Natl. Acad. Sci. USA* 92:3948–52

77. Calegari F, Coco S, Taverna E, Bassetti M, Verderio C, et al. 1999. A regulated secretory pathway in cultured hippocampal astrocytes. *J. Biol. Chem.* 274:22539–47

78. Attwell D. 1994. Glia and neurons in dialogue. *Nature* 369:707–8

79. Szatkowski M, Barbour B, Attwell D. 1990. Non-vesicular release of glutamate from glial cells by reversed electrogenic glutamate uptake. *Nature* 348:443–46

80. Araque A, Li N, Doyle RT, Haydon PG. 2000. SNARE protein-dependent glutamate release from astrocytes. *J. Neurosci.* 20:666–73

81. Kimelberg HK, Goderie SK, Higman S, Pang S, Waniewski RA. 1990. Swelling-induced release of glutamate, aspartate, and taurine from astrocyte cultures. *J. Neurosci.* 10:1583–91

82. Parpura V, Lui F, Brethorst S, Jeftinija K, Jeftinija S, Haydon PG. 1995. Alpha-latrotoxin stimulates glutamate release from cortical astrocytes in cell culture. *FEBS Lett.* 360:266–70

83. Girod R, Povov S, Alder J, Zheng JQ, Lohof A, Poo MM. 1995. Spontaneous quantal transmitter secretion from myocytes and fibroblasts: comparison with neuronal secretion. *J. Neurosci.* 15:2826–38

84. Morimoto T, Popov S, Buckley KM, Poo MM. 1995. Calcium-dependent transmitter secretion from fibroblasts: modulation by synaptotagmin I. *Neuron* 15:689–96

85. Parpura V, Fang Y, Basarsky T, Jahn R, Haydon PG. 1995. Expression of synaptobrevin II, cellubrevin and syntaxin but not SNAP-25 in cultured astrocytes. *FEBS Lett.* 377:489–92

86. Hepp R, Perrauat M, Chasserot-Golaz S, Galli T, Aunis D, et al. 1999. Cultured glial cells express the SNAP-25 analogue SNAP-23. *Glia* 27:181–87

87. Madison DL, Kruger WH, Kim T, Pfeiffer SE. 1996. Differential expression of rab3 isoforms in oligodendrocytes and astrocytes. *J. Neurosci. Res.* 45:258–68

88. Maienschein V, Marxen M, Volknandt W, Zimmermann H. 1999. A plethora of presynaptic proteins associated with ATP-storing organelles in cultured astrocytes. *Glia* 26:233–44

89. Jahn R, Hanson PI, Otto H, Ahnert-Hilger G. 1995. Botulinum and tetanus neurotoxins: emerging tools for the study of membrane fusion. *Cold Spring Harbor Symp. Quant. Biol.* 60:329–35

90. Blasi J, Binz T, Yamasaki S, Link E, Niemann H, Jahn R. 1994. Inhibition of neurotransmitter release by clostridial neurotoxins correlates with specific proteolysis of synaptosomal proteins. *J. Physiol.* 88:235–41

91. Link E, Blasi J, Chapman ER, Edelmann L, Baumeister A, et al. 1994. Tetanus and botulinal neurotoxins. Tools to understand exocytosis in neurons. *Adv. Second Messenger Phosphoprotein Res.* 29:47–58

92. Niemann H, Blasi J, Jahn R. 1994. Clostridial neurotoxins: new tools for dissecting exocytosis. *Trends-Pharmacol-Sci.* 4:179–85

93. Jeftinija SD, Jeftinija KV, Stefanovic G. 1997. Cultured astrocytes express proteins involved in vesicular glutamate release. *Brain Res.* 750:41–47

94. Carmignoto G, Pasti L, Zonta M, Pozzan T, Vicini S. 1999. $[Ca^{2+}]_i$ oscillations in atrocytes regulate a fast, quantal-like release of glutamate. *Soc. Neurosci. Abstr.* 25:17.12

95. Araque A, Sanzgiri RP, Parpura V, Haydon PG. 1998. Calcium elevation in astrocytes causes an NMDA receptor-dependent increase in the frequency of miniature synaptic currents in cultured hippocampal neurons. *J. Neurosci.* 18:6822–29

96. Robitaille R. 1998. Modulation of synaptic efficacy and synaptic depression by glial cells at the frog neuromuscular junction. *Neuron* 21:847–55

97. Newman EA, Zahs KR. 1998. Modulation of neuronal activity by glial cells in the retina. *J. Neurosci.* 18:4022–28

98. Cochilla AJ, Alford S. 1999. NMDA receptor-mediated control of presynaptic calcium and neurotransmitter release. *J. Neurosci.* 19:193–205

99. Glitsch M, Marty A. 1999. Presynaptic effects of NMDA in cerebellar Purkinje cells and interneurons. *J. Neurosci.* 19:511–19

100. Yokoi M, Kobayashi K, Manabe T, Takahashi T, Sakaguchi I, et al. 1996. Impairment of hippocampal mossy fiber LTD in mice lacking mGluR2. *Science* 273:645–47

101. Sulston JE, Schierenberg E, White JG, Thomson JN. 1983. The embryonic cell lineage of the nematode *Caenorhabditis elegans. Dev. Biol.* 100:64–119

102. McCall MA, Gregg RG, Behringer RR, Brenner M, Delaney CL, et al. 1996. Targeted deletion in astrocyte intermediate filament (Gfap) alters neuronal physiology. *Proc. Natl. Acad. Sci. USA* 93:6361–66

103. Shibuki K, Gomi H, Chen L, Bao S, Kim JJ, et al. 1996. Deficient cerebellar long-term depression, impaired eyeblink conditioning, and normal motor coordination in GFAP mutant mice. *Neuron* 16:587–99

104. Gerlai R, Wojtowicz JM, Marks A, Roder J. 1995. Overexpression of a calcium-binding protein, S100 beta, in astrocytes alters synaptic plasticity and impairs spatial learning in transgenic mice. *Learn. Mem.* 2:26–39

Annu. Rev. Physiol. 2001. 63:815–46

ON THE CELLULAR AND NETWORK BASES OF EPILEPTIC SEIZURES

David A McCormick[1] and Diego Contreras[2]

[1]Section of Neurobiology, Yale University School of Medicine, New Haven, Connecticut 06510; e-mail: david.mccormick@yale.edu
[2]Department of Neuroscience, School of Medicine, University of Pennsylvania, Philadelphia, Pennsylvania 19104; e-mail: diegoc@mail.med.upenn.edu

Key Words   epilepsy, rhythms, cerebral cortex, thalamus, hippocampus, electroencephalogram

■ **Abstract**   The highly interconnected networks of the mammalian forebrain can generate a wide variety of synchronized activities, including those underlying epileptic seizures, which often appear as a transformation of otherwise normal brain rhythms. The cerebral cortex and hippocampus are particularly prone to the generation of the large, synchronized bursts of activity underlying many forms of seizures owing to strong recurrent excitatory connections, the presence of intrinsically burst-generating neurons, ephaptic interactions among closely spaced neurons, and synaptic plasticity. The simplest form of epileptiform activity in these structures is the interictal spike, a synchronized burst of action potentials generated by recurrent excitation, followed by a period of hyperpolarization, in a localized pool of pyramidal neurons. Seizures can also be generated in response to a loss of balance between excitatory and inhibitory influences and can take the form of either tonic depolarizations or repetitive, rhythmic burst discharges, either as clonic or spike-wave activity, again mediated both by intrinsic membrane properties and synaptic interactions. The interaction of the cerebral cortex and the thalamus, in conjunction with intrathalamic communication, can also generate spike waves similar to those occurring during human absence seizure discharges. Although epileptic syndromes and their causes are diverse, the cellular mechanisms of seizure generation appear to fall into only two categories: rhythmic or tonic "runaway" excitation or the synchronized and rhythmic interplay between excitatory and inhibitory neurons and membrane conductances.

INTRODUCTION

Clinical epilepsy is a diverse disorder of which there are over 40 recognized types segregated into distinct epileptic syndromes (1). This diversity arises from both the numerous underlying cellular and molecular mechanisms, as well as from the spatial and temporal characteristics of the seizure. Most epileptic syndromes are grouped in two basic categories: partial and generalized. Partial seizures occur

0066-4278/01/0315-0815$14.00

within a localized area of the brain, whereas generalized seizures appear (at least on the level of the electroencephalogram) throughout the forebrain from the outset. If the partial seizure does not cause a disruption of consciousness or cognitive abilities, then it is said to be simple; if it does, then it is referred to as complex. There is great diversity in the pathologies leading to, and clinical manifestations of, the epileptic syndrome, yet it is thought that the actual generation of many of the different types of seizure may occur through common cellular mechanisms and networks. Although practically every part of the brain may generate an epileptic seizure, the investigation of the cellular and network mechanisms of epilepsy over the last several decades has focused largely on three structures: the cerebral cortex, the hippocampus (and related structures), and the thalamus. Investigation of the possible mechanisms for generation of partial, complex partial, and generalized seizures in these structures has demonstrated that every aspect of neuronal and glial function, from genes to synapses to networks, has at least a modulatory influence. Extensive and informative reviews of many of these aspects are available (see 2–14a). Here, we focus on the neurophysiological mechanisms for generation of epileptiform activity within thalamocortical, cortical, and hippocampal networks, with a particular emphasis on network mechanisms.

NEOCORTICAL AND HIPPOCAMPAL MECHANISMS OF EPILEPTIFORM ACTIVITIES

Both the neocortex and the hippocampus are prone to the generation of epileptiform activity and seizures. There are multiple factors contributing to the epileptogenicity of these structures, including the presence of massive recurrent excitatory connections, reliance upon inhibition for the regulation of excitability of this recurrent network, the ability of synaptic connections to strengthen or weaken with repetitive activation, the presence of intrinsically burst-generating cells, and finally a strong influence from ion regulation and perhaps other ephaptic (non-synaptic) interactions (reviewed in 5–7, 10, 14).

Single, Synchronized Bursts: Cellular Mechanisms of the Interictal Spike

The simplest identifiable unit of epileptiform activity in the central nervous system (CNS) is the interictal (between seizures) spike. Interictal spikes are brief (80–200 ms), large, sharp spikes in the EEG that occur in isolation on a background of otherwise normal activity (Figure 1A). They appear in a subpopulation of patients with focal epilepsy and are not, as individual events, associated with overt changes in cognitive abilities or behavior. Interictal spikes may serve to localize the epileptogenic focus, but they are not always detected from the primary focus from which seizures originate. The intracellular correlate of the interictal spike is an overt depolarization, called the paroxysmal depolarizing shift (PDS) (Figure 1B), that

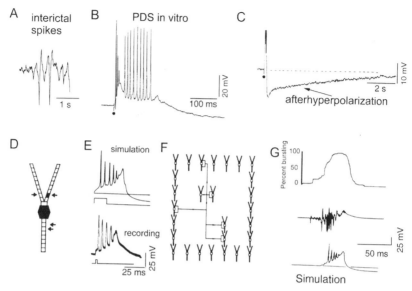

Figure 1 Interictal spike generation in hippocampus and cortex. (*A*) Example of two interictal spikes in the human EEG. Interictal spikes are brief (~0.1 s) events typically localized to a particular region of the forebrain. (*B*) Intracellular recording in a human cortical pyramidal cell maintained in a cortical slice in vitro during the generation of a epileptiform burst similar to that underlying the generation of interictal spikes. The depolarization underlying the epileptiform activity is termed a paroxysmal depolarization shift (PDS) and results in the initiation of a high-frequency burst of action potentials. (*C*) The PDS in the human cortical neuron is followed by a prolonged after-hyperpolarization that is generated by the activation of various K$^+$ currents. (*D*) Compartmental model of a single CA3 burst-generating pyramidal neuron. Arrows indicate location of excitatory inputs to modeled cells. (*E*) Intracellular injection of a short-duration depolarizing current pulse in a CA3 pyramidal neuron (bottom traces) or in the model of one of these cells (top traces) results in an intrinsic burst of action potentials. (*F*) Diagrammatic illustration of the modeled network of CA3 burst-generating pyramidal cells. Each pyramidal neuron synaptically excites multiple pyramidal cells. (*G*) Simulation of a synchronized burst of epileptiform activity in the stimulated network of CA3 pyramidal neurons. Initially, a few pyramidal neurons synchronously discharge, and this activity rapidly recruits other neurons into the epileptiform burst. The network activity fails as the percentage of neurons generating action potentials decreases dramatically, owing to spike inactivation and/or hyperpolarization. The simulated EEG (local field potential) includes high-frequency components from the synchronous action potential discharge of the neurons. The bottom trace is the membrane potential of one representative neuron (*B* and *C* from 43; *D-G* from 152).

last tens of milliseconds and can be so large that it leads to sodium-spike inactivation. The mechanisms for generation of interictal spikes derive from a basic and ubiquitous operation of neocortical and hippocampal networks: the activation of brief periods dominated by synaptic excitation between pyramidal cells followed by a period dominated by synaptic inhibition and/or activation of intrinsic hyperpolarizing conductances. Indeed, in cortical structures, most if not all epileptic activities derive from some type of imbalance between depolarizing and hyperpolarizing influences (synaptic, ion concentration regulation, or intrinsic membrane properties) in a large interconnected network of neurons. This imbalance in cortical networks can be experimentally induced by a variety of methods. Examples include reducing the efficiency of GABAergic inhibition through the application of $GABA_A$ receptor antagonists, increasing the excitability of neuronal elements and reducing the effectiveness of hyperpolarizing conductances by raising the extracellular concentration of K^+, and enhancing synaptic transmission by reducing some K^+ currents with the application of 4-aminopyridine. Additional methods such as modifying synaptic strength through repetitive electrical stimulation (e.g. kindling), enhancing excitatory synaptic transmission through NMDA receptors and reducing $GABA_A$ receptor–mediated inhibition by removing Mg^{2+} from the extracellular medium, and other manipulations may also induce epileptiform activities (see 5, 6, 10, 11). In all models of cortical epileptogenesis, except for the generation of epileptiform activity through ephaptic interactions (see below), the generation of seizures is completely dependent upon neurotransmission.

In the neocortex, cortical pyramidal cells in all layers project both locally and to other layers of the cortex, contacting other pyramidal cells (or spiny stellate neurons in layer IV) as well as local GABAergic interneurons. Typically, only one or a few synaptic contacts are made between each pyramidal cell and each of its target neurons (see 15), keeping the influence of most neurons on any other particular neuron relatively weak. However, each cortical neuron receives a large number (thousands) of excitatory synaptic inputs from a wide variety of sources, most of which are other cortical neurons, and therefore there is much divergence and convergence in cortical networks. The synaptic output of cortical pyramidal cells is often densest near the cell of origin, although patchy horizontal connections to functionally relevant and neighboring regions of cortex are also prominent (16, 17). Long-range and extensive connections to other cortical areas are characteristics of a subpopulation of cortical pyramidal cells (18), and functionally related cortical areas are highly interconnected, allowing for the rapid dissemination of neuronal activity (19). Each subclass of GABAergic interneuron exhibits its own unique connectivity (reviewed in 20), and each of the different types of synaptic connections within the cerebral cortex, both inhibitory and excitatory, have their own unique temporal properties (21, 22) that may be specifically modulated with experience and neurotransmitters (23). In addition to synaptic interactions, GABAergic neurons in the cortex also form gap junctions with other select subgroups of GABAergic cells, allowing for the fast synchronization of local networks (24–26).

Like the neocortex, the hippocampus contains a network of richly interconnected excitatory cells (e.g. pyramidal neurons) that are regulated by a wide diversity of inhibitory interneurons (reviewed by 27). In addition to the classic trisynaptic loop, from dentate granule cells, to CA3 pyramidal neurons, to CA1 pyramidal cells, there are also extensive associational connections (particularly within CA3), longitudinal connections along the length of the hippocampus, and commissural fibers connecting the two hippocampii, as well as extensive excitatory connections with related cortical structures such as the subiculum and entorhinal cortex.

The great complexity of cortical and hippocampal networks allows them to perform their varied tasks. However, one consequence of the massive interconnectivity of excitatory cells in both structures is the generation of "runaway" excitation if the recurrent excitation inherent in these networks is left unchecked. This is apparently the case, at least to some degree, in the generation of interictal spikes. The recurrent network of excitatory connections, both within the neocortex and hippocampus, results in a rapid excitation of other excitatory cells through the activation of non-NMDA and NMDA glutamatergic ionotropic receptors, causing a rapid recruitment of neurons into the epileptiform event (Figure 1*D–G*). Although all layers of the cerebral cortex and regions of the hippocampus appear to be capable of generating epileptiform activity, the cells that appear to discharge first during the generation of the so-called paroxysmal depolarizing shifts that underlie interictal spikes are layer V pyramidal neurons (28). Similarly, in the hippocampus, the CA3 field of pyramidal neurons exhibits a particular propensity to generate this pattern of abnormal activity (see 5, 10). This propensity, within layer V of the neocortex and CA3 of the hippocampus, relies not only on the excitatory interconnectivity of pyramidal neurons, but also on the presence of intrinsically burst-generating cells (Figure 1*E*).

Burst-Generating Cells in the Cortex and Hippocampus   A subset of layer V neocortical neurons and CA3 pyramidal cells can intrinsically generate bursts of 2 to 5 action potentials at 200–350 Hz upon activation by a brief depolarization (Figure 1*E*). These burst discharges are generated through the activation in the dendrites of slow action potentials that are mediated by Na^+ and Ca^{2+} currents (29, 30) and provide a prolonged depolarization of the soma and axon initial segment, thus promoting repetitive firing during the burst. The generation of burst discharges is not unidirectional from the dendrite to the soma because action potentials generated in the soma can back-propagate into the dendrites, and trigger dendritic spikes (31). Similarly, CA1 pyramidal neurons in the hippocampus and superficial (layer 2, 3) pyramidal cells of the cerebral cortex may generate high-frequency bursts of action potentials, under particular circumstances, through an interaction between the activation of traditional action potentials in the soma/initial segment and the activation of Na^+-dependent after-depolarizations following each action potential through the electrogenic properties of the dendrite (32–34). Recent investigations have confirmed earlier studies that CA1 pyramidal cells may also generate intrinsic bursts of spikes in response to strong or prolonged depolarization of the dendrites through the activation of a dendritic Ca^{2+} spike (35, 36). These pyramidal neurons exhibit a relatively uniform distribution along the soma-dendritic axis of both Na^+ and Ca^{2+} channels (although individual subtypes are distributed non-homogenously), but with a striking non-uniformity in the distribution of K^+ channels (reviewed in 36). Near the soma of CA1 pyramidal cells, there is a high density of BK Ca^{2+}-activated K^+ channels; the dendrites appear to have a higher density of transient K^+ channels (such as I_A and I_D). This distribution of depolarizing and hyperpolarizing channels limits the back-propagation of action potentials from the soma to the dendrites (owing to the strong activation of BK channels and transient K^+ channels by action potentials), while at the same time allowing the dendrites to generate Na^+/Ca^{2+} spikes in response to dendritic depolarization (owing to the presence of Na^+ and Ca^{2+} channels and the reduced concentration of BK channels in the dendrites). Thus strong or prolonged depolarization of CA1 pyramidal cells, such as during a seizure, may result in the generation of intrinsic burst discharges in these cells, while less synchronous or weaker depolarizations may result in trains of single spikes only.

A general mechanism for the generation of burst-discharges in cortical pyramidal neurons therefore appears to be through a "ping-pong" interaction between somatic and dendritic compartments (36a). Whether cortical cells generate action potential bursts is dependent upon both the neuromodulators being released onto the cell and the recent electrophysiological history of the neuron (see 34). Known burst-promoting states include slow-wave sleep for layer V pyramidal cells (reviewed in 37), repetitive and prolonged stimulation and increases in $[K^+]_o$ in at least superficial cortical pyramidal cells (34), and dendritic depolarization for CA1 hippocampal pyramidal cells (see 35). Changes in the prevalence of burst discharges in cortical neurons may contribute to the state dependence of some forms of epileptic seizures in vivo. Likewise, the generation of epileptiform activity may promote the generation of burst discharges, at least in some cortical neurons, thereby forming a positive feedback mechanism for the initiation of paroxysmal events.

The functional consequence of burst generation in cortical neurons is the amplification of inputs. The excitation of these cells with a short duration excitatory postsynaptic potential (EPSP) may result in the activation of several postsynaptic EPSPs, which, being generated at a relatively high frequency, will summate temporally and may increase synaptic reliability, owing to the low probability of neurotransmitter release at many cortical synapses (reviewed by 15, 30). Physiological and anatomical evidence suggests that burst-generating neurons may excite other such neurons through local axonal collaterals (see 38), giving rise to a network of cells that can generate powerful recurrent excitation. Indeed, following the block of inhibition in CA3 in vitro, bursting in a single CA3 pyramidal cell can evoke, if occurring at the right time, a synchronized burst throughout the population (38a).

The termination of burst discharges in cortical and hippocampal neurons appears to be largely achieved through the activation of outward K^+ currents and possibly through the inactivation of inward currents (39). Of the many different subtypes of K^+ channels distinct from one another in their voltage dependence, kinetics, and sensitivity to second messengers, those that are activated by increases in $[Ca^{2+}]_i$ (such as I_C and I_{AHP}) (40) and/or voltage are particularly important in the termination of single cell and network (e.g. interictal spike) burst discharges (Figure 1C). The discovery of K^+ channels that are sensitive to increases in $[Na^+]_o$ raises the possibility that they are also involved in the generation of prolonged (seconds) periods of hyperpolarization of cortical pyramidal neurons following the generation of intense bursts of activity (41, 42) and, therefore, could contribute to the termination of single cell or network burst discharges.

During network burst discharges, the activation of GABAergic inhibitory conductances, both $GABA_A$ and $GABA_B$, contribute to the termination of these synchronized events or PDSs (43, 44), and the block of these receptors may result in the generation of prolonged periods of after-discharges (see below). Interictal spikes, therefore, appear to be generated through a brief period of runaway excitation that spreads rapidly through a large local network of neurons, lasting ~80–200 ms and being terminated largely by the activation of inhibitory synaptic conductances and intrinsic K^+ currents (Figure 1) (39). Recent evidence suggests that an additional factor in the termination of burst discharges is a decrease in excitatory synaptic transmission owing to depletion of the readily releasable vesicles in presynaptic terminals (45). If this hypothesis is true, then the generation of prolonged discharges would be achieved by virtue of the large number of synapses involved, of which any single one might release transmitter only occasionally.

Another influence identified in the generation of synchronous discharges, especially in the CA1 field of the rodent hippocampus, is ephaptic (non-synaptic) interactions. The close proximity of cell bodies and dendrites in the hippocampus results in direct activation of neighbor cells by currents circulating in the extracellular space (referred to as an electrical field effect; see 6). The entry of positive charge into one neuron results in a negative charge in the extracellular space, thereby causing a decrease in the potential difference (e.g. depolarization) across the membrane of neighboring neurons. This apparent depolarization may then influence the timing of action potential generation in neighboring cells and therefore bring the network into synchrony. It is not yet clear how significant these electrical field effects are in the human hippocampus or neocortex, where pyramidal cell bodies are not as closely spaced as in the rodent hippocampal CA1 region.

Another form of non-synaptic interaction is the change in the extracellular concentration of ions. Periods of intense activity, from brief synchronized bursts of action potentials in a population of neurons to more prolonged discharges, result in significant increases in $[K^+]_o$ and decreases in $[Ca^{2+}]_o$. These changes in ion concentration may significantly increase neuronal excitability and promote epileptogenesis (Figure 2C) (46–48) (see below). Finally, changes in the extracellular space may facilitate these electrical field and ionic influences on synchronized burst generation and epileptogenesis. Decreases in the size of the extracellular space increase the electrical field effects and exacerbate increases in $[K^+]_o$ with activity (see 6). The interaction of these varied factors in positive feedback loops may lead to the generation of repetitive barrages of activity that qualify as the generation of epileptic seizures.

Sustained, Synchronized After-Discharges: Cortical Mechanisms for the Generation of Seizures

Interictal spikes denote a local disruption of normal function in cortical circuits and as such are useful in the diagnosis and localization of the underlying pathology

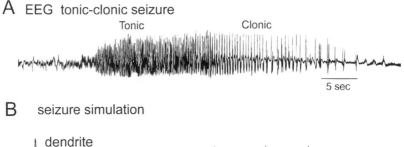

A EEG tonic-clonic seizure

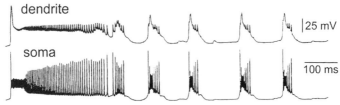

B   seizure simulation

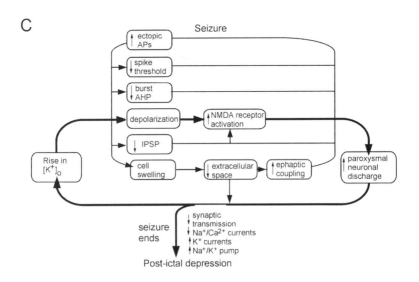

C

generating epileptic seizures. In addition to interictal spikes, epileptiform activity can also appear as the generation of after-discharges following the initial spike, as well as full tonic or tonic-clonic seizures (49). The transition from the generation of single PDSs during interictal spikes to full seizures in vivo has been associated with the gradual loss of the burst after-hyperpolarization and the progressive appearance of repetitive bursts of activity during a more and more prolonged after-depolarization (49, 50). The transition to a full seizure is associated with the maintained or tonic depolarization of the membrane potential and repetitive generation of action potentials at a few to tens of Hz (e.g. Figure 2*B*). This period of tonic activity is often followed by a period of irregular periodic bursts of action potentials (Figure 2*B*; the clonic phase), with relatively little synaptic or action potential activity in between synchronized bursts. Finally, as the clonic period of activity ends, there is a relatively quiet and hyperpolarized membrane potential corresponding to a period of "post-ictal depression."

Slice preparations, often of the hippocampus, have been utilized to develop models of repetitive after-discharges and electrographic seizures. Many of the manipulations that generate brief burst discharges in hippocampal slices also initiate seizure-like events. These include the block of $GABA_A$ receptor–mediated inhibition, induction of rapid kindling through repetitive local electrical stimulation of synaptic pathways, raising $[K^+]_o$, application of the K^+ channel blocker 4-aminopyridine, and reduction of $[Mg^{2+}]_o$ to very low levels (see 5, 6, 10, 13, 51–54). Additional manipulations that can generate prolonged after-depolarizations

---

←

Figure 2 Possible mechanisms of tonic-clonic seizures. (*A*) Single EEG trace from a curare-treated patient undergoing a tonic-clonic seizure. Note that the tonic portion of the seizure is associated with high-frequency discharge in cortical networks and that this high-frequency discharge gradually gives way to the lower-frequency synchronized discharges of the clonic portion of the seizure. (*B*) Simulated tonic-clonic seizure in a network of hippocampal pyramidal neurons induced by block of $GABA_A$ receptors. The tonic component is associated with the prolonged depolarization of both the dendritic and somatic compartments of the cell, which results in the generation of high-frequency action potential discharge, whereas the clonic component is associated with synchronized rhythmic burst generation mediated by the activation of slow spikes in the dendrites. (*C*) The importance of $[K^+]_o$ regulation and feedback mechanisms in the generation of seizures. Increases in $[K^+]_o$ initially promote the generation of epileptiform activity through multiple mechanisms including the enhancement of ectopic action potentials, decreases in action potential threshold, decreases in the amplitude of after-hyperpolarizations that terminate action potential bursts, depolarization of neurons, decreases in inhibitory synaptic potentials, and cell swelling. Secondary consequences include the increased activity of NMDA receptors and increased ephaptic coupling between neighboring neurons. All these events promote the generation of paroxysmal activity, which again increases $[K^+]_o$. Epileptiform activity fails when there is sufficient build up of decreases in synaptic transmission, the amplitude of Na^+ and Ca^{2+} currents, and through the activation of K^+ currents and electrogenic ion pumps (*A* from 153; *B* from 154; *C* modified from 47).

and/or electrographic seizures in hippocampal slices include the prior administration of tetanus toxin (which acutely disrupts synaptic transmission by cleaving synaptobrevin), the prolonged administration of cAMP analogues or stimulants of adenlylyl cyclase (see 5), and the activation of group I metabotropic glutamate receptors (55).

In many of these models (reduction of $GABA_A$ inhibition, increases in $[K^+]_o$, repetitive stimulation), the initial burst of epileptiform action potential activity is blocked only by antagonism of both non-NMDA and NMDA receptors, whereas the repetitive bursts of action potentials that follow this initial burst (Figure 2B) are sensitive to block of NMDA receptors alone (see 10). In contrast, both the primary and secondary bursts that occur in low $[Mg^{2+}]_o$ are abolished by block of NMDA receptors (51). Computational models of the generation of these after-depolarizations in a network of CA3 pyramidal cells by Traub et al (56) suggest that they are generated as a network of coupled oscillators in which the activation of NMDA receptors provides a prolonged depolarization of the dendrites of these cells, resulting in regenerative dendritic Na^+/Ca^{2+} spikes at 10–20 Hz, which then drive the repetitive bursts of action potentials at the soma (Figure 2B). The periodic activation of AMPA receptors at the synaptic connections between this pool of modeled pyramidal cells provides the timing signal that synchronizes the network.

During the generation of after-depolarizations and repetitive burst discharges, $[K^+]_o$ may increase considerably, from a normal level of approximately 3 mM up to 10 to 12 mM (e.g. 57). Initially, increases in $[K^+]_o$ will result in epileptogenic changes in network mechanisms by providing a depolarizing influence, decreasing the hyperpolarizing influence of compensatory K^+ currents, decreasing inhibitory synaptic transmission, decreasing action potential threshold, and increasing ephaptic interactions (Figure 2C) (see 47). However, strong increases in $[K^+]_o$ can also lead to decreases in neuronal and axonal excitability and, indeed, axonal conduction may become blocked (57a). Additionally, long-term changes in functional synaptic connections induced by bursts may also play a significant role in epileptogenesis (58, 59). These functional changes include the potentiation of excitatory synapses between pyramidal neurons, as well as potential functional decreases in inhibitory synaptic connections (51).

The generation of antidromic action potentials in the axon terminals of excitatory cells is important in the transition of single, interictal-like bursts to repetitive burst discharges, both in vivo (60, 61) and in vitro (62–64). Ectopic action potentials may travel throughout the axonal arbor and invade local and distal synaptic terminals, generating either a burst of synaptic transmitter release, or, on the population level, a periodic increase in excitation of the neurons in the network. Increases in ectopic action potential generation are often the consequence of increases in $[K^+]_o$, although other mechanisms are possible (Figure 2C) (62, 63). Ectopic action potentials, either following an initial burst of neuronal activity or during periods of intense neuronal firing, may be prevalent and facilitate the continuation of reverberating excitatory activity, thus promoting the transition from interictal spikes to seizures.

Local Propagation of Epileptiform Activity in Cortical Networks

Interictal spike-like epileptiform activity and associated after-discharges, generated in response to reduction of inhibition, propagate locally in hippocampal and cortical networks at a rate of approximately 70 to 200 mm/s (65a, 66). This propagation rate is substantially below that of axon conduction velocities and most likely is limited by the integration time required to bring each successive neuron to firing threshold. Thus the more quickly each neighboring neuron in the cortical slice is depolarized, the quicker the epileptiform burst may propagate (56). Obviously, the rate of depolarization of each neuron will be strongly influenced by many factors that include the strength and axonal length of excitatory and inhibitory connections in the network, the distance to firing threshold, the generation of burst discharges, and the membrane time constant. Epileptiform activity generated in response to lowering $[Mg^{2+}]_o$ propagates at a significantly lower rate than that following block of $GABA_A$ receptor–mediated inhibition, presumably owing to the intact nature of inhibitory interactions and their ability to slow the rapid depolarization of each successive neuron in the network (67). The propagation of primary and secondary (after-discharges) bursts of action potentials in hippocampal networks may not, however, follow the same rules. While primary bursts typically propagate in an orderly fashion away from the site of initiation, secondary bursts may jump to more distal points and propagate in a reverse direction, presumably in relation to the gradient of some important variable such as the density of excitatory or inhibitory connections (56).

Propagation of epileptiform activity in neocortical slices reveals a periodicity that depends on the direction of travel (66) and is indicative of some type of periodic functional connectivity, presumably related to functional columns in the neocortex. Isolation of different layers of cortex reveal that epileptiform activity may propagate through any layer, although it shows a preference for layer V (68).

These results reveal that epileptiform activities similar to those occurring in vivo during partial or complex-partial seizures may be generated on a local scale within small networks of hippocampal and cortical neurons. However, in vivo, it is expected that much larger networks of neurons are involved in the generation of each seizure that expresses itself clinically. Seizures in vivo may be partial, and therefore localized and limited to a particular cortical region, or may be initiated as apparently generalized, or become secondarily generalized, throughout the forebrain. It seems likely that in all these seizures, the epileptiform activity is initiated in a single location, and in all but the most localized forms of epileptiform activity, the abnormal discharges spread to involve multiple cortical and sub-cortical regions. The mechanisms by which seizure activity spreads and synchronizes between these multiple regions is still only poorly understood, although it is clear that corticocortical connections, as well as the interaction of cortical and subcortical structures, are highly involved. Thalamocortical interactions have received particular attention in the generation of certain types of seizures, especially in the primary generalized seizures of absence.

THALAMOCORTICAL MECHANISMS
AND EPILEPTIC SEIZURES

One form of generalized epilepsy that has received particular attention during the last two decades is absence (or petit-mal) epilepsy (69). Typical absence seizures are characterized in the EEG by a few seconds or more of sudden generalized and bilaterally synchronous spike-wave discharges at 2.5–3.5 Hz (Figure 3B), most often occurring in 2–16-year old children, and associated with a loss of cognitive abilities and behavioral arrest. One of the characteristics of absence seizures is that immediately following the ictal event there appears to be little if any disruption of either cognitive abilities or neurophysiological activities in the forebrain (70). This is in marked contrast to tonic-clonic or complex-partial seizures involving the neocortex or hippocampus, where both a behavioral and neurophysiological post-ictal depression is characteristic.

When discussing the cellular mechanisms of absence seizures and its associated EEG pattern of 3 Hz spike wave, it must be remembered that although typical absence seizures are always associated with spike-wave activity, the opposite is not true because there are multiple forms of spike-wave activity that are not associated with clinical absence and appear during other types of seizures (71). Therefore, it is particularly important in animal models of absence seizures to examine not only the spike-wave components of the EEG but also the behavioral and pharmacological aspects of these seizures. Two animal models of human absence are of particular note: the feline penicillin-generalized epilepsy (FPGE) model (reviewed in 72, 73) and the GAERS or WAG/Rij rat models (reviewed in 74–76). Spike-wave seizures in these animal models are similar to human absence attacks in that they exhibit a sudden onset and offset associated with behavioral arrest and lack of attentiveness. These seizures can be interrupted by an increase in arousal or by a sensory stimulus, and the frequency of attacks is decreased in response to drugs typically used to treat this type of epilepsy in humans (however, significant differences do exist, see below). Studies using these and other animal models, as well as human investigations, have implicated an abnormality in cortical and thalamic activity in the generation of spike-wave seizures (e.g. 4, 77, 78). For example, field potential recordings from cortical and thalamic loci in humans during absence seizures have shown spike-wave activity in both structures (reviewed in 9), and recent examinations of regional blood flow in thalamic structures using PET scans indicate an increase in thalamic activity during typical absence attacks (79).

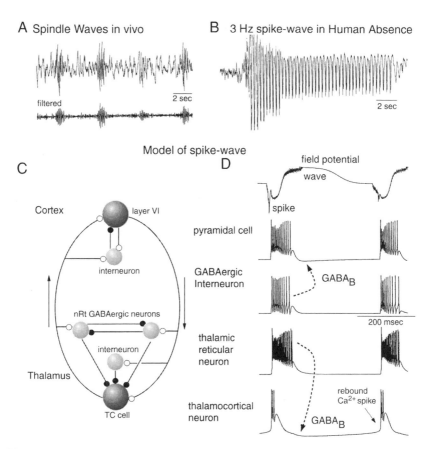

Figure 3 Possible cellular mechanisms of the generation of spike-wave seizures in human absence. (A) Spindle waves during slow-wave sleep in the normal EEG are intermixed with delta waves and recur once every few seconds. (B) Single EEG trace during an absence attack illustrating the striking 3-Hz spike-wave activity that characterizes this state. This spike-wave activity is widely synchronized throughout the EEG (not shown). (C) Simplified diagram of thalamocortical interactions proposed to underlie the generation of some forms of spike-wave activities. Cortical pyramidal cells and thalamocortical cells form mutually excitatory connections (open circles) that are regulated through the activation of GABAergic interneurons within the thalamus and cortex and thalamic reticular nucleus (inhibitory synaptic connections are denoted with filled circles). (D) Simulation of one cycle of a spike-wave seizure in corticothalamic networks. A burst of spikes in a thalamocortical neuron activates the cortical network, which generates a strong burst of action potentials through intracortical recurrent excitatory connections. This activity strongly activates both local GABAergic neurons and thalamic reticular neurons. The buildup of K^+ currents, including the activation of $GABA_B$ receptors and the inactivation of the depolarizing currents such as the low-threshold Ca^{2+} spike in thalamocortical cells, results in the cessation of activity in the network. The generation of a rebound Ca^{2+} spike in the thalamocortical cell, ~300 ms later, initiates the next cycle of the oscillation (A from 155; B from 156; D from 157).

Of particular relevance to the cellular mechanisms of absence seizures in humans and other primates is the observation that these paroxysmal EEG events are typically much more numerous during slow-wave sleep than during waking or rapid-eye-movement sleep (80, 80a). Indeed, animal models indicate that spike-wave seizures may be generated through a perversion of the normal cellular and network mechanisms underlying the generation of a normal slow-wave sleep EEG rhythm: the spindle wave (72, 73).

Spindle Waves and Their Relation to Spike-Wave Activity

Spindle waves are epochs of 6–15 Hz oscillation in the EEG that wax and wane over a period of 1 to 2 s and recur approximately once every 5 to 10 s during the early stages of slow-wave sleep (Figure 3A). Spindle waves are generated in the thalamus (reviewed in 3, 81), with neurons in the cerebral cortex being relatively weakly activated owing to the presence of strong feed-forward inhibition. Spindle waves are generated as an interaction between the GABAergic neurons of the thalamic reticular nucleus and thalamocortical neurons in which a brief burst of action potentials in the GABAergic cells hyperpolarizes their target thalamocortical cells through the activation of a Cl^- conductance mediated by $GABA_A$ receptors (see 3, 81). This hyperpolarization can be rather large because the equilibrium potential for Cl^- in thalamocortical cells is relatively negative, and burst firing in thalamic reticular cells results in both temporal summation of the unitary inhibitory postsynaptic potentials (IPSPs) and facilitation of these events (82, 83). The summated IPSP may result in the removal of inactivation of enough low-threshold Ca^{2+} current in the recipient thalamocortical cell to result in a rebound low-threshold spike (LTS) (84, 85) which then activates a burst of 1 to 4 Na^+ action potentials. Because thalamocortical and thalamic reticular cells are reciprocally connected (86, 87), the burst of action potentials in thalamocortical cells once again excites the thalamic reticular cells, thereby initiating the next cycle of the spindle oscillation (Figure 3C). The frequency of spindle-wave generation (6–15 Hz) appears to be dictated mainly by the cycle time required to complete a loop of activity between thalamic reticular and thalamocortical neurons ($\sim$70–150 ms) (88, 89). Local GABAergic neurons within the thalamus are not excited by thalamocortical cells but may participate in the generation of spindle waves in vivo owing to their excitation by corticothalamic axons. Present evidence suggests that local GABAergic neurons in the thalamus are either only weakly or not inhibited by thalamic reticular cells (88–90), although this finding remains to be explored.

The generation of spindle waves requires that both thalamocortical cells and thalamic reticular cells be in a relatively hyperpolarized membrane potential so that the low threshold Ca^{2+} current may be activated. In thalamocortical cells, low-threshold Ca^{2+} spikes are initiated by the rising phase of IPSPs, whereas in thalamic reticular cells, these Ca^{2+} spikes are initiated by EPSPs from thalamocortical neurons mediated via NMDA and non-NMDA receptors (88, 89, 91). This difference between the two cell types arises largely from the different subtypes of low-threshold Ca^{2+} currents present: The voltage dependence of the subtype of I_T present in thalamic reticular neurons is shifted to more depolarized levels (see 92) and probably has a more dendritic localization than in thalamocortical cells (93). The requirement for a hyperpolarized membrane potential for the generation of spindle waves explains the suppression of these by arousal. Increased activity in ascending and descending activating systems that underlie arousal results in a net depolarization of thalamocortical, thalamic reticular, and some cortical neurons through the reduction of K^+ conductances and, at least for thalamocortical cells, the enhancement of the h-current (reviewed in 37). Importantly, thalamic reticular neurons inhibit each other through dendrodendritic and axonal synaptic connections that activate mainly $GABA_A$, but also, longer lasting $GABA_B$ receptor–mediated IPSPs (94, 95). This lateral inhibition controls the amplitude and duration of excitation of these cells by thalamic and cortical activity (88, 89), which may have important consequences for the generation of some forms of spike-wave activity (96, 97).

Thalamic GABAergic mechanisms are not only involved in the generation of spindle waves, but also at least some forms of spike-wave seizures. In particular, intrathalamic injection of $GABA_A$ or $GABA_B$ (98) receptor agonists in the GAERS or WAG/Rij rat models of spike-wave seizures in vivo result in an enhancement of this epileptiform activity in these animals, presumably through hyperpolarization of thalamocortical neurons and promotion of the rebound oscillatory state. Administration of $GABA_B$ antagonists results in a marked reduction in these seizures in epileptic mice (99), suggesting that the activation of $GABA_B$ receptors may be particularly important. Extracellular recordings during spike-wave seizures reveal robust activity in thalamocortical and thalamic reticular neurons during these paroxysmal events, and lesions of the thalamic reticular nucleus abolish spike-wave seizures throughout the thalamocortical system (100, 101).

In vitro investigations of ferret thalamic slices suggest possible cellular and network mechanisms involved in the generation of paroxysmal 2–4 Hz thalamocortical activity (reviewed in 80). Dual intracellular recordings between thalamic reticular and thalamocortical neurons in vitro reveal that a physiological burst of 2 to 6 action potentials in reticular thalamic cells activates IPSPs predominately through $GABA_A$ receptors similar to those underlying the generation of spindle waves. Increasing the train of action potentials in these cells to >10 results in the additional activation of $GABA_B$ receptors and consequently a slow IPSP through a G protein–mediated increase in K^+ conductance (Figure 3D) (96). The requirement for strong release of GABA for the activation of $GABA_B$ receptor–mediated IPSPs by thalamic reticular neurons suggests that these receptors may be extrasynaptic (see 102) because their sensitivity to exogenous GABA itself appears similar or even higher than that of $GABA_A$ receptors (103). However, an additional explanation is that the opening of the K^+ channels activated by $GABA_B$ receptors requires the binding of multiple (four?) G proteins, such as one G protein to each receptor subunit (104). Functionally, the activation of $GABA_B$ receptors results in a slowing of the reverberatory activity between thalamic reticular and thalamocortical neurons, owing to the slow kinetics and prolonged duration (150–300 ms) of these IPSPs. In thalamic slices maintained in vitro, the block of $GABA_A$ receptors results in a pronounced increase in action potential activity in thalamic reticular neurons, presumably from disinhibition from other reticular neurons (88, 89). Following disinhibition from each other, thalamic reticular cells respond to barrages of EPSPs with the generation of a prolonged burst of action potentials and subsequently activate slow, $GABA_B$-mediated IPSPs in their post-synaptic thalamocortical cells (88, 89, 96, 105, 106). Following the near complete block of $GABA_A$ receptors, the time to complete a loop of activity between thalamic reticular cells and thalamocortical neurons lengthens to ∼300–400 ms, and therefore the network generates a rhythmic oscillation at ∼2–3 Hz. Because this frequency is similar to that at which thalamocortical cells prefer to endogenously oscillate, owing to the properties of I_T and the pacemaker current I_h (107, 108), the thalamocortical cells discharge with several action potentials on every cycle of the network oscillation (Figure 3D). The block of $GABA_A$ receptors in the thalamus may therefore result in the transformation of spindle waves into a paroxysmal event at 2–3 Hz, in which thalamocortical and thalamic reticular neurons discharge strongly and in synchrony. This manipulation provides a model for how the same diencephalic network can generate oscillations at two different frequencies characteristic of spindles (6–15 Hz) and absence-like events (2–3 Hz).

Similar results are obtained in vivo, by intrathalamic injections of the $GABA_A$ receptor antagonist bicuculline (109). Injection of bicuculline into the thalamus of otherwise intact cats greatly increases the number of spikes and the duration of burst discharges both in reticular thalamic and thalamocortical cells. This increase in burst activity is concomitant with a progressive decrease in the frequency of rhythmic activity from ∼10 Hz down to 2–3 Hz and a parallel increase in the synchrony among thalamic cells.

However, one important difference between the spike-wave seizures generated in rodents and those associated with human absence seizures, or the abnormal activity generated in thalamic slices, is their respective frequencies. Whereas the spike-wave activity in the EEG during human absence seizures is typically around 2.5 to 3.5 Hz, those spontaneously occurring in the rodent are ∼6–9 Hz, a frequency that would seem too high to be driven by IPSP through the activation of $GABA_B$ receptors in thalamocortical neurons. Indeed, intracellular recordings in rodent thalamocortical neurons reveal typical fast IPSPs, presumably mediated by $GABA_A$ receptors during the generation of these seizures (110). One possible solution to this apparent paradox has been suggested by computational modeling of both the 2–3 Hz thalamic rhythm and the 6–9 Hz oscillation (111). By reducing the strength of $GABA_B$ receptor activation (but not blocking it completely), the higher frequency oscillation may be generated. This rhythm still depends critically on the activation of $GABA_B$ receptors because this activation provides a prolonged hyperpolarization of thalamocortical cells that keeps these neurons in the range for the generation of rebound low-threshold Ca^{2+} spikes in response to the large $GABA_A$ receptor–mediated IPSPs. Thus the block of $GABA_B$ receptors would be expected to result in the cessation of these seizures, as observed, even though it is the activation of $GABA_A$ receptors that drives the oscillation with each cycle.

There are multiple possible reasons for the frequency differences between absence-like seizures in humans and rodents. Perhaps one of the most prominent is the general lack of local GABAergic circuit neurons in the rodent thalamus (see 91). In the primate, approximately 20–30% of neurons within each of the primary relay nuclei are local circuit GABAergic neurons, which are strongly innervated by corticothalamic inputs (see 91). These local circuit neurons activate both $GABA_A$ and $GABA_B$ receptor–mediated IPSPs (112) and therefore may contribute to the generation of large, slow IPSPs in thalamocortical neurons, thus facilitating the generation of 3-Hz spike-wave seizures in higher species. One implication of this is that the cognitive disruption associated with absence seizures is not related to the frequency of the spike-wave discharge per se but rather to the brain structures involved.

Investigations of spike-wave seizures in cats have emphasized the important role of abnormal discharge in the cerebral cortex and the interaction of this discharge with thalamocortical mechanisms. In the FPGE model of absence epilepsy, the intramuscular injection of a weak $GABA_A$ receptor antagonist, penicillin, results in the gradual transformation of spindle waves into spike-wave seizures (reviewed in 73). The critical locus for action of penicillin appears to be the cerebral cortex, since injection of this agent into the thalamus directly did not initiate spike-wave seizures in the EEG (although the spread of intrathalamic injections of penicillin are limited), whereas the topical application of penicillin directly to the cerebral cortex can initiate spike-wave events as long as the thalamocortical networks are intact. During the transition from spindle waves to spike-wave seizures with the systemic administration of penicillin, cortical neurons, including corticothalamic cells, undergo marked increases in action potential discharges. Initially, these cells discharge only weakly and intermittently in response to each phase of the spindle wave, while the development of spike-wave discharges is associated with strong bursts of action potentials in these cells during the spike and with hyperpolarization during the wave.

Results from systemic (i.v.) injections of bicuculline in cats in which the cerebral cortex had been completely removed from one hemisphere showed that seizures only occurred in the intact hemisphere, indicating that the thalamus cannot generate seizures alone (109). Furthermore, removal of the cortex in the seizing hemisphere caused the underlying thalamus to generate normal spindle waves without seizures. Because the lack of effect in thalamus of the systemic injections could be the result of an increased threshold for seizures in isolated thalamic networks, large injections of bicuculline were made intrathalamically. This resulted in the progressive substitution of sleep spindles by high-amplitude oscillations at 2–3 Hz that had characteristics intemediate between normal spindle waves and spike-wave seizures (109).

These studies indicate that disinhibition of neuronal activities in either the cerebral cortex or thalamus may result in abnormal 2–4 Hz activities in the EEG in both structures, with disinhibition of the neocortex resulting in activity that is most similar to spike-wave activities in human epilepsies (73, 113). One possibility is that the abnormal discharge of corticothalamic neurons, owing to an imbalance of excitation and inhibition in the cerebral cortex, results in the strong phasic excitation of thalamic reticular, thalamocortical, and local GABAergic neurons. Thus the strong activation of the corticothalamic pathway may result in both the direct excitation of thalamocortical cells and the hyperpolarization of these cells through disynaptic inhibition via thalamic reticular and local GABAergic cells (91, 114). Although this disynaptic inhibition may silence some thalamocortical cells, others generate rebound low-threshold Ca^{2+} spikes and bursts of action potentials that may initiate the next cycle of paroxysmal activity (Figure 3D) (115). Thus the critical feature in the transition from normal spindle wave to paroxysmal 2–3 Hz activity in the thalamus may be the initiation of prolonged barrages of action potentials simultaneously in many thalamic reticular GABAergic neurons. Indeed, the spike bursts of reticular neurons increase substantially in duration in the transition from normal sleep rhythms to spike-wave activity and become tightly related to the spike component of the seizure (115).

In vitro (116, 116a) and in vivo (116b) studies confirm the ability of strong synchronous activation of thalamic reticular cells by corticothalamic (or thalamocortical) afferents to convert the thalamic network from one generating normal spindle waves to one generating 2–3 Hz paroxysmal discharges. Again, these thalamic oscillations depend critically on the activation of $GABA_B$ receptor–mediated IPSPs for their generation (116, 116a). Therefore, even if thalamocortical mechanisms are responsible for the generation of 3-Hz spike-wave activity in human absence, the primary deficit need not be localized to the thalamus, but rather may occur within the cerebral cortex. The abnormal activity of cortical networks may then lead to pronounced discharge, followed by periods of silence and hyperpolarization, in both cortical and of thalamic cells (Figure 3D). At this point, the suggested mechanisms for the generation of abnormal spike-wave activities are the loss of $GABA_A$ receptor–mediated inhibition between thalamic reticular cells (97), the abnormally strong activation of thalamic GABAergic neurons by corticothalamic or thalamocortical afferents (e.g. 116, 116a), the loss of K^+ currents regulating burst length in thalamic reticular neurons, or the enhancement of the low threshold Ca^{2+} current (117).

Some of the cellular actions reported for one of the drugs typically used in the treatment of absence seizures, ethosuximide, are consistent with this model of these seizures. In particular, application of ethosuximide and related compounds reduces the amplitude of the low threshold Ca^{2+} current in thalamocortical neurons (reviewed in 118), although this effect is not seen by all investigators (119). In addition, the critical role of GABAergic inhibition in the generation of this form of spike-wave seizures is also consistent with the well known seizure-promoting side effects of barbiturates (which enhance GABAergic synaptic transmission) in patients with absence epilepsy (120).

Possible Mechanisms for the Waxing and Waning of Spindles and Thalamocortical Spike-Wave Seizures   Both in vivo and in vitro spindle waves can recur with a remarkable periodicity at approximately once every 5 to 10 s (see Figure 3*A*) (121). The waxing or growth phase of the spindle wave and 2–3 Hz paroxysmal activity in vitro is explained by the cyclical recruitment of neurons into the oscillation, as well as the increasing strength of the oscillation in thalamocortical cells (represented by increasing amplitude of IPSPs and rebound Ca^{2+} spikes) and in thalamic reticular cells (involving increasing amplitude of EPSP barrages and low-threshold Ca^{2+} spike–mediated burst discharges). The mechanisms underlying waning of these network oscillations is less obvious. However, one clue is that in thalamocortical cells the waning of spindle waves is followed by the generation of a slow after-depolarization, the duration of which matches the duration of the inter-spindle interval (87). This after-depolarization is generated through the persistent activation of the hyperpolarization-activated cation current I_h and although small (1–4 mV) is large enough to reduce significantly the ability of IPSPs arriving in thalamocortical cells to generate rebound low-threshold Ca^{2+} spikes (87, 122, 123). The persistent activation of I_h following the generation of a network oscillation may involve the Ca^{2+}-dependent activation of a Ca^{2+}-sensitive adenylyl cyclase and, subsequently, an increase in $[cAMP]_i$ (124). Cyclic AMP appears to bind directly, in an allosteric manner, to single h-channels, and in so doing stabilizes the open state (124, 125), providing the prolonged depolarization that inhibits oscillatory activity in thalamocortical networks.

Could the cessation of spike-wave activity in thalamocortical networks during seizures also involve the persistent activation of the h-current? This intriguing hypothesis remains to be tested, but it is possible that the cessation of spike-wave seizures that require rebound burst firing in thalamocortical neurons may cease owing to the build up of I_h activation and depolarization of thalamocortical cells. If a similar mechanism occurs in absence seizures in children, then it would help explain the lack of post-ictal depression because the seizures would be followed by a slight depolarization of thalamocortical cells, which, if anything, should actually facilitate the operation of forebrain networks.

Synchronizing Mechanisms in Normal and Abnormal Thalamocortical Activity

All the cellular models of EEG rhythm and seizure generation have focused on the operation of relatively local neuronal circuits, yet generalized spike-wave seizures typically exhibit widespread synchronization and rapid generalization. How is it that neural networks come to oscillate in a widely coordinated manner? Since widespread synchronization is also exhibited by brain rhythms associated with slow-wave sleep and anesthesia, i.e. spindling, delta, and the slow (<1 Hz) oscillation (127–129), this intriguing question has begun to be addressed, by studying the mechanisms of synchronization of these normal thalamic and cortical rhythms.

Synchronization of Spindle Waves and Spike-Wave Seizures   Recordings in vitro demonstrate that spindle waves in slices typically propagate along the horizontal plane at a slow rate (approximately 1 mm/s) as each adjacent portion is recruited into the network oscillation (126). Yet, recordings of these sleep rhythms in vivo often reveal spindle waves that appear almost simultaneously throughout the cerebral cortex, although local generation can still occur (127). This widespread synchronization is brought about by corticocortical and corticothalamocortical connections (127–129). Thus removal of the cerebral cortex leaves a thalamus that generates spindle waves that are only locally (within a couple of mm) coherent. On the other hand, when the cortex is present, local stimulation in the cerebral cortex results in spindle waves in the thalamus that are synchronized beyond the region stimulated (129). The mechanisms of this synchronization of thalamocortical rhythms is believed to rely largely on the divergence and convergence of axonal connections, including those between layer VI of the cerebral cortex and neurons in the thalamic reticular and relay nuclei (130), the divergence of axonal connections from the thalamic reticular nucleus to thalamocortical neurons (90, 131, 132), from the thalamus to the cerebral cortex, and within the cerebral cortex itself (19, 133).

Computational simulations of synchronization in thalamocortical circuits suggest that the activation of thalamic reticular neurons, with their divergent connections to multiple thalamocortical cells, may be a particularly powerful synchronizing mechanism (114). For example, the activation of a single GABAergic perigeniculate neuron, which is equivalent to a thalamic reticular neuron, may simultaneously inhibit 100 or more thalamocortical cells in the dorsal lateral geniculate nucleus that are separated by up to 1 mm (82). The subsequent rebound burst firing generated in these thalamocortical cells may then excite an even larger portion of the neocortex, and the subsequent feedback excitation from layer VI to the thalamus is expected to excite a considerably larger portion of the GABAergic neurons of the perigeniculate nucleus.

Severing the corpus callosum abolishes or severely reduces the inter-hemispheric synchrony of spindles waves as well as spike-wave seizures (73, 121). In contrast, local knife cuts through the depth of the cortex do not result in a loss of synchrony of spindle waves between the tissues on either side of the cut (129). Thus although local corticocortical connections are undoubtedly important in the synchronization of these thalamocortical rhythms, they are not necessary, whereas at least some long-range corticocortical connections are critical.

An important feature of synchronized rhythm generation in the thalamocortical system is the ability of these rhythms to be initiated in many different parts of the network. In thalamic slices, for example, spindle waves that propagate throughout the network can be initiated by the activation of a single GABAergic neuron (126). Thus the point of initiation of spindle waves, or of spike-wave seizures, may vary from event to event, depending on the state of the local network. The rapid generalization of these rhythms throughout the network and the inability to monitor the activity of all the neurons involved prevent the experimental or clinical detection of the true initiation and spread of these synchronized oscillations, which causes them to appear as "generalized from the outset." This synchronized, but distributed, nature of spike-wave activity is in marked contrast to the centrencephalic theory, which holds that a central pacemaker generates these seizures.

The synchronization of thalamocortical networks depends not only on anatomical connections, but also on the physiological state of the network. The deepening of slow-wave sleep or anesthesia is associated with increases in the synchronization of spindle waves and other slow rhythms (134). Hyperpolarization of the membrane potential of thalamic neurons, which occurs during deepening of sleep or anesthesia (see 37), markedly enhances slow rhythms in this structure, largely through the removal of inactivation of the low-threshold Ca^{2+} spike, but also through an increase in neuronal input resistance owing to the deactivation of various K^+ currents (135). A similar enhancement of synchronized burst firing may also occur within the cerebral cortex (136), and this enhancement of the local cellular mechanisms for the generation of slow rhythms may then translate at a more global level into a marked enhancement of widespread synchrony of these rhythms (137). However, deepening the state of sleep and anesthesia may abolish the generation of some thalamocortical rhythms and promote the occurrence of others. Spindle waves are most pronounced in the early stages of sleep, while slower rhythms such as delta waves are more prominent during the deep stages of slow-wave sleep. Spike-wave seizures in the rodent model of absence epilepsy are also prevalent during the early stages of sleep, but abolished in the later stages (80). Again, these transitions appear to depend largely on the state of the membrane potential of thalamic and cortical neurons, in that strong hyperpolarization of these neurons reduces the ability of these cells to generate rebound low-threshold Ca^{2+} spikes in response to the arrival of barrages of IPSPs, while promoting the generation of intrinsic, slow oscillatory rhythms (138). In summary, absence may be facilitated by moderate but not extreme hyperpolarization of diencephalic neurons.

SLOW OSCILLATION IN THE CEREBRAL CORTEX
AND ITS CONVERSION TO EPILEPTIC SEIZURES

During periods of anesthesia and slow-wave sleep, cortical and thalamocortical networks can generate recurrent synchronized activity at 0.1–0.9 Hz in animals and humans, the so-called slow oscillation (Figure 4A) (139–142). The slow oscillation is generated within the cerebral cortex because it survives complete lesions of the thalamus, isolation of cortical slabs from subcortical structures, and occurs in cortical slices maintained in vitro (143). However, the slow oscillation strongly influences activities in subcortical structures such as the caudate (144) and thalamus (139–141), and at least some EEG rhythms are generated through an interaction of the slow oscillation and other thalamocortical rhythms. For example, K-complexes, a normal human EEG rhythm occurring during slow-wave sleep, appear as the onset of a cycle of the slow oscillation in the cerebral cortex followed by the activation of a spindle wave within the thalamus (145).

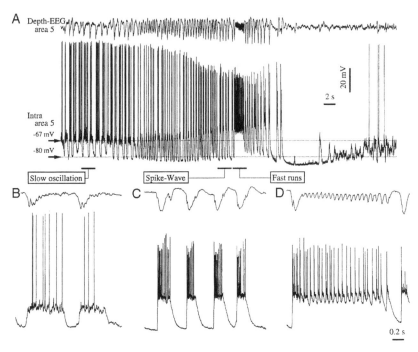

Figure 4   Cortical slow oscillations spontaneously develop into a seizure consisting of spike waves at 2–3 Hz and fast runs at ~15 Hz. (*A*) Intracellular recording from a regular-spiking cell and depth-EEG from neocortex area 5 in a cat under ketamine-xylazine anesthesia. The cortical slow oscillation is characterized by a depolarized up state at −67 mV and a hyperpolarized down state at −80 mV (expanded in *B* for detail). The transition to the seizure is associated with an increase in frequency of transitions between the up and down state, resulting in a spike-wave pattern in the EEG (expanded in *C*), that was interrupted by occasional fast runs of activity characterized by rhythmic 10–15 Hz activity riding on top of a sustained depolarization (expanded in *D*). The seizure lasted for ~25 s and was followed by an after-hyperpolarization and an apparent flattening of the EEG (from 113).

Intracellular recordings in vivo and in vitro reveal that the slow oscillation is characterized by the alternation between a depolarized "up" state and a hyperpolarized "down" state (Figure 4) (140, 143). Simultaneous recording of different identified cell types in the cerebral cortex and/or thalamus, as well as the local field potential or multiple unit activity, revealed that all cortical and thalamic neurons discharge during the up state and exhibit either no or reduced activity during the down state. Similarly, intracellular recordings from cortical pyramidal cells reveal that the up state is mediated by the arrival of barrages of both excitatory and inhibitory postsynaptic potentials, whereas the down state is associated with a relative reduction in the frequency of these events. These results indicate that the slow oscillation is generated by the initiation and failure of recurrent excitation within cortical circuits, with the activation of inhibitory neurons regulating the intensity of discharges during the depolarized up state (139, 141, 143).

In vitro investigations of the slow oscillation reveal that it can occur throughout layers II-VI of the cerebral cortex but that layer V has the lowest threshold for generation, and therefore this oscillation often is initiated in this layer. Following the initiation of the slow oscillation, it then propagates horizontally through the slice at the relatively slow rate of approximately 10 mm/s (143). In vivo recordings of the slow oscillation also point to the generation of this activity throughout layers II-VI, and simultaneous recordings from widely spaced cortical regions reveal synchronization of this rhythm in a manner that is consistent with a propagation rate of approximately 100 mm/s (137), which is ten times faster than observed in vitro. The role of corticocortical connections in the synchronization of the slow oscillation is suggested by the finding that vertical knife cuts through the cortex, or the local block of activity with the application of lidocaine, abolish the synchronization of this rhythm between adjacent areas (137, 146). Thus, in contrast to spindle waves, the slow oscillation depends critically on local intracortical connections for synchronization and is not as capable in synchronizing different cortical regions through corticothalamocortical interactions.

The down state of the slow oscillation is generated largely through a failure of the recurrent excitatory activity that maintains the depolarized up state (139–143). Intracellular recordings in vivo and in vitro reveal that the down state is associated with a relatively hyperpolarized membrane potential in pyramidal neurons and a slow after-hyperpolarization similar to that generated following repetitive action potentials in these cells (140, 142). Thus the slow oscillation may be generated through the interaction between the depolarizing influence of the recurrent activity characteristic of corticocortical interactions and the slow build-up and dissipation of outward K^+ currents activated by this activity (143). Additionally, the activation of K^+ currents through the release of neuromodulators, such as adenosine, has been suggested to contribute to the down state (147).

In response to repetitive local electrical stimulation, injections of bicuculline, or spontaneously, the slow oscillation in vivo may convert to epileptic seizures. These seizures are characterized by periods of fast runs of 10–15 Hz activity and/or spike/polyspike-wave activity at 3–4 Hz (Figure 4) (4, 115). As with slow oscillation, these seizures survive thalamectomy and therefore can be generated intracortically (109). This pattern of seizure activity is similar to that occurring in the Lennox-Gastaut epileptic syndrome, which clinically is associated with frequent seizures, sudden falls, marked resistance to pharmacological therapy, and mental and behavioral disturbances. In Lennox-Gastant syndrome, clinical and electrographic seizures are activated during sleep in a pattern consisting of diffuse slow spikes-waves and bursts of fast rhythms at 10 to 12 Hz.

The transition from the slow oscillation into a seizure is initially associated with a progressive increase in amplitude of the EEG slow waves followed by the appearance of runs of activity at 10–15 Hz that give way to sequences of spike/polyspike-wave complexes at 2 to 4 Hz. This gradual transformation of the cortical slow wave into a spike-wave seizure is correlated with a marked increase in synchrony of activity between cortical areas as well as between cortical and thalamic regions (148, 149). Intracellularly, during the fast runs at 10–15 Hz, most cortical cells are tonically depolarized and discharge at high frequencies (Figure 4D); an exception is a special class of cortical cells named chattering (150) or fast repetitive bursting cells that fire rhythmic spike-bursts time locked with the 10–15 Hz EEG spikes (113). The intense, synchronized burst discharges of these neurons, which include superficial and deep lying pyramidal cells, suggest that they play an important role in the generation, synchronization, and propagation of these seizures.

Although these seizures can be generated entirely within the cerebral cortex, in intact animals the thalamus is also involved. Both thalamocortical and reticular thalamic cells are depolarized and discharge trains of spikes during the 10–15 Hz component of these seizures (115, 151). During spike/polyspike components, the GABAergic neurons of the thalamic reticular nucleus are strongly and phasically excited, discharging prolonged bursts of action potentials in phase with the EEG spikes. These bursts of action potentials in thalamic reticular cells generate either a sustained or cyclical inhibition of thalamocortical neurons, which results in a silencing of the activity of approximately 60% of these cells and the generation of rebound bursts of action potentials that are in synchrony with the EEG spikes in the remaining neurons (115). Therefore, although these seizures can be generated entirely within the cerebral cortex of athalamic cats, in the intact animal there is a marked synchronization of cortical, thalamic reticular, and a substantial fraction of thalamocortical neurons (109, 149). It is likely that this synchronization of corticocortical and thalamocortical activities reinforces the spread and generation of these seizures.

SUMMARY

The normal connectivity and functional properties of the neocortex, hippocampus, and thalamus give rise to the ability to generate either local or large-scale normal synchronized oscillations. The generation of epileptic seizures is also mediated by these same networks and cellular mechanisms and therefore often appear as perversions of normal rhythmic activities. Although there are many clinical epileptic syndromes, experimental models have revealed only a few forms of seizure-like activities. The first, which is a model of partial, complex-partial, and tonic-clonic seizures, is based on recurrent excitatory interactions between pyramidal cells in either the cerebral cortex or hippocampus; the second form, which is the leading model of human absence seizures, is based on the reverberation of oscillatory activity between excitatory and inhibitory neurons within the thalamus and cerebral cortex. Thus although the initiating insults that result in the development of epileptic seizures may be diverse, the cellular mechanisms underlying the expression of these seizures may be relatively similar and therefore form a reasonable target for pharmacological intervention.

ACKNOWLEDGMENTS

We thank Roger Traub, Mircea Steriade, Maria Sanchez-Vives, and Alain Destexhe for helpful discussions. Supported by the National Institutes of Health (DAM) and by the Klingenstein Fund (DC). Additional information if available at: www.mccormicklab.org.

Visit the Annual Reviews home page at www.AnnualReviews.org

LITERATURE CITED

1. Commission on Classification and Terminology of the International League Against Epilepsy. Proposal for revised classification of epilepsies and epileptic syndromes. 1989. *Epilepsia* 30:389–99

2. Dichter MA, Ayala GF. 1987. Cellular mechanisms of epilepsy: a status report. *Science* 237:157–64

3. Steriade M, McCormick DA, Sejnowski TJ. 1993. Thalamocortical oscillations in the sleeping and aroused brain. *Science* 262:679–85

4. Steriade M, Contreras D, Amzica F. 1994. Synchronized sleep oscillations and their paroxysmal developments. *Trends Neurosci.* 17:199–208

5. Jefferys JG. 1994. Experimental neurobiology of epilepsies. *Curr. Opin. Neurol.* 7:113–22

6. Jefferys JG. 1995. Nonsynaptic modulation of neuronal activity in the brain: electric currents and extracellular ions. *Physiol. Rev.* 75:689–723

7. McNamara JO. 1994. Cellular and molecular basis of epilepsy. *J. Neurosci.* 14:3413–25

8. McNamara JO. 1999. Emerging insights into the genesis of epilepsy. *Nature* 399(Suppl):A15–22

9. Huguenard JR, Prince DA. 1997. Basic mechanisms of epileptic discharge in the thalamus. In *Thalamus Vol II. Experimental and Clinical Aspects*, ed. M Steriade, EG Jones, DA McCormick, pp. 295–330, New York: Elsevier

10. Jefferys JG, Traub RD. 1998. Electro-physiological substrates for focal epilepsies. *Prog. Brain Res.* 116:351–58

11. Mody I. 1998. Ion channels in epilepsy. *Int. Rev. Neurobiol.* 42:199–226

12. Mody I. 1999. Synaptic plasticity in kindling. *Adv. Neurol.* 79:631–43

13. Clark S, Wilson WA. 1999. Mechanisms of epileptogenesis. *Adv. Neurol.* 79:607–30

14. Delgado-Escueta AV, Wilson WA, Olsen RW, Porter RJ, eds. 1999. *Advances in Neurology Vol. 79. Jaspers Basic Mechanisms of the Epilepsies*. Philadelphia: . Lippincott, Williams & Wilkins. 3rd ed.

14a. Rogawski MA. 2000 KCNQ2/KCNQ3 K^+ channels and the molecular pathogenesis of epilepsy: implications for therapy. *Trends Neurosci.* 23:393–98

15. Thomson AM, Deuchars J. 1997. Synaptic interactions in neocortical local circuits: dual intracellular recordings in vitro. *Cerebral Cortex* 7:510–22

16. Gilbert CD. 1992. Horizontal integration and cortical dynamics. *Neuron* 9:1–13

17. Douglas RJ, Koch C, Mahowald M, Martin KA, Suarez HH. 1995. Recurrent excitation in neocortical circuits. *Science* 269:981–85

18. Rockland KS, Drash GW. 1996. Collateralized divergent feedback connections that target multiple cortical areas. *J. Comp. Neurol.* 373:529–48

19. Felleman DJ, Van Essen DC. 1991. Distributed hierarchical processing in the primate cerebral cortex. *Cerebral Cortex* 1:1–47

20. Peters A, Jones EG, eds. 1984. *Cerebral Cortex. Vol. 1. Cellular Components of the Cerebral Cortex.* New York: Plenum

21. Gupta A, Wang Y, Markram H. 2000. Organizing principles for a diversity of GABAergic interneurons and synapses in the neocortex. *Science* 287:244–46

22. Thomson AM. 2000. Facilitation, augmentation and potentiation at central synapses. *Trends Neurosci.* 23:305–12

23. Gil Z, Connors BW, Amitai Y. 1997. Differential regulation of neocortical synapses by neuromodulators and activity. *Neuron* 19:679–86

24. Swadlow HA, Beloozerova IN, Sirota MG. 1998. Sharp, local synchrony among putative feed-forward inhibitory interneurons of rabbit somatosensory cortex. *J. Neurophysiol.* 79:567–82

25. Gibson JR, Beierlein M, Connors BW 1999. Two networks of electrically coupled inhibitory neurons in neocortex. *Nature* 402:75–79

26. Galarreta M, Hestrin S. 1999. A network of fast-spiking cells in the neocortex connected by electrical synapses. *Nature* 402:72–75

27. Freund TF, Buzsaki G. 1996. Interneurons of the hippocampus. *Hippocampus* 6:347–470

28. Connors BW. 1984. Initiation of synchronized neuronal bursting in neocortex. *Nature* 310:685–87

29. Traub RD, Jefferys JG. 1994. Are there unifying principles underlying the generation of epileptic after-discharges in vitro? *Prog. Brain Res.* 102:383–94

30. Traub RD, Jefferys JG. 1994. Simulations of epileptiform activity in the hippocampal CA3 region in vitro. *Hippocampus* 4:281–85

31. Larkum ME, Zhu JJ, Sakmann B. 1999. A new cellular mechanism for coupling inputs arriving at different cortical layers. *Nature* 398:338–41

32. Azouz R, Jensen MS, Yaari Y. 1996. Ionic basis of spike after-depolarization and burst generation in adult rat hippocampal CA1 pyramidal neurons. *J. Physiol.* 492:211–23.

33. Jensen MS, Azouz R, Yaari Y. 1996. Spike after-depolarization and burst generation in adult rat hippocampal CA1 pyramidal cells. *J. Physiol.* 492:199–210

34. Brumberg JC, Nowak LG, McCormick DA. 2000. Ionic mechanisms underlying repetitive high frequency burst firing in supragranular cortical neurons. *J. Neurosci.* 20:4829–43

35. Golding NL, Jung H-Y, Mickus T, Spruston N. 1999. Dendritic calcium spike initiation and repolarization are controlled by distinct potassium channel subtypes in CA1 pyramidal neurons. *J. Neurosci.* 19:8789–98

36. Johnston D, Hoffman DA, Magee JC, Poolos NP, Watanabe S, et al. 2000. Dendritic potassium channels in hippocampal pyramidal neurons. *J. Physiol.* 525:75–81

36a. Traub RD, Wong RK, Miles R, Michelson H. 1991. A model of a CA3 hippocampal pyramidal neuron incorporating voltage-clamp data on intrinsic conductances. *J. Neurophysiol.* 66:635–60

37. McCormick DA. 1992. Neurotransmitter actions in the thalamus and cerebral cortex and their role in neuromodulation of thalamocortical activity. *Prog. Neurobiol.* 39:337–88

38. Markram H. 1997. A network of tufted layer 5 pyramidal neurons. *Cerebral Cortex* 7:523–33

38a. Miles R, Wong RK. 1983. Single neurones can initiate synchronized population discharge in the hippocampus. *Nature* 306:371–73

39. Alger BE, Williamson A. 1988. A transient calcium-dependent potassium component of the epileptiform burst afterhyperpolarization in rat hippocampus. *J. Physiol.* 399:191–205

40. Vergara C, Latorre R, Marrion NV, Adelman JP. 1998. Calcium-activated

potassium channels. *Curr. Opin. Neurobiol.* 8:321–29

41. Schwindt PC, Spain WJ, Crill WE. 1989. Long-lasting reduction of excitability by a sodium-dependent potassium current in cat neocortical neurons. *J. Neurophysiol.* 61:233–44

42. Sanchez-Vives MV, Nowak LG, McCormick DA. 2000. Cellular mechanisms of long-lasting adaptation in visual cortical neurons in vitro. *J. Neurosci.* 20:4286–99

43. McCormick, D.A. 1989. GABA as an inhibitory neurotransmitter in the human cerebral cortex. *J. Neurophysiol.* 62:1018–27

44. Scanziani M, Debanne D, Muller M, Gahwiler BH, Thompson SM. 1994. Role of excitatory amino acid and GABA_B receptors in the generation of epileptiform activity in disinhibited hippocampal slice cultures. *Neuroscience* 61:823–32

45. Staley KJ, Longacher M, Bains JS, Yee A. 1998. Presynaptic modulation of CA3 network activity. *Nat. Neurosci.* 1:201–9

46. Heinemann U, Lux HD, Gutnick MJ. 1977. Extracellular free calcium and potassium during paroxysmal activity in the cerebral cortex of the cat. *Exp. Brain Res.* 27:237–43

47. Traynelis SF, Dingledine R. 1988. Potassium-induced spontaneous electrographic seizures in the rat hippocampal slice. *J. Neurophysiol.* 59:259–76

48. Jensen MS, Yaari Y. 1997. Role of intrinsic burst firing, potassium accumulation, and electrical coupling in the elevated potassium model of hippocampal epilepsy. *J. Neurophysiol.* 77:1224–33

49. Matsumoto H, Ajmone-Marsan C. 1964. Cortical cellular phenomena in experimental epilepsy: ictal manifestations. *Exp. Neurol.* 9:305–26

50. Ayala GF, Matsumoto H, Gumnit RJ. 1970. Excitability changes and inhibitory mechanisms in neocortical neurons during seizures. *J. Neurophysiol.* 33:73–85

51. Le Beau FEN, Alger BE. 1998. Transient

suppression of GABA_A-receptor-mediated IPSPs after epileptiform burst discharges in CA1 pyramidal cells. *J. Neurophysiol.* 79:659–69

52. Lopantsev V, Avoli M. 1998. Laminar organization of epileptiform discharges in the rat entorhinal cortex in vitro. *J. Physiol.* 509:785–96

53. Borck C, Jefferys JG. 1999. Seizure-like events in disinhibited ventral slices of adult rat hippocampus. *J. Neurophysiol.* 82:2130–42

54. Demir R, Haberly LB, Jackson MB. 1999. Sustained plateau activity precedes and can generate ictal-like discharges in low-Cl^- medium in slices of rat piriform cortex. *J. Neurosci.* 19:10738–46

55. Galoyan SM, Merlin LR. 2000. Long-lasting potentiation of epileptiform bursts by group I mGluRs is NMDA receptor independent. *J. Neurophysiol.* 83:2463–67

56. Traub RD, Miles R, Jefferys JG. 1993. Synaptic and intrinsic conductances shape picrotoxin-induced synchronized after-discharges in the guinea-pig hippocampal slice. *J. Physiol.* 461:525–47

57. Lothman EW, Somjen GG. 1976. Functions of primary afferents and responses of extracellular K^+ during spinal epileptiform seizures. *Electroencephalogr. Clin. Neurophysiol.* 41:253–67

57a. Poolos NP, Mauk MD, Kocsis JD. 1987. Activity-evoked increases in extracellular potassium modulates presynaptic excitability in the CA1 region of the hippocampus. *J. Neurophysiol.* 58:404–16

58. Anderson WW, Swartzwelder HS, Wilson WA. 1987. The NMDA receptor antagonist 2-amino-5-phosphonovalerate blocks stimulus train-induced epileptogenesis but not epileptiform bursting in rat hippocampal slice. *J. Neurophysiol.* 57:1–21

59. Stasheff SF, Anderson WW, Clark S, Wilson WA. 1989. NMDA antagonists differentiate epileptogenesis from seizure

expression in an in vitro model. *Science* 245:648–51

60. Pinault D, Pumain R. 1989. Antidromic firing occurs spontaneously on thalamic relay neurons: triggering of somatic intrinsic burst discharges by ectopic action potentials. *Neuroscience* 31:625–37

61. Pinault D. 1995. Back propagation of action potentials generated at ectopic axonal loci: hypothesis that axon terminals integrate local environmental signals. *Brain Res. Rev.* 21:42–92

62. Stasheff SF, Hines M, Wilson MA. 1993. Axon terminal hyperexcitability associated with epileptogenesis in vitro. I. Origin of ectopic spikes. *J. Neurophysiol.* 70:961–75

63. Stasheff SF, Mott DD, Wilson WA. 1993. Axon terminal hyperexcitability associated with epileptogenesis in vitro. II. Pharmacological regulation by NMDA and GABA$_A$ receptors. *J. Neurophysiol.* 70:976–84

64. Traub RD, Colling SB, Jefferys JGR. 1995. Cellular mechanisms of 4-aminopyridine-induced synchronized afterdischarges in the rat hippocampal slice. *J. Physiol.* 489:127–40

65. Pinault D. 1992. Ectopic axonal firing in an epileptic cortical focus is not triggered by thalamocortical volleys during the interictal stage. *Brain Res.* 576:175–80

65a. Traub RD, Jeffrey JG, Miles R. 1993. Analysis of the propagation of disinhibition-induced after-discharges along the guinea-pig hippocampal slice in vitro. *J. Physiol.* 472:267–87

66. Chervin RD, Pierce PA, Connors BW. 1988. Periodicity and directionality in the propagation of epileptiform discharges across neocortex. *J. Neurophysiol.* 60:1695–713

67. Telfeian AE, Connors BW. 1999. Epileptiform propagation patterns mediated by NMDA and non-NMDA receptors in rat neocortex. *Epilepsia* 40:1499–506

68. Telfeian AE, Connors BW. 1998. Layer-specific pathways for the horizontal propagation of epileptiform discharges in neocortex. *Epilepsia* 39:700–8

69. Porter RJ. 1993. The absence epilepsies. *Epilepsia* 34:S42–48

70. Brown TR, Kiffin-Penry J, Porter RJ, Dreifuss FE. 1974. Responsiveness before, during, and after spike-wave paroxysms. *Neurology* 24:659–65

71. Engel J, Pedley TA, eds. 1998. *Epilepsy. A Comprehensive Textbook.* Vols. 1, 2, 3. Philadelphia: Lippencott-Raven

72. Gloor P, Fariello RG. 1988. Generalized epilepsy: some of its cellular mechanisms differ from those of focal epilepsy. *Trends Neurosci.* 11:63–68

73. Gloor P, Avoli M, Kostopoulos G. 1990. Thalamocortical relationships in generalized epilepsy with bilaterally synchronous spike-and-wave discharge. In *Generalized Epilepsy. Neurobiological Approaches*, ed. M Avoli, P Gloor, G Kostopoulos, R Naquet, pp. 190–212. Boston: Birkhauser

74. Coenen AM, Drinkenburg WH, Inoue M, van Luijtelaar EL. 1992. Genetic models of absence epilepsy, with emphasis on the WAG/Rij strain of rats. *Epilepsy Res.* 12:75–86

75. Danober L, Deransart C, Depaulis A, Vergnes M, Marescaux C. 1998. Pathophysiological mechanisms of genetic absence epilepsy in the rat. *Prog. Neurobiol.* 55:27–57

76. Snead OC III, Depaulis A, Vergnes M, Marescaux C. 1999. Absence epilepsy: advances in experimental animal models. *Adv. Neurol.* 79:253–78

77. Luhmann HJ, Mittmann T, van Luijtelaar G, Heinemann U. 1995. Impairment of intracortical GABAergic inhibition in a rat model of absence epilepsy. *Epilepsy Res.* 22:43–51

78. Avanzini G, de Curtis M, Franceschetti S, Sancini G, Spreafico R. 1996. Cortical versus thalamic mechanisms underlying spike and wave discharges in GAERS. *Epilepsy Res.* 26:37–44

79. Prevett MC, Lammertsma AA, Brooks DJ, Bartenstein PA, Patsalos PN, et al. 1995. Benzodiasepine-GABA$_A$ receptors in idiopathic generalized epilepsy measured with [^{11}C]flumazenil and positron emission tomography. *Epilepsia* 36:113–21

80. Kellaway P. 1985. Sleep and epilepsy. *Epilepsia* 26:S15–30

80a. Steriade M. 1974. Interneuronal epileptic discharges related to spike-and-wave cortical seizures in behaving monkeys. *Electroencephal. Clin. Neurophysiol.* 37:247–63

81. McCormick DA, Bal T. 1997. Sleep and arousal: thalamocortical mechanisms. *Annu. Rev. Neurosci.* 20:185–215

82. Kim U, McCormick DA. 1998. The functional influence of burst and tonic firing mode on synaptic interactions in the thalamus. *J. Neurosci.* 18:9500–16

83. Ulrich D, Huguenard JR. 1997. Nucleus-specific chloride homeostasis in rat thalamus. *J. Neurosci.* 17:2348–54

84. Jahnsen H, Llinás R. 1984. Electrophysiological properties of guinea-pig thalamic neurons: an in vitro study. *J. Physiol.* 349:205–26

85. Jahnsen H, Llinás R. 1984. Ionic basis for the electroresponsiveness and oscillatory properties of guinea-pig thalamic neurons in vitro. *J. Physiol.* 349:227–47.

86. Warren RA, Agmon A, Jones EG. 1994. Oscillatory synaptic interactions between ventroposterior and reticular neurons in mouse thalamus in vitro. *J. Neurophysiol.* 72:1993–2003

87. Bal T, McCormick DA. 1996. What stops synchronized thalamocortical oscillations? *Neuron* 17:297–308

88. Bal T, von Krosigk M, McCormick DA. 1995. Role of the ferret perigeniculate nucleus in the generation of synchronized oscillations in vitro. *J. Physiol.* 483:665–85

89. Bal T, von Krosigk M, McCormick DA. 1995. Synaptic and membrane mechanisms underlying synchronized oscillations in the ferret lateral geniculate nucleus in vitro. *J. Physiol.* 483:641–63

90. Liu XB, Warren RA, Jones EG. 1995. Synaptic distribution of afferents from reticular nucleus in ventroposterior nucleus of cat thalamus. *J. Comp. Neurol.* 352:187–202

91. Steriade M, Jones EG, McCormick DA, eds. 1997. *Thalamus. Vol. 1. Organisation and Function.* New York: Elsevier

92. Huguenard JR. 1996. Low-threshold calcium currents in central nervous system neurons. *Annu. Rev. Physiol.* 58:329–48

93. Destexhe A, Contreras D, Steriade M, Sejnowski TJ, Huguenard JR. 1996. In vivo, in vitro, and computational analysis of dendritic calcium currents in thalamic reticular neurons. *J. Neurosci.* 16:169–85

94. Ulrich D, Huguenard JR. 1996. GABA$_B$ receptor-mediated responses in GABAergic projection neurones of rat nucleus reticularis thalami in vitro. *J. Physiol.* 493:845–54

95. Sanchez-Vives MV, Bal T, McCormick DA. 1997. Inhibitory interactions between perigeniculate GABAergic neurons. *J. Neurosci.* 17:8894–908

96. Kim U, Sanchez-Vives MV, McCormick DA. 1997. Functional dynamics of GABAergic inhibition in the thalamus. *Science* 278:130–34

97. Sohal VS, Huntsman MM, Huguenard JR. 2000. Reciprocal inhibitory connections regulate the spatiotemporal properties of intrathalamic oscillations. *J. Neurosci.* 20:1735–45

98. Liu Z, Vergnes M, Depaulis A, Marescaux C. 1992. Involvement of intrathalamic GABA$_B$ neurotransmission in the control of absence seizures in the rat. *Neuroscience* 48:87–93

99. Hosford DA, Clark S, Cao Z, Wilson WA Jr, Lin FH, et al. 1992. The role of GABA$_B$ receptor activation in absence seizures of lethargic (lh/lh) mice. *Science* 257:398–401

100. Buzsaki G, Bickford RG, Ponomareff G, Thal LJ, Mandel R, Gage FH. 1988. Nucleus basalis and thalamic control of neocortical activity in the freely moving rat. *J. Neurosci.* 8:4007–26

101. Avanzini G, Vergnes M, Spreafico R, Marescaux C. 1993. Calcium-independent regulation of genetically determined spike and waves by the reticular nucleus of rats. *Epilepsia* 34:1–7

102. Fritschy JM, Meskenaite V, Winmann O, Honer M, Benke D, Mohler H. 1999. GABA$_B$-receptor splice variants GB1a and GB1b in rat brain: developmental regulation, cellular distribution and extrasynaptic localization. *Eur. J. Neurosci.* 11:761–68

103. Sodickson DL, Bean BP. 1996. GABA$_B$ receptor-activated inwardly rectifying potassium current in dissociated hippocampal CA3 neurons. *J. Neurosci.* 16:6374–85

104. Thomson AM, Destexhe A. 1999. Dual intracellular recordings and computational models of slow inhibitory postsynaptic potentials in rat neocortical and hippocampal slices. *Neuroscience* 92:1193–215

105. Huguenard JR, Prince DA. 1994. Clonazepam suppresses GABA$_B$-mediated inhibition in thalamic relay neurons through effects in nucleus reticularis. *J. Neurophysiol.* 71:2576–81

106. Sanchez-Vives MV, McCormick DA. 1997. Functional properties of perigeniculate inhibition of dorsal lateral geniculate nucleus thalamocortical neurons in vitro. *J. Neurosci.* 17:8880–93

107. McCormick DA, Pape HC. 1990. Properties of a hyperpolarization-activated cation current and its role in rhythmic oscillation in thalamic relay neurones. *J. Physiol.* 431:291–318

108. Soltesz I, Lightowler S, Leresche N, Jassik-Gerschenfeld D, Pollard CE, Crunelli V. 1991. Two inward currents and the transformation of low-frequency oscillations of rat and cat thalamocortical cells. *J. Physiol.* 441:175–97

109. Steriade M, Contreras D. 1998. Spike-wave complexes and fast components of cortically generated seizures. I. Role of neocortex and thalamus. *J. Neurophysiol.* 80:1439–55

110. Pinault D, Leresche N, Charpier S, Deniau JM, Marescaux C, et al. 1998. Intracellular recordings in thalamic neurones during spontaneous spike and wave discharges in rats with absence epilepsy. *J. Physiol.* 509:449–56

111. Destexhe A. 1999. Can GABA$_A$ conductances explain the fast oscillation frequency of absence seizures in rodents? *Eur. J. Neurosci.* 11:2175–81

112. Soltesz I, Crunelli V. 1992. GABA$_A$ and pre-and post-synaptic GABA$_B$ receptor-mediated responses in lateral geniculate nucleus. *Prog. Brain Res.* 90:151–69

113. Steriade M, Amzica F, Neckelmann D, Timofeev I. 1998. Spike-wave complexes and fast components of cortically generated seizures. II. Extra- and intracellular patterns. *J. Neurophysiol.* 80:1456–79

114. Destexhe A, Contreras D, Steriade M. 1998. Mechanisms underlying the synchronizing action of corticothalamic feedback through inhibition of thalamic relay cells. *J. Neurophysiol.* 79:999–1016

115. Steriade M, Contreras D. 1995. Relations between cortical and thalamic cellular events during transition from sleep patterns to paroxysmal activity. *J. Neurosci.* 15:623–42

116. Blumenfeld H, McCormick DA. 2000. Corticothalamic inputs control the pattern of activity generated in thalamocortical networks. *J. Neurosci.* 20:5153–62

116a. Bal T, Debay D, Destexhe A. 2000. Cortical feedback controls the frequency and synchrony of oscillations in the visual thalamus. *J. Neurosci.* 20:7478–88

116b. Steriade M, Oakson G. Diallo A. 1976.

Cortically elicited spike-wave afterdischarges in thalamic neurons. *Electroencephal. Clin. Neurophysiol.* 41:641–44

117. Tsakiridou E, Bertollini L, de Curtis M, Avanzini G, Paper HC. 1995. Selective increase in t-type calcium conductance or reticular thalamic neurons in a rat model of absence epilepsy. *J. Neurosci.* 15:3110–17

118. Huguenard JR. 1999. Neuronal circuitry of thalamocortical epilepsy and mechanisms of anti-absence drug action. *Adv. Neurol.* 79:991–99

119. Leresche N, Parri HR, Erdemli G, Guyon A, Turner JP, et al. 1998. On the action of the anti-absence drug ethosuximide in the rat and cat thalamus. *J. Neurosci.* 18:4842–53

120. Bazil CW, Pedley TA. 1998. Advances in the medical treatment of epilepsy. *Annu. Rev. Med.* 49:135–62

121. Andersen P, Andersson SA. 1968. *Physiological Basis of the Alpha Rhythm.* New York: Appleton-Century-Crofts

122. Luthi A, McCormick DA. 1998. Periodicity of thalamic synchronized oscillations: the role of Ca^{2+}-mediated upregulation of I_h. *Neuron* 20:553–63

123. Luthi A, McCormick DA. 1998. Periodicity of thalamic spindle waves is abolished by ZD7288. *J. Neurophysiol.* 79:3284–89

124. Luthi A, McCormick DA. 1999. Modulation of a pacemaker current through Ca(2+)-induced stimulation of cAMP production. *Nat. Neurosci.* 2:634–41

125. DiFrancesco D. 1999. Dual allosteric modulation of pacemaker (f) channels by cAMP and voltage in rabbit SA node. *J. Physiol.* 515:367–76

126. Kim U, Bal T, McCormick DA. 1995. Spindle waves are propagating synchronized oscillations in the ferret LGNd in vitro. *J. Neurophysiol.* 74:1301–23

127. Contreras D, Destexhe A, Sejnowski TJ, Steriade M. 1997. Spatiotemporal patterns of spindle oscillations in cortex and thalamus. *J. Neurosci.* 17:1179–96

128. Contreras D, Destexhe A, Steriade M. 1997. Spindle oscillations during cortical spreading depression in naturally sleeping cats. *Neuroscience* 77:933–36

129. Contreras D, Destexhe A, Sejnowski TJ, Steriade M. 1996. Control of spatiotemporal coherence of a thalamic oscillation by corticothalamic feedback. *Science* 274:771–74

130. Deschenes M, Veinante P, Zhang ZW. 1998. The organization of corticothalamic projections: reciprocity versus parity. *Brain Res. Rev.* 28:286–308

131. Pinault D, Bourassa J, Deschenes M. 1995. The axonal arborization of single thalamic reticular neurons in the somatosensory thalamus of the rat. *Eur. J. Neurosci.* 7:31–40

132. Cox CL, Huguenard JR, Prince DA. 1996. Heterogenous axonal arborizations of rat thalamic reticular neurons in the ventrobasal nucleus. *J. Comp. Neurol.* 366:416–30

133. Zhang ZW, Deschenes M. 1997. Intracortical axonal projections of lamina VI cells of the primary somatosensory cortex in the rat: a single-cell labeling study. *J. Neurosci.* 17:6365–79

134. Contreras D, Steriade M. 1997 State-dependent fluctuations of low-frequency rhythms in corticothalamic networks. *Neuroscience* 76:25–38

135. McCormick DA. 1991. Functional properties of a slowly inactivating potassium current in guinea pig dorsal lateral geniculate relay neurons. *J. Neurophysiol.* 66:1176–89

136. Wang Z, McCormick DA. 1992. Control of firing mode of corticotectal and corticopontine layer V burst generating neurons by norepinephrine, acetylcholine and 1S,3R-ACPD. *J. Neurosci.* 13:2199–216

137. Amzica F, Steriade M. 1995. Short- and long-range neuronal synchronization of the slow (<1 Hz) cortical oscillation. *J. Neurophysiol.* 73:20–38

138. Nunez A, Curro Dossi R, Contreras D,

Steriade M. 1992. Intracellular evidence for incompatibility between spindle and delta oscillations in thalamocortical neurons of cat. *Neuroscience* 48:75–85

139. Steriade M, Nunez A, Amzica F. 1993. A novel slow (1 Hz) oscillation of neocortical neurons in vivo: depolarizing and hyperpolarizing components. *J. Neurosci.* 13:3252–65

140. Steriade M, Nunez A, Amzica F. 1993. Intracellular analysis of relations between the slow (1 Hz) neocortical oscillation and other sleep rhythms of the electroencephalogram. *J. Neurosci.* 13:3266–83

141. Steriade M, Contreras D, Curro Dossi R, Nunez A. 1993. The slow (1 Hz) oscillation in reticular thalamic and thalamocortical neurons: scenario of sleep rhythm generation in interacting thalamic and neocortical networks. *J. Neurosci.* 13:3284–99

142. Metherate R, Ashe JH. 1993. Ionic flux contributions to neocortical slow waves and nucleus basalis-mediated activation: whole cell recordings in vivo. *J. Neurosci.* 13:5312–23

143. Sanchez-Vives MV, McCormick DA. 2000. Cellular and network mechanisms of rhythmic recurrent activity in neocortex. *Nat. Neurosci.* 3:1027–34

144. Stern EA, Kincaid AE, Wilson CJ. 1997. Spontaneous subthreshold membrane potential fluctuations and action potential variability of rat corticostriatal and striatal neurons in vivo. *J. Neurophysiol.* 77:1697–15

145. Amzica F, Steriade M. 1997. The K-complex: its slow (1-Hz) rhythmicity and relation to delta waves. *Neurology* 49:952–59

146. Amzica F, Steriade M. 1995. Disconnection of intracortical synaptic linkages disrupts synchronization of a slow oscillation. *J. Neurosci.* 15:4658–77

147. Contreras D, Destexhe A, Steriade M. 1997. Intracellular and computational characterization of the intracortical inhibitory control of synchronized thalamic inputs in vivo. *J. Neurophysiol.* 78:335–50

148. Steriade M, Amzica F. 1994. Dynamic coupling among neocortical neurons during evoked and spontaneous spike-wave seizure activity. *J. Neurophysiol.* 72:2051–69

149. Neckelmann D, Amzica F, Steriade M. 1998. Spike-wave complexes and fast components of cortically generated seizures. III. Synchronizing mechanisms. *J. Neurophysiol.* 80:1480–94

150. Gray C. McCormick DA. 1996. Chattering cells: superficial pyramidal neurons contributing to the generation of synchronous oscillations in the visual cortex. *Science* 274:109–13

151. Timofeev I, Grenier F, Steriade M. 1998. Spike-wave complexes and fast components of cortically generated seizures. IV. Paroxysmal fast runs in cortical and thalamic neurons. *J. Neurophysiol.* 80:1495–513

152. Traub RD, Wong RK. 1982. Cellular mechanism of neuronal synchronization in epilepsy. *Science* 216:745–47

153. Gastaut H, Broughton R. 1972. *Epileptic Seizures.* Springfield, IL: Thomas

154. Traub RD, Colling SB, Jefferys JG. 1995. Cellular mechanisms of 4-aminopyridine-induced synchronized afterdischarges in the rat hippocampal slice. *J. Physiol.* 489:127–40

155. Steriade M, Llinas R. 1988. The functional states of the thalamus and the associated neuronal interplay. *Physiol. Rev.* 68:649–742

156. Niedermeyer E. 1993. Epileptic seizure disorders. In *Electroencephalography. Basic Principles, Clinical Applications, and Related Fields*, ed. E Niedermeyer, F Lopes da Silva, pp. 461–564. Baltimore: Williams & Wilkins

157. Destexhe A. 1998. Spike-and-wave oscillations based on the properties of $GABA_B$ receptors. *J. Neurosci.* 18:9099–111

Annu. Rev. Physiol. 2001. 63:847–69

MAINTAINING THE STABILITY OF NEURAL FUNCTION: A Homeostatic Hypothesis

Graeme W Davis[1] and Ilya Bezprozvanny[2]

[1]Department of Biochemistry, University of California, San Francisco, San Francisco, California 94143-0448; e-mail: gdavis@biochem.ucsf.edu; [2]Department of Physiology, University of Texas Southwestern Medical Center, Dallas, Texas 75390-9040; e-mail: bezprozv@swvx12.sw

Key Words learning, synaptic plasticity, calcium, synaptogenesis, growth

■ **Abstract** The precise regulation of neural excitability is essential for proper nerve cell, neural circuit, and nervous system function. During postembryonic development and throughout life, neurons are challenged with perturbations that can alter excitability, including changes in cell size, innervation, and synaptic input. Numerous experiments demonstrate that neurons are able to compensate for these types of perturbation and maintain appropriate levels of excitation. The mechanisms of compensation are diverse, including regulated changes to synaptic size, synaptic strength, and ion channel function in the plasma membrane. These data are evidence for homeostatic regulatory systems that control neural excitability. A model of neural homeostasis suggests that information about cell activity, cell size, and innervation is fed into a system of cellular monitors. Intracellular- and intercellular-signaling systems transduce this information into regulated changes in synaptic and ion channel function. This review discusses evidence for such a model of homeostatic regulation in the nervous system.

INTRODUCTION

An increasing body of experimental evidence demonstrates that neurons have the capacity to respond to perturbations such as inappropriate synaptic function or altered innervation and thereby maintain their function within a normal physiological range (1). These experiments suggest that neurons have the capacity to monitor their own activity levels and transduce this information into regulated changes in excitability. For example, a neuron or muscle that is challenged by excessive innervation can regulate the function of each impinging synaptic terminal, decreasing the strength of each synapse such that the sum total excitation is normal despite the presence of abnormal innervation (1–3). The mechanisms that monitor excitation and maintain the functional properties of neurons and muscle are by definition homeostatic. These experiments have led to an emerging theory of neural homeostasis that may provide a basis for understanding how the stability of neural circuitry is maintained. Homeostatic regulation of neural activity could maintain the robust function of the nervous system during the restructuring and refinement of neural circuits that occur during postembryonic development. Homeostatic mechanisms may also ensure that neurons in all areas of the brain continue to function appropriately throughout life. Most neural circuits remain robust throughout life. During this time, most cellular components are recycled many times. One implication is that synaptic connections, once established, must be continually maintained (1, 4).

Homeostasis is one of the most basic cellular processes by which a cell responds to a change in the intracellular or extracellular environment and maintains a constant physiology. Homeostatic processes have been revealed in systems ranging from the cellular response to changing extracellular osmolarity to the system-level maintenance of blood pressure (5). In the nervous system, the maintenance of nerve cell excitation within reasonable physiological limits is a form of electrical homeostasis ensuring that an individual neuron is neither induced to fire action potentials excessively nor silenced.

Our ability to learn and adapt to our environment is thought to require changes in synaptic connectivity and neural excitation (6). It is essential, therefore, that the homeostatic regulation of neural activity does not preclude activity-dependent modification of neural circuitry. Rather, homeostatic mechanisms might establish limits beyond which activity-dependent changes may not reasonably modify cellular activity. As such, homeostatic regulation will ensure the stability of neural function without impairing our capacity for neural change. Thus whereas synaptic competition, activity-dependent synaptic plasticity, and neurotrophism encompass mechanisms that can generate precise change in synaptic structure and function (7–9), homeostasis is thought to constrain this change within reasonable physiological limits.

The mechanisms of homeostatic regulation in the nervous system remain to be characterized in any detail. The experimental data suggest that there are many different types of regulation. Regulatory changes can be cell autonomous or can involve intercellular-signaling events. Homeostatic changes in ion channel density and neurotransmitter receptor function have been observed that allow neurons to modulate excitability cell autonomously. In other examples, *trans*-synaptic signals have been implicated in the homeostatic regulation of synaptic function (1, 4). It is also possible that homeostasis may be expressed at a circuit or system level.

The types of perturbation to which neurons have been demonstrated to respond in a homeostatic manner are also diverse. Homeostatic compensation has been demonstrated in response to altered innervation, altered synaptic function, and altered cellular depolarization (1, 4). In addition, it is hypothesized that homeostatic mechanisms allow neurons and muscle to remain functional during the dramatic changes in cell shape and size that occur in normal development. The presence of multiple, redundant types of homeostatic signaling may be a consequence of the many different perturbations to which a cell must respond. Alternatively, such mechanistic diversity may ensure a robust regulatory system. The implicit importance of homeostasis to appropriate neural function suggests that there are links to neural disease. Homeostatic regulation has been observed as a response to disease and damage in the nervous system. Ultimately, a thorough understanding of homeostatic signaling at a cellular and molecular level will be required before impaired homeostatic systems can be investigated as a cause of neural disease.

EVIDENCE FOR HOMEOSTATIC REGULATION IN THE NERVOUS SYSTEM

In systems ranging from the invertebrate neuromuscular junction (NMJ) to synapses in the vertebrate cortex, increasing evidence supports the hypothesis that homeostatic processes maintain stable levels of neuronal activity. In each experiment, synaptic or neuronal functions are examined before and after experimental perturbations that alter innervation, excitation, or cell growth. The data demonstrate that neurons and muscle have a remarkable capacity to respond to these perturbations and return to function within their normal physiological range—an indication of homeostatic regulation. Evidence for homeostatic regulation in the nervous system has been the focus of two recent reviews (1, 4). In this section we highlight several additional experiments and add further discussion.

Homeostatic Response to Altered Post-Synaptic Excitability at the Vertebrate and Invertebrate Neuromuscular Junction

Two independent genetic manipulations have been used to impair post-synaptic excitation at the *Drosophila* NMJ. The *Drosophila* NMJ is glutamatergic. Electrophysiological analysis of glutamate receptor knockouts reveals a reduction in quantal size (most likely owing to the altered conductance of the channels formed by the remaining glutamate receptor subunits). Remarkably, impaired post-synaptic receptor function is precisely compensated for by increased presynaptic transmitter release, resulting in normal muscle depolarization (10). Identical results were obtained by muscle-specific overexpression of protein kinase A. Increased protein kinase A activity decreases quantal size (11). Again, presynaptic release precisely compensates for reduced quantal size, and the evoked depolarization of the muscle remains normal. Thus two independent genetic manipulations that alter post-synaptic glutamate receptor function demonstrate that presynaptic transmitter release is modulated in response to changes in post-synaptic excitability. In each example, it is hypothesized that homeostatic-signaling systems modulate presynaptic release via a retrograde signal from muscle to nerve. Either this retrograde signal may enhance release, or these effects may be achieved by the repression of a negative regulator of presynaptic release (12).

A similar homeostatic change has been observed at the vertebrate NMJ in experiments examining neuromuscular function in neuregulin-knockout mice. In heterozygous knockout mice, post-synaptic acetylcholine receptor clustering is reduced, and, as a result, there is a decrease in the post-synaptic sensitivity to acetylcholine (13). As in *Drosophila*, there is a compensatory increase in presynaptic transmitter release at these synapses. Thus despite the large safety factor at the vertebrate NMJ, homeostatic regulatory mechanisms can be revealed. This raises the possibility that such homeostatic compensation may play a significant role in the maintenance of the vertebrate neuromuscular synapse during normal growth and function.

The observed compensatory increase in synaptic efficacy, at both the *Drosophila* and vertebrate NMJs, is achieved during development. Therefore, the changes could be mediated by an increased rate of active-zone insertion. Alternatively, a portion of active zones at the wild-type synapse might normally be silent during development (14). Unveiling silent synapses could act as a compensatory response. Finally, a change in presynaptic release at the wild-type complement of active zones is also consistent with the observed data.

Homeostatic Response to Altered Post-Synaptic Excitability at Central Synapses

Neurons of the lobster stomatogastric ganglion show a remarkable ability to regenerate their stereotypic bursting properties after acute isolation from their normal synaptic circuitry (15, 16). In these experiments, single neurons are isolated from their surrounding synaptic circuitry and placed in single-cell culture. Remarkably, these single cells regenerate their endogenous bursting properties in the absence of patterned synaptic input by modifying the balance of their voltage-gated channel densities. This homeostatic modification of channel density can be blocked by supplying patterned activity, and it can also be blocked by preventing calcium entry to the neuron (15–17). The implication is that calcium entry is utilized as a means to monitor altered activity levels in the neuron. In this case, since cells are isolated from their surrounding synaptic connections, the source of calcium is likely to be calcium channels. The ability of calcium to act as an activity sensor is discussed at length in later sections.

An alternate form of compensation has been observed in vitro at vertebrate central synapses. Cortical synapses in culture have the capacity to modulate post-synaptic sensitivity to neurotransmitters in response to either increased or decreased excitation (18, 19). In these experiments, increased excitation is achieved by chronically blocking inhibitory synaptic input. Reduced excitation is achieved by bathing cultures in tetrodotoxin (TTX). A remarkable feature of the observed compensation is the demonstration that quantal size not only compensates for altered excitation (increased quantal size compensates for TTX treatment and vice versa) but that compensation is achieved by factorial scaling of the size of the quantal current (18). These results implicate mechanisms of receptor insertion as a form of compensation (20). More recently, the activity of brain-derived neurotrophic factors has been implicated in this homeostatic response (21).

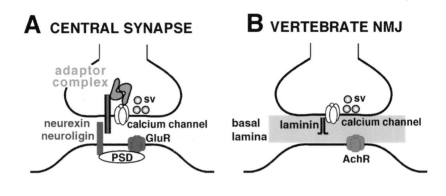

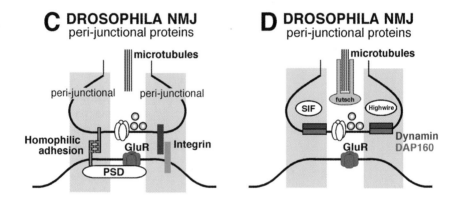

Figure 4 Synaptic organization and *trans*-synaptic signaling. (*A*) The constituents of a neuroligin-neurexin *trans*-synaptic complex are diagrammed. Presynaptic neurexin interacts with the evolutionarily conserved protein complex consisting of CASK, MINT, and Veli (adapter complex) that, in turn, binds to the presynaptic calcium channel. (*B*) A *trans*-synaptic complex that parallels the neuroligin-neurexin complex has been identified at the vertebrate NMJ. Synaptic laminin interacts with a complex that includes the presynaptic calcium channel alpha subunit. (*C*) A periactive zone (perijunctional) complex is diagrammed for the *Drosophila* NMJ. Within this region directly adjacent to the active zone (gray shading) are cell adhesion molecules, including integrins and Fasciclin II, capable of signaling across the synapse. PDZ-containing molecules in the post-synaptic density (PSD), including *discs-large,* may organize the post-synaptic density in a manner analogous to vertebrate central synapses. (*D*) Additional molecules have been localized to the perijunctional region, including proteins involved in endocytosis [Dynamin and DAP160 (87)]. Recently a number of very large proteins have been identified that are present within the perisynaptic region, including Highwire and Futsch.

Homeostatic Response to Altered Innervation at Central and Neuromuscular Synapses

The homeostatic control of neuronal or muscle function implies that the summed strength of all synaptic inputs should remain within certain bounds. According to this hypothesis, increasing the number of synaptic contacts to a single target should result in reduced synaptic efficacy at all (or a portion) of the synaptic terminals on a given target, and reducing the number of synaptic contacts should have the opposite effect. These phenomena have been observed at both central and neuromuscular synapses (1–3).

At a vertebrate central synapse in vitro, focal recordings from individual boutons (a single active zone) demonstrate that total target innervation is inversely correlated with the efficacy of transmission at each individual active zone (3). Cells that receive increased innervation show decreased efficacy at each individual active zone and vice versa. The apparent compensatory response is achieved by an altered post-synaptic response to neurotransmitter (3). One possible interpretation is that the post-synaptic cell senses increased innervation, potentially through altered excitation, and this cell generates a compensatory change in synaptic efficacy. Alternatively, if quantal size is determined by post-synaptic receptor density, then the distribution of a fixed number of receptors across various numbers of synaptic inputs could, in theory, account for this result.

Another test of the homeostatic response to altered innervation was recently achieved at the *Drosophila* NMJ (2). These experiments exploited a natural pattern of muscle innervation in which a pair of motoneurons each contacts two adjacent muscle targets. Innervation from these two motoneurons was biased onto one muscle target and away from the adjacent muscle target by overexpression of the cell adhesion molecule Fasciclin II (Fas II) exclusively in one of the two target muscles. The total bouton number was conserved such that one muscle received increased innervation (the muscle overexpressing Fas II) and the adjacent target received decreased innervation (having normal levels of Fas II expression) (22). Despite experimentally induced altered innervation (either an increase or decrease in bouton number), the muscles were normally depolarized, demonstrating a homeostatic response to altered innervation (Figure 1). At the target with fewer boutons, there was an increase in quantal size that produced a compensatory increase in muscle excitability, thereby generating normal depolarization. At the muscle target receiving increased innervation, there was a decrease in presynaptic release from each synaptic bouton, which allowed, once again, normal muscle depolarization. Taken together, these results demonstrate that homeostatic regulation of synaptic function is not only target specific, but it can be achieved through independent mechanisms at the terminals of a single neuron (2; Figure 1).

Synaptic competition drives many of the rewiring events that occur during postembryonic development (8, 9). A remarkable feature of synaptic competition is the ability of the post-synaptic cell to remain functional despite the pruning

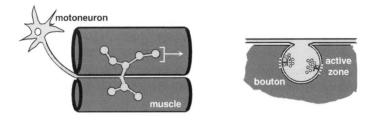

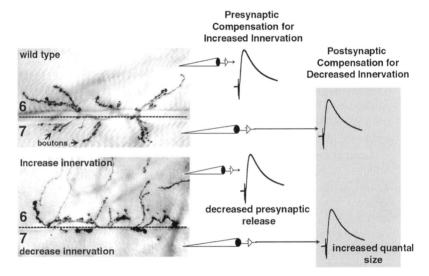

Figure 1 Homeostatic compensation for altered innervation at the *Drosophila* neuromuscular junction. (*Top*) A diagram of the motoneuron innervation to muscle 6 and muscle 7 in *Drosophila*. A single synaptic bouton is diagrammatically enlarged. Single boutons at the mature synapse contain multiple active zones (∼12 on average). (*Bottom*) Two images of the neuromuscular synapse are shown, the wild-type synapse at muscles 6 and 7 and an example of altered innervation after the overexpression of the cell adhesion molecule Fasciclin II only on muscle 6. The neuromuscular synapse is biased toward growth on muscle 6 and is biased away from muscle 7. At right, the results of quantal analysis are summarized for each muscle. Despite increased innervation at muscle 6, muscle depolarization is wild type. There is a compensatory decrease in per-bouton transmitter release resulting in normal total transmitter release. Despite reduced innervation at muscle 7, the muscle depolarization is wild type. There is a compensatory increase in quantal size that allows normal muscle depolarization despite fewer synaptic boutons. Thus two independent forms of compensation occur at the terminals of a single motoneuron contacting neighboring muscle targets.

and sprouting of presynaptic input(s). An interesting possibility is that synaptic competition is played out in a background of homeostatic regulation.

Homeostatic Response to Cellular Growth

The physiological changes caused by cellular growth are some of the most drastic perturbations that an individual cell will confront. During postembryonic development, a muscle cell can achieve a tremendous increase in size and mass (>50-fold growth in many vertebrate and invertebrate systems). Muscle has a requirement for homeostatic regulation of depolarization during this growth. As muscle size increases, input resistance decreases (23, 24). Decreased input resistance causes decreased depolarization for a given amount of synaptic current. Yet muscle must receive nearly constant levels of depolarization so that appropriate contractile properties are maintained. Developmental observation of neuromuscular transmission during a period of 40-fold growth at the crayfish NMJ demonstrates that constant levels of muscle depolarization are maintained by an increase in presynaptic transmitter release (achieved through growth of the motoneuron terminal) and an increase in the quantal size (23, 24). Thus compensatory changes are observed both pre- and post-synaptically to compensate for growth-related changes in muscle excitability. It has been proposed that a signal from muscle to nerve regulates presynaptic growth and function to compensate for the drop in muscle input resistance that occurs during growth (23–25). Recent experiments at the *Drosophila* NMJ provide experimental evidence supporting the presence of a homeostatic, retrograde-signaling system that couples synaptic development to muscle growth (1, 10).

Several experiments demonstrate that neurons are able to preserve their unique response properties during profound cellular growth—a form of homeostatic regulation. An insect giant interneuron, for example, preserves its response properties to sensory input during an ~50-fold increase in cell size by precisely coordinating the growth of dendrite diameter and dendrite length. This type of growth (termed ISO-electronic growth) alters the physical dimensions of the cell to preserve cellular response properties (26). There appear to be other solutions to this problem. As the dendrites of a central neuron grow, pre-existing sites of synaptic input become physically and electrically more distant from the soma. The presence of voltage-gated channels in the dendrite plasma membrane of vertebrate central neurons has been proposed as a mechanism to help propagate synaptic inputs made in distal regions of the dendritic tree to the site of synaptic integration (27, 28). It is not known whether these dendritic voltage-gated currents change in a coordinated manner during dendrite growth. In other instances, neurons appear to have evolved to take advantage of the changing response properties caused by growth to generate new functionality (29).

Homeostasis During Disease and Injury

The hypothesis that homeostatic regulation maintains the stability of neural function in the nervous system implies that this process should be revealed in the etiology of neural disease. Myasthenia gravis affects the neuromuscular synapse, causing a progressive loss of post-synaptic acetylcholine receptors. Decreased receptor function is compensated for by increased presynaptic release at human myasthenic muscle (30, 31), a result that parallels experimental observations at the *Drosophila* NMJ (10, 11) and at the NMJ of neuregulin-knockout mice (13).

Postpolio syndrome describes the gradual loss of neuromuscular function in a current population of people who survived polio as children (32). The neuromuscular synapses of these survivors are regenerated synapses that can be smaller than normal but are able to function at wild-type levels. In some cases, there is evidence of a compensatory enhancement of presynaptic release at these terminals. The cause of postpolio (the regression of these regenerated synapses after many years of nearly wild-type function) is not well understood, but it may include a gradual loss of compensatory mechanisms that are normally required to maintain wild-type function at regenerated, postpolio, neuromuscular synapses (32).

The disruption of homeostatic regulation might adversely alter the function of neural circuits, resulting in seizure-like activity or degeneration. Moreover, homeostatic mechanisms that normally ensure a balance of synaptic efficacy in the central nervous system might lead to various clinical syndromes of the injured central nervous system (1). For example, spinal cord injury leads to the removal of major classes of descending and ascending inputs. As a result, homeostatic mechanisms controlling synaptic strength might lead to the observed, inappropriate strengthening of persisting inputs, resulting in debilitating post-traumatic disorders. As another example, lesions of mature axons in a hippocampal slice induce numerous changes, including the formation of new axon collaterals, an increase in synaptic connectivity between neurons, and hyperexcitability (33). These results implicate a homeostatic response to injury that could be deleterious and may be related to the cause of post-traumatic epilepsy (33). We understand very little about the underlying mechanisms of the diverse homeostatic regulatory mechanisms that have been observed. We can only speculate on the relationship between homeostatic signaling and the basis for a broad spectrum of other neurological disorders and diseases.

Model for Homeostatic Regulation

The types of perturbations to which neurons and muscle are known to respond in a homeostatic manner include changes in cell growth, innervation, and excitability. Each of these perturbations ultimately impacts post-synaptic depolarization. Thus it seems likely that neurons and muscle are endowed with the capacity to monitor levels of activity or depolarization to initiate a compensatory response. It is also possible that neurons and muscle can monitor cell growth and innervation independently of the effects of these parameters on cellular depolarization. This is suggested by the observation that perturbations producing the same effects on post-synaptic depolarization do not always initiate the same compensatory response. For example, there are different responses to decreased innervation vs decreased post-synaptic receptor sensitivity at the *Drosophila* NMJ. Furthermore, increased innervation and increased post-synaptic receptor sensitivity will both increase post-synaptic depolarization, but increased receptor sensitivity is not compensated for, and the muscles become super excited (1, 2, 11).

The experiments and developmental observations made to date suggest a model of homeostatic regulation in the nervous system (Figure 2). Information about cell activity, cell size, and innervation is fed into a system of cellular monitors. Cellular monitors are likely to reside in the soma so that summated activity or size can be monitored. Important components may also be localized at synaptic sites to achieve specificity. Information regarding activity, size, or growth is then transduced from various monitors to intracellular signals (potentially requiring transcriptional regulation) that act on effectors such as post-synaptic transmitter receptors or ion channels in the plasma membrane. Modulation of presynaptic release via retrograde signaling, as demonstrated at the *Drosophila* NMJ, will require trans-synaptic signaling to receptors and effectors at presynaptic terminals. The mechanism by which various monitors are coupled to compensatory signaling may be continuous, or a cell may establish thresholds beyond which changes

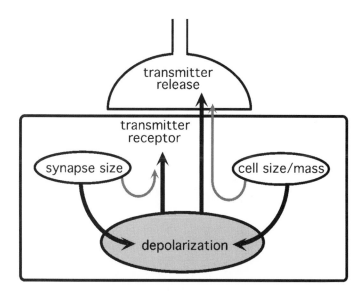

Figure 2 A model for homeostatic regulation at the *Drosophila* neuromuscular junction. A homeostatic regulatory system that assures proper muscle depolarization will include a system of post-synaptic monitors of muscle depolarization. It is possible that muscle size and synapse sizes are monitored simultaneously through their respective effects on muscle depolarization. It is equally likely that there will be independent systems that can monitor muscle size and synapse sizes independent of each other and independent of muscle depolarization (thin versus thick arrows). The assimilation of this information into meaningful *trans*-synaptic signals will likely include both positive and negative regulators.

in activity, size, or innervation are not tolerated. The next sections describe evidence for cellular monitors that may transduce activity or growth into meaningful chemical signaling within or between cells.

CELLULAR MONITORS OF CELL MASS AND GROWTH

The connection between cellular growth (increased cell mass) and other cellular processes is a well-established feature of the developmental program. Experiments at the intersection of cell cycle control and embryonic development demonstrate that cells have the capacity to monitor cell mass and control both cellular growth and cellular proliferation (34). One example is the presence of a cell mass checkpoint during progression through the cell cycle. Cells must attain a certain mass to progress through the cell cycle (35). If cells in culture are limited in their growth, they stop proliferating, and synchronous proliferation begins upon the addition of nutrients or growth factors. Progress through the cell cycle can be driven experimentally by activation of cell cycle regulators (34). However, when division occurs without cellular growth, the cells continue to decrease in size until catastrophe. The systems that monitor cell size can be coupled to intercellular signaling and regulatory events, which demonstrates that monitors of cell mass can be coupled to other cellular regulatory systems, including intercellular signaling (34). Thus it seems plausible that monitors of cell mass may also be coupled to homeostatic systems that regulate neuronal and muscle excitability during growth. The presence of cell mass monitors raises the issue of the extent to which differences in neuronal size and complexity are impacted by cell-autonomous monitors of growth vs extrinsic factors that influence, for example, dendrite outgrowth and branching. It is almost certain that both cell-autonomous and exogenous factors are involved (36).

CELLULAR MONITORS OF ACTIVITY

Intracellular calcium levels can provide a sensitive readout of cellular activity in both neurons and muscle (37–39). Activity-induced calcium oscillations can be generated by calcium entry through neurotransmitter receptors, voltage-gated calcium channels, and calcium release from intracellular stores. Each source of calcium can provide temporal information about changes in activity and spatial information from different subcellular localization and diffusion within the cell. It has been demonstrated in a number of systems that information can be encoded in the frequency, amplitude, duration, and number of calcium oscillations (39–42).

There are many questions related to calcium-dependent monitors of neural activity. How are calcium transients reliably encoded in the intracellular-signaling machinery (what are the calcium sensors)? If homeostatic regulatory machinery acts downstream of calcium sensors within the cell, how is flexibility achieved such that each cell can establish different calcium-sensitive responses or a similar homeostatic response to a very different calcium signal? For example, a tonic-firing neuron has different requirements for homeostatic regulation compared with a phasic-firing neuron. Furthermore, over time the properties of a cell may change and the homeostatic system that monitors activity must, therefore, be adaptable.

The hypothesis that calcium-dependent signaling could be the basis for a homeostatic monitor of neuronal activity was originally proposed in experiments that modeled the changes in ion channel density observed in stomatogastric neurons of the lobster after acute isolation in cell culture (15, 43). A series of calcium-sensitive frequency filters were modeled that were sensitive to different frequencies of calcium oscillation. By coupling information from the calcium filters to ion channel densities, the authors were able to effectively model the homeostatic regulation of ion channel density that was observed experimentally. The use of calcium frequency filters takes advantage of information encoded in the timing of calcium oscillations and is therefore more elaborate than invoking calcium set points beyond which changes in calcium concentration are not tolerated.

CamKII

Calcium-calmodulin-dependent protein kinase II (CamKII) has many of the required features of a calcium sensor of neural activity. CamKII can act as a frequency monitor for calcium spikes (38, 39). The frequency response of this enzyme is dependent on the properties of calmodulin (CaM) trapping and autophosphorylation (39, 44). The properties of autophosphorylation also allow this enzyme to retain information of previous activity. For example, if the threshold for autophosphorylation is met during an initial stimulus and only a portion of the holoenzyme subunits are autophosphorylated, then the response to subsequent low-frequency stimuli may be increased (39, 45). Furthermore, CamKII is demonstrated, in vitro and in vivo, to have functional output that is relevant to the modulation of neuronal excitability, synaptic function, gene expression, and cell shape (46–48).

There are several ways that the frequency response properties of CamKII might be modulated to accommodate different cellular set points as a homeostatic-activity sensor. CamKII activation is sensitive to a number of cellular variables including CaM concentration, phosphatase activity, enzyme localization, and the subunit composition of the holoenzyme (37, 44, 46). Modulation of any of these variables will potentially modulate CamKII function. The subunit composition of the holoenzyme may be a particularly potent parameter for altering the CamKII activity as an activity sensor. Neuronal CamKII consists primarily of two subunits, alpha and beta. These subunits can form homomeric and heteromeric enzymes composed of 6–12 subunits. The subunit composition influences the frequency response properties of the enzyme (39, 44). Several experiments indicate that subunit composition may be a modifiable feature of the kinase. Increased expression of the alpha subunit but not the beta subunit has been observed after long-term potentiation in the freely moving rat (49). Altered subunit composition may also change the subcellular targeting of CamKII, and this could be a potent means of modulating kinase sensitivity and function (50).

Calcineurin

The serine/threonine phosphatase calcineurin is another example of a calcium-signaling molecule that has recently been implicated in signaling systems that can generate oscillation-specific changes in gene transcription (40, 51). This is most clearly demonstrated in experiments examining the signal transduction cascade of calcium, calcineurin, and NF-AT in lymphocytes and more recently in hippocampal neurons (40, 41, 52). Several important features of this signaling system are worth highlighting. It can mediate calcium oscillation-specific changes in gene expression that include both changes in transcriptional selectivity and changes in the magnitude of the transcriptional response. Signaling via calcineurin and NF-AT is cell type specific, depending on the NF-ATc family members expressed within each cell. Finally, this signaling system is responsive to cellular context because the transcriptional response can be strongly influenced by convergent signaling systems including ras and protein kinase C (40). This last point is particularly important because it means that a calcium signal can be interpreted by the cellular context in which the signal is delivered.

Calcium signaling and CamKII signaling have essential functions during synaptic and neuronal development. Two recent studies are particularly relevant to the topic of homeostatic regulation. In *Caenorhabditis elegans*, synapse number at central neurons remains constant during normal larval development. A genetic analysis demonstrates that the maintenance of synapse number during development requires voltage-gated calcium channels and CamKII (47). These results implicate a system for maintaining synapse number and thereby maintaining post-synaptic function that is sensitive to both voltage and calcium signaling through voltage-gated channels.

Calcineurin, likewise, has functional output that is relevant to the regulation of neuronal excitability (53, 54). Post-synaptic calcineurin has been implicated in muscle-to-nerve retrograde-signaling systems that modulate synaptic strength at the vertebrate NMJ, in vitro (55). More recently, calcineurin modulation of inhibitory synaptic function has been implicated in the altered neuronal excitability after long-term potentiation (56).

Calcium Channels

The decoding of neural activity via calcium signaling is not achieved solely in the properties of the second messenger and transcriptional regulatory systems. Some of the selective properties of a calcium sensor for neural activity may be established by the properties of the voltage-gated channels themselves. L-type calcium channels provide a source of calcium influx capable of triggering calmodulin mobilization to the nucleus and activation of CREB-mediated transcription (48, 57). L-type calcium channels may be preferentially activated by synaptic potentials [excitatory post-synaptic potentials (EPSPs)] as opposed to action potentials. This is suggested by experiments monitoring the L-type calcium current in response to simulated EPSP or action potential waveforms (57a). The differential activation of L-type calcium channels is linked to the observation that L-type channels are activated at relatively negative potentials and have slow activation kinetics. Both features favor activation by slow, low-amplitude EPSPs as opposed to action potentials. One can imagine that information regarding both synaptic and action potential activity might be necessary for a neuron to accurately achieve homeostatic regulation. Action potentials provide information about the summed total cellular depolarization. EPSPs can provide information about the localized sources of depolarization within the dendritic tree.

In conclusion, calcium entry into a cell via calcium channels or transmitter receptors can be transduced into changes in calcium and second-messenger signaling that allow a cell to decode the voltage activity of a neuron into chemical signaling. There is the potential for this signaling to distinguish information about summed neuronal depolarization from information about local regions of synaptic activity in the dendrites. The responses downstream of calcium sensors can be cell type specific and context dependent within a given cell type. These are essential features of a system capable of monitoring neuronal activity and generating a homeostatic, compensatory response to altered activity or innervation. Many questions remain. How does a cell establish its own particular activity set points? Is this a cell-autonomous property linked to the genetic phenotype of a cell or is it influenced by early activity-dependent events? If early activity-dependent events participate in establishing the set points for the homeostasis of neuronal activity, is there a critical period for determining the calcium sensitivity (or set points) that will maintain cellular activity within a particular range? Can these properties be modulated?

Specificity of Homeostatic Synaptic Regulation

The specificity of homeostatic regulatory mechanisms has yet to be explored in any depth. A series of experiments at the *Drosophila* NMJ demonstrated that homeostatic regulation of synaptic function can be target specific at the terminals of a single neuron (2). Every other experiment has used cell-wide perturbation of activity or innervation, and, as a result, our current understanding of homeostatic signaling points to cell-wide regulatory change (4, 19). In theory, however, some forms of synaptic regulation must be synapse specific if homeostatic regulation is going to maintain the stability of neural circuitry as opposed to generating change (thereby functioning as another expression of synaptic plasticity).

For a cell to regulate its own excitability, it requires a mechanism to monitor summed, total excitation. One possibility is that a cell can monitor some aspect of action-potential-induced depolarization, potentially via calcium-dependent signaling (15, 57). If a cell monitors summed depolarization in this manner, how might a homeostatic regulatory system be established such that specificity could be achieved? Two candidate solutions to this problem draw on models for synapse-specific activity-dependent plasticity (Figure 3).

One possibility is that activity monitors are present in the cell soma, at a central location capable of integrating action-potential-induced activity. This would allow homeostatic signaling to include a transcriptional response at the nucleus. A homeostatic signal could be sent throughout the entire dendritic tree. If this homeostatic signal required a synaptic cofactor that was sensitive to local synaptic activity such as CaMII or calcineurin, then the a cell-wide homeostatic signal would be active only at sites of inappropriate activity (Figure 3A). Synaptic microdomains of elevated calcium have been observed, mediated by signaling via metabotropic glutamate receptors and inositol-1,4,5-triphosphate receptors (58, 59). Because homeostatic regulation is expected to respond to persistent and inappropriate synaptic activity, these local sites of elevated calcium signaling will not require synaptic "memory" of previous activity or "synaptic tagging," both of which have been proposed as mechanisms for synapse-specific long-term synaptic plasticity (60, 61).

A second possibility is that the entire homeostatic-signaling mechanism is localized post-synaptically at each synapse. Information about sum total excitation could be conveyed to every synapse via action potential back propagation. In this model, each synapse would be endowed with a mechanism for comparing the activity of back propagating action potentials with local synaptic activity (Figure 3B). There is evidence that modulation of synaptic strength via correlated activity might be highly sensitive to the timing of synaptic and action-potential-mediated depolarization (62), and this could conceivably be utilized to mediate homeostatic regulation of synapses in this manner. However, purely Hebbian mechanisms may not be sufficient to account for homeostatic synaptic regulation because synapses that participate in firing a post-synaptic cell, but do so inappropriately, should be downregulated according to a homeostatic hypothesis.

SIGNALING AT THE SYNAPSE

The evidence for homeostatic regulation of synaptic and neuronal function implies the presence of elaborate intracellular- and intercellular-signaling mechanisms. Signaling from the site of activity integration to sites of synaptic input is essential. At the synapse, there is evidence for modulation of transmitter receptor function or insertion. There is also evidence for *trans*-synaptic signaling systems that can modulate presynaptic release.

Trans-Synaptic Signaling

Nerve growth factors and neurotrophins are among the most intensively studied *trans*-synaptic signaling molecules. Neurotrophins in particular have been implicated as both survival factors and as mediators of activity-dependent synapse modification (7). Alternatively, biochemical and cell-biological evidence is

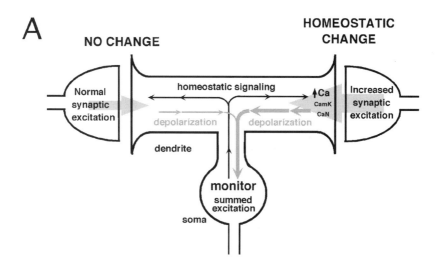

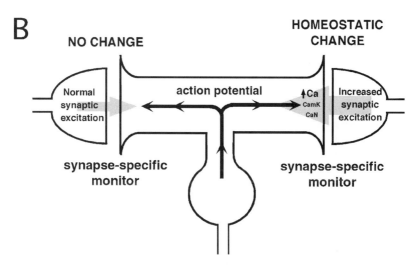

Figure 3 Synapse-specific homeostatic signaling. A neuron with two sources of synaptic input is diagrammed. (*A*) Monitors of summed excitation may be located in the soma. Depolarization is transmitted to the soma via passive or active dendritic propagation. Homeostatic regulatory signals are then sent back to the dendrites in a uniform manner, but they only generate regulatory changes at synapses with inappropriate synaptic activity [increased synaptic excitation (*right*)]. Sites of inappropriate synaptic activity may be recognized by the homeostatic signals owing to localized calcium-dependent signaling, potentially involving the activity of Cam kinase or calcineurin. (*B*) An alternate model proposes that information of summed excitation is monitored via back propagating action potentials. Activity sensors at each synapse (synapse-specific monitors) could achieve homeostatic change through the comparison of synaptic vs action potential activity at each individual synapse.

accumulating to suggest a model of *trans*-synaptic signaling that is achieved via a *trans*-synaptic scaffold of proteins that spans the synaptic cleft from the post-synaptic density to the presynaptic cytoskeleton.

Biochemical data have linked proteins of the pre- and post-synaptic densities via a *trans*-synaptic, asymmetric neuroligin-neurexin junction (63, 64). Neurexins have a single *trans*membrane domain and a short carboxy tail with protein 4.1 and CASK-PDZ domain-binding sequence motifs (65). Proteins with similarities to neurexins have been shown to mediate axon-glia interactions (66, 67). The sub-cellular localization of neurexins within central neurons remains to be determined. However, neuroligin-1 is localized postsynaptically at central synapses and has been shown to be a beta-neurexin ligand (68–70).

Three neuroligins have been identified in the rat, and two neuroligins have been recently identified in mice (71). All three neuroligins possess an extracellular domain that shares homology with acetylcholinesterase, although this domain does not have enzymatic activity (68). All of the neuroligins have a cytoplasmic domain with a PDZ-binding motif capable of binding synaptic adapter proteins including post-synaptic density protein (PSD)-95 (72). Thus the neuroligin-neurexin asymmetric junction is linked to a large network of synaptic proteins through the binding of modular adapter proteins such as CASK and PSD-95 via PDZ-mediated interactions.

Biochemical data have been assembled that describe a core *trans*-synaptic protein scaffold around the neurexin-neuroligin asymmetric junction that is hypothesized to participate in the organization of the synapse (Figure 4*A*, see color insert). This model assumes an asymmetric junction with presynaptic neurexin and post-synaptic neuroligin. Presynaptic neurexin interacts with an evolutionarily conserved protein complex consisting of CASK, MINT1, and Veli (63). CASK, MINT1, and Veli are modular adapter proteins that contain multiple protein interaction domains including PDZ and SH3 domains. Significantly, both CASK and MINT1 are linked biochemically to the presynaptic calcium channel (64). The CASK SH3 domain has been shown to interact with a proline-rich sequence in the presynaptic calcium channel (64). The carboxy terminus of the aphala and alpha1b calcium channel subunits also binds to the first PDZ domain of MINT1. Post-synaptically, neuroligin interacts with PSD-95 (72). Many other constituents of the post-synaptic density interact with PSD-95 including CamKII, nitric oxide synthase, and potassium channels (73). Thus an extensive *trans*-synaptic protein complex is linked biochemically to presynaptic calcium channels (64).

This extensive, *trans*-synaptic protein complex could serve to regulate the localization or function of presynaptic calcium channels. Because transmitter release is exquisitely sensitive to the function and most likely the localization of the presynaptic calcium channel, this *trans*-synaptic protein complex may have a potent influence on synapse organization and function. This model is supported by genetic analysis of an analogous Lin-10/Lin-2/Lin-7 protein complex in *C. elegans*. The Lin-10/Lin-2/Lin-7 complex is necessary and sufficient for basolateral localization of the epidermal growth factor receptor tyrosine kinase Let-23 and is necessary for post-synaptic glutamate receptor localization in *C. elegans* (74, 75). Until recently, however, there has not been experimental evidence supporting a role for the neurexin-neuroligin *trans*-synaptic complex in either synapse formation or modulation.

An elegant series of recent experiments demonstrated a role for the neuroligin-neurexin interaction in synapse formation (71). In these experiments, neuroligin expression was demonstrated to be sufficient to induce presynaptic differentiation in vitro. Neuroligin-induced synapse formation was analyzed both at the light level and ultrastructurally. This synaptogenic activity is mediated by specific sequences in the esterase domain of neuroligin, and evidence suggests that this signaling is mediated through interaction with presynaptic beta-neurexin (71). Among the synaptic proteins that are assembled by the neuroligin-neurexin interaction are synapsin and the modular adapter protein CASK/lin2. These data provide the first evidence of a cell-contact-mediated signaling event that is sufficient to drive synapse formation in the central nervous system. It remains to be determined whether similar signaling may occur at a mature synapse. The function of this complex, in vivo, also remains to be clarified. A neuroligin knockout is remarkably healthy (68). Neuroligins have widespread expression, however, and it is possible that different neuroligins have partially overlapping functions (68, 71).

A recent result by Hsueh et al (76) offers a further glimpse of possible signaling from this extensive *trans*-synaptic protein complex. The modular adapter protein CASK/Lin2 is concentrated at central synapses and binds to neurexin and syndecan proteins at the plasma membrane as well as binding the cytoplasmic proteins Mint and Veli. Recent work demonstrated that CASK can enter the cell nucleus and bind to specific DNA sequences (called T elements) in a transcriptional coactivation complex with Tbr-1 (76). Among the T-element-containing genes that may be regulated by the CASK/Tbr-1 complex is *reelin*, a gene implicated in cerebrocortical development. Thus an integral element of the *trans*-synaptic protein complex can signal to the nucleus and modulate transcription. Parallels can be drawn to cadherin signaling via beta-catenin from the cell plasma membrane to the nucleus (77), suggesting that this scenario may become a more common aspect of synaptic signaling and regulation. The mechanism by which CASK nuclear translocation is initiated and the role of this signaling in synaptic regulation remain unclear.

The generality of such a *trans*-synaptic signaling scaffold is suggested by the recent demonstration of a similar system at the vertebrate NMJ (78). In this system, biochemical data link synaptic alpha 4-beta 2-gamma 1 laminin to a presynaptic protein complex that includes a calcium channel subunit (Figure 4*B*). A potential *trans*-synaptic protein complex can be achieved through the synaptic basal lamina that traverses the neuromuscular synaptic cleft. Thus biochemical data at both central and neuromuscular synapses implicate a network of protein-protein interactions that may unify the pre- and postsynaptic densities.

A role for *trans*-synaptic adhesion in synaptic regulation is not unique to the neurexin-neuroligin junction. Homophilic cell adhesion molecules with the potential to signal across the synapse have been implicated in the mechanisms of synapse stabilization, growth, and activity-dependent plasticity (22, 79–81). Cell adhesion-dependent changes in synaptic morphology are demonstrated to be necessary, in some systems, for activity-dependent changes in synaptic function (82). However, signaling via cell adhesion molecules has not been demonstrated to directly influence the mechanisms of either transmitter release or post-synaptic transmitter detection (Figure 4*C*).

The complexity and extent of the synaptic signaling complex are yet to be completely realized. Forward genetic studies have begun to elucidate new elements of the synapse that may have escaped traditional biochemical techniques owing to their extreme size. These proteins are among a growing number of proteins that define a perijunctional region of the synapse, just adjacent to the active zone (Figure 4*D*). Perijunctional proteins include Piccolo, Bassoon, Still-life, Highwire, and Futsch (83). The Highwire protein (5233 amino acids) has recently been demonstrated to control presynaptic growth (83, 84). Mutations in *highwire* show a dramatic synaptic overgrowth phenotype, suggesting that *highwire* may represent a repressor of synapse elaboration (84). The Futsch protein is also extremely large (5327 amino acids). It is associated with the synaptic microtubule cytoskeleton and is necessary for synaptic microtubule organization and normal synaptic growth (85, 86). Among the constituents of the periactive zone are molecules implicated in synaptic vesicle endocytosis. Dynamin and dynamin-associated protein (DAP160) are localized to the periactive zone in a honeycomblike lattice that surrounds active zones in the *Drosophila* neuromuscular bouton (87, 88). The function of a potential periactive-zone protein complex remains to be determined. However, since *highwire* and *futsch* are potent regulators of synaptic growth and function, signaling via proteins in the periactive zone may be important during homeostatic regulation.

Regulation of Post-Synaptic Neurotransmitter Receptors

An altered post-synaptic response to neurotransmitters is implicated in many of the known examples of homeostatic regulation. A variety of different mechanisms could account for altered post-synaptic sensitivity to neurotransmitters, including altered receptor insertion, localization, or altered function of existing receptors. Rapid, activity-dependent cycling of α-AMPA-type glutamate receptors appears to be a potent mechanism for altering synaptic function during acute synaptic plasticity (20). Green fluorescent protein-tagged receptors are delivered to dendritic spines and clusters after tetanic stimulation, and this receptor trafficking requires activation of the NMDA receptors (89). Agents that block processes of exocytosis and endocytosis have effects on synaptic function that are consistent with a mechanism by which receptors are trafficked to and from the synaptic membrane (90, 91). Most recently, it has been shown that the insertion of α-AMPA-type receptors requires CamKII activity and a PDZ protein interaction (92). In principle, intracellular-signaling systems that are coupled to the mechanisms of receptor cycling could represent a potent mechanism for homeostatic regulation of synaptic strength.

CONCLUSION

The mechanisms of neural homeostasis are complex and may comprise diverse, interrelated signaling systems. Neurons and muscle are capable of responding in a homeostatic manner to diverse types of perturbation that include altered cell size, innervation, and excitation. The mechanisms of compensation are equally diverse, including regulated changes to synaptic size, presynaptic release, post-synaptic transmitter sensitivity, and the balance of voltage-gated channels. The complexity and diverse nature of homeostatic regulation may assure that neurons and muscle have a robust system with which to regulate excitability. Ultimately, the role of homeostatic signaling during neuronal development, the maintenance of neural function, and the etiology of neural disease will require an in-depth understanding of these homeostatic regulatory events at a molecular and cellular level. Given a limited molecular understanding of neural homeostasis, a forward genetic approach in model systems such as *C. elegans* and *Drosophila* may provide initial insight into these processes.

ACKNOWLEDGMENTS

We thank Kurt Marek, Suzanne Paradis, and Peter Clyne for critical comments on earlier versions of this manuscript. The writing of this review was supported in part by the BWF and National Institutes of Health grant NS39313-01 to GWD and grant NS39552 to IB.

Visit the Annual Reviews home page at www.AnnualReviews.org

LITERATURE CITED

1. Davis GW, Goodman CS. 1998. Genetic analysis of synaptic development and plasticity: homeostatic regulation of synaptic efficacy. *Curr. Opin. Neurobiol.* 8:149–56
2. Davis GW, Goodman CS. 1998. Synapse-specific control of synaptic efficacy at the terminals of a single neuron. *Nature* 392:82–86
3. Liu G, Tsien RW. 1995. Properties of synaptic transmission at single hippocampal synaptic boutons. *Nature* 375:404–8
4. Turrigiano GG. 1999. Homeostatic plasticity in neuronal networks: the more things change, the more they stay the same. *Trends Neurosci.* 22:221–27
5. Philips J, Herskowitz I. 1997. Osmotic balance regulates cell fusion during mating

in *Saccharomyces cerevisiae. J. Cell. Biol.* 138:961–74
6. Bliss TV, Collingridge GL. 1993. A synaptic model of memory: long-term potentiation in the hippocampus. *Nature* 361:31–39
7. McAllister AK, Katz LC, Lo DC. 1999. Neurotrophins and synaptic plasticity. *Annu. Rev. Neurosci.* 22:295–318
8. Sanes JR, Lichtman JW. 1999. Development of the vertebrate neuromuscular junction. *Annu. Rev. Neurosci.* 22:389–442
9. Katz LC, Shatz CJ. 1996. Synaptic activity and the construction of cortical circuits. *Science* 274:1133–38
10. Petersen SA, Fetter RD, Noordermeer JN, Goodman CS, DiAntonio A. 1997. Genetic analysis of glutamate receptors in

Drosophila reveals a retrograde signal regulating presynaptic transmitter release. *Neuron* 19:1237–48

11. Davis GW, DiAntonio A, Petersen SA, Goodman CS. 1998. Postsynaptic PKA controls quantal size and reveals a retrograde signal that regulates presynaptic transmitter release in *Drosophila*. *Neuron* 20:305–15

12. Marek KW, Ng N, Fetter R, Smolik S, Goodman CS, Davis GW. 2000. A genetic analysis of synaptic development: pre- and postsynaptic dCBP control transmitter release at the *Drosophila* NMJ. *Neuron* 25:537–47

13. Sandrock A, Dryer S, Rosen K, Gozani S, Kramer R, et al. 1997. Maintenance of acetylcholine receptor number by neuregulins at the neuromuscular junction in vivo. *Science* 276:599–604

14. Liao D, Zhang X, O'Brien R, Ehlers MD, Huganir RL. 1999. Regulation of morphological postsynaptic silent synapses in developing hippocampal neurons. *Nat. Neurosci.* 2:37–43

15. Marder E, Abbott LF, Turrigiano GG, Liu Z, Golowasch J. 1996. Memory from the dynamics of intrinsic membrane currents. *Proc. Natl. Acad. Sci. USA* 93:13481–86

16. Turrigiano G, Abbott LF, Marder E. 1994. Activity-dependent changes in the intrinsic properties of cultured neurons. *Science* 264:974–77

17. Turrigiano G, LeMasson G, Marder E. 1995. Selective regulation of current densities underlies spontaneous changes in the activity of cultured neurons. *J. Neurosci.* 15:3640–52

18. Turrigiano GG, Leslie KR, Desai NS, Rutherford LC, Nelson SB. 1998. Activity-dependent scaling of quantal amplitude in neocortical neurons. *Nature* 391:892–96

19. O'Brien RJ, Kamboj S, Ehlers MD, Rosen KR, Fischbach GD, Huganir RL. 1998. Activity-dependent modulation of synaptic AMPA receptor accumulation. *Neuron* 21:1067–78

20. Turrigiano GG. 2000. AMPA receptors unbound: membrane cycling and synaptic plasticity. *Neuron* 26:5–8

21. Desai NS, Rutherford LC, Turrigiano GG. 1999. BDNF regulates the intrinsic excitability of cortical neurons. *Learn. Mem.* 6:284–91

22. Davis GW, Schuster CM, Goodman CS. 1997. Genetic analysis of the mechanisms controlling target selection: target-derived Fasciclin II regulates the pattern of synapse formation. *Neuron* 19:561–73

23. Lnenicka GA, Mellon D, Jr. 1983. Changes in electrical properties and quantal current during growth of identified muscle fibres in the crayfish. *J. Physiol.* 345:261–84

24. Lnenicka GA, Mellon D, Jr. 1983. Transmitter release during normal and altered growth of identified muscle fibres in the crayfish. *J. Physiol.* 345:285–96

25. Frank E. 1973. Matching of facilitation at the neuromuscular junction of the lobster: a possible case for influence of muscle on nerve. *J. Physiol.* 233:635–58

26. Hill AA, Edwards DH, Murphey RK. 1994. The effect of neuronal growth on synaptic integration. *J. Comput. Neurosci.* 1:239–54

27. Stuart G, Sakmann B. 1995. Amplification of EPSPs by axosomatic sodium channels in neocortical pyramidal neurons. *Neuron* 15:1065–76

28. Schwindt PC, Crill WE. 1995. Amplification of synaptic current by persistent sodium conductance in apical dendrite of neocortical neurons. *J. Neurophysiol.* 74:2220–24

29. Edwards DH, Yeh SR, Barnett LD, Nagappan PR. 1994. Changes in synaptic integration during the growth of the lateral giant neuron of crayfish. *J. Neurophysiol.* 72:899–908

30. Cull-Candy SG, Miledi R, Trautmann A, Uchitel OD. 1980. On the release of transmitter at normal, myasthenia gravis and myasthenic syndrome affected human endplates. *J. Physiol.* 299:621–38

31. Plomp JJ, van Kempen GT, Molenaar

PC. 1992. Adaptation of quantal content to decreased postsynaptic sensitivity at single endplates in alpha-bungarotoxin-treated rats. *J. Physiol.* 458:487–99

32. Agre JC, Rodriquez AA, Tafel JA. 1991. Late effects of polio: critical review of the literature on neuromuscular function. *Arch. Phys. Med. Rehabil.* 72:923–31

33. McKinney RA, Debanne D, Gahwiler BH, Thompson SM. 1997. Lesion-induced axonal sprouting and hyperexcitability in the hippocampus in vitro: implications for the genesis of posttraumatic epilepsy. *Nat. Med.* 3:990–96

34. Su TT, O'Farrell PH. 1998. Size control: cell proliferation does not equal growth. *Curr. Biol.* 8:R687–89

35. Murray A. 1994. Cell cycle checkpoints. *Curr. Opin. Cell. Biol.* 6:872–76

36. Gao FB, Brenman JE, Jan LY, Jan YN. 1999. Genes regulating dendritic outgrowth, branching, and routing in *Drosophila. Genes Dev.* 13:2549–61

37. Schulman H, Heist K, Srinivasan M. 1995. Decoding Ca^{2+} signals to the nucleus by multifunctional CaM kinase. *Prog. Brain Res.* 105:95–104

38. Schulman H, Hanson PI, Meyer T. 1992. Decoding calcium signals by multifunctional CaM kinase. *Cell Calcium* 13:401–11

39. De Koninck P, Schulman H. 1998. Sensitivity of CaM kinase II to the frequency of Ca^{2+} oscillations. *Science* 279:227–30

40. Crabtree GR. 1999. Generic signals and specific outcomes: signaling through Ca^{2+}, calcineurin, and NF-AT. *Cell* 96:611–14

41. Graef IA, Mermelstein PG, Stankunas K, Neilson JR, Deisseroth K, et al. 1999. L-type calcium channels and GSK-3 regulate the activity of NF-ATc4 in hippocampal neurons. *Nature* 401:703–8

42. Buonanno A, Fields RD. 1999. Gene regulation by patterned electrical activity during neural and skeletal muscle development. *Curr. Opin. Neurobiol.* 9:110–20

43. LeMasson G, Marder E, Abbott LF. 1993. Activity-dependent regulation of conductances in model neurons. *Science* 259:1915–17

44. Brocke L, Srinivasan M, Schulman H. 1995. Developmental and regional expression of multifunctional Ca^{2+}/calmodulin-dependent protein kinase isoforms in rat brain. *J. Neurosci.* 15:6797–808

45. Meyer T, Hanson PI, Stryer L, Schulman H. 1992. Calmodulin trapping by calcium-calmodulin-dependent protein kinase. *Science* 256:1199–202

46. Braun AP, Schulman H. 1995. The multifunctional calcium/calmodulin-dependent protein kinase: from form to function. *Annu. Rev. Physiol.* 57:417–45

47. Rongo C, Kaplan JM. 1999. CaMKII regulates the density of central glutamatergic synapses in vivo. *Nature* 402:195–99

48. Deisseroth K, Heist EK, Tsien RW. 1998. Translocation of calmodulin to the nucleus supports CREB phosphorylation in hippocampal neurons. *Nature* 392:198–202

49. Thomas KL, Laroche S, Errington ML, Bliss TV, Hunt SP. 1994. Spatial and temporal changes in signal transduction pathways during LTP. *Neuron* 13:737–45

50. Srinivasan M, Edman CF, Schulman H. 1994. Alternative splicing introduces a nuclear localization signal that targets multifunctional CaM kinase to the nucleus. *J. Cell. Biol.* 126:839–52

51. Naya FJ, Mercer B, Shelton J, Richardson JA, Williams RS, Olson EN. 2000. Stimulation of slow skeletal muscle fiber gene expression by calcineurin in vivo. *J. Biol. Chem.* 275:4545–48

52. Meldolesi J. 1998. Calcium signalling: oscillation, activation, expression. *Nature* 392:863–66

53. Lai MM, Hong JJ, Ruggiero AM, Burnett PE, Slepnev VI, et al. 1999. The calcineurin-dynamin 1 complex as a calcium sensor for synaptic vesicle endocytosis. *J. Biol. Chem.* 274:25963–66

54. Mulkey RM, Endo S, Shenolikar S,

Malenka RC. 1994. Involvement of a calcineurin/inhibitor-1 phosphatase cascade in hippocampal long-term depression. *Nature* 369:486–88

55. Wan J, Poo M. 1999. Activity-induced potentiation of developing neuromuscular synapses. *Science* 285:1725–28

56. Lu YM, Mansuy IM, Kandel ER, Roder J. 2000. Calcineurin-mediated LTD of GABAergic inhibition underlies the increased excitability of CA1 neurons associated with LTP. *Neuron* 26:197–205

57. Deisseroth K, Bito H, Tsien RW. 1996. Signaling from synapse to nucleus: postsynaptic CREB phosphorylation during multiple forms of hippocampal synaptic plasticity. *Neuron* 16:89–101

57a. Mermelstein PG, Bito H, Deisseroth K, Tsien RW. 2000. Critical dependence of cAMP response element-binding protein phosphorylation on L-type channels supports a selective response to EPSPs in preference to action potentials. *J. Neurosci.* 20:266–73

58. Finch EA, Augustine GJ. 1998. Local calcium signalling by inositol-1,4,5-trisphosphate in Purkinje cell dendrites. *Nature* 396:753–56

59. Takechi H, Eilers J, Konnerth A. 1998. A new class of synaptic response involving calcium release in dendritic spines. *Nature* 396:757–60

60. Frey U, Morris RG. 1998. Synaptic tagging: implications for late maintenance of hippocampal long- term potentiation. *Trends Neurosci.* 21:181–88

61. Casadio A, Martin KC, Giustetto M, Zhu H, Chen M, et al. 1999. A transient, neuron-wide form of CREB-mediated long-term facilitation can be stabilized at specific synapses by local protein synthesis. *Cell* 99:221–37

62. Bi GQ, Poo MM. 1998. Synaptic modifications in cultured hippocampal neurons: dependence on spike timing, synaptic strength, and postsynaptic cell type. *J. Neurosci.* 18:10464–72

63. Butz S, Okamoto M, Sudhof TC. 1998. A tripartite protein complex with the potential to couple synaptic vesicle exocytosis to cell adhesion in brain. *Cell* 94:773–82

64. Maximov A, Sudhof TC, Bezprozvanny I. 1999. Association of neuronal calcium channels with modular adaptor proteins. *J. Biol. Chem.* 274:24453–56

65. Hata Y, Butz S, Sudhof TC. 1996. CASK: a novel dlg/PSD95 homolog with an N-terminal calmodulin-dependent protein kinase domain identified by interaction with neurexins. *J. Neurosci.* 16:2488–94

66. Bellen HJ, Lu Y, Beckstead R, Bhat MA. 1998. Neurexin IV, caspr and paranodin—novel members of the neurexin family: encounters of axons and glia. *Trends Neurosci.* 21:444–49

67. Missler M, Sudhof TC. 1998. Neurexins: three genes and 1001 products. *Trends Genet.* 14:20–26

68. Song JY, Ichtchenko K, Sudhof TC, Brose N. 1999. Neuroligin 1 is a postsynaptic cell-adhesion molecule of excitatory synapses. *Proc. Natl. Acad. Sci. USA* 96:1100–5

69. Ichtchenko K, Hata Y, Nguyen T, Ullrich B, Missler M, et al. 1995. Neuroligin 1: a splice site-specific ligand for beta-neurexins. *Cell* 81:435–43

70. Nguyen T, Sudhof TC. 1997. Binding properties of neuroligin 1 and neurexin 1 beta reveal function as heterophilic cell adhesion molecules. *J. Biol. Chem.* 272:26032–39

71. Scheiffele P, Jinhong F, Choih J, Fetter R, Serafini T. 2000. Neuroligin expressed in non-neuronal cells triggers presynaptic development in contacting axons. *Cell* 101:1–10

72. Irie M, Hata Y, Takeuchi M, Ichtchenko K, Toyoda A, et al. 1997. Binding of neuroligins to PSD-95. *Science* 277:1511–15

73. Kennedy MB. 1997. The postsynaptic density at glutamatergic synapses. *Trends Neurosci.* 20:264–68

74. Kaech SM, Whitfield CW, Kim SK. 1998. The LIN-2/LIN-7/LIN-10 complex

mediates basolateral membrane localization of the *C. elegans* EGF receptor LET-23 in vulval epithelial cells. *Cell* 94:761–71

75. Rongo C, Whitfield CW, Rodal A, Kim SK, Kaplan JM. 1998. LIN-10 is a shared component of the polarized protein localization pathways in neurons and epithelia. *Cell* 94:751–59

76. Hsueh YP, Wang TF, Yang FC, Sheng M. 2000. Nuclear translocation and transcription regulation by the membrane- associated guanylate kinase CASK/LIN-2. *Nature* 404:298–302

77. Bredt DS. 2000. Cell biology. Reeling CASK into the nucleus. *Nature* 404:241–42

78. Sunderland WJ, Son YJ, Miner JH, Sanes JR, Carlson SS. 2000. The presynaptic calcium channel is part of a transmembrane complex linking a synaptic laminin (alpha4beta2gamma1) with non-erythroid spectrin. *J. Neurosci.* 20:1009–19

79. Schuster CM, Davis GW, Fetter RD, Goodman CS. 1996. Genetic dissection of structural and functional components of synaptic plasticity. I. Fasciclin II controls synaptic stabilization and growth. *Neuron* 17:641–54

80. Martin KC, Kandel ER. 1996. Cell adhesion molecules, CREB, and the formation of new synaptic connections. *Neuron* 17:567–70

81. Tanaka H, Shan W, Phillips GR, Arndt K, Bozdagi O, et al. 2000. Molecular modification of N-cadherin in response to synaptic activity. *Neuron* 25:93–107

82. Davis GW, Schuster CM, Goodman CS. 1996. Genetic dissection of structural and functional components of synaptic plasticity. III. CREB is necessary for presynaptic functional plasticity. *Neuron* 17:669–79

83. Chang Q, Balice-Gordon RJ. 2000. Highwire, rpm-1, and futsch: balancing synaptic growth and stability. *Neuron* 26:287–90

84. Wan HI, DiAntonio A, Fetter RD, Bergstrom K, Strauss R, Goodman CS. 2000. Highwire regulates synaptic growth in *Drosophila. Neuron* 26:313–29

85. Hummel T, Krukkert K, Roos J, Davis G, Klambt C. 2000. *Drosophila* Futsch/22C10 is a MAP1B-like protein required for dendritic and axonal development. *Neuron* 26: 357–70

86. Roos J, Hummel T, Ng N, Klambt C, Davis GW. 2000. *Drosophila* Futsch regulates synaptic microtubule organization and is necessary for synaptic growth. *Neuron* 26:371–82

87. Roos J, Kelly RB. 1998. Dap160, a neural-specific Eps15 homology and multiple SH3 domain-containing protein that interacts with *Drosophila* dynamin. *J. Biol. Chem.* 273:19108–19

88. Roos J, Kelly RB. 1999. The endocytic machinery in nerve terminals surrounds sites of exocytosis. *Curr. Biol.* 9:1411–14

89. Shi SH, Hayashi Y, Petralia RS, Zaman SH, Wenthold RJ, et al. 1999. Rapid spine delivery and redistribution of AMPA receptors after synaptic NMDA receptor activation. *Science* 284:1811–16

90. Carroll RC, Beattie EC, Xia H, Luscher C, Altschuler Y, et al. 1999. Dynamin-dependent endocytosis of ionotropic glutamate receptors. *Proc. Natl. Acad. Sci. USA* 96:14112–17

91. Luscher C, Xia H, Beattie EC, Carroll RC, von Zastrow M, et al. 1999. Role of AMPA receptor cycling in synaptic transmission and plasticity. *Neuron* 24:649–58

92. Hayashi Y, Shi SH, Esteban JA, Piccini A, Poncer JC, Malinow R. 2000. Driving AMPA receptors into synapses by LTP and CaMKII: requirement for GluR1 and PDZ domain interaction. *Science* 287:2262–67

Annu. Rev. Physiol. 2001. 63:871–94

RESURGENCE OF SODIUM CHANNEL RESEARCH

Alan L Goldin

*Department of Microbiology and Molecular Genetics, University of California Irvine,
California 92697-4025; e-mail: agoldin@uci.edu*

Key Words cloning, expression, mutations, resurgent current

■ **Abstract** A variety of isoforms of mammalian voltage-gated sodium channels
have been described. Ten genes encoding sodium channel α subunits have been identified, and nine of those isoforms have been functionally expressed in exogenous systems. The α subunit is associated with accessory β subunits in some tissues, and three
genes encoding different β subunits have been identified. The α subunit isoforms have
distinct patterns of development and localization in the nervous system, skeletal and
cardiac muscle. In addition, many of the isoforms demonstrate subtle differences in
their functional properties. However, there are no clear subfamilies of the channels,
unlike the situation with potassium and calcium channels. The subtle differences in the
functional properties of the sodium channel isoforms result in unique conductances
in specific cell types, which have important physiological effects for the organism.
Small alterations in the electrophysiological properties of the channel resulting from
mutations in specific isoforms cause human diseases such as periodic paralysis, long
QT syndrome, and epilepsy.

INTRODUCTION

Voltage-gated sodium channels are the primary molecules responsible for the rising
phase of action potentials in electrically excitable cells. Because of their fundamental importance, much of the early work on ion channels involved characterizing
the electrophysiological and biochemical properties of sodium channels. In recent
years, however, the rapidly expanding number and diversity of potassium and calcium channels has overshadowed the field of sodium channel research, particularly
given the fact that all voltage-gated sodium channels are relatively similar. For a
number of reasons this situation is beginning to change with a resurgence of interest in the biology of sodium channels. First, a variety of different sodium channel
isoforms have been identified, cloned, functionally expressed, and characterized.
Second, these isoforms are distinct in terms of developmental and regional expression, and they demonstrate subtle differences in their electrophysiological
characteristics. These different properties can result in distinct conductances that
are physiologically significant to the organism, such as resurgent currents that
are uniquely expressed in cerebellar Purkinje cells. Finally, minor changes in the

0066-4278/01/0315-0871$14.00

properties of specific isoforms result in human diseases of muscle, heart, and the nervous system. The purpose of this review is to summarize the distinguishing characteristics of the different sodium channel isoforms. This review does not include detailed information about the structure and function of voltage-gated sodium channels because this topic has recently been reviewed by Catterall (1).

The voltage-gated sodium channel consists of a highly processed α subunit, $\sim$260 kDa, that is associated with accessory β subunits in some tissues, such as brain and muscle (2, 3). Although sodium channels are not as varied as potassium and calcium channels, sodium channels with different functional or pharmacological properties have been observed by electrophysiological recording. Consistent with this variation, a number of different α subunit isoforms have been detected by biochemical purification and molecular cloning. Unfortunately, the cDNA clones have been named in many different ways, often based on the tissue of origin for the clone, which does not always reflect the overall distribution of the specific isoform. To add to the confusion, the same isoform from different species has been assigned multiple names. Recently, a systematic nomenclature for sodium channels has been proposed (4). This nomenclature is similar to the ones that were developed for potassium (5) and calcium (6) channels, and it has been used for the purposes of this review.

The isoforms have been classified as a single family based on evolutionary relationships, and the names are assigned in numerical order. The name consists of the chemical symbol of the principal permeating ion (Na) with the principal physiological regulator (voltage) indicated as a subscript (Na_v). The number following the subscript indicates the gene subfamily (currently Na_v1 is the only subfamily), and the number following the decimal point identifies the specific channel isoform (e.g. $Na_v1.1$). That number has been assigned according to the approximate order in which each gene was identified, with some exceptions. Splice variants of each family member are identified by lowercase letters following the numbers (e.g. $Na_v1.1a$). The assigned names appear in Table 1, along with the original names, the gene names, Genbank Accession numbers, various characteristics of each isoform, and the references. The relationships among the various isoforms are shown as a phylogenetic tree in Figure 1, which is similar to the tree determined by Plummer & Meisler (7).

Previously, the mammalian sodium channels had been divided into three subfamilies, based on sequence comparisons (reviewed in 8). However, this distinction is not supported by the phylogenetic tree (Figure 1) in which there is no clear separation of sodium channels into separate subfamilies, unlike the case with potassium and calcium channels. Therefore, in this review, the mammalian sodium channel isoforms have all been classified as members of a single family, $Na_v1.x$ (Table 1). There are 10 distinct sodium channel isoforms. $Na_v1.1$–1.8 were previously classified as type 1 channels, as the sequences of these isoforms have the most similarity. $Na_v1.9$ consists of an isoform that is approximately 50% identical to most of the other channels, so that it was originally considered to represent a separate family, type 3 (9). $Na_v1.9$ is not significantly more divergent than any of the other

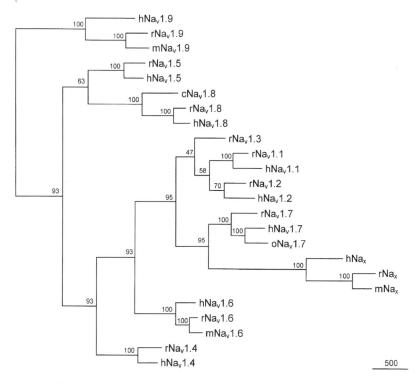

Figure 1   The proposed phylogenetic tree for mammalian voltage-gated sodium channel
α subunits was generated using sequences of channels for which the full-length coding regions have been determined, as listed in Table 1. This tree represents the optimal tree based
on parsimony analysis of nucleotide sequences. To perform the analysis, the amino acid sequences for all the isoforms were aligned using Clustal W (135). The amino acid sequences
in the alignments were then replaced with the published nucleotide sequences, and the nucleotide sequence alignments were subjected to analysis using the program PAUP* (136).
Divergent portions of the terminal regions and the cytoplasmic loops between domains I-II
and II-III were excluded from the PAUP* analysis. The tree was rooted by including the
invertebrate sodium channel sequences during the generation of the tree, although these sequences are not shown in the figure. The numbers at the nodes indicate the bootstrap values
for 100 replications. The scale bar represents 500 substitutions. The species of origin is
indicated as follows: h = *Homo sapiens* (human), r = *Rattus norvegicus* (rat), m = *Mus
musculus* (mouse), c = *Canis familiaris* (dog), o = *Oryctolagus cuniculus* (rabbit).

isoforms based on phylogeny, however, so that it does not clearly define a new
subfamily (Figure 1). Na_x includes isoforms with sequences that are also approximately 50% identical to the other sodium channels, and these were originally
considered to represent a new family, type 2 (10). Based on phylogeny, however,
Na_x appears to be a very late branch that diverged from $Na_v1.7$. Because none
of the Na_x channels have been functionally expressed, it is possible that these

TABLE 1 Mammalian sodium channel α subunits

Channel name	Original name	Species[a]	Splice variants	Function	TTX IC$_{50}$	Tissue	Size	Gene symbol	Chromosomal location[b]	Genebank access #
Na$_v$1.1	rat I (12)	Rat	Na$_v$1.1a	Yes (99)	10 nM (99)	CNS PNS	2009	SCN1A	M 2 [36] (29) H 2q24 (137)	X03638
	HBSCI (16)	Human		No		CNS	Partial			X65362
	SCN1A (18)	Human		No		CNS	2009			
	GPBI (17)	Guinea pig		No		CNS	Partial			AF003372
Na$_v$1.2	rat II (12) rat IIA (20)	Rat	Na$_v$1.2a	Yes (20, 111)	10 nM (111) 9 nM (99)	CNS	2005	SCN2A	M 2 [36] (29) H 2q23–24 (16, 138)	X03639 X61149
	HBSCII (16)	Human		No		CNS	Partial			X65361
	HBA (19)	Human		Yes (19)		CNS	2005			M94055
Na$_v$1.3	rat III (13, 112)	Rat	Na$_v$1.3a Na$_v$1.3b	Yes (112, 139)	2 nM (112) 15 nM (139)	CNS	1951	SCN3A	M 2 [36] (29) H 2q24 (140)	Y00766
Na$_v$1.4	SkM1, μ1 (45)	Rat		Yes (45)	5 nM (45)	Skeletal muscle	1840	SCN4A	M 11 [64] (141) H 17q23–25 (48, 142)	M26643
	SkM1 (48, 49)	Human		Yes (143)	25 nM (143)	Skeletal muscle	1836			M81758
Na$_v$1.5	SkM2 (46) rH1 (47)	Rat		Yes (61)	2 μM (61)	Denervated skeletal muscle, heart	2018	SCN5A	M 9 [70] (144) H 3p21 (144)	M27902
	H1 (50)	Human		Yes (50)	6 μM (50)	Heart	2016			M77235
Na$_v$1.6	NaCh6 (14)	Rat	Na$_v$1.6a	No		CNS PNS	1976	SCN8A	M 15 [64] (15) H 12q13 (15, 23)	L39018
	PN4 (21)	Rat		Yes (21)	1 nM (21)	CNS PNS	1976			AF049239 AF049240
	Scn8a (15, 22)	Mouse		Yes (22)	6 nM (22)	CNS	1976			U26707 AF049617
	Scn8a (23)	Human		No		CNS	1980			AF050736 AF225988

Na$_v$1.7	CerIII (17)	Guinea pig		No		CNS	Partial			AF003373
	PN1 (70, 71)	Rat		Yes (70)	4 nM (70)	PNS	1984	SCN9A	M 2 [36] 2 (145, 146) H 2q24^c	AF000368
	hNE-Na (72)	Human		Yes (72)	25 nM (72)	Medullary thyroid Ca	1977			U79568
	Nas (73)	Rabbit		No		Schwann cells	1984			X82835
Na$_v$1.8	SNS (74)	Rat		Yes (74)	~60 μM (74)	PNS (DRG)	1957	SCN10A	M 9 [67] (146) H 3p22–24	X92184
	PN3 (75)	Rat		Yes (75)	>100 μM (75)	PNS (DRG)	1956			U53833
	SNS (76)	Mouse		No		PNS	1958			Y09108
	NaNG (77)	Dog					1962			U60590
Na$_v$1.9	SNS2 (78)	Rat	Na$_v$1.9a	Yes (78)	1 μM (78)	PNS	1765	SCN11A	M 9 [71] (79, 147) H 3p21–24 (81, 147)	AJ237852
	NaN (9)	Rat		No		PNS	1765			AF059030
	PN5	Rat		Yes			1765			AF126739
	NaN (9)	Mouse		No			1765			AF118044
	NaT (79)	Mouse		No			1765			AB031389
	NaN (80)	Human		No			1791			AF188679
	SCN12A (81)	Human		No			1791			AF109737
										AF150882
Na$_x$	Na$_v$2.1 (10)	Human		No		Heart uterus muscle	1682	SCN6A^d	H 2q21–23 (148)	M91556
	Na-G (88)	Rat		No		Astrocytes PNS (DRG)	Partial	SCN7A^d	M 2 [41] (149)	M96578
	SCL11 (87)	Rat		No			1702			Y09164
	Na$_v$2.3 (86)	Mouse		No		Heart uterus muscle	1681			L36179

^{a}Complete species names are as follows: Rat = *Rattus norvegicus*, Human = *Homo sapiens*, Mouse = *Mus musculus*, Guinea pig = *Cavia porcellus*, Dog = *Canis familiaris*, Rabbit = *Oryctolagus cuniculus*.

^{b}Chromosomal locations are shown for mouse (M) and human (H) chromosomes.

^{c}Human map location for *SCN9A* is inferred from the mouse mapping data.

^{d}*SCN6A* and *SCN7A* most likely represent the same gene, as they were mapped in human and mouse, respectively (7).

genes do not encode voltage-gated sodium channels. Therefore, these genes have not been assigned numerical names in the proposed nomenclature, although they are discussed in this review.

Although the sequences of the mammalian sodium channels are sufficiently similar so that there are no distinct subfamilies, some of the isoforms are more closely related to each other from an evolutionary point of view, as indicated by the phylogenetic tree (Figure 1) and the chromosomal localization (Table 1) (7). The genes for five isoforms ($Na_v1.1$, $Na_v1.2$, $Na_v1.3$, $Na_v1.7$, and Na_x) are located on chromosome 2 in mouse and human, and all but Na_x are tightly clustered in both species. These five isoforms are also more closely related to each other in the phylogenetic tree. The genes for the three isoforms that are resistant to nanomolar concentrations of tetrodotoxin ($Na_v1.5$, $Na_v1.8$, and $Na_v1.9$) are located on chromosome 9 in mouse and 3 in human, and these isoforms are closely related in the phylogenetic tree. The genes for two isoforms ($Na_v1.4$ and $Na_v1.6$) are located on two different chromosomes, and each can be considered a separate group. The organization of the sodium channel genes is consistent with the hypothesis that the four groups of sodium channel genes resulted from the early genomic duplications that generated the four vertebrate HOX clusters and that additional duplications on chromosomes 2 and 9 in mouse (2 and 3 in human) generated the two sodium channel gene clusters (7).

The sodium channel isoforms are discussed based on the tissue in which they are most abundant. Four sodium channel isoforms, $Na_v1.1$, $Na_v1.2$, $Na_v1.3$ and $Na_v1.6$, are expressed at high levels in the central nervous system (CNS) (Table 1). Two isoforms are abundant in muscle: $Na_v1.4$ in adult skeletal muscle and $Na_v1.5$ in embryonic and denervated skeletal muscle and heart muscle. Three isoforms, $Na_v1.7$, $Na_v1.8$ and $Na_v1.9$, are expressed primarily in the peripheral nervous system. The channels making up the Na_x isoform are considered atypical because the sequences contain significant differences in regions that are critical for channel function, and this is the only isoform that has not been expressed in an exogenous system (10). Because of the lack of expression, it is possible that this isoform does not encode a functional, voltage-gated sodium channel. Na_x channels are expressed in a variety of tissues, including heart, uterus, muscle, astrocytes, and the dorsal root ganglion (DRG). Complementary DNA clones encoding the three accessory β subunits, $Na_v\beta1.1$, $Na_v\beta1.2$ and $Na_v\beta1.3$, have also been isolated, and these are listed in Table 2. The relationship among the three β subunits is shown as a phylogenetic tree in Figure 2.

SODIUM CHANNEL α SUBUNITS

Central Nervous System Channels

$Na_v1.1$, $Na_v1.2$, $Na_v1.3$, and $Na_v1.6$ are expressed abundantly in the CNS. In addition, $Na_v1.5$ is present in limbic regions of the brain (11), but this isoform is discussed with the channels expressed in muscle. $Na_v1.1$, $Na_v1.2$, and $Na_v1.3$ cDNAs were originally isolated from the rat CNS and were called types (or rat)

TABLE 2   Mammalian sodium channel β subunits

Name	Gene symbol	Original name	Species	Splice variants	Tissue	Size[a]	Chromosomal location[b]	Genbank access #
Na$_v\beta$1.1	*SCN1B*	β1 (98)	Rat	Naβ1.1A	CNS	218 [199]	M 7 [10] (150)	M91808
		β1 (151)	Human		CNS	218 [199]	H 19q13 (152)	L10338
		β1 (153)	Rabbit		CNS	218 [199]		U35382
Na$_v\beta$2.1	*SCN2B*	β2 (95)	Rat		CNS	215 [186]	M 9 [26] (154)	U37026
								U37147
		β2 (155)	Human		CNS	215 [186]	H 11q22-qter (155)	AF007783
Na$_v\beta$3.1	*SCN3B*	β3 (97)	Rat		CNS	215 [191]		AJ243395
		β3 (97)	Human		CNS	215 [191]	H 11q23.3 (97)	AJ243396

[a]The numbers in brackets indicate the sizes of the processed proteins.
[b]Chromosomal locations are shown for mouse (M) and human (H) chromosomes.

I, II, and III (12, 13). Na$_v$1.6 cDNA was isolated from rat brain, retina, and DRG (NaCh6) (14) and from mouse brain (Scn8a) (15). Partial cDNA clones have since been isolated for Na$_v$1.1 from human (HBSCI) (16) and guinea pig (GPBI) (17), and the full-length sequence has been determined from human (SCN1A) (18). Partial cDNA clones for Na$_v$1.2 have been isolated from human and called HBSCII (16) and HBA (19). A splice variant of Na$_v$1.2, originally termed rat IIA (20), has often been considered synonymously with rat II. Full-length sequences of Na$_v$1.6 have been isolated from rat (PN4) (21), mouse (Scn8a) (22), and human (Scn8a) (23), and a partial clone has been isolated from guinea pig (CerIII) (17).

The Na$_v$1.1 isoform was originally identified in the CNS (12), although it has since been shown to be expressed at high levels in the PNS (24). In contrast, the levels of Na$_v$1.2 and Na$_v$1.3 are significantly higher in the CNS than in the PNS (24). Na$_v$1.6 is the most abundantly expressed channel in the CNS, and it can also be detected in DRG cells (14). Each of these isoforms is present in neurons (14, 25) and glia (14, 26, 27), although the function of the channels in glial cells is not well understood (28). All of the CNS isoforms are inhibited by nanomolar concentrations of tetrodotoxin (TTX).

The genes for the CNS sodium channels have been localized on mouse and human chromosomes (Table 1). Na$_v$1.1, Na$_v$1.2, and Na$_v$1.3 are clustered on chromosome 2 in mice and humans. In the mouse, Na$_v$1.2 and Na$_v$1.3 are within 600 kb by physical mapping, and Na$_v$1.1 and Na$_v$1.2 are within 0.7 centimorgan by genetic linkage (29). Alternative splicing of all four isoforms has been demonstrated, which has resulted in isoforms termed Na$_v$1.1a, Na$_v$1.2a, Na$_v$1.3a, Na$_v$1.3b, and Na$_v$1.6a (21, 23, 30–33).

The isoforms in the CNS are present at different times in development, which has been studied most extensively in the rat. Na$_v$1.1, Na$_v$1.2, and Na$_v$1.6 are present at significant levels in the adult CNS. Na$_v$1.1 expression increases during the third postnatal week and peaks at the end of the first postnatal month, after which levels decrease by about 50% in the adult (34). Na$_v$1.2 expression also increases during the third postnatal week, but then continues to increase until reaching maximal

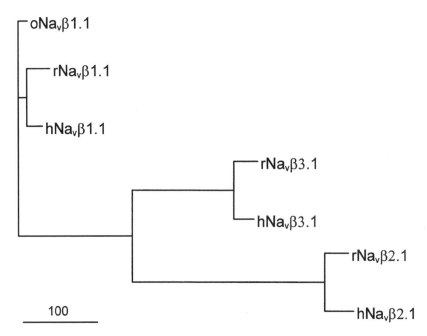

Figure 2 The proposed phylogenetic tree for mammalian voltage-gated sodium channel β subunits was generated using sequences of the cDNA clones listed in Table 2. This unrooted tree represents the optimal tree based on parsimony analysis using a branch-and-bound search, following the procedures described in the legend to Figure 1. The scale bar represents 100 substitutions. The species of origin is indicated as follows: h = *Homo sapiens* (human), r = *Rattus norvegicus* (rat), o = *Oryctolagus cuniculus* (rabbit).

levels during adulthood (34, 35). Na$_v$1.6 was detected during the embryonic period in brain (33), and levels increased shortly after birth and peaked by 2-weeks of age (23, 36, 37). This is the most abundantly expressed isoform in the CNS during adulthood (14). Levels of Na$_v$1.3 peak at birth but remain detectable at a lower level in adulthood (35–37).

Different isoforms are present in different locations in the adult CNS. Na$_v$1.1 is the predominant channel in the caudal regions and the spinal cord. Levels of Na$_v$1.2 are highest in the rostral regions (35, 38). Specifically, Na$_v$1.1 was detected at high levels in the cell bodies within the hippocampus, cerebellum, spinal cord, brainstem, cortex, substantia nigra, and caudate (34, 39), and Na$_v$1.2 was observed at high levels in the axons within the globus pallidus, hippocampus, and thalamus (34). There is no rostral-caudal gradient of Na$_v$1.6 mRNA (14), but it is present in a somato-dendritic distribution in output neurons of the cerebellum, cerebral cortex, and hippocampus (40), as well as in Purkinje cells in the cerebellar granule cell layer (41, 42). This isoform is present in both sensory and motor pathways, and its subcellular distribution includes axons, nodes, dendrites, cell bodies, and pre- and post-synaptic sites (42, 43). In the cerebellum, $Na_v1.1$ is detectable in Purkinje cells but not in granule cells, and $Na_v1.2$ is expressed in both Purkinje (25) and granule cells (44).

Skeletal and Heart Muscle Channels

Two sodium channel isoforms ($Na_v1.4$ and $Na_v1.5$) are expressed at significant levels in skeletal or cardiac muscle. $Na_v1.4$ was originally isolated from rat skeletal muscle and was called SkM1 or $\mu1$ (45). $Na_v1.5$ was isolated from rat skeletal muscle and called SkM2 (46), and it was also isolated from rat heart and called rH1 (47). Human versions of both isoforms have since been isolated and given the same names, SkM1 and H1 (48–50).

Expression of the $Na_v1.4$ and $Na_v1.5$ isoforms has been characterized most extensively in the rat. $Na_v1.4$ is expressed at high levels in adult skeletal muscle, at low levels in neonatal skeletal muscle, and not at all in brain or heart (51). $Na_v1.5$ is present at high levels in heart, but not in liver, kidney, or uterus (46, 47). This isoform was not originally detected in brain, but more sensitive approaches have demonstrated expression in the piriform cortex and subcortical limbic nuclei (11), which may explain the observation of sodium currents in the entorhinal cortex, with properties similar to those in cardiac muscle (52). $Na_v1.5$ is not observed in adult skeletal muscle, but it is detectable in neonatal skeletal muscle and after denervation of adult muscle (46). Although both isoforms are present in denervated skeletal muscle, the increase in the level of sodium channel mRNA following denervation results from an induction of $Na_v1.5$ expression (53).

The two muscle sodium channel isoforms can easily be distinguished from each other and from the CNS isoforms on the basis of toxin sensitivity. Sodium channels present in adult skeletal muscle are sensitive to nanomolar concentrations of TTX, as are the CNS channels. These channels are also sensitive to nanomolar concentrations of μ conotoxin GIIIA, to which the CNS channels are resistant (54, 55). Similar sensitivities are observed when the $Na_v1.4$ channel is expressed in an exogenous system (45, 56). In addition, $Na_v1.4$ is inhibited by nanomolar concentrations of μ conotoxin PIIIA, whereas $Na_v1.2$ is approximately 15-fold less sensitive, and $Na_v1.7$ requires micromolar concentrations for inhibition (57).

Sodium channels expressed in cardiac muscle cells are resistant to nanomolar concentrations of TTX, and require micromolar concentrations for inhibition (58). On the other hand, these channels are more sensitive to inhibition by lidocaine than are CNS channels (59). Similar sensitivities are observed when the $Na_v1.5$ channel is expressed in *Xenopus* oocytes, with an IC_{50} between 2 and 6 μM for TTX (60, 61). The presence of a cysteine instead of an aromatic residue in the pore region of domain I (the TTX resistance site) in $Na_v1.5$ is primarily responsible for the relative resistance to TTX (62–64). The same substitution is responsible for the greater sensitivity of $Na_v1.1$ to block by cadmium and zinc (62–65).

The electrophysiological properties of $Na_v1.4$ and $Na_v1.5$ are generally similar to those of the CNS channels, but with some important distinctions. $Na_v1.5$ has a more negative voltage-dependence of steady-state inactivation than either Na$_v$1.4 or any of the CNS isoforms (66, 67). Na$_v$1.5 also inactivates more rapidly than either Na$_v$1.4 or the CNS isoforms when the α subunit is expressed alone in *Xenopus* oocytes (61, 68), and co-expression of the β1 subunit does not accelerate inactivation of Na$_v$1.5 (69).

Peripheral Nervous System Channels

Three sodium channel isoforms, Na$_v$1.7, Na$_v$1.8, and Na$_v$1.9, are expressed primarily in the PNS. In addition, Na$_v$1.1 (24) and Na$_v$1.6 (14, 21), discussed above with the other CNS channels, are present at lower levels in the PNS. Na$_v$1.7 has been isolated from rat DRG (PN1) (70, 71), from human medullary thyroid cancer cells (hNE-NA) (72), and a partial clone has been isolated from rabbit Schwann cells (Nas) (73). Na$_v$1.8 was isolated from rat DRG and called both SNS (74) and PN3 (75), and it has been isolated from mouse (SNS) (76) and dog nodose ganglion (NaNG) (77). Na$_v$1.9 was isolated from rat DRG and called NaN (9), SNS2 (78), and PN5. It has also been isolated from mouse and called NaN (9) and NaT (79). One clone isolated from human DRG was called NaN (80), and another clone isolated from human brain was considered to represent a new isoform, and thus called SCN12A (81). However, this channel most likely represents the human version of the Na$_v$1.9 isoform, based on the phylogenetic tree (Figure 1).

Na$_v$1.1, which was discussed earlier with the CNS channels, is present at high levels in DRG and the lower spinal cord and at lower levels in sciatic nerve (24). Na$_v$1.6 is abundantly expressed in the PNS, having been detected in both gray and white matter in the spinal cord and in all diameter cells in the DRG, including both motor and primary sensory neurons (41, 43). In addition, this channel is present at the nodes of Ranvier in the sciatic nerve, spinal cord, and optic nerve, locations at which the other isoforms were not detected (41–43).

Na$_v$1.7 is widespread in the PNS, present in all types of DRG neurons, in Schwann cells, and in neuroendocrine cells (70, 72, 73). Within neurons, Na$_v$1.7 is localized to the neurite terminals, thus it is likely to have an important role in shaping the action potential (71). It is expressed in PC12 cells in which the level is induced by NGF (82, 83). The channel is sensitive to nanomolar concentration of TTX (70, 72), is slowly inactivating in oocytes, and is not modulated by the β1 or β2 subunits (70).

The expression of Na$_v$1.8 is more localized and found primarily in small-diameter sensory neurons of the DRG and trigeminal ganglion, in which the channel has been observed during both neonatal and adult periods (74–76, 80). This limited localization may have clinical significance because the C fibers that transmit nociceptive impulses are small-diameter neurons (74, 75). The Na$_v$1.8 channel is more resistant to TTX than any of the other isoforms, with an IC$_{50}$ of greater than 50 μM (74, 75). Resistance is from the presence of a serine rather than an aromatic residue at the TTX resistance site in domain I. Na$_v$1.8 demonstrates slow inactivation in oocytes without modulation by the β subunits (75). Mutant mice that completely lack $Na_v1.8$ are viable and express only TTX-sensitive, slow current in DRG neurons (84).

The $Na_v1.9$ channel is expressed in small fibers (sensory neurons) of the DRG and trigeminal ganglion, and the level of expression is down-regulated after axotomy (9, 80). Axonal injury of DRG neurons also leads to expression of $Na_v1.3$, which is not normally present in these cells (85). The $Na_v1.9$ channel is resistant to nanomolar concentrations of TTX, but it is half maximally blocked by 1 μM TTX (78).

Atypical Sodium Channels

The Na_x sodium channels were originally considered to be members of a different gene family (type 2), in that these sequences are less than 50% identical to those of the other sodium channel isoforms (10, 86, 87). Three different full-length clones have been isolated. The channel originally called $Na_v2.1$ was isolated from human heart (10), SCL11 was isolated from rat DRG (87), and the channel originally called $Na_v2.3$ was isolated from a mouse atrial tumor cell line (86). A partial clone (Na-G) was also isolated from rat astrocytes (88). It is likely that these clones represent the same isoform because the sequences are quite similar and they were derived from three different species (7). The phylogenetic tree is consistent with this interpretation (Figure 1). Therefore, in this review, these channels have all been classified as Na_x. The Na_x isoform is present at high levels in heart, skeletal muscle, and uterus, at low levels in brain, kidney, and spleen, and not at all in liver or smooth muscle. This isoform has also been detected in astrocytes, suggesting that it may represent a glial-specific channel.

The Na_x isoform has been considered an atypical sodium channel because there are sequence differences in two major regions shown to be critical for normal sodium channel function (10). First, there are significantly fewer charges in the S4 regions, which are essential for voltage-sensitive gating (89, 90). Second, the interdomain III-IV linker, which is involved in fast inactivation (91, 92), is poorly conserved. In particular, the critical IFM residues that form the nucleus of the inactivating particle have been replaced with IFI. However, it is not possible to evaluate the functional significance of these differences because none of these channels has been functionally expressed in an exogenous system, despite numerous efforts (86, 87). There are a number of possible reasons for the inability to observe functional currents from any of these channels. The channels may require accessory subunits that have not yet been identified, or the full-length sequences may contain cloning artifacts. It is possible that these sequences represent pseudogenes, although the fact that all three clones contain uninterrupted reading frames makes this hypothesis less likely. It is also possible that the Na_x isoform does not represent a true voltage-gated sodium channel (87), which is why it has not been assigned a number in the proposed nomenclature (4).

SODIUM CHANNEL β SUBUNITS

Many of the mammalian sodium channel α subunits are associated with accessory β subunits in vivo. Two β subunits were originally identified by biochemical purification. The $\beta 1$ subunit is noncovalently attached to the α subunit, and the $\beta 2$ subunit is covalently linked to the α subunit by disulfide bonds (93). Channels in the adult CNS are associated with both $\beta 1$ and $\beta 2$ subunits, and channels in adult skeletal muscle are associated with just $\beta 1$ (3). Complementary DNA clones encoding both of these subunits have been isolated from rat and human (Table 2). In addition, cDNA clones encoding a $\beta 3$ subunit have been isolated from the same two species, and a splice variant of the $\beta 1$ subunit has been identified in rat (94). The sequences of the three β subunits are not homologous, but they are all clearly related based on the phylogenetic tree (Figure 2). Each of the β subunit sequences predicts a protein with an amino-terminal signal sequence and single membrane-spanning region, indicative of an extracellular amino terminus. All three β subunits contain immunoglobulin-like folds similar to those found in neural cell adhesion molecules (95–97). The $\beta 3$ subunit RNA is expressed in a complementary fashion to $\beta 1$ subunit RNA in the CNS, which suggests that α subunits may be associated with either $\beta 1$ or $\beta 3$ (97).

Co-expression of the $\beta 1$ subunit with many of the α subunits in *Xenopus* oocytes modulates the electrophysiological properties of the channel, including accelerating inactivation and shifting the voltage-dependence of steady-state inactivation in the negative direction (22, 98, 99). These effects require the extracellular domain of the $\beta 1$ subunit, but not the intracellular domain (100–102). The region on the α subunit that is most important for modulation by $\beta 1$ includes the extracellular loops between S2 and S6 in domain IV (103). Co-expression of the $\beta 3$ subunit modulates gating of the α subunit sodium channels to a lesser extent than does co-expression of $\beta 1$ (97), and co-expression of the $\beta 2$ subunit modulates α subunit gating the least of the β subunits (95). The β subunits are also important for sodium channel interactions with cellular proteins. The $\beta 2$ subunit significantly increases membrane capacitance, which may indicate that it is involved in insertion of the channels into the cellular membrane (104, 105). Both $\beta 1$ and $\beta 2$ interact with the extracellular matrix proteins tenascin-C and tenascin-R, suggesting that the proteins may function as cellular adhesion molecules (106, 107). Consistent with this hypothesis, both $\beta 1$ and $\beta 2$ subunits recruit ankyrin to sites of cell-cell contact, and this recruitment requires the cytoplasmic domains of the subunits (108).

FUNCTIONAL ROLES OF DIFFERENT
CHANNEL ISOFORMS

Functional differences among the sodium channel isoforms have been inferred from correlation between electrophysiological recordings from native tissues and identification of the isoforms present in those tissues. One example that has been extensively studied is the sodium current in cerebellar Purkinje cells, which demonstrates unique persistent and resurgent properties (109, 110). Three iso-forms ($Na_v1.1$, $Na_v1.2$, and $Na_v1.6$) have been detected in these cells (17, 25), and Vega-Saenz de Miera et al (17) suggest that $Na_v1.1$ mediates a transient current in Purkinje neurons whereas $Na_v1.6$ mediates a persistent current. Raman et al (110) examined the persistent and resurgent currents in normal Purkinje cells and in cells from mice containing a null mutation for $Na_v1.6$. Both currents were greatly reduced in cells lacking $Na_v1.6$, suggesting that this channel is a major contributor to persistent and resurgent currents.

One means of determining whether the different sodium channel isoforms medi-ate distinct conductances is to examine the properties of each isoform in isolation, which is most easily performed using an exogenous expression system. All four of the sodium channel isoforms that have been identified thus far in the CNS have been functionally expressed in exogenous systems (Table 1). The electrophysiological properties of the isoforms examined in *Xenopus* oocytes are generally similar, particularly when compared with the great variation observed for the voltage-gated potassium and calcium channels. All the isoforms demonstrate fast inactivation, are blocked by nanomolar concentrations of TTX, and are modulated by the $\beta1$ and $\beta2$ subunits (20–22, 95, 98, 99, 111).

There are subtle differences, however. In the absence of β subunits, the $Na_v1.6$ channel inactivates more rapidly than any of the other isoforms (22), and the $Na_v1.3$ channel inactivates significantly more slowly (112). Co-expression of the β sub-units results in similar inactivation kinetics for $Na_v1.1$, $Na_v1.2$, and $Na_v1.6$ (22), but $Na_v1.3$ inactivates with biphasic kinetics, suggesting only partial modulation by the $\beta1$ subunit (113). The $Na_v1.6$ isoform has a more positive voltage-dependence of activation and a more negative voltage-dependence of steady-state inactivation compared with $Na_v1.1$ and $Na_v1.2$ in the absence of the β subunits (22). However, co-expression of the β subunits causes a large hyperpolarizing shift in the voltage dependence of activation for $Na_v1.6$, with no significant effect on the voltage-depen-dence of steady-state inactivation. Therefore, the voltage-dependent properties of $Na_v1.1$, $Na_v1.2$, and $Na_v1.6$ are generally similar in the presence of the β subunits.

There are significant differences among the three isoforms with respect to per-sistent current (22). $Na_v1.2$ has the least amount of persistent current at all depolar-izations, with less than 1%. $Na_v1.1$ demonstrates a persistent current that is large at negative potentials (greater than 5%) and decreases with more positive membrane potentials. In contrast, $Na_v1.6$ demonstrates a persistent current that increases with more positive membrane potentials, reaching a maximum of greater than 5% at the most positive potentials. These results are consistent with the hypothesis that $Na_v1.6$ channels mediate a persistent current that is largest when an action potential is fired, which might play a critical role in the repetitive firing of action potentials seen in Purkinje neurons. However, the persistent current from $Na_v1.1$ may also have important consequences for the firing properties of Purkinje neurons.

The resurgent current in cerebellar Purkinje cells is a small sodium current elicited by a waveform that simulates an action potential (109, 110). This current was observed both in normal Purkinje cells and in cells from mice lacking $Na_V1.6$, but it was much larger in the normal Purkinje cells expressing $Na_V1.6$. These results suggest that $Na_V1.6$ is the primary sodium channel responsible for the resurgent current. However, no resurgent current was observed from $Na_V1.6$ channels when they were expressed in *Xenopus* oocytes, either in the presence or absence of the β subunits (22). In addition, no resurgent current was observed in oocytes expressing $Na_V1.1$, $Na_V1.2$, or various combinations of the three isoforms (22). There are several possible reasons for the lack of resurgent current from $Na_V1.6$ channels expressed in *Xenopus* oocytes. First, it is possible that the $Na_V1.6$ channel undergoes post-translational modification in Purkinje neurons, which may change some of the electrophysiological properties of the channel. Second, there may be accessory proteins other than the β subunits in Purkinje neurons that could alter the properties of the channel. Third, it is possible that the resurgent current may be a property of one specific splice variant of the $Na_V1.6$ sodium channel, since multiple splice variants exist (21, 23, 33). All of these alternatives are based on the hypothesis that resurgence depends on cellular properties or factors in addition to the specific sodium channel isoform. Consistent with this hypothesis, resurgent current was not observed in mouse spinal neurons, in which $Na_V1.6$ is the major component of sodium current density (114).

CLINICAL SIGNIFICANCE OF SODIUM CHANNELS

A number of human diseases have been identified that result from aberrant sodium channel activity. Mutations in $Na_V1.4$ have been shown to cause three neuromuscular diseases: hyperkalemic periodic paralysis (HYPP), paramyotonia congenita (PMC), and the potassium-aggravated myotonias (115). HYPP is a disease in which increased levels of serum potassium lead to muscle hypoexcitability and paralysis. PMC patients experience cold-induced weakness and paralysis that is aggravated by increased muscle activity. These diseases are inherited in an autosomal-dominant manner and result from mutations in many different regions of the channel, each of which causes defects in either voltage-dependent activation or inactivation (115). Mutations in $Na_V1.5$ have been shown to cause long QT syndrome, which is also inherited in a dominant manner (116). The mutations that cause long QT syndrome are located in multiple regions of the channel, and they all cause defects in sodium channel inactivation (117, 118).

There is less information about the effects of sodium channel abnormalities in the CNS. Mutations in $Na_V1.6$ have been identified as causing a number of diseases in mice. Unlike the muscle disorders, the $Na_V1.6$ mutations are recessive, causing a variety of symptoms ranging from mild ataxia to dystonia, paralysis, and juvenile lethality (119). The mutations include *med* and *med^tg*, both of which result in complete disruption of the $Na_V1.6$ gene (15, 120, 121), and *med^jo*, which is a single point mutation of alanine to threonine in the domain III S4-S5 linker (122). This mutation produces an ataxic phenotype that is most likely caused by changes in the voltage-dependent properties of the $Na_V1.6$ channel (122, 123). Limbic seizures and behavioral abnormalities were observed in transgenic mice expressing an $Na_v1.2$ mutation that caused a small increase in persistent current (124). The seizures progressed in severity with age, ultimately leading to premature death (124).

Recently, two types of general epilepsy with febrile seizures plus (GEFS+) have been demonstrated to result from mutations in human CNS sodium channel genes. GEFS+ type 1 results from a mutation in the gene encoding the $\beta1$ subunit (*SCN1B*) (125), and GEFS+ type 2 results from mutations in the gene encoding $Na_v1.1$ (*SCN1A*) (18). Both types of GEFS+ are autosomal-dominant disorders. The mutation in the $\beta1$ subunit replaces a conserved cysteine in an extracellular immunoglobulin-like fold, which prevents modulation of the α subunit when expressed in *Xenopus* oocytes (125). Two mutations in $Na_v1.1$ have been identified thus far, one in domain II S4 and the other in domain IV S4 (18). The domain IV mutation, which is a substitution of histidine for arginine, shifted the voltage dependence of steady-state inactivation in the positive direction and caused slower inactivation when it was made in the $Na_v1.2$ channel and examined in *Xenopus* oocytes (126). However, the effects of either of these mutations in the original $Na_v1.1$ channel have not been examined. The $Na_v1.1$ isoform may be particularly important for the generation of epileptic seizures, as the ratio of mRNA encoding $Na_v1.1$ was increased compared with that encoding $Na_v1.2$ in specific brain regions of patients undergoing surgery to relieve intractable seizures (127).

A number of studies have suggested that changes in the expression of specific sodium channel isoforms contribute to the pathophysiology of inflammatory pain (128, 129) and that aberrant expression of TTX-resistant currents are involved (130, 131). The two TTX-resistant sodium channel isoforms present in the PNS are $Na_v1.8$ and $Na_v1.9$. Both channels are expressed in small-diameter sensory DRG neurons, which include the C fibers that transmit nociceptive impulses (9, 74, 75, 80). In addition, both isoforms are observed at increased levels in some peripheral nerve fibers proximal to injury in humans (132). The importance of $Na_v1.9$ in nociceptive transmission is suggested by the localization of this isoform in un-myelinated fibers, at some nodes of thinly myelinated fibers, and in corneal terminals that are primarily nociceptive (133). There is more direct evidence for the role of $Na_v1.8$ in neuropathic pain. The symptoms of experimental, neuropathic pain can be attenuated by interfering with the expression of $Na_v1.8$ (134). In addition, mutant mice lacking $Na_v1.8$ demonstrate significant analgesia to noxious mechanical stimuli and other defects in the ability to respond to painful stimuli, indicating that this isoform is involved in pain pathways (84). The data strongly suggest that these isoforms, particularly $Na_v1.8$, have important roles in the transmission of painful impulses in the nervous system.

CONCLUSIONS

The mammalian voltage-gated sodium channels represent a collection of isoforms with distinct patterns of expression and subtle differences in functional properties. There are no clear subfamilies of the isoforms, unlike the situation with potassium and calcium channels. The relative similarity of electrophysiological characteristics reflects the fact that sodium channels carry out the fundamental role of membrane depolarization during an action potential. However, the subtle differences can result in unique conductances in specific cell types, which have important physiological effects for the organism. In addition, mutations leading to small alterations in channel properties result in human diseases of muscle, heart, and the nervous system.

ACKNOWLEDGMENTS

I thank Dr. Miriam Meisler for critical reading of the manuscript and Dr. George Gutman for help with the phylogenetic analysis. Work in the author's laboratory is supported by grants from the National Institutes of Health, American Heart Association, and The National Alliance for Research on Schizophrenia and Depression.

Visit the Annual Reviews home page at www.AnnualReviews.org

LITERATURE CITED

1. Catterall WA. 2000. From ionic currents to molecular mechanisms: the structure and function of voltage-gated sodium channels. *Neuron* 26:13–25

2. Catterall WA. 1993. Structure and function of voltage-gated ion channels. *Trends Neurosci.* 16:500–6

3. Isom LL, DeJongh KS, Catterall WA. 1994. Auxiliary subunits of voltage-gated ion channels. *Neuron* 12:1183–94

4. Goldin AL, Barchi RL, Caldwell JH, Hofmann F, Howe JR, et al. 2000. Nomenclature of voltage-gated sodium channels. *Neuron* 28:365–68

5. Chandy KG. 1991. Simplified gene nomenclature. *Nature* 352:26

6. Ertel EA, Campbell KP, Harpold MM, Hofmann F, Mori Y, et al. 2000. Nomenclature of voltage-gated calcium channels. *Neuron* 25:533–35

7. Plummer NW, Meisler MH. 1999. Evolution and diversity of mammalian sodium channel genes. *Genomics* 57:323–31

8. Goldin AL. 1999. Diversity of mammalian voltage-gated sodium channels. In *Molecular and Functional Diversity of Ion Channels and Receptors*, ed. B Rudy, P Seeburg, pp. 38–50. New York: NY Acad. Sci.

9. Dib-Hajj SD, Tyrrell L, Black JA, Waxman SG. 1998. NaN, a novel voltage-gated Na channel, is expressed preferentially in peripheral sensory neurons and down-regulated after axotomy. *Proc. Natl. Acad. Sci. USA* 95:8963–68

10. George AL Jr, Knittle TJ, Tamkun MM. 1992. Molecular cloning of an atypical voltage-gated sodium channel expressed in human heart and uterus: evidence for a distinct gene family. *Proc. Natl. Acad. Sci. USA* 89:4893–97

11. Hartmann HA, Colom LV, Sutherland ML, Noebels JL. 1999. Selective localization of cardiac SCN5A sodium channels in limbic regions of rat brain. *Nat. Neurosci.* 2:593–95

12. Noda M, Ikeda T, Kayano T, Suzuki H, Takeshima H, et al. 1986. Existence of distinct sodium channel messenger RNAs in rat brain. *Nature* 320:188–92

13. Kayano T, Noda M, Flockerzi V, Takahashi H, Numa S. 1988. Primary structure of rat brain sodium channel III deduced from the

cDNA sequence. *FEBS Lett.* 228:187–94

14. Schaller KL, Krzemien DM, Yarowsky PJ, Krueger BK, Caldwell JH. 1995. A novel, abundant sodium channel expressed in neurons and glia. *J. Neurosci.* 15:3231–42

15. Burgess DL, Kohrman DC, Galt J, Plummer NW, Jones JM, et al. 1995. Mutation of a new sodium channel gene, *Scn8a*, in the mouse mutant 'motor endplate disease'. *Nat. Genet.* 10:461–65

16. Lu C-M, Han J, Rado TA, Brown GB. 1992. Differential expression of two sodium channel subtypes in human brain. *FEBS Lett.* 303:53–58

17. Vega-Saenz de Miera E, Rudy B, Sugimori M, Llinas R. 1997. Molecular characterization of the sodium channel subunits expressed in mammalian cerebellar Purkinje cells. *Proc. Natl. Acad. Sci. USA* 94:7059–64

18. Escayg A, MacDonald BT, Meisler MH, Baulac S, Huberfeld G, et al. 2000. Mutations of *SCN1A*, encoding a neuronal sodium channel, in two families with GEFS+2. *Nat. Genet.* 24:343–45

19. Ahmed CMI, Ware DH, Lee SC, Patten CD, Ferrer-Montiel AV, et al. 1992. Primary structure, chromosomal localization, and functional expression of a voltage-gated sodium channel from human brain. *Proc. Natl. Acad. Sci. USA* 89:8220–24

20. Auld VJ, Goldin AL, Krafte DS, Marshall J, Dunn JM, et al. 1988. A rat brain Na$^+$ channel α subunit with novel gating properties. *Neuron* 1:449–61

21. Dietrich PS, McGivern JG, Delgado SG, Koch BD, Eglen RM, et al. 1998. Functional analysis of a voltage-gated sodium channel and its splice variant from rat dorsal root ganglion. *J. Neurochem.* 70:2262–72

22. Smith MR, Smith RD, Plummer NW, Meisler MH, Goldin AL. 1998. Functional analysis of the mouse Scn8a sodium channel. *J. Neurosci.* 18:6093–102

23. Plummer NW, Galt J, Jones JM, Burgess DL, Sprunger LK, et al. 1998. Exon organization, coding sequence, physical mapping, and polymorphic intragenic markers for the human neuronal sodium channel gene *SCN8A*. *Genomics* 54:287–96

24. Beckh S. 1990. Differential expression of sodium channel mRNAs in rat peripheral nervous system and innervated tissues. *FEBS Lett.* 262:317–22

25. Black JA, Yokoyama S, Higashida H, Ransom BR, Waxman SG. 1994. Sodium channel mRNAs I, II and III in the CNS: cell-specific expression. *Mol. Brain Res.* 22:275–89

26. Black JA, Yokoyama S, Waxman SG, Oh Y, Zur KB, et al. 1994. Sodium channel mRNAs in cultured spinal cord astrocytes: in situ hybridization in identified cell types. *Mol. Brain Res.* 23:235–45

27. Oh Y, Black JA, Waxman SG. 1994. The expression of rat brain voltage-sensitive Na$^+$ channel mRNAs in astrocytes. *Mol. Brain Res.* 23:57–65

28. Sontheimer H, Black JA, Waxman SG. 1996. Voltage-gated Na$^+$ channels in glia: properties and possible functions. *Trends Neurosci.* 19:325–31

29. Malo D, Schurr E, Dorfman J, Canfield V, Levenson R, Gros P. 1991. Three brain sodium channel alpha-subunit genes are clustered on the proximal segment of mouse chromosome 2. *Genomics* 10:666–72

30. Schaller KL, Krzemien DM, McKenna NM, Caldwell JH. 1992. Alternatively spliced sodium channel transcripts in brain and muscle. *J. Neurosci.* 12:1370–81

31. Sarao R, Gupta SK, Auld VJ, Dunn RJ. 1991. Developmentally regulated alternative RNA splicing of rat brain sodium channel mRNAs. *Nucleic Acids Res.* 19:5673–79

32. Ahmed CMI, Auld VJ, Lester HA, Dunn R, Davidson N. 1990. Both sodium channel II and IIA α subunits are expressed in rat brain. *Nucleic Acids Res.* 18:5907

33. Plummer NW, McBurney MW, Meisler MH. 1997. Alternative splicing of the

sodium channel *SCN8A* predicts a truncated two-domain protein in fetal brain and non-neuronal cells. *J. Biol. Chem.* 272:24008–15

34. Gong B, Rhodes KJ, Bekele-Arcuri Z, Trimmer JS. 1999. Type I and type II Na$^+$ channel α-subunit polypeptides exhibit distinct spatial and temporal patterning, and association with auxiliary subunits in rat brain. *J. Comp. Neurol.* 412:342–52

35. Beckh S, Noda M, Lübbert H, Numa S. 1989. Differential regulation of three sodium channel messenger RNAs in the rat central nervous system during development. *EMBO J.* 8:3611–36

36. Felts PA, Yokoyama S, Dib-Hajj S, Black JA, Waxman SG. 1997. Sodium channel α-subunit mRNAs I, II, III, NaG, Na6 and hNE (PN1): different expression patterns in developing rat nervous system. *Mol. Brain Res.* 45:71–82

37. Schaller KL, Caldwell JH. 2000. Developmental and regional expression of sodium channel isoform NaCh6 in the rat central nervous system. *J. Comp. Neurol.* 420:84–97

38. Gordon D, Merrick D, Auld V, Dunn R, Goldin AL, et al. 1987. Tissue-specific expression of the R$_I$ and R$_{II}$ sodium channel subtypes. *Proc. Natl. Acad. Sci. USA* 84:8682–86

39. Westenbroek RE, Merrick DK, Catterall WA. 1989. Differential subcellular localization of the R$_I$ and R$_{II}$ Na$^+$ channel subtypes in central neurons. *Neuron* 3:695–704

40. Whitaker W, Faull R, Waldvogel H, Plumpton C, Burbidge S, et al. 1999. Localization of the type VI voltage-gated sodium channel protein in human CNS. *NeuroReport* 10:3703–9

41. Tzoumaka E, Tischler AC, Sangameswaran L, Eglen RM, Hunter JC, Novakovic SD. 2000. Differential distribution of the tetrodotoxin-sensitive rPN4/NaCh6/Scn8a sodium channel in the nervous system. *J. Neurosci. Res.* 60:37–44

42. Caldwell JH, Schaller KL, Lasher RS, Peles E, Levinson SR. 2000. Sodium channel Na$_v$1.6 is localized at nodes of Ranvier, dendrites, and synapses. *Proc. Natl. Acad. Sci. USA* 97:5616–20

43. Krzemien DM, Schaller KL, Levinson SR, Caldwell JH. 2000. Immunolocalization of sodium channel isoform NaCh6 in the nervous system. *J. Comp. Neurol.* 420:70–83

44. Furuyama T, Morita Y, Inagaki S, Takagi H. 1993. Distribution of I, II and III subtypes of voltage-sensitive Na$^+$ channel mRNA in the rat brain. *Mol. Brain Res.* 17:169–73

45. Trimmer JS, Cooperman SS, Tomiko SA, Zhou J, Crean SM, et al. 1989. Primary structure and functional expression of a mammalian skeletal muscle sodium channel. *Neuron* 3:33–49

46. Kallen RG, Sheng Z-H, Yang J, Chen L, Rogart RB, Barchi RL. 1990. Primary structure and expression of a sodium channel characteristic of denervated and immature rat skeletal muscle. *Neuron* 4:233–42

47. Rogart RB, Cribbs LL, Muglia LK, Kephart DD, Kaiser MW. 1989. Molecular cloning of a putative tetrodotoxin-resistant rat heart Na$^+$ channel isoform. *Proc. Natl. Acad. Sci. USA* 86:8170–74

48. Wang J, Rojas CV, Zhou J, Schwartz LS, Nicholas H, Hoffman EP. 1992. Sequence and genomic structure of the human adult skeletal muscle sodium channel alpha subunit gene on 17q. *Biochem. Biophys. Res. Commun.* 182:794–801

49. George AL Jr, Komisarof J, Kallen RG, Barchi RL. 1992. Primary structure of the adult human skeletal muscle voltage-dependent sodium channel. *Ann. Neurol.* 31:131–37

50. Gellens ME, George AL Jr, Chen L, Chahine M, Horn R, et al. 1992. Primary structure and functional expression of the human cardiac tetrodotoxin-insensitive voltage-dependent sodium channel. *Proc. Natl. Acad. Sci. USA* 89:554–58

51. Trimmer JS, Cooperman SS, Agnew WS, Mandel G. 1990. Regulation of muscle

sodium channel transcripts during development and in response to denervation. *Dev. Biol.* 142:360–67

52. White JA, Alonso A, Kay AR. 1993. A heart-like Na$^+$ current in the medial entorhinal cortex. *Neuron* 11:1037–47

53. Yang JSJ, Sladky JT, Kallen RG, Barchi RL. 1991. TTX-sensitive and TTX-insensitive sodium channel mRNA transcripts are independently regulated in adult skeletal muscle after denervation. *Neuron* 7:421–27

54. Cruz LJ, Gray WR, Olivera BM, Zeikus RD, Kerr L, et al. 1985. *Conus geographus* toxins that discriminate between neuronal and muscle sodium channels. *J. Biol. Chem.* 260:9280–88

55. Moczydlowski E, Olivera BM, Gray WR, Strichartz GR. 1986. Discrimination of muscle and neuronal Na-channel subtypes by binding competition between [^{3}H]saxitoxin and mu-conotoxins. *Proc. Natl. Acad. Sci. USA* 83:5321–25

56. Ukomadu C, Zhou J, Sigworth FJ, Agnew WS. 1992. μI Na$^+$ channels expressed transiently in human embryonic kidney cells: biochemical and biophysical properties. *Neuron* 8:663–76

57. Safo P, Rosenbaum T, Shcherbatko A, Choi D-Y, Han E, et al. 2000. Distinction among neuronal subtypes of voltage-activated sodium channels by μ-conotoxin PIIIA. *J. Neurosci.* 200:76–80

58. Brown AM, Lee KS, Powell T. 1981. Voltage clamp and internal perfusion of single rat heart muscle cells. *J. Physiol.* 318:455–77

59. Bean BP, Cohen CJ, Tsien RW. 1983. Lidocaine block of cardiac sodium channels. *J. Gen. Physiol.* 81:613–42

60. Cribbs LL, Satin J, Fozzard HA, Rogart RB. 1990. Functional expression of the rat heart I Na$^+$ channel isoform. Demonstration of properties characteristic of native cardiac Na$^+$ channels. *FEBS Lett.* 275:195–200

61. White MM, Chen L, Kleinfield R, Kallen RG, Barchi RL. 1991. SkM2, a Na$^+$ channel cDNA clone from denervated skeletal muscle, encodes a tetrodotoxin-insensitive Na$^+$ channel. *Mol. Pharmacol.* 39:604–8

62. Backx PH, Yue DT, Lawrence JH, Marbán E, Tomaselli GF. 1992. Molecular localization of an ion-binding site within the pore of mammalian sodium channels. *Science* 257:248–51

63. Heinemann SH, Terlau H, Imoto K. 1992. Molecular basis for pharmacological differences between brain and cardiac sodium channels. *Pflügers Arch.* 422:90–92

64. Satin J, Kyle JW, Chen M, Bell P, Cribbs LL, et al. 1992. A mutant of TTX-resistant cardiac sodium channels with TTX-sensitive properties. *Science* 256:1202–5

65. Chen L-Q, Chahine M, Kallen RG, Horn R. 1992. Chimeric study of sodium channels from rat skeletal and cardiac muscle. *FEBS Lett.* 309:253–57

66. Makielski JC. 1996. The heart sodium channel phenotype for inactivation and lidocaine block. *Jpn. Heart J.* 37:733–39

67. Nuss HB, Tomaselli GF, Marbán E. 1995. Cardiac sodium channels (hH1) are intrinsically more sensitive to block by lidocaine than are skeletal muscle (μ1) channels. *J. Gen. Physiol.* 106:1193–209

68. Satin J, Kyle JW, Chen M, Rogart RB, Fozzard HA. 1992. The cloned cardiac Na channel α-subunit expressed in *Xenopus* oocytes show gating and blocking properties of native channels. *J. Membr. Biol.* 130:11–22

69. Qu Y, Isom LL, Westenbroek RE, Rogers JC, Tanada TN, et al. 1995. Modulation of cardiac Na$^+$ channel expression in *Xenopus* oocytes by β1 subunits. *J. Biol. Chem.* 270:25696–701

70. Sangameswaran L, Fish LM, Koch BD, Rabert DK, Delgado SG, et al. 1997. A novel tetrodotoxin-sensitive, voltage-gated sodium channel expressed in rat and

human dorsal root ganglia. *J. Biol. Chem.* 272:14805–9

71. Toledo-Aral JJ, Moss BL, He Z-J, Koszowski AG, Whisenand T, et al. 1997. Identification of PN1, a predominant voltage-dependent sodium channel expressed principally in peripheral neurons. *Proc. Natl. Acad. Sci. USA* 94:1527–32

72. Klugbauer N, Lacinova L, Flockerzi V, Hofmann F. 1995. Structure and functional expression of a new member of the tetrodotoxin-sensitive voltage-activated sodium channel family from human neuroendocrine cells. *EMBO J.* 14:1084–90

73. Belcher SM, Zerillo CA, Levenson R, Ritchie JM, Howe JR. 1995. Cloning of a sodium channel α subunit from rabbit Schwann cells. *Proc. Natl. Acad. Sci. USA* 92:11034–38

74. Akopian AN, Sivilotti L, Wood JN. 1996. A tetrodotoxin-resistant voltage-gated sodium channel expressed by sensory neurons. *Nature* 379:257–62

75. Sangameswaran L, Delgado SG, Fish LM, Koch BD, Jakeman LB, et al. 1996. Structure and function of a novel voltage-gated, tetrodotoxin-resistant sodium channel specific to sensory neurons. *J. Biol. Chem.* 271:5953–56

76. Souslova VA, Fox M, Wood JN, Akopian AN. 1997. Cloning and characterization of a mouse sensory neuron tetrodotoxin-resistant voltage-gated sodium channel gene, Scn10a. *Genomics* 41:201–9

77. Chen J, Ikeda SR, Lang W, Isales CM, Wei X. 1997. Molecular cloning of a putative tetrodotoxin-resistant sodium channel from dog nodose ganglion neurons. *Gene* 202:7–14

78. Tate S, Benn S, Hick C, Trezise D, John V, et al. 1998. Two sodium channels contribute to the TTX-R sodium current in primary sensory neurons. *Nat. Neurosci.* 1:653–55

79. Ogata K, Jeong S-Y, Murakami H, Hashida H, Suzuki T, et al. 2000. Cloning and expression study of the mouse tetrodotoxin-resistant voltage-gated sodium channel α subunit NaT/Scn11a. *Biochem. Biophys. Res. Commun.* 267:271–77

80. Dib-Hajj SD, Tyrrell L, Cummins TR, Black JA, Wood PM, Waxman SG. 1999. Two tetrodotoxin-resistant sodium channels in human dorsal root ganglion neurons. *FEBS Lett.* 462:117–20

81. Jeong S-Y, Goto J, Hashida H, Suzui T, Ogata K, et al. 2000. Identification of a novel human voltage-gated sodium channel α subunit gene, *SCN12A. Biochem. Biophys. Res. Commun.* 267:262–70

82. D'Arcangelo G, Paradiso K, Shepherd D, Brehm P, Halegoua S, Mandel G. 1993. Neuronal growth factor regulation of two different sodium channel types through distinct signal transduction pathways. *J. Cell Biol.* 122:915–21

83. Toledo-Aral JJ, Brehm P, Halegoua S, Mandel G. 1995. A single pulse of nerve growth factor triggers long-term neuronal excitability through sodium channel gene induction. *Neuron* 14:607–11

84. Akopian AN, Souslova V, England S, Okuse K, Ogata N, et al. 1999. The tetrodotoxin-resistant sodium channel SNS has a specialized function in pain pathways. *Nat. Neurosci.* 2:541–48

85. Black JA, Cummins TR, Plumpton C, Chen YH, Hormuzdiar W, et al. 1999. Upregulation of a silent sodium channel after peripheral, but not central, nerve injury in DRG neurons. *J. Neurophysiol.* 82:2776–85

86. Felipe A, Knittle TJ, Doyle KL, Tamkun MM. 1994. Primary structure and differential expression during development and pregnancy of a novel voltage-gated sodium channel in the mouse. *J. Biol. Chem.* 269:30125–31

87. Akopian AN, Souslova V, Sivilotti L, Wood JN. 1997. Structure and distribution of a broadly expressed atypical sodium channel. *FEBS Lett.* 400:183–87

88. Gautron S, Dos Santos G, Pinto-Henrique D, Koulakoff A, Gros F, Berwald-Netter

Y. 1992. The glial voltage-gated sodium channel: cell- and tissue-specific mRNA expression. *Proc. Natl. Acad. Sci. USA* 89:7272–76

89. Stühmer W, Conti F, Suzuki H, Wang X, Noda M, et al. 1989. Structural parts involved in activation and inactivation of the sodium channel. *Nature* 339:597–603

90. Yang N, Horn R. 1995. Evidence for voltage-dependent S4 movement in sodium channels. *Neuron* 15:213–18

91. Patton DE, West JW, Catterall WA, Goldin AL. 1992. Amino acid residues required for fast sodium channel inactivation. Charge neutralizations and deletions in the III-IV linker. *Proc. Natl. Acad. Sci. USA* 89:10905–9

92. West JW, Patton DE, Scheuer T, Wang Y, Goldin AL, Catterall WA. 1992. A cluster of hydrophobic amino acid residues required for fast Na^+ channel inactivation. *Proc. Natl. Acad. Sci. USA* 89:10910–14

93. Messner DJ, Catterall WA. 1985. The sodium channel from rat brain—separation and characterization of subunits. *J. Biol. Chem.* 260:10597–604

94. Kazen-Gillespie KA, Ragsdale DS, D'Andrea MR, Mattei LN, Rogers KE, Isom LL. 2000. Cloning, localization, and functional expression of sodium channel β1A subunits. *J. Biol. Chem.* 275:1079–88

95. Isom LL, Ragsdale DS, De Jongh KS, Westenbroek RE, Reber BFX, et al. 1995. Structure and function of the β_2 subunit of brain sodium channels, a transmembrane glycoprotein with a CAM motif. *Cell* 83:433–42

96. Isom LL, Catterall WA. 1996. Na^+ channel subunits and Ig domains. *Nature* 383:307–8

97. Morgan K, Stevens EB, Shah B, Cox PJ, Dixon AK, et al. 2000. β3: an additional auxiliary subunit of the voltage-sensitive sodium channel that modulates channel gating with distinct kinetics. *Proc. Natl. Acad. Sci. USA* 97:2308–13

98. Isom LL, DeJongh KS, Patton DE, Reber BFX, Offord J, et al. 1992. Primary structure and functional expression of the β_1 subunit of the rat brain sodium channel. *Science* 256:839–42

99. Smith RD, Goldin AL. 1998. Functional analysis of the rat I sodium channel in *Xenopus* oocytes. *J. Neurosci.* 18:811–20

100. Chen C, Cannon SC. 1995. Modulation of Na^+ channel inactivation by the β_1 subunit: a deletion analysis. *Pflügers Arch.* 431:186–95

101. McCormick KA, Isom LL, Ragsdale D, Smith D, Scheuer T, Catterall WA. 1998. Molecular determinants of Na^+ channel function in the extracellular domain of the β1 subunit. *J. Biol. Chem.* 273:3954–62

102. McCormick KA, Srinivasan J, White K, Scheuer T, Catterall WA. 1999. The extracellular domain of the β1 subunit is both necessary and sufficient for β1-like modulation of sodium channel gating. *J. Biol. Chem.* 274:23638–46

103. Qu Y, Rogers JC, Chen S-F, McCormick KA, Scheuer T, Catterall WA. 1999. Functional roles of the extracellular segments of the sodium channel α subunit in voltage-dependent gating and modulation by β1 subunits. *J. Biol. Chem.* 274:32647–54

104. Schmidt JW, Rossie S, Catterall WA. 1985. A large intracellular pool of inactive Na channel alpha subunits in developing rat brain. *Proc. Natl. Acad. Sci. USA* 82:4847–51

105. Schmidt JW, Catterall WA. 1986. Biosynthesis and processing of the alpha subunit of the voltage-sensitive sodium channel in rat brain. *Cell* 46:437–45

106. Srinivasan J, Schachner M, Catterall WA. 1998. Interaction of voltage-gated sodium channels with the extracellular matrix molecules tenascin-C and tenascin-R. *Proc. Natl. Acad. Sci. USA* 95:15753–57

107. Xiao Z-C, Ragsdale DS, Malhotra JD, Mattei LN, Braun PE, et al. 1999. Tenascin-R is a functional modulator of

sodium channel β subunits. *J. Biol. Chem.* 274:26511–17

108. Malhotra JD, Kazen-Gillespie K, Hortsch M, Isom LL. 2000. Sodium channel β subunits mediate homophilic cell adhesion and recruit ankyrin to points of cell-cell contact. *J. Biol. Chem.* 275:11383–88

109. Raman IM, Bean BP. 1997. Resurgent sodium current and action potential formation in dissociated cerebellar Purkinje neurons. *J. Neurosci.* 17:4517–26

110. Raman IM, Sprunger LK, Meisler MH, Bean BP. 1997. Altered subthreshold sodium currents and disrupted firing patterns in Purkinje neurons of *Scn8a* mutant mice. *Neuron* 19:881–91

111. Noda M, Ikeda T, Suzuki H, Takeshima H, Takahashi T, et al. 1986. Expression of functional sodium channels from cloned cDNA. *Nature* 322:826–28

112. Joho RH, Moorman JR, VanDongen AMJ, Kirsch GE, Silberberg H, et al. 1990. Toxin and kinetic profile of rat brain type III sodium channel expressed in *Xenopus* oocytes. *Mol. Brain Res.* 7:105–13

113. Patton DE, Isom LL, Catterall WA, Goldin AL. 1994. The adult rat brain β_1 subunit modifies activation and inactivation gating of multiple sodium channel α subunits. *J. Biol. Chem.* 269:17649–55

114. Pan F, Beam KG. 1999. The absence of resurgent sodium current in mouse spinal neurons. *Brain Res.* 849:162–68

115. Cannon SC. 1997. From mutation to myotonia in sodium channel disorders. *Neuromusc. Disord.* 7:241–49

116. Kass RS, Davies MP. 1996. The roles of ion channels in an inherited heart disease: molecular genetics of the long QT syndrome. *Cardiovasc. Res.* 32:443–54

117. Wang Q, Shen J, Li Z, Timothy K, Vincent GM, et al. 1995. Cardiac sodium channel mutations in patients with long QT syndrome, an inherited cardiac arrhythmia. *Hum. Mol. Genet.* 4:1603–7

118. Wang DW, Yazawa K, George AL Jr, Bennett PB. 1996. Characterization of human cardiac Na^+ channel mutations in the congenital long QT syndrome. *Proc. Natl. Acad. Sci. USA* 93:13200–5

119. Meisler MH, Sprunger LK, Plummer NW, Escayg A, Jones JM. 1997. Ion channel mutations in mouse models of inherited neurological diseases. *Ann. Med.* 29:569–74

120. Kohrman DC, Plummer NW, Schuster T, Jones JM, Jang W, et al. 1995. Insertional mutation of the motor endplate disease (*med*) locus on mouse chromosome 15. *Genomics* 26:171–77

121. Kohrman DC, Harris JB, Meisler MH. 1996. Mutation detection in the *med* and *med^J* alleles of the sodium channel *Scn8a*. *J. Biol. Chem.* 271:17576–81

122. Kohrman DC, Smith MR, Goldin AL, Harris J, Meisler MH. 1996. A missense mutation in the sodium channel Scn8a is responsible for cerebellar ataxia in the mouse mutant *jolting*. *J. Neurosci.* 16:5993–99

123. Smith MR, Goldin AL. 1999. A mutation that causes ataxia shifts the voltage-dependence of the Scn8a sodium channel. *NeuroReport* 10:3027–31

124. Kearney JA, Plummer NW, Smith MR, Kapur J, Cummins TR, et al. 2000. A gain-of-function mutation in the sodium channel gene Scn2a results in seizures and behavioral abnormalities. *Neuroscience.* In press

125. Wallace RH, Wang DW, Singh R, Scheffer IE, George AL Jr, et al. 1998. Febrile seizures and generalized epilepsy associated with a mutation in the Na^+-channel $\beta 1$ subunit gene *SCN1B*. *Nat. Genet.* 19:366–70

126. Kühn FJP, Greeff NG. 1999. Movement of voltage sensor S4 in domain 4 is tightly coupled to sodium channel fast inactivation and gating charge immobilization. *J. Gen. Physiol.* 114:167–83

127. Lombardo AJ, Kuzniecky R, Powers

RE, Brown GB. 1996. Altered brain sodium channel transcript levels in human epilepsy. *Mol. Brain Res.* 35:84–90

128. Waxman SG, Dib-Hajj S, Cummins TR, Black JA. 1999. Sodium channels and pain. *Proc. Natl. Acad. Sci. USA* 96:7635–39

129. Waxman SG, Cummins TR, Dib-Hajj S, Fjell J, Black JA. 1999. Sodium channels, excitability of primary sensory neurons, and the molecular basis of pain. *Muscle Nerve* 22:1177–87

130. Gold MS, Reichling DB, Shuster MJ, Levine JD. 1996. Hyperalgesic agents increase a tetrodotoxin-resistant Na^+ current in nociceptors. *Proc. Natl. Acad. Sci. USA* 93:1108–12

131. Gold MS. 1999. Tetrodotoxin-resistant Na^+ currents and inflammatory hyperalgesia. *Proc. Natl. Acad. Sci. USA* 96:7645–49

132. Coward K, Plumpton C, Facer P, Birch R, Carlstedt T, et al. 2000. Immunolocalization of SNS/PN3 and NaN/SNS2 sodium channels in human pain states. *Pain* 85:41–50

133. Fjell J, Hormuzdiar W, Milenkovic M, Aglieco F, Tyrrell L, et al. 2000. Localization of the tetrodotoxin-resistant sodium channel NaN in nociceptors. *NeuroReport* 11:199–202

134. Porreca F, Lai J, Bian D, Wegert S, Ossipov MH, et al. 1999. A comparison of the potential role of the tetrodotoxin-insensitive sodium channels, PN3/SNS and NaN/SNS2, in rat models of chronic pain. *Proc. Natl. Acad. Sci. USA* 96:7640–44

135. Thompson JD, Higgins DG, Gibson TJ. 1994. CLUSTAL W: improving the sensitivity of progressive multiple sequence alignment through sequence weighting, positions-specific gap penalties and weight matrix choice. *Nucleic Acids Res.* 22:4673–80

136. Swofford DL. 1998. PAUP*. *Phylogenetic Analysis Using Parsimony (*and other methods).* Sunderland, MA: Sinauer

137. Malo MS, Blanchard BJ, Andresen JM, Srivastava K, Chen X-N, et al. 1994. Localization of a putative human brain sodium channel gene (SCN1A) to chromosome band 2q24. *Cytogenet. Cell Genet.* 67:178–86

138. Litt M, Luty J, Kwak M, Allen L, Magenis RE, Mandel G. 1989. Localization of a human brain sodium channel gene (*SCN2A*) to chromosome 2. *Genomics* 5:204–8

139. Suzuki H, Beckh S, Kubo H, Yahagi N, Ishida H, et al. 1988. Functional expression of cloned cDNA encoding sodium channel III. *FEBS Lett.* 228:195–200

140. Malo MS, Srivastava K, Andresen JM, Chen X-N, Korenberg JR, Ingram VM. 1994. Targeted gene walking by low stringency polymerase chain reaction: assignment of a putative human brain sodium channel gene (*SCN3A*) to chromosome 2q24–31. *Proc. Natl. Acad. Sci. USA* 91:2975–79

141. Ambrose C, Cheng S, Fontaine B, Nadeau JH, MacDonald M, Gusella JF. 1992. The alpha-subunit of the skeletal muscle sodium channel is encoded proximal to Tk-1 on mouse chromosome 11. *Mamm. Genome* 3:151–55

142. George AL Jr, Ledbetter DH, Kallen RG, Barchi RL. 1991. Assignment of a human skeletal muscle sodium channel alpha-subunit gene (*SCN4A*) to 17q23.1–25.3. *Genomics* 9:555–56

143. Chahine M, Bennett PB, George AL Jr, Horn R. 1994. Functional expression and properties of the human skeletal muscle sodium channel. *Pflügers Arch.* 427:136–42

144. George AL Jr, Varkony TA, Drabkin HA, Han J, Knops JF, et al. 1995. Assignment of the human heart tetrodotoxin-resistant voltage-gated Na^+ channel α-subunit gene (SCN5A) to band 3p21. *Cytogenet. Cell Genet.* 68:67–70

145. Beckers M-C, Ernst E, Belcher S, Howe J, Levenson R, Gros P. 1996. A new sodium channel α-subunit gene (*Scn9a*) from Schwann cells maps to the *Scn1a, Scn2a, Scn3a* cluster of mouse chromosome 2. *Genomics* 36:202–5

146. Kozak CA, Sangameswaran L. 1996. Genetic mapping of the peripheral sodium channel genes, *Scn9a* and *Scn10a*, in the mouse. *Mamm. Genome* 7:787–92

147. Dib-Hajj SD, Tyrrell L, Escayg A, Wood PM, Meisler MH, Waxman SG. 1999. Coding sequence, genomic organization, and conserved chromosomal localization of the mouse gene *scn11a* encoding the sodium channel NaN. *Genomics* 59:309–18

148. George AL Jr, Knops JF, Han J, Finley WH, Knittle TJ, et al. 1994. Assignment of a human voltage-dependent sodium channel α-subunit gene (*SCN6A*) to 2q21-q23. *Genomics* 19:395–97

149. Potts JF, Regan MR, Rochelle JM, Seldin MF, Agnew WS. 1993. A glial-specific voltage-sensitive Na channel gene maps close to clustered genes for neuronal isoforms on mouse chromosome 2. *Biochem. Biophys. Res. Commun.* 197:100–4

150. Tong J, Potts JF, Rochelle JM, Seldin MF, Agnew WS. 1993. A single beta1 subunit mapped to mouse chromosome 7 may be a common component of Na channel isoforms from brain, skeletal muscle and heart. *Biochem. Biophys. Res. Commun.* 195:679–85

151. McClatchey AI, Cannon SC, Slaugenhaupt SA, Gusella JF. 1993. The cloning and expression of a sodium channel beta1-subunit cDNA from human brain. *Hum. Mol. Genet.* 2:745–49

152. Makita N, Sloan-Brown K, Weghuis DO, Ropers HH, George AL Jr. 1994. Genomic organization and chromosomal assignment of the human voltage-gated Na$^+$ channel β_1 subunit gene (*SCN1B*). *Genomics* 23:628–34

153. Belcher SM, Howe JR. 1996. Cloning of the cDNA encoding the sodium channel $\beta1$ subunit from rabbit. *Gene* 170:285–86

154. Jones JM, Meisler MH, Isom LL. 1996. *Scn2b*, a voltage-gated sodium channel $\beta2$ gene on mouse chromosome 9. *Genomics* 34:258–59

155. Eubanks J, Srinivasan N, Dinulos MB, Disteche CM, Catterall WA. 1997. Structure and chromosomal localization of the $\beta2$ subunit of the human brain sodium channel. *NeuroReport* 8:2775–79

Subject Index

A

Absence seizures
  cellular and network bases
    of epileptic seizures,
    815–38
Accelerated
    re-endothelialization
  somatic gene therapy in
    cardiovascular system
    and, 436, 440
Acetylation
  histone
    estrogen receptor ß and,
    172
Acetylcholine (ACH)
  NAADP, cADPr, and IP$_3$ in
    Ca^{2+} signaling, 99–112
  pacemaker ion channels
    and, 237
Acid secretion
  gastrin, CCK, signaling,
    and cancer, 49–66
  gastrins and, 119–32
Acinar cells
  pancreatic
    cholecystokinin-
      regulating synthesis
      and, 77–91
    NAADP, cADPr, and IP$_3$
      in Ca^{2+} signaling, 99,
      104
Acquired immunity
  surfactant proteins A and D
    and pulmonary host
    defense, 539–42
Actins
  cholecystokinin-regulating
    synthesis and, 77
  gastrin, CCK, signaling,
    and cancer, 49,
    61–63

phosphagen systems and,
  301
Action potentials
  cellular and network bases
    of epileptic seizures,
    815–38
Activation
  cholecystokinin-regulating
    synthesis and, 77, 82–83
  circadian rhythms in
    Neurospora and, 757–86
  gastrin, CCK, signaling,
    and cancer, 56–60, 62, 64
  NAADP, cADPr, and IP$_3$ in
    Ca^{2+} signaling, 99–112
  pacemaker ion channels
    and, 235, 246–48
Adenosine triphosphate
    (ATP)
  cell oxygen sensing and,
    259, 265, 269
  phosphagen systems and,
    289–314
Adenoviruses
  nephrogenic diabetes
    insipidus and, 619–20
  somatic gene therapy in
    cardiovascular system
    and, 433
  surfactant proteins A and D
    and pulmonary host
    defense, 537
Adenylyl cyclase
  guanylyl cyclase family
    and, 215–27
Adrenals
  StAR protein and
    steroidogenesis, 194–203
Adrenocorticotropic hormone
    (ACTH)
  StAR protein and

steroidogenesis, 194–96
After-discharges
  cellular and network bases
    of epileptic seizures,
    822–25
al-3 gene
  circadian rhythms in
    Neurospora and, 783
Alanine
  antifreeze proteins of
    teleost fishes and, 369
  gastrin, CCK, signaling,
    and cancer, 56
  surfactant proteins B and
    C, 556–57
Aldosterone
  history of research and, 8
  StAR protein and
    steroidogenesis, 194, 197
Algae
  endogenous timekeepers
    and, 695–722
Allopregnanolone
  StAR protein and
    steroidogenesis, 194
Allosteric enzymes
  ^{13}C NMR of intermediary
    metabolism and, 15,
    17–21, 24, 28–32
Alveoli
  lung development and,
    485–86
  pulmonary collectins and
    surfactant metabolism,
    495, 508–9
  surfactant proteins A and D
    and pulmonary host
    defense, 521–42
Amidation
  gastrin, CCK, signaling,
    and cancer, 53–54, 65

895

CUMULATIVE INDEXES

CONTRIBUTING AUTHORS, VOLUMES 59–63

CHAPTER TITLES, VOLUMES 59–63

Cardiovascular Physiology

936

Cell Physiology

Comparative Physiology

Endocrinology

Neurophysiology

Perspectives

Renal and Electrolyte Physiology

Respiratory Physiology

Special Topics
Apoptosis

Circadian Rhythms